# Teacher's Resource Book



Scott Foresman

**Editorial Offices:** Glenview, Illinois • Parsippany, New Jersey • New York, New York
**Sales Offices:** Parsippany, New Jersey • Duluth, Georgia • Glenview, Illinois
Coppell, Texas • Ontario, California

**Credits**
**Illustrations**
**Paula Becker:** 6, 11, 24, 28, 31, 42, 46, 50, 58, 66, 69, 70, 71, 72, 76, 84, 87, 88, 89, 90, 102, 104 **Doug Cushman:** 5, 9, 15, 16, 17, 18, 29, 33, 34, 35, 36, 41, 57, 59, 65, 77, 81, 83, 86, 93, 96, 99, 101 **Karen Dugan:** 10, 14, 23, 30, 39, 40, 45, 47, 48, 51, 52, 53, 54, 60, 64, 68, 75, 78, 82, 85, 94, 100, 105, 106 **Diane Teske Harris:** 20, 56, 74

**Photos**
All photos shot for Scott Foresman by Russell Phillips Photography, except for the following:
***PhotoDisc, Inc.:*** 2 (apple, baseball, cat, dog, elephant, feather, goat, hat, jacks, kangaroo, lion, monkey, nest, rat, saw, turtle, umbrella, X ray, yo-yo, zebra) 12 (horse, monkey, ring, sandwich, saw, seal) 21 (camel, can, cap, car, carrot, turtle) 22 (can, cat) 32 (can, cat, hat, rat) 67 (cat, dog)





ISBN 0-328-02230-6

ISBN 0-328-04057-6

5 6 7 8 9 10 11-V004-10 09 08 07 06 05 04

5 6 7 8 9 10 11-V004-10 09 08 07 06 05 04

# Table of Contents

**Unit 1**

## Unit 2

| *Take a Closer Look* | Family Times | Phonics | High-Frequency Words | Comprehension | Grammar | Vocabulary/ High-Frequency Words | Research and Study Skills | Phonics Review | Spelling | Selection Test | Writing Process |
|---|---|---|---|---|---|---|---|---|---|---|---|
| The Nap<br>Oh, Cats! | 1-2 | 3-4 | 5 | 6 | 7, 11<br>17-18 | 8 | | 9, 15 | 10, 16 | 13-14 | |
| Look at That!<br>Can You Find It? | 19-20 | 21-22 | 23 | 24 | 25, 29<br>35-36 | 26 | | 27, 33 | 28, 34 | 31-32 | |
| What Did I See?<br>I Went Walking | 37-38 | 39-40 | 41 | 42 | 43, 47<br>53-54 | 44 | | 45, 51 | 46, 52 | 49-50 | |
| Fish Mix<br>How Many Fish? | 55-56 | 57-58 | 59 | 60 | 61, 65<br>71-72 | 62 | | 63, 69 | 64, 70 | 67-68 | |
| Jog, Frog, Jog<br>Tadpole to Frog | 73-74 | 75-76 | 77 | 78 | 79, 83<br>89-90 | 80 | | 81, 87 | 82, 88 | 85-86 | |
| A Big Job<br>Sweet Potato Pie | 91-92 | 93-94 | 95 | 96 | 97, 102<br>107-108 | 98 | | 99, 105 | 100, 106 | 103-104 | 101, 109 |

## Unit 3

| *Let's Learn Together* | Family Times | Phonics | High-Frequency Words | Comprehension | Grammar | Vocabulary/ High-Frequency Words | Research and Study Skills | Phonics Review | Spelling | Selection Test | Writing Process |
|---|---|---|---|---|---|---|---|---|---|---|---|
| The Big Mess<br>The Little Red Hen | 1-2 | 3-4 | 5 | 6 | 7, 11<br>17-18 | 8 | | 9, 15 | 10, 16 | 13-14 | |
| Yes, We Want Some Too!<br>Cat Traps | 19-20 | 21-22 | 23 | 24 | 25, 29<br>35- 36 | 26 | | 27, 33 | 28, 34 | 31-32 | |
| My Buddy, Stan<br>Biscuit | 37-38 | 39-40 | 41 | 42 | 43, 47 | 44 | | 45, 51 | 46, 52 | 49-50 | |
| Trucks<br>Communities | 55-56 | 57-58 | 59 | 60 | 61, 66<br>71-72 | 62 | 63 | 64, 69 | 65, 70 | 67-68 | |
| Fox and Bear<br>Fox and Bear Look at the Moon | 73-74 | 75-76 | 77 | 78 | 79, 83<br>89-90 | 80 | | 81, 87 | 82, 88 | 85-86 | |
| I Can Read<br>Lilly Reads | 91-92 | 93-94 | 95 | 96 | 97, 102<br>107-108 | 98 | | 99, 105 | 100, 106 | 103-104 | 101, 109 |

## Unit 4

### *Favorite Things Old and New*

| | Family Times | Phonics | High-Frequency Words | Comprehension | Grammar | Vocabulary/ High-Frequency Words | Research and Study Skills | Phonics Review | Spelling | Selection Test | Writing Process |
|---|---|---|---|---|---|---|---|---|---|---|---|
| The Red Stone Game<br>The Gingerbread Man | 1-2 | 3-4 | 5 | 6 | 7, 11<br>17-18 | 8 | | 9, 15 | 10, 16 | 13-14 | |
| The Same as You<br>Cherry Pies and Lullabies | 19-20 | 21-22 | 23 | 24 | 25, 30<br>35-36 | 26 | 27 | 28, 33 | 29, 34 | 31-32 | |
| Rose and Grandma Make the Sun Shine<br>Our Family Get-Together | 37-38 | 39-40 | 41 | 42 | 43, 47<br>53-54 | 44 | | 45, 51 | 46, 52 | 49-50 | |
| The Rolling Rice Cake: A Story from Japan<br>The Rat and the Cat | 55-56 | 57-58 | 59 | 60 | 61, 65<br>71-72 | 62 | | 63, 69 | 64, 70 | 67-68 | |
| June and the Mule: A Tall Tale<br>Slim, Luke, and the Mules | 73-74 | 75-76 | 77 | 78 | 79, 84<br>89-90 | 80 | 81 | 82, 87 | 83, 88 | 85-86 | |
| Riddle-dee Fiddle-dee-dee<br>The Riddles | 91-92 | 93-94 | 95 | 96 | 97, 102<br>107-108 | 98 | | 99, 105 | 100, 106 | 103-104 | 101, 109 |

## Unit 5

### *Take Me There*

| | Family Times | Phonics | High-Frequency Words | Comprehension | Grammar | Vocabulary/ High-Frequency Words | Research and Study Skills | Phonics Review | Spelling | Selection Test | Writing Process |
|---|---|---|---|---|---|---|---|---|---|---|---|
| A Real Gift<br>Arthur's Reading Race | 1-2 | 3-4 | 5 | 6 | 7, 11<br>17-18 | 8 | | 9, 15 | 10, 16 | 13-14 | |
| A Big Day for Jay<br>Lost! | 19-20 | 21-22 | 23 | 24 | 25, 29<br>35-36 | 26 | | 27, 33 | 28, 34 | 31-32 | |
| Baby Otter Grows Up<br>Foal | 37-38 | 39-40 | 41 | 42 | 43, 47<br>53-54 | 44 | | 45, 51 | 46, 52 | 49-50 | |
| What a Sight!<br>Lost in the Museum | 55-56 | 57-58 | 59 | 60 | 61, 66<br>71-72 | 62 | 63 | 64, 69 | 65, 70 | 67-68 | |
| Chompy's Afternoon<br>Dinosaur Babies | 73-74 | 75-76 | 77 | 78 | 79, 83<br>89-90 | 80 | | 81, 87 | 82, 88 | 85-86 | |
| The True Story of Abbie Burgess<br>The Bravest Cat! The True Story of Scarlett | 91-92 | 93-94 | 95 | 96 | 97, 102<br>107, 108 | 98 | | 99, 105 | 100, 106 | 103-104 | 101, 109 |

## Unit 6

| Surprise Me! | Family Times | Phonics | High-Frequency Words | Comprehension | Grammar | Vocabulary/ High-Frequency Words | Research and Study Skills | Phonics Review | Spelling | Selection Test | Writing Process |
|---|---|---|---|---|---|---|---|---|---|---|---|
| Bluebirds in the Garden<br>The Garden | 1-2 | 3-4 | 5 | 6 | 7, 11<br>17-18 | 8 | | 9, 15 | 10, 16 | 13-14 | |
| Jordan Makes a New Friend<br>Ice-Cold Birthday | 19-20 | 21-22 | 23 | 24 | 25, 29<br>35-36 | 26 | | 27, 33 | 28, 34 | 31-32 | |
| Show Time: Your First Play<br>Do You Live in a Nest? | 37-38 | 39-40 | 41 | 42 | 43, 48<br>53-54 | 44 | 45 | 46, 51 | 47, 52 | 49-50 | |
| What's New in Mrs. Powell's Class?<br>Fox on Stage | 55-56 | 57-58 | 59 | 60 | 61, 65<br>71-72 | 62 | | 63, 69 | 64, 70 | 67-68 | |
| Doggy Art<br>The Snow Glory | 73-74 | 75-76 | 77 | 78 | 79, 83<br>89-90 | 80 | | 81, 87 | 82, 88 | 85-86 | |
| I'll Join You<br>Leon and Bob | 91-92 | 93-94 | 95 | 96 | 97, 102<br>107-108 | 98 | | 99, 105 | 100, 106 | 103-104 | 101, 109 |

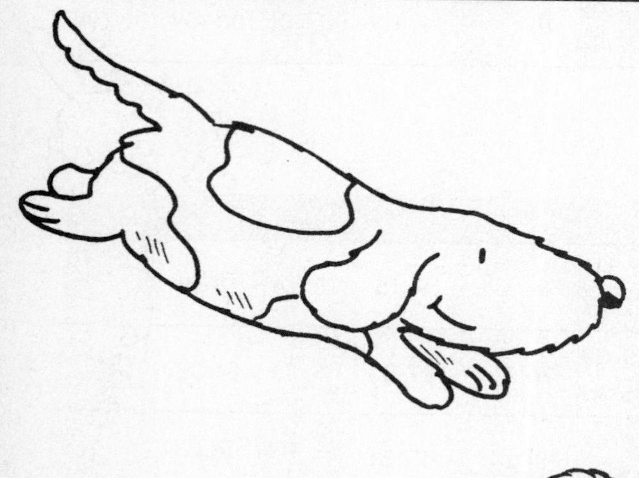

**You are your child's first and best teacher!**

**Here are ways to help your child practice skills while having fun!**

**Day 1** Write each letter of the alphabet on a slip of paper, place the slips of paper in a paper bag, and shake them up. Invite your child to grab a letter from the bag and name the letter.

**Day 2** Read a story to your child. Stop at the end of each page and ask your child to tell what will happen next. Then read on, and have your child make a new prediction.

**Day 3** Write the words *red*, *yellow*, and *blue* on cards. Point to the word *blue* and ask your child to hunt for blue items (blue sock or blue pencil) and place them next to the word *blue*. Give the same instructions for red and yellow items.

**Day 4** Point to an item in the house and ask your child to "name it" (tell what it is). Start with easy items such as *book* and add more difficult things.

**Day 5** Practice making rhyming words. Say the word *hat* and help your child name rhyming words, giving clues for words such as *bat*, *cat*, *fat*, *pat*, *rat*, and *sat*. Continue with *can* (*fan*, *man*, *pan*, *ran*, *van*) and *cap* (*lap*, *map*, *nap*, *rap*, *tap*, *zap*).

**Read with your child EVERY DAY!**



(fold here)

# Family Times

Date ________________

Dear Parent:

Welcome to "Family Times," your link to your child's reading program. In the reading program for this level, your child will learn about

- the alphabet
- the letter sounds
- beginning reading words

Please use the ideas in "Family Times" to share the learning experiences with your child. Each issue of "Family Times" will present new ways to help you practice the lessons presented in the reading program.

Sincerely,

________________________

Name: ______________________________

# The Alphabet

Your child is working with the alphabet in school. Say the letters of the alphabet with your child. Ask your child to point to specific capital and small letters, for example, "Point to capital *M*." "Point to small *s*."

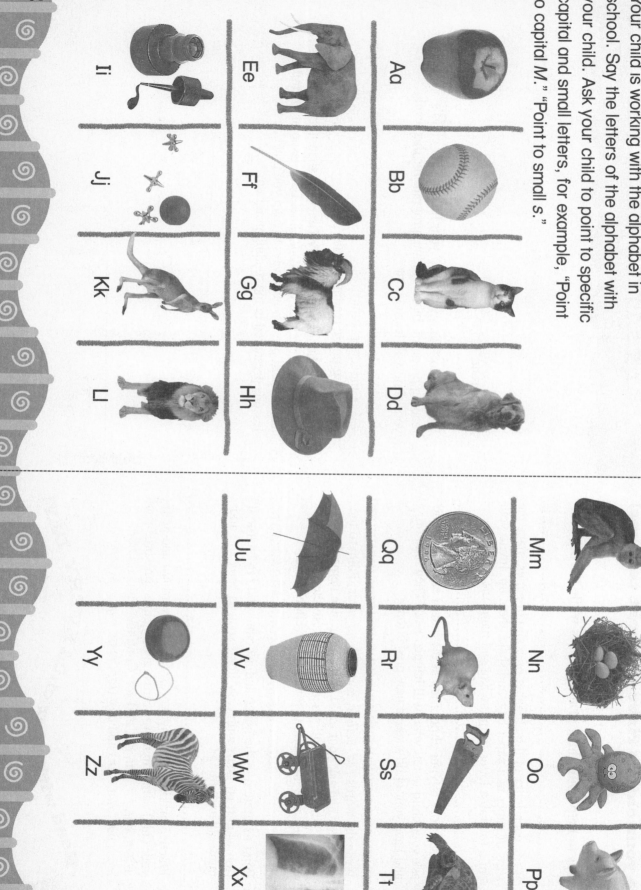

| | | | |
|---|---|---|---|
| Aa | Bb | Cc | Dd |
| Ee | Ff | Gg | Hh |
| Ii | Jj | Kk | Ll |

| | | | |
|---|---|---|---|
| Mm | Nn | Oo | Pp |
| Qq | Rr | Ss | Tt |
| Uu | Vv | Ww | Xx |
| | Yy | Zz | |

Name ______________________ Lunch

Circle.

| | | | | | |
|---|---|---|---|---|---|
| L | B | L | L | T | L |

| | | | | | |
|---|---|---|---|---|---|
| F | T | F | E | F | F |

| | | | | | |
|---|---|---|---|---|---|
| S | S | K | C | S | S |

| | | | | | |
|---|---|---|---|---|---|
| G | C | G | J | G | G |

| | | | | | |
|---|---|---|---|---|---|
| M | M | N | M | W | M |

| | | | | | |
|---|---|---|---|---|---|
| B | B | D | B | R | B |

**Directions:** Circle the letters that are alike in each row.

**Home Activity:** Use magazines and help your child look for letters that are alike.

Name ______________________

Lunch

| | | | | | | | |
|---|---|---|---|---|---|---|---|
| L | t | l | b | R | b | n | r |
| A | o | c | a | N | h | n | m |
| H | h | f | b | V | w | r | v |
| K | t | k | h | E | e | a | c |
| P | b | q | p | D | p | d | b |
| S | r | c | s | C | o | c | e |
| U | v | u | x | Y | j | g | y |

**Directions:** Look at the capital letter. Circle its lowercase letter.

**Home Activity:** Write capital and lowercase letters and ask your child to name the letters.

Name ______________________________

## Color.

**Directions:** Color the picture that tells what will happen next.

**Home Activity:** Show pictures and have your child predict what might happen next.

Name ____________________

Lunch

## Circle.

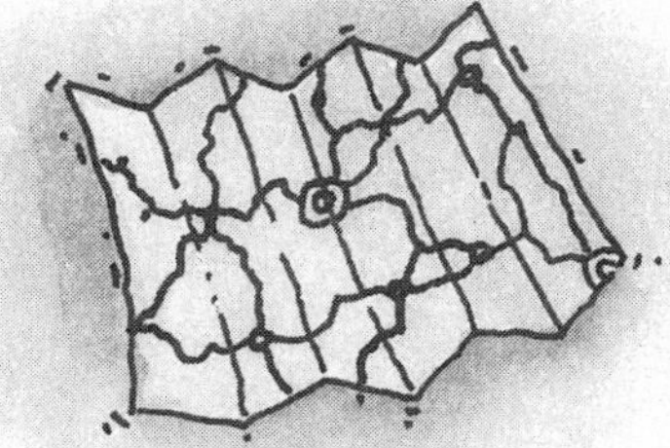

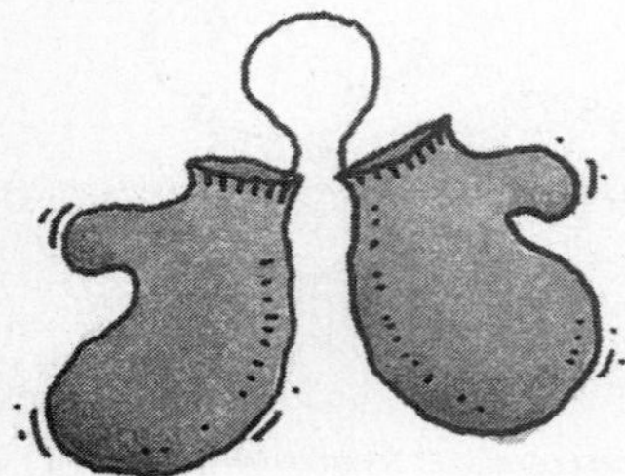

## Draw.

**Directions:** Circle things that begin with /m/. Then make an /m/ picture.

**Home Activity:** Make an *M* with things your child collects that begin with *m*.

Name ______________________________

| | |
|---|---|
| see | I |
| a | red |
| yellow | blue |

**Directions:** Have children cut along the dotted lines to make word cards.

Name ______________________________

Lunch

| | |
|---|---|
| I | See |
| Red | A |
| Blue | Yellow |

Name ______________________________

Color.

Circle.

Draw a line.

Color.

**Directions:** Find the mouse in each picture. Follow the directions.

**Home Activity:** Play "Directions" by asking your child to do things such as "Get the book from the table."

Name ______________________________

Lunch

Circle.

Rr

Draw.

**Directions:** Circle things that begin with /r/. Then make an /r/ picture.

**Home Activity:** Name two words. Have your child tell which word begins with *r*: rug—bug, turtle—rabbit.

Name ______________________________

# Color.

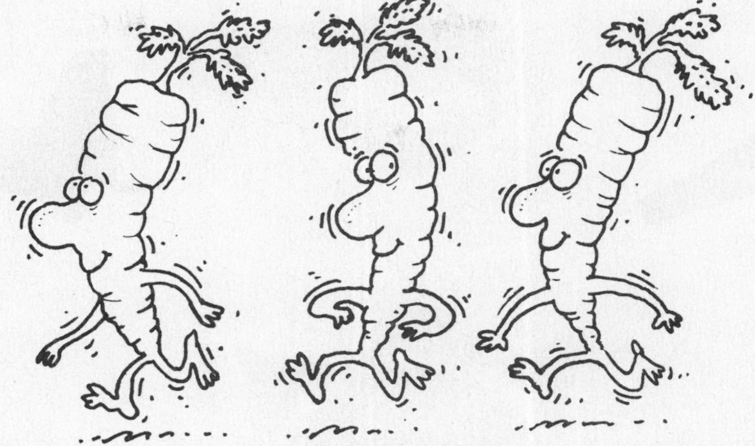

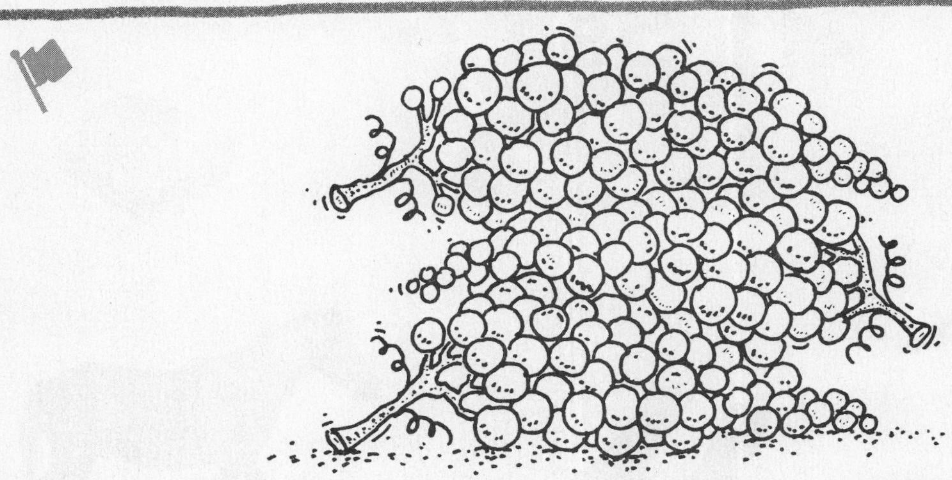

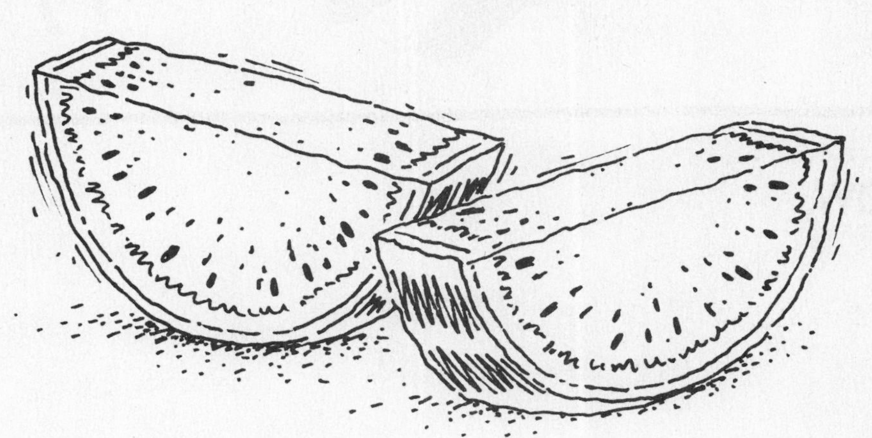

**Directions:** Color the first carrot in line, the bunch of grapes on top, and the watermelon on the right.

**Home Activity:** Look for things in the room and tell which is on top/bottom, left/right, or first/next/last.

Name ______________________________

Circle.

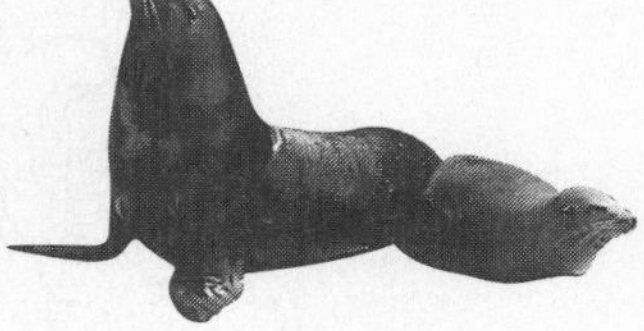

6

Ss

7

Draw.

**Directions:** Circle things that begin with /s/. Then make an /s/ picture.

**Home Activity:** Find things in the kitchen that begin with *s*—sink, soup, salt, soap.

Name ______________________

Draw.

**Directions:** Draw a picture of your favorite thing. Label your picture.

**Home Activity:** Share favorites with your child—books, toys, foods—and tell why they are favorites.

Name ______________________

# Circle.

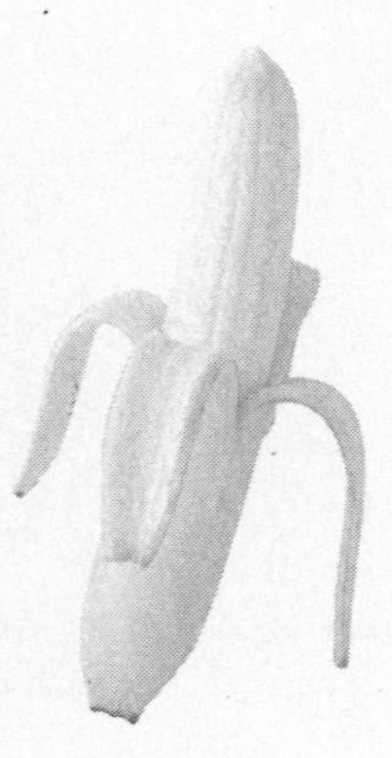

**Directions:** Circle an animal, a person, and a place.

**Home Activity:** Look at pictures and label persons, places, aminals, and things.

Name ______________________

Lunch

Bb

Tt

**Directions:** Draw lines to things that begin with /b/, then /t/. Make /b/ and /t/ pictures.

**Home Activity:** Play a guessing game for words that begin with *b* or *t*. *You can throw me. I'm a _____. (ball)*

I see red.
I see yellow.
I see blue.



(fold here)

Name: ________________________

# Red, Yellow, Blue

I see red.

I see red.
I see yellow.
I see blue.

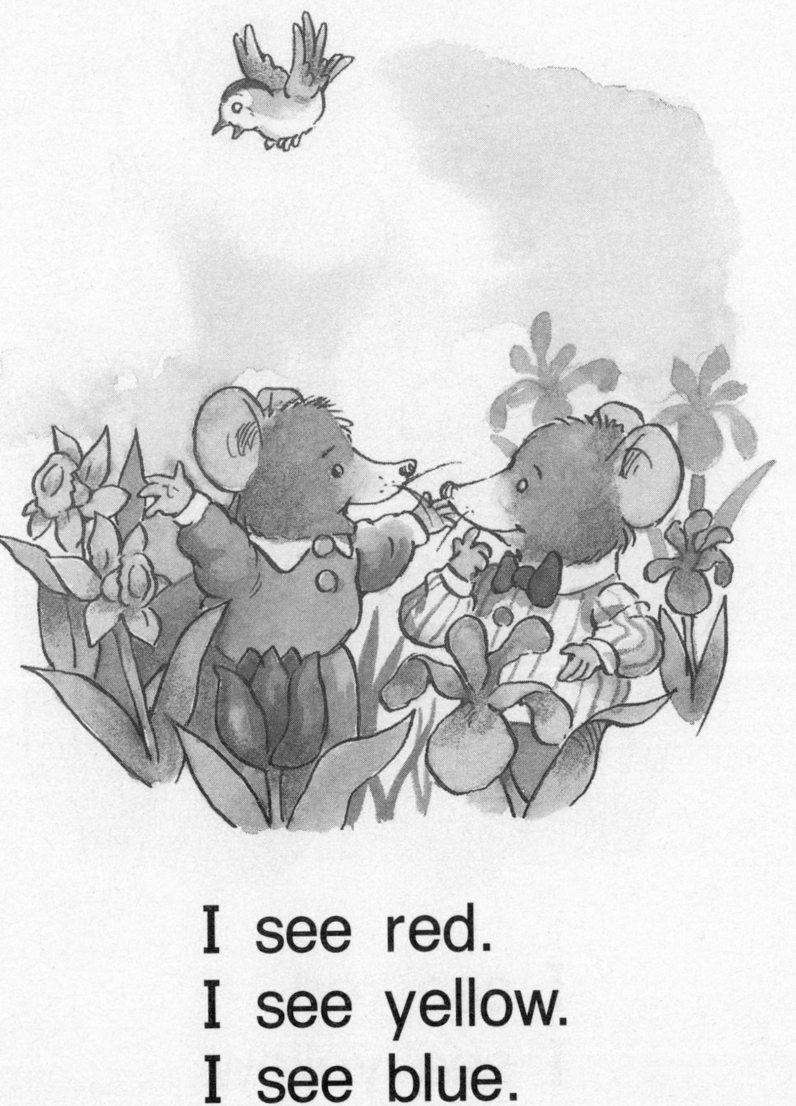

I see red.
I see yellow.
I see blue.



(fold here)

I see red.

I see red.
I see yellow.

I see red.
I see yellow.

**You are your child's first and best teacher!**

**Here are ways to help your child practice skills while having fun!**

**Day 1** Write the letter *c* and __*ap*, __*an*, and __*at* on a sheet of paper. Have your child name a word that begins with *c* and write the letter *c*.

**Day 2** Name the category *Animals*. Have your child name as many animals as he or she can. Write the animal names.

**Day 3** Point to items around the house. Have your child tell whether the items are the same or different. Use two identical or two different items such as pencils, pens, pans, socks, or sheets of paper.

**Day 4** Ask your child to name words that tell things to do—*run*, *jump*, *hop*, *skip*. As each word is named, have your child pantomime it.

**Day 5** Draw eight boxes on a large sheet of paper. Write one of these words in each box: *cat*, *tap*, *pat*, *can*, *nap*, *pan*, *bat*, *cap*. Put the paper on the floor and have your child throw a beanbag onto a box. Have your child read the word. Continue until many of the words have been read.

**Read with your child EVERY DAY!**



(fold here)

# Family Times

Can You Do That?
I can hit a ball with a bat.
I can nap on my nice new mat.
I can tap, tap, tap like that.
I can do this. Can you do that?
I can ride in a purple van.
I can cool off with a fan.
I can pat my tan cat, Dan.
I can do this. Can you do that?


The rhyme has words that begin with the consonants *c*, *n*, and *p* and words with a short *a* vowel sound as in *cat*. The short vowel *a* words include words with the rhyming patterns *-at*, *-an*, and *-ap*. Read the rhyme with your child and look for words that begin with *c*, *n*, or *p*. Then look for rhyming words.

Name: ____________________

# Begin It!

**Materials** cards with the numbers 1 to 3, button or marker for each player

## Game Directions

1. Take a number card and move your marker the number of spaces shown.

2. Name a word that begins with the same sound as the name of the picture in the space.

3. If your answer is correct, stay on that space. If you are not correct, return to the space where you began your turn.

4. The first player to reach the end wins!

Name ______________________________

Lunch

Circle.

Cc

5

Draw.

**Directions:** Circle things that begin with /c/. Then make a /c/ picture.

**Home Activity:** Help your child find pictures of things that begin with *c*.

Name ______________________

## Write.

___at

___at

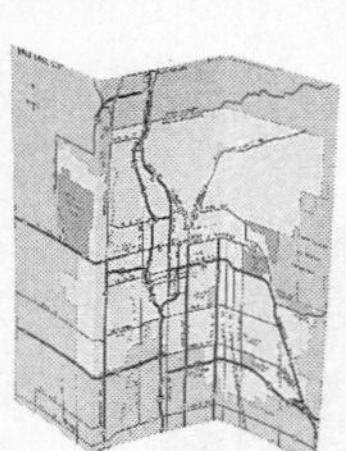

___ap

___ap

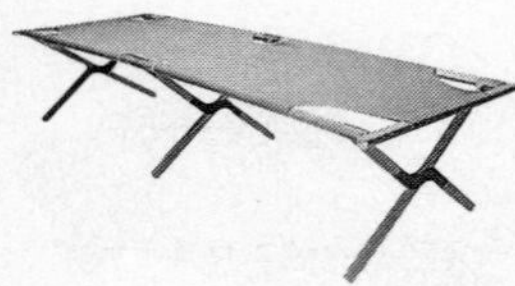

___ot

___ot

___an

___an

___up

___up

**Directions:** Write the letter for the beginning sound on the line.

**Home Activity:** Help your child write other rhyming words and draw a picture for each word.

Name ______________________

# Color.

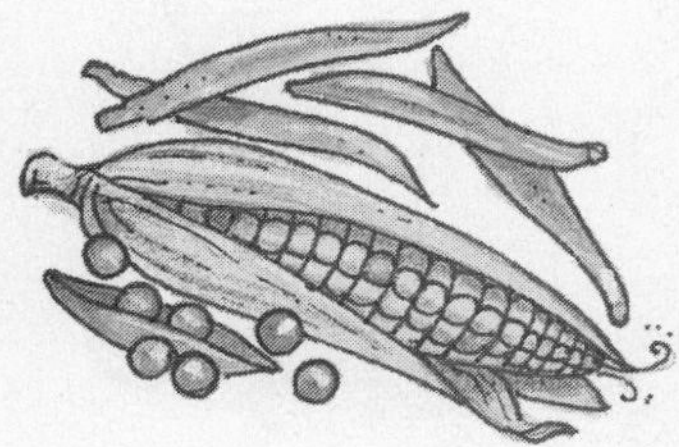
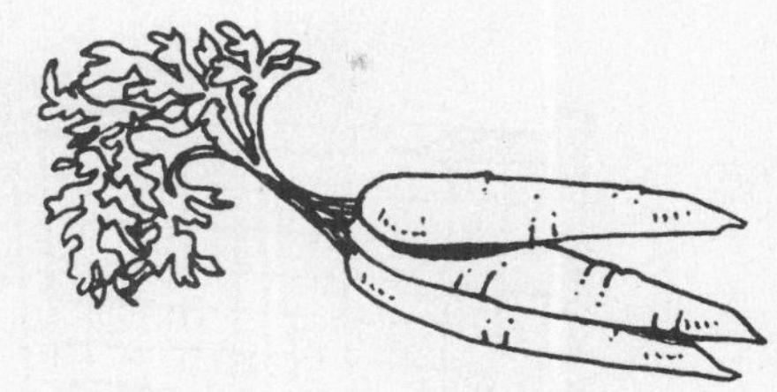

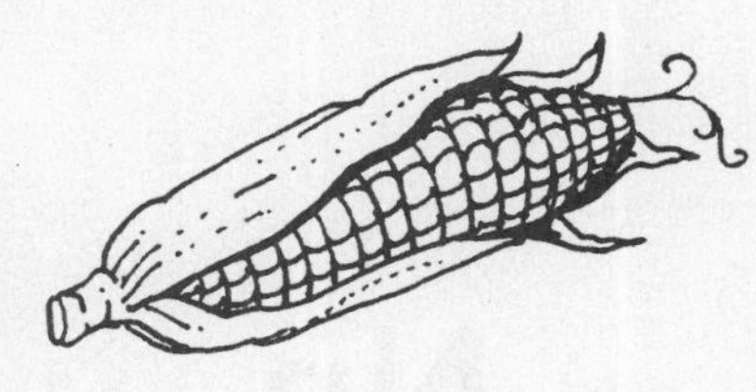

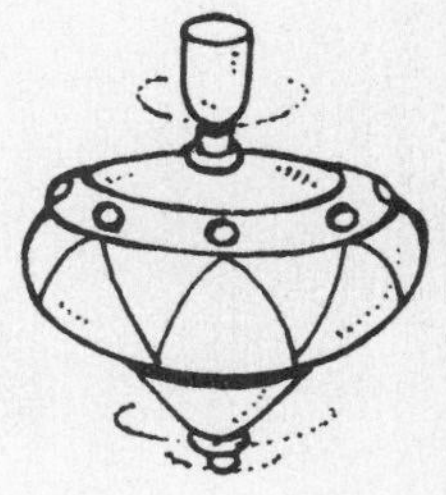

**Directions:** Color the picture that belongs in each group.

**Home Activity:** Help your child name words that belong in groups such as *toys*, *foods*, *colors*, and *animals*.

Name ______________________________

## Circle.

Nn

## Draw.

**Directions:** Circle things that begin with /n/. Then make an /n/ picture.

**Home Activity:** Help your child find things that begin with *n*.

Name ______________________________

| | |
|---|---|
| can | look |
| at | the |
| my | and |

**Directions:** Have children cut along the dotted lines to make word cards.

Name ______________________

Lunch

| | |
|---|---|
| Look | Can |
| The | At |
| And | My |

Name ______________________________

## Draw a line.

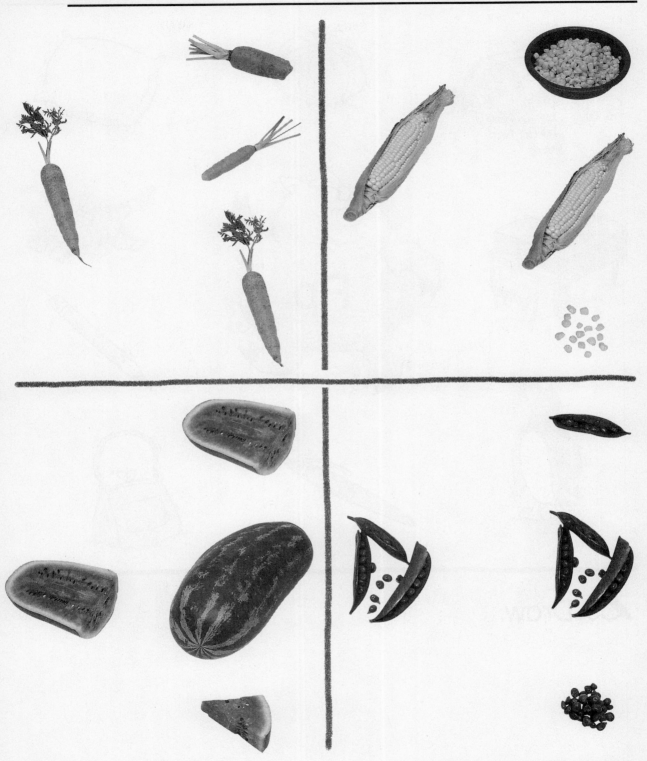

**Directions:** Draw a line to the picture that is the same.

**Home Activity:** Look at pictures together to find things that are alike and things that are different.

Name ______________________________

Circle.

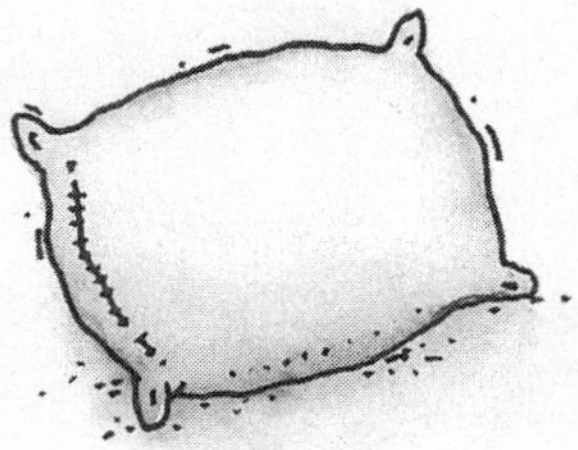

Pp

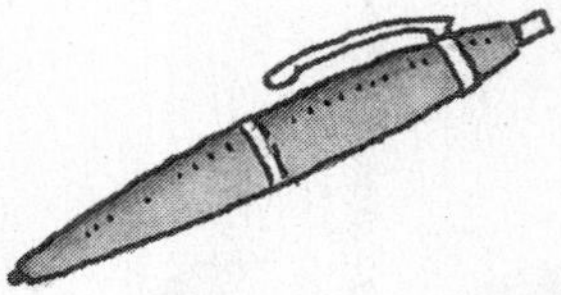

Draw.

**Directions:** Circle things that begin with /p/. Then make a /p/ picture.

**Home Activity:** Make a set of cards with pictures that begin with *p*. Use the cards to name things that begin alike.

Name ______________________________

## Draw a line.

A mouse ate lunch.

I see a little mouse.

The house is red.

The mouse ran fast.

The mouse had food.

**Directions:** Draw a line between the words in each sentence.

**Home Activity:** Help your child find the words and sentences you read from a page in a book.

Name ______________________________

Circle.

cat

cap

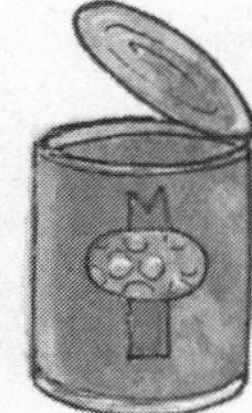

can

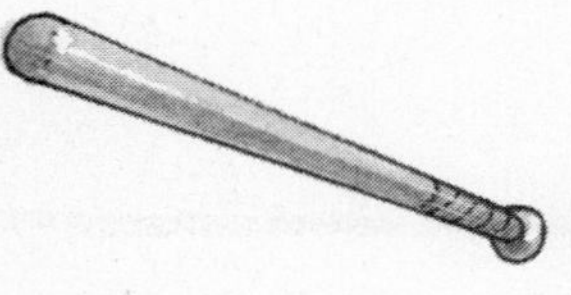

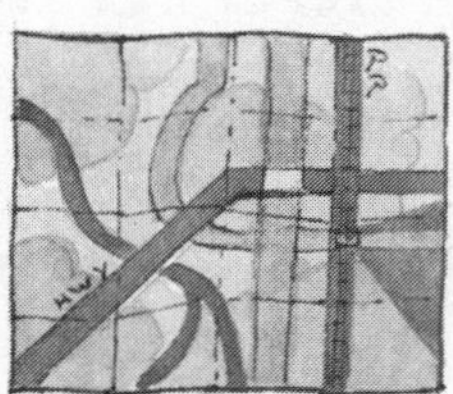

**Directions:** In each column, circle the pictures whose names rhyme.

**Home Activity:** Have your child say the rhyming words and use each word in a sentence.

Name ____________________

Draw.

**Directions:** Circle the pictures that show things you can do. Draw something you can do.

**Home Activity:** Work with your child to make a list of "Things We Can Do."

Name ______________________________

Circle.

**Directions:** Circle three things you can do.

**Home Activity:** Ask your child to tell about his or her favorite activity.

Name ______________________

# Write.

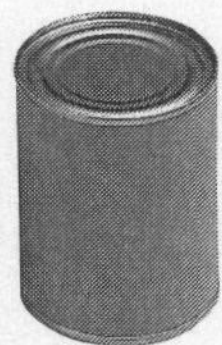

___an

___at

___an

___at

___an

___at

___an

___at

___an

___at

**Directions:** Write the letter for the beginning sound to make rhyming words.

**Home Activity:** Make word cards and practice reading the words.

Look at the blue and yellow .
Look at my .



(fold here)

# My Book

I can see the .



I can see the blue and yellow .

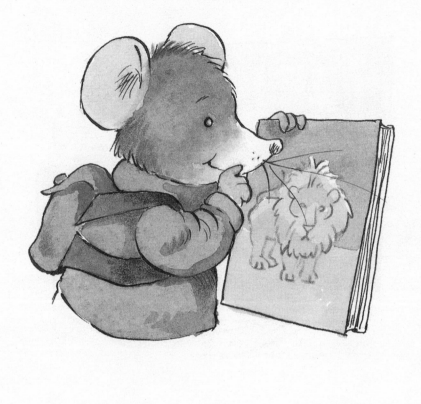

Look at the yellow .



(fold here)

I can see the red .

Look at the red [book icon].

I can see the yellow [book icon].

**You are your child's first and best teacher!**

**Here are ways to help your child practice skills while having fun!**

**Day 1** Help your child look through catalogs or magazines to find pictures whose names begin with *f*. Have your child paste the pictures on a paper labeled with the letters *Ff*.

**Day 2** Show a picture and have your child tell what the picture is all about. This will help your child identify the main idea of each picture. Use a picture book or other pictures.

**Day 3** Write these words: *fit*, *cat*, *cap*, *big*, *man*. Read the words together. Then say the word *bat* and have your child find the word that rhymes with *bat*. Continue with *hit*, *can*, *nap*, *pig*.

**Day 4** Practice using naming words (nouns) for people by having your child identify the people in your family—mother, father, cousins, aunts, uncles, etc.

**Day 5** Write these words on small cards: *big*, *dig*, *fig*, *jig*, *pig*, *sit*, *hit*, *fit*, *kit*, *bit*. Mix the cards and place them facedown on a table. Have your child take two cards and read the words. If the words rhyme, the child keeps the cards. Continue until all the rhyming pairs are made.

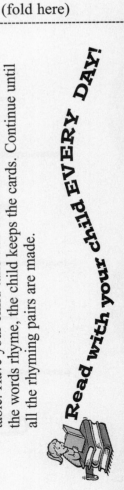

**Read with your child EVERY DAY!**



(fold here)

# Family Times

### A Big Family

My family is big.
We like to dance the jig.
We live on a farm with goats and geese,
And I'm the littlest pig!

We like to fish a bit.
We like to giggle and sit.
We hit the ball and run so fast.
We stay so trim and fit.

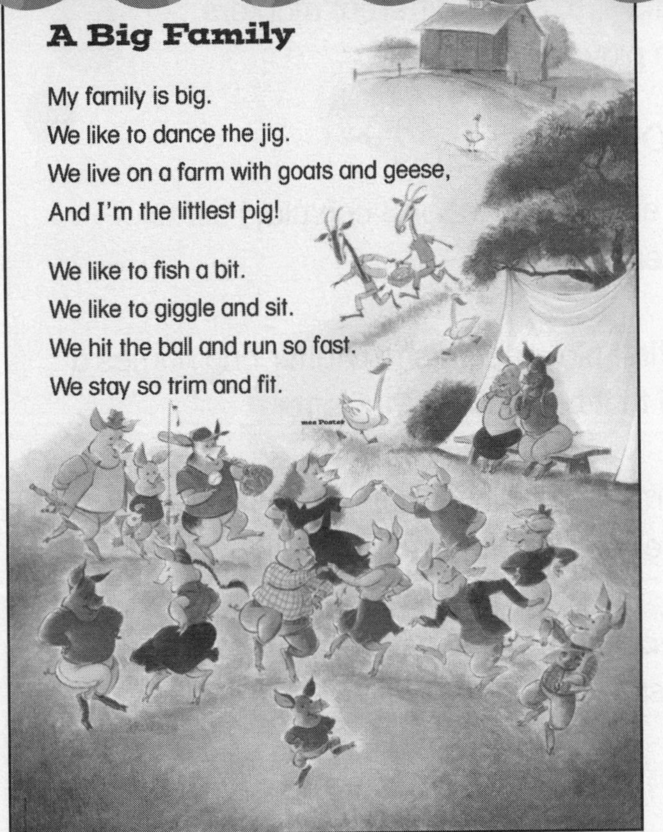

The rhyme has words that begin with the consonants *f*, *g*, and *l* and words with a short *i* vowel sound as in *pig*. The short vowel *i* words include words with the rhyming patterns *-ig* and *-it*. Read the rhyme with your child and look for rhyming words. Then look for words that begin with *f*, *g*, or *l*.

Name: ______________________

# Pick a Letter

**Materials** a set of different markers for each player

**Game Directions**

**1.** Give each player (2 or 3 can play) some markers.

**2.** The first player points to a letter and names a word that begins with that letter.

**3.** If correct, the player puts a marker on that space. The next player has a turn.

**4.** Play continues until a player covers a row across, down, or diagonally.

| | | | |
|---|---|---|---|
| g | f | l | f |
| l | f | g | l |
| f | g | l | f |
| l | f | l | g |

Name ______________________

## Circle.

## Draw.

**Directions:** Circle things that begin with /f/. Then make an /f/ picture.

**Home Activity:** Help your child make a list of words that begin with *f*.

Name ____________________

## Write.

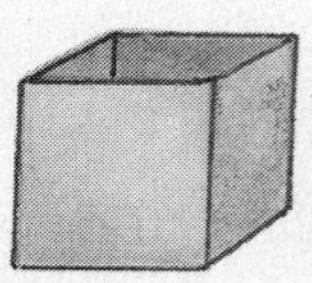

box

___ox

man

___an

run

___un

ball

___all

dish

___ish

**Directions:** Change the first letter to make a new word that names the picture.

**Home Activity:** Help your child create a sentence for a pair of words such as *man—fan. I see a man holding a fan.*

Name ______________________

## Circle.

animals    people

animals    people

animals    people

**Directions:** Circle the word that tells what the picture is all about.

**Home Activity:** Show pictures to your child and have your child tell what the picture is all about (the main idea).

Name ______________________________

Circle.

Gg

Draw.

**Directions:** Circle things that begin with /g/. Then make a /g/ picture.

**Home Activity:** Help your child find pictures of things that begin with *g*.

Name ______________________________

| big | it |
|---|---|
| is | in |
| little | have |

**Directions:** Have children cut along the dotted lines to make word cards.

Name ______________________



| It | Big |
|---|---|
| In | Is |
| Have | Little |

Name ____________________

## Draw a line.

STOP

**Directions:** Draw lines to the pictures that rhyme.

**Home Activity:** Have your child name a rhyming word for words such as *ball, fish, car, hot, cold, book, rake, boat, pin, pet.*

Name ______________________

## Circle.

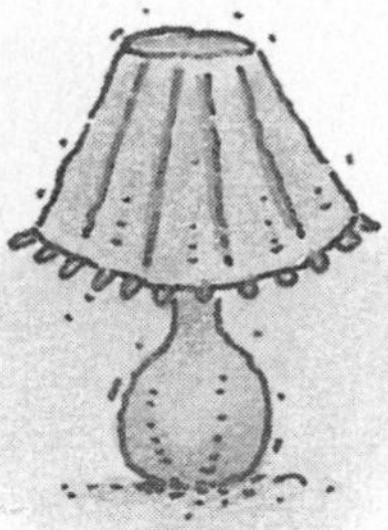

Ll

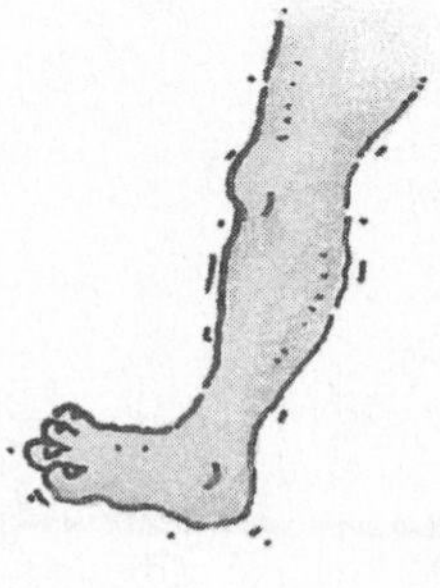

## Draw.

**Directions:** Circle things that begin with /l/. Then make an /l/ picture.

**Home Activity:** Write the letters *Ll* on paper. Have your child draw pictures that begin with *l*.

Name ____________________

Color.

in

up

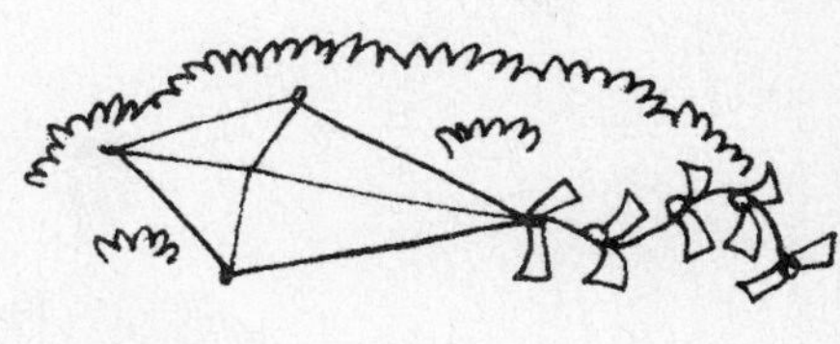

hot

day

big

**Directions:** Color the picture that shows the opposite.

**Home Activity:** Play "opposites" by saying a word and having your child name the opposite: *sad* (happy).

Name ______________________

## Circle.

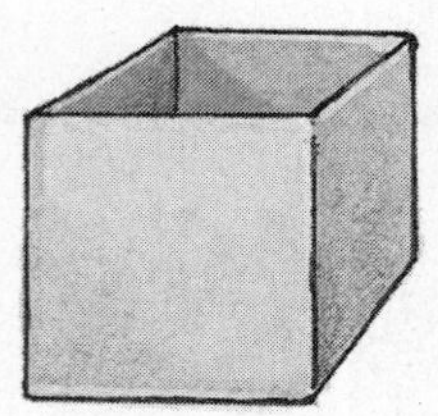

**Directions:** Circle the pictures that rhyme.

**Home Activity:** Have your child name other rhyming words for each set. (*big, fig, jig, twig; fit, kit, lit, pit*)

Name ____________________

## Circle.

mom

dad

sister

brother

pet

car

house

grandmother

grandfather

## Draw.

**Directions:** Circle the pictures that show people. Draw the people in your family.

**Home Activity:** Help your child label the people in the family picture and draw other family members.

Name ______________________________

## Circle.

**Directions:** Circle the person in each row.

**Home Activity:** Have your child draw and label a picture of himself or herself playing with friends.

Name ______________________

Circle.

pig

wig

sit

lit

dig

pig

bit

hit

big

dig

kit

bit

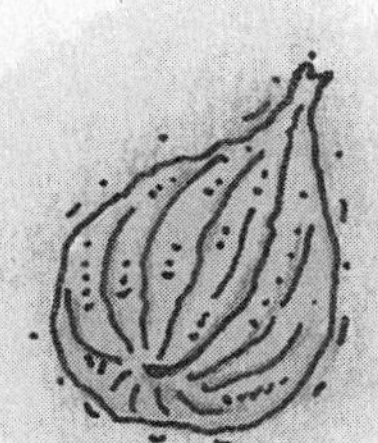

fig

wig

fit

lit

**Directions:** Circle the word that names the picture.

**Home Activity:** Make word cards for words that rhyme with *win* and *will.*

I can have it!



(fold here)

# I See It!

Look at it!
It is big.

Can I have it?

I see it.
It is little.



(fold here)

I see it.
It is big!

Can I have it?

Look at it!
It is little.

**You are your child's first and best teacher!**

**Here are ways to help your child practice skills while having fun!**

**Day 1** Draw a house on a sheet of paper. Ask your child to name words that begin like the word *house*. Each time an *h* word is named, have your child write the letter *h* on the house.

**Day 2** Help your child tell the difference between fact and fantasy by giving examples of things that can happen and things that are make-believe: a duck driving a jet, a worker fixing the street, firefighters putting out a fire, turtles shopping.

**Day 3** Sing the "Alphabet Song" with your child and write the letters of the alphabet together. Then give directions to find letters: name the letter that comes after *h* or the letter that comes between *b* and *d*.

**Day 4** Write the words *car*, *a big car*, *I see a big car*. Read the items together and have your child tell which one is a complete sentence. Use other words and word groups.

**Day 5** Play "Make More Words." Say the word *cot*. Ask your child to say the word with you and to change the beginning sound to "make more words." (*dot*, *got*, *hot*, *not*, *pot*, *lot*, *rot*, *tot*) Continue with *hop*. (*mop*, *pop*, *top*)

**Read with your child EVERY DAY!**



(fold here)

# Family Times

## My Friend Is a Kitten

My friend is a kitten.
We dance and we hop.
We spot a big hill, and
We hike to the top.

We like to dig big holes.
We like kites a lot.
We dive in the water
When it gets too hot.

The rhyme uses words that begin with the consonants *h*, *d*, and *k* and words with a short *o* vowel sound as in *cot*. The rhyming patterns *-ot* and *-op* have the short *o* vowel sound. Help your child find the rhyming words as you read the rhyme together. Also look for words that begin with *h*, *d*, or *k*.

Name: ______________________

**Materials** I paper circle, paper clip, pencil, marker for each player

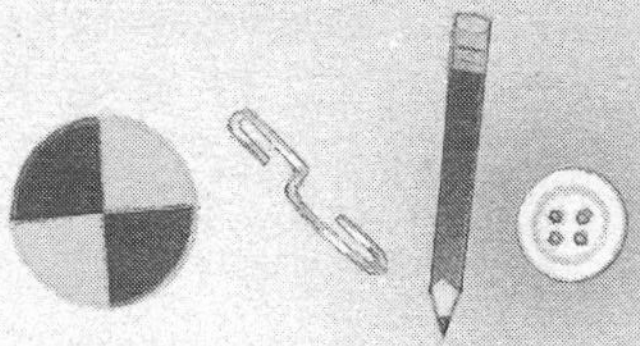

## Game Directions

1. Make a spinner as shown.

2. The first player spins the spinner and names a word that begins with the same sound as the picture name.

3. If the player is correct, he or she moves the number of spaces shown on the spinner. The next player has a turn.

4. The first player to reach the end wins!

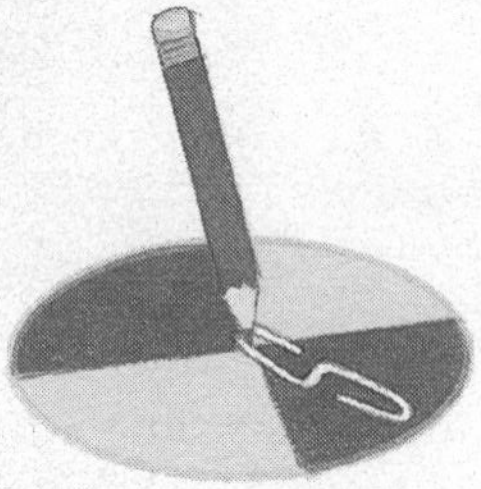

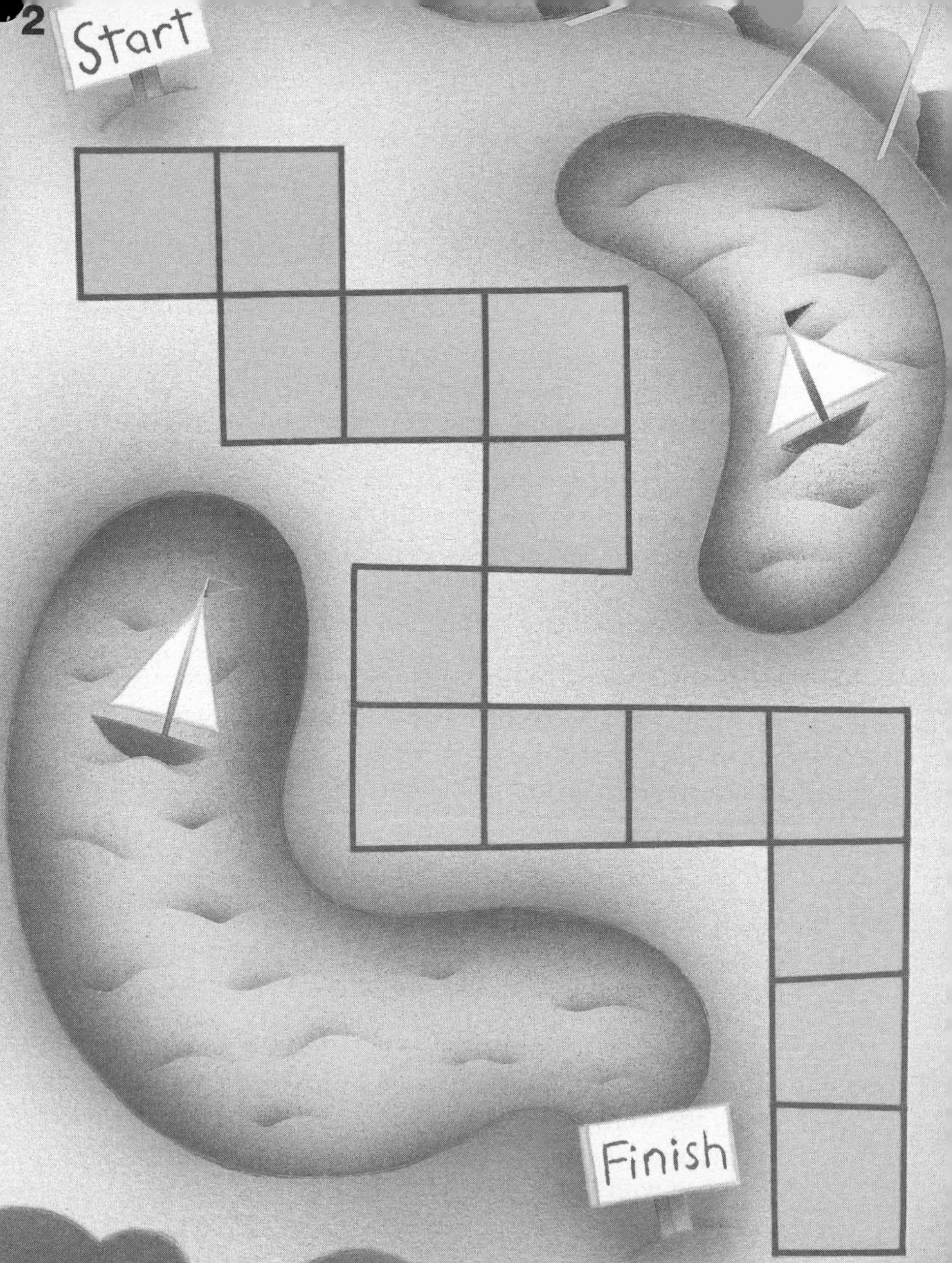

Start

Finish

Name ________________________________

## Circle.

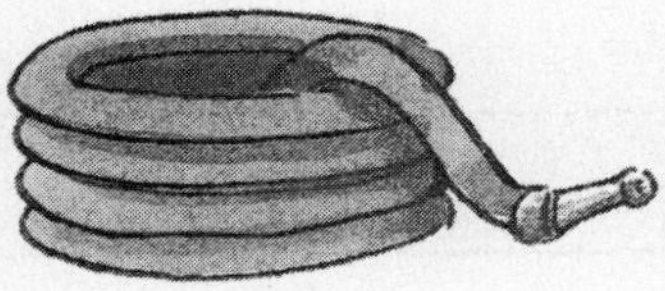

Hh

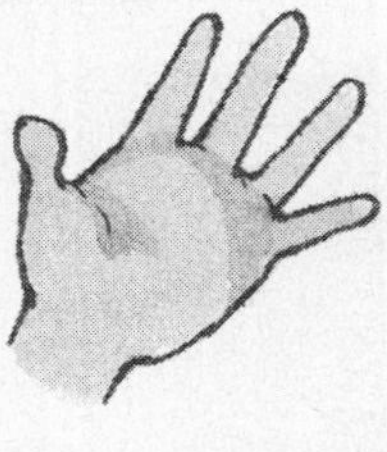

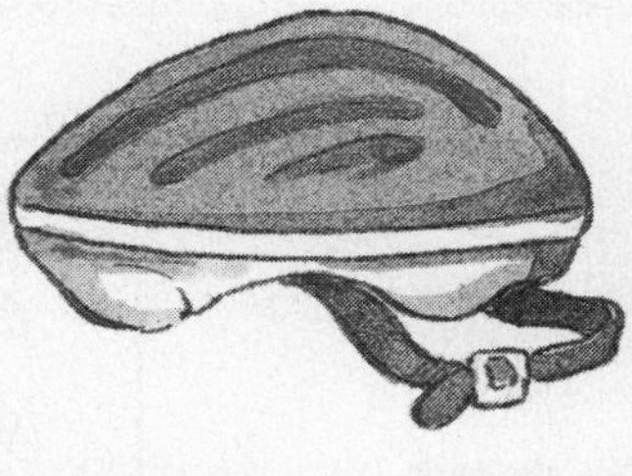

## Draw.

**Directions:** Circle things that begin with /h/. Then make an /h/ picture.

**Home Activity:** Help your child find pictures of things that begin with *h*.

Name ____________________

## Write.

pen

top

cat

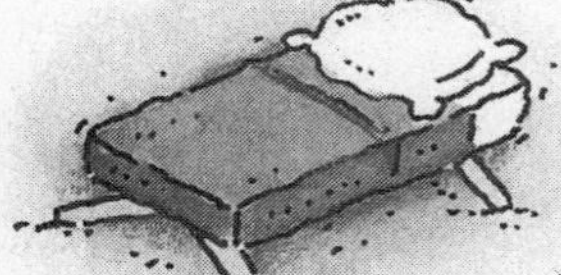

cot

jam

**Directions:** Change the first letter to make a new word that names the picture. Write the word.

**Home Activity:** Help your child write other words that begin with *h* (*hit*, *hut*, *hid*, *had*).

Name ________________________________

Circle.

**Directions:** Circle the picture that shows something make-believe.

**Home Activity:** Have your child tell you why each picture on the page is real or make-believe.

Name ______________________________

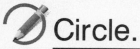

## Circle.

Dd

## Draw.

**Directions:** Circle things that begin with /d/. Then make a /d/ picture.

**Home Activity:** Help your child make a list of words that begin with *d.*

Name ______________________________

| | |
|---|---|
| not | to |
| you | that |
| do | like |

**Directions:** Have children cut along the dotted lines to make word cards.

Name ______________________________

| | |
|---|---|
| To | Not |
| That | You |
| Like | Do |

Name ______________________

## Draw a line.

J• •K

•G •H •I •L M• N•

F• •O

•E D• •Q •P

C• X• •W •R

B• Y• •V •S

A•  Z•—•U •T

## Write.

a b c ___ e f g

___ i j k ___ m n

___ p q r s ___ u

v w ___ y z

**Directions:** Draw a line to connect the letters in the order of the alphabet. Write the missing letters.

**Home Activity:** Make a set of letter cards. Have your child put the letters in the order of the alphabet.

Name ______________________

## Circle.

Kk

## Draw.

**Directions:** Circle things that begin with /k/. Then make a /k/ picture.

**Home Activity:** Say two words. Ask your child to tell which word begins with *k* (*kick—pick*).

Name ______________________

## Color.

## Write.

## Circle.

| | | | |
|---|---|---|---|
| H | b | F | H |
| M | M | n | N |

| | | | |
|---|---|---|---|
| K | B | K | t |
| D | P | b | D |

**Directions:** Color the make-believe picture. Write your name. Circle the matching letters.

**Home Activity:** Give directions like the ones on the page and have your child follow the directions.

Name ______________________________

# Circle.

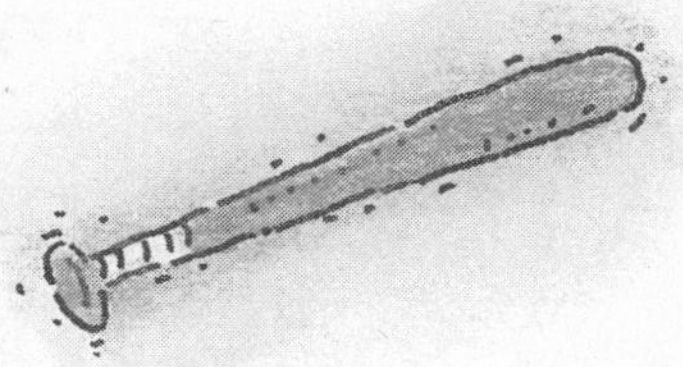

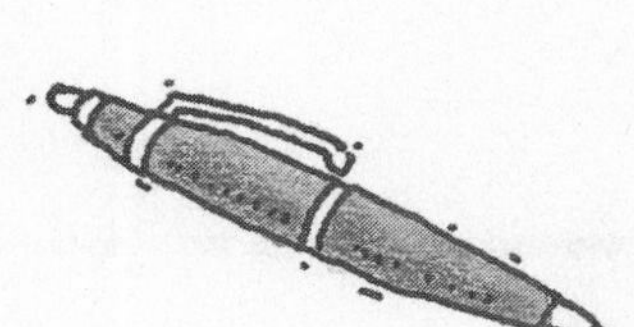

**Directions:** Circle the pictures that rhyme.

**Home Activity:** Have your child think of other words that rhyme with *pot* and *top*.

Name ______________________________

## Draw a line.

cat

two cats

See a cat and a dog.

## Draw.

I see a yellow cat and a red dog.

**Directions:** Draw lines to match the words and pictures. Draw a picture of the sentence.

**Home Activity:** Say a sentence and have your child draw a picture about the sentence.

Name ______________________________

## Draw a line.

bats

hats

See a bat and a hat.

---

## Draw.

I see a big bat and a tall hat.

**Directions:** Draw lines to match the words and pictures. Draw a picture of the sentence.

**Home Activity:** Have your child make up a sentence and draw a picture of it.

Name

## Write.

dot

pop

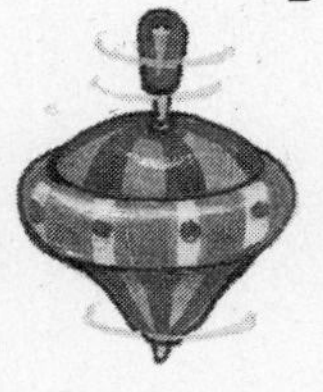

**Directions:** Write a rhyming word to name each picture.

**Home Activity:** Read rhymes or poems and have your child name the words that rhyme.

I like to do that!



(fold here)

# Do That!

Do you like to do that?

I do not like to do that.

Do you like to do that?



(fold here)

I do not like to do that.

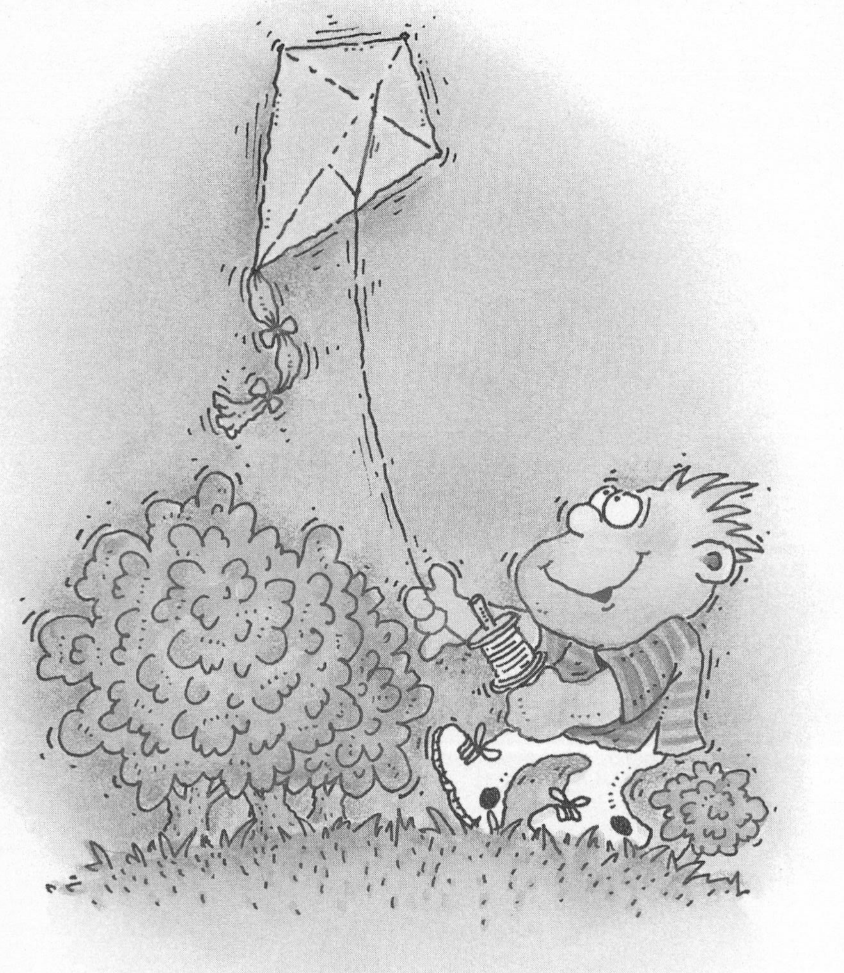

Do you like to do that?

I do not like to do that.

**You are your child's first and best teacher!**

**Here are ways to help your child practice skills while having fun!**

**Day 1** Give riddle clues for *j* words and have your child solve the riddle: It flies in the sky. (*jet*) It makes you laugh. (*joke*) It goes on toast. (*jam* or *jelly*)

**Day 2** Tell your child something to do in three steps and have him or her tell what to do first, next, and last. Then read a story. After each page ask your child to tell what happened, giving the events in the correct sequence.

**Day 3** Practice rhyme by saying a sentence with rhyming words: My *hen* has a new *pen*. My *pet* will *get* a toy. Our *cat* can *bat*. I *see three* trucks.

**Day 4** Write a sentence on a strip of paper: *The big cat likes yarn.* Cut the sentence into words. Work with your child to arrange the words into a sentence. Continue with other sentences.

**Day 5** Write the words *hen* and *net* as headings on a paper. Have your child write rhyming words for each word. As each word is written, have your child read the word.

Read with your child EVERY DAY!

(fold here)

# Family Times

**A Jolly Pair**

My name is Jenny Jackson.
I am a jolly hen.
I wiggle and I waddle
All around my pen.

I have a friend named Vera.
We're very close, you see.
We like to juggle vegetables.
A jolly pair are we.

We want to catch a nice worm.
We'll let him be our pet.
Vera is a jolly friend.
I'm glad that we have met.

The rhyme includes words that your child is working with in school: words that begin with the consonants *j*, *w*, and *v* and words with a short *e* vowel sound as in *hen*. The rhyming patterns *-et* and *-en* have the short *e* vowel sound. Read the rhyme together and have your child find the words that begin with *j*, *w*, or *v*. Then ask your child to name the rhyming words.

Name: ______________________

# Mark One

**Materials** different markers for each player

## Game Directions

1. Give each player a set of markers. Choose someone to begin.
2. The first player names a word that begins like the name of one of the pictures on the gameboard.
3. If the player is correct, he or she puts a marker on that space. The next player can choose the same or a different space and must name a new word.
4. The player who uses all of his or her markers first wins!

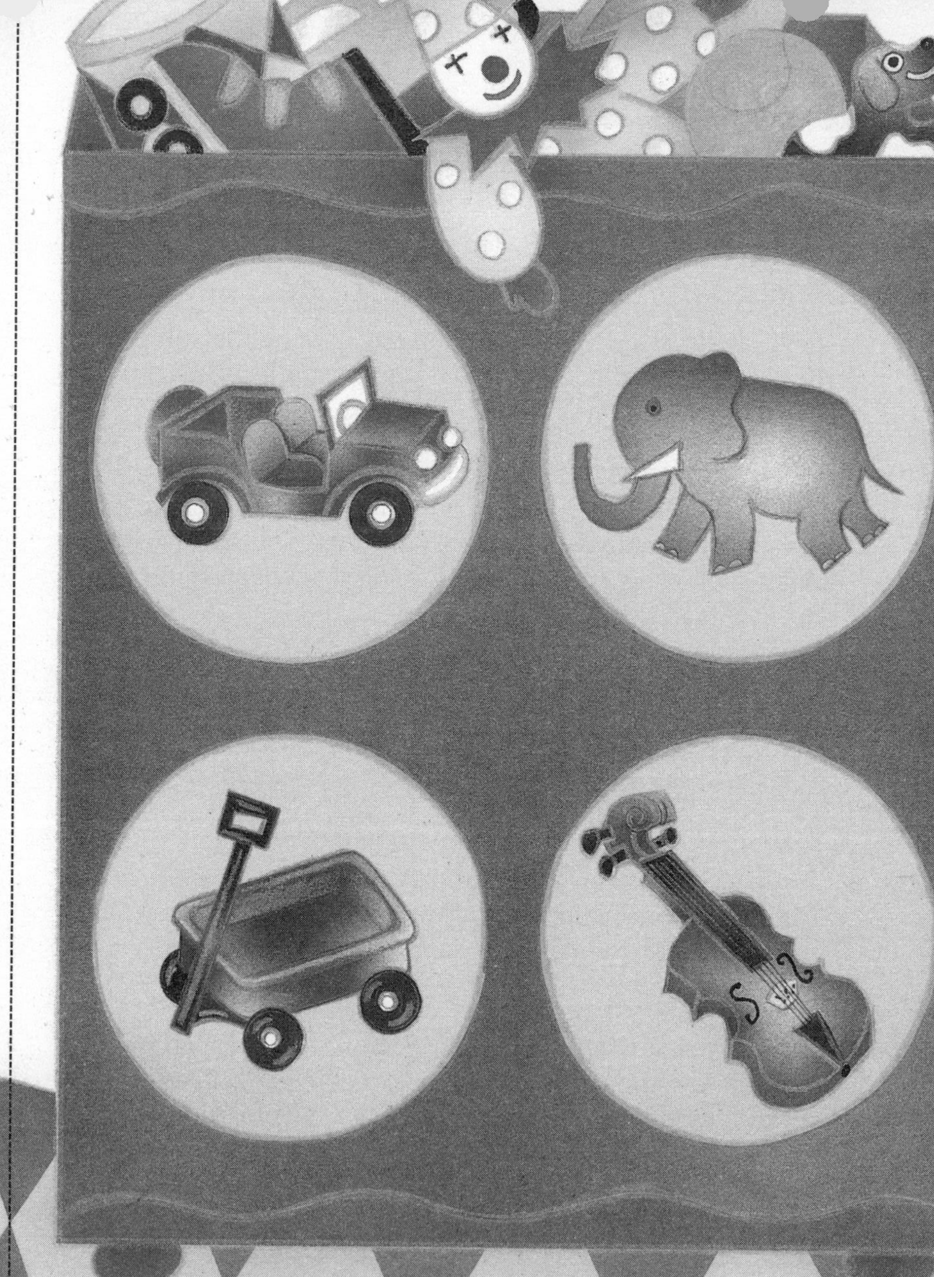

Name ______________________

Circle.

Jj

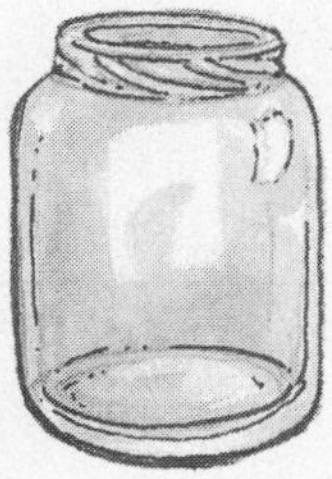

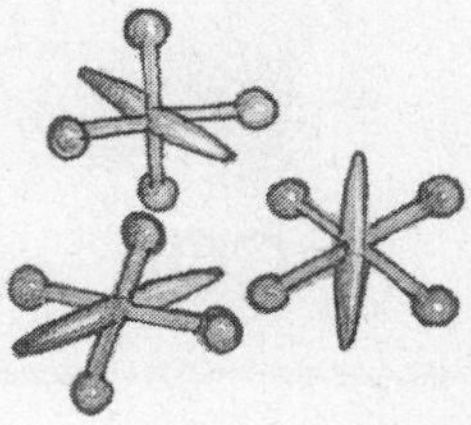

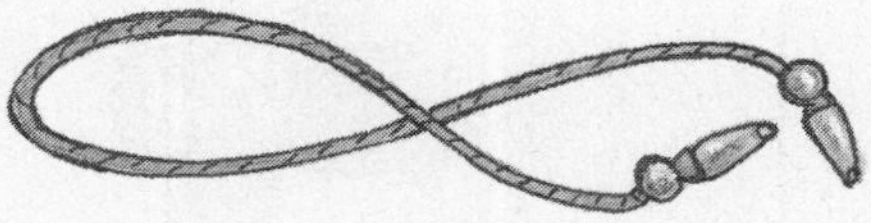

Draw.

**Directions:** Circle things that begin with /j/. Then make a /j/ picture.

**Home Activity:** Help your child find things around the house that begin with *j*.

Name ______________________

## Write.

net

ham

car

bug

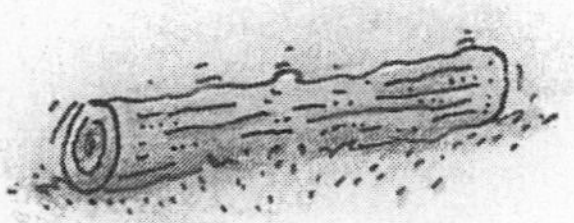

log

**Directions:** Change the first letter to make a new word that names the picture. Write the word.

**Home Activity:** Ask your child to read the rhyming words and use each word in a sentence.

Name ______________________

## Write.

**Directions:** Number the pictures 1, 2, and 3 to tell the order that things happened.

**Home Activity:** Read a story and ask your child to retell the story.

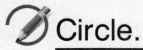

Name ______________________________

## Circle.

Ww

## Draw.

**Directions:** Circle things that begin with /w/. Then make a /w/ picture.

**Home Activity:** Help your child look for pictures of things that begin with *w*.

Name ______________________________

| | |
|---|---|
| get | what |
| we | one |
| two | three |

**Directions:** Have children cut along the dotted lines to make word cards.

Name ______________________

| | |
|---|---|
| What | Get |
| One | We |
| Three | Two |

Name ______________________________

## Circle.

**Directions:** Circle the two things in each picture whose names rhyme.

**Home Activity:** Ask your child to name the rhyming pictures and give other rhyming words.

Name ______________________________

 Circle.

Vv

Draw.

 **Directions:** Circle things that begin with /v/. Then make a /v/ picture.

 **Home Activity:** Help your child make a list of words that begin with *v*.

Name ______________________

## Write.

We get one.

I have two.

We have three.

**Directions:** Write each word used in the sentence.

**Home Activity:** Read the sentences together. Have your child copy each sentence.

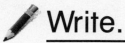

Name ______________________

## Write.

___et

___et

___et

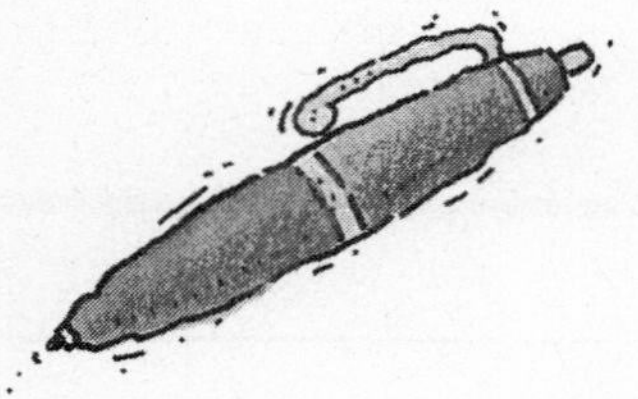

___en

___en

___en

**Directions:** Write the letter to make each rhyming word.

**Home Activity:** Help your child use the words to make rhymes: *Jack and Jill had a pet. They took it to a vet.*

Name ______________________________

## Circle.

## Draw.

**Directions:** Circle the pictures that show places. Draw a picture of a place you know.

**Home Activity:** Help your child name places in the neighborhood.

Name ______________________

Circle.

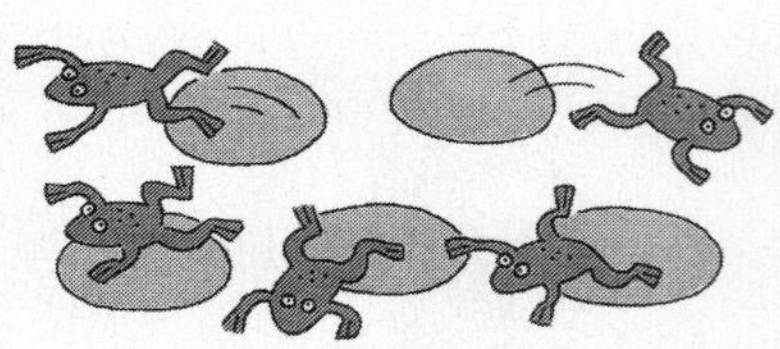

**Directions:** Circle the pictures of places.

**Home Activity:** Help your child label places in pictures.

Name ____________________

## Write.

pet

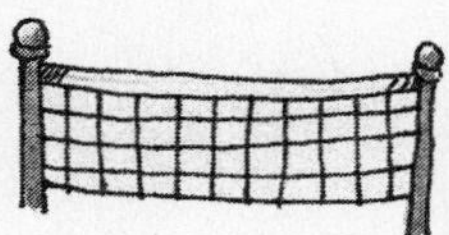

---

pen

10

**Directions:** Write a rhyming word to name each picture.

**Home Activity:** Ask your child to make other rhyming words for each set. (*bet*, *set*, *let*, *vet*; *then*, *when*, *den*)

We can get three.



(fold here)

# Get One!

What can we get?

Can we get three?

We can get two.



(fold here)

Can we get one?

We can get one.

Can we get two?

**You are your child's first and best teacher!**

**Here are ways to help your child practice skills while having fun!**

**Day 1** Play "Going to Yellowstone." Say "I'm going to Yellowstone and I will take a yo-yo." Have your child say the sentence and add another *y* word: "I'm going to Yellowstone and I will take a yo-yo and a yam." Continue adding other words.

**Day 2** Ask your child to retell a story you have read or a story from school. Encourage him or her to keep the events in the correct order.

**Day 3** Say the word *el-e-phant* and ask your child to tell how many word parts (syllables) the word has. Continue with these words: *cir-cus*, *bus*, *hel-i-cop-ter*, *truck*, *rab-bit*, *pur-ple*.

**Day 4** Ask your child to give the opposite for each word you say. (*small—large*, *big—little*, *in—out*, *up—down*, *high—low*, *back—front*, *on—off*, *empty—full*)

**Day 5** Say the word *net*. Have your child write the word. Then say the word *nut* and have your child change the vowel letter in *net* to make the new word. Continue with these words: *tab—tub*, *cot—cut*, *cap—cup*, *hot—hut*, *bag—bug*.

**Read with your child EVERY DAY!**



(fold here)

# Family Times

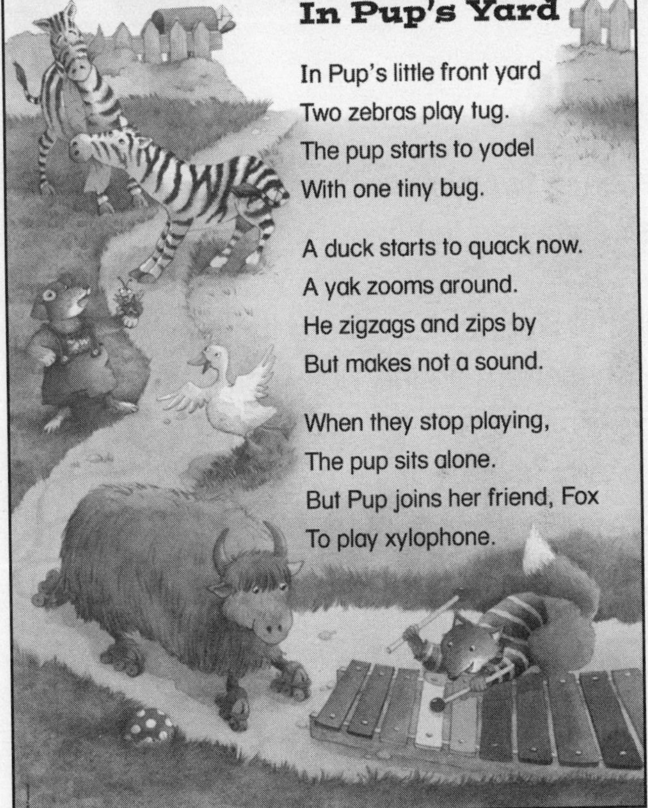

**In Pup's Yard**

In Pup's little front yard
Two zebras play tug.
The pup starts to yodel
With one tiny bug.

A duck starts to quack now.
A yak zooms around.
He zigzags and zips by
But makes not a sound.

When they stop playing,
The pup sits alone.
But Pup joins her friend, Fox
To play xylophone.

The rhyme includes words that your child is working with in school: words that begin with *z*, *x*, *y*, and *qu* and words with a short *u* vowel sound as in *cut*. The rhyming patterns *-ut*, *-up*, and *-ug* have the short *u* vowel sound. Sing the rhyme together to the tune of "Down in the Valley." Have your child find the words that begin with *z*, *x*, *y*, or *qu*.

Name: ______________________

# Tick-Tack-Toe

**Materials** marker for each player

**Game Directions**

1. Give each of two players a set of markers. Choose someone to begin.
2. The first player names a word that begins with one of the letters on the Tick-Tack-Toe board.
3. If the player is correct, he or she puts a marker on that space. The second player takes a turn.
4. The first player who fills a row across, down, or diagonally wins.



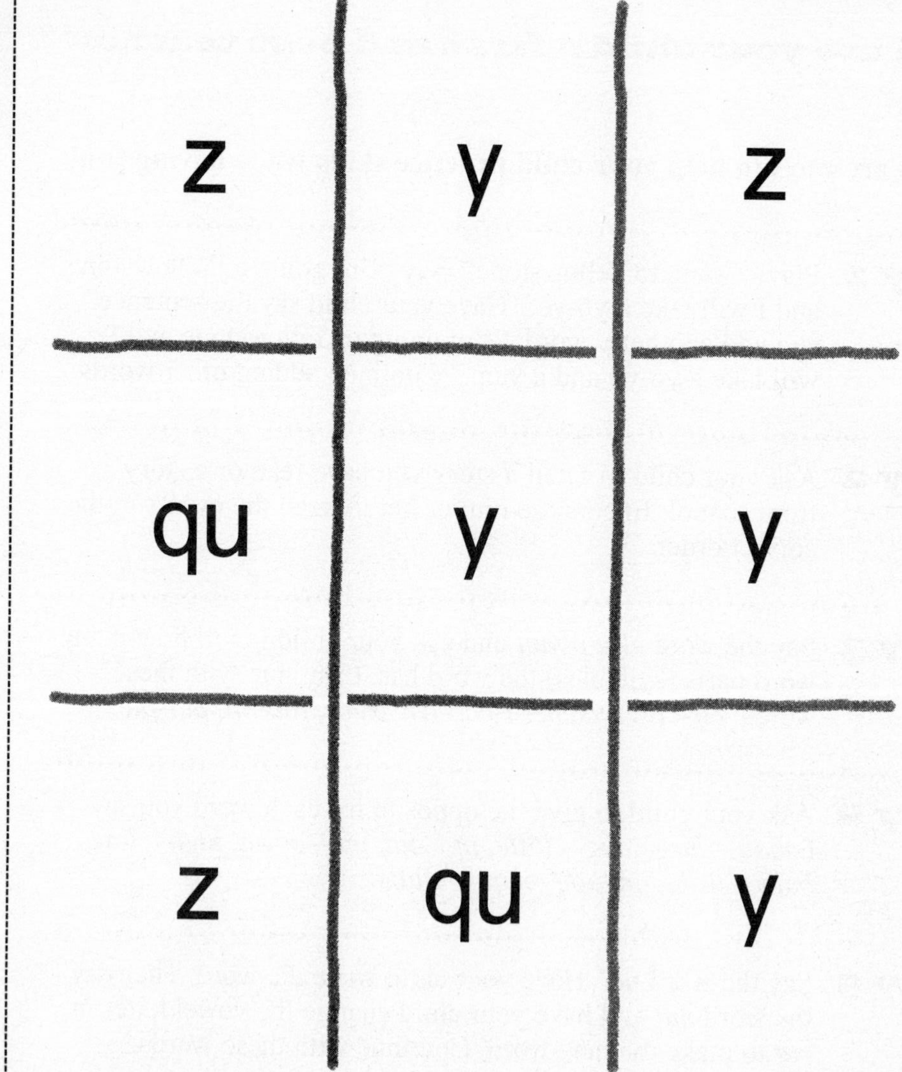

Name ____________________

## Circle.

# Yy

## Color.

# Xx

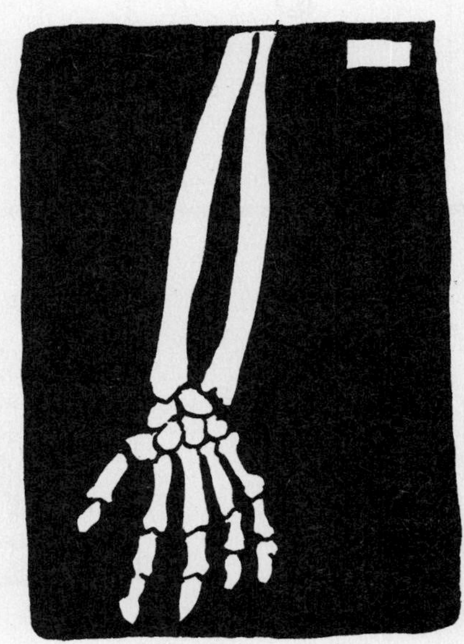

**Directions:** Circle things that begin with /y/. Color the thing that begins with *x*.

**Home Activity:** Help your child make a list of words that begin with *y*.

Name ______________________

## Write.

barn

bell

card

**Directions:** Change the first letter to make a new word that names the picture. Write the word.

**Home Activity:** Ask your child to look in books for other words that begin with *y*.

Name ______________________________



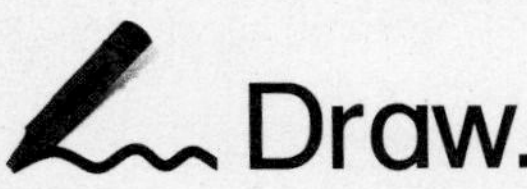

# Draw.

**Directions:** Draw something that happened in *Tumble Bumble*.

**Home Activity:** Have your child tell you the story in the book *Tumble Bumble*.

Name ______________________

## Circle.

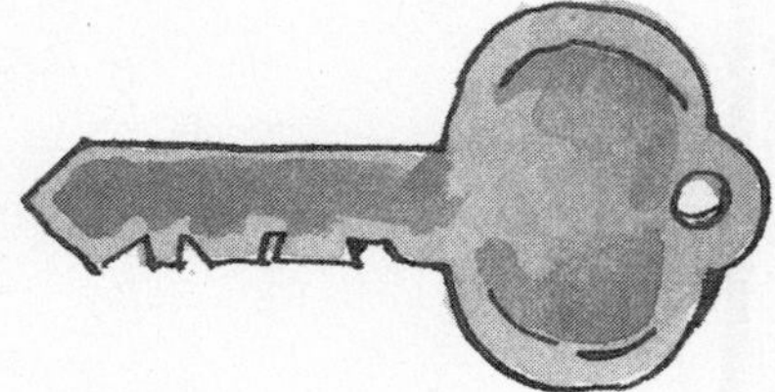

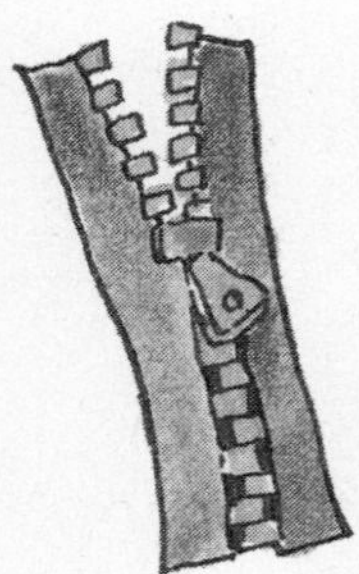

## Write.

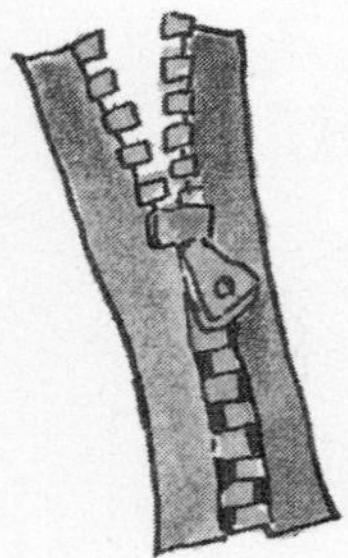

zip

______________________

**Directions:** Circle things that begin with /z/. Write the word for the picture.

**Home Activity:** Help your child write some /z/ words (*zoo*, *zoom*).

Name ______________________________

| | |
|---|---|
| up | but |
| go | where |
| here | am |

**Directions:** Have children cut along the dotted lines to make word cards.

Name ______________________________

| | |
|---|---|
| But | Up |
| Where | Go |
| Am | Here |

Name ______________________

# Write.

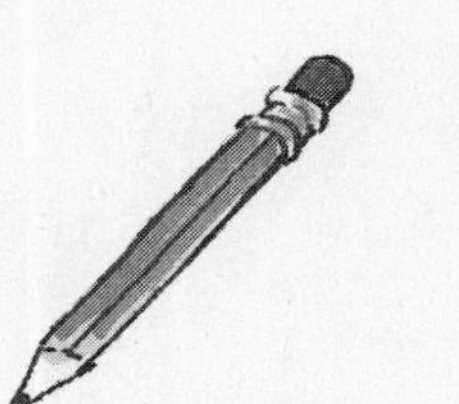

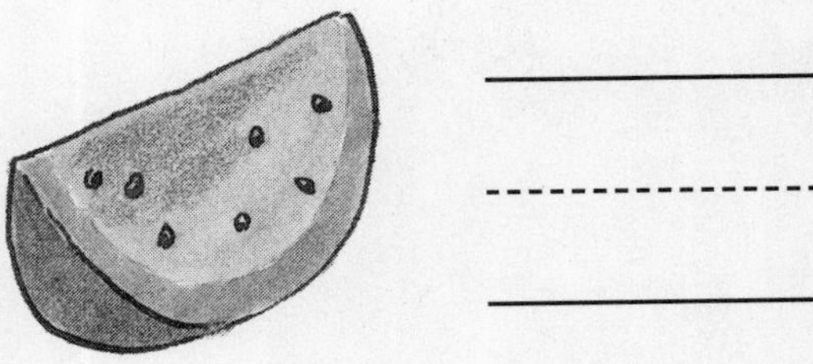

**Directions:** Say each picture name and clap the syllables. Write the number for the syllables.

**Home Activity:** Say words and have your child count how many parts the word has.

Name ______________________



## Circle.

qu

## Draw.

**Directions:** Circle things that begin with *qu* /kw/. Then make a /qu/ picture.

**Home Activity:** Say two words. Ask your child to tell which word begins with *qu* (*quit/hit*, *pack/quack*, *pick/quick*).

Name ______________________________

Draw.

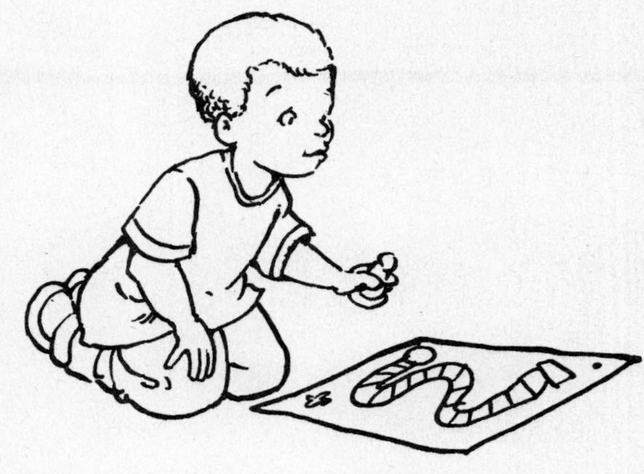

**Directions:** Draw things that go with playing a game or playing soccer.

**Home Activity:** Talk to your child about the activity in each picture. Ask your child to tell what he or she added and why.

Name ______________________________

## Circle.

up

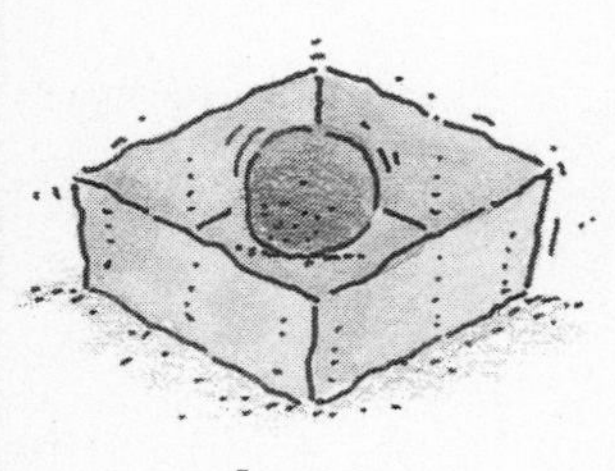

in

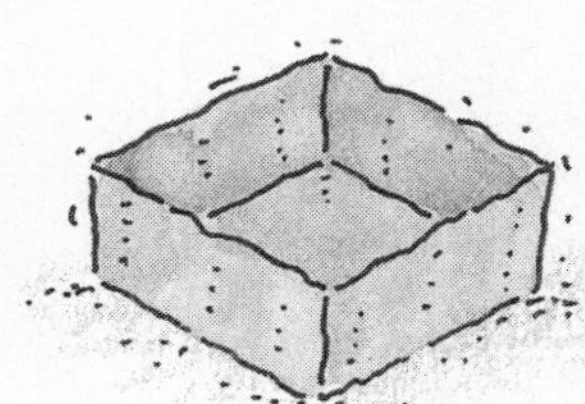

big

on

**Directions:** Circle the picture that shows the opposite of the first picture.

**Home Activity:** Have your child name the opposite of a word you name: *stop* (go).

Name ______________________

## Write.

___ug

___ug

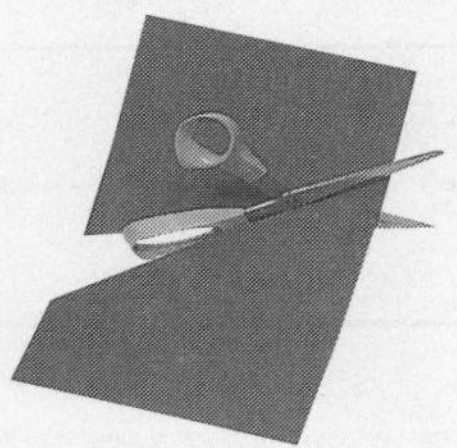

___ut

___ut

___up

___up

**Directions:** Write the letter to make each rhyming word.

**Home Activity:** Have your child find two things whose names rhyme.

Name ______________________

## Circle and write.

hug

bug

______________________

tug

rug

______________________

cut

nut

______________________

pup

cup

______________________

**Directions:** Circle the word that names the picture. Write the word.

**Home Activity:** Read the pair of words in each box and make sentences using both of the words.

# Where Am I?

Here I am.

(fold here)

I can go up,
but where do I go?

Here I am.



(cut here)

I can go up,
but where do I go?

Here I am.

(cut here)

Here I am.
What can I do?



(fold here)

I can go up, but
where do I go?

Name ____________________ 

## Write.

I like to play ________.

## Draw.

**Directions:** Finish the sentence and write it on the lines. Draw a picture to show your sentence.

**Home Activity:** Have your child tell about the picture and the things he or she likes to play. Make a list of games.

Name ______________________________

I read ______________________________

______________________________

It was about

## You *are* your child's first *and* best teacher!

**Here are ways to help your child practice skills while having fun!**

**Day 1** On small sticky notes or cards, write _____n, _____ t, _____d, _____p, _____g, _____m. Have your child stick the notes on household things that end with these sounds.

**Day 2** Ask your child to use the words *away, come, down, no,* and *will* in sentences with rhyming words, for example: *They were away all day.*

**Day 3** Read aloud to your child. Encourage your child to figure out the meaning of each unfamiliar word by using the first letter in the word and clues in the story and in the pictures.

**Day 4** Your child is learning that people speak for many reasons: to share ideas, to give information, and to ask questions. Challenge your child to listen for different uses of language.

**Day 5** Your child learned how to write a caption for a poster. Help him or her make a poster with a caption that tells about something that happens in your house.

**Read with your child EVERY DAY!**



(fold here)

# Family Times

The Nap

Oh, Cats!

### My Cat, Sam

I'm very glad
Sam is my cat.
Sam likes to nap
On his tan mat.

Sam likes to eat
From his big pan.
Sam likes to play
With his red can.

Sam likes to jump
Into my bag.
Sam likes to tug
On a blue rag.

This rhyme includes words your child is working with at school: words with the short *a* sound *(cat, nap)* and those that end with *n, t, d, p, g,* or *m.* Sing the rhyme together. Then think of other words with the short *a* sound. Work together to create a new verse with some of these short *a* words.

Name: ______________________________

# Fast Draw

**Materials** yellow crayon, index cards

**Game Directions**

1. Make 24 word part cards as shown. Use the yellow crayon to color both sides of all the cards that have two letters.
2. Place all 24 cards facedown on a table.
3. Players take turns picking two yellow cards and four white cards.
4. Each player uses the cards to try to make as many three-letter words as possible.

| | | | |
|---|---|---|---|
| an | an | at | at |
| ad | ad | ap | ap |
| ag | ag | am | am |
| b | c | d | f |
| h | m | n | p |
| r | s | t | w |

Name ____________________



**Circle** a word to finish each sentence.
**Write** it on the line.

---

cat cup

1. Here is the big ____________ .

---

bag big

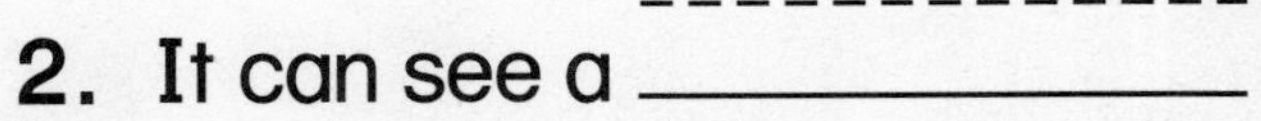

2. It can see a ____________ .

---

mat mop

3. See the cat on the ____________ .

---

nip nap

4. It can have a ____________ now.

---

pat pit

5. We ____________ the cat.

**Notes for Home:** Your child practiced reading words with the short *a* sound heard in *cat*.
***Home Activity:*** Work with your child to make words that rhyme with the short *a* words above.

Name ______________________________

**Draw** a line to show how Tad can go through the maze.

TAD

In

Out

**Write** the words that name the 5 things the cat goes past.
**Use** words from the box.

| bag | jam | van | ham | cap | map | fan | mat |
|---|---|---|---|---|---|---|---|

1. ______________ 2. ______________ 3. ______________

4. ______________ 5. ______________

**Notes for Home:** Your child practiced words that end in *n, t, d, p, g,* and *m*. ***Home Activity:*** Encourage your child to hunt through the house for things with names that end in these letters. Together, draw a picture for each item and label it.

Name ______________________



**Pick** a word from the box to finish each sentence.
**Write** it on the line.

| away | come | down | no | will |
|---|---|---|---|---|

1. No, Nan. I ______________ not get up.

2. ______________, Pam. Do not get up here.

3. Go ______________, you two!

4. Get ______________, Nan!

5. Nan and Pam, ______________ here and see.

**Notes for Home:** This week your child is learning to read the words *away*, *come*, *down*, *no* and *will*. ***Home Activity:*** As you read with your child, encourage him or her to point out these words in print.

Name ______________________________

**Look** at the underlined word.
**Circle** the picture that matches the sentence.

1. The cat is orange.

2. The boy is down below the cat.

3. He has a big balloon.

4. It is up in the sky.

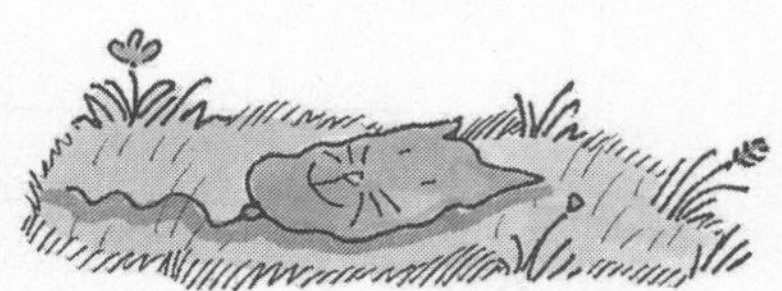

5. That little cat is so tiny!

**Notes for Home**: Your child figured out the meanings of unfamiliar words by finding clues in text and art. ***Home Activity:*** Read a story. As you come across unfamiliar words, encourage your child to use context clues to find the meaning of these words.

Name ______________________

A **sentence** is a group of words that tells a complete idea.

This is a sentence: The cat will come down.
This is not a sentence: The cat.

**Circle** the words to finish each sentence.

1. Sam and Pat ______ .  to nap / like to nap

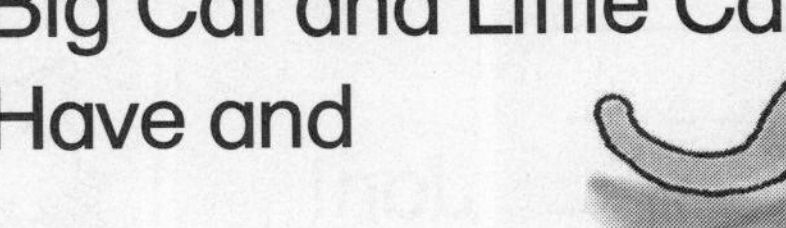

2. ______ do not nap.  Big Cat and Little Cat / Have and

3. Big Cat and Little Cat ______ .  go up / and Pat

4. ______ will not get up.  Ran / Sam

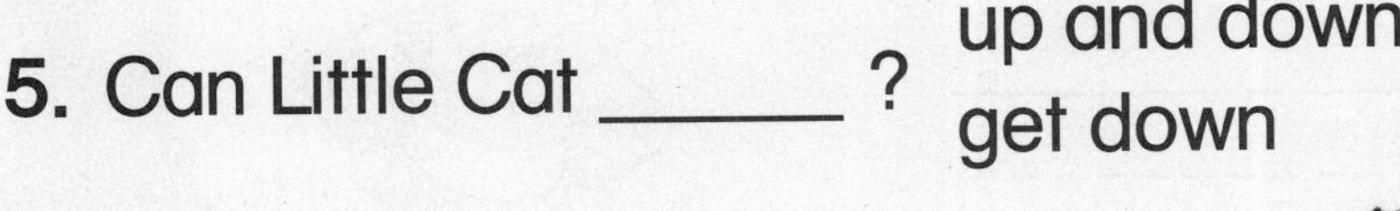

5. Can Little Cat ______ ?  up and down / get down

**Notes for Home:** Your child practiced recognizing complete sentences. ***Home Activity:*** Write five incomplete sentences that your child can read. Have him or her finish the sentences.

Name ______________________________

**Circle** a word to finish each sentence.
**Write** it on the line.

have     will

1. Jan, ________________ you get up?

See     Stay

2. ________________ here, Jan.

No     So

3. ________________, Jan!
Do not do that!

up     away

4. Do not go ________________, Jan!

Can     Come

5. ________________ here you bad cat!

down     do

6. You come ________________!

**Notes for Home:** Your child practiced reading and writing the words *away, come, down, no, stay,* and *will*. ***Home Activity:*** Help your child write a brief story using these words and then practice reading it aloud.

Name ______________________________

bug fox mat rug seal

**Say** the word for each picture.
**Write** the first letter of the word.
**Use** a letter from the box.

| b | f | m | r | s |
|---|---|---|---|---|

1. 
2. 
3. 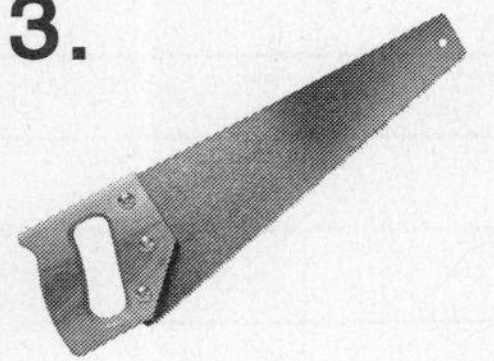
4. 
5. 
6. 
7. 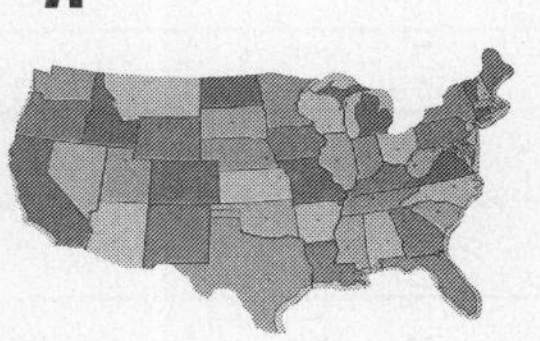
8. 

**Find** the word that has the same beginning sound as .
**Mark** the ⬭ to show your answer.

9. 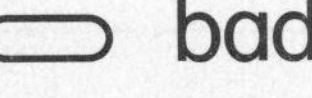
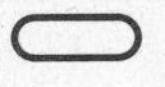
⬭ bad
⬭ sad
⬭ ran

10. ⬭ Sam
⬭ ram
⬭ fan

**Notes for Home:** Your child reviewed words that begin with *b, f, m, r,* and *s*. ***Home Activity:*** Have your child name as many objects as he or she can see in your home that begin with these letters.

Name ______________________________

**Look** at each word. **Say** it.
**Listen** for the middle and ending sounds in **b<u>at</u>** and **f<u>an</u>**.

| | **Write** each word. | **Check** it. |
|---|---|---|
| 1. at | | |
| 2. sat | | |
| 3. cat | | |
| 4. an | | |
| 5. ran | | |
| 6. man | | |

## Word Wall Words

**Write** each word.

| | | |
|---|---|---|
| 7. will | | |
| 8. no | | |

**Notes for Home:** Your child spelled words that end with *-at* and *-an* and two frequently used words: *will, no.* ***Home Activity:*** Ask your child to draw different pictures showing a man and a cat. Challenge your child to use these spelling words to label the pictures.

Name ______________________________

**Circle** a word to finish each sentence.
**Write** the sentence on the line.

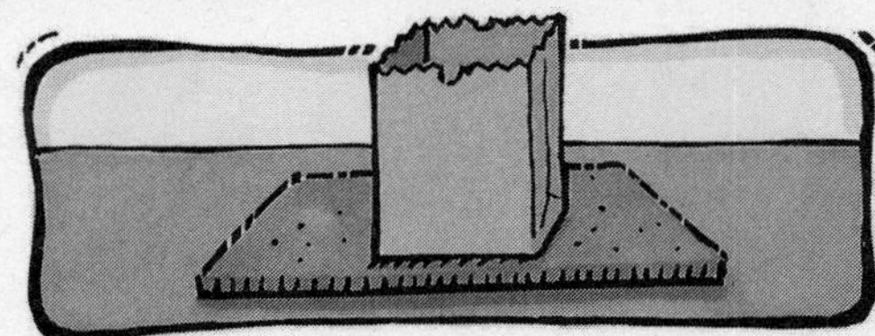

bag rag

1. The ______ is on the mat.

go red

2. The cats ______ in the bag.

bat cat

3. The bad ______ will not come.

big like

4. We ______ the cats.

**Notes for Home:** Your child wrote simple sentences. ***Home Activity:*** Help your child write simple sentences to describe a picture. Make sure your child capitalizes the beginning of a sentence and puts a period at the end.

Name ______________________________



# Test-Taking Tips

1. Write your name on the test.
2. Read each question twice.
3. Read all the answer choices for the question.
4. Mark your answer carefully.
5. Check your answer.

Name ______________________________

# Part 1: Vocabulary

**Read** each sentence.
**Mark** the ⬭ for the word that fits.

1. The cat ______ go in.
   ⬭ will ⬭ big ⬭ see

2. My cat will ______ .
   ⬭ can ⬭ come ⬭ three

3. The cat sat ______ .
   ⬭ down ⬭ get  no

4. ______ , cat, do not go in.
    To ⬭ It  No

5. The cat ran ______ .
    red 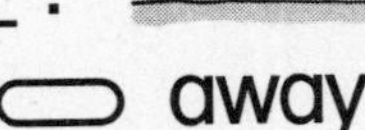 away ⬭ but

GO ON

Name ______________________________



# Part 2: Comprehension

**Read** each question.
**Mark** the ⬭ for the answer.

**6.** How many cats are there?
- ⬭ three
- ⬭ one
- ⬭ ten

**7.** The girl wants the cats to
- ⬭ run away.
- ⬭ come and play.
- ⬭ go up the tree.

**8.** When the cats hide, the girl
- ⬭ gets a new pet.
- ⬭ looks for them.
- ⬭ goes home.

**9.** How does the story end?
- ⬭ The girl hides.
- ⬭ The cats run away.
- ⬭ The cats come back.

**10.** The cats are
- ⬭ sad.
- ⬭ big.
- ⬭ fun.

STOP

Name ________________________

can

girl

nest

pan

top

**Say** the word for each picture.
**Write** the first letter of the word.
**Use** a letter from the box.

c g n p t

1. 

2. 

3. 

4. 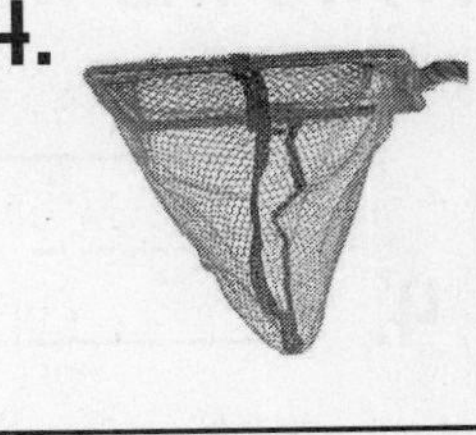

5. 

6. 

7. 

8. 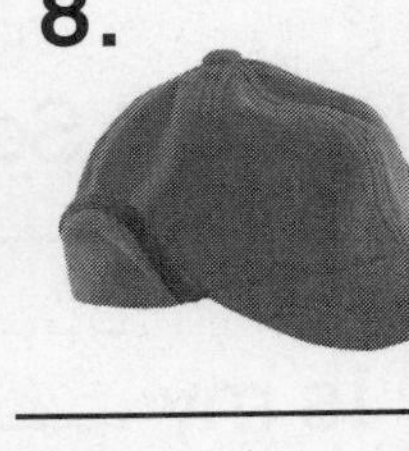

**Find** the word that has the same beginning sound as .
**Mark** the ⬭ to show your answer.

9. ⬭ mop
⬭ not
⬭ has

10. ⬭ mat
⬭ can
⬭ nap

**Notes for Home:** Your child reviewed words that begin with the letters *c, g, n, p,* and *t.*
***Home Activity:*** Help your child make a list of animals that begin with these letters.

Name ______________________________

at sat cat an ran man

**Write** the words from the box that rhyme with  .

1. ____________ 2. ____________ 3. ____________

**Write** the words from the box that rhyme with 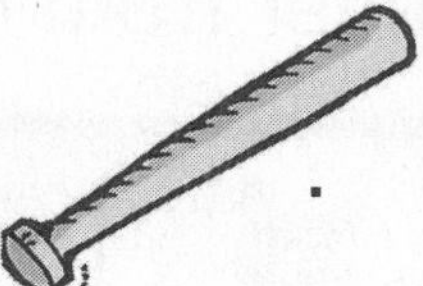 .

4. ____________ 5. ____________ 6. ____________

**Pick** a word from the box to finish each sentence.
**Write** it on the line.

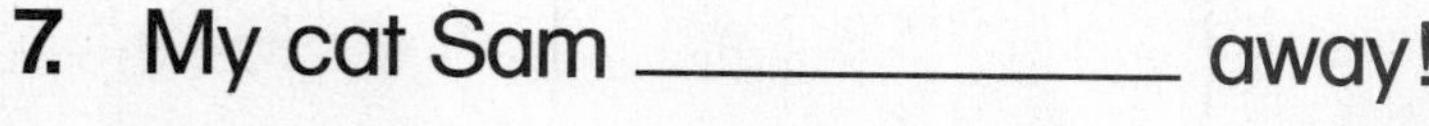

7. My cat Sam ____________ away!

8. Is my ____________ in that can?

---

**Pick** a word from the box to finish each sentence.
**Write** it on the line.

will
no

9. Sam ____________ not come.

10. There is ____________ cat in the can!

**Notes for Home:** Your child spelled words that end with *-at* and *-an* and two frequently used words: *will, no*. ***Home Activity:*** Have your child use these words to make up simple sentences. Help your child write each sentence.

Name ______________________________

The children ride bikes.

A **sentence** is a group of words that tells a complete idea.

**Find** each sentence.
**Draw** a line under each one.

1. Two girls
   books
   Two girls read books.

2. Bob paints a picture.
   Bob
   a picture

3. sings a song
   Ms. Fox
   Ms. Fox sings a song.

**Notes for Home:** Your child identified complete sentences. ***Home Activity:*** Talk about what you did today. Have your child write a complete sentence that describes one thing you did.

Name ______________________

**Find** the sentence.
**Write** the sentence.

1. Kim found    Kim found a cat.

2. She pats her pet.    her pet

3. The cat    The cat eats food.

4. drinks milk    The cat drinks milk.

**Notes for Home:** Your child wrote complete sentences. ***Home Activity:*** Have your child make up two sentences about a favorite game.

## You *are* your child's first *and* best teacher!

**Here are ways to help your child practice skills while having fun!**

**Day 1** Write a simple short *a* word such as *bag*. Have your child change one letter to make a new word with short *a*, such as *bat*. Take turns changing that word to *mat* and *mad* and so on.

**Day 2** Work with your child to make up a story about a treasure hunt using the words: *all, are, find, make,* and *play.*

**Day 3** Read a story with your child. For each important event in the story, pause and ask your child to tell you what happened (effect) and why it happened (cause).

**Day 4** Your child is learning to listen to predict outcomes or tell what will happen next. Read aloud a story to your child. Pause often and ask: *What will happen next?*

**Day 5** Ask your child to make up some sentences about family members or pets. Then work with your child to identify the subject of each sentence that tells who or what does something.

**Read with your child EVERY DAY!**



(fold here)

# Family Times

**Look at That!** **Can You Find It?**

### What Will We Find?

Please come with us now.
We look at our maps.
We bring our snack bags
And wear our pink caps.

We find an ant hill.
We find four fat cats.
We find a big web.
We even find bats.

We find a brown snail.
It sits on a tree.
We find a green leaf
And one bumble bee.

This rhyme includes words your child is working with in school: words with the short *a* vowel sound *(fat)* and words that end with *b, k, s, r, f,* and *l.* Sing "What Will We Find?" with your child. Then find things around your home that end with *b, k, s, r, f,* or *l.*

Name: ______________________

# Last Letters

**Materials** paper circle, paper clip, pencil, 1 button per player

**Game Directions**

1. Make a simple spinner as shown.

2. Take turns spinning for a letter. Players need to name a word that ends with that letter. If a player can name a word, he or she may move the number of spaces shown on the spinner. Follow the directions on the gameboard spaces. If the player cannot name a word, the turn is over.

3. The first player to reach the end wins!

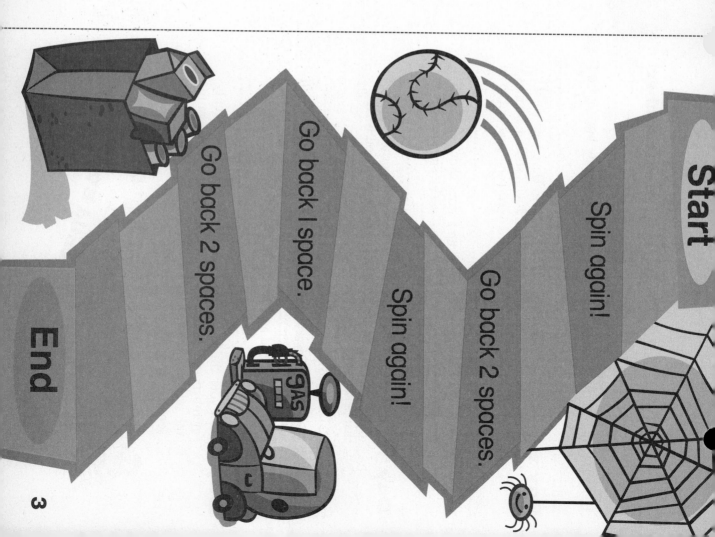

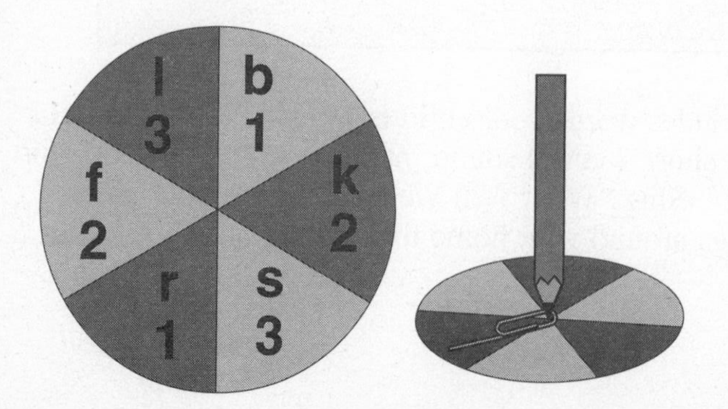




Start

Spin again!

Go back 2 spaces.

Spin again!

Go back 1 space.

Go back 2 spaces.

End

Name ______________________________

**Circle** the word for each picture.

bag

1. cat cop

2. rat rug

3. pan pin

4. hot hat

5. bet bat

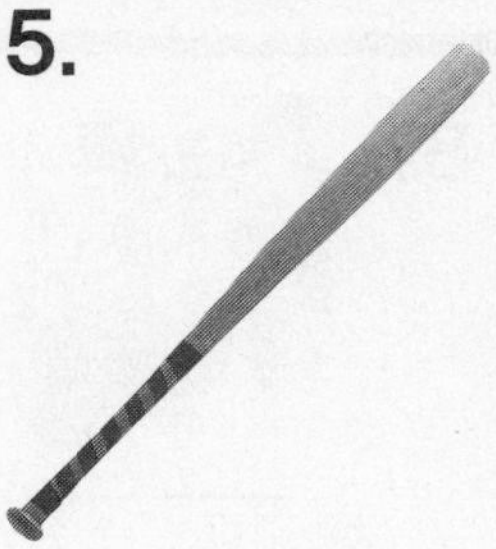

6. map mop

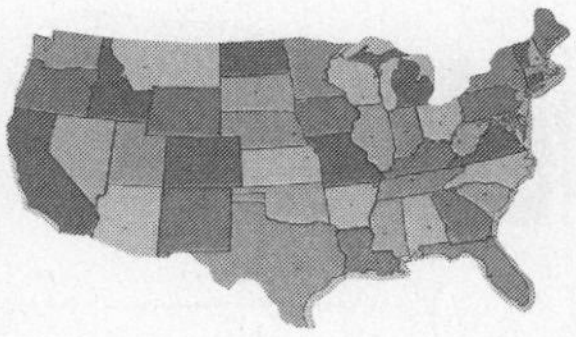

7. fin fan

8. can cot

**Draw** a picture for each word.

9. cap

10. man

**Notes for Home:** Your child practiced reading one-syllable words with the short *a* sound as in b<u>a</u>g. ***Home Activity:*** Help your child write sentences using short *a* words. Encourage your child to try to write some rhymes. (*The fat cat sat on the mat.*)

Name ______________________________

**Pick** a letter from the box to finish each word.
**Write** it on the line.

| b | k | s | r | f | l |
|---|---|---|---|---|---|

snai<u>l</u>

1. 
pai ____

2. 
loc ____

3. 
we ____

4. 
sta ____

5. 
lea ____

6. 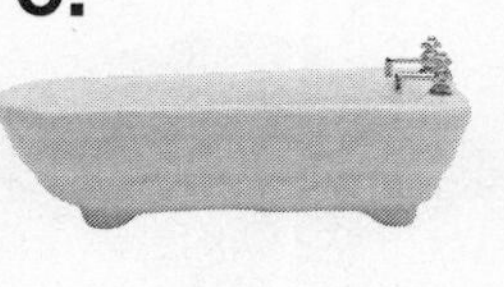
tu ____

7. 

bu ____

8. 

boo ____

**Draw** a picture for each word.

9. car

10. jar

**Notes for Home:** Your child is learning to read words that end with the letters *b*, *k*, *s*, *r*, *f*, and *l*. ***Home Activity:*** Go on a "Last Letter Hunt" around your home with your child. Together make a list of all the things you can find whose names end with *b*, *k*, *s*, *r*, *f*, or *l*.

Name ____________________



**Pick** a word from the box to finish each sentence.
**Write** it on the line.

| all | are | find | make | play |
|---|---|---|---|---|

1. Can you come and ____________ tag?

2. Will you ____________ play?

3. We will ____________ Pat go look.

4. Can Pat ____________ Jan and Dan?

5. Jan and Dan ____________ not here!

**Notes for Home:** This week your child is learning to read the words *all, are, find, make,* and *play*. ***Home Activity:*** Write these words on cards. Take turns drawing two cards. Try to use both words in one sentence. Help your child write his or her sentences.

Name ______________________________

**Look** at the picture that shows what happened.
**Circle** the picture that shows why it happened.

1.

2.

3.

**Look** at the picture that shows what happened.
**Draw** a picture that shows why it happened.

4.

**Notes for Home:** Your child learned about cause (why something happens) and effect (what happens). ***Home Activity:*** Give your child some causes and challenge him or her to guess what might happen. (For example: *It was raining, and Nan does not have a coat. Nan will get wet.*)

Name ____________________________

The **naming part** of a sentence names a person, animal, or thing.

<u>**Pat and Nan**</u> run.

**Circle** the naming part of each sentence.

1. Sal and the cat play.

2. Mom and Dad sat down.

3. The cat runs away.

4. Mom and Sal look.

5. The man gets it down.

**Notes for Home:** Your child identified the subject in simple sentences. ***Home Activity:*** Read a story along with your child. Ask your child to point out the naming part of different sentences.

Name ______________________

**Pick** a word from the box to finish each sentence.
**Write** it on the line.

**find snack make**

1. Sam will ______________ the cat.

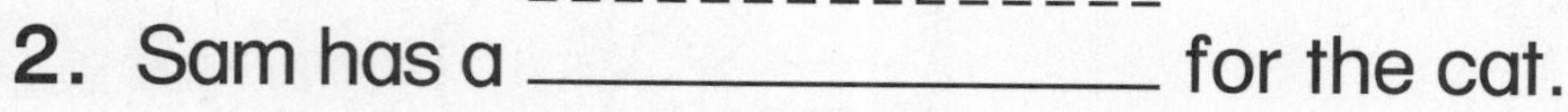

2. Sam has a ______________ for the cat.

3. It will ______________ the cat come out!

---

**Pick** a word from the box to finish each sentence.
**Write** it on the line.

**all are play**

4. We ______________ at the park.

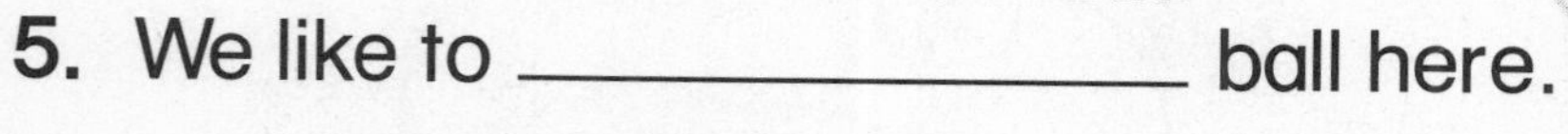

5. We like to ______________ ball here.

6. We ______________ have fun!

**Notes for Home:** Your child finished sentences using the words *all*, *are*, *find*, *make*, *play*, and *snack*. ***Home Activity:*** Say each word and ask your child to use it in a sentence. Help your child to draw pictures for the sentences.

Name ______________________

**Look at That!**
**Can You Find It?**

doll

hat

jam

kite

lock

**Say** the word for each picture.
**Write** the first letter of the word.
**Use** a letter from the box.

d h j k l

1. 

2. 

3. 

4. 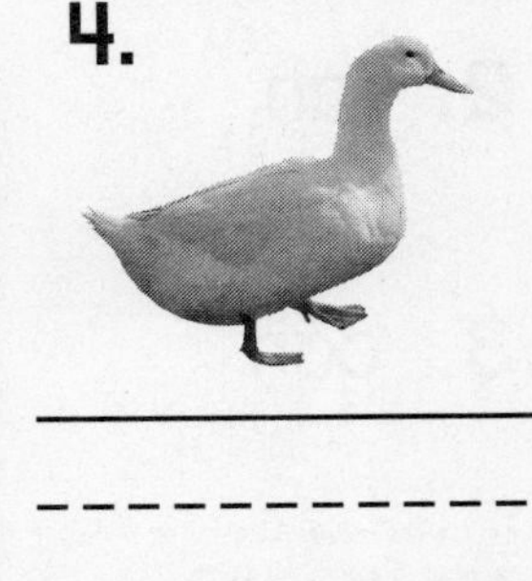

5. 

6. 

7. 

8. 

**Find** the word that has the same beginning sound as the picture.
**Mark** the ⬭ to show your answer.

9. ⬭ dad
⬭ lap
⬭ had

10. ⬭ jet
⬭ king
⬭ Dan

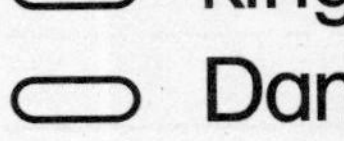

**Notes for Home:** Your child reviewed words that begin with the letters *d, h, j, k,* and *l.*
***Home Activity:*** Help your child make a list of people's names that begin with these sounds.

Name ______________________________

**Look** at each word. **Say** it.
**Listen** for the **short a** sound in .

| | **Write** each word. | **Check** it. |
|---|---|---|
| 1. am | | |
| 2. fan | | |
| 3. can | | |
| 4. bad | | |
| 5. had | | |
| 6. sad | | |

## Word Wall Words

**Write** each word.

| | | |
|---|---|---|
| 7. find | | |
| 8. all | | |

**Notes for Home:** Your child spelled words with the short *a* sound heard in c*a*p and two frequently used words: *find, all*. ***Home Activity:*** Work with your child to make up a story about a hot day. Help your child write it, using these spelling words.

Name ______________________________

**Circle** the word or words that are the naming part of each sentence.
**Write** the word or words on the line.

Pam My

1. ______________ has a hat.

Where The hat

2. ______________ is big.

A big A bat

3. ______________ is in the hat.

The cats I look

4. ______________ see the hat.

They Make

5. ______________ find the bat.

**Notes for Home:** Your child identified and wrote the subject, or naming part, of a sentence. ***Home Activity:*** Read aloud some simple sentences in ads and on signs. Have your child pick out the naming parts of the sentences.

Name ______________________________

# Test-Taking Tips

1. Write your name on the test.

2. Read each question twice.

3. Read all the answer choices for the question.

4. Mark your answer carefully.

5. Check your answer.

Name ______________________________

# Part 1: Vocabulary

**Read** each sentence.
**Mark** the ⬭ for the word that fits.

1. Sam and Dan like to ______ .

⬭ find ⬭ here ⬭ play

2. What will Dad ______ ?

⬭ make ⬭ see ⬭ did

3. The ants ______ little.

⬭ no ⬭ come ⬭ are

4. What do the ants ______ ?

⬭ find ⬭ can ⬭ big

5. ______ the ants come to see.

⬭ Am ⬭ All ⬭ At

GO ON

Name ______________________



# Part 2: Comprehension

**Read** each question.
**Mark** the ⊂⊃ for the answer.

6. The big girl makes a
   - ⊂⊃ hat.
   - ⊂⊃ rag.
   - ⊂⊃ map.

7. What do the children play?
   - ⊂⊃ Have a snack.
   - ⊂⊃ Get a nest.
   - ⊂⊃ Find the snail.

8. What does Sam find?
   - ⊂⊃ a spider web
   - ⊂⊃ a nest
   - ⊂⊃ an ant

9. What is in the hole?
   - ⊂⊃ a bird
   - ⊂⊃ a spider
   - ⊂⊃ an ant

10. Who finds the snail?
    - ⊂⊃ Pat
    - ⊂⊃ Nat
    - ⊂⊃ Jan

STOP

Name ______________________

Look at That!

Can You Find It?

van

wagon

yellow

zero

**Say** the word for each picture.
**Write** the first letter of the word.
**Use** a letter from the box.

v w y z

1. 

2. 

3. 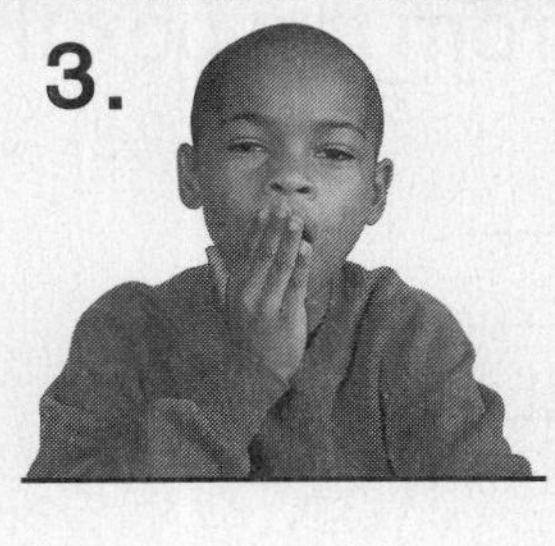

4. 

5. 

6. 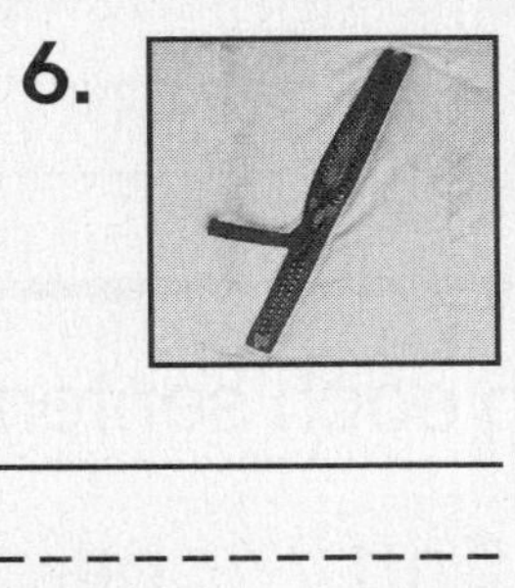

7. 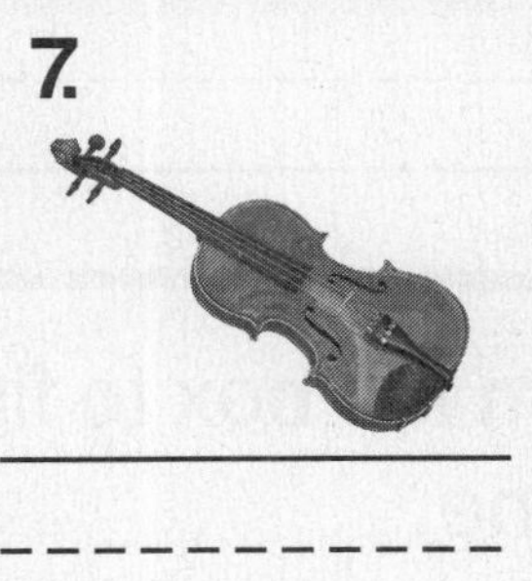

8. 

**Find** the word that has the same beginning sound as the picture.
**Mark** the ⬭ to show your answer.

9. ⬭ vat
⬭ was
⬭ yak

10. ⬭ wad
⬭ yap
⬭ van

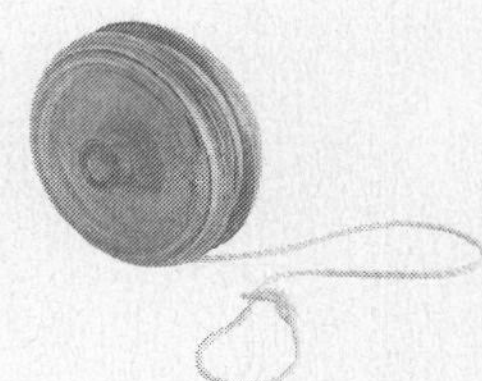

**Notes for Home:** Your child reviewed words that begin with the letters *v, w, y,* and *z.*
***Home Activity:*** Read a story aloud to your child. Pause at the beginning of each page and ask your child to listen for words with these sounds.

Name ______________________

am fan can bad had sad

**Write** three words from the box that rhyme with **Dad**.

1. __________ 2. __________ 3. __________

**Write** the word from the box that rhymes with 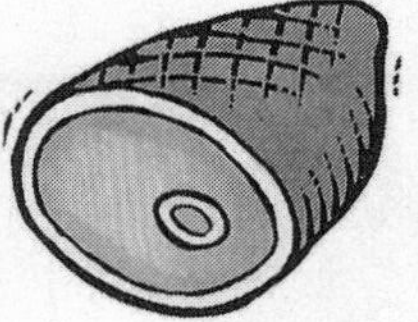 .

4. __________

**Write** two words from the box that rhyme with  .

5. __________ 6. __________

**Pick** a word from the box to finish each sentence.
**Write** it on the line.

find all

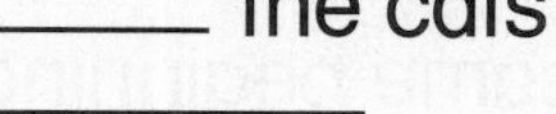

7. Can you __________ the cats?

8. The cats are __________ here.

**Notes for Home:** Your child spelled words with the short *a* sound heard in *Dad* and two frequently used words: *find, all*. ***Home Activity:*** Say simple sentences for your child to write. Use these spelling words.

Name ______________________________

RETEACHING

**The hat** is big.

The **naming part** of a sentence names a person, animal, or thing. It usually tells who or what does something.

**Draw** lines to match the two parts to make sentences.
**Circle** the naming part.

| | |
|---|---|
| This card | says hello. |
| Grandpa | was fun. |
| The zoo | is from Chicago. |
| I | miss you. |

**Notes for Home:** Your child matched sentence parts. ***Home Activity:*** Write subjects (*Our dog, Your hat, My nose*) on cards. Have your child choose a card and use the subject to make up or write a sentence.

Name ______________________________

Complete each sentence.
**Write** the naming part.

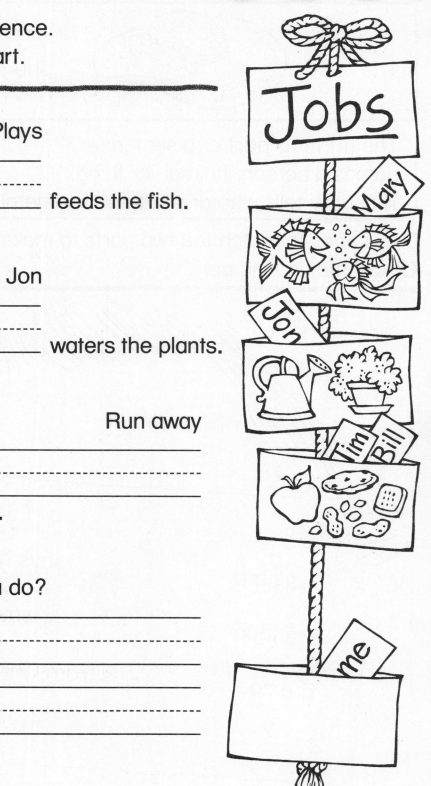

Mary Plays

1. ______________ feeds the fish.

Look at Jon

2. ______________ waters the plants.

Bill and Tim Run away

3. ______________
pass out snacks.

4. What job can you do?

______________________________

______________________________

______________________________

**Notes for Home:** Your child wrote naming parts of sentences. ***Home Activity:*** Have your child draw a picture of a family member. Then have him or her write a sentence, using that family member's name as the subject of the sentence.

**You *are* your child's first *and* best teacher!**

**Here are ways to help your child practice skills while having fun!**

**Day 1** Write the words *pit, did, fin, pig, sick,* and *pink* on slips of paper and place in a bowl. Take turns drawing a slip and naming a word that rhymes with the word on the slip.

**Day 2** Have your child draw pictures of himself or herself going on a walk and then use the words *did, me, saw, walk,* and *went* to write captions for the drawings.

**Day 3** As you read stories to your child, pause to encourage him or her to make predictions by asking: *What do you think will happen next? Why?*

**Day 4** Your child is learning that good speakers speak clearly, slowly, and distinctly. Encourage your child to take his or her time when telling you about something that happened in school.

**Day 5** The children in your child's class are beginning to keep a class journal. Help your child begin a home journal to describe events at home.

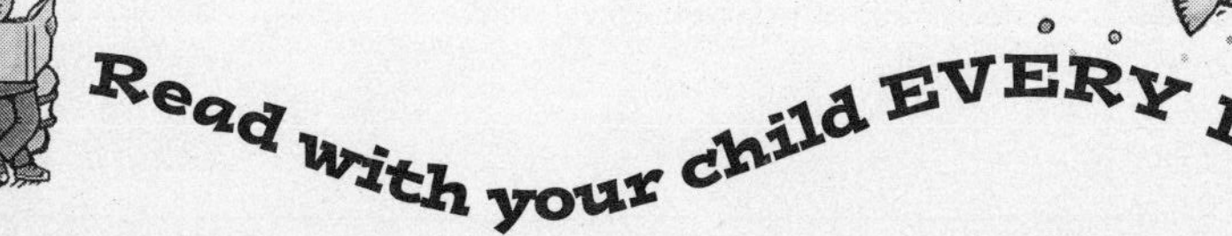

**Read with your child EVERY DAY!**



(fold here)

# Family Times

**What Did I See?** **I Went Walking**

### A Park, a Farm

I saw a big red ball to kick.
I saw a puppy with a stick.
I saw a big cone I could lick.
All in a park together.

I saw a duck and a little chick.
I saw a pink pig do a trick.
I saw some corn that I could pick.
All on a farm together.

This rhyme includes words your child is working with in school: words with the short *i* sound *(pig, pink)* and words ending in *-ck (duck)*. Sing the rhyme together and make up new verses. End the first three lines of each verse with short *i* words ending in *-ig, -in, -ink, -ip,* or *-it.*

Name: ______________________________

# Make a Match

**Materials** index cards, marker, bag

**Game Directions**

1. Make 10 picture cards of words that rhyme with those shown, such as *tack, sack; peck, deck; stick, brick; lock, rock;* and *truck, stuck*. Put the cards in a bag.

2. Each player starts by picking two cards. If words on the cards rhyme, the player puts them aside. The player then points to the card on the game board that rhymes with the card pair.

3. Players continue taking turns picking cards until all cards are gone.

4. The player with the most pairs wins!

Name ________________________________



**Draw** a line from each word to the part of the picture it matches.

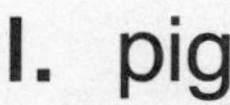

1. pig

2. lick

3. sink

4. lid

5. rip

**Notes for Home:** Your child matched words with the short *i* sound heard in *it* to parts of a picture. ***Home Activity:*** Help your child write simple sentences about the picture, using short *i* words.

Name ______________________

**Circle** a word that ends like **black** to finish each sentence.
**Write** it on the line.

black

Jack Nan

1. Here is ______________.

pal duck

2. Zack is his ______________.

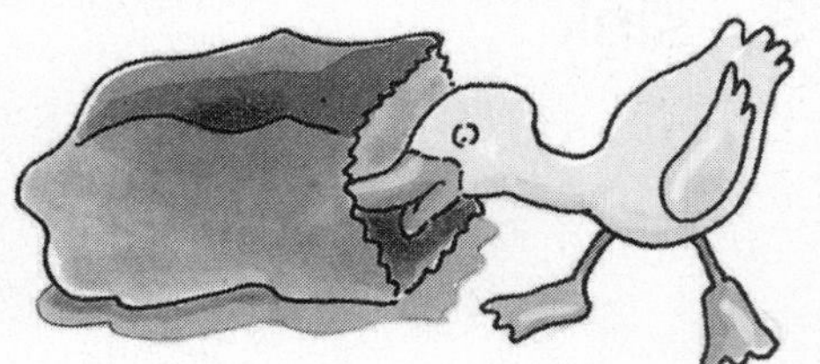

bag sack

3. What is in the ______________?

Zack Kim

4. Oh, ______________, do not do that!

sick sad

5. Zack is ______________.

**Notes for Home:** Your child practiced reading and writing words that end in *-ck*. ***Home Activity:*** Help your child write and read words that rhyme with the words ending in *-ck,* such as *sack* and *back.*

Name ______________________________

**Pick** a word from the box to finish each sentence.
**Write** it on the line. Use each word only once.

| did | me | saw | walk | went |
|---|---|---|---|---|

1. Sal and I like to ______________ .

2. Sal ______________ a big, fat cat.

3. Where ______________ the cat go?

4. The cat ______________ up and hid.

5. Come back to ______________ , Sal!

**Notes for Home:** This week your child is learning to read the words *did, me, saw, walk,* and *went.* ***Home Activity:*** Work with your child to use these words to write about a walk you have taken.

Name ______________________________

**Look** at the picture.
**Circle** the sentence that tells what will happen next.

1. Jan and Pal will nap.
   Jan and Pal will walk.

2. Jan and Pal will play.
   Jan will get mad.

3. Jan will walk to the van.
   Jan will sit in the van.

4. Pal will sit on it.
   Pal will lick it up.

5. Jan and Pal will play tag.
   Jan and Pal will go in.

**Notes for Home:** Your child used picture clues to make predictions about what event will happen next. ***Home Activity:*** As you read a story to your child, pause to ask your child what he or she thinks will happen next in the story. Discuss why your child thinks so.

Name ______________________________

A **sentence** has two parts.
The **action part** of a sentence tells what someone or something does.

The pups walk fast.

Circle the action part in each sentence.
Draw a line from the sentence to the picture it matches.

1. The two cats see the big can.

2. The two cats go in the can.

3. The two pups walk up to the can.

4. The two pups look in the can.

5. The two cats do not stay!

6.

7.

8.

9.

10.

**Notes for Home:** Your child identified the predicates of sentences—the parts of sentences that describe the action. ***Home Activity:*** Write some sentence beginnings, telling who or what the sentence is about. Have your child say the action parts of the sentences.

Name ______________________________

**Circle** a word to finish each sentence.
**Write** it on the line.

went    have

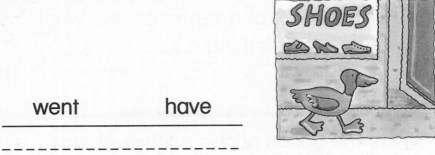

1. Mick the Duck ________________ on a walk.

---

saw    can

2. Mick ________________ a fat duck.

did    looking

3. That duck is ________________ at me.

---

went    walk

4. Mick will ________________ to that duck.

did    had

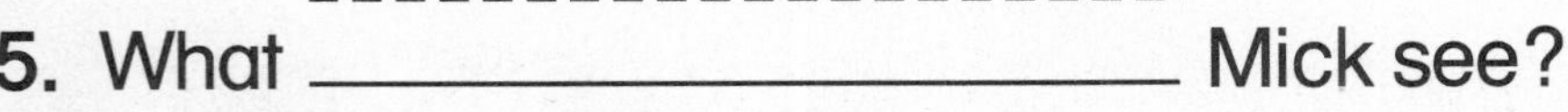

5. What ________________ Mick see?

---

me    my

6. Is that you or is that ________________ ?

**Notes for Home:** Your child practiced reading and writing the words *did, looking, me, saw, walk,* and *went.* ***Home Activity:*** Help your child use these words to write a story about something else that Mick the Duck did.

Name ______________________________

**Read** the word.
**Circle** the picture for each word.

can 

1. fan  

2. bag  

3. hat 

4. pan 

5. man  

6. van  

7. map 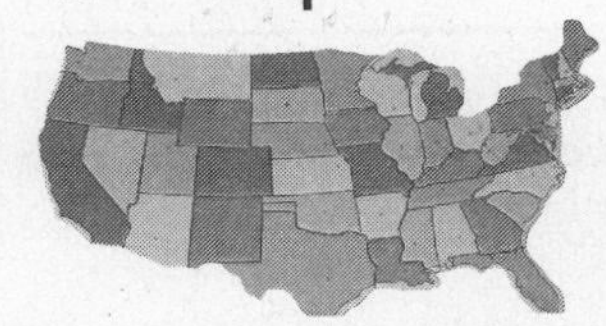 

8. bat 

**Find** the word that has the same middle sound as .
**Mark** the ⬭ to show your answer.

9. ⬭ sad
⬭ big
⬭ not

10. ⬭ red
⬭ hit
⬭ tap

**Notes for Home:** Your child reviewed words with the short *a* sound heard in *can*. ***Home Activity:*** Point out words on posters and headlines that have this sound. Help your child read these words.

Name ______________________

**Look** at each word. **Say** it.
**Listen** for the **short i** sound and the ending sounds.

| | **Write** each word. | **Check** it. |
|---|---|---|
| 1. it | | |
| 2. sit | | |
| 3. hit | | |
| 4. pick | | |
| 5. sick | | |
| 6. kick | | |

## Word Wall Words

**Write** each word.

| | | |
|---|---|---|
| 7. saw | | |
| 8. went | | |

**Notes for Home:** Your child spelled words that end with *-it* and *-ick* and two frequently used words: *saw, went.* ***Home Activity:*** Help your child write a sentence using each spelling word. Together, draw pictures to go with each sentence.

Name ______________________

**Circle** the word that is the action part of each sentence.
**Write** it on the line.

two see

1. The pigs ____________ a big rip.

walk no

2. The pink pigs ____________ in.

**Match** the naming part with the action part to make a sentence that makes sense.
**Write** the sentence on the line.

| | |
|---|---|
| My dad | is in the jar. |
| The cat | has a van. |
| The jam | naps in my lap. |

3. ______________________________

4. ______________________________

5. ______________________________

**Notes for Home:** Your child identified predicates—the parts of sentences that describe what a person or thing does. ***Home Activity:*** Read a story with your child. As you read, cover the predicates of some sentences. Ask your child to think of a way to complete each sentence.

Name ___________________________



# Test-Taking Tips

1. Write your name on the test.
2. Read each question twice.
3. Read all the answer choices for the question.
4. Mark your answer carefully.
5. Check your answer.

Name ______________________

# Part 1: Vocabulary

**Read** each sentence.
**Mark** the ⬭ for the word that fits.

1. The boy ______ up.
   - ⬭ find
   - ⬭ away
   - ⬭ went

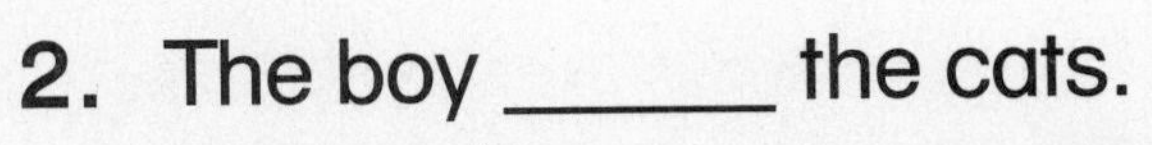

2. The boy ______ the cats.
   - ⬭ make
   - ⬭ saw
   - ⬭ walk

3. The dog will come to ______ .
   - ⬭ me
   - ⬭ did
   - ⬭ down

4. See me ______ !
   - ⬭ make
   - ⬭ walk
   - ⬭ find

5. What ______ I find?
   - ⬭ went
   - ⬭ all
   - ⬭ did

GO ON

Name ______________________________

## Part 2: Comprehension

**Read** each question.
**Mark** the ⬭ for the answer.

6. What did the boy do?
   - ⬭ went for a walk
   - ⬭ had a nap
   - ⬭ hid in a sack

7. First, he saw a
   - ⬭ cow.
   - ⬭ duck.
   - ⬭ cat.

8. What did all the animals do?
   - ⬭ run
   - ⬭ follow
   - ⬭ sit

9. The boy
   - ⬭ is sad.
   - ⬭ went back.
   - ⬭ likes animals.

10. What will the boy do?
    - ⬭ get a cat
    - ⬭ play with the animals
    - ⬭ see two ducks

STOP

Name ______________________________

pin

bat

red

nap

dog

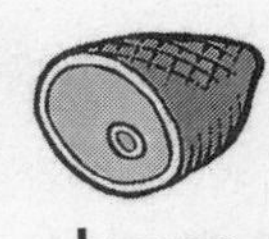
ham

**Circle** the word for each picture.

1. 
dad
dab

2. 
rag
rack

3. 
pick
pig

4. 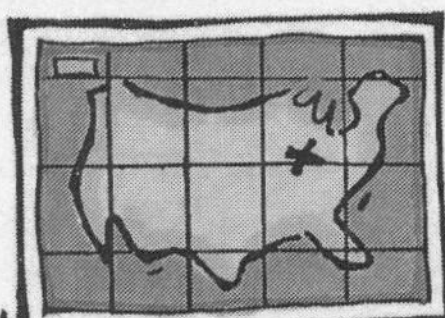
mat
map

5. 
cab
cap

6. 
hat
had

7. 

hit
hip

8. 
lip
lid

**Find** the word that has the same ending sound as .
**Mark** the ⬭ to show your answer.

9. ⬭ fin
⬭ has
⬭ jam

10. ⬭ man
⬭ him
⬭ his

**Notes for Home:** Your child reviewed words that end in the letters *n, t, d, p, g,* and *m.* ***Home Activity:*** Have your child look through a storybook and find short words that end in each of these letters. Help your child say the words.

Name ______________________

it sit hit pick sick kick

**Write** three words from the box that rhyme with .

1. __________ 2. __________ 3. __________

**Write** three words from the box that rhyme with .

4. __________ 5. __________ 6. __________

**Write** two words from the box to tell what the hippo is doing.

7. ____________________

8. ____________________

**Pick** a word from the box to finish each sentence.
**Write** it on the line.

saw went

9. I __________ you!

10. Dan __________ away.

**Notes for Home:** Your child spelled words that end with *-it* and *-ick* and two frequently used words: *saw, went*. ***Home Activity:*** Have your child use these spelling words and others like them to write a story about a pig.

Name ______________________________

**RETEACHING**

| My father plants a tree. | |
|---|---|
| **Naming Part:** | **Action Part:** |
| My father | plants a tree. |

A sentence has two parts.
The **action part** tells what a person or thing does.

**Underline** the action part.

1. Tom and I plant many seeds.

2. A bird eats some seeds.

3. Other seeds grow into flowers.

4. My father waters the flowers.

**Notes for Home:** Your child identified predicates—parts of sentences that tell action—in sentences. ***Home Activity:*** Say the name of a favorite television show character or story character. Have your child make up a sentence about what that character can do.

Name ______________________________

**Finish** each sentence.
**Read** each naming part.
**Write** the correct action part from the box.

| runs fast | fly away | play ball |
|---|---|---|

1. The boys ______________________________.

2. Lee ______________________________.

3. The birds ______________________________.

**Notes for Home:** Your child wrote predicates in sentences. ***Home Activity:*** Visit a favorite place. Have your child describe in complete sentences what people or animals are doing. Then ask him or her to repeat the action parts of their sentences.

## You *are* your child's first *and* best teacher!

**Here are ways to help your child practice skills while having fun!**

**Day 1** Help your child write sentences, using as many words that end in *x* in each sentence as possible. Some words to use are: *box, fix, fox, Max, ox, six, wax.*

**Day 2** Take turns making up questions for one another to answer, using any of the following words in your questions or answers: *how, many, on, they, why.*

**Day 3** Your child is learning to identify where a story takes place. As you and your child read stories and watch stories on television, encourage him or her to describe where the story takes place.

**Day 4** Your child is learning about word order in sentences. Write a simple sentence and cut it into words. Help your child reorder the words to make the sentence.

**Day 5** Your child is working together with classmates to write a poem. For additional practice, make up pairs of rhyming lines, using familiar, simple words.

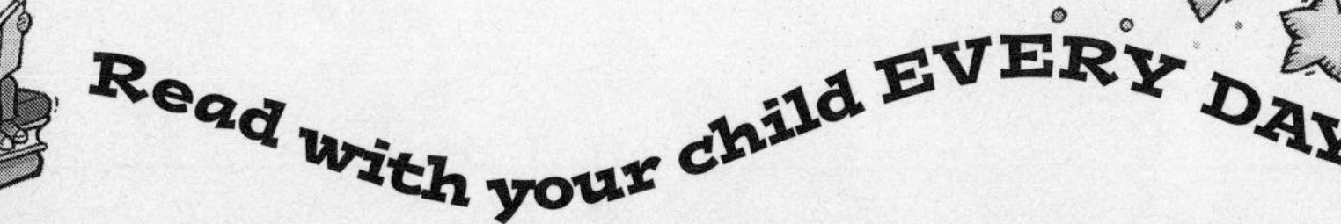
Read with your child EVERY DAY!

(fold here)

# Family Times

Fish Mix — How Many Fish?

### It's a Fish!

I think I see a fin.
I see it swish and spin.
I see six pink dots on the fin.
I don't think I'll jump in!

The fish is big and thin.
It winks and waves its fin.
I wink at it and then I grin.
I do think I'll jump in!

This rhyme includes words your child is working with at school: words with the short *i* sound you hear in *fin, fish,* and *pink,* and words that end in *x*. Have your child sing the rhyme to you. Then sing the rhyme together. Singers clap their hands each time a short *i* word is sung.

Name: ______________________

# The Ones That Didn't Get Away

**Materials** paper, marker, scissors, 10 paper clips, 24″ piece of string, small magnet, ruler or wooden spoon

**Game Directions**

1. Prepare a set of 10 paper fish as shown.

2. Tie one end of string to magnet and the other end to a ruler or wooden spoon.

3. Put a paper clip on each fish. Scatter fish on the floor and take turns catching them with the magnet "bait."

4. When a player catches a fish, the player spells a word ending with the letters on that fish.

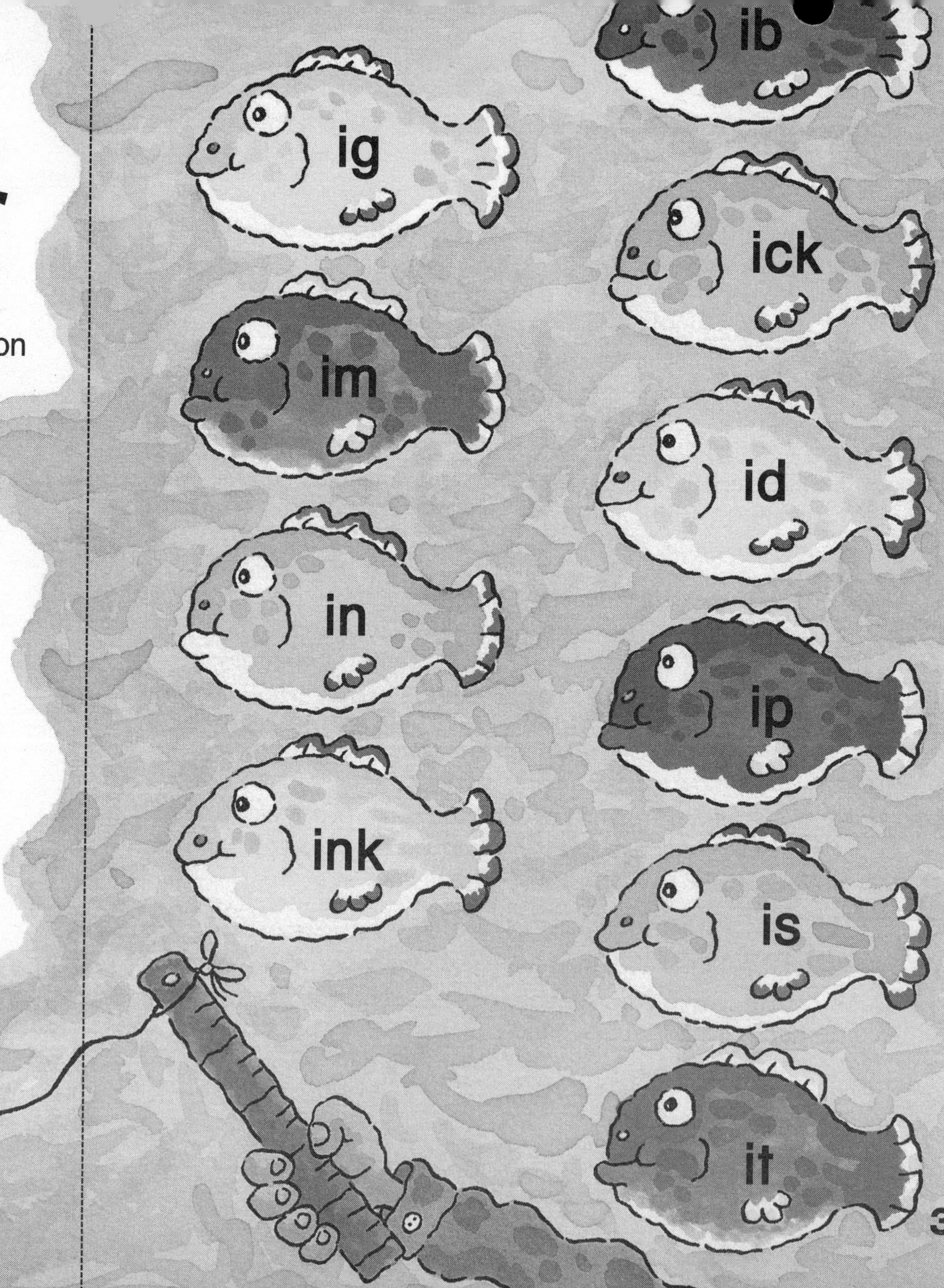

Name ______________________



**Pick** a word from the box to match each clue.
**Write** the words in the puzzles.

| dish | pin | bib | six | lid |
|---|---|---|---|---|

fish

1. 

2.

3. 

1. 2. 3.

4. 5.

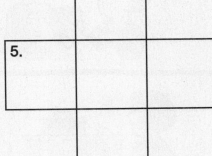

4. 

5. 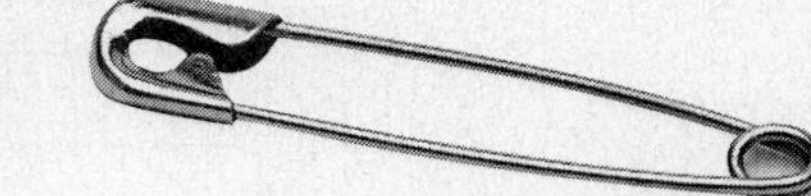

**Notes for Home:** Your child solved two puzzles using words that have the short *i* sound as in *fish*. ***Home Activity:*** Together, make a list of simple words with the short *i* sound for your child to practice reading.

Name ____________________

**Circle** a word to finish each sentence.
**Write** it on the line.

6 six

box bag

1. The fish are in a ____________ .

six two

2. I have ____________ fish.

mix make

3. I ____________ up the fish.

fit fix

4. Can you ____________ it?

back box

5. Get me the red ____________ .

**Notes for Home:** Your child practiced reading words that end with *-x*. ***Home Activity:*** On cards, write *box, fix, mix,* and *six*. Show each card to your child to give him or her practice reading these words.

Name ______________________

**Pick** a word from the box to finish each sentence.
**Write** it on the line.

| how | many | on | they | why |
|---|---|---|---|---|

1. We go ______ a walk.

2. How ______ fish did Tim see?

3. ______ many fish did the cat see?

4. ______ did the cat not see the fish?

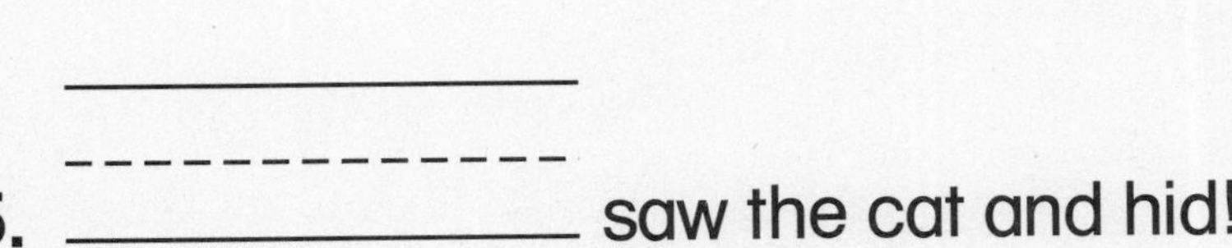

5. ______ saw the cat and hid!

**Notes for Home:** This week your child is learning to read the words *how, many, on, they,* and *why. **Home Activity:*** Have your child use these words to ask and answer questions. Take turns asking and answering questions.

Name ________________________________

**Look** at each picture that shows when a story happens.
**Circle** the picture that shows **today**.

1.  

2.  

**Look** at each picture that shows where a story happens.
**Circle** the picture that shows a **real** place.

3.  

4.  

**Draw** a picture of a make-believe place.

5.

**Notes for Home:** Your child identified when and where stories happen. ***Home Activity:*** As you read stories with your child, ask him or her questions such as: *Could this story happen today? Does the story happen in a place that could be real?*

Name ______________________________

The **order of words** tells what a sentence means.

Matches the meaning of the picture:
Dan can make a hat.

Does not match the meaning of the picture:
A hat can make Dan.

**Look** at each picture.
**Circle** the sentence that matches the meaning of the picture.

1. 
The rock is on Dan.
Dan is on the rock.

2. 
Max and Sam look at fish.
Fish look at Max and Sam.

3. 
Kim and Pam make a fish and a cat.
A fish and a cat make Kim and Pam.

4. 
Dad ran to Nan.
Nan ran to Dad.

**Write** a sentence for the picture.
**Make** sure the words are in the right order.

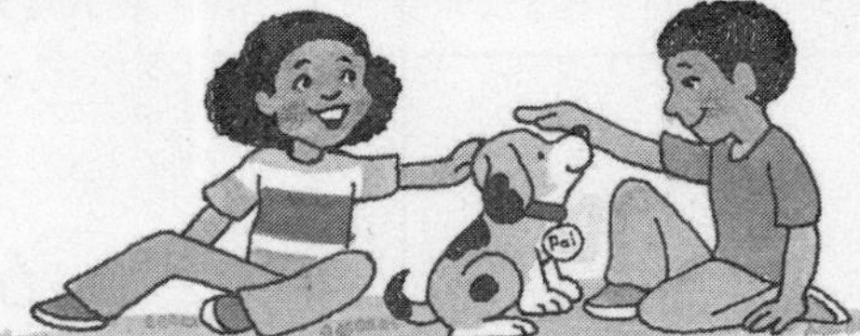

5. ______________________________

**Notes for Home:** Your child practiced using words in sentences in an order that makes sense for each picture. ***Home Activity:*** On strips of paper, write simple sentences your child can read. Cut them up and have him or her reassemble the words into a sentence that makes sense.

Name ______________________



**Pick** a word from the box to match each clue.
**Write** the words in the puzzles.

| happy | how | many | on | they | why |
|---|---|---|---|---|---|

1. a lot
2. The fish has a yellow dot ______ his fin.
3. ______ like it here.
4. Pam is ______ .
5. ______ is it so big?
6. ______ many do you see?

**Notes for Home:** Your child read and wrote the words *happy, how, many, on, they,* and *why*. ***Home Activity:*** Write each word on a slip of paper. Then have your child read the word and use it to tell about a day at a beach or at a pool.

Name ______________________________



**Read** the word.
**Circle** the picture for each word.

pan

1. can

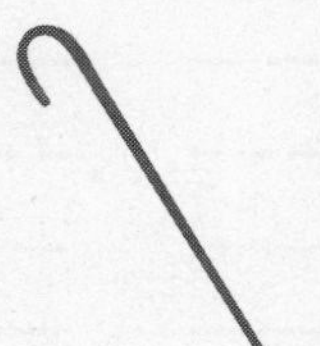

2. map

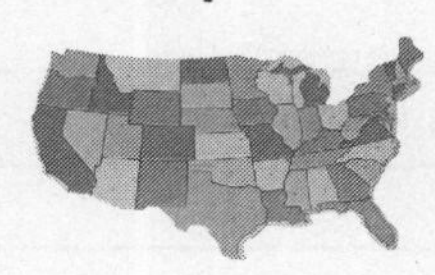

3. bat

4. bag

5. cat

6. jam

7. cap

8. ax

**Find** the picture whose name has the **short a** sound.
**Mark** the ⬭ to show your answer.

9. ⬭ ⬭ ⬭

10. ⬭ ⬭ ⬭

**Notes for Home:** Your child reviewed words with the short *a* sound heard in *cat*. ***Home Activity:*** As you read with your child, encourage your child to find short *a* words that he or she can read aloud.

Name ______________________________

**Look** at each word. **Say** it.
**Listen** for the **short i** sound in  .

| | **Write** each word. | **Check** it. |
|---|---|---|
| 1. fix | | |
| 2. mix | | |
| 3. six | | |
| 4. in | | |
| 5. him | | |
| 6. did | | |

# Word Wall Words

**Write** each word.

| | | |
|---|---|---|
| 7. on | | |
| 8. they | | |

**Notes for Home:** Your child spelled words with the short *i* sound heard in *pig* and two frequently used words: *on, they*. ***Home Activity:*** Help your child tell a story about someone who wins six pigs. Write the story with your child, using as many spelling words as possible.

Name ________________________________

**Circle** the sentence that tells about the picture.

1. The ball hit Pam.

   Pam hit the ball.

2. A fish has the man.

   The man has a fish.

3. The rat hid in the can.

   The can hid in the rat.

4. Sid and Tim like the caps.

   The caps like Sid and Tim.

**Write** a sentence to tell about the picture.

5.

________________________________________________

**Notes for Home:** Your child identified the correct word order in sentences. ***Home Activity:*** Write short complete sentences that your child can read *(Ted is sad)*. Cut each sentence into words and have your child reassemble them to make a sentence.

Name ______________________



# Test-Taking Tips

1. Write your name on the test.

2. Read each question twice.

3. Read all the answer choices for the question.

4. Mark your answer carefully.

5. Check your answer.

Name ______________________________



# Part 1: Vocabulary

**Read** each sentence.
**Mark** the ⬭ for the word that fits.

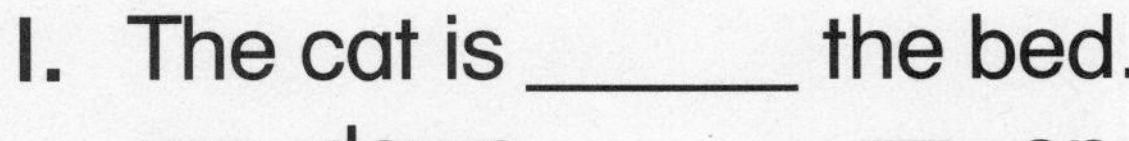

1. The cat is ______ the bed.
   ⬭ down ⬭ on ⬭ why

2. ______ like to walk.
   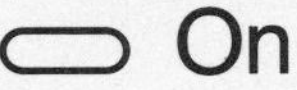 
   ⬭ On ⬭ Me ⬭ They

3. ______ is the sun red?

   ⬭ Why ⬭ On ⬭ Happy

4. There are ______ fish.

   ⬭ they ⬭ many ⬭ come

5. The boy is ______ .
   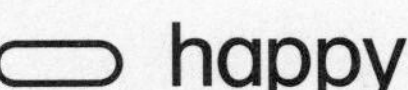
   ⬭ down ⬭ happy ⬭ how

GO ON

Name ______________________



# Part 2: Comprehension

**Read** each question.

**Mark** the ⬭ for the answer.

6. How many fish are in this story?
   - ⬭ two
   - ⬭ six
   - ⬭ ten

7. The fish live in a
   - ⬭ sink.
   - ⬭ pail.
   - ⬭ bay.

8. The pail is
   - ⬭ yellow.
   - ⬭ blue.
   - ⬭ red.

9. One yellow fish
   - ⬭ hid in a can.
   - ⬭ had a wish.
   - ⬭ lost its way.

10. The yellow fish was happy to
    - ⬭ stay lost.
    - ⬭ go to the sink.
    - ⬭ get away.

Name ______________________

bib

book

plus

door

leaf

snail

**Pick** a letter from the box to finish each word.
**Write** it on the line.

b f k l r s

1. 
ja ____

2. 
bu ____

3. 
coo ____

4. 
roo ____

5. 
cri ____

6. 
sea ____

7. 
tu ____

8. 
nai ____

**Find** the word that has the same ending sound as the picture.
**Mark** the ⬭ to show your answer.

9. ⬭ gas
⬭ gab
⬭ bag

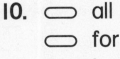

10. ⬭ all
⬭ for
⬭ is

**Notes for Home:** Your child reviewed words that end with the letters *b, k, s, r, f,* and *l.*
***Home Activity:*** As you read with your child, pause when you come to a word that ends with one of these letters. Read the word. Have your child name the letter that stands for the ending sound.

Name ______________________

**Pick** a word from the box to finish each sentence.
**Write** it on the line.

| fix | mix | six | in | him | did |
|---|---|---|---|---|---|

1. The cat is __________ the bag.
2. How __________ he get in there?
3. Can you get __________ out?

**Write** three words from the box that have the same ending sound as **fox.**

4. __________ 5. __________ 6. __________

**Read** the words in the box.
**Write** the letters to finish each word.

| on | they |
|---|---|

7. ______ n 8. ______ ______ ______ y

**Notes for Home:** Your child spelled words with the short *i* sound heard in *him* and two frequently-used words: *on, they*. ***Home Activity:*** Have your child use one or two of these words each day in a sentence that describes something that really happened.

Name ______________________________

**RETEACHING**

**Bike rides a Dad.**

This group of words does not make sense.

The words are not in the correct order.

**Dad rides a bike.**

This group of words makes sense.

The words are in the correct order.

**Draw** a line under the words in the correct order.

1. We ride in the park. Park ride in the we.
2. My flat is tire. My tire is flat.
3. Bike fixes my Dad. Dad fixes my bike.
4. Do you ride a bike? Do bike ride a you?

**Write** each missing word.

5. My fast moves bike.

My ______________ moves ______________.

**Notes for Home:** Your child identified the correct word order in sentences. ***Home Activity:*** Write a sentence with your child. Use scissors to cut between the words, and have your child put the words in the correct order.

Name ______________________________

**Write** an X next to the words that are **not** in sentence order. **Write** them in sentence order. Do not write the sentences that are in the correct order already.

1. Pets have many we. ________

2. Rabbits live in our yard. ________

3. Pets feeds the Mom. ________

4. What pet do you want? ________

**Notes for Home:** Your child wrote words in the correct order in sentences. ***Home Activity:*** Have your child look at magazine pictures. Say two sentences (one incorrectly) to describe it. Have your child identify the sentence with words in the correct order.

**You are your child's first and best teacher!**

**Here are ways to help your child practice skills while having fun!**

**Day 1** Look at a storybook with your child. Help your child find and list all the nouns (words that name people, places, and things) that end in *-s* and that show more than one *(frogs, boys)*.

**Day 2** Ask your child to draw a picture of a pond. Then write about it, using these words: *does, he, into, this, water.*

**Day 3** Your child is learning why authors write books and is using this information to predict what a book might be about. Look at nonfiction books. Ask your child: *What do you think this book is about? Why?*

**Day 4** Your child is learning to recognize sentences that tell something. Point out sentences in print. Ask your child to tell whether each is a telling sentence and how he or she knows that.

**Day 5** Before reading a poem to your child, ask him or her to listen for something specific, such as the rhythm, rhyme, or certain sounds.

**Read with your child EVERY DAY!**



(fold here)

# Family Times

Jog, Frog, Jog

Tadpole to Frog

## Hip, Hop, Hip!

Hip, hop, hip! In the fog,
I see frogs hop to a log.
With a hip, hop, polliwog,
Hopping to a log.
How many frogs hop to a log?

Hip, hop, hip! In the fog,
I see hogs jog to a log.
With a hip, hop, polliwog,
Jogging to a log.
How many hogs jog to a log?

Hip, hop, hip! In the fog,
I see frogs and hogs on a log.
With a hip, hop, polliwog,
Sitting on a log.
I see frogs and hogs on a log.

This rhyme includes words your child is working with at school: words with the short *o* sound you hear in *hop* and plural words ending in *-s*. Sing the rhyme together, hopping forward each time you hear a word with the short *o* sound and clapping each time you hear a word ending in *-s*.

Name: ______________________

# Hip, Hop Don't Stop

**Materials** paper, marker, scissors, bag, 1 button per player

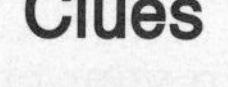

**Game Directions**

1. Copy the clues shown on a sheet of paper. Cut the clues apart and put them in the bag.
2. Players put buttons on Start. Take turns drawing and reading clues.
3. Each time a player can answer a clue with a short *o* word, that player's button may hop to the next lily pad. (Answers to the clues are given below.)
4. The first player to hop to the end wins!

**Answers (in order): hog, top, clock, pot, dog, shop, hot, hop, mop, frog**

**Clues**

| | |
|---|---|
| a fat farm animal that grunts | not the bottom |
| hangs on the wall and tells time | something to cook in |
| a friendly pet that wags its tail | a store |
| not cold | jump |
| something to wash the floor with | an animal that swims and croaks |

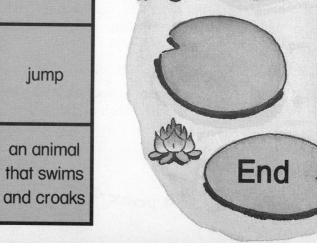

Name ______________________________

**Say** the word for each picture.
**Circle** the picture if the word has
the **short o** sound in **top.**

top 

1. 

2. 

3. 

4. 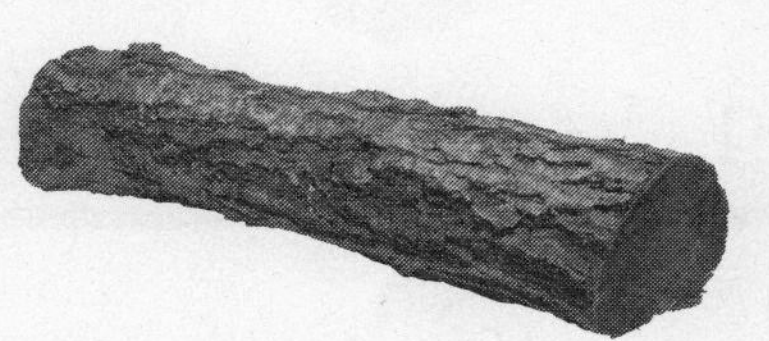

5. 

6. 

7. 

8. 

9. 

10. 

11. 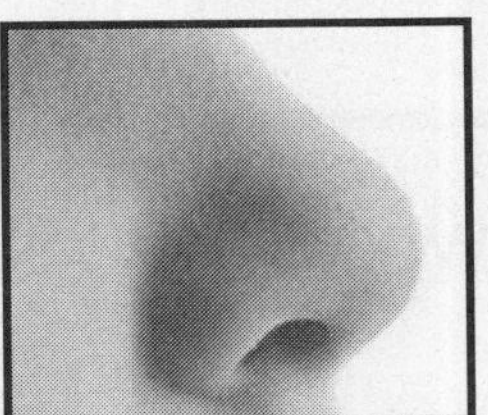

12. 

13. 

14 

15. 

**Notes for Home:** Your child identified words that contain the short *o* sound in *top*. ***Home Activity:*** Encourage your child to use any of the short *o* words pictured above in sentences. Challenge your child to think of other short *o* words.

Name ______________________________



**Circle** a word to match each picture.

1. 
frog frogs

2.  
pig pigs

3. 
hat hats

4. 
log logs

5. 
dog dogs

6. 
bag bags

7. 
egg eggs

8. 
sink sinks

**Draw** a picture for each word.

9. cats

10. duck

**Notes for Home:** Your child identified singular and plural nouns. ***Home Activity:*** Have your child name items on a shelf or in a closet. Listen for the use of *-s* at the end of many plural words, such as *books, hats,* and *gloves.*

Name ______________________

**Circle** a word to finish each sentence.
**Write** it on the line.

1. What a lot of ______________ is in there! water many

2. Look at ______________ big fish! they this

3. ______________ he like it in there? Has Does

4. What will ______________ do now? he has

5. See him go ______________ the big rocks. into up

**Notes for Home:** This week your child is learning to read the words *does, he, into, this,* and *water.* ***Home Activity***: Help your child make up sentences that contain these words. Draw pictures to match each sentence.

Name ______________________________

**Circle** the four books that may tell you about something real.

1. 

2. 

3. 

4. 

5. 

6. 

7. 

8. 

---

**Think** of a book that tells you about something real.
**Write** its name on the line.
**Draw** a picture in the box that shows what the book is about.

9. ______________________________

10. 

**Notes for Home:** Your child has learned to tell what a book might be about by figuring out why it was written. ***Home Activity:*** As you read various materials with your child, ask what he or she thinks each is about and why the author wrote it.

Name ______________________

A **statement** tells something.
It begins with a capital letter. It ends with a **.**.

He can see many fish.

**Correct** each statement.
**Write** it on the line.

1. here are six fish

2. one fish has a yellow dot

3. two fish are blue

4. one is like a cat

5. one has a fin like a fan

**Notes for Home:** Your child wrote and punctuated sentences that tell something. ***Home Activity:*** Take turns writing statements that tell what you see in the room. Help your child write words, as needed.

Name ______________________



**Pick** a word from the box to finish each sentence.
**Write** the words in the puzzles.

| body | does | he | into | this | water |
|---|---|---|---|---|---|

1. ______ sees a frog.
2. The frog is by the ______.
3. ______ frog is big!

4. A tadpole's ______ does not look like a frog.
5. Soon it will grow ______ a frog.
6. How long ______ it take?

**Notes for Home:** Your child used newly learned words to solve puzzles. ***Home Activity:*** Help your child make up a short story using some of these words. Help your child to write down the sentences and illustrate his or her ideas.

Name ______________________

**Say** the word for each picture.
**Write i** on the line if you hear the **short i** sound.

pig

1.

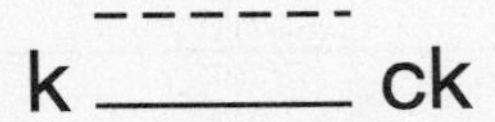
k ____ ck

2.
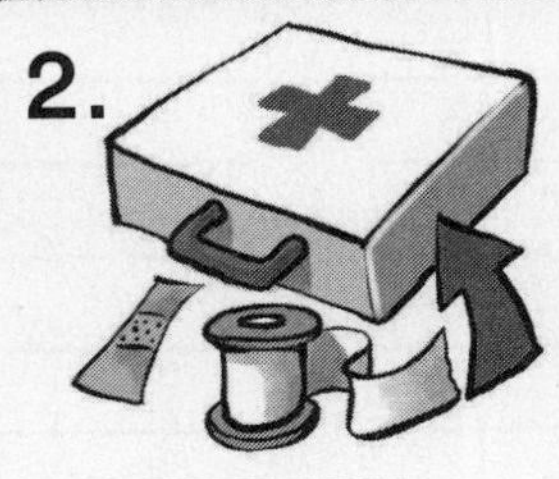
k ____ t

3.

t ____ ck

4.

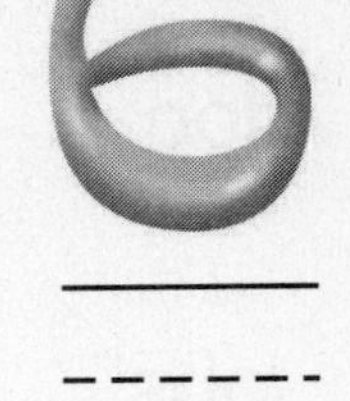
s ____ x

5.
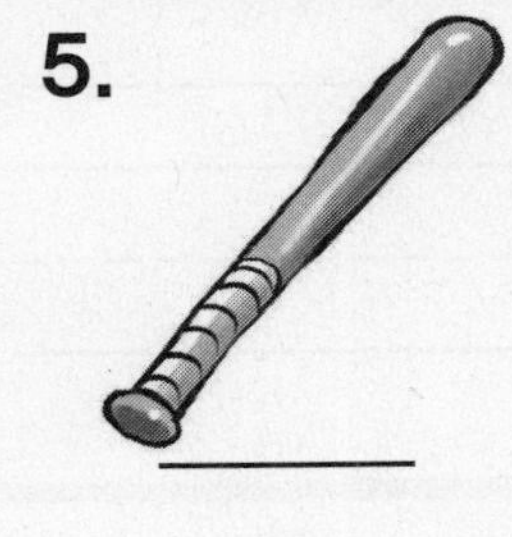
b ____ t

6.

m ____ x

7.

f ____ sh

8.

d ____ g

**Find** the word that has the same middle sound as [picture].
**Mark** the ⬭ to show your answer.

9. ⬭ wax
⬭ hid
⬭ red

10. ⬭ like
⬭ packs
⬭ tip

**Notes for Home:** Your child reviewed words with the short *i* sound heard in *pig*. ***Home Activity:*** Help your child make up fun rhymes using short *i* words, such as *The big pig in the wig likes to dig and do a jig.*

Name ______________________

**Look** at each word. **Say** it.
**Listen** for the ending sound that names more than one.

| | **Write** each word. | **Check** it. |
|---|---|---|
| 1. job | | |
| 2. log | | |
| 3. dog | | |
| 4. jobs | | |
| 5. logs | | |
| 6. dogs | | |

## Word Wall Words

**Write** each word.

| | | |
|---|---|---|
| 7. this | | |
| 8. into | | |

**Notes for Home:** Your child spelled short *o* words that are used to name one and more than one, as well as two frequently used words: *this, into.* ***Home Activity:*** Have your child tell what is the same and different about the first six spelling words above.

Name ______________________________



**Circle** the group of words that is a telling sentence.
**Write** it on the line.
**Add** a capital letter and a period.

1. does the dog like the frog    the dog sees the frog

2. what is it    it is a big frog

3. it does not hop away    can it hop

4. will the dog get in the pond    the dog gets in the pond

5. the frog will go away    will the frog go away

**Notes for Home:** Your child reviewed declarative sentences—sentences that tell something. ***Home Activity:*** Have your child choose some subjects for dinner table discussion by writing a list of sentences on a page. Invite family members to read aloud a sentence and discuss the topic.

Name ______________________________

# Test-Taking Tips

1. Write your name on the test.
2. Read each question twice.
3. Read all the answer choices for the question.
4. Mark your answer carefully.
5. Check your answer.

Name ______________________

# Part 1: Vocabulary

**Read** each sentence.
**Mark** the ⬭ for the word that fits.

1. ______ is a log.

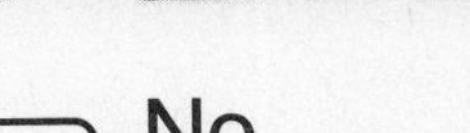

⬭ Did ⬭ No 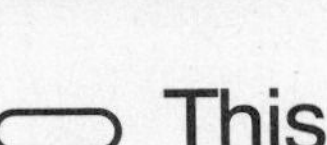 ⬭ This

---

2. The frog can hop ______ the log.

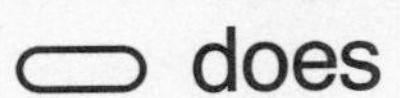 ⬭ does  ⬭ into ⬭ how

---

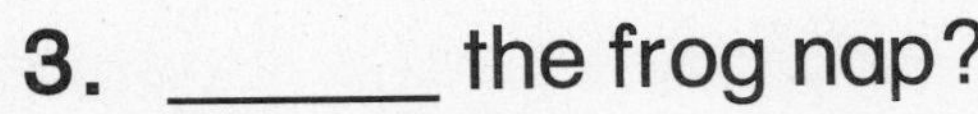
3. ______ the frog nap?

 ⬭ Does  ⬭ It  ⬭ Who

---

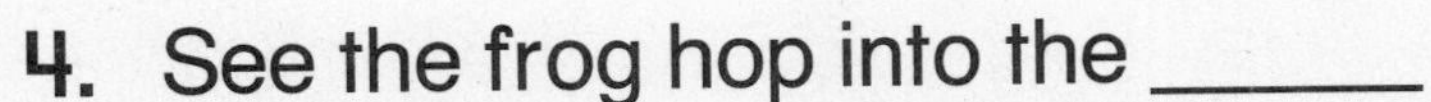
4. See the frog hop into the ______ .

 ⬭ find  ⬭ water  ⬭ away

---

5. ______ is happy to play.

 ⬭ He ⬭ Me  ⬭ No

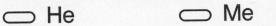

Name ______________________________

## Part 2: Comprehension

**Read** each question.
**Mark** the ⊂⊃ for the answer.

6. First, there are
   - ⊂⊃ tails.
   - ⊂⊃ legs.
   - ⊂⊃ eggs.

7. Where do tadpoles live?
   - ⊂⊃ in water
   - ⊂⊃ on logs
   - ⊂⊃ in a bag

8. A frog has
   - ⊂⊃ six legs.
   - ⊂⊃ no legs.
   - ⊂⊃ four legs.

9. Frogs like to
   - ⊂⊃ jump.
   - ⊂⊃ dig.
   - ⊂⊃ walk.

10. What do we find out?
    - ⊂⊃ why frogs have a tail
    - ⊂⊃ how tadpoles turn into frogs
    - ⊂⊃ how frogs jump

STOP

Name ______________________________

**Circle** the word for each picture.

fi<u>x</u>

1.  fox fog

2.  wag wax

3.  sits six

4. 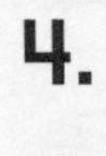 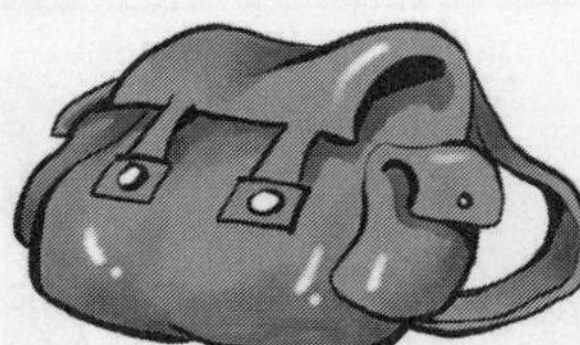 sax sack

5.  box boss

6. 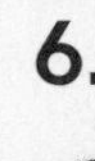 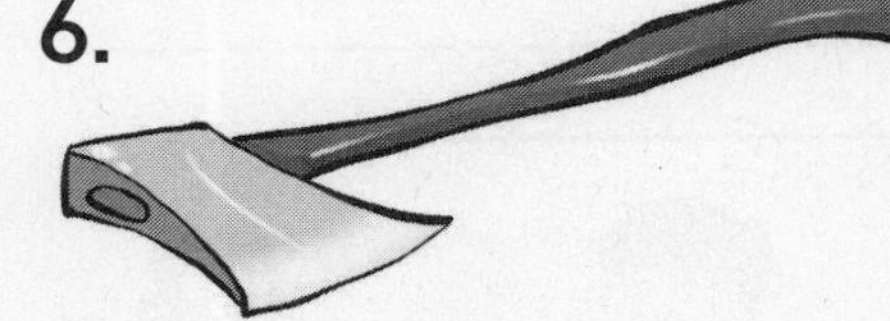 ax as

7.  mix miss

8.  sick six

**Find** the word that has the same ending sound as [picture].
**Mark** the ⬭ to show your answer.

9.  ⬭ hop
⬭  ox
⬭ has

10. ⬭ tack
⬭  taps
⬭ tax

**Notes for Home:** Your child reviewed words that end with the letter *x*. ***Home Activity:*** Draw pictures with your child for the words with *x* listed above. Have your child label each picture.

Name ______________________

**Write** a word from the box to match each picture.

job log dog jobs logs dogs

1. ______________________

2. ______________________

3. ______________________

4. ______________________

5. ______________________

6. ______________________

**Pick** a word from the box to finish each sentence.
**Write** it on the line.

this into

7. The rat ran ______________ a hog.

8. ______________ hog did not like that!

**Notes for Home:** Your child spelled pairs of short *o* words that name one and more than one, as well as two frequently used words: *this, into*. ***Home Activity:*** Say simple sentences using each spelling word. Have your child write each sentence.

Name ______________________________

**Mom has a paint can.**

A **statement** tells something.
Begin a statement with a **capital letter.**
End a statement with a **period.**

**Draw** a line from each statement to the correct picture.

1. Jen moves the chair.

2. Mom paints the door.

3. Don feeds the cat.

4. Dad cleans the floor.

**Notes for Home:** Your child identified statements that matched pictures. ***Home Activity:*** Have your child draw a picture of a friend doing something. Then have him or her write a statement about what the friend is doing.

Name ______________________________

**Match** the sentence parts.
**Write** the statements.

| The dog | gets cut. |
|---|---|
| The wood | is my pet. |
| Today | is red. |
| My hat | it rains. |

1. ______________________________

2. ______________________________

3. ______________________________

4. ______________________________

**Notes for Home:** Your child wrote statements correctly. ***Home Activity:*** Have your child make up statements about the weather today.

## You *are* your child's first *and* best teacher!

**Here are ways to help your child practice skills while having fun!**

**Day 1** Take turns acting out a simple short *o* word such as *chop* or *hop*. The other person guesses the word and writes it.

**Day 2** Have your child recite silly sentences containing the words *Shoo Fly Pie* (a pie dessert originated by the Amish) along with one of these words: *by, eat, sing, stop,* and *them*.

**Day 3** Your child has identified causes and effects. When looking at action photographs, ask questions such as: *What happened?* (effect) *Why did it happen?* (cause)

**Day 4** Your child has been learning about questions. Draw a question mark on an index card. During a family conversation, challenge your child to hold up the card each time a question is asked.

**Day 5** Ask your child to draw a portrait of herself or himself. Label the picture *All About Me* and work together to write captions for it.

**Read with your child EVERY DAY!**



(fold here)

# Family Times

**A Big Job** **Sweet Potato Pie**

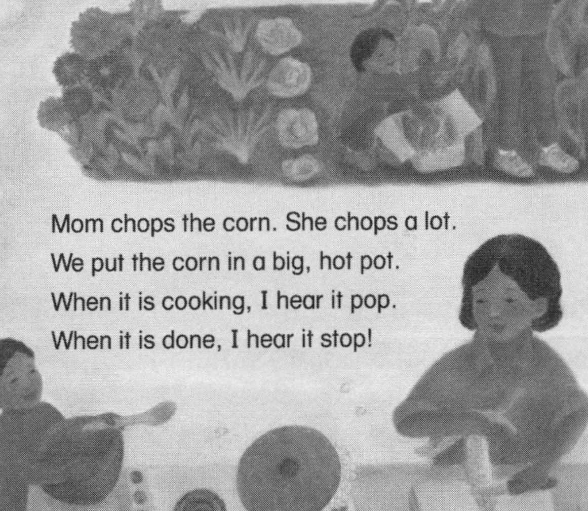

### I Like Popcorn

I like popcorn. My name is Bob.
I pop the popcorn. That is my job.
Mom picks the corncobs from the crop,
Filling the box up to the top.

Mom chops the corn. She chops a lot.
We put the corn in a big, hot pot.
When it is cooking, I hear it pop.
When it is done, I hear it stop!

This rhyme includes words your child is working with at school: words with the short *o* sound you hear in *pop* and action words ending in *-ing* and *-s*. Sing the rhyme with your child. As you sing, act out the actions described in the song.

Name: ____________________

# What's Happening?

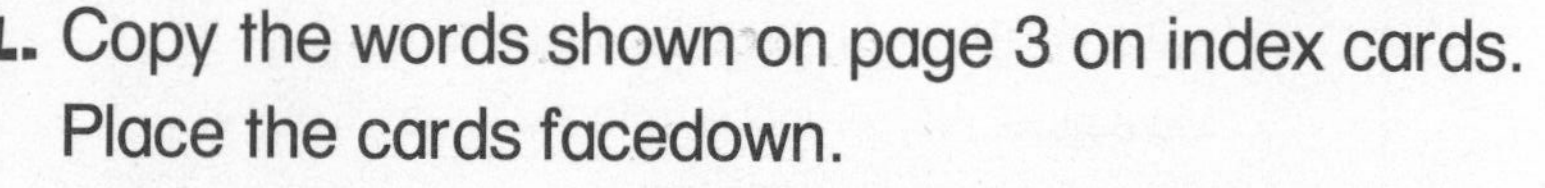

**Materials** index cards, marker

**Game Directions**

1. Copy the words shown on page 3 on index cards. Place the cards facedown.
2. Players take turns each drawing six cards and using as many as they can to make a sentence.
3. After each turn, the player returns the cards to the pile.
4. Each word card used earns one point. The first player to earn 15 points wins!

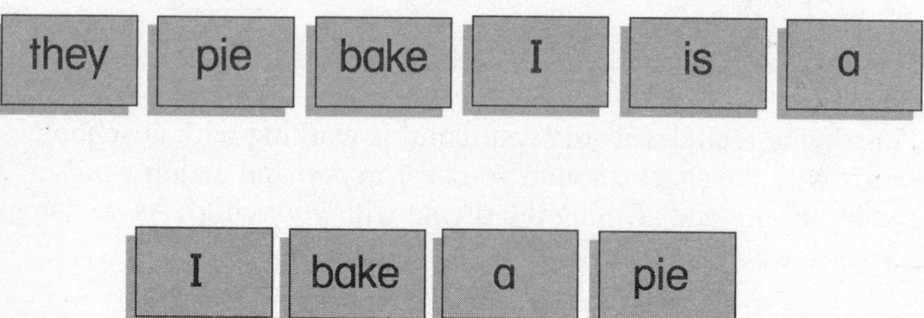




| I | they | Nan | are |
|---|---|---|---|
| is | the | a | with |
| pie | mat | cat | dog |
| pat | patting | bake | bakes |
| sit | sits | play | playing |

Name ________________________

**Circle** the word for each picture.

top

1. 
map mop

2. 
dog dig

3. 
fox fix

4. 
lick lock

5. 
pot pit

6. 
log leg

7. 
rack rock

8. 
ax ox

9. 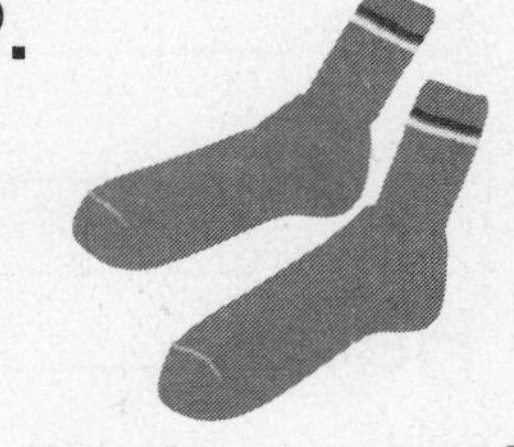
sack sock

**Write** your own **short o** word.
**Draw** a picture of it in the box.

10. ________________________

**Notes for Home:** Your child practiced reading words with the short *o* sound as in *top.* ***Home Activity:*** Write the endings *-ock, -od, -og, -op, -ot,* and *-ox* on slips of paper. Have your child use different beginning letters to write words with these endings.

Name ______________________

**Add -ing** to each word.
**Write** the new word on the line.

She is play<u>ing</u>.

1. eat ____________ 2. pick ____________

**Add -s** to each word.
**Write** the new word on the line.

He play<u>s</u>.

3. make ________ 4. like ________ 5. see ________

**Use** the words you wrote to finish the sentences.
**Write** the words on the lines.

6. She ____________________ them.

7. He is ____________________ them.

8. He ____________________ it.

9. They are ____________________ it.

10. He ____________________ it a lot!

**Notes for Home:** Your child added *-s* or *-ing* to verbs. ***Home Activity:*** Have your child write verbs like *get, hop, jog, mop, nap, nod, pat, rip, stop, tap, walk,* and *zip,* and add an *-s* to each verb. Act out each verb together.

Name ______________________

**Pick** a word from the box to finish each sentence.
**Write** it on the line.

| by | eat | sing | stop | them |
|---|---|---|---|---|

1. We ______________ walking.

2. We sit ______________ the water.

3. I ______________ two yams.

4. I like ______________ hot!

5. They like to ______________ .

**Notes for Home:** This week your child is learning to read the words *by, eat, sing, stop,* and *them.* ***Home Activity:*** Encourage your child to use these words to make up a story about a person or animal that cannot sing. Help your child write the story and read it aloud.

Name ______________________________



**Look** at the first picture.
**Circle** the picture that shows what made this happen.

1.   

2.   

3.   

4.   

---

**Look** at the picture. **Draw** what happened first.

5. 

**Notes for Home:** Your child identified causes (why something happens) and effects (what happens). ***Home Activity:*** Call your child's attention to causes and effects by asking questions such as: *What do you think made that happen? What would happen if …?*

Name ______________________________

A **question** asks something.
It begins with a capital letter.
It ends with a ?.
This is a question: Is everybody here?

**Correct** each sentence.
**Write** it on the line.

1. do you like ham

2. can I have that

3. is this my bag

4. where is his bag

5. will you sit by me

**Notes for Home:** Your child practiced writing questions. ***Home Activity:*** Play a game with your child. Hide an object. Then have your child ask questions to find out where the object is hidden. Help your child write some of the questions asked.

Name ______________________

**Pick** a word from the box to finish each sentence.
**Write** it on the line.

1. Sit ______________ me.

2. Do you like ______________ ?

3. Will you ______________ that?

4. No! Sam, ______________ that!

5. It likes to ______________ .

**Notes for Home:** Your child practiced using the words *by, eat, sing, stop,* and *them.* ***Home Activity:*** Help your child use these words to write a story about a family party.

Name ______________________

A Big Job

Sweet Potato Pie

**Circle** the word for each picture.

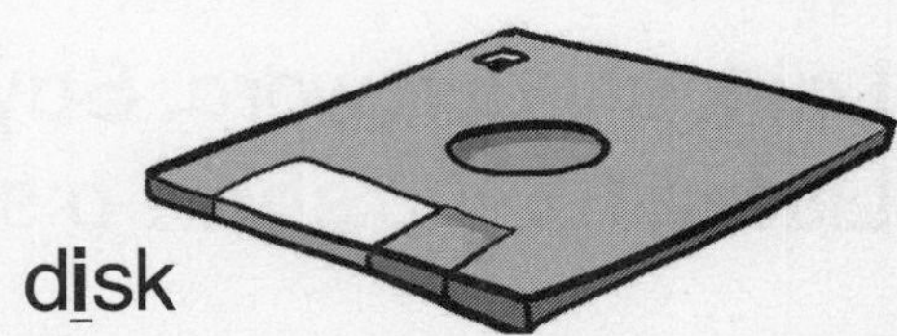

di̲sk

1.  hall / hill

2. 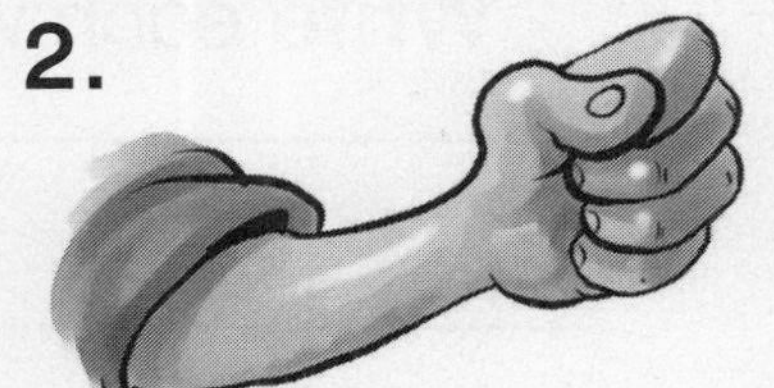 fuss / fist

3.  bill / ball

4.  has / hiss

5. 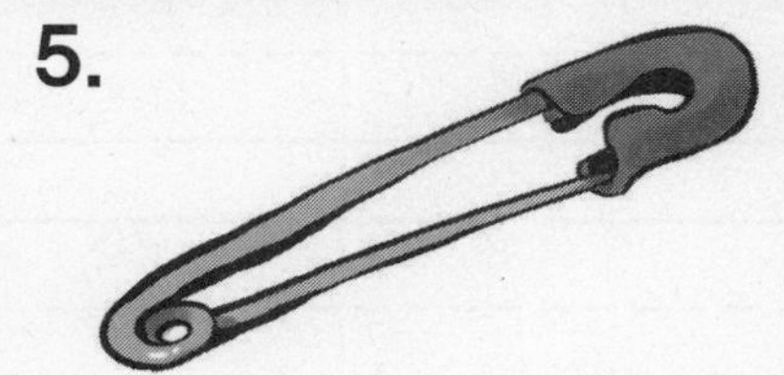 pan / pin

6.  sip / sap

7.  will / wall

8. 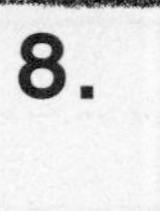  lock / lick

**Find** the word that has the same middle sound as .
**Mark** the ⬭ to show your answer.

9. ⬭ likes
⬭ sees
⬭ sits

10. ⬭ find
⬭ this
⬭ wash

**Notes for Home:** Your child reviewed words with the short *i* sound heard in *di̲sk*. ***Home Activity:*** Find other words with the short *i* sound in storybooks. Help your child to read these words.

Name ______________________________

**Look** at each word. **Say** it.
**Listen** for the **short o** sound in .

| | **Write** each word. | **Check** it. |
|---|---|---|
| 1. hot | | |
| 2. not | | |
| 3. got | | |
| 4. mop | | |
| 5. hop | | |
| 6. top | | |

## Word Wall Words

**Write** each word.

| | | |
|---|---|---|
| 7. eat | | |
| 8. stop | | |

**Notes for Home:** Your child spelled words with the short *o* sound heard in *dog* and two frequently used words: *eat, stop*. ***Home Activity:*** Help your child draw a cartoon strip and use these spelling words to write the dialogue.

Name ______________________

Add words to tell more about something.

Nan likes to eat fish.

Nan likes to eat <u>big</u> fish.

---

What would make each sentence better?

**Pick** a word from the box to finish each sentence.

**Write** it on the line. Use each word only once.

| red | hot | little | many |
|---|---|---|---|

1. Jill likes to eat ______________ jam.

2. Bob likes to eat ______________ nuts.

3. I like to eat ______________ ham.

4. My cat likes to eat ______________ fish!

---

**Write** a sentence about what you like to eat.

5. ________________________________________

________________________________________

**Notes for Home:** Your child added details to simple sentences to make them more interesting. ***Home Activity:*** Write some simple sentences about favorite foods for your child. Work with your child to add interesting details to each sentence.

Name ______________________________

**Make up** a question for each answer.
**Write** the question on the line.

______________________________

1. Bob has a little pig.

______________________________

2. Bob likes the pig a lot!

______________________________

3. The cat does not like the pig at all.

______________________________

4. Jan can give the cat a pat.

______________________________

5. The cat will like that.

**Notes for Home:** Your child wrote questions. ***Home Activity:*** Have your child use the words *how, what,* and *where* to write questions to ask you. Help your child with spelling as needed. Check to be sure your child uses a question mark at the end of each sentence.

Name ______________________________



# Part I: Vocabulary

**Read** each sentence.

**Mark** the ⬭ for the word that fits.

1. They ______ all day.

⬭ find ⬭ make ⬭ sing

2. The pigs walk one ______ one.

⬭ by ⬭ all ⬭ down

3. I can see ______ in the water.

⬭ on ⬭ why ⬭ them

4. Nan will ______ picking them.

⬭ make ⬭ stop ⬭ does

5. Nan will ______ the pie.

⬭ eat ⬭ walk ⬭ stop

Name ____________________________

# Part 2: Comprehension

**Read** each question.

**Mark** the ⊂⊃ for the answer.

6. Who picks the sweet potatoes?
   - ⊂⊃ Pa
   - ⊂⊃ Tom
   - ⊂⊃ Bob

7. What does Grandma do?
   - ⊂⊃ chops
   - ⊂⊃ digs
   - ⊂⊃ bakes

8. They all come in to
   - ⊂⊃ wash.
   - ⊂⊃ sing.
   - ⊂⊃ eat.

9. What happens last?
   - ⊂⊃ Everybody eats pie.
   - ⊂⊃ Everybody walks inside.
   - ⊂⊃ Everybody starts singing.

10. Do they like sweet potato pie?
    - ⊂⊃ Yes, they eat it all.
    - ⊂⊃ No, they let the pets eat it.
    - ⊂⊃ No, they like to sing.

STOP

Name ______________________________

**Circle** the word for each picture.

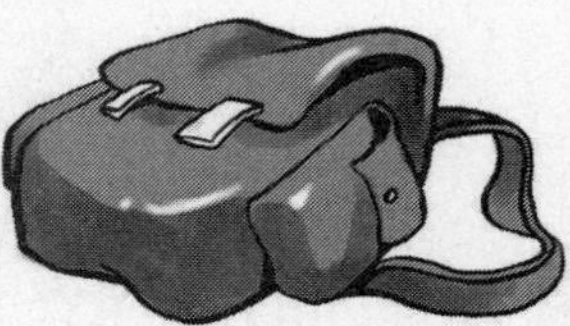

backpack

1. 
rack
rats

2. 
robs
rock

3. 
kiss
kick

4. 
bags
back

5. 
pick
pig

6. 
look
lock

7. 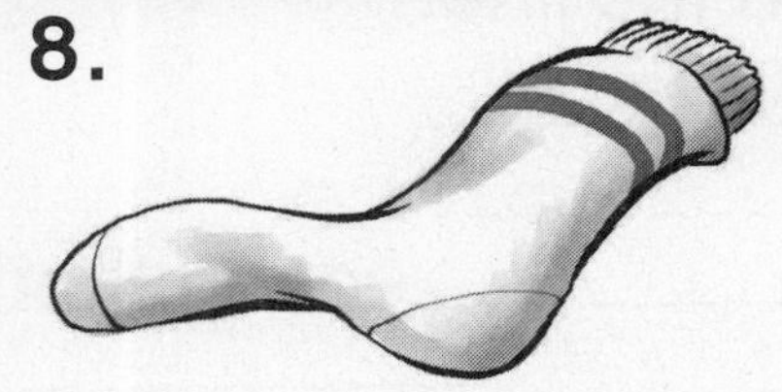
lick
lock

8. 
sock
stop

**Find** the word that has the same ending sound as .
**Mark** the ⬭ to show your answer.

9. ⬭ dogs
⬭ dock
⬭ dots

10. ⬭ tick
⬭ this
⬭ wish

**Notes for Home:** Your child reviewed words that end with *-ck*. ***Home Activity:*** Help your child write words that end in *-ck*. Then use them to make up nonsense rhymes together (For example: *On top of the rocks stood a goat in pink socks.*).

Name ______________________

| hot | not | got | mop | hop | top |
|---|---|---|---|---|---|

**Write** a word from the box to match each picture.

1. ____________ 2. ____________ 3. ____________

**Write** the words from the box that rhyme with **pot**.

4. ____________ 5. ____________ 6. ____________

**Pick** a word from the box to finish each sentence.
**Write** it on the line.

| eat | stop |
|---|---|

7. ____________ eating that!

8. He did not ____________ it all.

**Notes for Home:** Your child spelled words with the short *o* sound heard in *hot* and two frequently used words: *eat, stop*. ***Home Activity:*** Have your child use some of the spelling words to tell a story about a frog that goes exploring. Help your child write the story.

Name ______________________________

**Are you my friend?**

A **question** asks something.
It begins with a capital letter.
It ends with a question mark.

**Draw** a line under each question.

1. Can I come?
   You can come.

2. We can play.
   Can we play?

3. The game is fun.
   Is the game fun?

4. May I have one?
   You may have one.

5. Can you stay?
   I can stay.

**Notes for Home:** Your child correctly identified questions. ***Home Activity:*** Write two statements and two questions. Have your child find the questions and answer them.

Name ______________________________

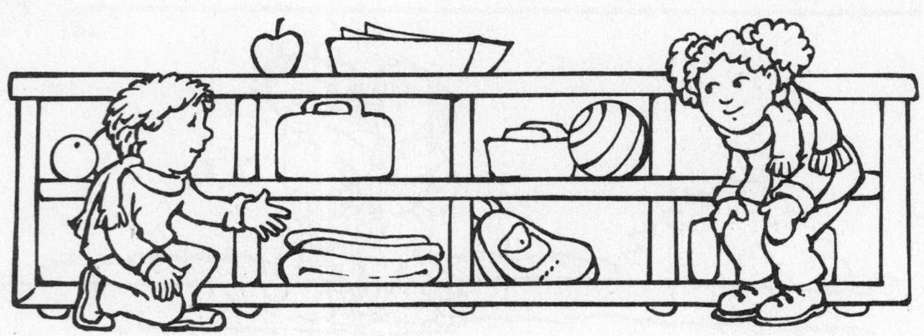

**Look** at the words.
Use them to **write** a question.

1. my book who has

______________________________

2. will snow fall

______________________________

3. my hat where is

______________________________

4. my ball do you see

______________________________

**Notes for Home:** Your child wrote questions. ***Home Activity:*** Write two sentences about animals. Have your child make up questions about the animals.

Name ______________________________

**Correct** each sentence.
**Write** it on the line.
Hint: Each sentence should begin with a capital letter.
It should end with a . or a ? .

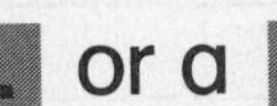

1. i like to eat blue fish

______________________________

2. tim eats six nuts

______________________________

3. does Sam like hot ham

______________________________

4. we like hot buns and jam

______________________________

5. what do you like to eat

______________________________

**Notes for Home:** Your child corrected sentences using capitalization and end marks. ***Home Activity:*** Write simple statements and questions about food, but do not use capital letters or end marks. Challenge your child to correct each sentence.

Name

I read

It was about

Words I Can Now Read and Write

**You *are* your child's first *and* best teacher!**

**Here are ways to help your child practice skills while having fun!**

**Day 1** Write the short *e* word *pet*. Have your child say it. Then, cross out the *p* and add a *b* to make *bet*. Have your child say that word. Continue changing the first letter using *g, j, l, m, n, s, w,* and *y*. List all the short *e* words you make.

**Day 2** Write simple sentences using these words that your child is learning to read: *help, now, said, so,* and *who*. Help your child read each sentence aloud.

**Day 3** Read aloud one of your child's favorite stories. Have your child tell how the story's characters are alike and how they are different.

**Day 4** Your child is learning to read aloud. Read a favorite story together. Ask your child to read the words spoken by the main character, while you read the other parts.

**Day 5** Choose a catalog or story with pictures in it. Ask your child to identify any nouns—words that name people, places, animals, and things—shown in the pictures.

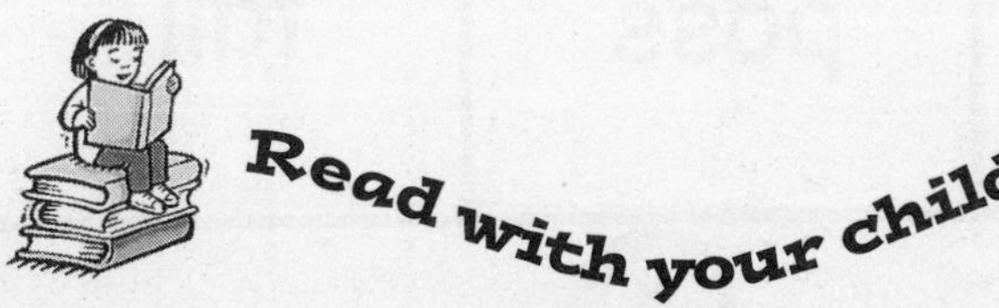

**Read with your child EVERY DAY!**



(fold here)

# Family Times

**The Big Mess** **The Little Red Hen**

### Ted Helps

Ted feeds his pet named Ned.
And then he makes his bed.
Ted helps to paint the little shed.
He paints it blue and red.

Ted helps his sister Jen,
Spell words and count to ten.
Ted sets the table. And what then?
He then plays ball with Jen!

This rhyme includes words your child is working with in school: words with the short *e* sound *(pet, bed)* and words with double final consonants *(spell, ball)*. Sing "Ted Helps" with your child. Then work together to draw Ted's pet Ned.

Name: ____________________

# Cover Up!

**Materials** paper, marker, bag, 9 buttons per player

**Game Directions**

1. Use the 18 words below to make 3 X 3 cards like those shown on page 3. Words can be in any order.
2. Write the same 18 words on paper. Cut the words apart and place them in a bag.
3. Players take turns picking a word from the bag and reading it aloud. Players use buttons to cover this word if it is on their cards.
4. The first person to cover three words in a row—across, up, down, or diagonally—wins!

**Words**
hill, ball, mess, call, doll, bell, yell, kiss, will, miss, tell, sell, bill, wall, pass, tall, fill, fall

sell

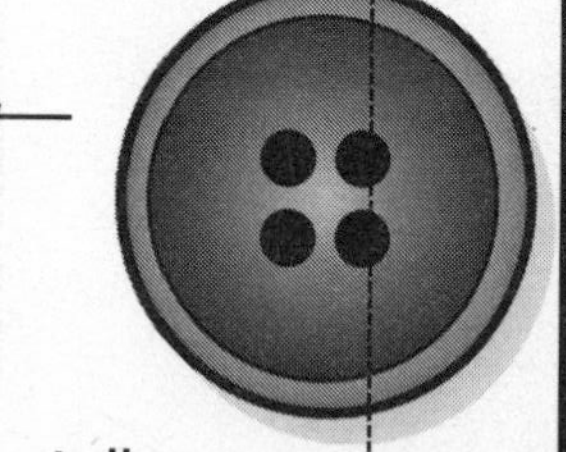



| hill | call | yell |
|---|---|---|
| ball | doll | kiss |
| mess | bell | will |

| miss | bill | tall |
|---|---|---|
| tell | wall | fill |
| sell | pass | fall |

Name ______________________________

**Circle** a word to finish each sentence.
**Write** it on the line.

hen

pen pan

1. The hen is in the ______________ .

pot pet

2. Ken likes to ______________ the hen.

bag beg

3. What is in the ______________ ?

fed fan

4. The hen wants to be ______________ .

miss mess

5. The hen makes a ______________ .

**Notes for Home:** Your child practiced reading and writing words with the short *e* sound heard in *hen*. ***Home Activity:*** Work with your child to make a list of all the words on this page with a short *e*.

Name ______________________________

**Say** the word for each picture.
**Circle** the letters to finish each word.
**Write** the letters on the line.

ball

1. all ell
b ______

2. ell all
w ______

3. oll ill
d ______

4. all ell
c ______

5. ess iss
k ______

6. ell ill
w ______

7. all ell
y ______

8. ill all
f ______

9. ill all
b ______

10. oss ess
m ______

**Notes for Home:** Your child is learning words with double final consonants *(wall, hill, kiss)*.
***Home Activity:*** Have fun taking turns naming words that rhyme with the ones your child wrote on this page.

Name ______________________________

**Pick** a word from the box to finish each section.

**Write** it on the line.

| help | now | said | so | who |
|---|---|---|---|---|

1. ____________ can get the cat?

2. Ben can ____________ the cat get down.

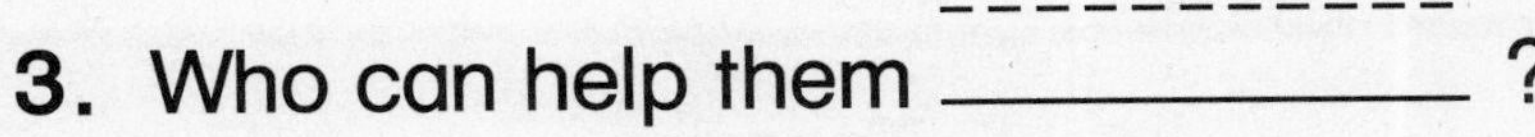

3. Who can help them ____________ ?

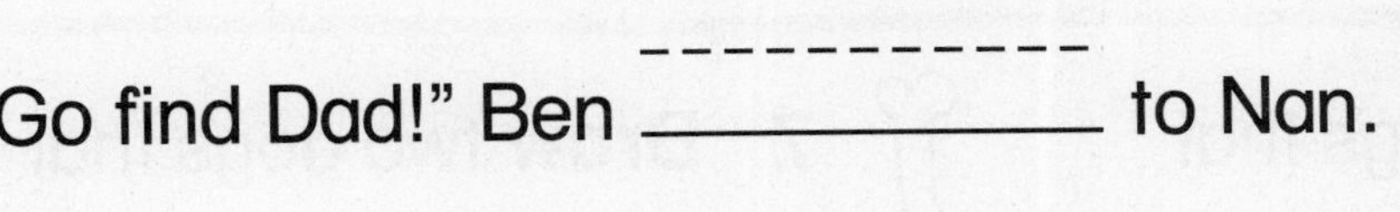

4. "Go find Dad!" Ben ____________ to Nan.

5. He is here!
____________ now we can get down.

**Notes for Home:** This week your child is learning to read the words *help, now, said, so,* and *who*. ***Home Activity:*** Ask your child to use each word in a spoken sentence.

Name ________________________________

**Look** at the picture.
**Circle** the answer to each question.
**Hint:** One question will have two answers.

| | | |
|---|---|---|
| 1. Who is little? | Tess | Bess |
| 2. Who is big? | Tess | Bess |
| 3. Who is sitting up? | Tess | Bess |
| 4. Who is sleeping? | Tess | Bess |
| 5. Who is a dog? | Tess | Bess |

6. **Draw** two dogs that are the same.

7. **Draw** two dogs that are different.

**Notes for Home**: Your child compared and contrasted two animal characters.
***Home Activity:*** Choose two animals that your child likes. Have your child tell how they are alike and different.

Name ______________________________

A **noun** names a person, place, animal, or thing.

**Circle** the noun in each sentence.
**Draw** a picture of it in the box.

1. The man walks.

2. The cat likes to eat.

3. The frog jumps.

4. The girl jogs.

5. The dog ran away.

**Notes for Home:** Your child circled and drew nouns that name a person, place, animal, or thing. ***Home Activity:*** Help your child draw and label pictures of people, places, animals, and things that are in or near your home.

Name ______________________

**Pick** a word from the box to finish each sentence.
**Write** it on the line.

help    now    said    so    want    who

1. "I need ______________ !" said Tim.

2. "I need it ______________ !"

3. " ______________ will help me?"

4. "I ______________ to help you," said Dan.

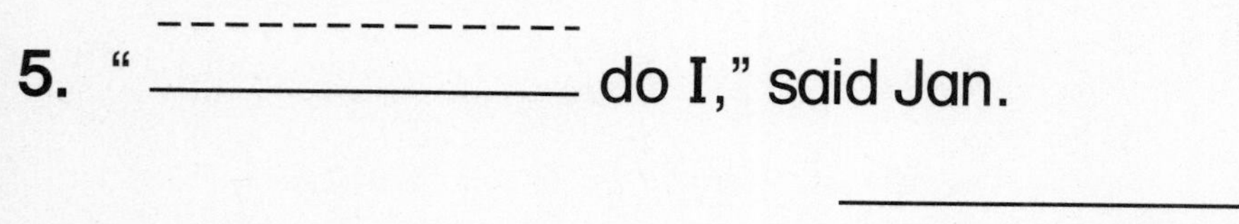

5. " ______________ do I," said Jan.

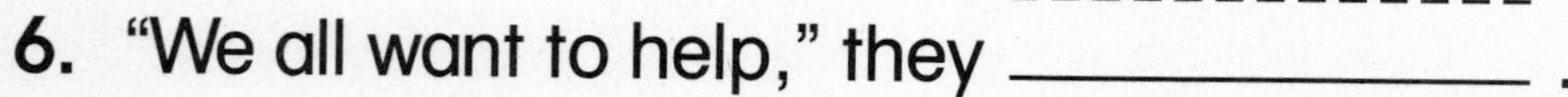

6. "We all want to help," they ______________ .

**Notes for Home:** Your child read and wrote the words *help, now, said, so, want,* and *who* to complete sentences. ***Home Activity:*** Ask your child to use each vocabulary word in a short sentence. Work together to write each sentence.

Name ______________________________

**Say** the word for each picture.
**Write o** if the word has a **short o** sound.

| 1. | 2. | 3. | 4. |
|---|---|---|---|
| f ___ x | h ___ t | fr ___ g | c ___ t |

| 5. | 6. | 7. | 8. |
|---|---|---|---|
| p ___ n | t ___ p | cl ___ ck | l ___ ck |

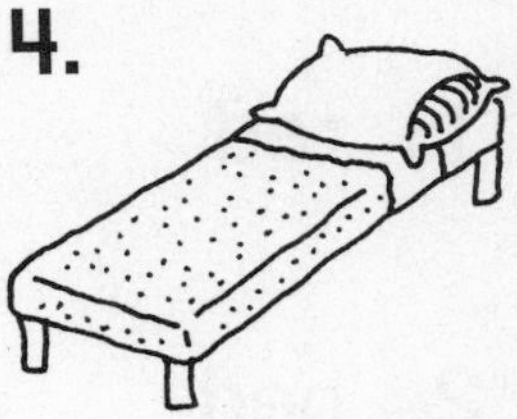

**Find** the word that has the same middle sound as .
**Mark** the ⬭ to show your answer.

9. ⬭ look
⬭ so
⬭ stop

10. ⬭ how
⬭ jog
⬭ you

**Notes for Home:** Your child reviewed words containing the short *o* sound heard in *hog*.
***Home Activity:*** Ask your child questions which can be answered with a short *o* word (For example: *What do you do with your head to say yes?*). Have your child say the answer and spell it *(nod)*.

Name ______________________

**Look** at each word. **Say** it.
**Listen** for the **short e** sound in
**Listen** for different ending sounds.

| | **Write** each word. | **Check** it. |
|---|---|---|
| 1. red | | |
| 2. bed | | |
| 3. fed | | |
| 4. well | | |
| 5. tell | | |
| 6. mess | | |

## Word Wall Words

**Write** each word.

| | | |
|---|---|---|
| 7. said | | |
| 8. who | | |

**Notes for Home:** Your child spelled words with *-ed, -ell,* and *-ess* and two frequently used words: *said, who.* ***Home Activity:*** Have your child add other letters before *-ed, -ell,* and *-ess* to form new words, such as *led, bell,* and *Bess.*

Name ______________________

**Circle** the noun that matches each picture.

many little fish

1. ______________

hog fat sit

2. ______________

hot pans three

3. ______________

hen eat peck

4. ______________

**Write** a noun to go with each picture.

5.

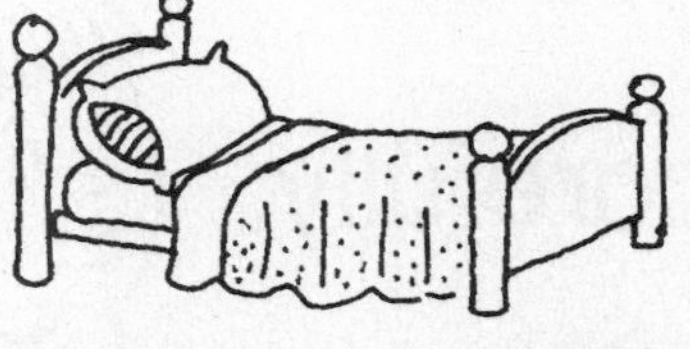

______________

6.

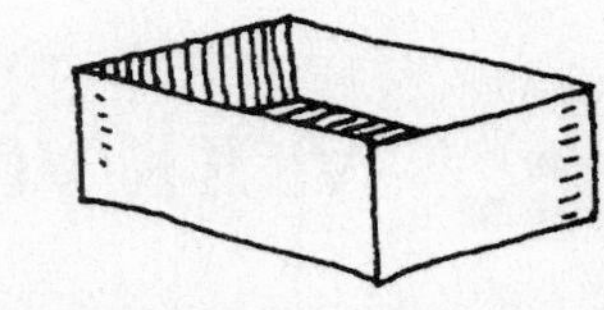

______________

7.

______________

8.

______________

**Notes for Home:** Your child reviewed nouns—words that name people, places, animals, or things. ***Home Activity:*** Read a story book with your child and look for words that are nouns. Then ask your child to use those nouns in new sentences.

# Test-Taking Tips

1. Write your name on the test.
2. Read each question twice.
3. Read all the answer choices for the question.
4. Mark your answer carefully.
5. Check your answer.

Name ______________________________

# Part 1: Vocabulary

**Read** each sentence.
**Mark** the ⬭ for the word that fits.

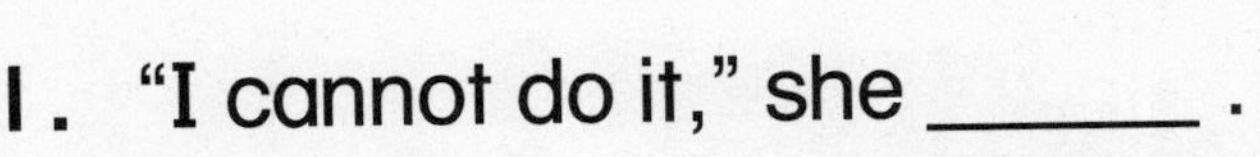

1. "I cannot do it," she ______ .

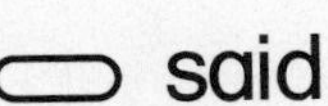

⬭ saw ⬭ now ⬭ said

2. "______ will help me?"

⬭ Who ⬭ On ⬭ Why

3. Miko comes to ______ .

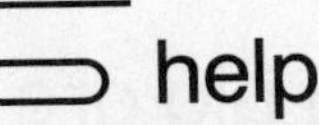

⬭ into ⬭ help ⬭ went

4. ______ they walk up.

⬭ So ⬭ All ⬭ Many

5. ______ they go down.

⬭ Who ⬭ By ⬭ Now

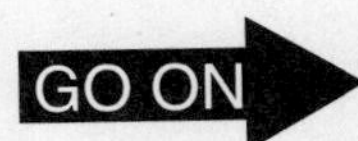

Name ___________________________________



## Part 2: Comprehension

**Read** each question.

**Mark** the ⬭ for the answer.

6. What does the Little Red Hen want?
   - ⬭ help
   - ⬭ pans
   - ⬭ a job

7. The dog, cat, and pig are not like the Little Red Hen. All they do is
   - ⬭ play.
   - ⬭ sing.
   - ⬭ eat.

8. Who makes the food?
   - ⬭ the Little Red Hen
   - ⬭ the cat
   - ⬭ the dog and the pig

9. At the end, the dog, cat, and pig are
   - ⬭ happy.
   - ⬭ sad.
   - ⬭ sick.

10. Was the Little Red Hen mean to eat by herself?
    - ⬭ Yes, because her friends helped.
    - ⬭ No, because she did all the work.
    - ⬭ Yes, because she made too much food.

STOP

Name ____________________

**The Big Mess**

**The Little Red Hen**

**Say** the word for each picture.
**Write -s** if the picture shows more than one.

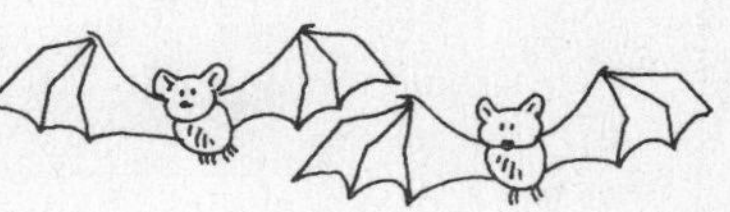

bats

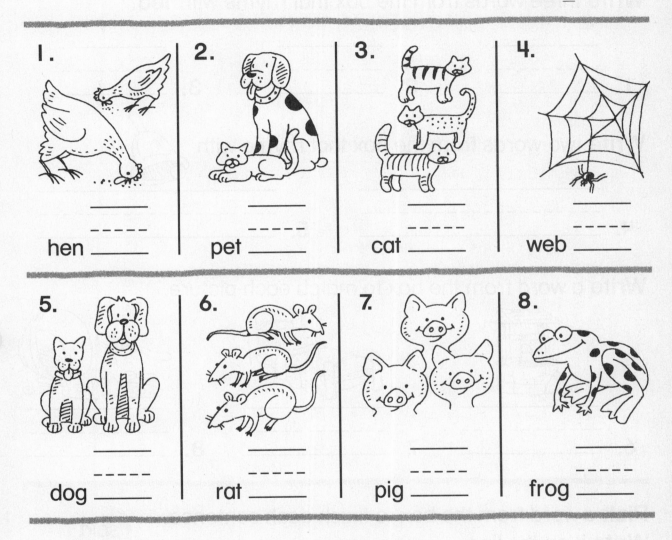

1.

hen ____

2.

pet ____

3.

cat ____

4.

web ____

5.

dog ____

6.

rat ____

7.

pig ____

8.

frog ____

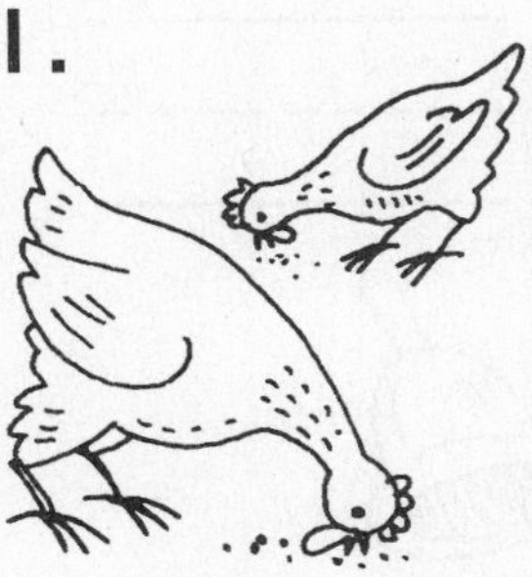

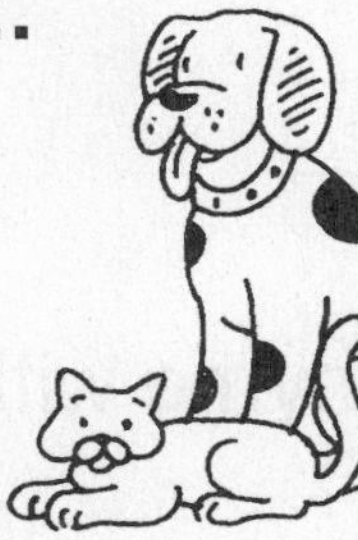

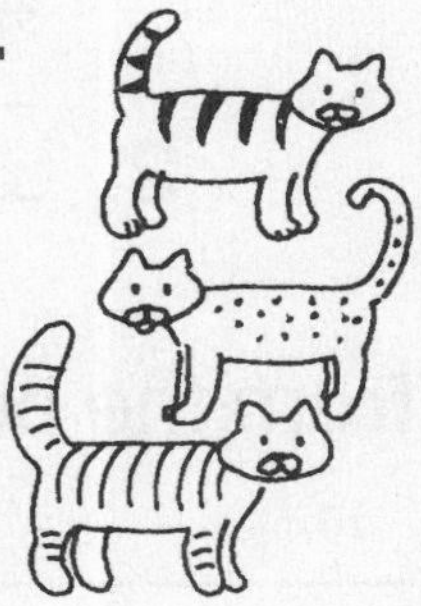

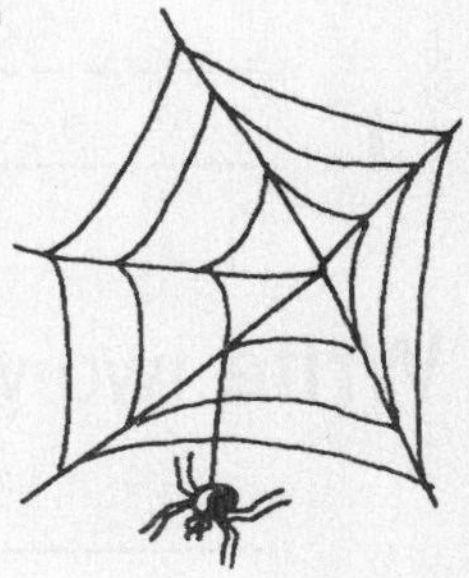

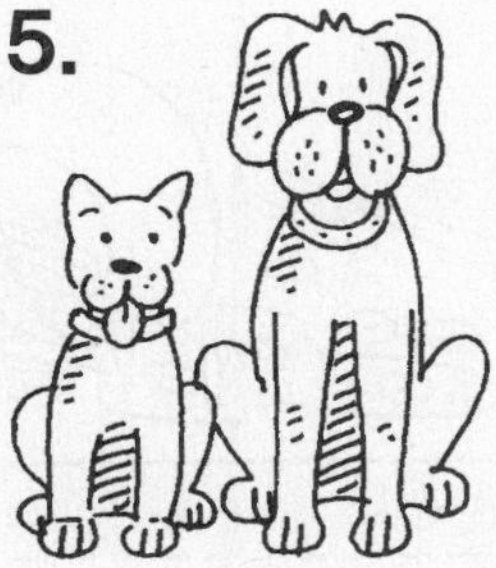

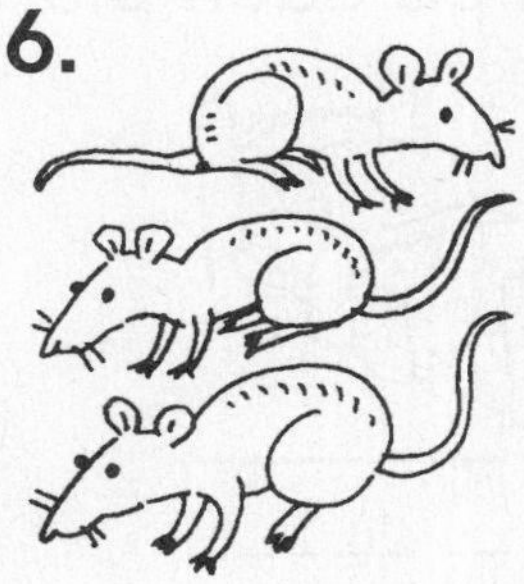

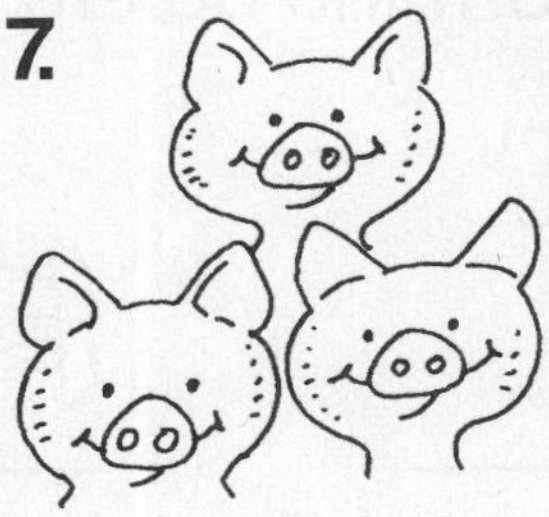

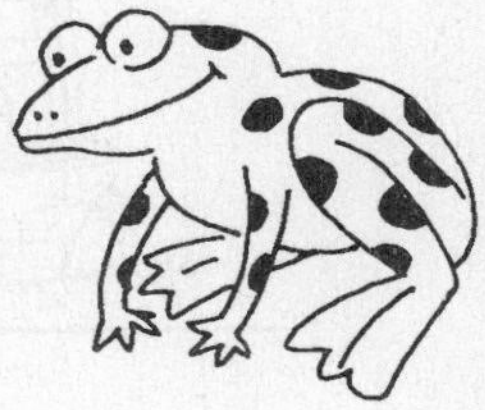

**Find** the word that means more than one.
**Mark** the ⬭ to show your answer.

9. ⬭ boss
⬭ hats
⬭ his

10. ⬭ has
⬭ digs
⬭ pens

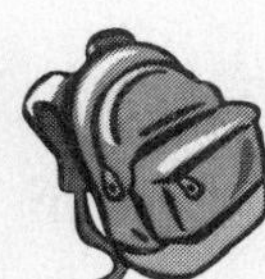

**Notes for Home:** Your child reviewed plural nouns that show more than one. ***Home Activity:*** Together, count and list objects in your home. Choose words that form their plurals by adding just an *-s*. Help your child spell the names of the objects, having him or her supply the *-s* endings.

Name ______________________________

red bed fed well tell mess

**Write** three words from the box that rhyme with **Ted**.

1. ____________ 2. ____________ 3. ____________

**Write** two words from the box that rhyme with  .

4. ______________________ 5. ______________________

**Write** a word from the box to match each picture.

6. ____________ 7. ____________ 8. ____________

**Pick** a word from the box to finish each sentence.
**Write** it on the line.

said
who

9. Oh, ____________ will help me?

10. Is that what she ____________ ?

**Notes for Home:** Your child spelled words that end with *-ed, -ell,* and *-ess* and two frequently-used words: *said, who*. ***Home Activity:*** Work with your child to make up fun rhymes using the spelling words. Help your child write the rhymes and draw pictures for the rhymes.

Name ______________________________



RETEACHING

| Person | Place | Thing |
|---|---|---|
| woman | zoo | tree |

The word **woman** names a person.
The word **zoo** names a place.
The word **tree** names a thing.

A **noun** names a person, place, or thing.

**Circle** the noun for each picture.
**Write** the word.

| Person | Place | Thing |
|---|---|---|
| boy run | park fun | ride bike |
| 1. ________ | 2. ________ | 3. ________ |

**Notes for Home:** Your child identified nouns—words that name people, places, or things. ***Home Activity:*** Have your child use nouns to label four people, places, and things in your home.

Name ______________________________

Color **blue** the nouns that name people.
Color **yellow** the nouns that name things.
Color **green** the nouns that name places.

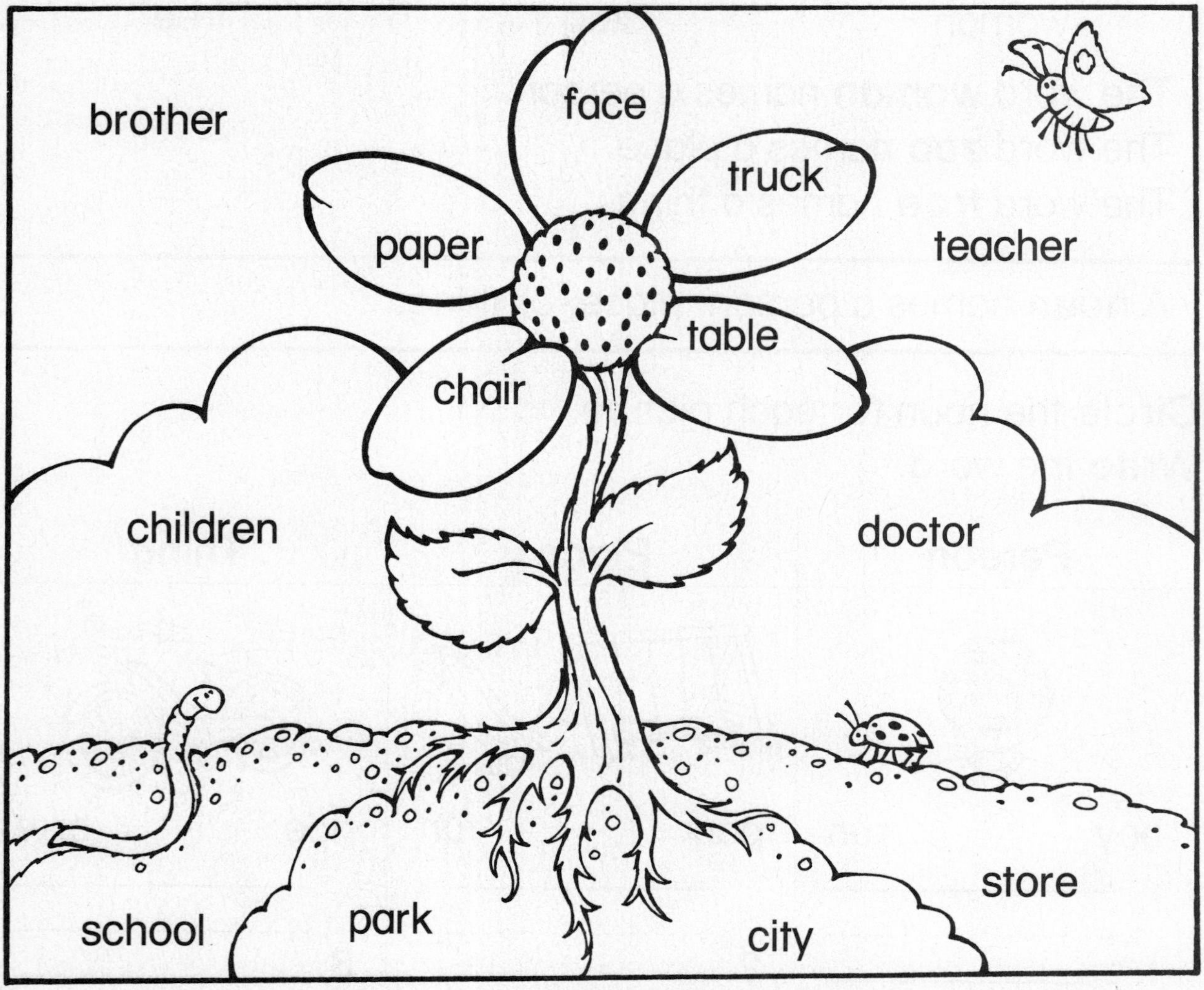

brother
face
truck
paper
teacher
table
chair
children
doctor
school
park
city
store

**Notes for Home:** Your child identified nouns—words that name people, places, or things. ***Home Activity:*** Together, make up a song about people, places, and things you might see in a park.

## You *are* your child's first *and* best teacher!

**Here are ways to help your child practice skills while having fun!**

**Day 1** Write these blends on slips of paper: *dr, fr, tr, bl, cl, pl.* Invite your child to pick a slip and say a word that begins with that blend, such as *drop, frog,* or *trip.*

**Day 2** At dinnertime, ask your child to use each of the following words in sentences about the food you will have: *for, good, some, too,* and *want.*

**Day 3** Describe an everyday task without saying what the task is. Ask your child to guess the task. For example, to describe making a bed, say: *I pull up the sheet. I pull up the blanket,* and so on.

**Day 4** After your child listens to a story or watches a favorite TV show, ask what happened in the story. Invite your child to write words and/or draw pictures that help retell the story.

**Day 5** Take turns pointing to individual household objects, naming each object, and then telling the word that would mean more than one of that same object. For example, use *chair* and *chairs.*

**Read with your child EVERY DAY!**



(fold here)

# Family Times

**Yes, We Want Some Too!** **Cat Traps**

### Oh, Yes! They Do!

Blue jays like to peck and peck.
Oh, yes! They do!
Blackbirds eat fruit on the deck.
Oh, yes! They do!
I will watch them. Oh, yes! I will!
I will watch them. Oh, yes! I will!

Green frogs play next to a duck.
Oh, yes! They do!
Ten red hens say, "Cluck, cluck, cluck."
Oh, yes! They do!
I will watch them. Oh, yes! I will!
I will watch them. Oh, yes! I will!

This rhyme includes words your child is working with in school: words with the short *e* sound *(peck, yes)* and words with initial *r* and *l* blends *(blue, fruit, cluck)*. Sing "Oh, Yes! They Do!" with your child. Then work together to draw the animals named in the rhyme.

Name: ____________________

# Follow the Patch

**Materials** 15 index cards, marker, 1 button per player

**Game Directions**

1. Write the 15 letters shown below on index cards.
2. Shuffle the cards and place them facedown in a pile.
3. Players take turns picking a card from the pile and writing as many short *e* words as possible beginning with the letter on the card.
4. Each player moves his or her button forward for every word named.
5. The first player to reach the end wins!

| b | d | f | g | h |
|---|---|---|---|---|
| j | l | m | n | p |
| r | s | t | w | y |

Name ______________________________

**Circle** the word for each picture.

web

1. 

pets men man

2. 

bed beg bad

3. 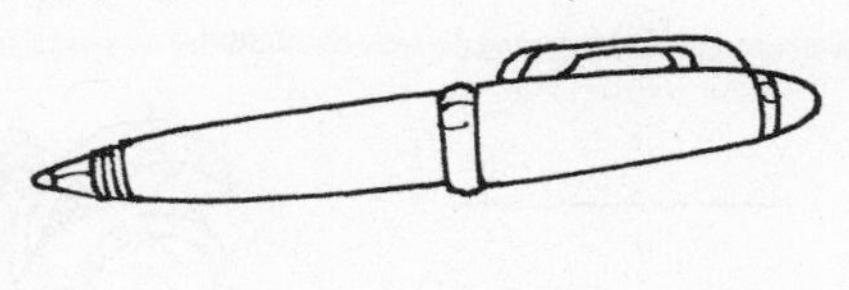

pen pan pin

4. 

tin tan ten

5. 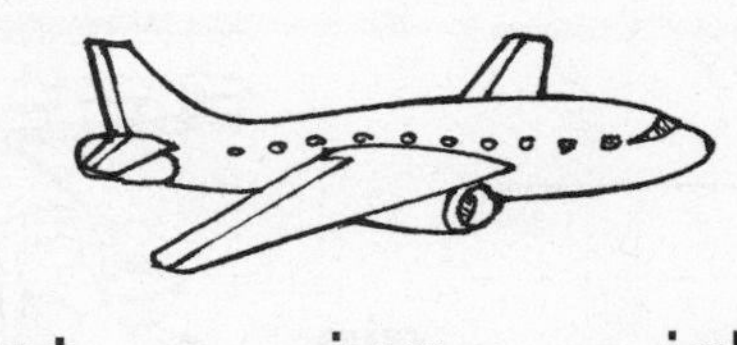

jet jug jab

6. 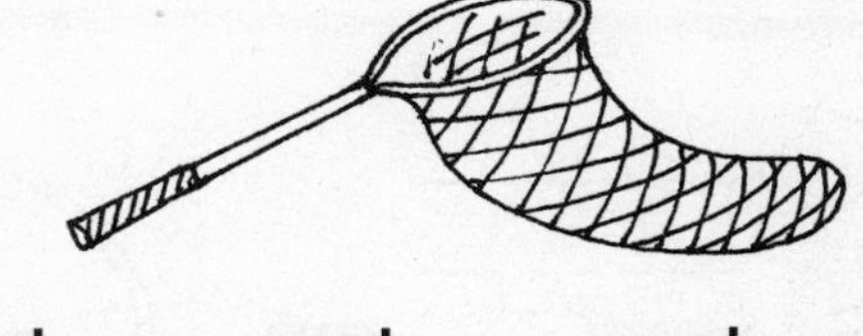

net not wet

7. 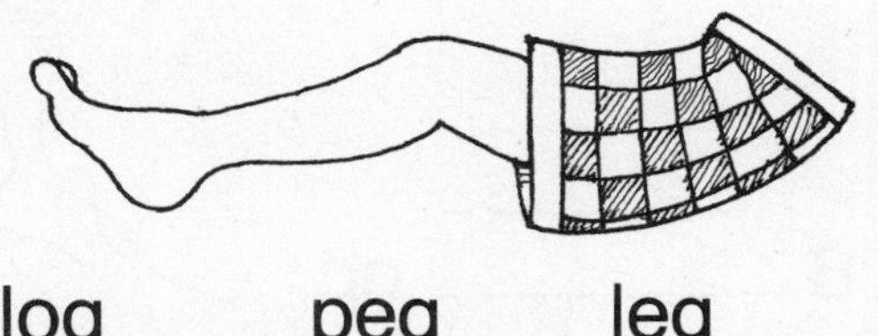

log peg leg

8. 

men man hen

9. 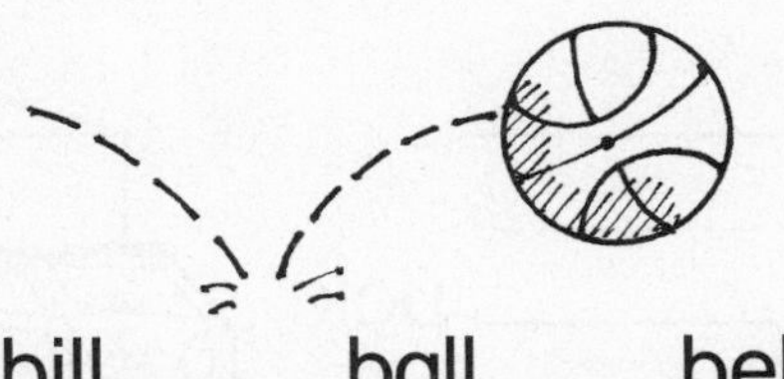

bill ball bell

10. 

hot hen den

**Notes for Home:** Your child practiced reading words with the short *e* sound *(leg, web)*.
***Home Activity:*** Help your child write a short story using the short *e* words on this page.

Name ________________________________

**Pick** letters from the box to finish each word.
**Write** the letters on the line.

| dr | fr | tr | bl | cl | pl |
|---|---|---|---|---|---|

cl ock

1. ________ op 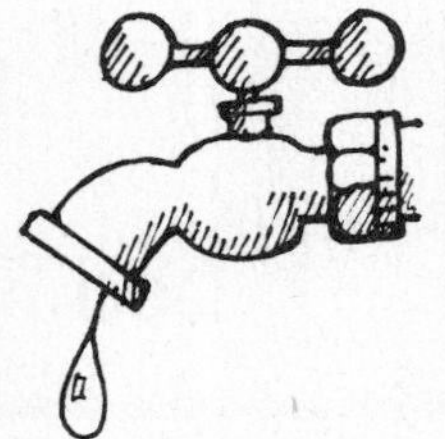

2. ________ ee 

3. ________ ock 

4. ________ ant 

5. ________ am 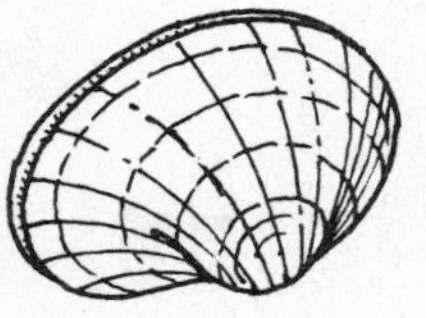

6. ________ ain 

7. ________ og 

8. ________ ap 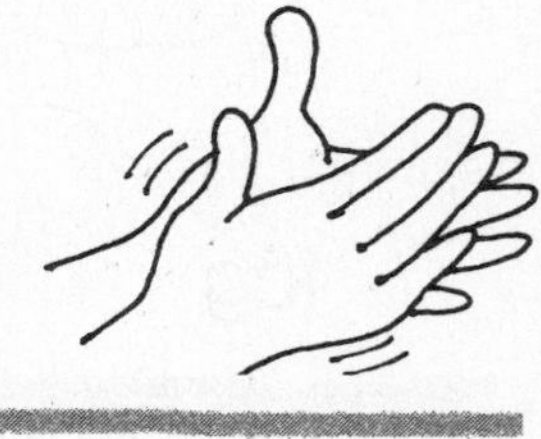

9. ________ ess 

10. ________ uck 

**Notes for Home:** Your child is learning to read words with initial *r* and *l* blends *(trap, frog, clam)*.
***Home Activity:*** Ask your child to make up silly sentences that each contain words beginning with just one blend, such as *Freddy frog likes French fries.*

Name ________________________

**Pick** a word from the box to finish each sentence.
**Write** it on the line. Use each word only once.

| for | good | some | too | want |
|---|---|---|---|---|

1. Do you ______________ to eat?

2. Yes, I want ______________ food.

3. Here is some food ______________ you.

4. That looks ______________ .

5. I will eat some ______________ .

**Notes for Home:** This week your child is learning to read the words *for*, *good*, *some*, *too,* and *want. **Home Activity:*** Get puppets or use washable markers to draw a face on closed fingers for puppets. Use the puppets to have a dialogue with your child using these new words.

Name ______________________________

**Look** at each picture.
**Make** an X after the sentence that tells what happened.

1. Tom got a cat. ______
Tom fell in the water. ______

2. Ming likes pets. ______
Ming likes fish. ______

3. Tess likes to sing. ______
Tess ran up the big hill. ______

4. The cat wants the fish. ______
The fish like the cat. ______

**Look** at the picture.
**Write** a word to finish the sentence.

5. The girl is ____________ .

**Notes for Home:** Your child is learning about drawing conclusions about story events and characters. ***Home Activity:*** Draw faces that show simple emotions: sadness, joy, anger, and so on. Ask your child to tell you how each person you drew feels, and explain how he or she knew this.

Name ______________________________



**Adding** an **-s** can make a noun mean more than one.

**Cat** shows one.
**Cats** show more than one. **cat**  **cats** 

**Look** at each picture and the noun in ( ).
**Add -s** to the noun if needed.
**Write** it on the line to finish each sentence.

1. The three ______________ eat. (pig)

2. The ______________ are in the pen. (hen)

3. The ______________ hops on a log. (frog)

4. The ______________ go up and down. (cat)

5. They have a big ______________ . (ball)

**Notes for Home:** Your child learned that adding *-s* to a noun makes it mean more than one. ***Home Activity:*** Name some common animals, such as *cat, dog,* and *bird.* Ask your child to name more than one of each animal.

Name ____________________

**Pick** a word from the box to finish each sentence.
**Write** it in the puzzle.

| for | good | meow | some | too | want |
|---|---|---|---|---|---|

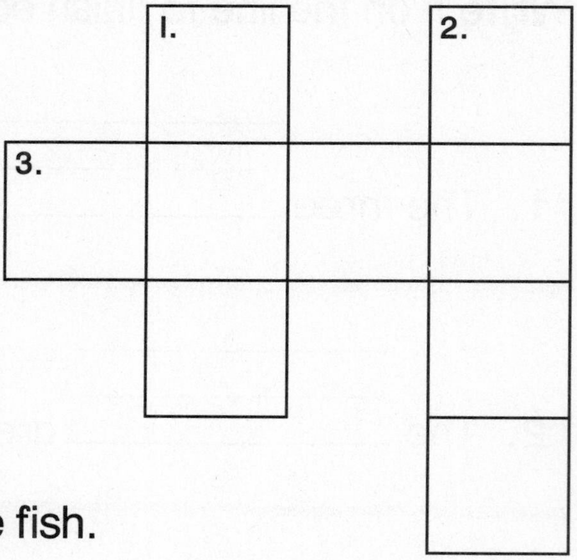

1. The fish is _____ the cat.
2. "_____!" said the cat.
3. I will give the cat _____ of the fish.

4. I _____ to play!
5. He likes to play _____!
6. We will have a _____ time.

*Notes for Home:* Your child solved puzzles using the words *for, good, meow, some, too,* and *want.* ***Home Activity:*** Say each word and ask your child to use it in a sentence. Help your child write each sentence.

Name ______________________________

**Say** the word for each picture.
**Write o** if the word has a **short o** sound.

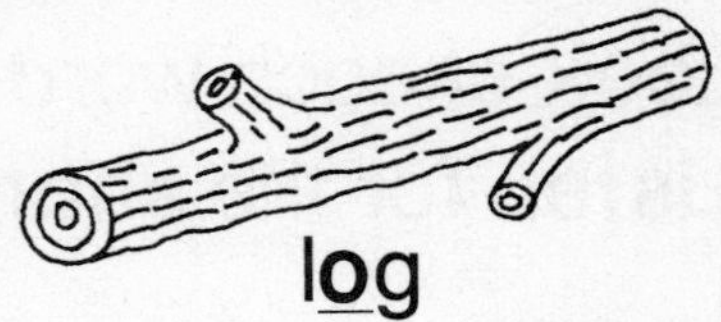


1. 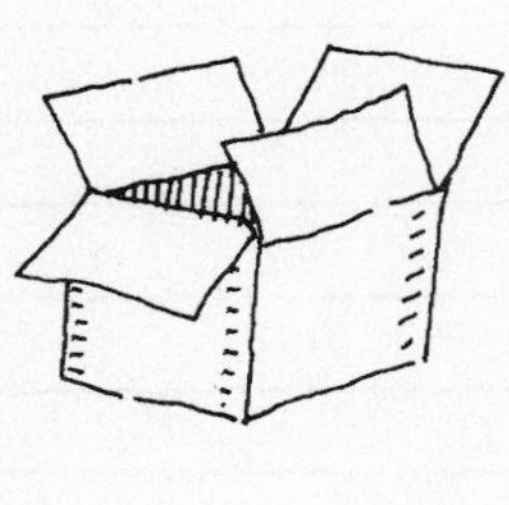
b ____ x

2. 
s ____ ck

3. 
r ____ ck

4. 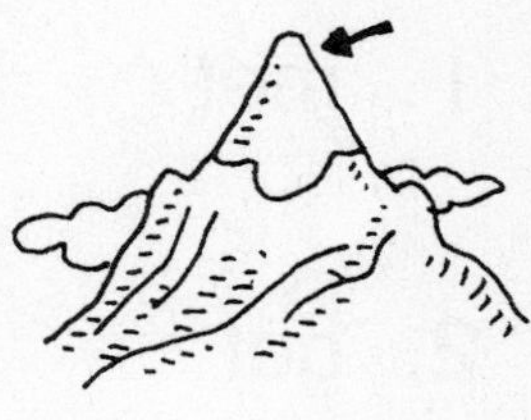
t ____ p

5. 
d ____ g

6. 
p ____ t

7. 
n ____ t

8. 
fr ____ g

**Find** the word that has the same **short o** sound as  .

**Mark** the ⊂⊃ to show your answer.

9. ⊂⊃ down
⊂⊃ lock
⊂⊃ into

10. ⊂⊃ hot
⊂⊃ go
⊂⊃ one

**Notes for Home:** Your child reviewed words with the short *o* sound heard in *log*.
***Home Activity:*** Have your child look through a book and find short *o* words. Together, list these words. Take turns using these words in sentences.

Name ______________________

**Look** at each word. **Say** it.
**Listen** for the **short e** sound in 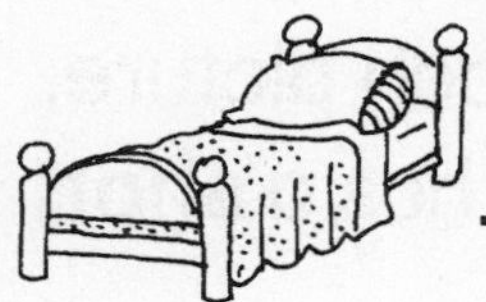 .

| | **Write** each word. | **Check** it. |
|---|---|---|
| 1. met | | |
| 2. get | | |
| 3. pet | | |
| 4. let | | |
| 5. ten | | |
| 6. yes | | |

## Word Wall Words

**Write** each word.

| | | |
|---|---|---|
| 7. want | | |
| 8. good | | |

**Notes for Home:** Your child spelled words with the short *e* sound heard in *bed* and two frequently used words: *want, good*. ***Home Activity:*** Encourage your child to use some of these words to write a story about a pet that takes a walk on a rainy day.

Name ______________________

**Say** the word for each picture.
**Write** the plural for each word.

1.

dog

2.
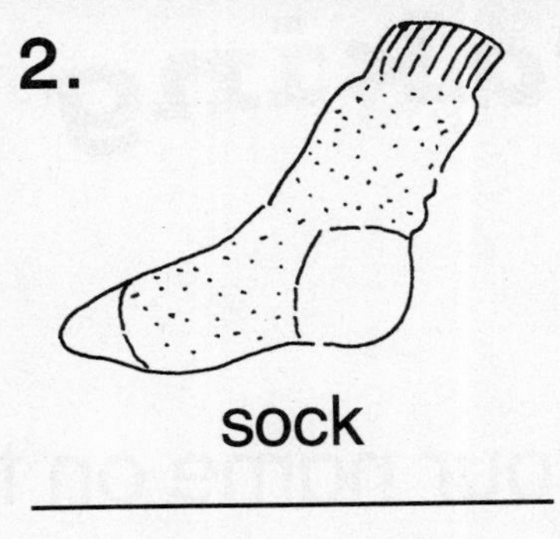
sock

3.

hen

4.
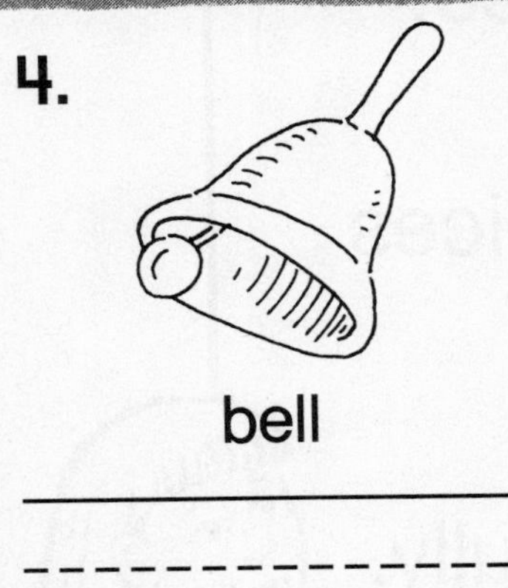
bell

5.

flag

6.

pet

7.

fish

8.
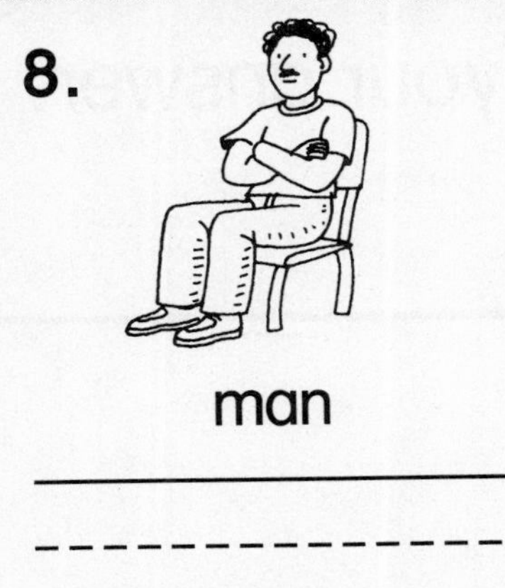
man

9.
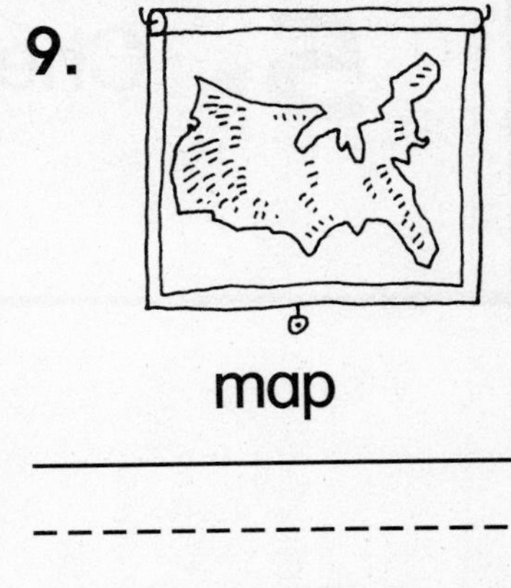
map

**Notes for Home:** Your child reviewed nouns that become plural when just *-s* is added and irregular plurals like *men* and *fish*. ***Home Activity:*** Look at a picture book with your child. List several nouns. Include both singular and plural nouns.

Name ______________________________

# Test-Taking Tips

1. Write your name on the test.

2. Read each question twice.

3. Read all the answer choices for the question.

4. Mark your answer carefully.

5. Check your answer.

Name ______________________________

## Part I: Vocabulary

**Read** each sentence.
**Mark** the ⬭ for the word that fits.

1. The cats ______ to eat.

 ⬭ make 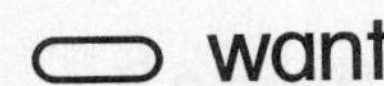 ⬭ want ⬭ sing

2. The cats get ______ chow.

 ⬭ on 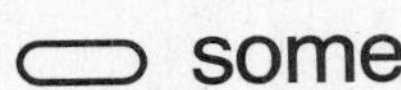 ⬭ some ⬭ into

3. Now they meow ______ more.

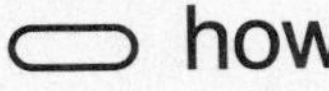 ⬭ how 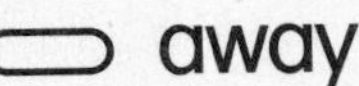 ⬭ away  ⬭ for

4. The chow was ______ .

⬭ good  ⬭ them 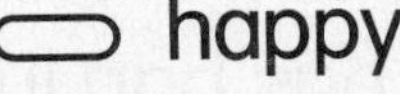 ⬭ happy

5. This cat is ______ fat!

⬭ all  ⬭ by ⬭ too

Name ______________________________



# Part 2: Comprehension

**Read** each question.

**Mark** the ⬭ for the answer.

6. In this story, the cat wants to
   - ⬭ nap.
   - ⬭ snack.
   - ⬭ fish.

7. What does the cat do many times?
   - ⬭ sets a trap
   - ⬭ gets a bug
   - ⬭ eats a snack

8. The cat gets a snack from a
   - ⬭ pig.
   - ⬭ duck.
   - ⬭ girl.

9. How does the cat feel at the end?
   - ⬭ mad
   - ⬭ sick
   - ⬭ happy

10. What can you tell about the cat?
    - ⬭ He runs fast.
    - ⬭ He has bad luck.
    - ⬭ He eats too much.

STOP

Name ______________________________

**Use** the word in ( ) to finish each sentence.
**Write** it on the line.
**Add** an **-s** if needed.

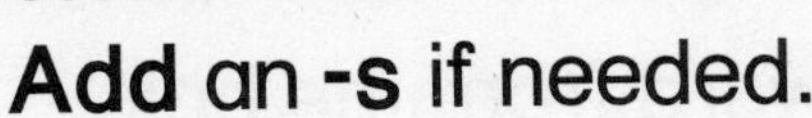

The cat **smells** a rat.
The rats **get** away.

(see)

1. The cat ______________ a fish.

(look)

2. The two fish ______________ at him.

(hit)

3. The cat ______________ the fish.

(get)

4. The cat ______________ wet!

**Find** the sentence that tells about the picture.
**Mark** the ⬭ to show your answer.

5. ⬭ The rat win.
   ⬭ The rats wins.
   ⬭ The rat wins.

**Notes for Home:** Your child reviewed verbs that end in *-s* that describe what just one person or thing does. ***Home Activity:*** With your child, watch television with the sound off. Have your child tell what is happening, using the appropriate verbs.

Name ______________________________

| met | get | pet | let | ten | yes |
|---|---|---|---|---|---|

**Change** one letter in each word to make a word from the box.
**Write** the new word on the line.

1. got __________
2. leg __________
3. pen __________
4. men __________
5. tin __________
6. yet __________

**Pick** a word from the box to match each clue.
**Write** it on the line.

7. not no __________
8. 5 + 5 = __________

**Pick** a word from the box to finish each sentence.
**Write** it on the line.

| want | good |
|---|---|

9. I ______________ a hen.

10. A hen is a ______________ pet.

**Notes for Home:** Your child spelled words with the short *e* sound heard in *get* and two frequently used words: *want, good*. ***Home Activity:*** Write the spelling words. Cut each word into letters. Have your child use the letters to spell each word.

Name ______________________________

boy

boys

boy + -s = boys

Many words add **-s** to mean more than one.

**Draw** a line from the word to the correct picture.

| 1. | | 2. | |
|---|---|---|---|
| | bed | | bears |
| | beds | | bear |

| 3. | | 4. | |
|---|---|---|---|
| | ball | | car |
| | balls | | cars |

**Notes for Home:** Your child labeled pictures with singular and plural nouns. ***Home Activity:*** Together, cut out pictures from magazines or newspapers. Have your child use nouns to label the pictures.

Name ______________________________

**Trace** the path.
**Follow** the words that mean more than one.

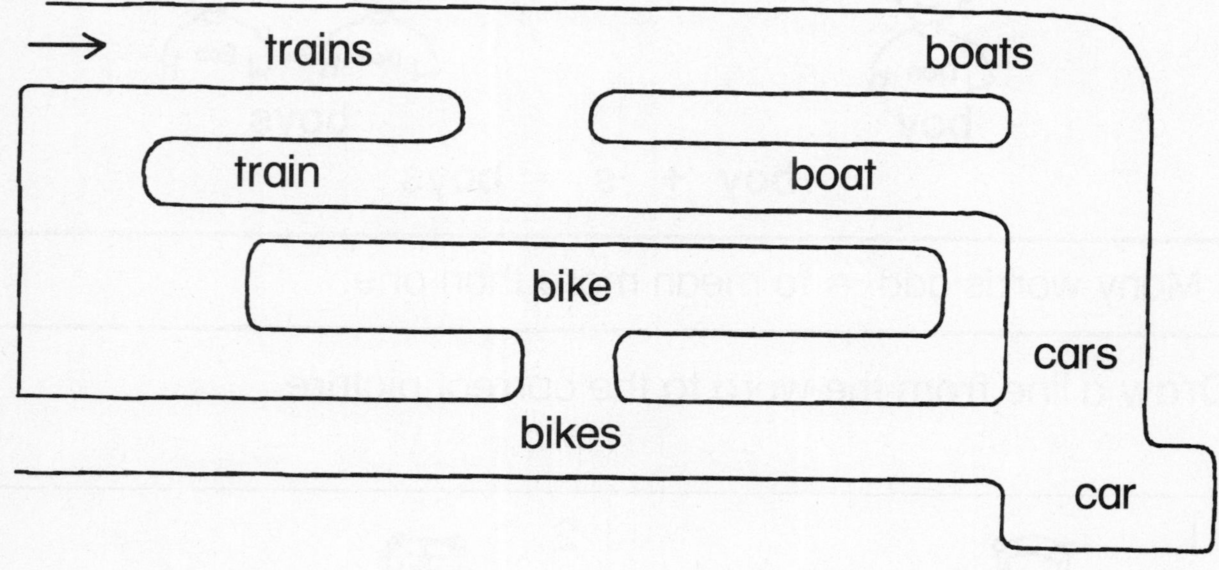


**Write** the correct word on the line.

| worker | workers |
|---|---|

1. The ____________________ fixes the road.

| car | cars |
|---|---|

2. Six ____________________ are on the street.

**Notes for Home:** Your child identified and wrote plural nouns—nouns that name more than one person, place, or thing. ***Home Activity:*** Ask your child to explain the rule for adding *-s* to nouns that name more than one.

**You are your child's first and best teacher!**

**Here are ways to help your child practice skills while having fun!**

**Day 1** Write a simple short *u* word, such as *hug*. Have your child change one letter to make a new word with short *u,* such as *bug*. Take turns changing that word to *bun* and *sun* and so on.

**Day 2** Encourage your child to make up sentences that include the following words: *jump, more, sleep, time,* and *with*. Then ask your child to draw a picture that illustrates each sentence.

**Day 3** Your child is learning to identify the main idea in a story. Read a story aloud to your child. Then ask your child: *What is the story all about?*

**Day 4** Your child is learning about grouping things that belong together. Give your child a category such as *pets* or *fruit*. Have your child name things that belong in that category.

**Day 5** Work with your child to make an address book filled with friends and family. Make sure that your child capitalizes all special names and places (proper nouns).

**Read with your child EVERY DAY!**



(fold here)

# Family Times

**My Buddy, Stan** **Biscuit**

**I'm a Happy Puppy**

I'm a happy puppy. I have fun.
I want to jump and swim and run.
When I want a snack, I find my cup.
I run right over and eat it up!

I'm a happy puppy. I have fun.
I like to skip and skate in the sun.
When I want to sleep, I find my rug.
I snuggle up and get a hug.

This rhyme includes words that your child is working with in school: words with the short *u* vowel sound *(fun, cup)* and words that begin with the letter *s* and another consonant *(skip, snack)*. Sing "I'm a Happy Puppy" with your child. Make up hand motions to match the words in the rhyme.

Name: ____________________

# S Is the Best

**Materials** paper circle, paper clip, pencils, 1 button per player

Start

## Game Directions

**1.** Make a simple spinner as shown.

**2.** Take turns spinning and naming a word that begins with the *s* blend spun.

**3.** If the player names a word, he or she may move that number of spaces. If the player cannot name a word, the turn is over.

**4.** The first player to reach the end wins!

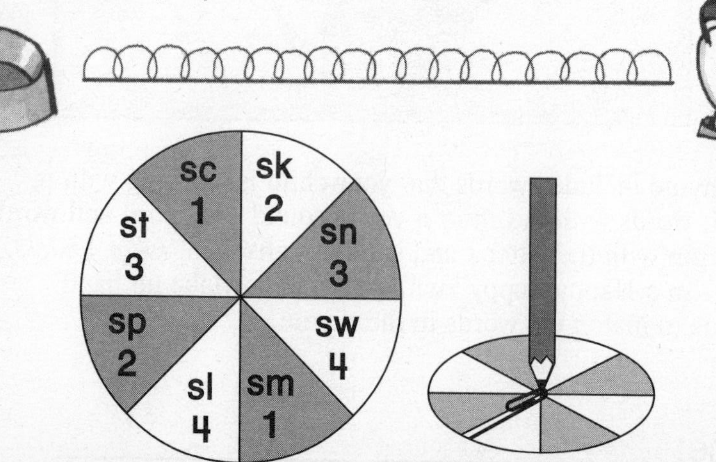

End

Name ____________________

**Circle** a word to finish each sentence.
**Write** it on the line.

pup

mud mad

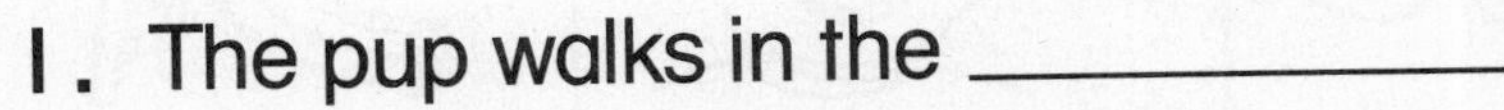

1. The pup walks in the ____________ .

tub tab

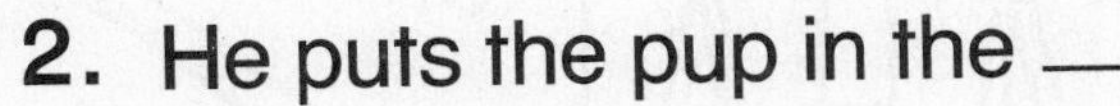

2. He puts the pup in the ____________ .

tag tug

3. This pup wants to ____________ .

bug bag

4. The pup plays with a ____________ .

hog hug

5. He wants to ____________ his pup.

**Notes for Home:** Your child practiced reading words with the short *u* sound heard in *pup*.
***Home Activity:*** Work with your child to write a story using as many of the short *u* words listed above as possible. Draw pictures to go along with the story you write.

Name ______________________________

**Pick** letters from the box to finish each word.
**Write** the letters on the line.

sk sl sm sn sp st sw

1. ________ ed
2. ________ ake
3. ________ ile
4. ________ ide
5. ________ ep
6. ________ ate
7. ________ ing
8. ________ oon

**Draw** a picture for each sentence.

9. Pat sleeps.

10. The pup has a spot.

**Notes for Home:** Your child identified words that begin with *s* blends such as *sp* and *sn* (*spool, snail*). ***Home Activity:*** Work with your child to find things around the house that begin with *s* blends. Make a list of these items.

Name ________________________________

**Pick** a word from the box to finish each sentence.
**Write** it on the line. Use each word only once.

| jump | more | sleep | time | with |
|---|---|---|---|---|

1. It is ______________ for bed.

2. Tim wants to ______________ .

3. The pup wants to ______________ .

4. The pup gets one ______________ hug.

5. The pup will sleep ______________ Tim.

**Notes for Home:** This week your child is learning to read the words *jump, more, sleep, time,* and *with*. ***Home Activity:*** Together with your child, write a short poem about a new puppy. Use as many of the words on this page as possible.

Name ______________________________

**Read** the story.
**Circle** the sentence that tells what the story is all about.
**Draw** a picture that shows what the story is all about.

---

1. Nan got a pup.
The pup is black.
Nan hugs the pup.
Nan calls the pup Bud.

2.

---

3. Ted jumps into the water.
Dan runs into the water.
Ted swims with Dan.
Ted and Dan have fun.

4.

---

**Write** the name of a story you have read.
**Draw** a picture that shows what the story is all about.

5. ______________________________

**Notes for Home:** Your child identified the main idea of a story. ***Home Activity:*** Read a story to your child. Discuss the story and ask your child to tell you what the story is all about. Invite your child to draw a picture that shows what the story is all about.

Name ______________________________

**Special names** for people, places, animals, and things begin with **capital letters.**

Jan Bass

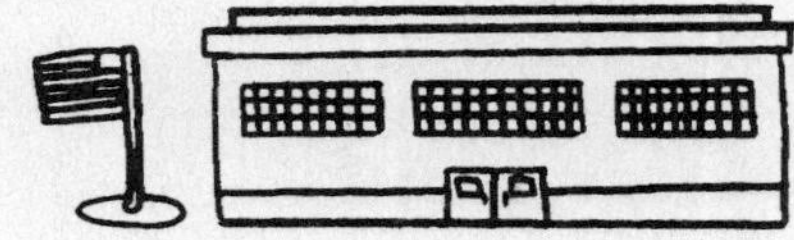

Brick Street School

Rex

**Correct** each name. **Write** it on the line.

1. bess

______________________________

2. bell school

______________________________

3. lake blue

______________________________

4. spot

______________________________

**Draw** a special person, place, thing, or animal.
**Write** its name on the line.

5.

______________________________

**Notes for Home:** Your child identified and wrote special names (proper nouns) with capital letters. ***Home Activity:*** Work with your child to think of the names of favorite people, places, or pets. Help your child to write a list of these names using capital letters.

Name ______________________________

**Pick** a word from the box to match each clue.
**Write** the words in the puzzles.

hear jump more sleep time with

1.

2. The pup wants one ______ hug.

3.

| 1. | | 2. | |
|---|---|---|---|

| 3. | | | | |
|---|---|---|---|---|

4. Can I go ______ you?

5. It is ______ for bed.

6.

| 4. | | 5. | |
|---|---|---|---|

| 6. | | | |
|---|---|---|---|

**Notes for Home:** Your child completed puzzles using words that he or she learned to read this week. ***Home Activity:*** Work with your child to write sentences using these words. Have him or her read the sentences aloud to you.

Name ______________________

**Circle** the word for each picture.
**Write** it on the line.

1. 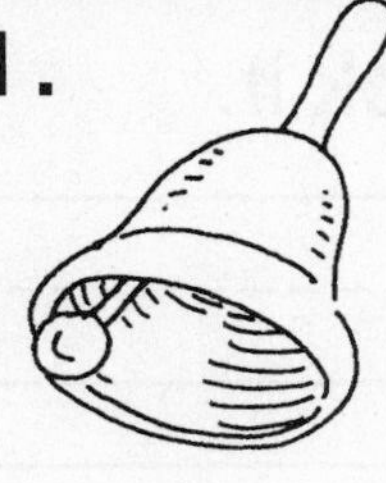
bell bill

2. 
pin pen

3. 
web won

4.
jug jet

5. 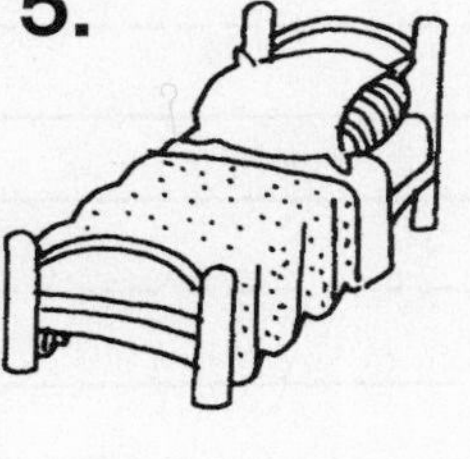
bad bed

6. 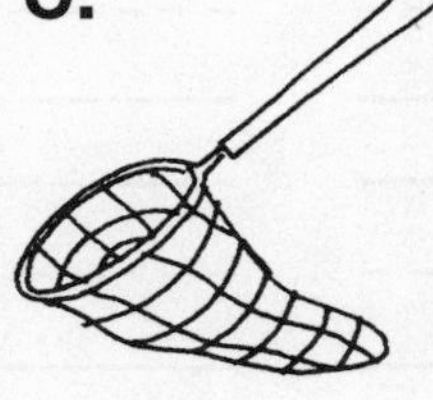
net not

7.
pet pit

8.
leg log

**Find** the word that has the same vowel sound as .
**Mark** the ⬭ to show your answer.

9. ⬭ sleep
⬭ sled
⬭ slap

10. ⬭ well
⬭ wall
⬭ we

**Notes for Home:** Your child reviewed words with the short *e* sound heard in *vet*. ***Home Activity:*** Help your child write a silly poem in which all the rhyming words have the short *e* sound. Encourage your child to read the poem aloud to other family members.

Name ______________________

**Look** at each word. **Say** it.
**Listen** for the **short u** sound in [picture].
**Listen** for different ending sounds.

| | **Write** each word. | **Check** it. |
|---|---|---|
| 1. fun | | |
| 2. run | | |
| 3. up | | |
| 4. cup | | |
| 5. stuff | | |
| 6. puff | | |

# Word Wall Words

**Write** each word.

| | | |
|---|---|---|
| 7. jump | | |
| 8. more | | |

**Notes for Home:** Your child spelled words with *-un, -up,* and *-uff* that have the short *u* sound heard in *cup* and two frequently used words: *jump, more.* ***Home Activity:*** Say each spelling word. Have your child use it in a sentence. Say the spelling word again and have your child write it.

Name ______________________________

**Circle** the special name in each sentence.

1. I call my dog Max.
2. Here is Meg.
3. Her cat, Sam, is big and fat.
4. That little cat is Pip.
5. Dan Yin has a pig.

**Circle** the special name in each sentence.
**Write** it with a capital letter on the line.

6. Where is bess? ____________________
7. She is with fran. ____________________
8. How many rats does kim have? ____________________
9. Let brad hold my frog. ____________________
10. Where did nan get all the bugs? ____________________

**Notes for Home:** Your child identified and wrote proper nouns—names for particular people, places, or things. ***Home Activity:*** Have your child write some address labels for your mail, making sure the proper names are capitalized.

Name ______________________________



# Test-Taking Tips

1. Write your name on the test.

2. Read each question twice.

3. Read all the answer choices for the question.

4. Mark your answer carefully.

5. Check your answer.

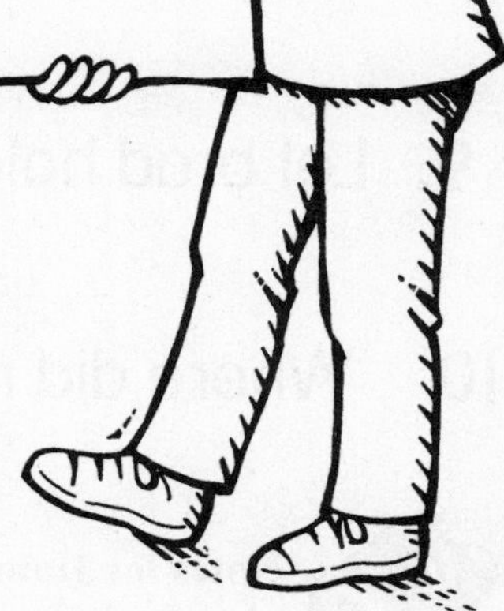

Name ________________________________



# Part 1: Vocabulary

**Read** each sentence.
**Mark** the ⬭ for the word that fits.

1. The pup likes to ______ .
   ⬭ more ⬭ make ⬭ jump

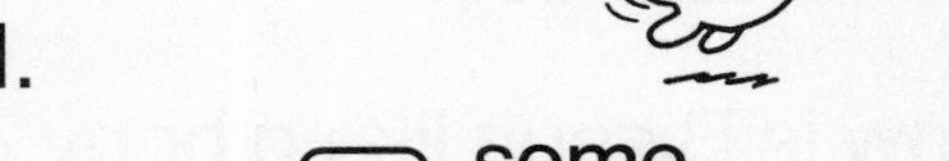

2. The pup plays ______ the girl.
   ⬭ with ⬭ this ⬭ some

3. The pup gets one ______ snack.
   ⬭ help ⬭ more ⬭ now

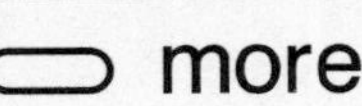

4. It is ______ for bed.
   ⬭ time ⬭ jump ⬭ sleep

5. The pup will ______ now.
   ⬭ some ⬭ sleep ⬭ time

Name ______________________



# Part 2: Comprehension

**Read** each question.
**Mark** the ⊂⊃ for the answer.

6. What is it time for Biscuit to do?
   - ⊂⊃ play
   - ⊂⊃ eat
   - ⊂⊃ sleep

7. Biscuit does not go to bed. Biscuit wants to
   - ⊂⊃ eat.
   - ⊂⊃ hear a story.
   - ⊂⊃ kiss a doll.

8. How is Biscuit like a baby?
   - ⊂⊃ He can say "Woof."
   - ⊂⊃ He can sing.
   - ⊂⊃ He likes hugs.

9. How does the story end?
   - ⊂⊃ The girl plays.
   - ⊂⊃ Biscuit sleeps.
   - ⊂⊃ Biscuit runs away.

10. What is a good name for this story?
    - ⊂⊃ "A Happy Girl"
    - ⊂⊃ "Time for Bed"
    - ⊂⊃ "One More Walk"

STOP

Name ______________________________

**Circle** the word for each picture.
**Write** it on the line.

doll

1.

puff pull

______________

2.

snip sniff

______________

3.

stuns stuff

______________

4.

miss mitt

______________

5.

kiss kick

______________

6.

bat ball

______________

7.

tops toss

______________

8.

buzz bull

______________

**Find** the word that has the same ending sound as .
**Mark** the ⬭ to show your answer.

9. ⬭ vet
⬭ still
⬭ walk

10. ⬭ smell
⬭ black
⬭ yellow

**Notes for Home:** Your child reviewed words that have double final consonants such as *doll*.
***Home Activity:*** Have your child collect words like these from signs and stories and then write the found words in lists. Invite him or her to keep a separate list for each letter pair.

Name ______________________

fun run up cup stuff puff

**Write** the words from the box that rhyme with each picture.

1. ____________ 2. ____________

3. ____________ 4. ____________

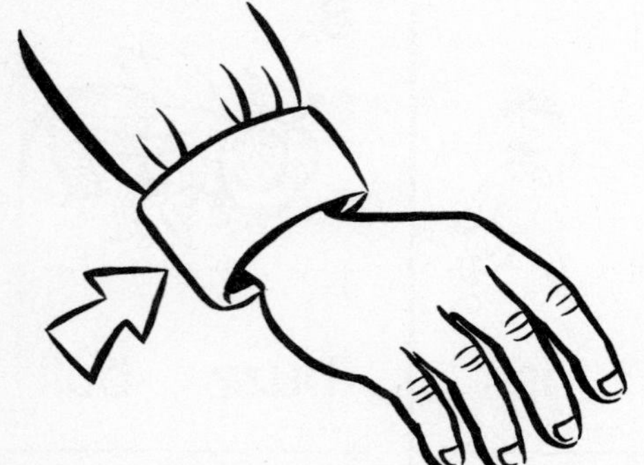

5. ____________ 6. ____________

**Pick** a word from the box to finish each sentence.
**Write** it on the line.

jump more

7. My pup likes to ____________ up.

8. He wants one ____________ hug.

**Notes for Home:** Your child spelled words with *-un, -up,* and *-uff* that have the short *u* sound heard in *cup* and two frequently used words: *jump, more*. ***Home Activity:*** Help your child make up rhymes using some of these spelling words.

Name ______________________

RETEACHING

**Special names** of people, pets, and places begin with capital letters.

**Look** at each picture.
**Write** the name on the line.

Denver  1. I live in ______________.

Spot  2. My dog is ______________.

Flo 3. My sister is ______________.

**Notes for Home:** Your child identified and wrote proper nouns—nouns that name specific people, places, or animals. ***Home Activity:*** Have your child explain the rule for beginning a proper noun with a capital letter.

Name ______________________________

**Circle** the special name in each box.
**Write** one special name in each sentence.

| boy | Bob | town | Salem |
|---|---|---|---|
| Fluffy | cat | Aunt Kate | woman |

1. ____________________ sits on a chair.

2. ____________________ runs around the house.

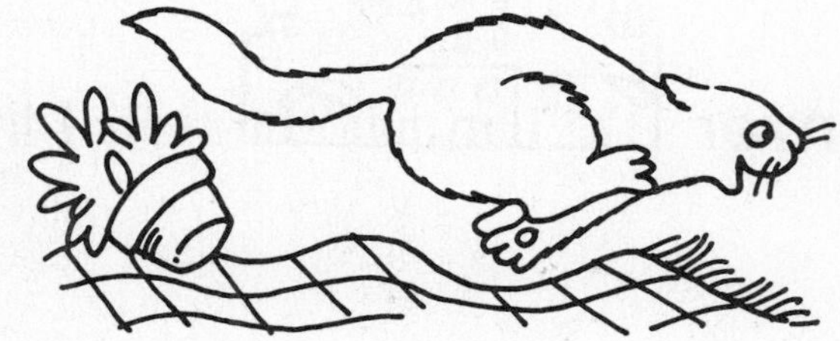

3. They live in ____________________.

**Notes for Home:** Your child identified and wrote proper nouns. ***Home Activity:*** Have your child draw a picture of family members. Have him or her use proper nouns to label the drawing. Make sure your child uses capital letters to write proper nouns.

**You *are* your child's first *and* best teacher!**

**Here are ways to help your child practice skills while having fun!**

**Day 1** With your child, practice saying these words that begin with the sound /s/: *cell, cellar, cement, cent, center, circle, circus, city,* and *cycle*. Hiss like a snake when you say the sound /s/.

**Day 2** Make up two-line rhymes with your child, using each of these words: *bring, carry, hold, our,* and *us*. For example: *I love to carry/My big pig, Harry*.

**Day 3** Write the phrase *Have Four Legs*. With your child, take turns thinking of things that have four legs, including animals and furniture.

**Day 4** Your child is learning to make announcements. Give your child the job of announcing your dinner menu.

**Day 5** Practice using special titles. Have fun with your child by using *Ms., Mrs., Mr.,* and *Dr.* before the names of your pets and other animals you both know.

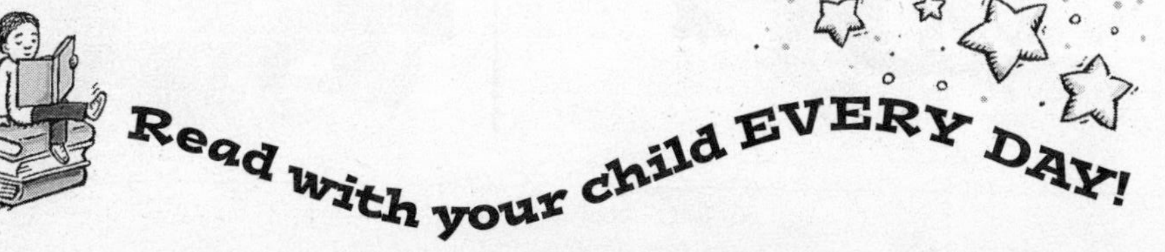
Read with your child EVERY DAY!

(fold here)

# Family Times

Trucks — Communities

**Trucks and Buses**

Cindy's a plumber.
She unclogs a tub.
She unclogs a sink too
And gives it a scrub!

George drives a big truck,
With his puppy in back.
George has all the lumber
In one giant stack.

Gene is a driver.
He drives a big bus.
Gene drives in the city
And drives all of us.

This rhyme includes words your child is working with in school: words with the short *u* sound *(tub, truck)* and words beginning with *g* and *c* that stand for the sounds /j/ and /s/ *(Gene, city)*. Sing "Trucks and Buses" with your child. Then draw and label pictures of trucks and buses.

Name: ______________________

# It's a Match

**Materials** paper, marker, bag

**Game Directions**

**1.** Write the short *u* words shown below on small squares of paper. Place the squares in a bag.

**2.** Players take turns picking squares from the bag, reading the words aloud, and placing each word over the picture it matches.

**3.** Play until the gameboard squares are all covered.

**4.** Make your own gameboard and set of matching short *u* words and play again.

**Matching Words**

bug, cup, duck, bus, tub, drum, skunk, truck

Name ______________________________

**Circle** a word to finish each sentence.
**Write** it on the line.

duck

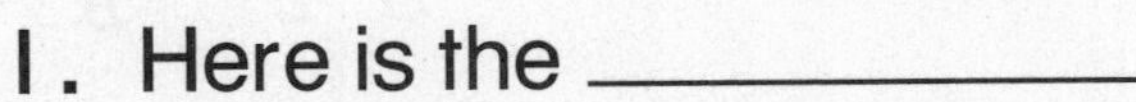

bun bat bus

1. Here is the ________________ .

hug tug tag

2. Rob sees the ducks ________________ .

run ran rip

3. Rob sees the ducks ________________ .

mad mud bud

4. One duck fell in the ________________ .

fan fin fun

5. Now the ducks have ________________ !

**Notes for Home:** Your child practiced reading and writing words with the short *u* sound heard in *bug* and *duck*. ***Home Activity:*** Work together to write a poem using as many of the short *u* words shown above as you can.

Name ________________________________



**Say** the word for each picture.
**Circle** the letter that begins each word.
**Write** the letter on the line.

circus

giraffe

g c

1. ______ ym

g c

2. ______ ent

g c

3. ______ ircle

g c

4. ______ ingerbread

g c

5. ______ erbil

g c

6. ______ erms

g c

7. ______ ity

g c

8. ______ ereal

**Notes for Home:** Your child practiced writing words that begin with *c* and *g* that stand for the /s/ sound in *circus* and the /j/ sound in *giraffe*. ***Home Activity:*** Ask your child to say the *c* /s/ and *g* /j/ words on this page out loud, emphasizing the initial sounds.

Name ______________________



**Pick** a word from the box to finish each sentence.
**Write** it on the line.

| bring | carry | hold | our | us |
|---|---|---|---|---|

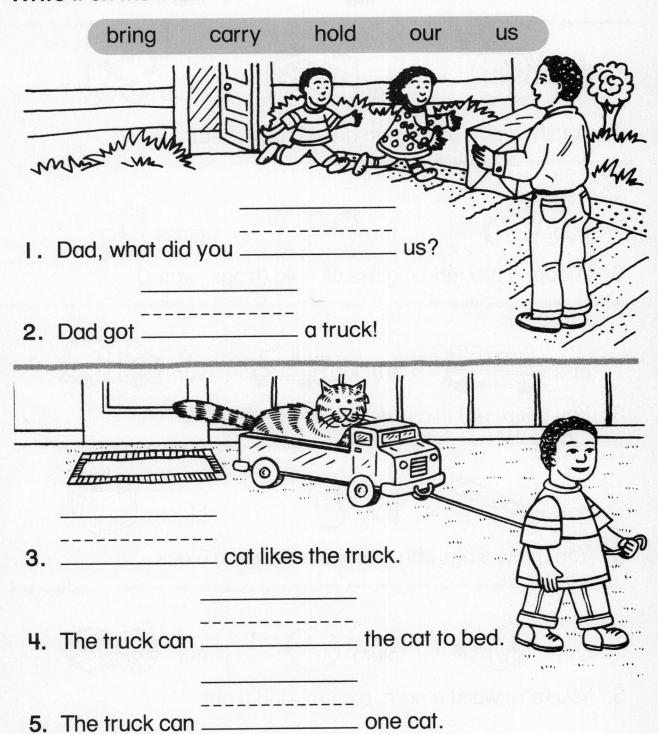

1. Dad, what did you ______________ us?

2. Dad got ______________ a truck!

3. ______________ cat likes the truck.

4. The truck can ______________ the cat to bed.

5. The truck can ______________ one cat.

**Notes for Home:** This week your child is learning to read the words *bring, carry, hold, our,* and *us*. ***Home Activity:*** Work with your child to write three sentences using all five words.

Name ______________________________

**Look** at the pictures. **Read** the sentence.
**Circle** the word in ( ) that tells how the objects are alike.

fish  cat pup 

1. A fish, a cat, and a pup are all (pets, red).

cup  tub 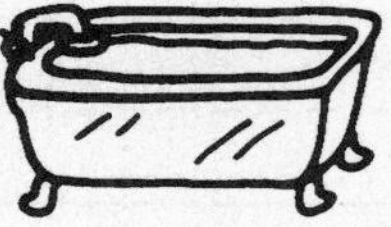 glass 

2. A cup, a tub, and a glass all hold (frogs, water).

bus  truck  van 

3. You (skip, go) in a bus, a truck, and a van.

bat  ball  block 

4. You (play, sing) with a bat, a ball, and a block.

ham 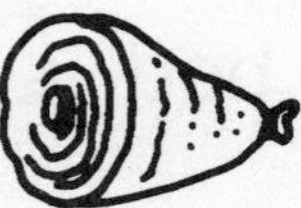 plum  nut 

5. You (eat, walk) a ham, a plum, and a nut.

**Notes for Home:** Your child is learning about classifying—grouping things belonging together. ***Home Activity:*** Draw three smiling faces and one sad one. Ask your child which one does not belong and why.

Name ______________________________

A **title** comes before a name.
A title and a name each begin with a capital letter.
A title ends with a **.** .

**Dr.** Ron

**Write** each title and name on the line.
**Use** capital letters and a period.

1. One man in the bus is mr hob.

______________________________

2. He brings ms woo to our class.

______________________________

3. He brings mrs dan to the city.

______________________________

4. We carry our pup, mr jump, on the bus.

______________________________

5. dr ron can help our pup.

______________________________

**Notes for Home:** Your child identified and wrote special titles, such as *Dr., Mr., Mrs.,* and *Ms.* ***Home Activity:*** Put titles before the names of family friends. Say the names out loud. Help your child write each title and name.

Name ______________________________



**Pick** the word from the box to finish each sentence.
**Write** it on the line. Use each word only once.

| bring | build | carry | hold | our | us |
|---|---|---|---|---|---|

1. Look at ____________ go.

2. We are in ____________ van.

3. Dad will ____________ us to the water.

4. We ____________ a cup, a ball, and a truck.

5. The cup can ____________ water.

6. We play and ____________ a city.

**Notes for Home:** Your child used newly learned words to fill in the blanks in a story.
***Home Activity:*** Say each vocabulary word aloud, and have your child write it down.

Name ______________________

**Write** the words in each box in **ABC order**.

**a b c d e f g h i j k l m n o p q r s t u v w x y z**

| help work fix save | truck dump rocks logs |
|---|---|
| 1. ________ | 5. ________ |
| 2. ________ | 6. ________ |
| 3. ________ | 7. ________ |
| 4. ________ | 8. ________ |

**Find** these words in Words to Know of your student book on page 130. **Draw** a picture to show what these words mean.

| 9. dentist | 10. coach |
|---|---|

**Notes for Home:** Your child put words in alphabetical order and used a glossary to find the meanings of two words. ***Home Activity:*** Write the names of family members on slips of paper. Each name should begin with a different letter. Ask your child to put them in ABC order.

Name ______________________________



**Say** the word for each picture.
**Add -s** to the word if it names more than one.

spots

1.

truck ______

2.

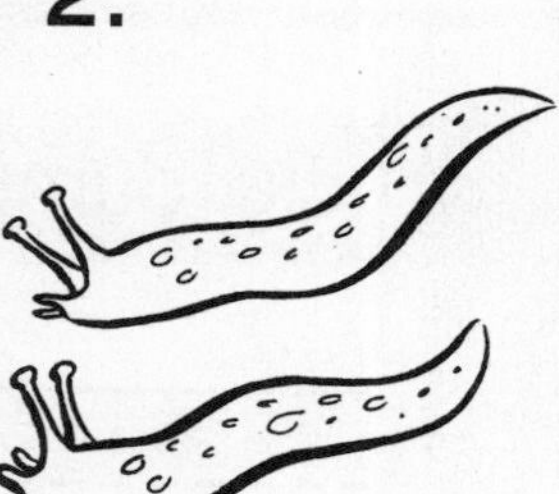

slug ______

3.

mat ______

4.

doll ______

5.

plum ______

6.

egg ______

7.

jug ______

8.

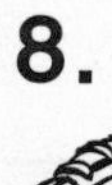

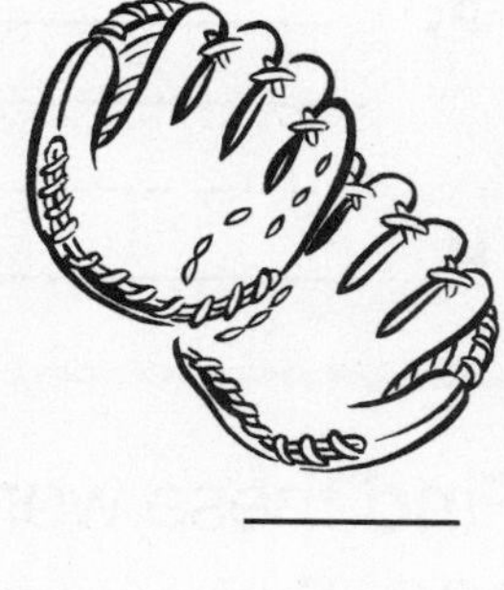

mitt ______

**Find** the words that tell about the picture.
**Mark** the ⬭ to show your answer.

9. ⬭ three frog
⬭ three frogs
⬭ frog

10. ⬭ rock
⬭ two rock
⬭ two rocks

**Notes for Home:** Your child reviewed writing plural nouns by adding *-s*. ***Home Activity:*** Go through a grocery flyer with your child. Look for fruits and vegetables that form their plurals by adding only *-s*. Have your child use the plural forms to make a pretend shopping list.

Name ______________________________

**Look** at each word. **Say** it.
**Listen** for the **short u** sound in  .

| | **Write** each word. | **Check** it. |
|---|---|---|
| 1. us | | |
| 2. bus | | |
| 3. cut | | |
| 4. but | | |
| 5. rug | | |
| 6. hug | | |

## Word Wall Words

**Write** each word.

| | | |
|---|---|---|
| 7. our | | |
| 8. bring | | |

**Notes for Home:** Your child spelled words with the short *u* sound heard in *cup* and two frequently used words: *our, bring*. ***Home Activity:*** Have your child cut out letters for these spelling words from an old magazine and then paste the letters on paper to spell the words.

Name ________________________

**Read** each name.
**Write** it correctly on the line.
**Use** a capital letter or a **.** if needed.

1. mr Lee ________________

2. mrs Bell ________________

3. miss fox ________________

4. dr Dunn ________________

**Make** a name tag for yourself.

**Notes for Home:** Your child reviewed writing special titles used with people's names. ***Home Activity:*** Have your child help you make a phone list of the people to be called in emergencies. Say the names for your child to write. Use titles, such as *Dr.* or *Mrs.*

Name ______________________________

## Part 1: Vocabulary

**Read** each sentence.
**Mark** the ⬭ for the word that fits.

1. This is ______ mom.
 ⬭ and ⬭ our ⬭ many

2. Mom will go with ______ .
⬭ all ⬭ by ⬭ us

3. She can ______ the bag.
⬭ stop ⬭ carry ⬭ come

4. I will ______ the door.
⬭ play ⬭ make ⬭ hold

5. Sal will ______ a bag in for Mom.
⬭ bring ⬭ sing ⬭ find

GO ON

Name ______________________________ 

# Part 2: Comprehension

**Read** each question.
**Mark** the ⊂⊃ for the answer.

6. Who helps us stay healthy?
   - ⊂⊃ doctors
   - ⊂⊃ police officers
   - ⊂⊃ coaches

7. Teachers help us to
   - ⊂⊃ sleep.
   - ⊂⊃ learn.
   - ⊂⊃ build.

8. Who can fix our teeth?
   - ⊂⊃ mail carriers
   - ⊂⊃ dentists
   - ⊂⊃ firefighters

9. What did you learn from what you read?
   - ⊂⊃ Mail carriers have the best job.
   - ⊂⊃ There are many kinds of work.
   - ⊂⊃ Kids can have jobs.

10. What is a good name for what you read?
    - ⊂⊃ "Go to the Doctor"
    - ⊂⊃ "Time to Play"
    - ⊂⊃ "Jobs People Do"

STOP

Name ______________________

**Pick** letters from the box to finish each word.
**Write** the letters on the line.

truck

| br | cr | dr | fr | gr | pr |
|---|---|---|---|---|---|

1. 
______ ick

2. 
______ og

3. 
______ um

4. ______ op

5. 
______ ack

6. 
______ in

7. 
______ ess

8. 
______ ib

**Find** the word that has the same beginning sound as .
**Mark** the ⬭ to show your answer.

9. ⬭ trip
⬭ drill
⬭ brim

10. ⬭ grab
⬭ trot
⬭ tan

**Notes for Home:** Your child reviewed words that begin with the letters *br, cr, dr, fr, gr, pr,* and *tr*. ***Home Activity:*** Read a story with your child. Look for words that begin with these letters. Encourage your child to read these words.

Name ______________________



us bus cut but rug hug

**Write** the words from the box that rhyme with **hut**.

1. ______________ 2. ______________

**Write** the words from the box that rhyme with **Gus**.

3. ______________ 4. ______________

**Write** the words from the box that rhyme with **dug**.

5. ______________ 6. ______________

---

**Pick** a word from the box to finish each sentence.
**Write** it in the puzzle.

our bring

7. I have my hat.
We have _______ hats.

8. _______ it to me.

| 7. | | | | |
|---|---|---|---|---|
| | | | | |
| 8. | | | | |

**Notes for Home:** Your child practiced spelling words with the short *u* sound in *pup* and two frequently used words: *our, bring*. ***Home Activity:*** Use these spelling words to make up letter games with your child. (For example: *Change rat to but in two turns. rat bat but.)*

Name ______________________________

RETEACHING

A **title** can come before the name of a person.
A title begins with a capital letter.
It ends with a period.

This is **Mrs. Vargas**.

**Read** the title and the name.
**Write** the title and the name correctly on the line.

1. mrs kay lyons

______________________________

2. dr sal miller

______________________________

3. mr john korn

______________________________

4. mr gil cruz

______________________________

**Notes for Home:** Your child wrote special titles, such as *Dr., Mr.,* and *Mrs.* ***Home Activity:*** Make name tags for family members. Have your child write a title for each person, using correct capitalization and punctuation.

Name ______________________



**Write** each name correctly.

Monday

dr. billy bear

1. ______________________

Tuesday

miss wendy wildcat

2. ______________________

Wednesday

mr. david deer

3. ______________________

Thursday

mrs. gretchen goat

4. ______________________

Friday

dr. bobby bee

5. ______________________

**Notes for Home:** Your child wrote titles, such as *Dr., Mr.,* and *Mrs.,* correctly. ***Home Activity:*** Together, write a story about funny characters with titles (*Dr. Fishface, Mrs. Peanutbutter*).

**You *are* your child's first *and* best teacher!**

**Here are ways to help your child practice skills while having fun!**

**Day 1** Take turns making up sentences containing mostly words with the same short vowel sounds. For example, a short *a* sentence might be: *Tad and Max had a cat in the van.*

**Day 2** Ask your child to use the words *came, know, out, she,* and *there* in sentences about doing something with a friend.

**Day 3** Look for pronouns like *he, him, she, her,* and *we* in your child's favorite stories. Ask your child to tell you whom each pronoun represents.

**Day 4** Read a favorite story with your child. Together find the nouns in the story that name people, places, or things.

**Day 5** Ask your child to draw a scene of a favorite game your child plays with a friend, such as tag. Then have your child describe to you what is happening in the picture he or she drew.

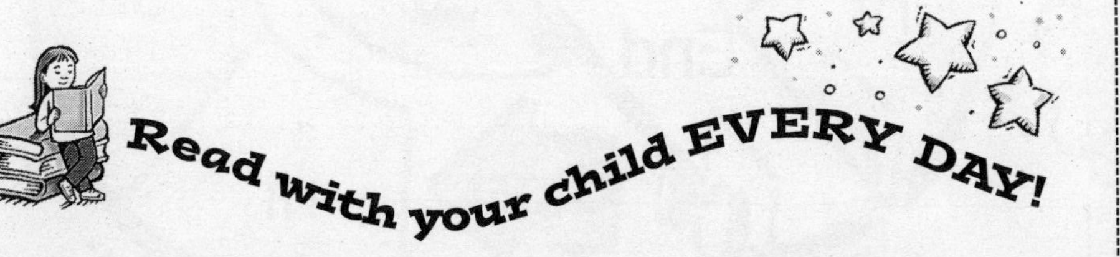
Read with your child EVERY DAY!

(fold here)

# Family Times

**Fox and Bear** **Fox and Bear Look at the Moon**

### My Pals

My pals help when I am ill.
My best pals are Pam and Jill.
Pam will fix a yummy lunch.
She will fix me toast to munch.
Jill will hand me my red cup.
It has milk. I drink it up.

We will sit and sing a lot.
We will play with my pet, Spot.
They will help to walk my pet.
Pam and Jill will not forget!
We just want to jump and run.
When I'm well, that will be fun.

This rhyme includes words your child is working with in school: words with short vowels *(sit, Pam, cup)* and words with final consonant blends *(help, jump, hand, want, toast)*. Sing "My Pals" together. Think up rhyming words for the words with the final blends.

Name: ______________________________

# Circle the Pond

**Materials** 1 button per player, 1 penny

**Game Directions**

**1.** Place buttons on gameboard and take turns flipping a penny. Heads moves ahead two spaces, and tails moves one space.

**2.** When landing on a space, a player must name a word ending with the blend shown. Words may only be used once. Make a list to keep track.

**3.** A player unable to name a word must go back to where he or she started the turn.

**4.** The first player to jump into the pond wins!

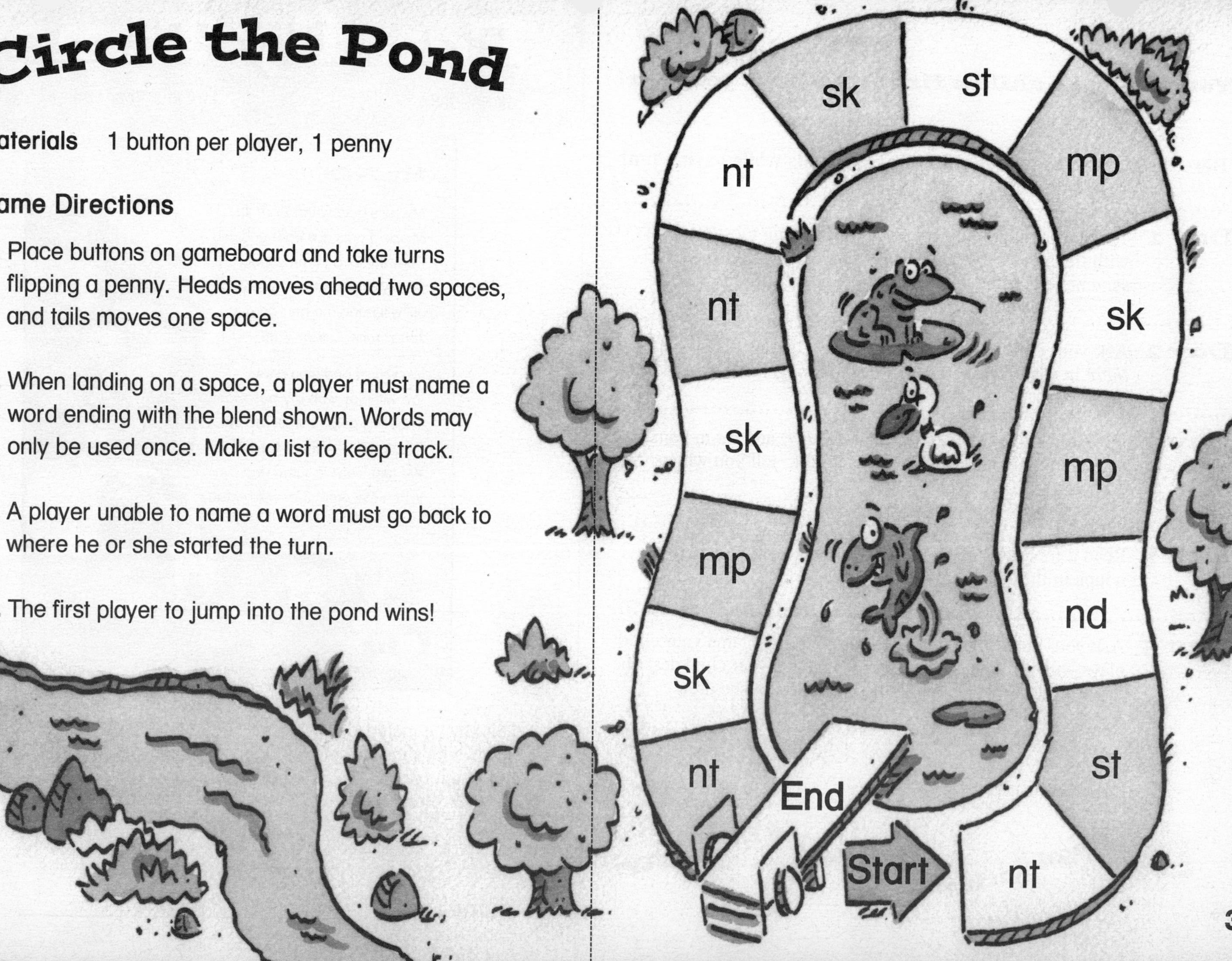

Name ______________________________

**Say** the word for each picture.
**Circle** the letter to finish each word.
**Write** the letter on the line.

Ted and Bud

a e i o u

1. b ______ s

a e i o u

2. h ______ t

a e i o u

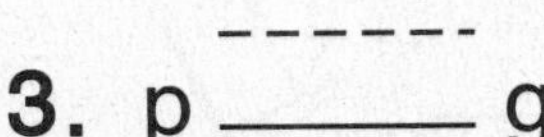

3. p ______ g

a e i o u

4. j ______ t

a e i o u

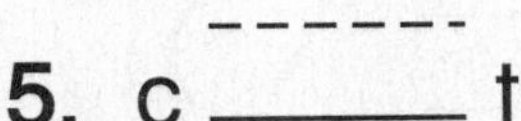

5. c ______ t

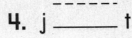

a e i o u

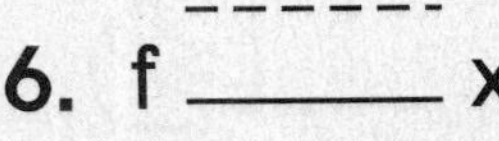

6. f ______ x

a e i o u

7. t ______ p

a e i o u

8. m ______ p

a e i o u

9. b ______ d

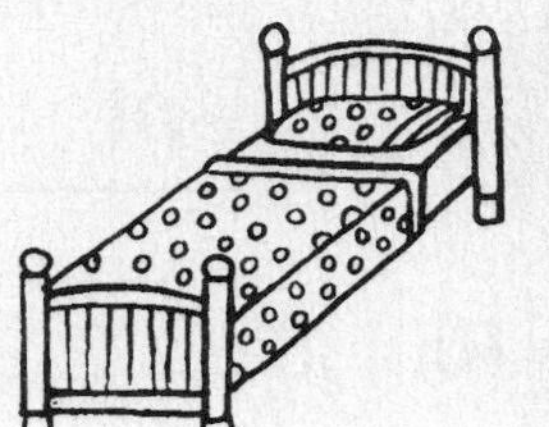

a e i o u

10. c ______ p

**Notes for Home:** Your child studied words with the short vowel pattern CVC (consonant-vowel-consonant) as in *ran* and *net*. ***Home Activity:*** Challenge your child to think of three new words that show this pattern for each vowel.

Name ______________________________

**Say** the word for each picture.
**Circle** the letters to finish each word.
**Write** the letters on the line.

sta**mp**

1. po ______ nd nt
2. fi ______ nt st
3. ce ______ mp nt
4. pu ______ st mp
5. la ______ st mp
6. ha ______ nt nd
7. ca ______ st nt
8. te ______ nt mp
9. sa ______ nd st
10. ju ______ nt mp

**Notes for Home:** Your child is studying final consonant blends such as *-mp, -nd, -nt,* and *-st.* ***Home Activity:*** Ask your child to make up two sentences that each have a word with a final consonant blend.

Name ______________________

**Pick** a word from the box to finish each sentence.
**Write** it on the line.

| came | know | out | she | there |
|---|---|---|---|---|

1. Meg ______________ to the pond.

2. ______________ saw a tent.

3. "I ______________ that tent," said Meg.

4. "I know Dan and Lucky will be in ______________."

5. Dan and Lucky ran ______________ of the tent!

**Notes for Home:** This week your child is learning to read the words *came, know, out, she,* and *there*. ***Home Activity:*** On a piece of paper, write the first and last letters of each word. Say each word aloud and ask your child to fill in the middle letter or letters.

Name ______________________________

**Read** each sentence.
**Circle** the word or words that mean the same as the underlined word.

1. Tim and Liz run fast.
They want to get to the pond.

Tim    Liz    Tim and Liz

2. Tim likes to sit by the water. He sees a duck.

Tim    Liz    the duck

3. Liz sees it too.

Tim    Liz    the duck

4. The duck calls out to them.

Liz    the duck    Tim and Liz

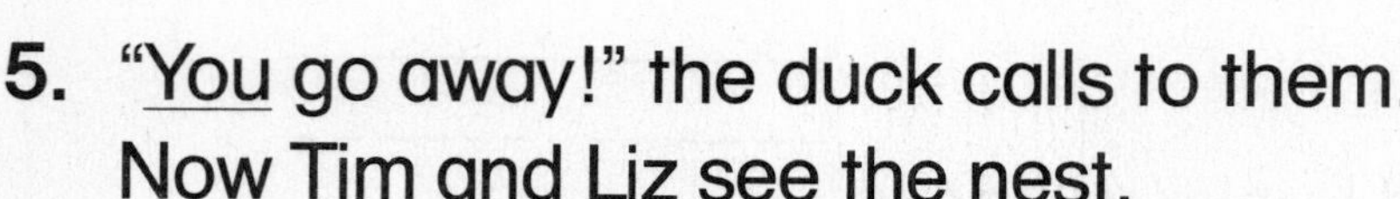

5. "You go away!" the duck calls to them.
Now Tim and Liz see the nest.

Tim and Liz    the duck    the eggs

**Notes for Home:** Your child used words and pictures to identify the person or thing that each pronoun represents. ***Home Activity:*** Read the above sentences with your child. Discuss the clues he or she used to figure out each answer.

Name ______________________________

A **noun** names a person, place, animal, or thing.
A noun can be in more than one part of a sentence.

The **cat** sees the **fish**.

The **dog** sees the **cat**!

**Underline** the nouns in each sentence.
**Draw** a picture to show each noun.

1. The truck holds rocks.
2. The man chops a log.
3. The frog eats a bug.
4. The bug is on the rug.
5. The black cat has a hat.

**Notes for Home:** Your child identified nouns in different parts of sentences.
***Home Activity:*** Make up a simple sentence that uses two nouns, one in the naming part of the sentence and one in the action part like those above. Ask your child to find the nouns.

Name ______________________

**Pick** a word from the box to finish each sentence.
**Write** it in the puzzle.

| came | know | out | she | there |
|---|---|---|---|---|

1. Do you ______ what is in the box?
2. The frog hops ______ of the box!
3. The frog does not like it in ______ .

1. 2.

3.

4. The frog ______ from the pond.
5. ______ wants to go back to her pond.

4.

5.

**Notes for Home:** Your child used newly learned vocabulary words to complete the crossword puzzle. ***Home Activity:*** Say each word from the box aloud, and ask your child to tell you what it means or use it in a sentence.

Name ______________________

**Circle** the word for each picture.
**Write** it on the line.

1.

tent tint

2.
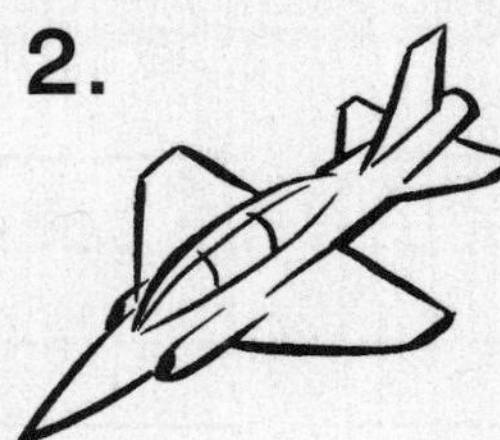
jet get

3.

pack peck

4.

bud bed

5.

nut net

6.

tan ten

7.

ball bell

8.

step stop

**Find** the word that has the same middle sound as .
**Mark** the ⬭ to show your answer.

9. ⬭ spell
⬭ spill
⬭ eat

10. ⬭ hand
⬭ cent
⬭ they

**Notes for Home:** Your child reviewed the short *e* sound heard in *net*. ***Home Activity:*** Start with the short *e* word *bed*. Take turns changing the first or last letters to make new short *e* words, such as *red* or *beg*.

Name ______________________________

**Look** at each word. **Say** it.
**Listen** for the end sounds in 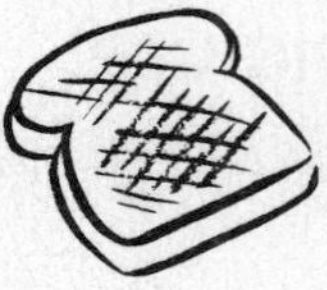 and .

**Write** each word. **Check** it.

1. fast
2. best
3. just
4. must
5. hand
6. and

## Word Wall Words

**Write** each word.

7. out
8. came

**Notes for Home:** Your child spelled words that end with *st* and *nd* and two frequently used words: *out, came*. ***Home Activity:*** Encourage your child to use these words to tell a story about a contest. Work with your child to write the story.

Name ______________________

**Circle** the nouns in each group of words.
**Use** them to write a sentence that makes sense.
**Write** the nouns on the lines.

this fox trots rocks

**1.–2.** The ____________ jumps over the ____________.

fast mat at cat

**3.–4.** The ____________ runs on the ____________.

jogs log frog down

**5.–6.** The ____________ hops off the ____________.

pig in jig sing

**7.–8.** The ____________ does a ____________.

jug run bug jog

**9.–10.** The ____________ hides in the ____________.

**Notes for Home:** Your child reviewed nouns that appear in different parts of sentences. ***Home Activity:*** Together, make up sentences in which the nouns can be reversed. *(The cat is on the hat. The hat is on the cat.)* Have your child write both versions, and draw what each one describes.

# Test-Taking Tips

1. Write your name on the test.
2. Read each question twice.
3. Read all the answer choices for the question.
4. Mark your answer carefully.
5. Check your answer.

Name ______________________________

# Part 1: Vocabulary

**Read** each sentence.
**Mark** the ⬭ for the word that fits.

1. Do you ______ what time it is?

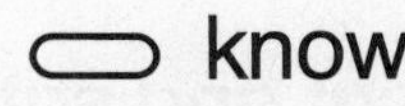

⬭ who ⬭ too ⬭ know

2. Ana went ______ to play.

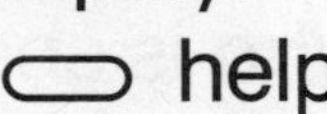
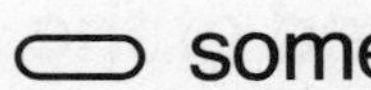

⬭ out ⬭ help ⬭ some

3. ______ brings a ball.

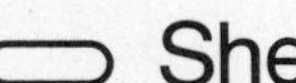

⬭ Our ⬭ She ⬭ So

4. Kim and Dan are ______ .

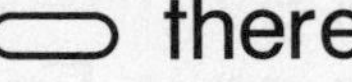

⬭ with ⬭ for ⬭ there

5. Ana ______ in at two.

⬭ came ⬭ hold ⬭ know

GO ON

Name ______________________________ 

# Part 2: Comprehension

**Read** each sentence.
**Mark** the ⬭ for the answer.

6. To Fox and Bear, the moon looked
   - ⬭ sad.
   - ⬭ red.
   - ⬭ fat.

7. As Bear sat and sat, Fox
   - ⬭ went to sleep.
   - ⬭ jumped in.
   - ⬭ played.

8. "She looked at the moon." Who is she?
   - ⬭ Fox
   - ⬭ Bear
   - ⬭ Cat

9. When the moon was gone, where did it go?
   - ⬭ in the water
   - ⬭ behind a cloud
   - ⬭ by the tree

10. What did Bear do at the end?
    - ⬭ Bear got the moon out.
    - ⬭ Bear gave Fox a pat.
    - ⬭ Bear had a nap.

STOP

Name ______________________________

**Circle** the word for each picture.

 black

1. 
block
flock

2. 
slant
plant

3. 
flag
glad

4. 
slip
slap

5. 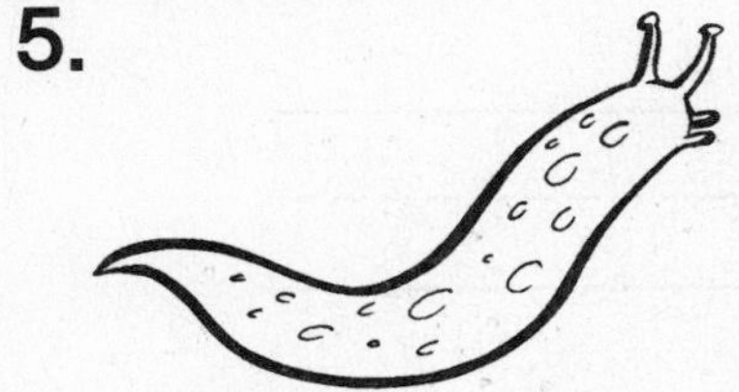
snug
slug

6. 
sled
fled

7. 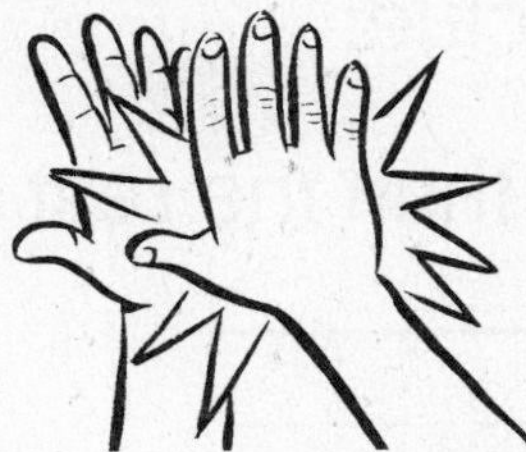
clap
flap

8. 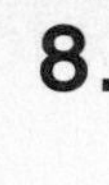 
class
glass

**Find** the word that has the same beginning sound as the picture.
**Mark** the ⬭ to show your answer.

9. 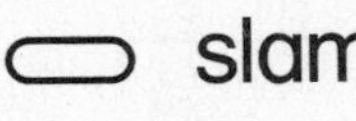 clink
 slam
⬭ like

10. 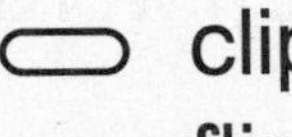 clip
⬭ flip
⬭ trip

**Notes for Home:** Your child reviewed words that begin with *bl, cl, fl, gl, pl,* and *sl.*
***Home Activity:*** Have your child tell you a sentence containing several words with the same beginning sounds. Help your child write and read the sentences. *(The slug slid down the slope.)*

Name ______________________

fast best just must hand and

**Write** the words from the box that rhyme with each picture.

1. ____________ 2. ____________

3. ____________ 4. ____________

**Write** the word from the box that rhymes with each word below.

5. last ____________ 6. test ____________

**Write** the word from the box to match each clue.

7. not slow ____________

8. better than the rest ____________

**Write** the word from the box that means the opposite of each word below.

out came

9. went ____________ 10. in ____________

**Notes for Home:** Your child spelled words that end with *st* and *nd* and two frequently used words: *out, came*. ***Home Activity:*** Have your child use these words to tell you a story about two friends. Help your child to write and read the finished story.

Name ______________________________

**RETEACHING**

The **boy** saw a **frog**.

A **noun** names a person, place, animal, or thing.
It can be in more than one place in a sentence.

**Circle** the noun in each sentence.
**Write** a noun from the box on the line.

| store | cat | bus | boy |
|---|---|---|---|

1. The ____________ is on the mat.

2. Children ride in a ____________.

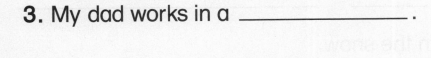

3. My dad works in a ____________.

4. The ____________ kicks a ball.

**Notes for Home:** Your child wrote nouns in sentences. ***Home Activity:*** Have your child draw a picture of people or animals doing something. He or she should use two nouns to write a sentence about the picture.

Name ______________________

**Read** each sentence.
**Circle** the nouns.
**Write** them on the lines.

In spring the fox can run in the rain.

1. ________ ________ ________

The rain wets his face.

2. ________ ________

In summer frogs swim in the lake.

3. ________ ________ ________

In fall my mom will rake the leaves.

4. ________ ________ ________

The leaves are loud under her feet.

5. ________ ________

In winter sleds slide on the snow.

6. ________ ________ ________

**Notes for Home:** Your child identified nouns in subjects and predicates of sentences.
***Home Activity:*** Together, write a poem about the seasons. Have your child supply the nouns.

## You are your child's first and best teacher!

**Here are ways to help your child practice skills while having fun!**

**Day 1** Discover how many real words can be created by using a new vowel *(a, e, i, o, u)* for each vowel in these words: *bag, bed, bit, cot,* and *log.*

**Day 2** Write the following words on index cards: *again, please, read, say,* and *word.* Have your child say each word aloud and use it in a sentence.

**Day 3** Tell or read your child a story, such as *The Three Little Pigs.* Then ask your child to tell you about each character in the story.

**Day 4** Your child is learning to describe things. When talking with your child, ask questions that will get your child to describe an experience, feeling, or idea.

**Day 5** Go through a calendar together, noting the names for the days of the week and months of the year. Help your child write each name, using a capital letter.

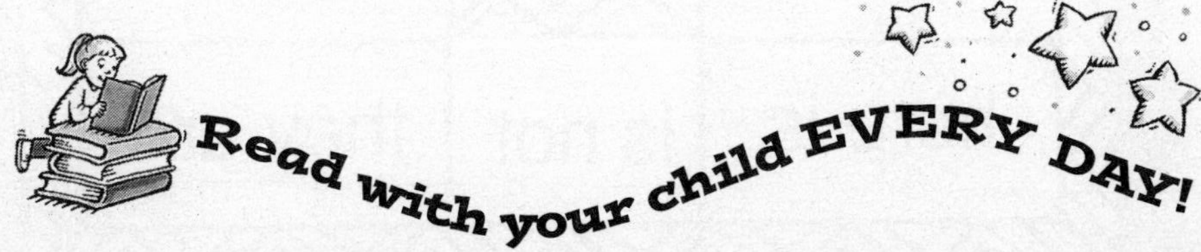
Read with your child EVERY DAY!

(fold here)

# Family Times

I Can Read

Lilly Reads

### Let's Read

Let's get a book. Let's read right now.
I'll read with you. I'll show you how!
We'll read on the bench. We'll read on the bus.
We'll read to Mom. She'll read to us.
We'll read all day. We'll read in the sun.
We'll read and snack. It's so much fun!

We'll read to Fred, our fish that's red.
And when we finish, we'll get in bed.
We'll read in bed. We'll read tonight.
And when we finish, we'll shut off the light.

This rhyme includes short vowel words *(get, with, bus)* and contractions *(Let's, I'll, We'll)*. Read aloud "Let's Read" with your child, taking turns reading the lines. Read these short sentences with a crisp snap.

Name: ______________________

# Contraction Race

**Materials** 1 coin, paper, pencil, 1 button per player

**Game Directions**

1. Players take turns tossing a coin and moving ahead one space for heads or two spaces for tails.

2. Each player writes the contraction for the two words in the gameboard space. Answers are given below.

3. Play continues until the first player crosses the finish line. The player with the most correct contractions wins!

**Answers (in order): we're, it's, he's, they'll, aren't, let's, we'll, doesn't, won't, she's, you'll, they're, isn't, here's, I'll, I'm, she'll, wasn't, he'll, don't**

Start

we are

it is

he is

they will

are not

let us

we will

does not

will not

she is

you will

they are

is not

here is

I will

I am

she will

was not

he will

do not

End

Name ______________________

**Read** each sentence.
**Pick** a letter from the box to finish each word.
**Write** the letter on the line.

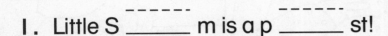

| a | e | i | o | u |
|---|---|---|---|---|

b<u>a</u>g b<u>e</u>g b<u>i</u>g b<u>o</u>g b<u>u</u>g

1. Little S ______ m is a p ______ st!

2. He likes to j ______ mp on my b ______ d.

3. He likes to sp ______ ll the water in the c ______ p.

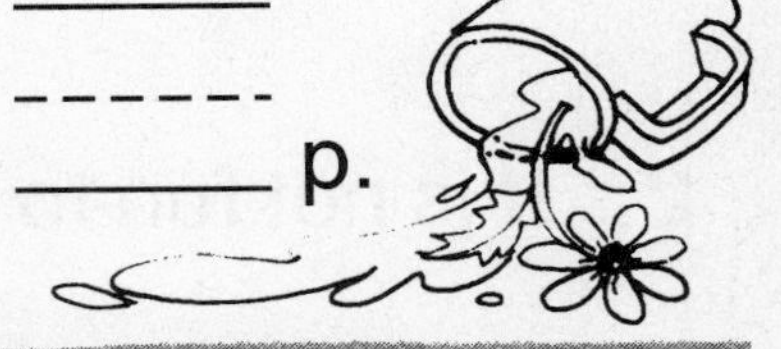

4. He likes to h ______ g fr ______ gs.

5. Why is a fr ______ g in my b ______ x?

**Notes for Home:** Your child wrote words with the short vowel pattern CVC (Consonant-Vowel-Consonant), such as *big* and *bag*. ***Home Activity:*** Challenge your child to write five new sentences with words that have the short vowel pattern CVC.

Name ________________________

**Read** each sentence.
**Write** the contraction for the underlined words.

I am sad! I'm sad!

1. I do not want to play with Sam! ____________

2. It is not fun to play with Sam. ____________

3. He will make a mess. ____________

4. He does not sit still. ____________

5. He is a pest! ____________

**Notes for Home:** Your child combined words to form contractions.
***Home Activity:*** Say five contractions aloud. have your child tell you the two words each contraction represents.

Name ______________________

**Pick** a word from the box to finish each rhyme.
**Write** it on the line.

| again | please | read | say | word |
|---|---|---|---|---|

1. I can ____________ to you.
Do you want me to?

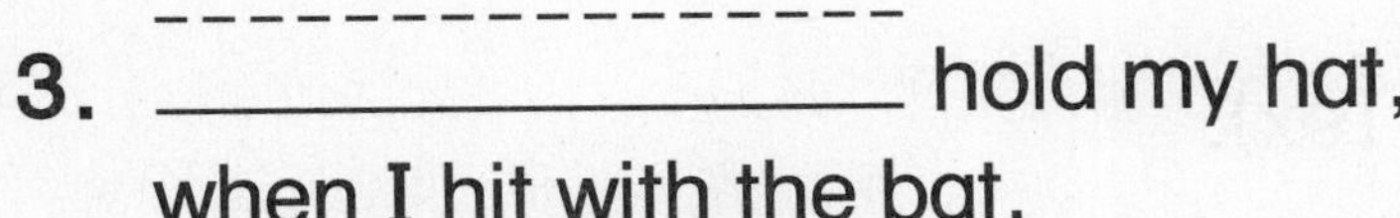

2. I want to play. ____________
What do you ____________ ?

3. ____________ hold my hat,
when I hit with the bat.

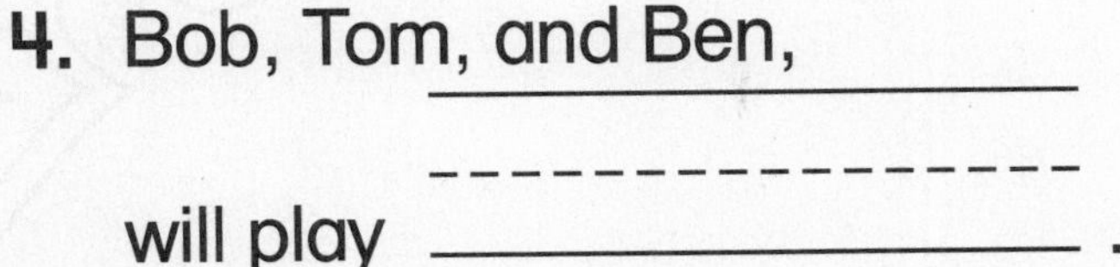

4. Bob, Tom, and Ben, ____________
will play ____________ .

5. I want that dress. ____________
Will you say the ____________ *yes*?

**Notes for Home:** This week your child is learning to read the words *again, please, read, say,* and *word.* ***Home Activity:*** Ask your child to use these words to make up additional rhymes.

Name ______________________________

**Look** at the pictures. **Read** the sentences.
**Underline** the words in ( ) that tell about the characters.

1. There are (one pig, two pigs, three pigs).

2. (Spot, Kim, Tex) likes to play in the mud.

3. (Spot, Kim, Tex) likes to eat.

4. Pam holds (Spot, Kim, Tex).

**Draw** the pig you like.

5.

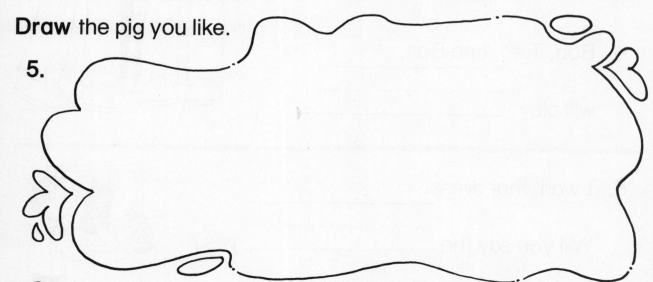

**Notes for Home:** Your child is learning about characters in stories. ***Home Activity:*** Read or tell the well-known story of *The Three Little Pigs* to your child. Talk about how the pigs were different from one another.

Name ________________________

**Days** begin with capital letters.
**Months** begin with capital letters.

**Pick** a letter from the box to finish each word.
**Write** it on the line.

M T W F S

1. ____onday
2. ____uesday
3. ____ednesday
4. ____hursday
5. ____riday
6. ____aturday

**Pick** a month from the box to finish each sentence.
**Write** it on the line.
**Use** a capital letter.

february july

7. We make a  in ____________.

8. It may get hot in ____________. 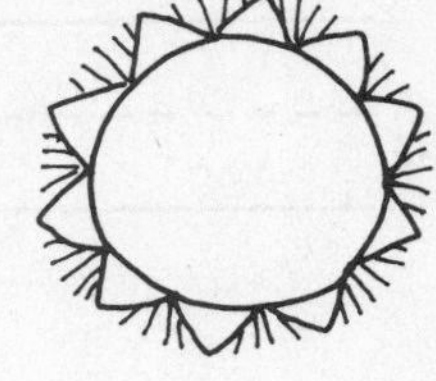

**Notes for Home:** Your child used capital letters to write the names of days and months. ***Home Activity:*** Work with your child to list all the days of the week and the months of the year. Be sure your child uses capital letters.

Name ______________________

**Pick** a word from the box to finish each sentence.
**Write** it on the line. Use each word only once.

| again | please | read | say | word |
|---|---|---|---|---|

1. "I want Peg to ______ to us," said Tim.

2. "Will you read us this story ______?" said Tim.

3. "Do ______ yes," said Bess.

4. "Say one more ______," said Peg.

5. "______!" said Tim and Bess.

**Notes for Home:** Your child worked with the new vocabulary words *again, please, read, say,* and *word. **Home Activity:*** Say each word and ask your child to write it and then use it in a sentence.

Name ______________________________

**Circle** the picture for each word.

sun

1. nut  

2. cut  

3. bug  

4. gum  

5. fun  

6. truck  

7. mutt  

8. cub  

**Find** the word that has the same middle sound as .
**Mark** the ⬭ to show your answer.

9. ⬭ you
⬭ jump
⬭ blue

10. ⬭ look
⬭ our
⬭ puff

**Notes for Home:** Your child reviewed words that have the short *u* sound heard in sun. ***Home Activity:*** Challenge your child to write as many words as he or she can with one of these endings: *-uff, -ug, -um, -ump,* and *-ut.*

Name ______________________________

**Look** at each word. **Say** it.
**Listen** for the beginning sounds and short vowel sounds of each word.

| | **Write** each word. | **Check** it. |
|---|---|---|
| 1. clap | ____________ | ____________ |
| 2. sled | ____________ | ____________ |
| 3. trip | ____________ | ____________ |
| 4. spot | ____________ | ____________ |
| 5. drop | ____________ | ____________ |
| 6. drum | ____________ | ____________ |

## Word Wall Words

**Write** each word.

| | | |
|---|---|---|
| 7. read | ____________ | ____________ |
| 8. please | ____________ | ____________ |

**Notes for Home:** Your child spelled words with short vowel sounds that begin with a consonant blend *(clap)*, and two frequently used words: *read, please*. ***Home Activity:*** Say each spelling word aloud. Have your child spell the word and use it in a sentence.

Name ______________________________

Leave out sentences that do not belong.

I like dogs.
~~My cat is brown~~.
My dog is big.

**Circle** four sentences to tell about a pond.

1. I like to go to the little pond.
2. I read my book beside the water.
3. It was hot on Friday.
4. I can smell the damp mud by the water.
5. I see two green frogs jump into the water.
6. I will not let my dog play inside.

**Write** a sentence about a pond.

7. ______________________________

**Notes for Home:** Your child identified sentences that do not belong in a group. ***Home Activity:*** Tell a short story to your child. Make up one or two sentences that do not belong with the rest. Ask your child to tell you which sentences do not belong and to explain why.

Name ______________________________

**Read** each sentence.
**Write** it correctly on the line.
**Use** capital letters as needed.

1. july has 31 days.

2. It is cold in february.

3. I like friday the best.

4. We have art on monday.

5. I will go on saturday.

**Notes for Home:** Your child wrote the days of the week and months of the year with capital letters. ***Home Activity:*** Have your child look at a calendar and list special days your family celebrates. Be sure your child uses capital letters wherever appropriate.

Name ______________________________

# Part I: Vocabulary

**Read** each sentence.
**Mark** the ⬭ for the word that fits.

1. Bret wants to ______ the book.
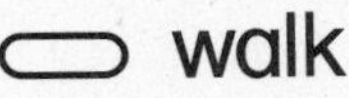 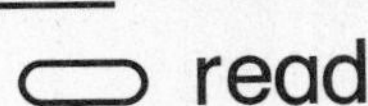
⬭ walk ⬭ read ⬭ play

2. He does not know a ______.
⬭ word ⬭ me ⬭ some

3. Bret will try to ______ the word.
⬭ jump ⬭ sleep ⬭ say

4. "Will you ______ help me?"
⬭ for ⬭ our ⬭ please

5. Mom said, "Look at it ______."
⬭ time ⬭ again ⬭ with

GO ON

Name ________________________________



## Part 2: Comprehension

**Read** each question.

**Mark** the ⬭ for the answer.

6. Mrs. Woo asks Lilly to
   - ⬭ find a list.
   - ⬭ read a page.
   - ⬭ sit up tall.

7. Why did Lilly stop?
   - ⬭ She got to the end.
   - ⬭ She wanted to play.
   - ⬭ She did not know a word.

8. What can you tell about Willy?
   - ⬭ He wants to read.
   - ⬭ He is Lilly's best pal.
   - ⬭ He knows an elf.

9. How did Lilly feel at the end?
   - ⬭ mad
   - ⬭ happy
   - ⬭ sad

10. Did Mrs. Woo help Lilly?
    - ⬭ Yes, she let Lilly rest.
    - ⬭ No, she let Willy read.
    - ⬭ Yes, she said for Lilly to try again.

STOP

Name ____________________________________



**Circle** the word for each picture.

1.  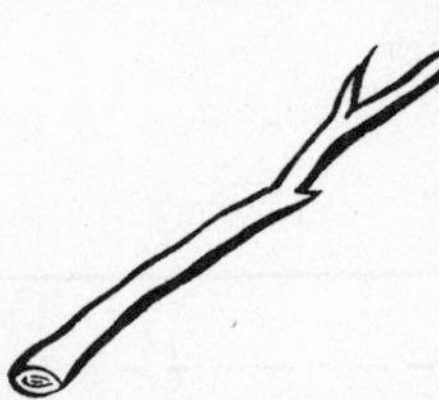
slick
stick

2. 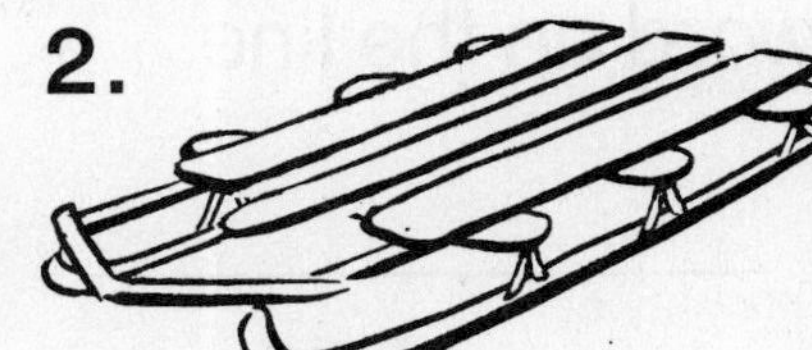
sled
sped

3. 
skunk
stuck

4. 
still
spill

5. 
smell
spell

6. 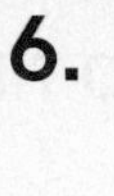 
slam
stamp

7. 
slacks
snack

8.  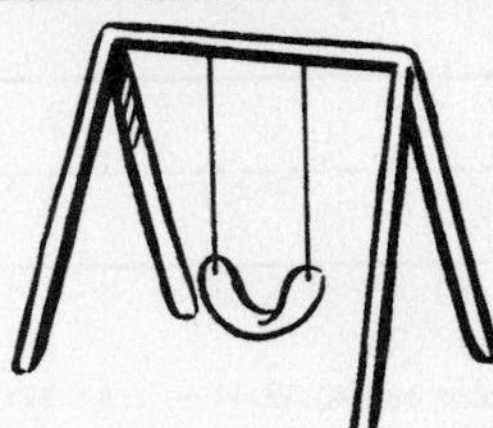
swing
sting

**Find** the word that has the same beginning sounds as the picture.
**Mark** the ⬭ to show your answer.

9. 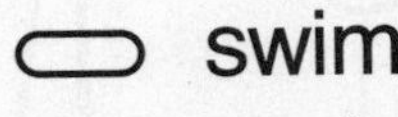 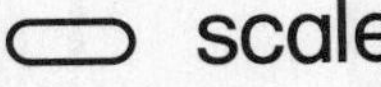
⬭ stall
⬭ swim
⬭ scale

10. 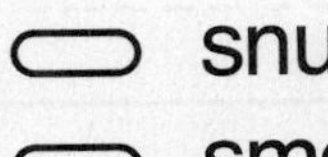 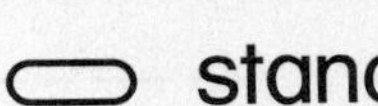
⬭ snug
⬭ small
⬭ stand

**Notes for Home:** Your child reviewed words that begin with a blend of *s* and another consonant. ***Home Activity:*** Read a story with your child. Have your child look for words that begin with an *s* blend. Ask your child to write these words in a list.

Name ______________________________

clap sled trip spot drop drum

**Add** one letter to each word to make a word from the box.
**Write** the word on the line.

1. rip ______________ 2. pot ______________

3. led ______________ 4. lap ______________

**Pick** a word from the box to finish each sentence.
**Write** it on the line.

5. I play on my ______________ .

6. Do not ______________ the sticks.

**Pick** a word from the box to finish each sentence.
**Write** it on the line.

read please

7. Will you ______________ to me?

8. Yes, if you say ______________ .

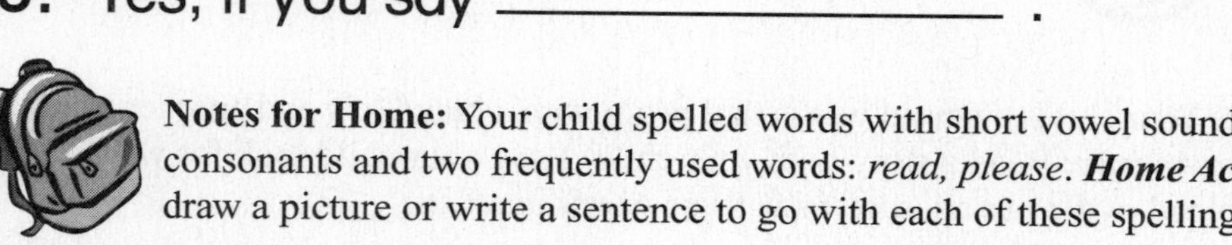

**Notes for Home:** Your child spelled words with short vowel sounds that begin with two consonants and two frequently used words: *read, please*. ***Home Activity:*** Have your child draw a picture or write a sentence to go with each of these spelling words.

Name ______________________

RETEACHING

| Sunday | Monday | Tuesday | Wednesday |
|---|---|---|---|
| Thursday | Friday | Saturday | |

January February March April May June

July August September October November December

**Days of the week** begin with capital letters.
**Months of the year** begin with capital letters.

**Write** the correct month.

1. People can fly kites in

______________________.

2. People can swim in

______________________.

**Circle** the name of each day that is written correctly.

3. Sunday monday tuesday Wednesday
thursday Friday Saturday

**Notes for Home:** Your child wrote names of months and identified names of days that were written correctly. ***Home Activity:*** Together, create a calendar of family activities. Have your child write the names of the days and months, using capital letters.

Name ______________________



**Circle** each month that is written correctly.

1. January February March april
may June july

**Read** the days of the week below.
**Write** one to complete each sentence.

2. Today is ________.

3. The next day is ________.

4. We do not go to school on ________.

| Sunday | Monday | Tuesday | Wednesday |
|---|---|---|---|
| Thursday | Friday | Saturday | |

**Notes for Home:** Your child identified names of months that were written correctly and used names of days in sentences. ***Home Activity:*** Have your child draw a picture of what he or she did today. Then have him or her label the picture with the day, date, and year.

Name ______________________

**Correct** each sentence.
**Write** it on the line.
Hint: Special names for days and months should begin with a capital letter.

1. I walk in the fog in april.

2. It is fun to roll on the grass in may.

3. The sun is hot in july.

4. I will play ball on friday.

5. I will rest on saturday.

**Notes for Home:** Your child identified and capitalized proper nouns for days of the week and months of the year in sentences. ***Home Activity:*** Help your child make a calendar. Check that all days, months, and holidays are capitalized. Together, fill in special events and holidays.

Name

I read

It was about

Words I Can Now Read and Write

**You *are* your child's first *and* best teacher!**

**Here are ways to help your child practice skills while having fun!**

**Day 1** Write a simple long *a* word that follows a consonant-vowel-consonant-*e* pattern, such as *cake* or *tale.* Have your child think of rhyming words that follow this pattern.

**Day 2** Ask your child to write or say a short story that uses any of the following words that your child is learning to read: *after, as, call, laugh, something.*

**Day 3** After you read a story to your child, ask your child to tell you which things in the story could really happen and which things are make-believe.

**Day 4** Your child is practicing his or her listening skills. Read a short paragraph or story to your child. Challenge him or her to retell the key parts of the material read.

**Day 5** Show your child some photographs or magazine cutouts of people in action. Help your child write or say a sentence to describe what the people are doing.

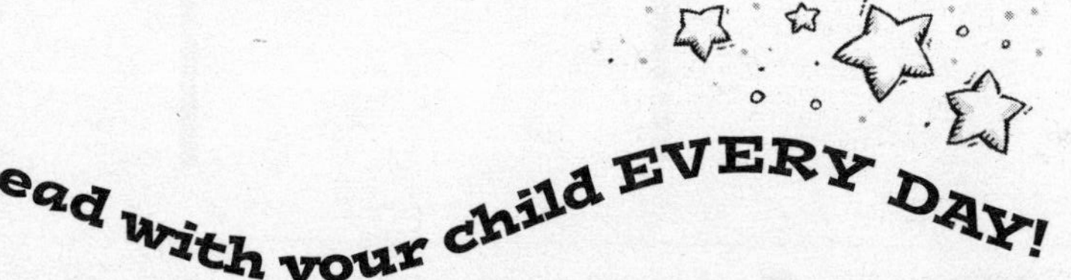

**Read with your child EVERY DAY!**



(fold here)

# Family Times

**The Red Stone Game** **The Gingerbread Man**

**Nate**

We have a friend . . .
He likes to bake . . .
His name is Nate . . .
He made a cake . . .

Nate gave us cake . . .
On a cake plate . . .
It was so good . . .
We ate and ate . . .

Then we cleaned up . . .
We washed our plates . . .
We walked right out . . .
The big red gate . . .

This rhyme includes words your child is working with in school: words with the long *a* sound that end in *e (Nate, bake, made)* and words that end in *-ed (cleaned, walked)*. Chant "Nate" with your child. Clap each time a long *a* word is said. Tap your feet for each word ending with *-ed.*

Name: ______________________

# Three in a Row

**Materials** index cards, markers

**Game Directions**

**1.** Write the action words shown below on index cards. Use the gameboard to play tick-tack-toe.

**2.** One player draws Xs. The other draws Os.

**3.** Players take turns picking a card, reading the word aloud, and marking either an X or an O on the same word with an *-ed* ending on the gameboard.

**4.** The first player who gets three marks in a row wins!

**Action Words**
jump, look, want, call, laugh, wash, cook, wish, pick

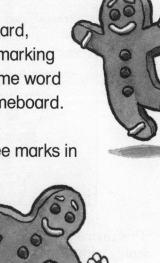

| jumped | looked | wanted |
|---|---|---|
| called | laughed | washed |
| cooked | wished | picked |

Name ______________________________

**Circle** the word for each picture.

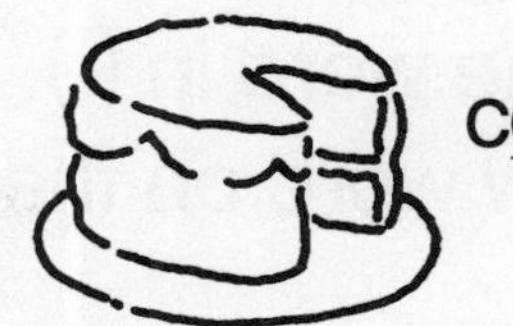
cake

| | | |
|---|---|---|
| 1. 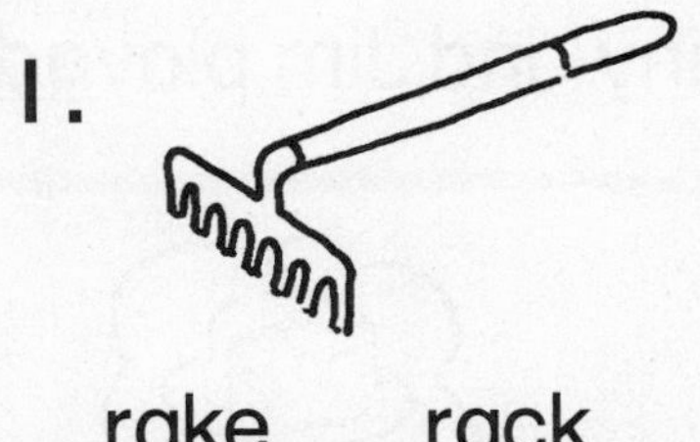 rake rack | 2.  sneak snake | 3. 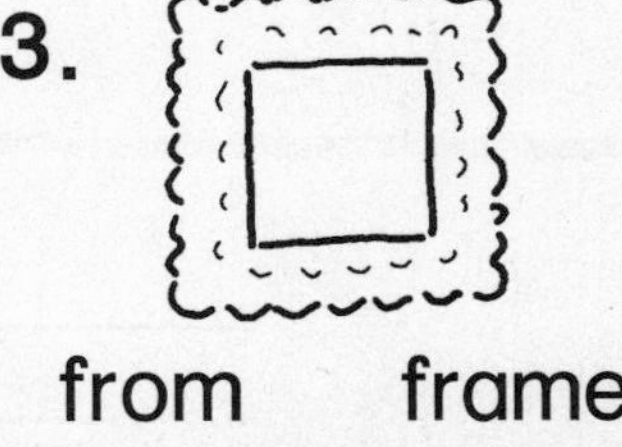 from frame |
| 4.  face fans | 5. 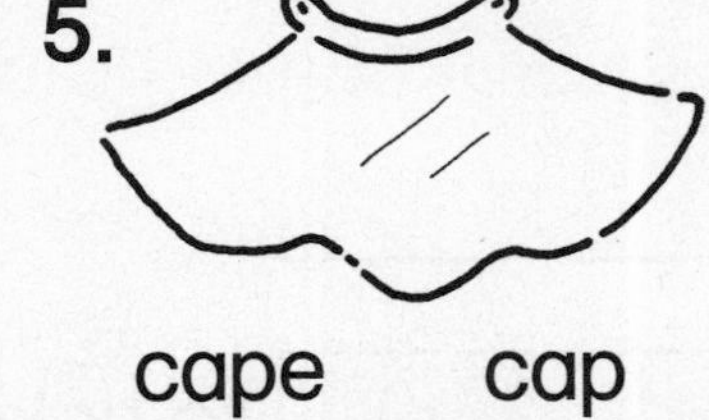 cape cap | 6. 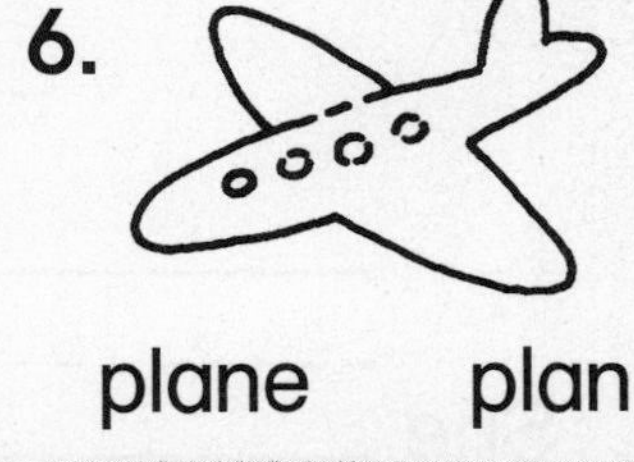 plane plan |
| 7.  lock lake | 8. 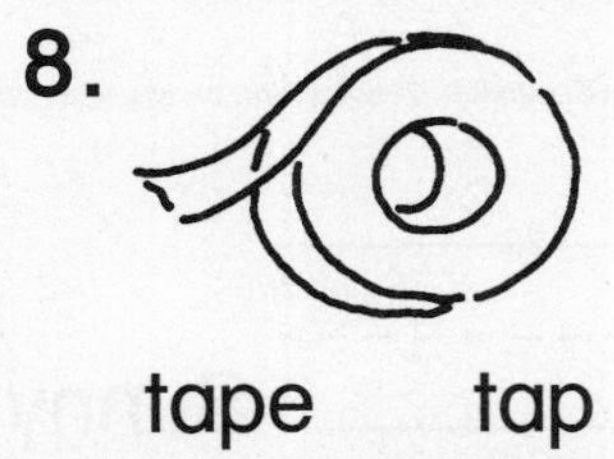 tape tap | 9. 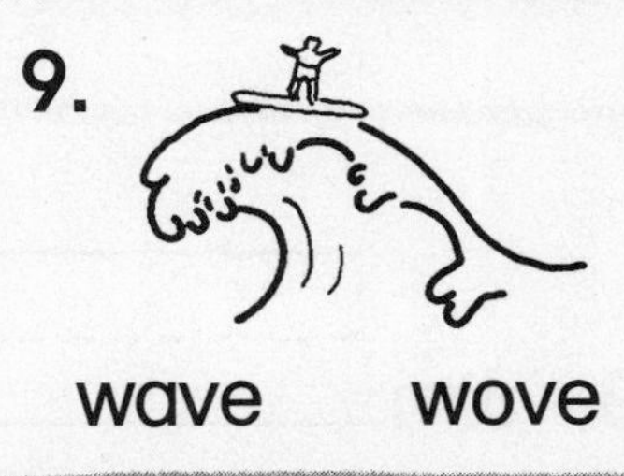 wave wove |
| 10.  scarf skate | 11. 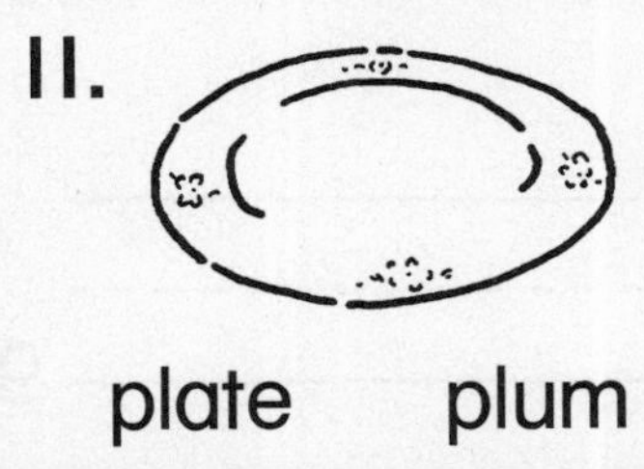 plate plum | 12. 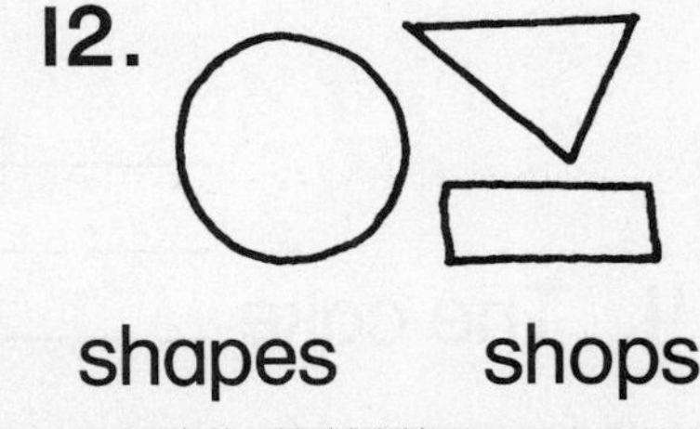 shapes shops |
| 13. 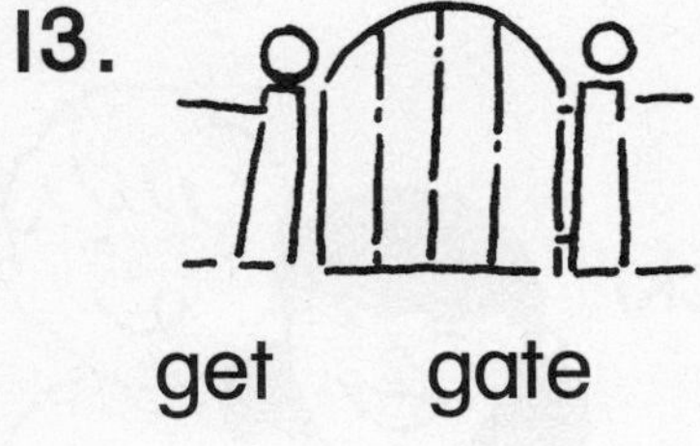 get gate | 14. 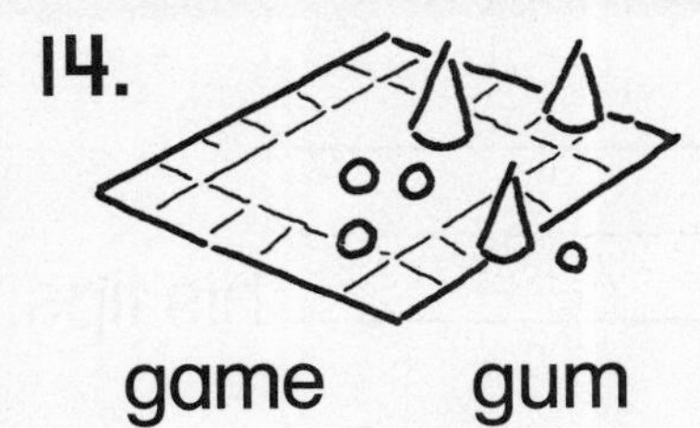 game gum | 15. 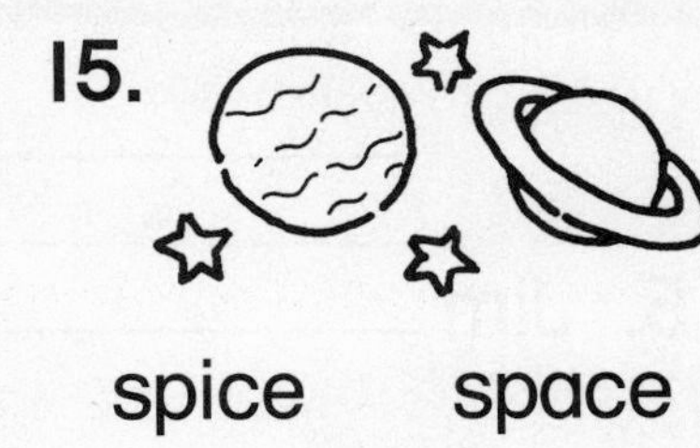 spice space |

**Notes for Home:** Your child practiced reading words with the long *a* sound that follows a consonant-vowel-consonant-*e*, pattern such as *cake*. ***Home Activity:*** Work with your child to use each of the long *a* words shown in a sentence.

Name ______________________________

**Add -ed** to the word in ( ).
**Write** the new word on the line to finish the sentence.

Sunny and Jim play**ed**.

1. Sunny ______________________ Jim. (call)

2. She ______________________ to bake a cake. (want)

3. Jim ______________________ Sunny. (help)

4. The cake ______________________ good. (look)

5. Jim ______________________ his lips. (lick)

**Notes for Home:** Your child practiced writing words that end with *-ed*. ***Home Activity:*** Work with your child to write a story using the *-ed* words above.

Name ______________________________

**Read** each sentence.
**Circle** the picture that tells about the sentence.

after as call laugh something

1. Sam gave a call to Jane.

2. He ran after Jane.

3. Sam gave something to Jane.

4. Jane wanted to laugh.

5. It looked the same as Jane.

**Notes for Home:** This week your child learned to read the words *after*, *as*, *call*, *laugh*, and *something*. ***Home Activity:*** Write each word in a simple sentence. Ask your child to read the sentences to you.

Name ______________________

**Look** at each pair of pictures.
**Circle** the picture that shows something that could really happen.
**Write** a sentence that tells about the picture you circled.

1.

______________________

2. ______________________

3.

______________________

4. ______________________

**Draw** a picture that shows something that could really happen.
**Write** a sentence that tells about the picture.

5.

______________________

______________________

**Notes for Home:** Your child made choices between events that could really happen and events that could not. ***Home Activity:*** Read a story with your child. Ask your child which parts of the story could really happen and which could not.

Name ______________________________

A **verb** is a word that can show action.
**Waves** is a verb.

Tom <u>**waves**</u> to Min.

---

**Circle** the verb in each sentence.
**Draw** a line from each sentence to the picture it matches.

1. The fox runs after the cat.

6. 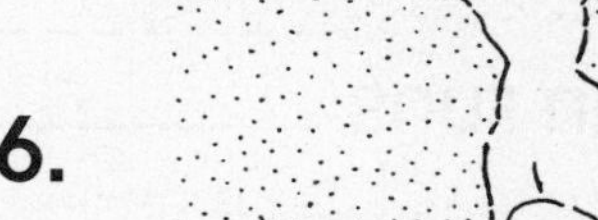

2. The cat jumps over the wall.

7. 

3. The fox stops at the wall.

8.  

4. The cat hops up on the wall.

9. 

5. The cat laughs.

10. 

**Notes for Home:** Your child circled verbs that show actions and matched each sentence to a picture. ***Home Activity:*** Together, write six verbs on separate slips of paper. Take turns. You or your child picks a slip and acts out the verb. The other guesses the action.

Name ____________________

**Pick** a word from the box to finish each sentence.
**Write** it on the line.

| after | as | call | catch | laugh | something |
|---|---|---|---|---|---|

1. Ann runs ____________ Nick.

2. But she is not as fast ____________ he is.

3. Ann can't ____________ him.

4. Ann can ____________ Nick.

5. She gives ____________ to him.

6. Now they ____________ and eat.

**Notes for Home:** Your child completed sentences using newly learned words.
***Home Activity:*** Work with your child to make up a story using as many of the words from the box as possible.

Name ______________________

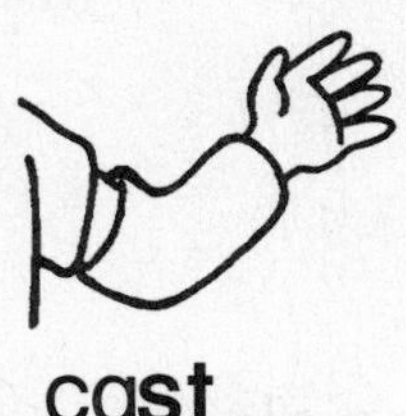

ca**st** plа**nt** ha**nd** stu**mp**

**Pick** letters from the box to finish each word.
**Write** the letters on the line.

st nt nd mp

1. te ______
2. sa ______
3. sta ______
4. li ______
5. po ______
6. ju ______
7. ce ______
8. ne ______

**Find** the word that has the same ending sound as the picture.
**Mark** the ⬭ to show your answer.

9. ⬭ lamp
   ⬭ last
   ⬭ land

10. ⬭ stand
    ⬭ rent
    ⬭ rust

**Notes for Home:** Your child reviewed words with final consonant blends *st, nt, nd,* and *mp* such as *cast, plant, hand,* and *stump*. ***Home Activity:*** Pick one final consonant blend such as *st* or *nd*. Have your child name as many words ending with that sound as possible.

Name ____________________

**Look** at each word. **Say** it.
**Listen** for the **long a** sound in  .

| | **Write** each word. | **Check** it. |
|---|---|---|
| 1. ate | | |
| 2. late | | |
| 3. gave | | |
| 4. make | | |
| 5. take | | |
| 6. bake | | |

## Word Wall Words

**Write** each word.

| | | |
|---|---|---|
| 7. as | | |
| 8. after | | |

**Notes for Home:** Your child learned to spell words with the long *a* sound heard in *cake.* ***Home Activity:*** Say each spelling word. Have your child use it in a sentence. Then say the spelling word again and have your child write it down.

Name ______________________________

**Read** the sentence.
**Underline** the verb.
**Write** the verb on the line.

1. Dan bakes a cake.

2. Mom eats the cake.

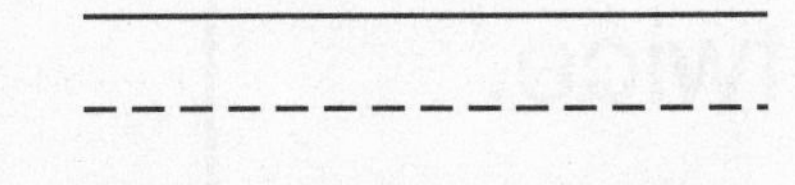

3. Dan calls Dad.

4. Dad runs home fast.

5. Dad asks for more!

**Notes for Home:** Your child identified and wrote verbs—words that show action. ***Home Activity:*** Read a story with your child. Ask your child to point out the verbs in the sentences. Later, make a list of some of the action words and take turns acting them out.

Name ______________________

# Test-Taking Tips

1. Write your name on the test.
2. Read each question twice.
3. Read all the answer choices for the question.
4. Mark your answer carefully.
5. Check your answer.

Name ______________________________



# Part 1: Vocabulary

**Read** each sentence.
**Mark** the ⬭ for the word that fits.

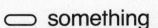

1. The dog sees ______.

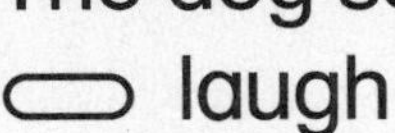 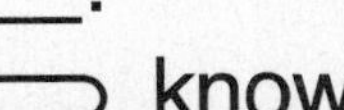 

⬭ laugh ⬭ know ⬭ something

2. The dog runs ______ the cat.

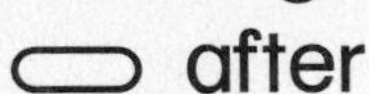 

⬭ after ⬭ as ⬭ now

3. Now they ______ the dog.

  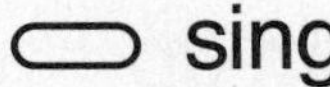

⬭ came ⬭ call ⬭ sing

4. They ______ at the dog.

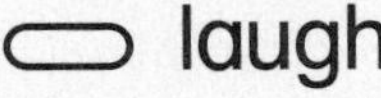  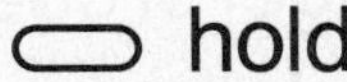

⬭ laugh ⬭ carry ⬭ hold

5. The dog did not ______ the cat.

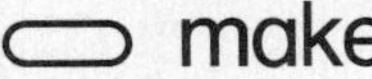 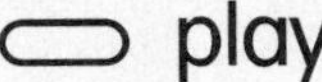 

⬭ make ⬭ play ⬭ catch

GO ON

Name ______________________________



# Part 2: Comprehension

**Read** each question.
**Mark** the ⬭ for the answer.

6. Who makes the Gingerbread Man?
   - ⬭ the man
   - ⬭ the woman
   - ⬭ the girl

7. What does the Gingerbread Man do first?
   - ⬭ runs from the farm
   - ⬭ sees some water
   - ⬭ takes a ride

8. Why does the Gingerbread Man laugh?
   - ⬭ No one can catch him.
   - ⬭ He wants to get wet.
   - ⬭ The fox is funny.

9. What does the Gingerbread Man think the fox will do?
   - ⬭ eat him up
   - ⬭ help him
   - ⬭ bring him water

10. What part of the story could be real?
    - ⬭ A gingerbread man runs away.
    - ⬭ A fox talks to a gingerbread man.
    - ⬭ A boy wants to eat a gingerbread man.

STOP

Name ________________________________

**Underline** the word that has the same beginning sound as **gingerbread**.
**Draw** a line from the sentence to the picture it matches.

1. He ran in the gym.
2. The ring has a gem in it.
3. I saw a giraffe at the zoo.
4. Do not get his germs!

5. 

6. 

7. 

8. 

**Find** the word that matches each picture.
**Mark** the ⬭ to show your answer.

9.  
⬭ giant
⬭ gift
⬭ gum

10. ⬭ girl
⬭ gerbil
⬭ gas

**Notes for Home:** Your child reviewed the soft *g* sound heard in *gingerbread*. ***Home Activity:*** Play a game in which you describe a soft *g* word on this page and you ask your child to guess the word. For example:

Name ______________________



ate late gave make take bake

**Pick** a word from the box to finish each sentence.
**Write** it on the line. Use each word only once.
**Hint:** The word rhymes with the underlined word.

1. Did you ____________ my big, red rake?

2. I want to ____________ a yummy cake.

3. I sat on the crate as I ____________ .

4. I hate to be ____________ .

**Pick** a word from the box to match each clue.
**Write** it on the line.

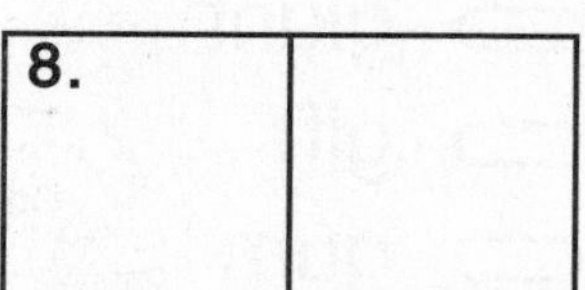

5. It begins with **m**.

____________

6. It rhymes with *cave*.

____________

**Pick** a word from the box that fits in each puzzle.
**Write** it in the puzzle.

as after

| 7. | | | | |
|---|---|---|---|---|
| | | | | |

| 8. | |
|---|---|
| | |

**Notes for Home:** Your child practiced spelling words with long *a* that end in *e* and two frequently used words: *as, after.* ***Home Activity:*** Have your child tell a short story that uses the spelling words. Work together to write the story.

Name ________________________________



**RETEACHING**

eat

read

A **verb** is a word that shows action.

**Read** each sentence.
**Draw** a line under each verb.

1. The children run.
2. They sit in the sun.
3. The dogs bark.
4. The birds fly in the sky.
5. Everyone plays in the park.
6. They eat lunch.

**Write** a verb in the sentence.

7. The cats ________________________________.

**Notes for Home:** Your child identified verbs—words that name actions—in sentences. ***Home Activity:*** Help your child create a two-box comic strip. Have him or her use verbs to label the action in the comic strip.

Name ______________________

**Write** the correct verb from the box under each picture.

| pet | feed |
|---|---|

1. ______________________

2. ______________________

**Write** the correct verb from the box in each sentence.

| walk | eats |
|---|---|

3. My dog ______________________ food.

4. We ______________________ in the park.

**Notes for Home:** Your child used verbs—words that name actions—in sentences. ***Home Activity:*** Look at photographs or pictures from magazines with your child. Have him or her use verbs in sentences that describe the pictures.

## You *are* your child's first *and* best teacher!

**Here are ways to help your child practice skills while having fun!**

**Day 1** Write a simple long *a* word that follows a consonant-vowel-consonant-*e* pattern, such as *lake* or *game*. Have your child name other long *a* words that rhyme with this word.

**Day 2** Help your child write sentences that use the words that he or she is learning to read this week: *every, made, mother, of,* and *was.*

**Day 3** After you read a story to your child, talk about things in his or her life that are similar to the story's characters or plot.

**Day 4** Your child is learning about choral, or group, reading. Practice reading "We Took Our Family to the Lake," shown on page 1, individually and then together.

**Day 5** Work with your child to name some verbs ending in *-s*. Then, have your child make up simple sentences using each verb along with the name of a family member, such as: *Dad sits. Jim runs.*

**Read with your child EVERY DAY!**



(fold here)

# Family Times

The Same as You — Cherry Pies and Lullabies

### We Took Our Family to the Lake

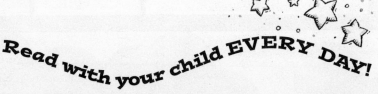

We took our family to the lake.
We thought of things
That we could take.
We brought chicken and a
Chocolate cake.
We took our family to the lake.

We took the cake plates
That are blue.
We took the games
And checkers too.
We took the chairs.
We brought a few.
We took our family to the lake.

This rhyme includes words your child is working with in school: words with the long *a* sound that end with an *e (lake, take)* and words that begin with *ch (chicken, chairs)* and *th (thought, things)*. Make a list of the things the family took to the lake.

Name: ______________________

# Coin Toss

**Materials** paper, marker, 1 coin

**Game Directions**

1. Make a large gameboard like the one shown.
2. Players take turns tossing the coin onto the gameboard and saying a word that begins with the letters shown in the square.
3. A correct answer earns the number of points shown in that square.
4. The first player to get 10 points wins!

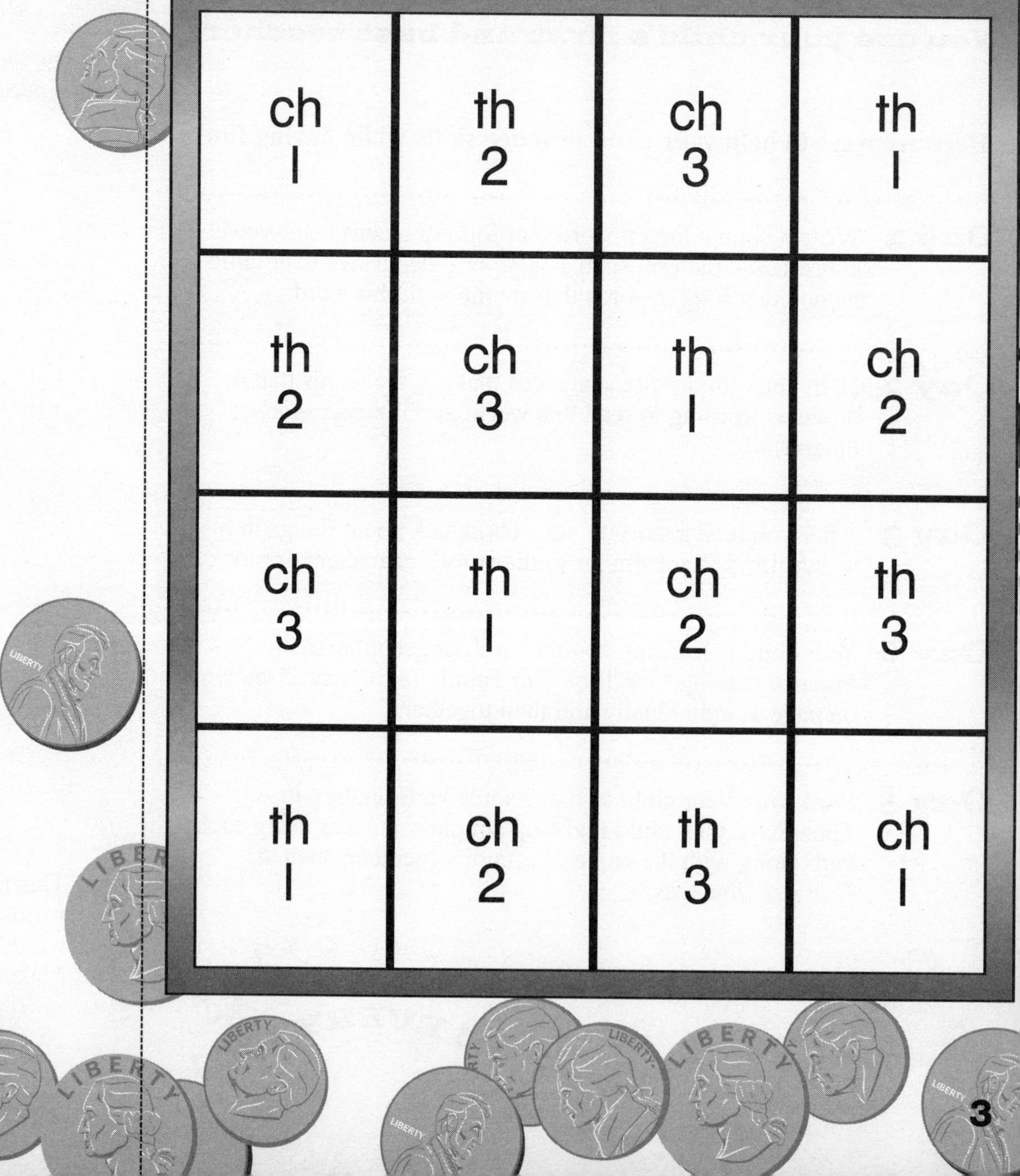

| ch<br>1 | th<br>2 | ch<br>3 | th<br>1 |
|---|---|---|---|
| th<br>2 | ch<br>3 | th<br>1 | ch<br>2 |
| ch<br>3 | th<br>1 | ch<br>2 | th<br>3 |
| th<br>1 | ch<br>2 | th<br>3 | ch<br>1 |

Name ______________________________

**Help** Kate get to the lake.
**Color** each box that has the **long a** sound in **lake.**
**Write** each **long a** word you color on the line.

Kate

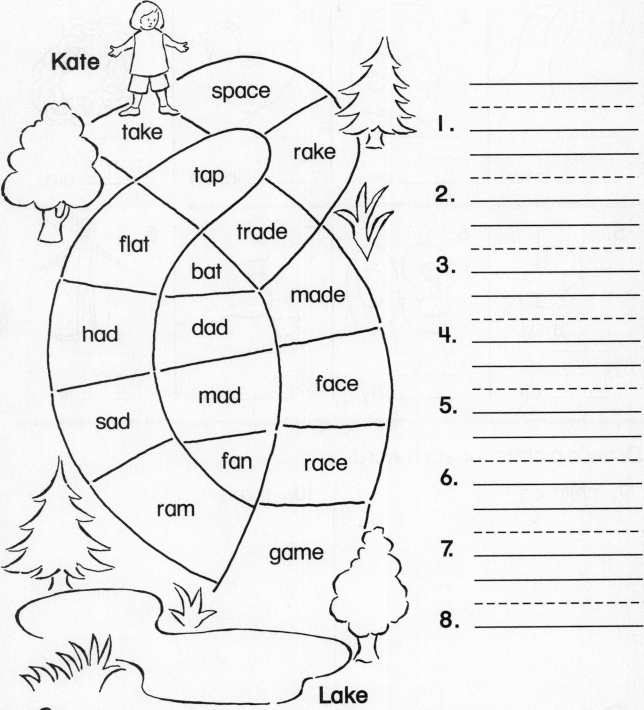

space
take
rake
tap
trade
flat
bat
made
had
dad
face
mad
sad
fan
race
ram
game

Lake

1. ______________________
2. ______________________
3. ______________________
4. ______________________
5. ______________________
6. ______________________
7. ______________________
8. ______________________

**Notes for Home:** Your child identified and wrote words with the long *a* sound that follow a consonant-vowel-consonant-*e* pattern, such as *lake*. ***Home Activity:*** Work with your child to name pairs of rhyming words that have the long *a* sound, such as *bake* and *take*.

Name ______________________________

**Say** the word for each picture.
**Write ch** or **th** to finish each word.

<u>ch</u>erry <u>th</u>anks

**Draw** a picture for each word.

9. children

10. three

**Notes for Home:** Your child added the initial digraphs *th* and *ch* (two letters that together stand for one sound) to complete words. ***Home Activity:*** Write down several words that begin with *ch* or *th*. Ask your child to read them to you.

Name ______________________________

**Pick** a word from the box to finish each sentence.
**Write** it on the line.

| every | made | mother | of | was |
|---|---|---|---|---|

1. My mother ____________ me a doll.

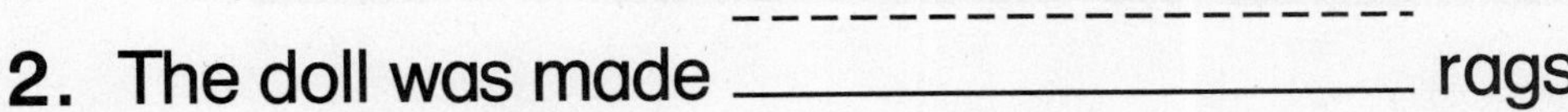

2. The doll was made ____________ rags.

3. It ____________ soft.

4. Now my ____________ sings.

5. She sings to us ____________ time we go to bed.

**Notes for Home:** This week your child learned to read the words *every*, *made*, *mother*, *of*, and *was*. ***Home Activity:*** Help your child write or tell you sentences that include these words.

Name ______________________________

**Read** the story.
**Follow** the directions below.

## Fun at the Lake

John and his mom and dad like to go to the lake.
John swims. They all play ball.
They have many good things to eat.
They laugh and have a good time.
The lake is fun for them all.

1. Which sentence tells the big idea? Underline it.

   Moms, dads, and kids do things to have fun.
   John likes to swim.
   It is fun to eat good things.

2.-4. How did you know the big idea? Underline three sentences in the story that helped you know.

5. Draw a picture to show the big idea in the story.

**Notes for Home:** Your child identified a story's theme, or its big idea. ***Home Activity:*** Read a story with your child. Discuss the story's big idea. Help your child connect this idea to something in his or her own life.

Name ______________________________

A **verb** is a word that shows action.
Put an **-s** at the end of a verb if there is **one** person, animal, or thing doing the action.

Jake **plays** with a ball.

**Add -s** to each verb in ( ).
**Write** the new verb on the line to finish each sentence.

1. Jill ________________ to Bill. (wave)

2. Mike ________________ the big book. (read)

3. Nick ________________ the van. (see)

4. Nan ________________ her mother. (call)

5. Tom ________________ on the mat. (jump)

**Draw** a picture to show the action of one of the sentences above.

**Notes for Home:** Your child added *-s* to verbs with a singular subject (one person, place, or thing). ***Home Activity:*** Work with your child to write and illustrate a story about one boy or girl. Then ask your child to underline the verbs he or she uses.

Name ______________________

**Pick** a word from the box to finish each sentence.
**Write** it on the line.

| every | made | mother | of | was |
|---|---|---|---|---|

1. My ______________ likes to bake.

2. This is one ______________ her cakes.

3. ______________ cake she bakes is good!

4. Once she ______________ a pink cake.

5. It ______________ good.

**Notes for Home:** Your child completed sentences using words that he or she learned this week. ***Home Activity:*** Recall with your child a time when the two of you baked or cooked together. Work together to write sentences about it using as many of these words as possible.

Name ______________________

**Read** the table of contents.
**Write** an answer to each question.

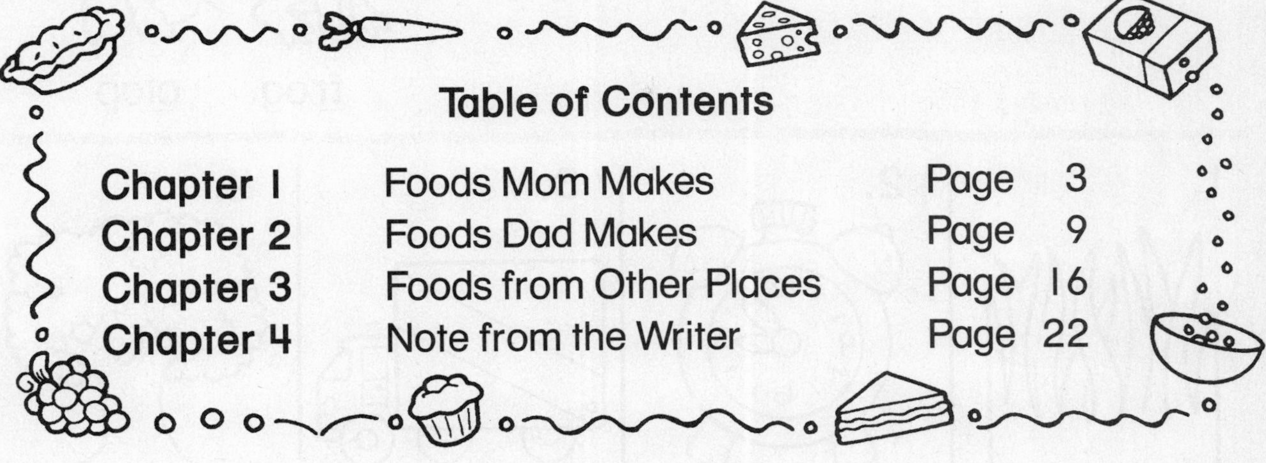

Table of Contents

| | | |
|---|---|---|
| **Chapter 1** | Foods Mom Makes | Page 3 |
| **Chapter 2** | Foods Dad Makes | Page 9 |
| **Chapter 3** | Foods from Other Places | Page 16 |
| **Chapter 4** | Note from the Writer | Page 22 |

1. How many chapters are in the book? ________

2. On what page does Chapter 1 start? ________

3. Which chapter comes after Foods Mom Makes?

________________________________________

4. On what page does Foods from Other Places start? ________

5. What is on page 22?

________________________________________

**Notes for Home:** Your child read a table of contents. ***Home Activity:*** Before you read a chapter book to your child, look at the table of contents together. Talk about the different chapter titles, the number of pages per chapter, and anything else listed in the table of contents.

Name ______________________________

**Circle** the word for each picture.

frog clap

1. grass glass
2. crack clock
3. tuck truck
4. tree tee
5. tack track
6. fog flag
7. glad grapes
8. crab claw

**Find** the word that has the same beginning sounds as the picture.
**Mark** the ⬭ to show your answer.

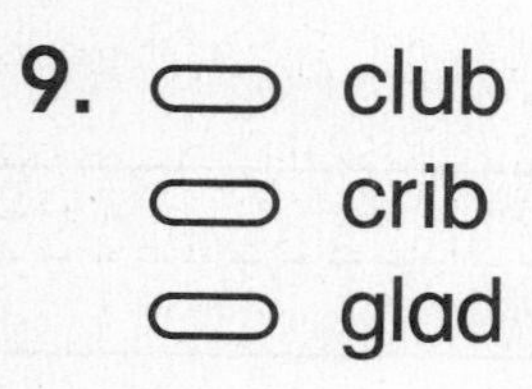

9. ⬭ club
   ⬭ crib
   ⬭ glad

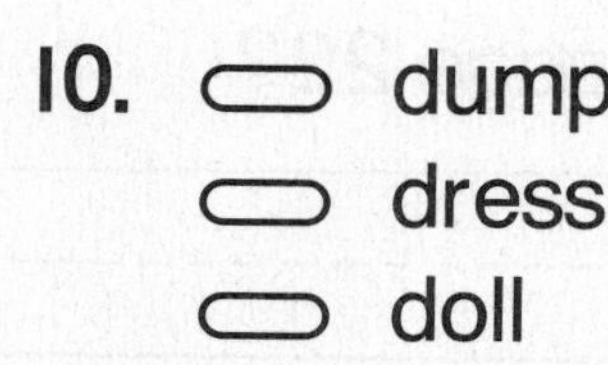

10. ⬭ dump
    ⬭ dress
    ⬭ doll

**Notes for Home:** Your child reviewed words with initial *r* and *l* blends, such as *frog* and *clap*. ***Home Activity:*** Help your child make flashcards for words with these blends. He or she can write the word on one side of a card and draw a picture to illustrate it on the other side.

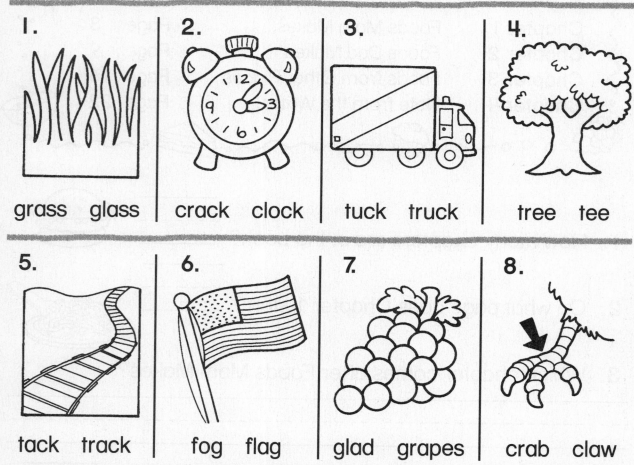

Name ______________________________

**Look** at each word. **Say** it.
**Listen** for the **short a** or **long a** sound.

| | **Write** each word. | **Check** it. |
|---|---|---|
| 1. tap | | |
| 2. cap | | |
| 3. mad | | |
| 4. tape | | |
| 5. cape | | |
| 6. made | | |

## Word Wall Words

**Write** each word.

| | | |
|---|---|---|
| 7. of | | |
| 8. was | | |

**Notes for Home:** Your child spelled words with the short *a* sound *(cap)* and the long *a* sound *(cape),* as well as two frequently used words: *of, was.* ***Home Activity:*** Read each word to your child. Have your child sort the words into short *a* words, long *a* words, and Word Wall Words.

Name ______________________________

**Circle** the verb that tells what one person or animal does.
**Write** the verb on the line to finish each sentence.

reads read

1. Mom ________________ a book.

sing sings

2. Dad ________________ a song.

sleep sleeps

3. Sally ________________ in her bed.

sits sit

4. Skip ________________ by the bed.

nap naps

5. Fluff ________________ on the bed.

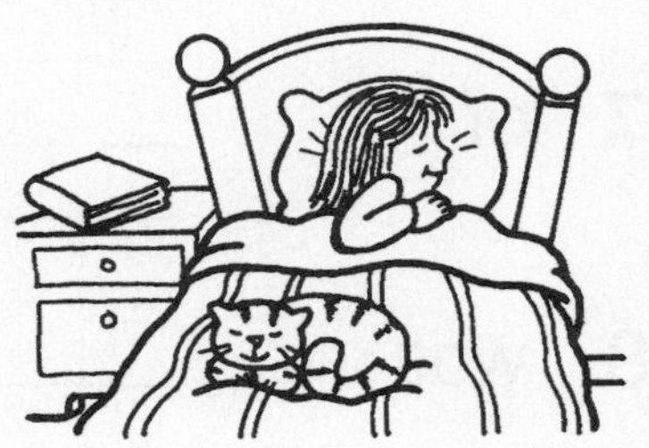

**Notes for Home:** Your child chose verbs to show the action of one person or animal. ***Home Activity:*** Have your child say a sentence about each of your family members. Ask your child to identify the verbs he or she uses in each sentence.

Name ______________________________

# Part 1: Vocabulary

**Read** each sentence.

**Mark** the ⬭ for the word that fits.

1. Fran ______ a cake.

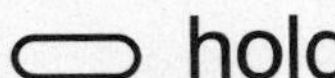

⬭ made ⬭ hold ⬭ said

2. "My _____ will like this," she said.

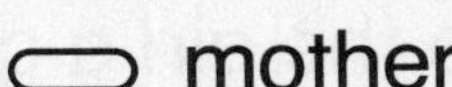
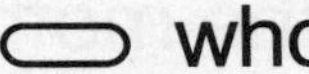

⬭ time ⬭ mother ⬭ who

3. Then it ______ time for bed.

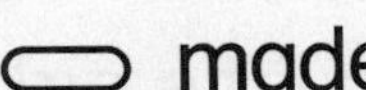

⬭ was ⬭ call ⬭ made

4. Mom will read a lot ______ books.

⬭ some ⬭ of ⬭ all

5. Fran likes _____ book.

⬭ for ⬭ as ⬭ every

Name ___________________________



# Part 2: Comprehension

**Read** each question.

**Mark** the ⬭ for the answer.

6. What does the grandmother bake?
   - ⬭ cherry pie
   - ⬭ hot dogs
   - ⬭ plum pie

7. Who made a crown of flowers for the girl?
   - ⬭ her great-grandmother
   - ⬭ her grandmother
   - ⬭ her mother

8. Why does the mother give the girl a quilt?
   - ⬭ The girl asks for one.
   - ⬭ The mother had one when she was small.
   - ⬭ The grandmother tells the mother to.

9. Every woman in this story
   - ⬭ has a little girl.
   - ⬭ plants flowers.
   - ⬭ bakes all day.

10. In this story, every woman
    - ⬭ does the same things in her own way.
    - ⬭ has the same crown of flowers.
    - ⬭ lives in the same place.

STOP

Name ______________________________

**Write qu** to finish each word.
**Draw** a line from the word to the sentence where it belongs.

1. ________ iet
2. ________ iz
3. ________ estion
4. ________ een

5. The ______ has many rings.
6. Ned is sleeping. Please be ______ .
7. We had a math ______ today.
8. May I ask a ______ ?

**Find** the word that has the same beginning sound as 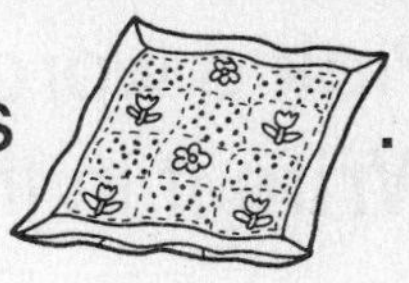 .
**Mark** the ⬭ to show your answer.

9. ⬭ gulp
   ⬭ quick
   ⬭ pick

10. ⬭ quit
    ⬭ grit
    ⬭ kit

**Notes for Home:** Your child reviewed the sound /kw/ that the letters *qu* represent as in *quilt*. ***Home Activity:*** Look in a dictionary to find simple words beginning with *qu* that your child will know. Give your child clues about the word's meaning and see if he or she can

Name ______________________

tap cap mad tape cape made

**Write** three words from the box that have a **short a** sound.

1. ____________ 2. ____________ 3. ____________

**Write** three words from the box that have a **long a** sound.

4. ____________ 5. ____________ 6. ____________

**Pick** a word from the box to finish each sentence.
**Write** it on the line.

7. He has a ____________.

8. She has a ____________.

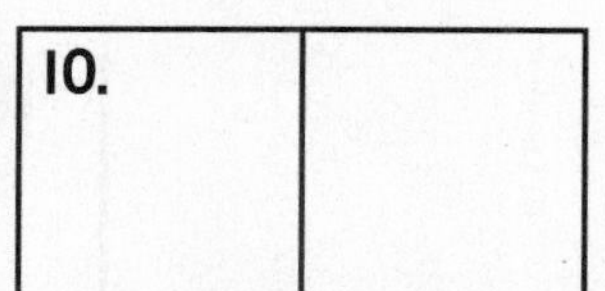

**Pick** a word from the box that fits in each puzzle.
**Write** it in the puzzle.

of
was

9.

10.

**Notes for Home:** Your child practiced spelling words with short *a (tap)* and long *a (tape)*, as well as two frequently used words: *of, was. **Home Activity:*** Say each spelling word and use it in a sentence. Repeat the spelling word and have your child write it down.

Name ______________________

**RETEACHING**

Add **-s** to the verb.

The girl **waters** the plant.

The boy **hits** the ball.

A **verb** may tell what one person, animal, or thing does.

**Read** the sentence.
**Write** the word on the line.

build builds

1. One pig ______________ a house.

blow blows

2. A wolf ______________ the house down.

make makes

3. One pig ______________ a house of sticks.

comes come

4. This house ______________ down too.

**Notes for Home:** Your child identified and wrote verbs to show the action of one animal or thing. ***Home Activity:*** Talk with your child about what you did today. Have him or her identify the verbs in your sentences.

Name ______________________________

**Draw** a line to the correct verb.

| | |
|---|---|
| 1. The teacher ______ at the girls. | smiles<br>smile |
| 2. The teacher ______ the children. | help<br>helps |
| 3. She ______ a book. | read<br>reads |
| 4. The teacher ______ to the children. | talks<br>talk |
| 5. The boy ______ on a chair. | sit<br>sits |

**Notes for Home:** Your child chose the correct verbs for sentences. ***Home Activity:*** Say sentences with singular subjects. (For example: *The cat jumps.*) Have your child repeat the verb in each sentence. *(jumps)*

**You are your child's first and best teacher!**

**Here are ways to help your child practice skills while having fun!**

**Day 1** Draw pictures with your child of objects whose names have the long *o* sound that follow a consonant-vowel-consonant-*e* pattern as in *rose* or *bone.* Write a label for each picture.

**Day 2** Ask your child to write or say aloud a thank-you note that uses any of the following words: *father, going, has, thank,* and *very.*

**Day 3** Your child is learning about a story's main idea. The next time you are reading together, ask your child to tell what the story is all about in a sentence or two.

**Day 4** Help your child write a family history that describes each family member.

**Day 5** Ask your child to name some verbs. Then have him or her use them in sentences about more than one person in your family, such as: *Mom and I jump. We sing.*

**Read with your child EVERY DAY!**



(fold here)

# Family Times

**Rose and Grandma Make the Sun Shine** **Our Family Get-Together**

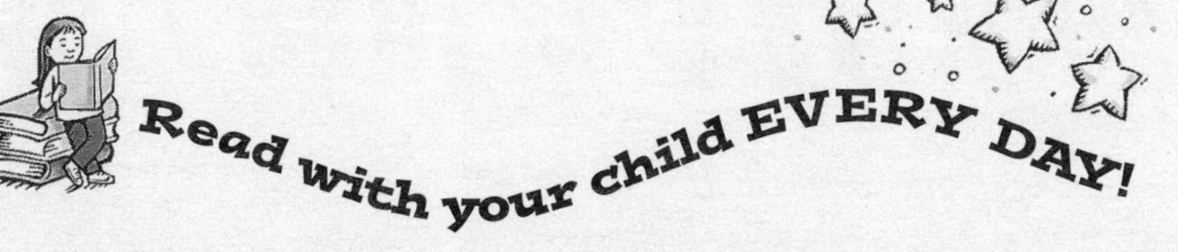

### Oh, Visit My Home

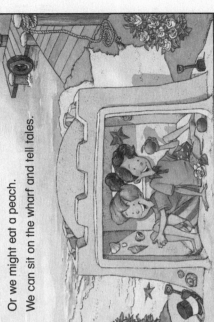

Oh, visit my home. It is shaped like a dome.
We can whistle and climb a tall rope.
We can pick a white rose.
We can find shells and doze.
We'll have fun when you visit. I hope.

Oh, visit my home.
We can look for tall ships and big whales.
We can see the white beach,
Or we might eat a peach.
We can sit on the wharf and tell tales.

This rhyme includes words your child is working with in school: words with the long *o* sound that end in *e (rope, home)* and words that begin with *sh (shells, ships)* and *wh (white, whales)*. Sing "Oh, Visit My Home" along with your child. Talk about all the fun things that can be done at your home.

Name: ______________________

# Color the Flower

**Materials** red and blue crayons

**Game Directions**

1. One flower is marked *sh*. The other flower is marked *wh*. Take turns adding *sh* or *wh* to each flower petal.
2. If the word makes sense, color the petal blue.
3. If the word does not make sense, color the petal red.

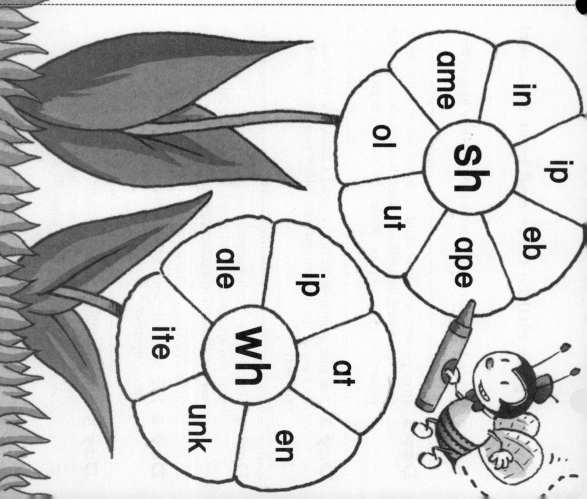

sh: in, ip, eb, ape, ut, ol, ame

wh: ip, at, en, unk, ite, ale

Name ______________________________

**Pick** the word with the **long o** sound to finish each sentence.
**Write** it on the line.

rope

home hot

1. Ben walked ________________ .

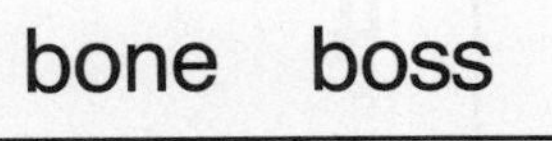

bone boss

2. Pug wants a ________________ .

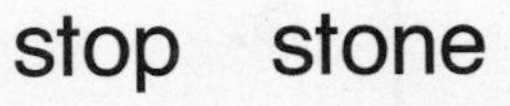

stop stone

3. Hal picks up a ________________ .

joke job

4. I told my best ________________ .

not nose

5. Sal bumped her ________________ .

**Notes for Home:** Your child identified and wrote words with the long *o* sound that follow the pattern consonant-vowel-consonant-*e* (CVC*e*) as in *rope*. ***Home Activity:*** Work with your child to write a story using as many long *o* words that follow the CVC*e* pattern as possible.

Name ______________________

**Say** the word for each picture.
**Write sh** or **wh** to finish each word.

<u>sh</u>irt <u>wh</u>eat

1. ________ op
2. ________ ip
3. ________ eel
4. ________ ale
5. ________ isper
6. ________ oe
7. ________ iskers
8. ________ eep
9. ________ istle
10. ________ ell

**Notes for Home:** Your child identified words that begin with *sh* and *wh* as in <u>*sh*</u>*irt* and <u>*wh*</u>*eat*. ***Home Activity:*** Write a list of words that begin with *sh* and *wh*. Help your child read the words aloud and draw pictures of them.

Name ______________________

**Pick** a word from the box to finish each sentence.
**Write** it on the line.

| father | going | has | thank | very |
|---|---|---|---|---|

1. Jim walks with his ______________.

2. They are ______________ to see Grandma.

3. Jim ______________ a cake for her.

4. He wants to ______________ her for the game she gave him.

5. He likes the game ______________ much.

**Notes for Home:** This week your child is learning to read the words *father, going, has, thank,* and *very*. ***Home Activity:*** Write simple sentences with these words. Help your child read the sentences aloud. Have your child point to the words he or she knows as you read.

Name ______________________________

**Read** the story.
**Circle** the sentence that tells what the story is all about.
**Draw** a picture that shows what the story is all about.

1. Everyone came to my home.
Bill, Jane, and Bob all came.
They came with food and games.
It was good to see them.

2.

3. Tom plays ball with his mother.
Tom goes on walks with his father.
Sometimes they all read books.
Tom has fun with his mother and father.

4.

**Write** a title for each story that tells what it is all about.

5. ______________________________

6. ______________________________

**Notes for Home:** Your child identified and illustrated the main idea of two stories.
***Home Activity:*** Invite your child to name his or her favorite story. Then ask your child to tell you in a sentence or two what the story is all about.

Name ______________________________

A **verb** may tell what two or more people, animals, or things do. Do not add **-s** to these verbs.

They <u>jog</u> home.

**Circle** a word in ( ) to finish each sentence.
**Draw** a picture for each sentence.

1. Sal and Tim (bake/bakes).
2. Joe and Pat (plays/play).
3. The girls (jump/jumps).
4. Mom and Dad (eats/eat).
5. They (walk/walks) the dog.

**Notes for Home:** Your child completed sentences by choosing verbs for plural subjects. ***Home Activity:*** Write a list of verbs such as *sing, walk,* and *look*. Ask your child to use each verb in a sentence that tells about more than one person doing the action.

Name ______________________________

**Pick** a word from the box to finish each sentence.
**Write** it on the line. Use each word only once.

| cousins | father | going | has | thank | very |
|---|---|---|---|---|---|

1. Her ____________ and mother took Jill on a trip.

2. They went to see all of her ____________ .

3. She ____________ a lot to tell them.

4. Jill had a ____________ good time.

5. She is ____________ to see them again.

6. Jill calls to ____________ them for the fun day.

**Notes for Home:** Your child completed sentences using words that he or she learned this week. ***Home Activity:*** Work with your child to write a story about a family gathering using as many of these words as possible.

Name ______________________

**Pick** a word from the box to match each picture.
**Write** it on the line.

lake cane plane frame face cage scale snake

1. 

2. 

3. 

4. 

5. 

6. 

7. 

8. 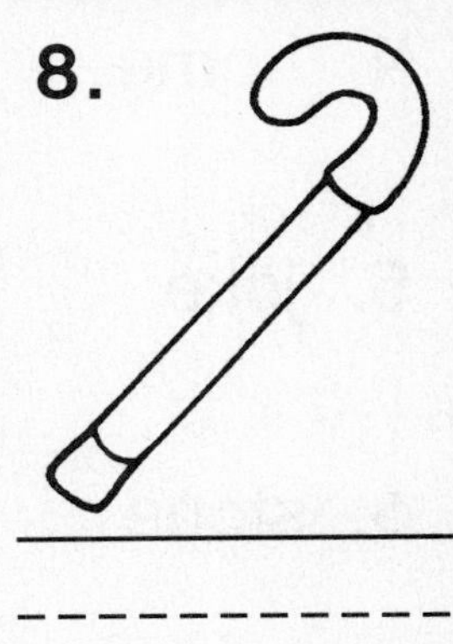

**Find** the word that has the same vowel sound as .
**Mark** the ⬭ to show your answer.

9. ⬭ tap
⬭ tape
⬭ trap

10. ⬭ plan
⬭ place
⬭ pan

**Notes for Home:** Your child reviewed words with the long *a* sound as in *grapes*. ***Home Activity:*** Write *face* on a sheet of paper. Have your child change the consonant letters to write a new long *a* word, such as *place*. Continue changing letters and building new words.

Name ______________________________

**Look** at each word. **Say** it.
**Listen** for the **long o** sound in 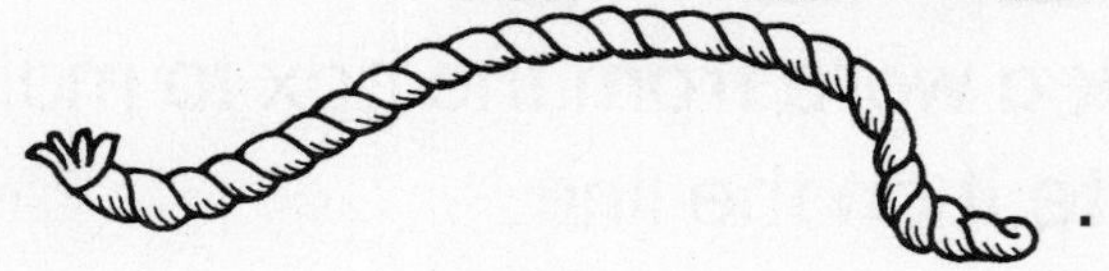 .

| | **Write** each word. | **Check** it. |
|---|---|---|
| 1. rode | | |
| 2. those | | |
| 3. hope | | |
| 4. home | | |
| 5. joke | | |
| 6. stone | | |

# Word Wall Words

**Write** each word.

| | | |
|---|---|---|
| 7. has | | |
| 8. very | | |

**Notes for Home:** Your child spelled words with the long *o* sound spelled consonant-vowel-consonant-*e* (CVC*e*) as in *rope,* and two frequently-used words: *has, very.* ***Home Activity:*** Challenge your child to spell other long *o* words that follow a CVC*e* pattern.

Name ______________________

**Circle** the verb that tells what more than one person does.
**Write** the verb on the line to finish each sentence.

play plays

1. The girls ____________ a game.

runs run

2. Kim and Jill ____________ away.

hides hide

3. They ____________ in a bush.

need needs

4. They ____________ more players.

asks ask

5. They ____________ Ken and Bill to play too.

**Notes for Home:** Your child chose verbs to show the action of two or more people. ***Home Activity:*** Have your child tell you a story about the children in his or her class. Encourage your child to use plural subjects (two or more people) as he or she tells the story.

Name ______________________________



# Test-Taking Tips

1. Write your name on the test.

2. Read each question twice.

3. Read all the answer choices for the question.

4. Mark your answer carefully.

5. Check your answer.

Name ______________________________

# Part 1: Vocabulary

**Read** each sentence.
**Mark** the ⬭ for the word that fits.

1. This is my ______ .

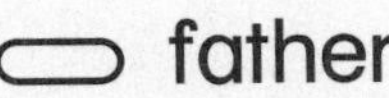

⬭ something ⬭ father ⬭ mother

2. He is ______ to get a pet.

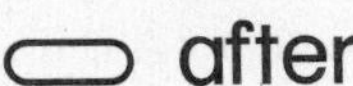
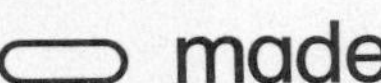
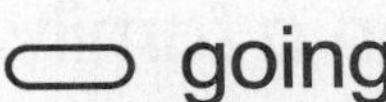

⬭ after ⬭ made ⬭ going

3. Dad ______ a dog for me.

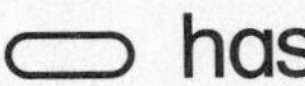

⬭ has ⬭ catch ⬭ was

4. I am ______ happy.

⬭ as ⬭ every ⬭ very

5. "______ you, Dad!"

⬭ Laugh ⬭ Call ⬭ Thank

GO ON

Name ______________________________



# Part 2: Comprehension

**Read** each question.
**Mark** the ⊂⊃ for the answer.

6. Where was the get-together?
   - ⊂⊃ Uncle Eddie's
   - ⊂⊃ Uncle Richard's
   - ⊂⊃ Grandma's

7. What did all the family do?
   - ⊂⊃ had fun
   - ⊂⊃ came by car
   - ⊂⊃ went up a tree

8. What is on a family tree?
   - ⊂⊃ frogs
   - ⊂⊃ jokes
   - ⊂⊃ names

9. How old was the boy who tells what happened?
   - ⊂⊃ three
   - ⊂⊃ six
   - ⊂⊃ ten

10. The boy tells mostly about
    - ⊂⊃ frogs.
    - ⊂⊃ a picture.
    - ⊂⊃ a family.

STOP

Name ______________________



**Pick** a contraction from the box to finish each sentence.
**Write** it on the line. Remember to use capital letters.

| | |
|---|---|
| he is = he's | she is = she's |
| they are = they're | they will = they'll |

1. ______________ reading a book.

2. ______________ asking Gram to play.

3. ______________ play a game.

4. ______________ having fun!

**Find** the contraction for the two words.
**Mark** the ⬭ to show your answer.

5. do not
   - ⬭ don't
   - ⬭ won't
   - ⬭ does

6. we are
   - ⬭ we'll
   - ⬭ we'd
   - ⬭ we're

**Notes for Home:** Your child wrote contractions to finish sentences. ***Home Activity:*** Say two words that could be joined together to make a contraction. Ask your child to name the contraction and use it in a sentence.

Name ______________________________

**Say** the word for each picture.
**Pick** a word from the box that rhymes with it.
**Write** the word on the line.

| rode | those | hope | home | joke | stone |
|---|---|---|---|---|---|

1. ______________________

2. ______________________

3. ______________________

4. ______________________

5. ______________________

6. ______________________

**Put** the letters in the correct order to make a word from the box.
**Write** it on the line.

| has | very |
|---|---|

7. sha ______________

8. yvre ______________

**Notes for Home:** Your child spelled words with long *o* that follow a consonant-vowel-consonant-*e* pattern *(rope)* and two frequently used words: *has, very.* ***Home Activity:*** Write *rope*. Have your child tell what letters to change to form different spelling words, such as *hope*.

Name ______________________



RETEACHING

The people **work**.

Two foxes **run**.

Do not add **-s** to a verb that tells what two or more people, animals, or things do.

**Read** the first sentence.
**Write** the verb in the second sentence.

1. He <u>plants</u> one flower.

   They ______________ many flowers.

2. He <u>waters</u> his flower.

   They ______________ their flowers.

3. His flower <u>grows</u> tall.

   Their flowers ______________ tall.

**Notes for Home:** Your child identified verbs in sentences with plural subjects. ***Home Activity:*** Write plural subjects on cards. *(The dogs, The pigs)* Have your child write a sentence for each subject.

Name ______________________________

**Circle** the correct word for each sentence.
**Write** the sentence.

1. The children __________. looks look

2. The winds __________. blow blows

3. Many leaves __________. falls fall

4. Some girls __________ the leaves. rake rakes

5. Those boys __________ the basket. hold holds

6. The puppies __________ in the pile! jumps jump

**Notes for Home:** Your child identified verbs that show the action of two or more people, animals, or things. ***Home Activity:*** Look at photographs of groups of people. Have your child say a sentence that describes what the people are doing in each photograph.

**You are your child's first and best teacher!**

**Here are ways to help your child practice skills while having fun!**

**Day 1** List some long *i* words that follow a consonant-vowel-consonant-*e* pattern, such as *rice* and *dine*. Take turns using them in sentences, for example: *The nice mice ate rice.*

**Day 2** Ask your child to write or say sentences about his or her friends using any of the following words your child is learning to read this week: *be, friend, pretty, soon,* and *your*.

**Day 3** Before reading a story, browse through the illustrations and some of the words together. Ask your child to use these clues to predict what the story will be about.

**Day 4** Your child is learning about making introductions. Encourage your child to practice introducing himself or herself to you.

**Day 5** Ask your child to tell about a family vacation or special trip that happened in the past. Listen for the use of past tense verbs. Ask questions that will help your child correct any errors using past tense verbs.

**Read with your child EVERY DAY!**



(fold here)

# Family Times

**The Rolling Rice Cake** | **The Rat and the Cat**

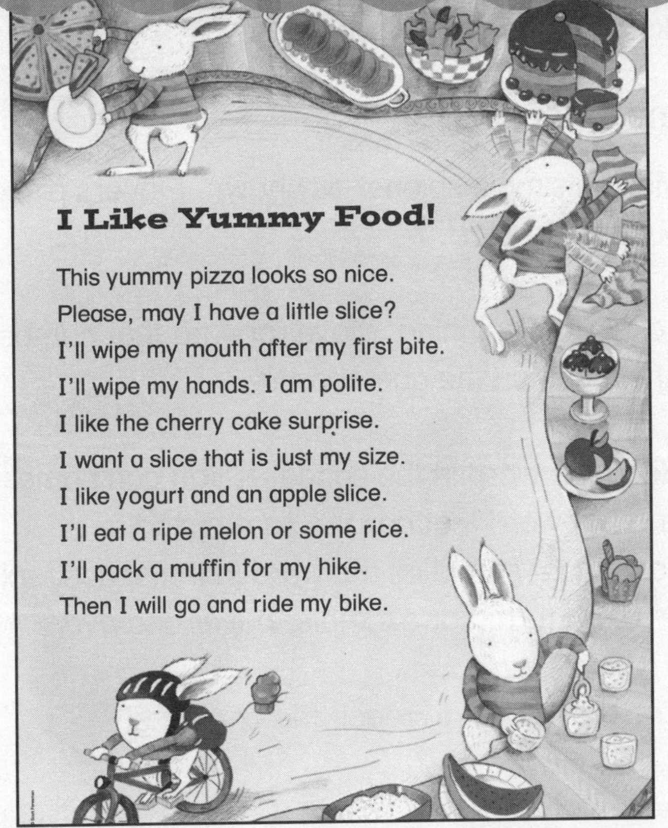

**I Like Yummy Food!**

This yummy pizza looks so nice.
Please, may I have a little slice?
I'll wipe my mouth after my first bite.
I'll wipe my hands. I am polite.
I like the cherry cake surprise.
I want a slice that is just my size.
I like yogurt and an apple slice.
I'll eat a ripe melon or some rice.
I'll pack a muffin for my hike.
Then I will go and ride my bike.

This rhyme includes words your child is working with in school: words with the long *i* sound that follow a consonant-vowel-consonant-*e* pattern *(nice, bite)* and words with single or double consonants in the middle *(melon, pizza)*. Sing "I Like Yummy Food" together and act out the lyrics.

Name: ______________________

# Spin It

**Materials** paper, paper clip, pencil, marker, 1 button per player

**Game Directions**

1. Make a simple spinner as shown. Players place buttons on Start.

2. Take turns spinning. Move forward that number of spaces on the gameboard.

3. Read the word in the space. If you can name another word that has the same middle consonant sound as the word in the space, spin an extra turn. For example: *never* and *river*.

4. The first player to reach the end wins!

Start

never

butter

cherry

muffin

water

melon

baby

silly

happy

rabbit

yummy

dresser

baker

slipper

End

Name ______________________________

**Pick** a word from the box to match each picture.
**Write** the word on the line.
**Circle** each picture whose name has the **long i** sound.

| bike | dime | fire | line |
|---|---|---|---|
| mice | pig | six | slide |

1. ______________________

2. ______________________

3. ______________________

4. ______________________

5. ______________________

6. ______________________

7. ______________________

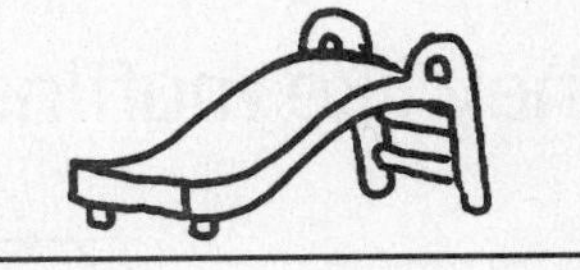

8. ______________________

**Notes for Home:** Your child practiced reading words with the long *i* sound that follow a consonant-vowel-consonant-*e* pattern such as *kite*. ***Home Activity:*** Work with your child to write a story using as many of the long *i* words listed above as possible.

Name ________________________________

**Pick** a letter or letters from the box to finish each word.
**Write** the letters on the lines.

ff m tt pp v

1. Tess is ha ________ y when she eats with Sid.

2. They like to eat mu ________ ins.

3. Yellow muffins are made from le ________ ons.

4. They like muffins be ________ er than cake.

5. They can ne ________ er have too many muffins!

**Notes for Home:** Your child completed words with single and double consonants in the middle, such as *water* and *butter*. ***Home Activity:*** List some of your family's favorite foods. Ask your child to identify the middle consonant sounds in the words.

Name ______________________________

**Pick** a word from the box to finish each sentence.
**Write** it on the line.

| be | friend | pretty | soon | your |
|---|---|---|---|---|

1. Sal is my best ____________________ .

2. She has a ____________________ doll.

3. This hat is for ____________________ doll.

4. It will be dark ____________________ .

5. Then it will ____________________ time to go.

**Notes for Home:** This week your child learned to read the words *be*, *friend*, *pretty*, *soon*, and *your*. ***Home Activity:*** Write these words on slips of paper and have your child practice reading each word you show.

Name ______________________________

**Look** at this book cover.
**Circle** or **write** your answers.

Hal and Sal Take a Trip

By
Bob Dog

1. Who wrote this book? ______________________________

2. What do you think this book will be about?

real dogs    silly dogs    a real trip

3. What do you think this book will be like?

funny    sad    full of facts

4. Why do you think the writer wrote this book?

to tell facts about dogs    to make you sad    to make you laugh

5. Would you want to read this book? Why or why not?

______________________________

______________________________

**Notes for Home:** Your child answered questions about why an author may have written a story. ***Home Activity:*** Before reading a story with your child, ask questions like the ones on this page to help your child think about the author's purpose for writing it.

Name ______________________________

**Verbs** can tell about action that takes place now.

Today Mom and I cook dinner.

**Verbs** can tell about action that happened in the past.
Add **-ed** to these verbs.

Yesterday Dad and Sam cooked dinner.

---

**Look** at the picture.
**Circle** the sentence that tells when the action happened.

1. We fix the bike.
   We fixed the bike.

2. We bake a cake.
   We baked a cake.

3. Ted and Ned jump on the bed.
   Ted and Ned jumped on the bed.

4. Pat and Jane water the plants.
   Pat and Jane watered the plants.

---

**Draw** a picture about the sentence.

5. Tim and Nan play in the sandbox.

**Notes for Home:** Your child used pictures to distinguish between present and past tense verbs in sentences. ***Home Activity:*** Write *bake, baked, mix,* and *mixed*. Work with your child to think of a sentence for each word.

Name ______________________________

**Pick** a word from the box to finish each sentence.
**Write** it on the line.

| alone | be | friend |
|---|---|---|
| pretty | soon | your |

1. Where will you eat ______________ lunch?

2. Matt eats his lunch ______________ .

3. Matt will ______________ happy to play after lunch.

4. He will play as ______________ as he can.

5. Matt likes to play with his ______________ Fran.

6. Fran has a ______________ dress.

**Notes for Home:** Your child used newly learned words in sentences. ***Home Activity:*** Ask your child to write simple sentences in which vocabulary words are missing. Then you fill in the missing words, and ask your child to check your answers.

Name ______________________________

**ch**ick **sh**ip **th**orn **wh**ip

**Say** the word for each picture.
**Write ch, sh, th,** or **wh** to finish each word.

1.  _____ op
2.  _____ in
3.  _____ ips
4.  _____ eck
5.  _____ ale
6.  _____ ink
7.  _____ irt
8.  _____ umb

**Find** the word that has the same beginning sound as the picture.
**Mark** the ⬭ to show your answer.

9. ⬭ chin
⬭ shin
⬭ thin

10. ⬭ chest
⬭ shorts
⬭ why

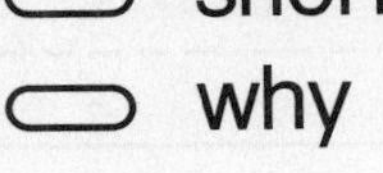

**Notes for Home:** Your child reviewed words that begin with *ch, sh, th,* and *wh*.
***Home Activity:*** Choose one of these letter combinations. Take turns with your child naming as many words beginning with that sound as you can.

Name ______________________

**Look** at each word. **Say** it.
**Listen** for the **long i** sound in  .

| | **Write** each word. | **Check** it. |
|---|---|---|
| 1. like | | |
| 2. nice | | |
| 3. time | | |
| 4. ride | | |
| 5. white | | |
| 6. five | | |

## Word Wall Words

**Write** each word.

| | | |
|---|---|---|
| 7. your | | |
| 8. friend | | |

**Notes for Home:** Your child spelled words with the long *i* sound heard in b*i*ke and two frequently used words: *your, friend*. ***Home Activity:*** Have your child tell you sentences using each spelling word. Write the sentences, leaving a blank space for each spelling word for your child to fill in.

Name ______________________

**Fill** in the table.
**Write** the words on the lines.

| | Now | In the Past |
|---|---|---|
| 1. | jump | ______________ |
| 2. | walk | ______________ |
| 3. | ______________ | laughed |
| 4. | ______________ | thanked |

**Circle** the verb that makes sense in each sentence.
**Write** it on the line.

ask asked

5. Last week, we ______________ Tim to come see us.

says said

6. He ______________ he had to check with his dad.

have had

7. Now, we play and ______________ fun.

**Notes for Home:** Your child wrote present and past tense verbs to complete sentences. ***Home Activity:*** Say a sentence about something happening now. Then ask your child to repeat the sentence using the past tense of the verb.

Name ______________________________

# Test-Taking Tips

1. Write your name on the test.

2. Read each question twice.

3. Read all the answer choices for the question.

4. Mark your answer carefully.

5. Check your answer.

Name ______________________________

# Part 1: Vocabulary

**Read** each sentence.
**Mark** the ⬭ for the word that fits.

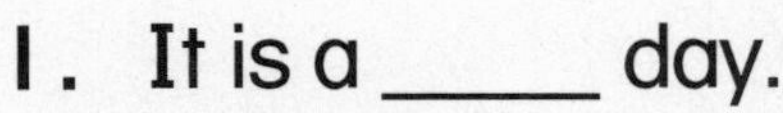
1. It is a _____ day.

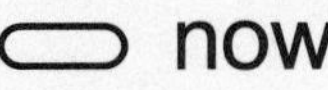 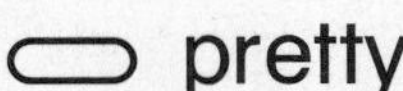
⬭ now ⬭ pretty ⬭ some

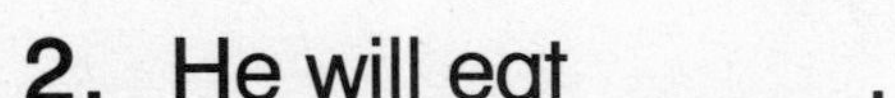
2. He will eat ______.

⬭ so ⬭ our ⬭ soon

3. A ______ comes by.

  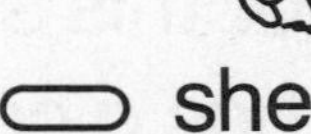
⬭ friend ⬭ there ⬭ she

4. "Is that ______ dog?"

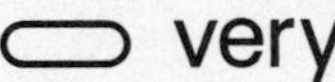  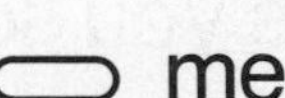
⬭ very ⬭ your ⬭ me

5. She will ______ good now.

⬭ into ⬭ there ⬭ be

GO ON

Name ______________________



# Part 2: Comprehension

**Read** each question.
**Mark** the ⊂⊃ for the answer.

6. The rat first sees the cat in
   - ⊂⊃ a shop.
   - ⊂⊃ a box.
   - ⊂⊃ his home.

7. The rat wants the cat to
   - ⊂⊃ do some tricks.
   - ⊂⊃ be his friend.
   - ⊂⊃ catch fish for him.

8. The man thinks the cat will
   - ⊂⊃ run away from the rat.
   - ⊂⊃ eat the rat.
   - ⊂⊃ have fun with the rat.

9. What part of this story could be real?
   - ⊂⊃ A rat has a cat for a pet.
   - ⊂⊃ A cat talks.
   - ⊂⊃ A man has a shop.

10. At the end, this story
   - ⊂⊃ makes you sad.
   - ⊂⊃ sings a song.
   - ⊂⊃ has a surprise.

STOP

Name ______________________

**Pick** a word from the box to match each picture.
**Write** it on the line.
**Circle** the picture if the **c** in the word has the same sound as in the beginning of **circle**.

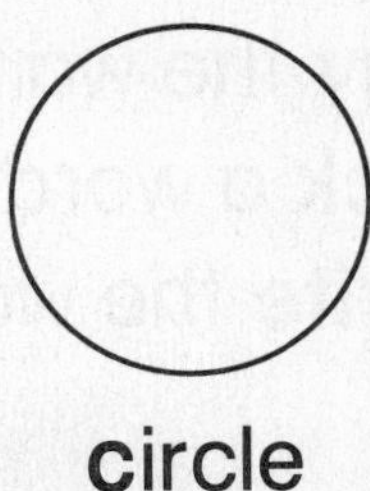

circle

| cap | cake | car | cent | city | face | ice | mice |
|---|---|---|---|---|---|---|---|

1. ____________
2. ____________
3. ____________
4. ____________
5. ____________
6. ____________
7. ____________
8. ____________

**Find** the word where **c** has the same sound as in **cent**.
**Mark** the ⬭ to show your answer.

9. ⬭ nice
   ⬭ nick
   ⬭ sick

10. ⬭ cape
    ⬭ lace
    ⬭ lock

**Notes for Home:** Your child reviewed words where the letter *c* represents the sound /s/ as in *cent. **Home Activity:*** Ask your child to say a sentence that uses a word with *c* where *c* stands for the sound /s/.

Name ______________________

**Say** the word for each picture.
**Pick** a word from the box that rhymes with it.
**Write** the word on the line.

like nice time ride white five

1. ______________________

2. ______________________

3. ______________________

4. ______________________

5. ______________________

6. ______________________

**Pick** a word from the box to finish each sentence.
**Write** it on the line.

your friend

7. Is this ______________ bike?

8. I want to play with my ______________ .

**Notes for Home:** Your child spelled words with long *i* and two frequently used words: *your, friend.* ***Home Activity:*** Say a spelling word aloud. Ask your child to spell the word and then name other words that rhyme with the spelling word.

Name ______________________________



She **claps.** (now) She **clapped.** (past)

Verbs can tell about action that takes place now.
Verbs can tell about action that happened in the past.

**Look** at each word in the boxes.
Does it tell about now or the past?
**Write** it under **Now** or **The Past**.

| Now | The Past |
|---|---|
| 1. ______ | 2. ______ |
| 3. ______ | 4. ______ |
| 5. ______ | 6. ______ |

| barked | calls | walked |
|---|---|---|
| jumps | needs | shouted |

**Notes for Home:** Your child identified verbs in the past and present tenses. ***Home Activity:*** Read a story with your child. Have him or her point out past-tense and present-tense verbs in the story.

Name ______________________________

**Circle** the correct word in ( ).

1. Last year he never (talks/talked).
2. Now he (talked/talks) too much.
3. Last year he never (walked/walks).
4. Now he (walked/walks) too much.
5. Last year he never (waves/waved).
6. Now he (waved/waves) too much.
7. Last year he never (jumps/jumped).
8. Now he (jumps/jumped) on me!

**Notes for Home:** Your child chose verbs in the past and present tenses to complete sentences. ***Home Activity:*** Sing a favorite song with your child. Have him or her identify past-tense and present-tense verbs in the song.

## You *are* your child's first *and* best teacher!

**Here are ways to help your child practice skills while having fun!**

**Day 1** Write the word *mule.* Challenge your child to make new long *u* words by substituting other letters for *m* and/or *l*. For example, *mule* becomes *flute* or *Luke*.

**Day 2** Work with your child to make up short riddles using any of these words: *four, funny, long, watch,* and *were.* For example: *I have four fingers and one thumb. What am I? (a hand)*

**Day 3** After you have read a story to your child, have your child describe the beginning, middle, and end of the story.

**Day 4** Your child is learning to listen for details. Describe something using as many details as possible. Challenge your child to guess what you are describing.

**Day 5** Ask your child to look at a picture and describe it by using simple sentences that include the words *is, are, was,* and *were.* For example: *He is running. They are eating.*

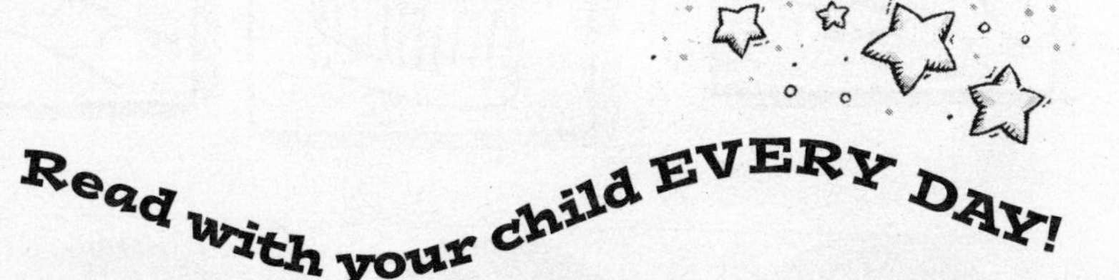

**Read with your child EVERY DAY!**



(fold here)

# Family Times

**June and the Mule** **Slim, Luke, and the Mules**

### The Dude Ranch

We're at the dude ranch.
We'll ride the big mules.
We'll brush them
And feed them
And follow the rules.

When it is lunch time,
We'll hear a bell ring.
We'll rush to the table
And eat everything.

Later this evening
On this cool night in June,
We'll stretch by the fire
And sing a nice tune.

This rhyme includes words your child is working with in school: words with the long *u* sound *(dude, tune)* and words that end with *ch, tch, sh,* and *ng*. Sing "The Dude Ranch" together. Underline the words with the long *u* sound and circle the words that end with *ch, tch, sh,* and *ng*.

Name: ______________________

# It's a Match

**Materials** index cards, markers

**Game Directions**

1. Make a picture card and a word card for these words: *ranch, lunch, wing, watch, long, fish, brush, math, bath, ditch.* Mix each set of cards and place each card in the set facedown.

2. Players take turns turning over two cards at a time, one card from each set.

3. If the word and picture cards match, the player keeps the pair. If not, the player mixes the cards back into each set.

4. Play until all cards have been matched up. The player with the most pairs wins!

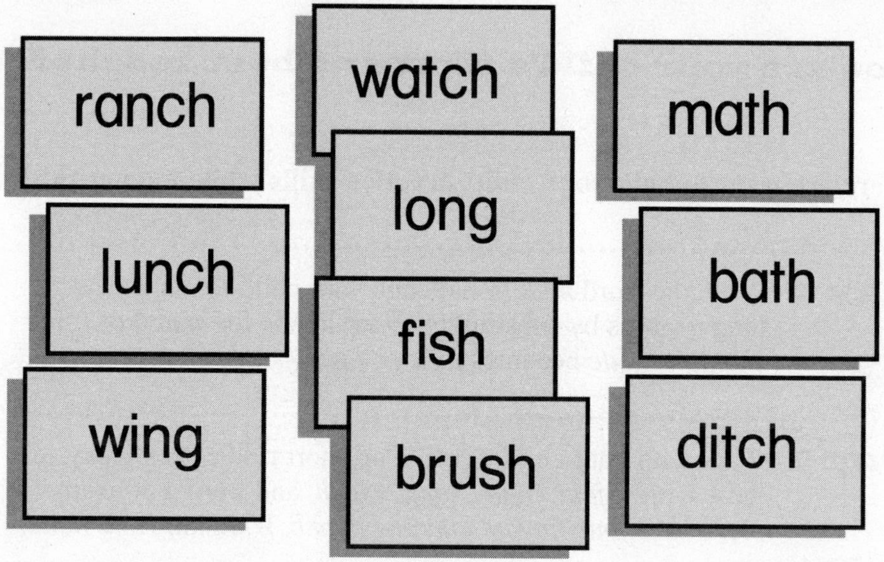

ranch watch math

lunch long bath

wing fish brush ditch

Name ______________________________

**Look** at each picture.
**Circle** the word to finish each sentence.
**Write** it on the line.

flute flop flood

1. Mike plays the ______________ .

tune tub tube

2. I filled the ______________ .

team tan tune

3. Do you like that ______________ ?

cute can cut

4. My cat is very ______________ .

cub cube cab

5. This is an ice ______________ .

**Notes for Home:** Your child practiced reading words with the long *u* sound that follow a consonant-vowel-consonant-*e* pattern, such as *mule*. ***Home Activity:*** Work with your child to think of pairs of rhyming words that have the long *u* sound.

Name ______________________

**Pick** letters from the box to finish each word.
**Write** the letters on the line.

| ch | tch | sh | th | ng |
|---|---|---|---|---|

ben<u>ch</u>

1. 
pa ______

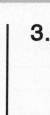

2. ki ______

3. ri ______

4. 
di ______

5. 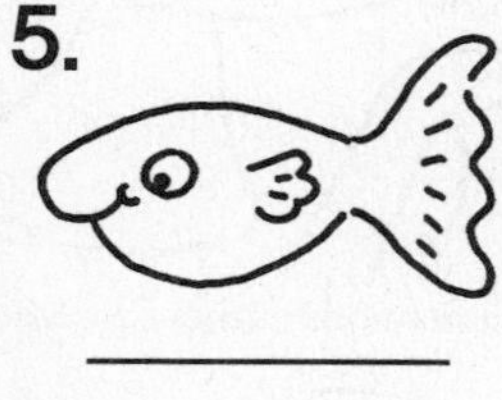
fi ______

6. 
lun ______

7. 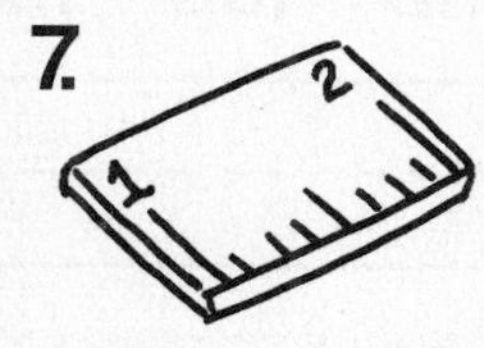

in ______

8. 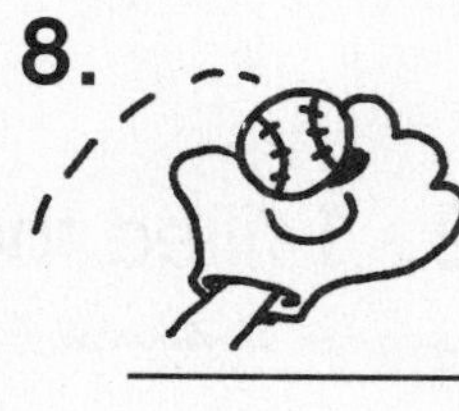
ca ______

**Draw** a picture for each word.

**9.** watch

**10.** moth

**Notes for Home:** Your child added the final digraphs *-ch, -tch, -sh, -th,* and *-ng* to complete words. ***Home Activity:*** Invite your child to make up sentences that include rhyming words with these endings. For example: *I wish I had a fish.*

Name ______________________

**Pick** a word from the box to match each clue.
**Write** it on the line.

four funny long watch

1. comes after one, two, three

______________

2. a ______________ rope

3. the same as *look*

______________

4. the same as *silly*

______________

**Write** a sentence using the word *were*.

5. ______________________________

**Notes for Home:** This week your child learned to read the words *four*, *funny*, *long*, *watch*, and *were*. ***Home Activity:*** Challenge your child to use as many of the vocabulary words as possible in one silly sentence, such as *I watched four long, funny clowns.*

Name ______________________

**Read** the sentences in the story.
**Number** them from 1 to 3 to show the right order.

1. ______ Then she let the mules go out in the pen.

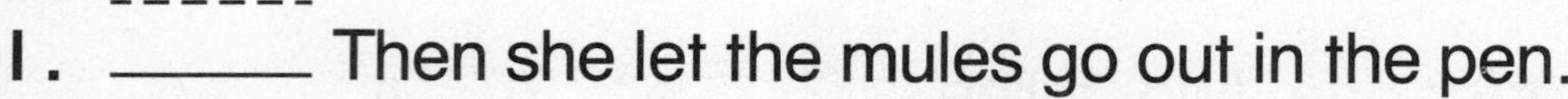

2. ______ After the mules ate, Ellen gave them water.

3. ______ Ellen fed the mules.

**Draw** a picture to show what happened at the **beginning.**
**Draw** a picture to show what happened at the **end**.

| 4. Beginning | 5. End |
| --- | --- |
| | |

**Notes for Home:** Your child numbered sentences and drew pictures to show the order of events in a story. ***Home Activity:*** Together, write a four-sentence story, with each sentence on a separate strip of paper. Help your child put the sentences in the correct order.

Name ______________________________

**Use is** and **are** to tell about now.

She **is** riding the mule.

**Use was** and **were** to tell about the past.

The ride **was** nice.

---

**Write** a word from the box to finish each sentence.
**Use** the clue in ( ) to help you.

| is | are | was | were |
|---|---|---|---|

1. He ______________ calling a friend. (now)
2. She ______________ late. (past)
3. They ______________ watching the mules. (now)
4. It ______________ nice out. (now)
5. We ______________ going home. (past)

**Notes for Home:** Your child used the words *is*, *are*, *was*, and *were* in sentences.
***Home Activity:*** Write the words *he*, *she*, *it*, *we,* and *they* on slips of paper. Have your child pick one slip at a time and use each word in a sentence with *is*, *are*, *was*, or *were*.

Name ______________________________

**Pick** a word from the box to finish each sentence.
**Write** it on the line.

| count | four | funny | long | watch | were |
|---|---|---|---|---|---|

1. We ______________ going to see the mules.

2. It is a ______________ walk to the pen.

3. We like to ______________ the mules.

4. Sam will ______________ how many mules are there.

5. There are ______________ mules in the pen.

6. I laugh at the ______________ mule.

**Notes for Home:** Your child completed sentences using words learned this week. ***Home Activity:*** Work with your child to write a story using as many of these words as possible.

Name ______________________________

This graph shows how many animals live on Jan's farm.
**Read** the graph.
**Use** the graph to answer each question.

1. How many pigs are on the farm? ______

2. How many horses and dogs are on the farm? ______

3. How many more cows are there than sheep? ______

4. What animal is there the most of? ______________

5. What animal is there the least of? ______________

**Notes for Home:** Your child read a bar graph and answered questions about it. ***Home Activity:*** Help your child make a bar graph that shows the number of different kinds of objects in your home. Then ask your child questions about the graph.

Name ______________________________

**Circle** the word for each picture.

five

1. 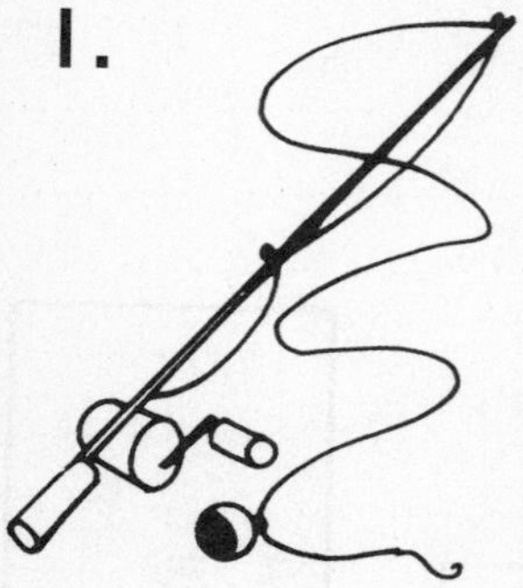 line lane
2.  mane mice
3.  kit kite
4.  bike bill
5.  pill pile
6.  lime lame
7.  fish file
8. 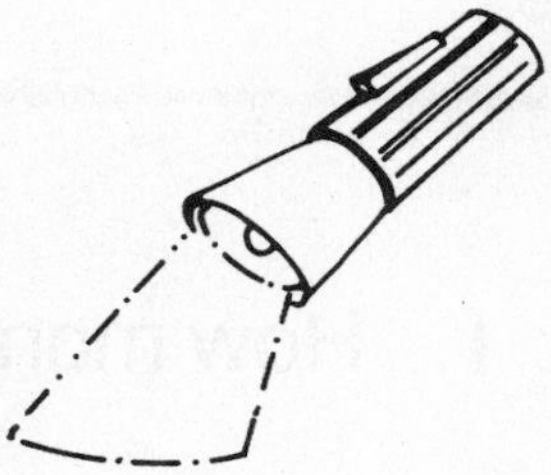 shine shin

**Find** the word that has the same **long i** sound as .
**Mark** the ⬭ to show your answer.

9. ⬭ flip
⬭ fine
⬭ fin

10. ⬭ slip
⬭ sip
⬭ slice

**Notes for Home:** Your child reviewed words with the long *i* sound heard in *five*. ***Home Activity:*** All the long *i* words above are spelled using a consonant-vowel-consonant-*e* pattern. Write the word *five*. Take turns changing the consonants to build new words, such as *fine, dine,* and *dime.*

Name ______________________

**Look** at each word. **Say** it.
**Listen** for the sounds that **th**, **ch**, **sh,** and **ng** stand for.

| | **Write** each word. | **Check** it. |
|---|---|---|
| 1. the | | |
| 2. that | | |
| 3. with | | |
| 4. such | | |
| 5. fish | | |
| 6. long | | |

## Word Wall Words

**Write** each word.

| | | |
|---|---|---|
| 7. four | | |
| 8. were | | |

**Notes for Home:** Your child spelled words with *th, ch, sh,* and *ng,* as well as two frequently used words: *four, were.* ***Home Activity:*** Help your child write a story about a fish, using these spelling words.

Name ______________________

**Circle** the verb that makes sense in each sentence.
**Write** the verb on the line.

1. Jim and Cara ____________ walking to the pen. is are

2. Jim ____________ going to give hay to the mules. is are

3. The mules ____________ awake. is are

4. Before, they ____________ sleeping. was were

5. Cara ____________ happy to give the mules water. was were

**Notes for Home:** Your child completed sentences using *is*, *are*, *was*, and *were*. ***Home Activity:*** Write the words *is*, *are*, *was*, and *were* on flashcards. Have your child pick a card, read the word, and use it in a sentence.

Name ____________________

# Part 1: Vocabulary

**Read** each sentence.
**Mark** the ⬭ for the word that fits.

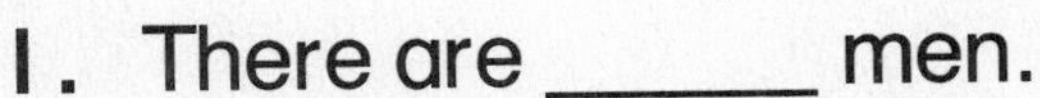
1. There are ______ men.

 four 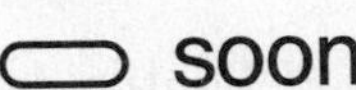 soon ⬭ after

2. They went for a ______ ride.

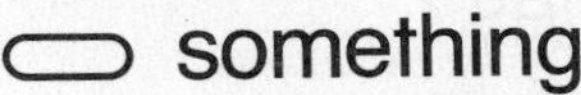 something 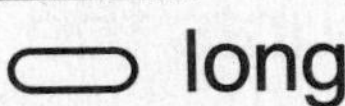 long ⬭ very

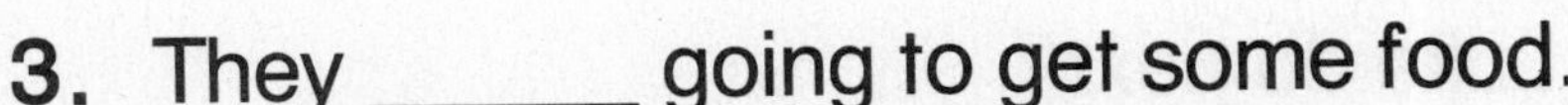
3. They ______ going to get some food.

 has  made ⬭ were

4. One man will ______ the truck.

 watch 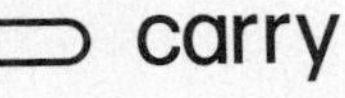 carry  funny

5. He will ______ the bags.

⬭ play  count  catch

Name ______________________________



# Part 2: Comprehension

**Read** each sentence.

**Mark** the ⊂⊃ for the answer.

6. What do Slim and Luke have to do?
   - ⊂⊃ go to town
   - ⊂⊃ rub down the mules
   - ⊂⊃ work on the ranch

7. How many mules do Slim and Luke have?
   - ⊂⊃ four
   - ⊂⊃ five
   - ⊂⊃ six

8. What happens when Slim counts the mules?
   - ⊂⊃ He does not count the one he is on.
   - ⊂⊃ A mule runs away.
   - ⊂⊃ He counts too many.

9. What will Slim and Luke do next?
   - ⊂⊃ go to buy food
   - ⊂⊃ count the mules again
   - ⊂⊃ let the mules go

10. Slim and Luke seem
    - ⊂⊃ sad.
    - ⊂⊃ mean.
    - ⊂⊃ silly.

STOP

Name ______________________________

**Add -ed** and **-ing** to each word.
**Write** the new words on the lines.

| | Add -ed | Add -ing |
|---|---|---|
| 1. play | ________ | ________ |
| 2. rest | ________ | ________ |
| 3. talk | ________ | ________ |
| 4. help | ________ | ________ |
| 5. ask | ________ | ________ |

**Find** the word that makes sense in each sentence.
**Mark** the ⬭ to show your answer.

6. Now, Kit is ______ her mom.
   - ⬭ called
   - ⬭ call
   - ⬭ calling

7. Before, Kit ______ in the park.
   - ⬭ play
   - ⬭ played
   - ⬭ playing

**Notes for Home:** Your child reviewed words with *-ed* and *-ing* endings. ***Home Activity:*** Make a list of action verbs like those above. Have your child add *-ed* and *-ing* to each word and use it in a sentence.

Name ______________________________

the that with such fish long

**Write** three words from the box that have **th**.

1. ____________ 2. ____________ 3. ____________

**Pick** a word from the box to finish each sentence.
**Write** it on the line.

4. This is a very ____________ pole.

5. Look at the ____________ jump!

6. This is ____________ a nice pond.

**Pick** a word from the box to finish each sentence.
**Write** it in the puzzle.

four
were

7. Two plus two is ______ .

8. The boys ______ running fast.

| 7. |
|---|
| |
| |
| |

| 8. | | | |
|---|---|---|---|
| | | | |

**Notes for Home:** Your child spelled words with *th, ch, sh,* and *ng,* as well as two frequently used words: *four, were.* ***Home Activity:*** Say a spelling word aloud. Ask your child to write the word and then use it in a sentence.

Name ______________________________

RETEACHING

A box **is** big.
Some toys **are** small.
The day **was** fun.
We **were** happy.

The words **is** and **are** tell about now.
Use **is** to tell about **one.**
Use **are** to tell about **more than one.**
The words **was** and **were** tell about the past.
Use **was** to tell about **one.**
Use **were** to tell about **more than one.**

**Draw** a line to complete each sentence.

| | |
|---|---|
| 1. The party | were pretty. |
| 2. The birthday signs | is over. |
| 3. Carlos | is happy. |
| 4. The games | is gone! |
| 5. The cake | are put away. |

**Notes for Home:** Your child used correct forms of the verb *to be* in sentences. ***Home Activity:*** Together, make up a poem about family members. Have your child tell you which forms of the verb *to be* to use.

Name ______________________________

**Use** the words in the boxes to complete the sentences.
One word will be used twice.

1. The dog ______________ outside. (now)

2. The birds ______________ on the grass. (now)

3. The tree ______________ not empty. (past)

4. Now one bird ______________ outside. (now)

5. The kittens ______________ small. (past)

| was | are | is | were |
|---|---|---|---|

**Notes for Home:** Your child used correct forms of the verb *to be*, such as *is, are, was,* and *were,* in sentences. ***Home Activity:*** Together, read a favorite story. Ask your child to point out where different forms of the verb *to be* are used in the story.

**You *are* your child's first *and* best teacher!**

**Here are ways to help your child practice skills while having fun!**

**Day 1** Write a list of long *e* words spelled *ee* or *e* such as *feet* and *me.* With your child, take turns thinking of sentences that tell a story. Use as many long *e* words as you can.

**Day 2** Ask your child to make up sentences using these words: *about, any, ask, kind,* and *over.*

**Day 3** On one side of a sheet of paper, draw a picture of something make-believe. On the other side, draw something from real life. Ask your child to label each drawing *make-believe* or *real.*

**Day 4** Your child is learning to follow oral directions. Give your child step-by-step directions for making something, such as a peanut butter and jelly sandwich. Have your child follow the directions as you say them.

**Day 5** After you have read a story with your child, ask him or her to point out any contractions that are formed by joining a verb and *not (wasn't).* Have your child tell you what two words each contraction represents.

**Read with your child EVERY DAY!**



(fold here)

# Family Times

**Riddle-dee Fiddle-dee-dee** **The Riddles**

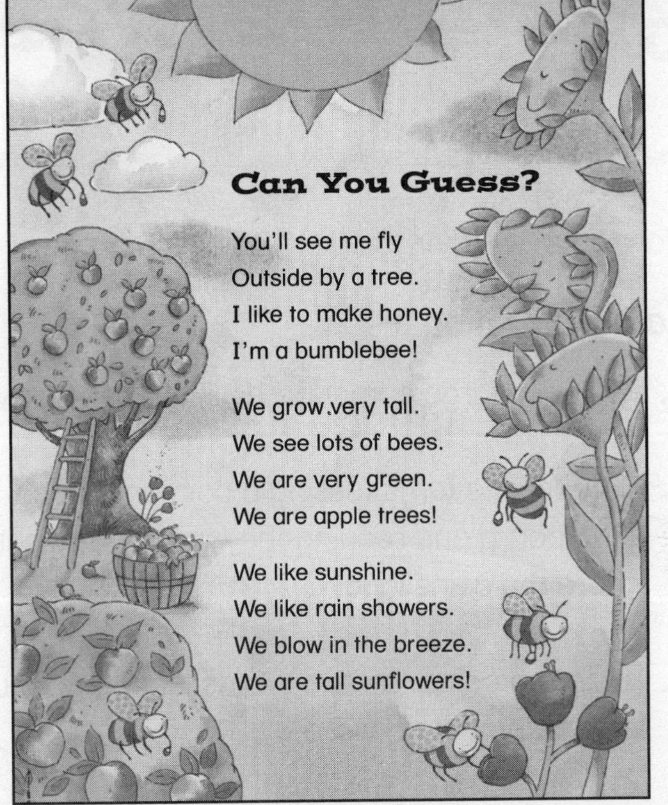

Can You Guess?

You'll see me fly
Outside by a tree.
I like to make honey.
I'm a bumblebee!

We grow very tall.
We see lots of bees.
We are very green.
We are apple trees!

We like sunshine.
We like rain showers.
We blow in the breeze.
We are tall sunflowers!


This rhyme includes words your child is working with in school: words with the long *e* sound spelled *ee* and *e (see, me)* and compound words *(outside, sunshine)*. Read "Can You Guess?" aloud with your child. Put your hands in the air for each long *e* word you say.

Name: ______________________

# Combining Words

**Materials** paper, marker, 2 coins per player

**Game Directions**

1. Make two large gameboards like those shown.
2. Players take turns tossing a coin onto each gameboard and reading the words in the squares where the coins land.
3. To earn a point, the two words landed on must form a compound word.
4. The first player to get 5 points wins!



| snow | air | sun | in |
|---|---|---|---|
| out | some | any | every |

| ball | plane | shine | side |
|---|---|---|---|
| doors | body | thing | one |

Name ______________________



**Help** the bee get home.
**Read** each word.
**Draw** a line that only goes past the **long e** words.
**Write** the **long e** words on the lines.

feet
bed
beet
wet
sheet
we
net
peel
jeep
he
jet
me
Home

1. ______________
2. ______________
3. ______________
4. ______________
5. ______________
6. ______________
7. ______________
8. ______________

**Notes for Home:** Your child practiced reading words with the long *e* sound spelled *ee* and *e*. ***Home Activity:*** Ask your child to use the long *e* words above in sentences, such as *She gave the beet to me.*

Name ______________________________

**Read** each compound word.
**Write** the two words you see in each compound word.

snowball = snow + ball

1. cannot = ______________ + ______________

2. anything = ______________ + ______________

3. airplane = ______________ + ______________

4. inside = ______________ + ______________

5. cowboy = ______________ + ______________

**Notes for Home:** Your child identified two smaller words in each compound word. ***Home Activity:*** Write a list of compound words. Ask your child to identify the two separate words in each compound word.

Name ______________________________

**Pick** a word from the box to finish each sentence.
**Write** it on the line.

1. Mo sees ______________ nine or ten bees.

2. Some bees fly ______________ her head.

3. Mo knows to be ______________ to the bees.

4. They do not hurt her in ______________ way.

5. Mo will ______________ her mom more about bees.

**Notes for Home:** This week your child learned to read the words *about*, *any*, *ask*, *kind*, and *over*. ***Home Activity:*** Write these words on slips of paper. Show each word to your child. Have him or her say the word and use it in a sentence.

Name ______________________________

**Look** at each picture.
**Write R** on the line if it could really happen.
**Write M** on the line if it is make-believe.

1.

______

2.

______

3.

______

4.

______

**Draw** a picture of something that could really happen.

5.

**Notes for Home:** Your child identified sentences as real or make-believe. ***Home Activity:*** Make up a story with your child. Include parts that are both real and make-believe.

Name ________________________________

A verb and the word *not* can be put together.
They make a shorter word called a **contraction**.
The letter *o* is left out of the word *not*.
An ' is used in place of the letter *o*.

were not = **weren't**    does not = **doesn't**

**Read** each sentence.
**Write** the contraction for the underlined words.

1. Those jokes were not good. ________________

2. It is not hard to tell good jokes. ________________

3. The jokes my mom tells are not bad.

4. But my dad does not get them.

5. He was not laughing like the rest of us.

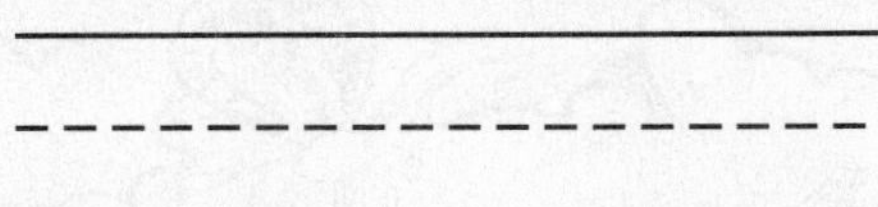

**Notes for Home:** Your child learned to write contractions using *not* with verbs.
***Home Activity:*** Have your child count the number of contractions used during five minutes of family conversation. Make a list to see which contractions use *not* with verbs.

Name ______________________________

**Pick** a word from the box to match each clue.
**Write** the words in the puzzles.

| about | answer | any | ask | kind | over |
|---|---|---|---|---|---|

1. I know a riddle ______ a bird.
2. not under
3. What do you give to a question?

1. 2.

3.

4. 5.

6.

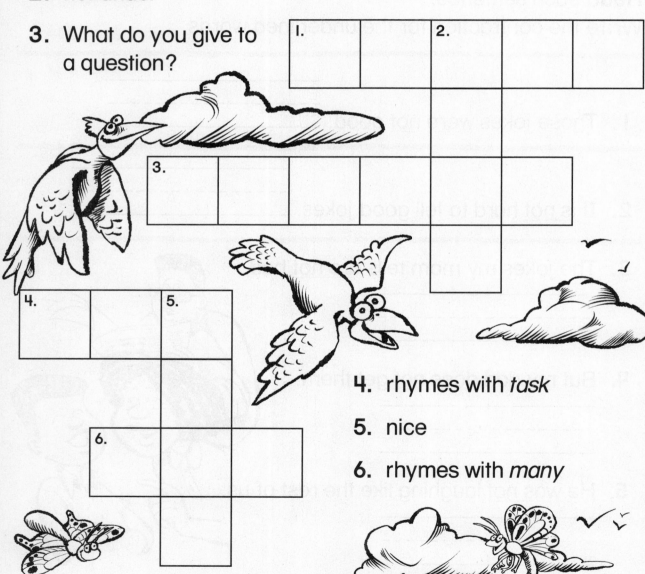

4. rhymes with *task*
5. nice
6. rhymes with *many*

**Notes for Home:** Your child solved puzzles using words that he or she learned this week. ***Home Activity:*** Help your child write a sentence using each word.

Name ______________________

**Say** the word for each picture.
**Write a, e, i, o,** or **u** to finish each word.

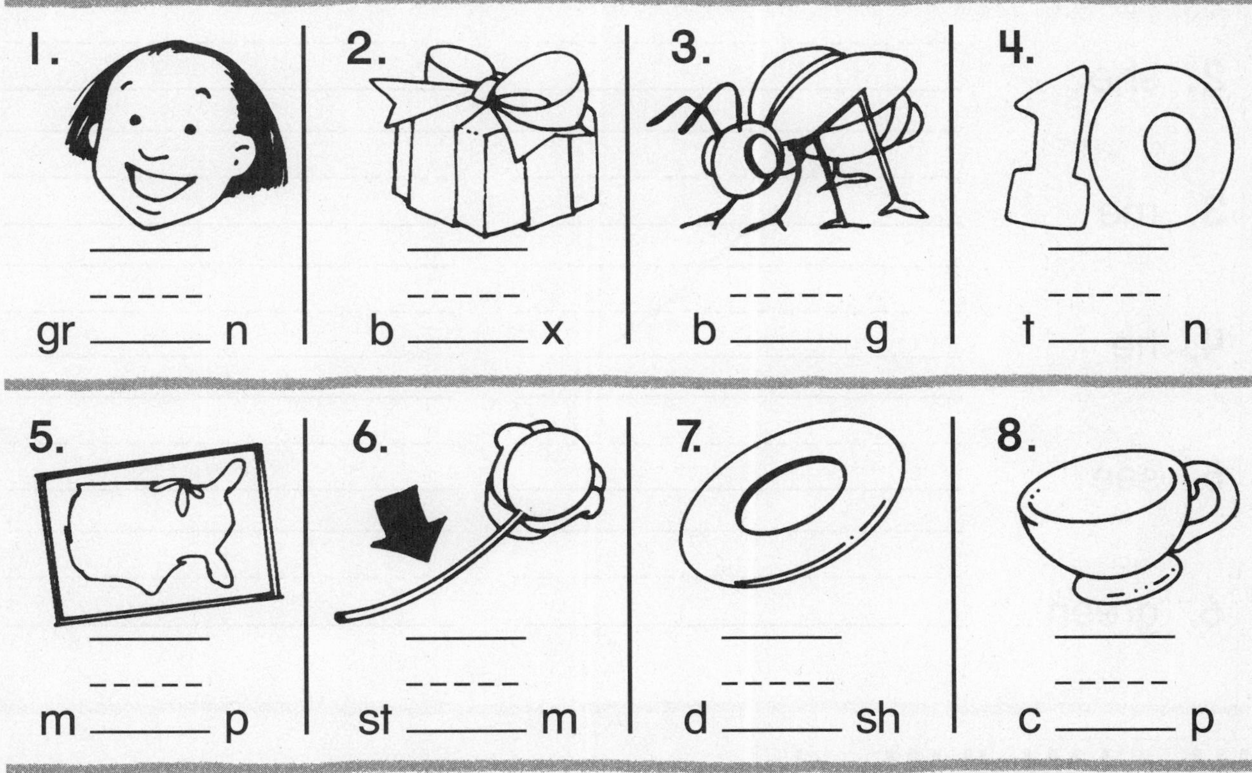


**Find** the word that has the same middle sound as the picture.
**Mark** the ⬭ to show your answer.

9. ⬭ dress
⬭ drum
⬭ drip

10. ⬭ pig
⬭ pen
⬭ pine

**Notes for Home:** Your child reviewed words with the short vowel sounds heard in *pan, bed, ship, pot,* and *cub.* ***Home Activity:*** Pick one of these short vowel words. Ask your child to name as many words as he or she can that have the same vowel sound.

Name ______________________________

**Look** at each word. **Say** it.
**Listen** for the **long e** sound in 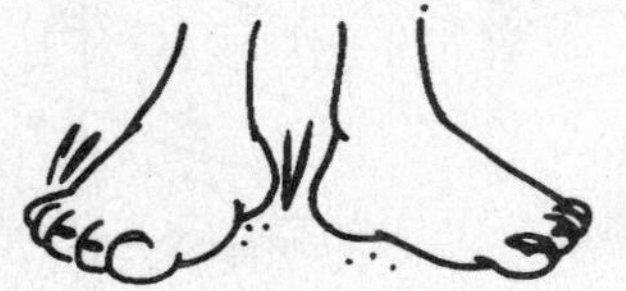.

| | **Write** each word. | **Check** it. |
|---|---|---|
| 1. we | | |
| 2. she | | |
| 3. me | | |
| 4. he | | |
| 5. see | | |
| 6. green | | |

# Word Wall Words

**Write** each word.

| | | |
|---|---|---|
| 7. any | | |
| 8. kind | | |

**Notes for Home:** Your child spelled words with the long *e* sound spelled *e* and *ee (me, see)* and two frequently used words: *any, kind.* ***Home Activity:*** Work together to write and illustrate a story about seeing a strange green animal. Include the spelling words in the story.

Name ______________________________

Put steps in the right order.

| **Wrong Order** | **Right Order** |
|---|---|
| She hits the ball. | He tosses the ball. |
| He tosses the ball. | She hits the ball. |

**Put** these sentences in the right order.
**Write** them on the lines.

Drop the bat at the plate.
Swing the bat.
Pick up the bat.
Hit the ball with the bat.

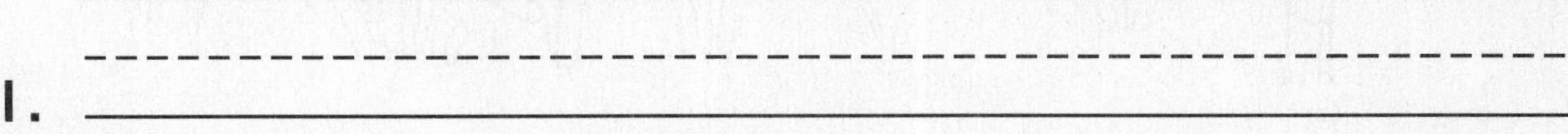

1. ______________________________

2. ______________________________

3. ______________________________

4. ______________________________

**Write** a sentence to tell what comes next.

5. ______________________________

**Notes for Home:** Your child identified and wrote steps in a process in the correct order. ***Home Activity:*** Invite your child to tell you about something that he or she does that has an order—getting ready for school or a game. Ask your child to write down the steps in order.

Name ______________________

**Read** each sentence.
**Pick** a contraction from the box to take the place of the underlined words.
**Write** it on the line.

| aren't | didn't | doesn't | isn't | wasn't |
|---|---|---|---|---|

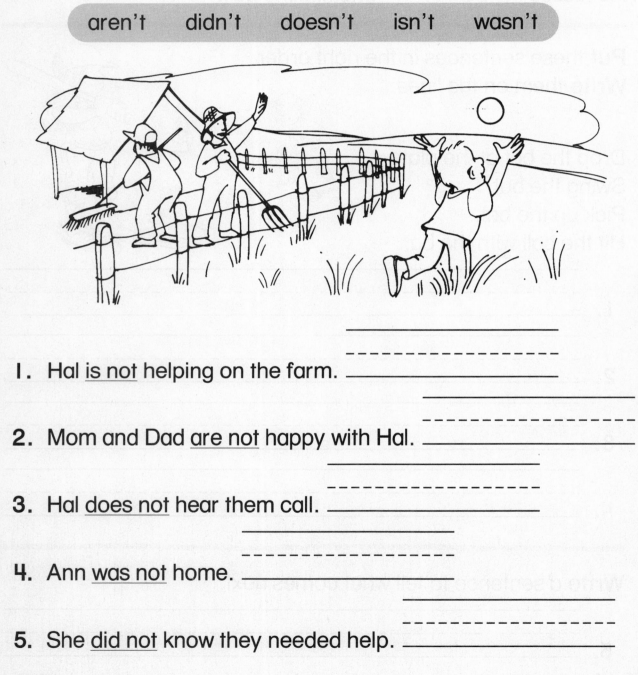

1. Hal is not helping on the farm. ______________
2. Mom and Dad are not happy with Hal. ______________
3. Hal does not hear them call. ______________
4. Ann was not home. ______________
5. She did not know they needed help. ______________

**Notes for Home:** Your child used *not* with verbs to make contractions. ***Home Activity:*** Write the words *is, are, was, were, do,* and *did* on flashcards. Have your child pick a card, add the word *not*, and tell you the contraction.

Name ______________________________

# Part 1: Vocabulary

**Read** each sentence.
**Mark** the ⬭ for the word that fits.

---

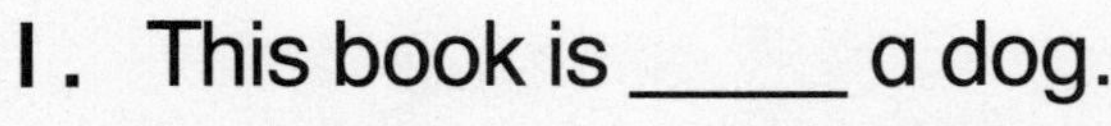

1. This book is _____ a dog.

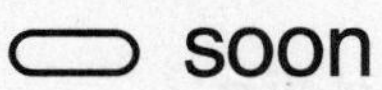

⬭ soon ⬭ as ⬭ about

---

2. What _____ of dog is it?

⬭ kind ⬭ answer ⬭ friend

---

3. Bill does not have _____ friends.

⬭ very ⬭ any ⬭ for

---

4. I will _____ Bill to play with us.

⬭ ask ⬭ catch ⬭ bring

---

5. Her hat is _____ her nose.

⬭ after ⬭ some ⬭ over

Name ______________________________



# Part 2: Comprehension

**Read** each question.
**Mark** the ⬭ for the answer.

6. What is the first thing Boris wants to do?
   - ⬭ go swimming
   - ⬭ take a plane ride
   - ⬭ tell riddles

7. What does Boris do when Morris answers a riddle?
   - ⬭ laughs
   - ⬭ growls and shouts
   - ⬭ claps his hands

8. What happens when Morris tells the riddles?
   - ⬭ He makes up new answers.
   - ⬭ He won't tell the answers.
   - ⬭ He likes the answers Boris gives.

9. Why does Boris go home?
   - ⬭ to eat dinner
   - ⬭ to think up new riddles
   - ⬭ to get away from Morris

10. How can you tell this story is make-believe?
    - ⬭ A bear tells a riddle.
    - ⬭ The riddles are funny.
    - ⬭ Morris the moose has a hoof.

STOP

Name ______________________________

**Circle** the word for each picture.

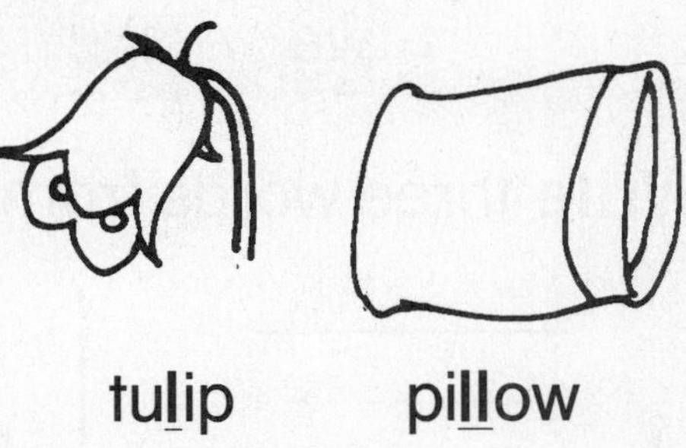

tulip pillow

| 1. | 2. | 3. | 4. |
|---|---|---|---|
| butter but | raft rabbit | carrot carpet | ladder letter |
| 5. | 6. | 7. | 8. |
| papers party | rubber ruler | carpet card | diver dinner |

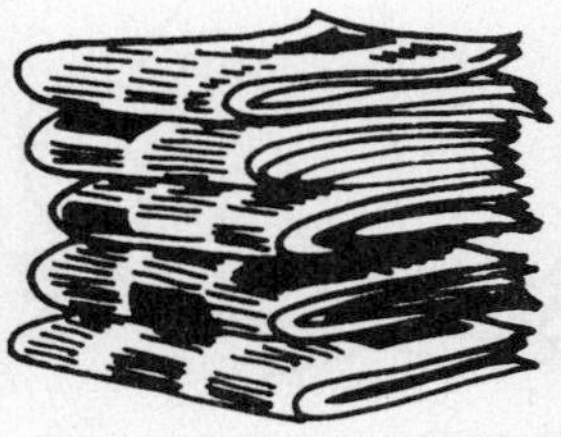

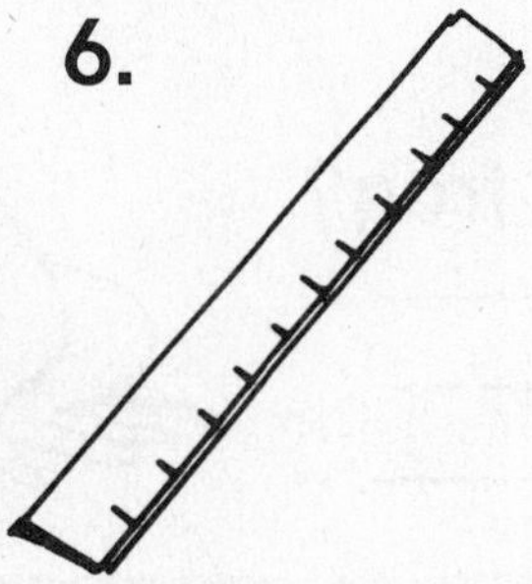

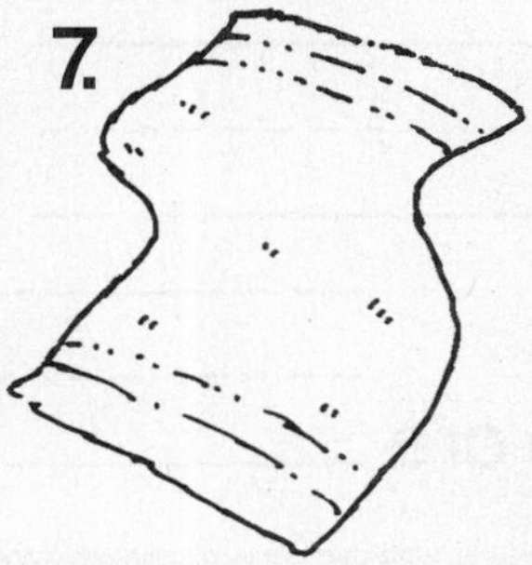

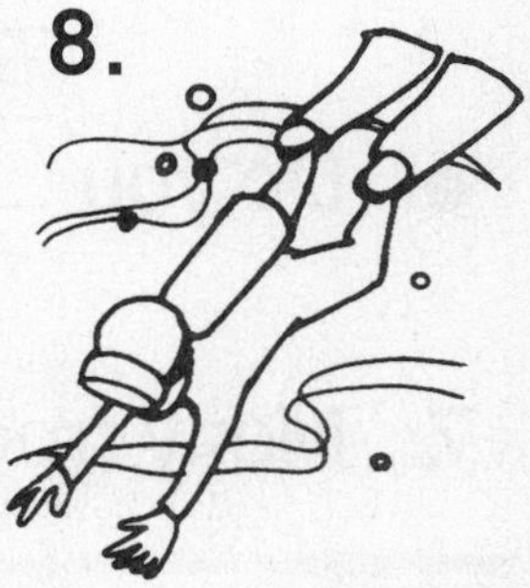

**Find** the word to match each picture.
**Mark** the ⬭ to show your answer.

9. ⬭ trigger
⬭ tiger
⬭ time

10. ⬭ kitten
⬭ kite
⬭ carrot

**Notes for Home:** Your child reviewed words with two syllables that have one or two consonants in the middle. ***Home Activity:*** Have your child choose words from the page and use each word in a sentence. Check that your child is clearly saying the middle consonant sounds.

Name ______________________

we she me he see green

**Write** three words from the box with just two letters.

1. ________ 2. ________ 3. ________

**Write** two words from the box with three letters.

4. ________ 5. ________

**Pick** a word from the box to finish each sentence.
**Write** it on the line.

6. Do you ________ the frog?

7. Many frogs are ________ .

**Pick** a word from the box to finish each sentence.
**Write** it in the puzzle.

any kind

8. Do you want ______ grapes?

9. It is ______ of you to ask me.

8.

9.

**Notes for Home:** Your child spelled words with the long *e* sound spelled *e* and *ee (me, see),* as well as two frequently used words: *any, kind.* ***Home Activity:*** Have your child write the spelling words and sort them into three groups: long *e* spelled *e*, long *e* spelled *ee*, and Word Wall Words.

Name ______________________

RETEACHING

A verb and the word **not** can be put together to make a contraction.

An **'** is used in place of the letter *o*.

is not = **isn't** are not = **aren't**

A **contraction** is a short way to put two words together.

**Read** each sentence.
**Write** the contraction for the underlined words.

1. The sun did not come out. ______________

2. Our pond was not full. ______________

3. It is not warm. ______________

4. The boys are not glad. ______________

5. My dogs are not sleeping. ______________

6. The day is not fun. ______________

**Notes for Home:** Your child wrote contractions using *not* with verbs. ***Home Activity:*** Say a sentence, using the verb *is, are, was, were, do,* or *did. (I was at the store.)* Have your child change the sentence by using a contraction of the verb and the word *not. (I wasn't at the store.)*

Name ______________________

## Word Bank

is not = isn't are not = aren't

was not = wasn't were not = weren't

**Read** each sentence.
**Write** the two words for each contraction.

1. The farm wasn't noisy.

2. Birds aren't flying.

3. The sky isn't dark.

4. The cows aren't mooing.

5. Our chicken isn't clucking.

6. Fields weren't plowed.

7. Aunt Marge wasn't coming.

**Write** a sentence. Use a contraction.

**Notes for Home:** Your child separated contractions of verbs and the word *not*. *(isn't, aren't, wasn't, weren't)* ***Home Activity:*** Sing a familiar song with your child. Change the words by using contractions of verbs and the word *not*.

Name ______________________________

**Correct** each sentence.
**Write** it on the line.
Hint: Verbs that tell what one person, animal, or thing does end in **-s**.

1. Sam want to play tag.

2. Anna and Bill tells him how to play.

3. Anna run to tag Bill.

4. He laugh and run away.

5. They likes to play tag!

**Notes for Home:** Your child corrected verbs in sentences. ***Home Activity:*** Write action words on slips of paper, such as *jump, run,* and *play.* Take turns choosing a verb and saying sentences about one person doing the action and more than one person doing the action.

Name

I read

It was about

Words I Can Now Read and Write

## You *are* your child's first *and* best teacher!

**Here are ways to help your child practice skills while having fun!**

**Day 1** Say a word in which the long *e* sound is spelled *ea* as in *beat.* Encourage your child to say and spell a rhyming word that also uses the letters *ea,* such as *seat*. See how many pairs of words the two of you can name.

**Day 2** Ask your child to make up a TV-commercial jingle, or song, that uses all of the following words: *buy, only, or, right,* and *think.* Help your child write the jingle.

**Day 3** Play a prediction game with your child. Name an action or event, for example: *Two football teams arrive at a stadium.* Ask your child to tell what might happen next.

**Day 4** Your child is learning about adjectives—words that describe people, places, and things. Name adjectives such as *happy, sad, angry,* or *silly,* and ask your child to draw faces to match these words.

**Day 5** Help your child write about a favorite TV show or the characters on the show.

Read with your child EVERY DAY!

(fold here)

# Family Times

**A Real Gift** **Arthur's Reading Race**

### Eat a Treat!

I stepped into my garden.
I saw a fuzzy peach.
I saw some peas and green beans.
They were within my reach.

I pulled off all the green beans.
I grabbed the pods with ease.
I picked the fuzzy big peach.
The peach was sure to please!

I made a little food stand.
I put out food to eat.
I wrote a sign for all to read
That listed every treat.

This rhyme includes words your child is working with at school: words with the long *e* sound spelled *ea (peach)* and words ending in *-ed (pulled)*. Sing the rhyme together and act out the words.

Name: ____________________

# Verb Match Up

**Materials** index cards, marker

**Game Directions**

**1.** Write each pair of verbs (with and without the *-ed* ending) on separate index cards.

**2.** Mix the cards and place each one facedown in rows and columns.

**3.** Players take turns turning over two cards at a time to match present and past tense verbs. If the cards match, the player keeps the cards. If not, the player returns the cards to their original positions.

**4.** When all matches have been made, the player with the most pairs wins!

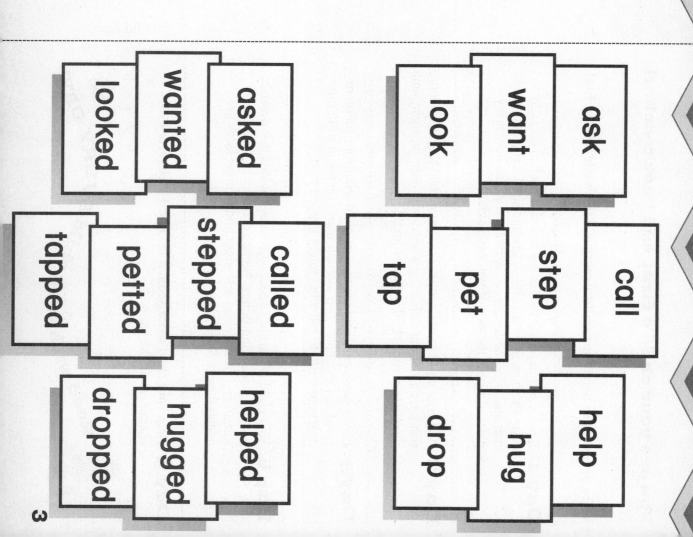

ask
want
look

call
step
pet
tap

help
hug
drop

asked
wanted
looked

called
stepped
petted
tapped

helped
hugged
dropped

Name ______________________________

**Circle** a word to finish each sentence.
**Write** it on the line.

peach 

read red

1. I will ________________ about a cat.

crate cream

2. My cat likes ________________ .

eat ant

3. My cat likes to ________________ .

tack teach

4. I want to ________________ my cat a trick.

flea fun

5. The trick is ________________ !

**Notes for Home:** Your child practiced reading words with the long *e* sound spelled *ea* as in *peach*. ***Home Activity:*** Work with your child to make a list of other words with the long *e* sound spelled *ea*. Ask your child to rhyme the new words with the words in these sentences.

Name ______________________

Jan stepp**ed** on the box.
step + p + ed = stepped

**Add -ed** to each word.
**Write** the new word on the line.

1. clap ____________ 2. jump ____________

3. stop ____________ 4. pet ____________

5. ask ____________ 6. tug ____________

7 call ____________ 8. rub ____________

9. jog ____________ 10. hug ____________

**Notes for Home:** Your child practiced writing words ending in *-ed*, like *stepped*.
***Home Activity:*** Think of three or four verbs (for example: *pat*). Say each word aloud. Ask your child to add *-ed* to each word, and then use each word in a sentence.

Name ______________________________

**Pick** a word from the box to finish each sentence.
**Write** it on the line.

| buy | only | or | right | think |
|---|---|---|---|---|

1. Tom wants to ______________ a hat.

2. He can get ______________ one hat.

3. Will he get this hat ______________ that one?

4. He has to ______________ a bit.

5. This hat fits just ______________ .

**Notes for Home:** This week your child is learning to read the words *buy, only, or, right,* and *think*. ***Home Activity:*** Write each word on a slip of paper. Put all the slips in a bowl or hat. Ask your child to pick a word, say it aloud, and use it in a sentence.

Name ______________________________

**Read** the first sentence. Then **read** the pair of sentences.
**Circle** the sentence that tells what will happen next.
**Draw** a picture in the box that shows what will happen next.

1. Bob wakes up late.

   Bob will get to the bus on time.
   Bob will miss the bus.

2.

3. Mom and Dad pack for a trip.

   Mom and Dad will buy a dog.
   Mom and Dad will drive away.

4.

**Look** at the pictures.
**Draw** what will happen next.

5.

**Notes for Home:** Your child predicted what will happen next in a story and drew a picture to show this prediction. ***Home Activity:*** Read a story to your child. At several points in the story, stop and ask your child to predict what will happen next.

Name ______________________________

An **adjective** can tell about size, shape, color, or how many. **Big** is an adjective.

Pat has a big hat.

**Circle** the adjective in each sentence.

1. Jim has a long bat.

2. Look at the black cat.

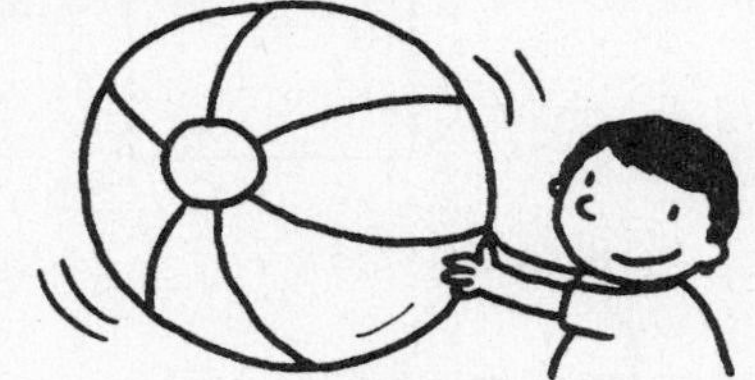

3. That's a huge ball.

4. Socks is a cute dog.

5. Pam has five hats.

**Notes for Home:** Your child identified adjectives that tell more about nouns—people, places, animals, or things. ***Home Activity:*** Look around the room. Point to an object and encourage your child to say an adjective that tells more about that object.

Name ______________________________

**Pick** a word from the box to match each clue.
**Write** the words in the puzzles.

| buy | eight | only | or | right | think |
|---|---|---|---|---|---|

1. Do you like cats _____ dogs?
2. not wrong
3. five, six, seven, _____

4. I have _____ one cat.
5. I _____ dogs are cute.
6. not sell

**Notes for Home:** Your child solved puzzles using words learned this week.
***Home Activity:*** Work with your child to write a story using as many of these words as possible.

Name ______________________________

**Circle** the word for each picture.

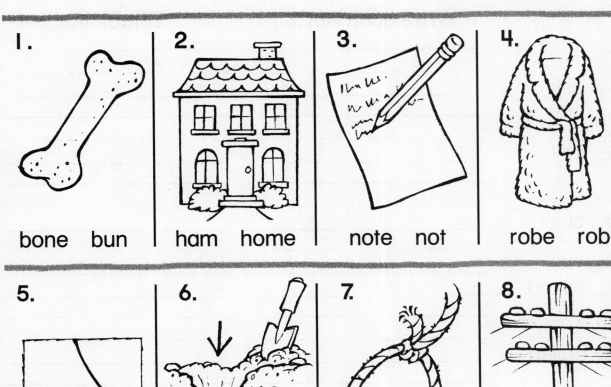

phone 

1. bone bun

2. 
ham home

3. 
note not

4. 
robe rob

5. knot nose

6. 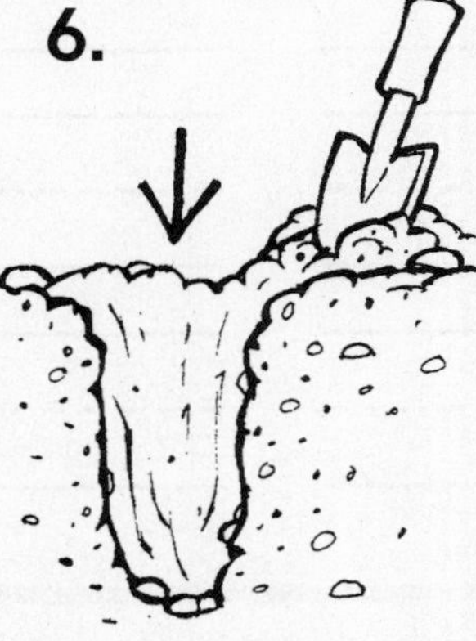
hold hole

7. 
rope ripe

8. 
pole pill

**Find** the word that has the same **long o** sound as .
**Mark** the ⬭ to show your answer.

9. ⬭ nod
⬭ rode
⬭ rod

10. ⬭ poke
⬭ dot
⬭ pot

**Notes for Home:** Your child reviewed words with the long *o* sound that follow the pattern consonant-vowel-consonant-*e (cone)*. ***Home Activity:*** Give a clue about each long *o* word shown above and challenge your child to guess it. For example: *What does a dog like to chew? (bone)*

Name ______________________________

**Look** at each word. **Say** it.
**Listen** for the **-ed** ending.

| | **Write** each word. | **Check** it. |
|---|---|---|
| 1. ask | | |
| 2. call | | |
| 3. clean | | |
| 4. asked | | |
| 5. called | | |
| 6. cleaned | | |

## Word Wall Words

**Write** each word.

| | | |
|---|---|---|
| 7. think | | |
| 8. only | | |

**Notes for Home:** Your child spelled words with and without the ending *-ed,* as well as two frequently used words: *think, only.* ***Home Activity:*** Have your child use each spelling word in a sentence. Check that your child uses *-ed* words to describe actions in the past.

Name ______________________________

**Pick** the adjective from the box that matches each picture.
**Write** it on the line.

| sad | black | three | tall | small |
|---|---|---|---|---|

1. ______________ man

2. ______________ cat

3. ______________ doll

4. ______________ dog

5. ______________ ducks

**Notes for Home:** Your child used adjectives to describe objects. ***Home Activity:*** Say an adjective that describes color, shape, size, kind, or number *(white, round, small, happy,* or *five).* Have your child use that adjective to describe a person or object.

Name ______________________________



# Test-Taking Tips

1. Write your name on the test.
2. Read each question twice.
3. Read all the answer choices for the question.
4. Mark your answer carefully.
5. Check your answer.

Name ______________________________

# Part I: Vocabulary

**Read** each sentence.
**Mark** the ⊂⊃ for the word that fits.

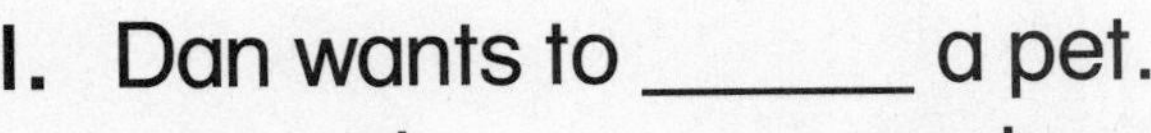
1. Dan wants to ______ a pet.

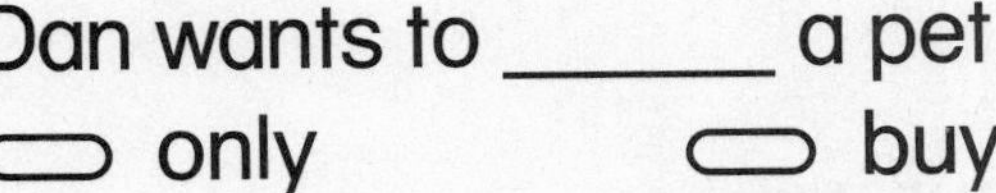
⊂⊃ only ⊂⊃ buy ⊂⊃ sleep

2. There are ______ four pets here.

 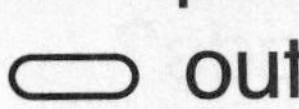 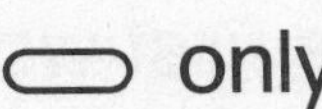
⊂⊃ or ⊂⊃ out ⊂⊃ only

Hmmm...

3. He has to ______.

 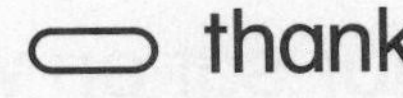
⊂⊃ think ⊂⊃ right ⊂⊃ thank

4. Does he want a dog ______ a cat?

⊂⊃ of ⊂⊃ or ⊂⊃ think

5. This cat is the ______ pet for Dan!

⊂⊃ right ⊂⊃ buy ⊂⊃ more

GO ON

Name ______________________



# Part 2: Comprehension

**Read** each question.

**Mark** the ⬭ for the answer.

6. What does Arthur like to do?
   - ⬭ sing
   - ⬭ read
   - ⬭ sleep

7. If D.W. reads ten words, Arthur will
   - ⬭ give her a book.
   - ⬭ take her home.
   - ⬭ buy her an ice cream.

8. What is the first word D.W. reads?
   - ⬭ zoo
   - ⬭ gas
   - ⬭ walk

9. At the end of the story, D.W. sees that
   - ⬭ Arthur sat on wet paint.
   - ⬭ Arthur can't read his book.
   - ⬭ Arthur lost his ice cream.

10. What do you think D.W. will do on the way home?
    - ⬭ buy an ice cream for Arthur
    - ⬭ read something
    - ⬭ eat a hot dog

STOP

Name ____________________________________

**Circle** the compound word in each sentence.

strawberry 

1. Jim swings by himself.
2. We played in the backyard.
3. Plants live everywhere.
4. We went inside.
5. Baseball is the best game!
6. Cupcakes are fun to bake.
7. I put on my bathrobe.
8. My friend has a ponytail.

**Find** the compound word.
**Mark** the ⊂⊃ to show your answer.

9. ⊂⊃ bathtub
   ⊂⊃ bath
   ⊂⊃ tube

10. ⊂⊃ driver
    ⊂⊃ dinner
    ⊂⊃ driveway

**Notes for Home:** Your child reviewed compound words—words formed by joining two or more other words. ***Home Activity:*** Write words such as *out*, *side*, *in*, *any*, *thing*, *basket*, *ball*, *some*, and *one* on separate index cards. Have your child use the cards to form compound words.

Name ______________________

ask call clean asked called cleaned

**Pick** the pairs of words from the box that are alike.
**Write** the shorter word on the left.
**Write** the word **+ -ed** on the right.

| Word | Word + -ed |
|---|---|
| 1. ______ | 2. ______ |
| 3. ______ | 4. ______ |
| 5. ______ | 6. ______ |

**Write** the word from the box that rhymes with each word below.

7. mean ______ 8. tall ______

**Pick** a word from the box that fits in each puzzle.
**Write** it in the puzzle.

think only

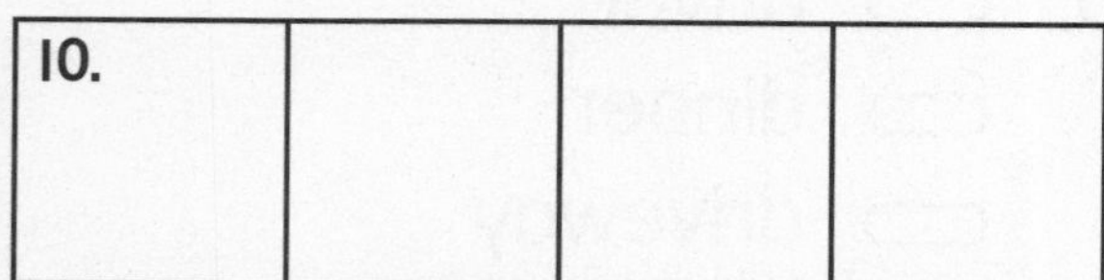

9.

10.

**Notes for Home:** Your child spelled words with and without the ending *-ed,* as well as two frequently used words: *think, only*. ***Home Activity:*** Say each spelling word. Ask your child to write it and use it in a sentence.

Name ______________________________

**hot** fire

An **adjective** tells more about a person, place, or thing.

**Circle** the adjective that tells about each picture.

1. **big** cat **small** cat

2. **sad** girl **happy** girl

3. **slow** rocket **fast** rocket

4. **funny** clown **sleepy** clown

5. **big** animal **tiny** animal

6. **happy** man **wet** man

**Notes for Home:** Your child identified adjectives—words that describe. ***Home Activity:*** Point to objects in the room. Have your child use adjectives to describe the objects.

Name ______________________________

**Read** each sentence.
**Choose** an adjective from the box to complete each sentence.
**Write** the word on the line.

| big | black | long | little |
|---|---|---|---|

1. The boys ride a ____________ bike.

2. They see a ____________ bus.

3. The ____________ dog walks with the girl.

4. The dog wears a ____________ bow.

**Notes for Home:** Your child used adjectives in sentences. ***Home Activity:*** Have your child draw an imaginary creature. Then ask him or her to use adjectives to label the drawing.

## You *are* your child's first *and* best teacher!

**Here are ways to help your child practice skills while having fun!**

**Day 1** Write a simple sentence using two words that can be made into a contraction, such as <u>She is</u> *at home.* Ask your child to rewrite the sentence using a contraction: <u>She's</u> *at home.*

**Day 2** Write simple sentences using these words: *don't, from, hear, live,* and *when.* Help your child read each sentence.

**Day 3** Look for pictures of two similar objects in a catalog. Ask your child to point out things that are different and things that are alike in the two pictures.

**Day 4** Your child is learning about solving problems. Present your child with a problem situation and ask: *What would you do if that happened to you?*

**Day 5** Look at newspapers with your child. Then encourage him or her to make up a news story about a child or animal who gets lost. Work together to write the story.

**Read with your child EVERY DAY!**



(fold here)

# Family Times

**A Big Day for Jay** **Lost!**

### Oh, What a Day!

It's Saturday . . .
We swim all day . . .
We like to play . . .
Down by the bay . . .

It starts to rain . . .
And we can't stay . . .
We waddle home . . .
But lose our way . . .

A kind gray snail . . .
Shows us the way . . .
We'll soon be home . . .
Oh, what a day!

This rhyme includes words your child is working with at school: words with the long *a* sound spelled *ay* and *ai (play, rain)* and contractions *(We'll)*. Read aloud "Oh, What a Day!" together. Think up more words that rhyme with the long *a* words in this rhyme.

Name: ______________________

# Name a Rhyme

**Materials** paper, 1 coin

**Game Directions**

1. Players take turns tossing a coin onto the gameboard and reading the word that the coin lands on.

2. A player earns a point for each rhyming word named that spells the long *a* sound the same way as the word landed on. Make a list of the words used. Do not use a word more than once. Possible rhyming words are given below.

3. The first player to get 15 points wins!

**Rhyming Words:**
snail, pail, mail, trail, fail, jail; hay, play, day, way, bay, stay, away; rain, train, drain, sprain, brain, main

Name ______________________

**Write** the word for each picture.

nail   hay

1. Put the ______________ in the ______________ .

 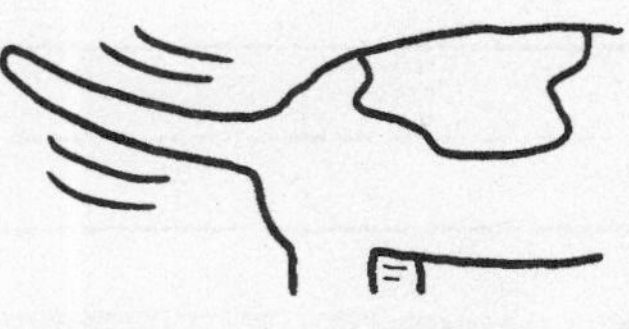

2. Does a ______________ have a ______________ ?

**Circle** the word in each sentence that has the **long a** sound.

3. Ben likes to play.
4. The ball rolls away.
5. Which way did it go?

**Notes for Home:** Your child practiced writing and reading words with the long *a* sound spelled *ai* (as in *nail*) and *ay* (as in *hay*). ***Home Activity:*** Work with your child to write a short story using as many of the long *a* words on the page as possible.

Name ______________________

**Pick** a word from the box that means the same as each pair of words.
**Write** it on the line.

__She is__ tall.
__She's__ tall.

| you'll | it's | that's | aren't |
|---|---|---|---|
| I'll | I'm | hadn't | don't |

1. it + is ______________________

2. that + is ______________________

3. are + not ______________________

4. you + will ______________________

5. I + will ______________________

6. I + am ______________________

7. do + not ______________________

8. had + not ______________________

**Notes for Home:** Your child learned to identify and write contractions, such as *I'll* and *She's*. ***Home Activity:*** Read each contraction on this page aloud. Challenge your child to use each one in a sentence. Work together to write each in a sentence.

Name ______________________

**Pick** a word from the box to finish each sentence.
**Write** it on the line.

| don't | from | hear | live | when |
|---|---|---|---|---|

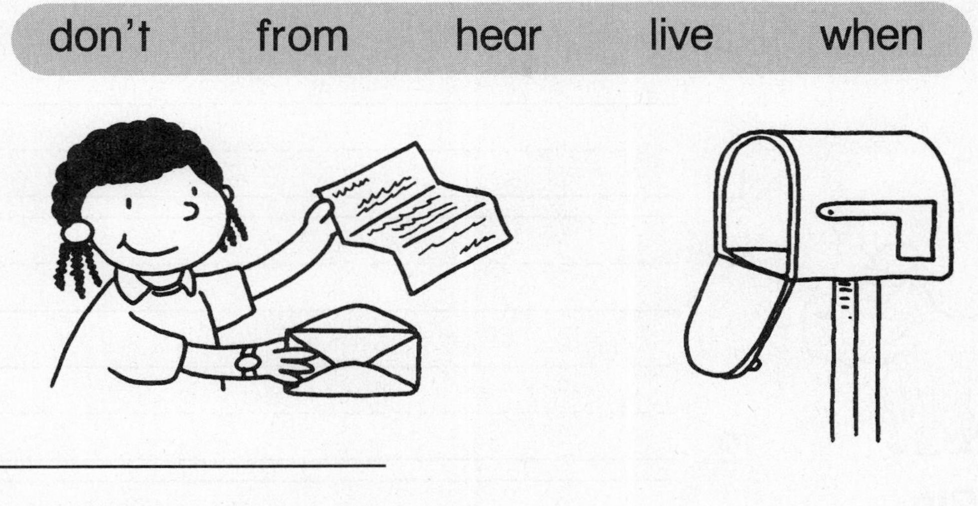

1. I ____________ the mail truck beep.

2. I got a note ____________ my friend.

3. My friend used to ____________ here.

4. Now I ____________ see him anymore.

5. I am glad ____________ he writes to me!

**Notes for Home:** This week your child is learning to read the words *don't, from, hear, live,* and *when*. ***Home Activity:*** Encourage your child to tell you a story using these words. Make a picture book of the completed story. Help your child write a caption for each picture.

Name ______________________________

**Look** at both pictures.
**Write** sentences to tell how the pictures are the same and different.

Pip

Rex

**Same**

1. ______________________________

2. ______________________________

**Different**

3. ______________________________

4. ______________________________

5. ______________________________

**Notes for Home:** Your child used pictures to tell how two things are alike and different. ***Home Activity:*** Point out two objects to your child. Encourage your child to tell you how they are the same and how they are different.

Name ______________________________

An **adjective** can tell what color or what shape something is.

The box is **square**. 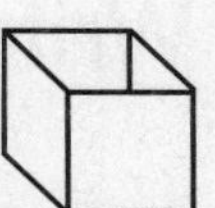

**Circle** the adjective in each sentence.
**Color** the picture to match the adjectives.

1. The ball is blue.

2. The clown has red hair.

3. He has a purple hat.

**Draw** a picture for each group of words.

4. a square clock

5. a wide river

**Notes for Home:** Your child identified adjectives for colors and shapes. ***Home Activity:*** Name a color or shape. Ask your child to point out an object that has that color or shape.

Name ______________________

**Pick** a word from the box to finish each sentence.
**Write** it on the line.

| don't | from | hear | hurt | live | when |
|---|---|---|---|---|---|

1. I ____________ a pup.

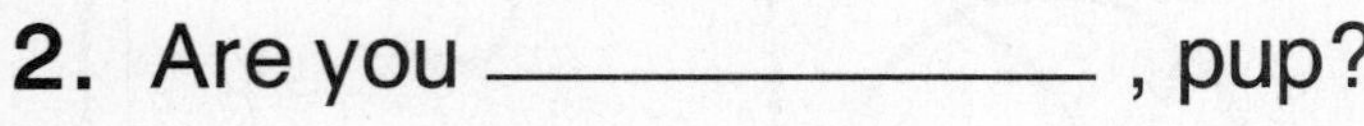

2. Are you ____________ , pup?

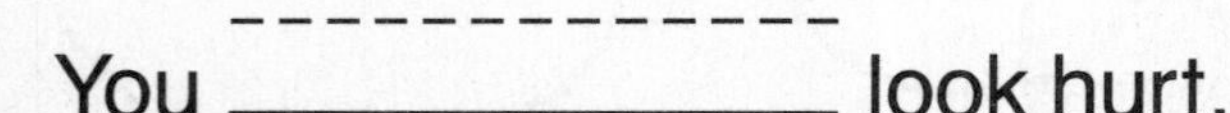

3. You ____________ look hurt.

4. Where do you ____________ ?

5. You are not ____________ this block.

6. You will be glad ____________ I find your home.

**Notes for Home:** Your child used new vocabulary words to complete a story. ***Home Activity:*** Read the vocabulary words aloud. Ask your child to write each word and explain its meaning.

Name ______________________

rake

Pete

bike

home

cube

**Circle** the word for each picture.

1. 
spice space

2. 
kite kit

3. 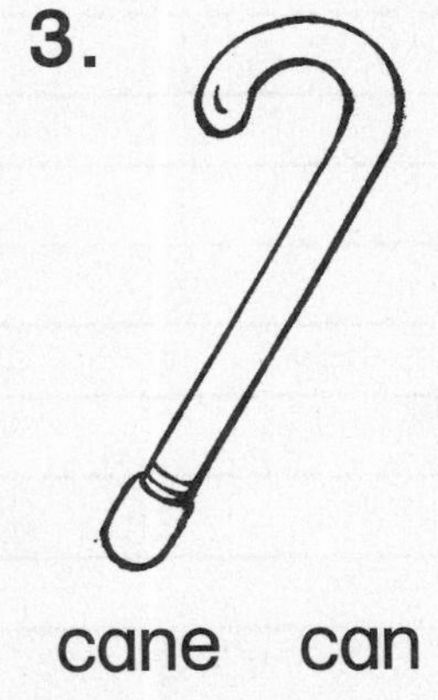
cane can

4. 
rose rise

5. 

get gate

6. 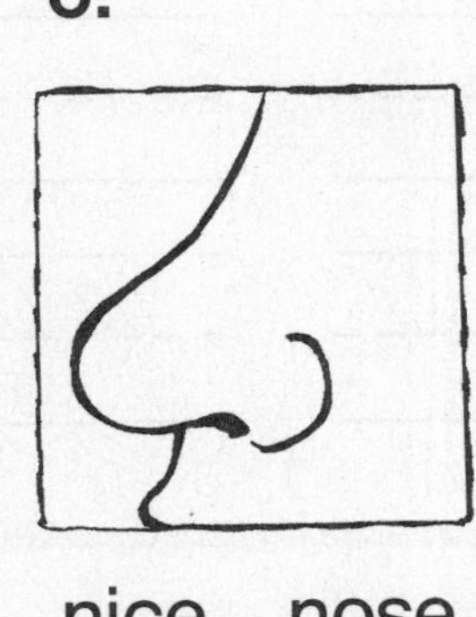
nice nose

7. 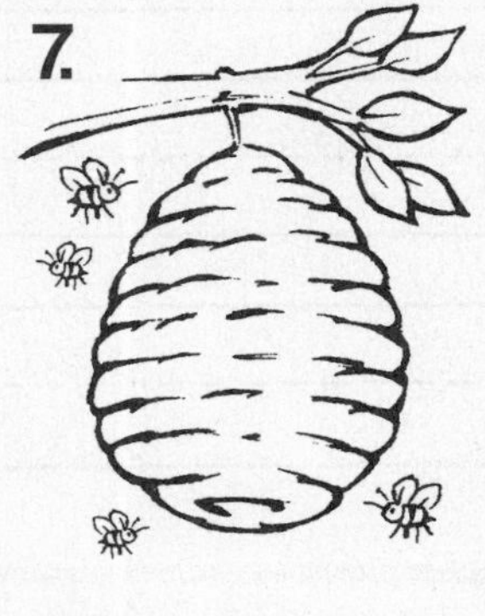
hive have

8. 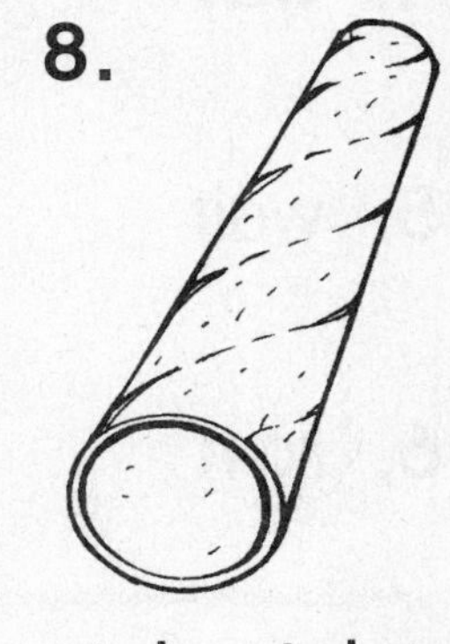
tub tube

**Find** the word that has the **long vowel** sound.
**Mark** the ⬭ to show your answer.

9. ⬭ late
⬭ plan
⬭ man

10. ⬭ bite
⬭ bit
⬭ brick

**Notes for Home:** Your child reviewed long vowel sounds in words ending with *e*. ***Home Activity:*** Write the words *Tim*, *rat*, *kit*, *can*, *rid*, and *rob* on a piece of paper. Ask your child to say each word. Then add *e* to the end of each word. Ask your child to say each new word.

Name ______________________

**Look** at each word. **Say** it.
**Listen** for the **long a** sound in  .

| | **Write** each word. | **Check** it. |
|---|---|---|
| 1. say | | |
| 2. play | | |
| 3. may | | |
| 4. way | | |
| 5. wait | | |
| 6. rain | | |

# Word Wall Words

**Write** each word.

| | | |
|---|---|---|
| 7. when | | |
| 8. from | | |

**Notes for Home:** Your child spelled words in which the long *a* sound is spelled *ai* and *ay* and two frequently used words: *when, from.* ***Home Activity:*** Say each spelling word. Ask your child to spell the word, and then use it in a sentence. Together, draw pictures for the sentences.

Name ______________________

**Follow** the directions.
Then, **pick** the best adjective
from the box to finish each sentence.
**Write** it on the line.

| square | round | green | red | yellow |
|---|---|---|---|---|

1. Color the hat green.

   This is a ______________ hat.

2. Draw a round stone.

   This is a ______________ stone.

3. Color the chick yellow.

   This is a ______________ chick.

4. Draw a square box.

   This is a ______________ box.

5. Color the fish red.

   This is a ______________ fish.

**Notes for Home:** Your child used adjectives to describe color and shape. ***Home Activity:*** Encourage your child to draw pictures showing objects of different colors and shapes. Work with your child to label each picture, for example, *a blue bear.*

Name ______________________________



# Test-Taking Tips

1. Write your name on the test.
2. Read each question twice.
3. Read all the answer choices for the question.
4. Mark your answer carefully.
5. Check your answer.

Name ______________________________



# Part 1: Vocabulary

**Read** each sentence.
**Mark** the ⊂⊃ for the word that fits.

1. I ______ something crying.

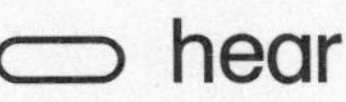 hear 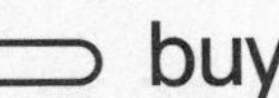 buy ⊂⊃ live

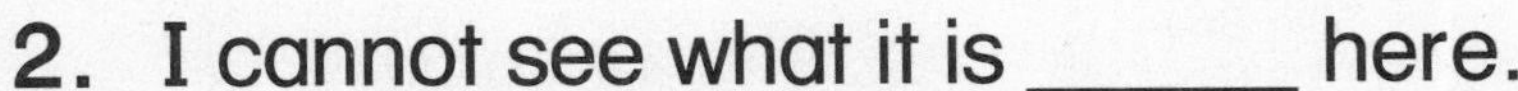

2. I cannot see what it is ______ here.

 don't 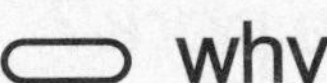 why ⊂⊃ from

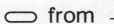

3. ______ I go out, I see it.

⊂⊃ For ⊂⊃ When ⊂⊃ Want

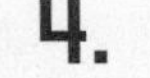

4. "______ be sad," I say.

⊂⊃ Down ⊂⊃ From ⊂⊃ Don't

5. "I think you _____ here."

⊂⊃ live ⊂⊃ bring ⊂⊃ think

Name ______________________________



# Part 2: Comprehension

**Read** each question.
**Mark** the ⬭ for the answer.

6. What does the bear want to find?
   - ⬭ some buildings
   - ⬭ a library
   - ⬭ his home

7. From the top of a building, he sees
   - ⬭ trees and water.
   - ⬭ friends.
   - ⬭ more bears.

8. What does the bear do in the park?
   - ⬭ read
   - ⬭ eat
   - ⬭ sleep

9. They go to the library to
   - ⬭ find out where the bear lives.
   - ⬭ have a good time.
   - ⬭ go for a bus ride.

10. How are the bear and his friend alike?
    - ⬭ They both sleep on the bus.
    - ⬭ They both get lost.
    - ⬭ They both like trucks.

STOP

Name ____________________________

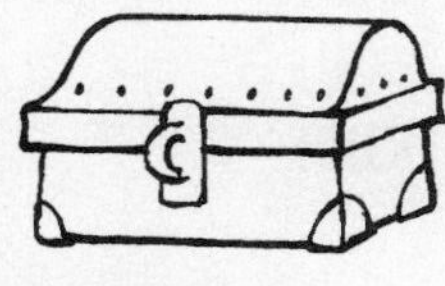

chest

shop

thin

whistle

**Circle** the word for each picture.

1.

sheep deep

2.

gale whale

3.

heat wheat

4.

thorn torn

5.

ship whip

6.

there chair

7.

thick chick

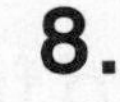

8.

sell shell

**Find** the word that has the same beginning sound as  .
**Mark** the ⬭ to show your answer.

9. ⬭ cheap
⬭ keep
⬭ care

10. ⬭ cold
⬭ calm
⬭ child

**Notes for Home:** Your child reviewed digraphs—two letters that represent one sound—as in *chest*, *shop*, *thin*, and *whistle*. ***Home Activity:*** Together, write words beginning with *ch, sh, th,* and *wh* that have the same beginning sounds as the words shown above.

Name ______________________

say play may way wait rain

**Write** four words from the box that rhyme with **day**.

1. ______________ 2. ______________

3. ______________ 4. ______________

**Write** the word from the box that rhymes with each word below.

5. bait ______________ 6. main ______________

**Pick** a word from the box to finish each sentence.
**Write** it on the line.

7. We like to ______________ games.

8. ______________ for me to hide.

**Write** the word from the box that has the same beginning sound as the picture.

when from

9. ______________

10. ______________

**Notes for Home:** Your child spelled words in which the long *a* sound is spelled *ai* and *ay,* as well as two frequently used words: *when, from.* ***Home Activity:*** Challenge your child to write other words with *ai* and *ay* that have a long *a* sound.

Name ______________________________

The water is **blue**. The **yellow** sun is hot.

Some adjectives describe colors.

The ball is **round**.

Some adjectives describe shapes.

**Draw** a line under each color word.
**Color** each picture.

1. The red truck goes fast.

2. The yellow sun is big.

3. The green leaves cover the tree.

**Circle** each word that describes a shape.

4. The square box was full.

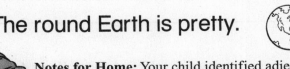

5. The round Earth is pretty.

**Notes for Home:** Your child identified adjectives that describe colors and shapes. ***Home Activity:*** Have your child cut out pictures from magazines or catalogs. Then have him or her label the pictures with words that describe colors and shapes.

Name ________________________

**Write** the color of each picture in the boxes.
**Write** one letter in each box.

| blue | green | orange | red | yellow |
|---|---|---|---|---|

1. 2. 3. 4. 5.

6. Write the new color word you made. ________________

| round | square |
|---|---|

7. **Write** a sentence, using a word that tells about a shape.

________________________________________

________________________________________

**Notes for Home:** Your child wrote adjectives that describe color and shape. ***Home Activity:*** Have your child write color and shape words on cards. Then have him or her place the cards near objects they describe.

## You *are* your child's first *and* best teacher!

**Here are ways to help your child practice skills while having fun!**

**Day 1** Act out words that end with *-ing*, such as *running, jumping, hopping,* and *eating.* See if your child can guess which word you are acting out.

**Day 2** Encourage your child to make up sentences that include the following words children are learning to read this week: *around, her, new, old,* and *show.*

**Day 3** Write the events of a familiar story, but put the events out of order. Ask your child to retell the story with the events in the proper order.

**Day 4** Your child is learning to identify the main idea in a story. Read a story aloud to your child. Then ask your child to write a sentence or two telling what the story was all about.

**Day 5** Go for a walk with your child. Point out objects or people along the way and ask your child to describe them using an adjective for size, such as a *small* dog or a *big* truck.

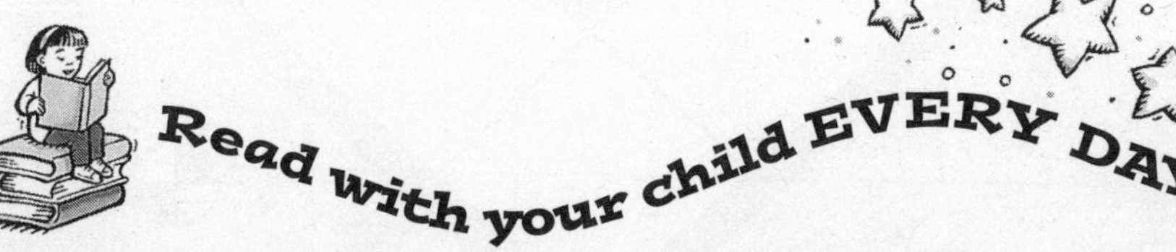
Read with your child EVERY DAY!

(fold here)

# Family Times

**Baby Otter Grows Up** **Foal**

### I See a Foal

I see a foal with a shiny coat.
I see a foal playing with a goat.

I see a foal roaming all around.
I see a foal jumping on the ground.

I see a foal looking at a crow.
I see a foal running in the snow.

This rhyme includes words your child is working with in school: words with the long *o* sound spelled *oa* and *ow (foal, crow)* and words that end in *-ing (playing)*. Sing "I See a Foal" with your child. Have your child act out the parts of the foal.

Name: ______________________

# Spin and Spell

**Materials** paper, scissors, paper clip, pencil, 1 button per player

## Game Directions

1. Make a simple spinner as shown.

2. Players take turns spinning and then naming and spelling a word with the long *o* sound spelled either *oa* as in *boat* or *ow* as in *row*. Words that could be used include: *boat, coat, soap, foal, goat, row, crow, grow, know, blow.*

3. If a player spells the word correctly, he or she moves that number of spaces.

4. The first player to reach the end wins!

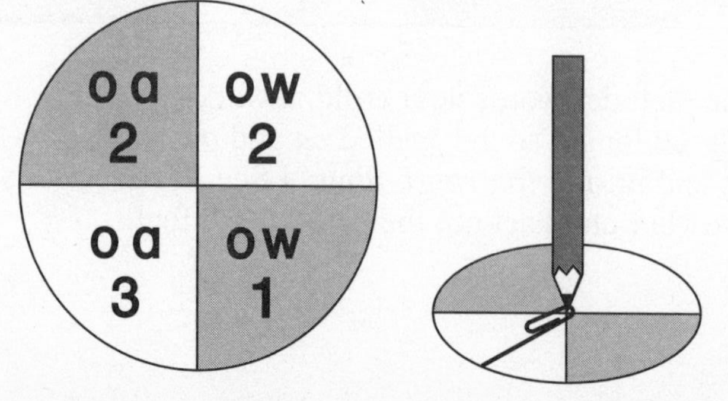

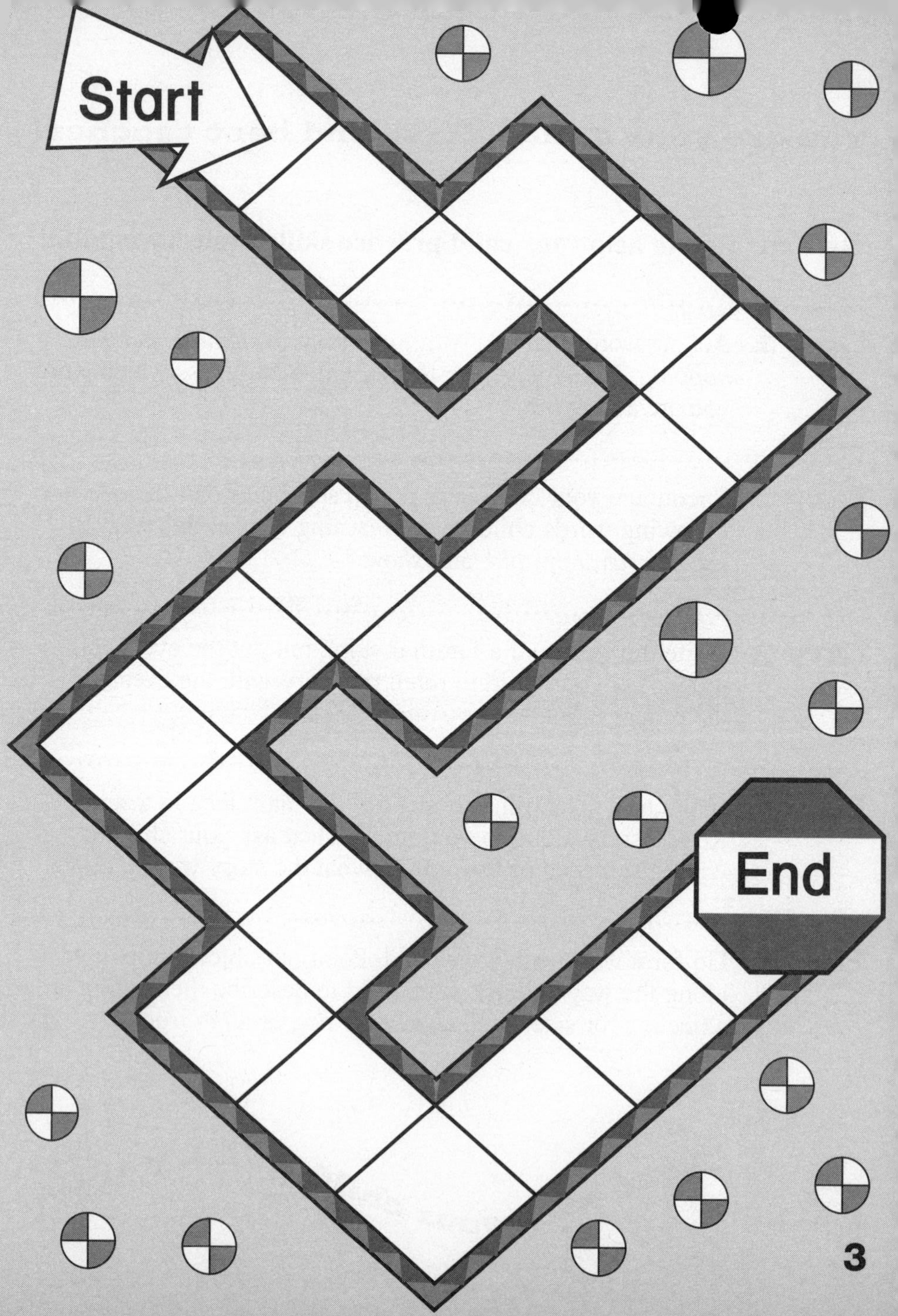

Start

End

Name ______________________

**Circle** the word for each picture.
**Write** it on the line.

coat

window

1. bat / boat / beet ______________

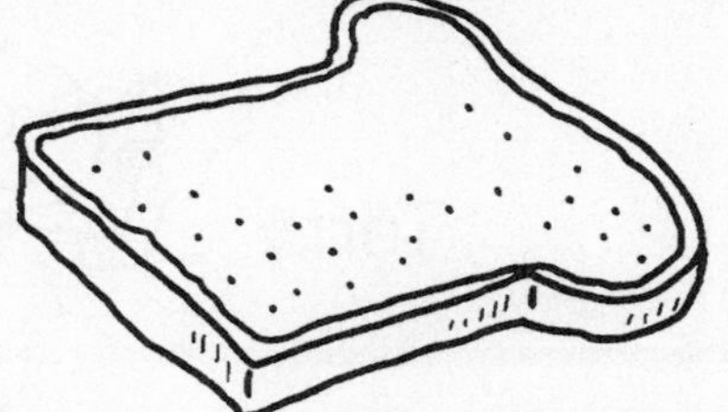

2. toast / tea / top ______________

3. road / run / red ______________

4. crop / cap / crow ______________

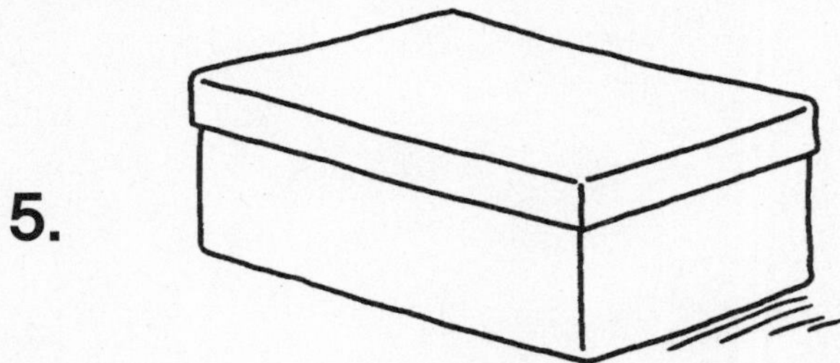

5. bill / bowl / box ______________

**Notes for Home:** Your child practiced reading words with the long *o* sound spelled *oa* (as in *coat*) and *ow* (as in *window*). ***Home Activity:*** Read each long *o* word on this page aloud. Encourage your child to think of a word that rhymes with each word.

Name ______________________________

**Pick** a word from the box that tells what each person is doing.
**Write** it on the line.

| eating | running | sitting |
|---|---|---|

jumping

1. Alex is ____________________.

Alex

2. Terry is ____________________.

Terry

3. Pat is ____________________.

Pat

**Draw** a picture to show each action.

4. reading

5. barking

**Notes for Home:** Your child read words ending in *-ing*, such as *jumping*. ***Home Activity:*** Encourage your child to point out verbs with *-ing* as you read together. Have your child say the verb with and without *-ing*.

Name ______________________________

**Pick** a word from the box to match each clue.
**Write** the words in the puzzles.

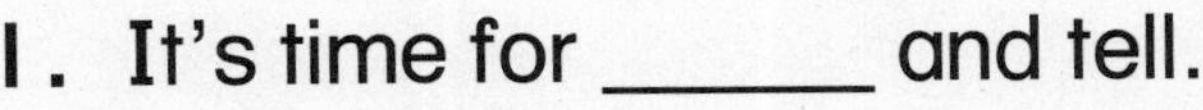

around her new old show

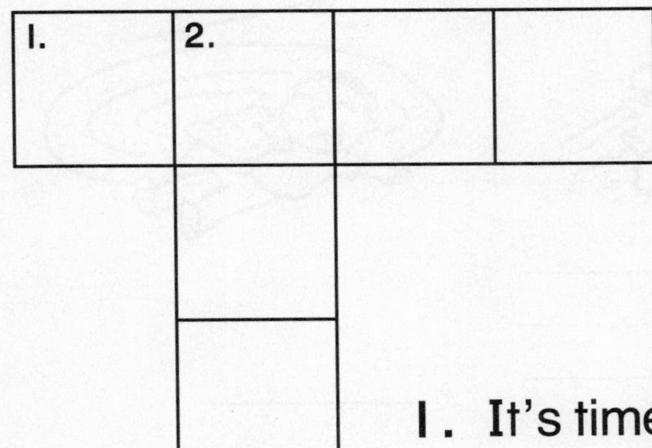

1. It's time for ______ and tell.

2. Kim holds ______ rabbit.

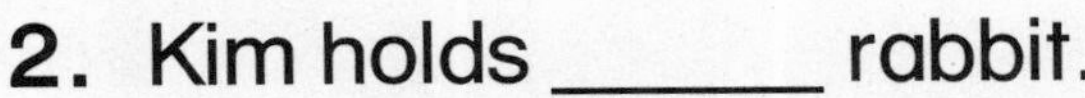

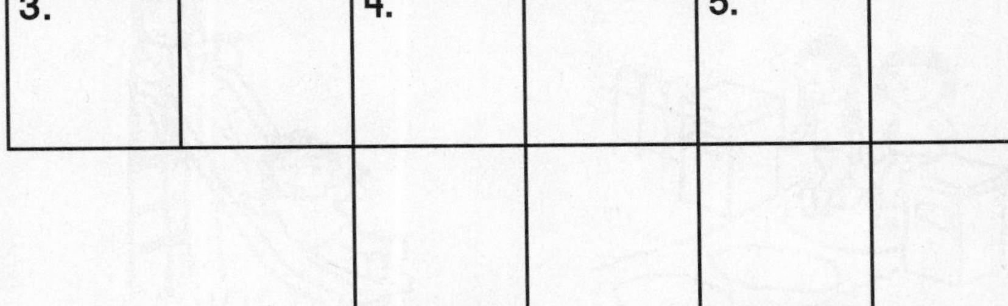

3. The top spins ______ .

4. not new

5. not old

**Notes for Home:** This week your child is learning to read the words *around, her, new, old,* and *show*. ***Home Activity:*** Encourage your child to make up a story or poem using these vocabulary words. Work together to write the story or poem and read it to other family members or friends.

Name ______________________

**Look** at the pictures.
**Write 1, 2, 3** to put the sentences in order.

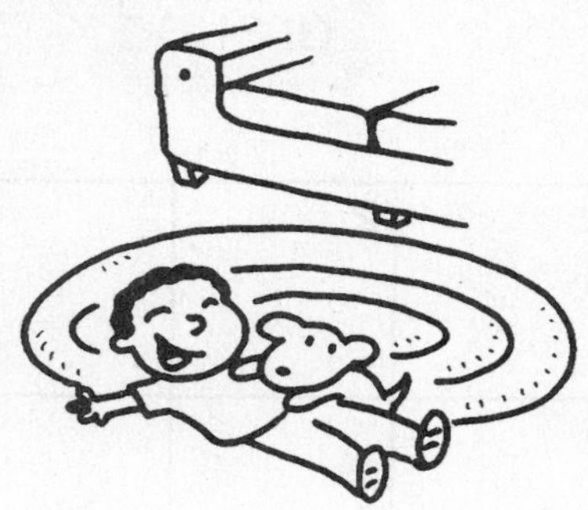

1. Then Dan picked a puppy. ________
2. Dan played with his new puppy at home. ________
3. Dan and his mother went to the pet store. ________

4. Jen and Sam went home. ________
5. First Jen and Sam went to the park. ________
6. Jen and Sam played on the slide. ________

**Notes for Home:** Your child put a sequence of events in order to form a story. ***Home Activity:*** Ask your child to draw a series of pictures showing three events in the order in which they happened.

Name ______________________________

An **adjective** can tell what size something is.

The **small** pup is in a **big** box.

**Pick** a word from the box to finish each sentence.
**Write** it on the line.

big short small long tiny

1. Ben has a ______________ string.

2. Jill has a ______________ string.

3. Tom has a ______________ box.

4. Jill has a ______________ box.

5. The cats are ______________ .

**Notes for Home:** Your child identified adjectives for sizes, such as *big* and *tiny*. ***Home Activity:*** Say each adjective in the box above. Encourage your child to use that adjective to describe something else.

Name ______________________

**Pick** a word from the box to finish each sentence.
**Write** it on the line.

| around | her | new | old | ponies | show |
|---|---|---|---|---|---|

1. Look at the ______________ .

2. One pony has a ______________ baby foal.

3. The foal looks ______________ for its mother.

4. The mother is close to ______________ foal.

5. The foal is new, but the mother is ______________ .

6. I want to ______________ the foal to my dad!

**Notes for Home:** Your child used newly learned words to finish a story. ***Home Activity:*** Spell each of the vocabulary words aloud. Ask your child to name each word.

Name ______________________________

me

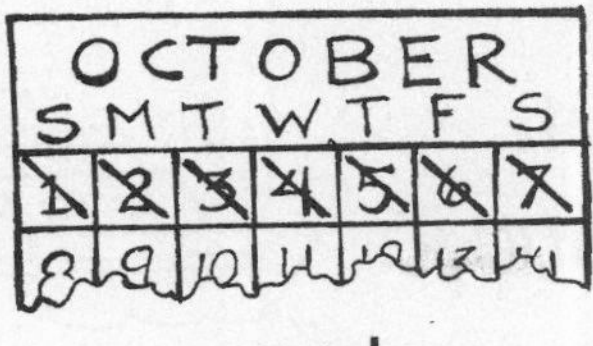

week

bean

**Say** the word for each picture.
**Write e**, **ee**, or **ea** to finish each word.

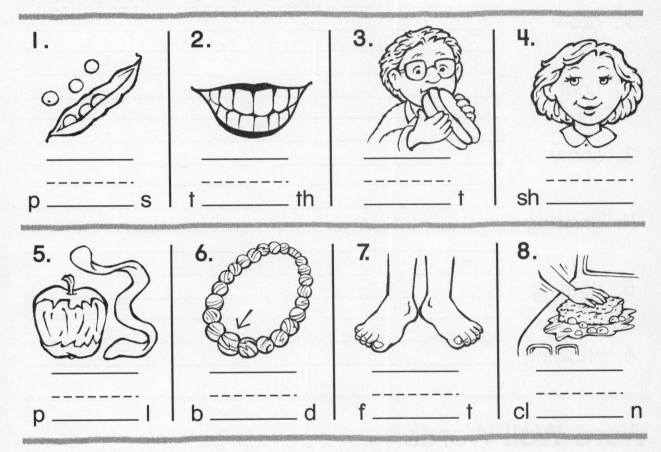

1. p ______ s
2. t ______ th
3. ______ t
4. sh ______
5. p ______ l
6. b ______ d
7. f ______ t
8. cl ______ n

**Find** the word that has the same **long e** sound as **bee**.
**Mark** the ⬭ to show your answer.

9. ⬭ we
⬭ wet
⬭ white

10. ⬭ ten
⬭ tent
⬭ tea

**Notes for Home:** Your child reviewed words in which the long *e* sound is spelled *e, ee,* and *ea*. ***Home Activity:*** Ask your child to think of a rhyming word for each long *e* word on this page. Write the words and look at how the vowel sound is spelled.

Name ______________________

**Look** at each word. **Say** it.
**Listen** for the **long o** sound in .

| | **Write** each word. | **Check** it. |
|---|---|---|
| 1. grow | | |
| 2. float | | |
| 3. show | | |
| 4. growing | | |
| 5. floating | | |
| 6. showing | | |

## Word Wall Words

**Write** each word.

| | | |
|---|---|---|
| 7. around | | |
| 8. old | | |

**Notes for Home:** Your child spelled words with and without the ending *-ing* and two frequently used words: *around, old.* ***Home Activity:*** Challenge your child to add *-ing* to other action words such as *jump, look, see,* and *help.*

Name ______________________________

**Follow** the directions.
Then, **pick** the best adjective from the box to finish each sentence.
**Write** it on the line. Use each word only once.

| thin | long | big | fat | little |
|---|---|---|---|---|

1. Color the big dog.

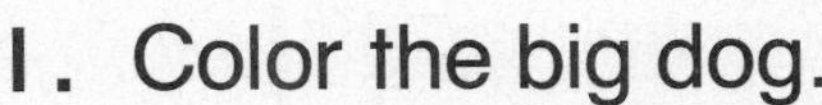

Rover is a ____________ dog.

2. Color the long rope.

The ____________ rope has a knot.

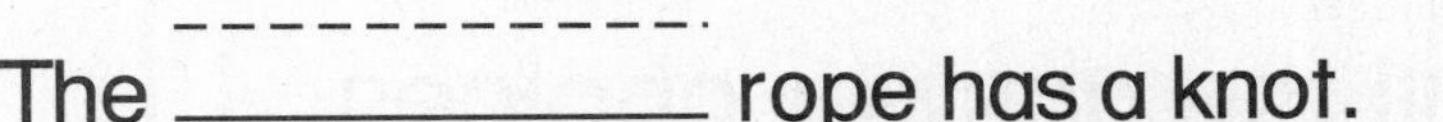

3. Color in the paws on the little pup.

Boots is a ____________ pup.

4. Draw a hat on a fat cat.

This ____________ cat has a hat.

5. Circle the thin line.

This line is ____________ .

**Notes for Home:** Your child used adjectives to describe size. ***Home Activity:*** Go for a walk with your child. Encourage him or her to describe the objects and people you see using size adjectives, such as *big, small, tall,* and *short, huge, tiny.*

Name ______________________________



# Test-Taking Tips

1. Write your name on the test.
2. Read each question twice.
3. Read all the answer choices for the question.
4. Mark your answer carefully.
5. Check your answer.

Name ______________________________

## Part 1: Vocabulary

**Read** each sentence.
**Mark** the ⬭ for the word that fits.

1. Jen has a ______ friend.
   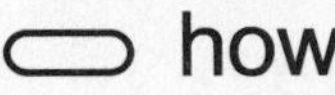 ⬭ how　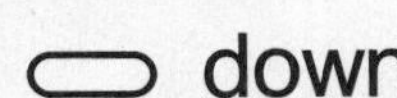 ⬭ down　⬭ new

2. Jen and Anna run ______ the tree.
    ⬭ around　 ⬭ old　⬭ with

3. Anna wants to ______ Jen something.
    ⬭ catch　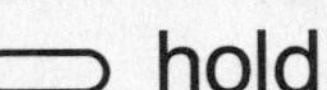 ⬭ hold　 ⬭ show

4. Look who is in ______ house!
   ⬭ any　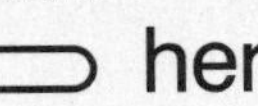 ⬭ her　 ⬭ new

5. He is only five days ______ .
   ⬭ old　⬭ or　⬭ around

Name ______________________________



# Part 2: Comprehension

**Read** each question.
**Mark** the ⬭ for the answer.

6. What does a foal eat when it is new?
   - ⬭ grass
   - ⬭ milk
   - ⬭ apples

7. What does the foal get when it is two weeks old?
   - ⬭ a new home
   - ⬭ a friend
   - ⬭ two new teeth

8. When the foal wants its mother, it
   - ⬭ runs around the field.
   - ⬭ neighs loudly.
   - ⬭ eats red apples.

9. The foal is nearly full-grown at
   - ⬭ one week.
   - ⬭ five weeks.
   - ⬭ five months.

10. You can tell that new foals
    - ⬭ are not very happy.
    - ⬭ eat what you eat.
    - ⬭ grow fast.

STOP

Name ______________________________

**Pick** a letter or letters to finish each word.
**Write** the letters on the lines.

kitten zebra

| bb | d | g | m | pp | rr | tt | z |
|---|---|---|---|---|---|---|---|

1. o ______ er

2. ti ______ er

3. spi ______ er

4. ra ______ it

5. pu ______ y

6. ca ______ el

7. pa ______ ot

8. li ______ ard

**Find** the word that has the same middle consonant sound as the picture.
**Mark** the ⬭ to show your answer.

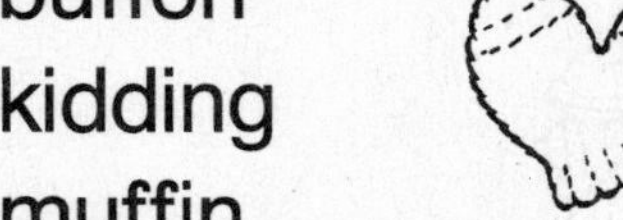

9. ⬭ button
⬭ kidding
⬭ muffin

10. ⬭ rice
⬭ never
⬭ rider

**Notes for Home:** Your child completed words with two syllables that have single or double consonants in the middle, such as *kitten* and *zebra*. ***Home Activity:*** Help your child name things around your home that have consonants in the middle *(sofa, radio, letters, pillows, papers)*.

Name ______________________

grow float show growing floating showing

**Pick** the pairs of words from the box that are alike.
**Write** the shorter word on the left.
**Write** the word + **-ing** on the right.

| Word | Word + -ing |
| --- | --- |
| 1. ______________ | 2. ______________ |
| 3. ______________ | 4. ______________ |
| 5. ______________ | 6. ______________ |

**Pick** a word from the box to finish each sentence.
**Write** the word in the puzzle.

around old

7. Rex is an ______ dog.
8. He likes to walk ______ the block.

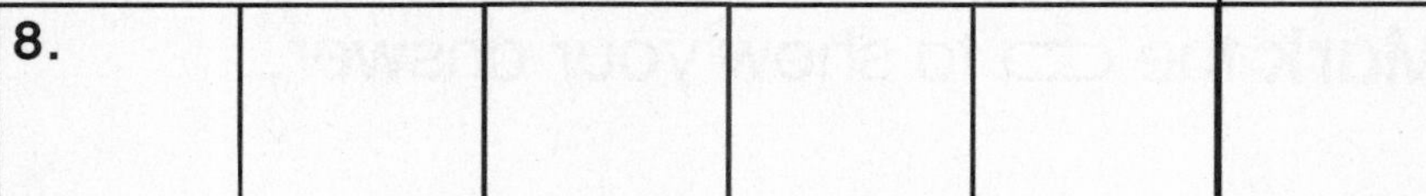

**Notes for Home:** Your child spelled words with and without the ending *-ing* and two frequently used words: *around, old.* ***Home Activity:*** Ask your child to use each spelling word in a sentence. Help your child write the sentences.

Name ________________________________



RETEACHING

big small

Some **adjectives** describe size.
The words **big, small, long, short,** and **tiny** describe size.

**Write** an adjective for each picture.

1. 

______________________

2. 

______________________

3. 

______________________

4. 

______________________

**Notes for Home:** Your child wrote adjectives that describe size. ***Home Activity:*** Have two friends or family members stand next to each other. Then have your child tell about them, using adjectives that describe size.

Name ________________

| small | big | tiny | short | tall |
|---|---|---|---|---|

**Look** at the pictures. Write an adjective for each sentence.

1. The dog has a ________ tail.

2. The ________ cat looks at the dog.

3. The ________ dog looks at the cat.

4. A boy paints a ________ fence.

**Notes for Home:** Your child wrote adjectives that describe size. ***Home Activity:*** Have your child look in a story for adjectives that describe size. Then have him or her make up sentences, using the adjectives from the story.

## You *are* your child's first *and* best teacher!

**Here are ways to help your child practice skills while having fun!**

**Day 1** Your child is learning to use possessives—words that show ownership. Encourage your child to make up a funny story using as many possessives as possible, such as *Mom's* and *Dad's.*

**Day 2** Your child is learning to read these words: *been, first, found, start,* and *together*. Ask your child to cut letters out of magazines or newspapers to spell these words.

**Day 3** Help your child draw a set of two pictures that shows what happens (effect) and why it happens (cause), such as a flat bike tire (effect) and a nail in the road (cause).

**Day 4** Create a simple graphic organizer with your child. Write a noun such as *dog* inside a circle, and ask your child to write words that might describe that noun around the outside of the center circle.

**Day 5** Name an adjective that tells what kind something is, such as *'ot, wet,* or *sad.* Ask your child to say the adiective that is he opposite of the one you named.

**Read with your child EVERY DAY!**



(fold here)

# Family Times

**What a Sight** | **Lost in the Museum**

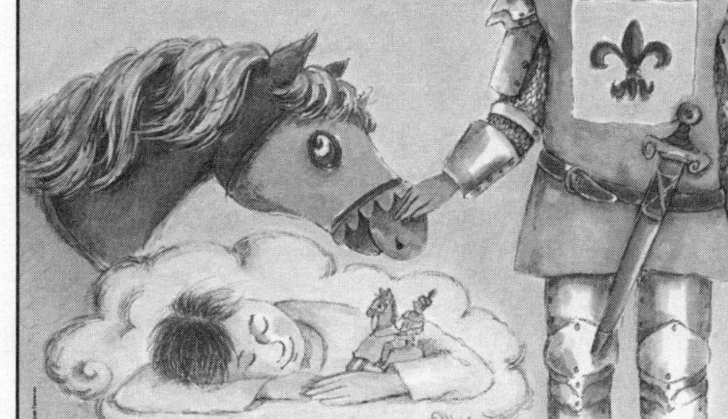

### Dwight the Knight

There was a boy named Dwight.
Dwight's school was a delight.
Dwight's class had gone to see some sights
Like kings and queens and knights.

When Dwight went home that night,
He dreamed he was a knight.
Dwight's horse was big.
Dwight's sword was light.
Dwight's armor shined so bright.

This rhyme includes words your child is working with in school: words with long *i* spelled *igh (night)* and words that are possessives *(Dwight's)*. Sing "Dwight the Knight" with your child. Then underline the long *i* words and circle the possessives.

Name: ______________________

# Phonics Dominoes

**Materials** index cards, marker, ruler

**Game Directions**

1. Use the long *i* words below to make dominoes like those shown on page 3. Write pairs of words on index cards. Words can be used more than once, but not on the same domino.

2. Shuffle the dominoes, place them facedown, and have each player select six.

3. Players take turns lining up the dominoes to match words with *igh* or words with *ie*. See the example on page 3. If a play is not possible, a player must draw a domino from the pile.

4. The first player to use all his or her dominoes wins!

**Long *i* Words**

| | | | |
|---|---|---|---|
| high | night | flight | pie |
| bright | right | fight | lie |
| tight | might | sight | die |
| sigh | light | fright | tie |



| flight | fright |
|---|---|

| bright | right |
|---|---|

| night | lie |
|---|---|

| tie | might |
|---|---|

| sigh | pie |
|---|---|

Name ______________________________

**Pick** a word from the box to finish each sentence.
**Write** it on the line.

| fright | light | night | pie | right |
|---|---|---|---|---|

I eat p**ie** at n**igh**t.

1. I had a dream last ______________.

2. There was something bad in my ______________.

3. It gave me such a ______________!

4. I woke up and put on the ______________.

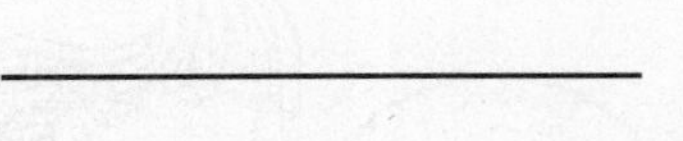

5. Then I was all ______________.

**Notes for Home:** Your child practiced reading words with the long *i* sound spelled *ie (pie)* and *igh (night)*. ***Home Activity:*** Read the long *i* words on this page aloud. Ask your child to think of a word that rhymes with each word.

Name ______________________________

**Add 's** to the end of each word.
**Write** the new word on the line.

**Meg's** hat

1. Jim ______ bat
2. baby ______ laugh
3. Max ______ book
4. Kate ______ kite
5. Mom ______ cup
6. boy ______ games
7. Ben ______ cat
8. Jill ______ horn

**Pick** a word from the box to match each picture.
**Write** it on the line.

Jen's Matt's

9. ______________ hat

10. ______________ ball

**Notes for Home:** Your child wrote words with *'s* to show ownership. ***Home Activity:*** Point out objects in your home or outside that are owned by one person. Ask your child to use a possessive to tell you who owns each object *(Mike's bike)*.

Name ________________________________

**Pick** a word from the box to finish each sentence.
**Write** it on the line. Use each word only once.

| been | first | found | start | together |
|---|---|---|---|---|

1. We went to the store ____________________.

2. ____________________ we went to buy fish.

3. My mother got lost.

   I had to ____________________ yelling.

4. Then I saw her.

   She had ____________________ looking for me.

5. I was glad I ____________________ her!

**Notes for Home:** This week your child is learning the words *been, first, found, start,* and *together.* ***Home Activity:*** Use each of these words in a simple sentence. Help your child read each sentence aloud.

Name ______________________________

**Draw** a line to match what happens with why it happens.

| | What Happens | Why It Happens |
|---|---|---|
| 1. |  |  |
| 2. |  |  |
| 3. |  |  |
| 4. |  |  |

**Notes for Home:** Your child connected pictures to show what happens (effect) and why it happens (cause). ***Home Activity:*** Describe an event to your child (For example: *A cat jumps onto a shelf full of glasses.*). Encourage your child to tell you what might happen next.

Name ______________________________

Some **adjectives** tell what kind.
**Wet** tells what kind of day it is.

It is a **wet** day.

**Circle** an adjective in ( ) to finish each sentence.

1. This is a (funny / yummy) cake.

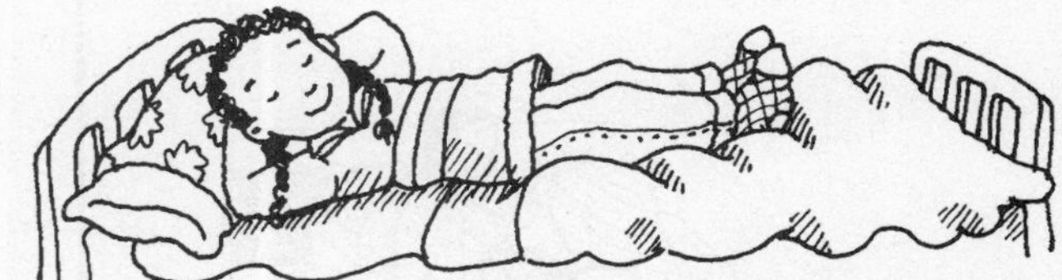

2. What a (hard / soft) bed!

3. The dog is (wet / dry) .

4. He has a (neat / messy) place.

5. I read a (sad / funny) book.

**Notes for Home:** Your child identified adjectives that tell what kind, such as *wet* or *soft*. ***Home Activity:*** Point out objects to your child. Encourage your child to name an adjective telling what kind of object each one is.

Name ______________________________

**Pick** a word from the box that is the opposite of each word below.
**Write** it on the line.

| been | first | found | start | together |
|---|---|---|---|---|

1. stop

______________________

2. last

______________________

3. lost

______________________

4. apart

______________________

**Write** a sentence with the word *been*.

5. ______________________________________

*Notes for Home:* Your child identified opposites and wrote a sentence using words learned this week. ***Home Activity:*** Encourage your child to make up a song or poem using as many of these words as possible.

Name ________________________________

**Look** at the map.
**Write** the answer to each question.

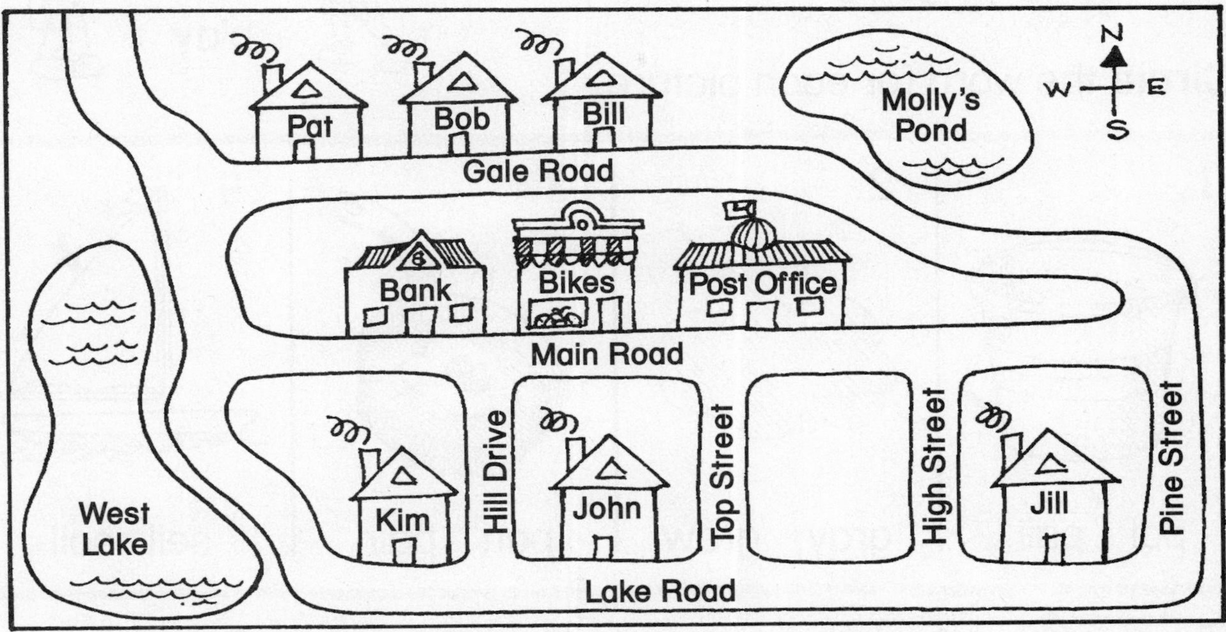


1. What road does Bob live on? ________________

2. What road is the bike shop on? ________________

3. Who lives closer to West Lake, Kim or Jill? ________________

4. What road would Jill take to get to Kim's home quickly?

________________________________________________

**Notes for Home:** Your child read a map and answered questions about it. ***Home Activity:*** Look at a map of your town with your child. Go over the different symbols and explain what they mean. Then point out two places and ask him or her to show you how to get from one place to the other.

Name ______________________

tail 

 play

**Circle** the word for each picture.

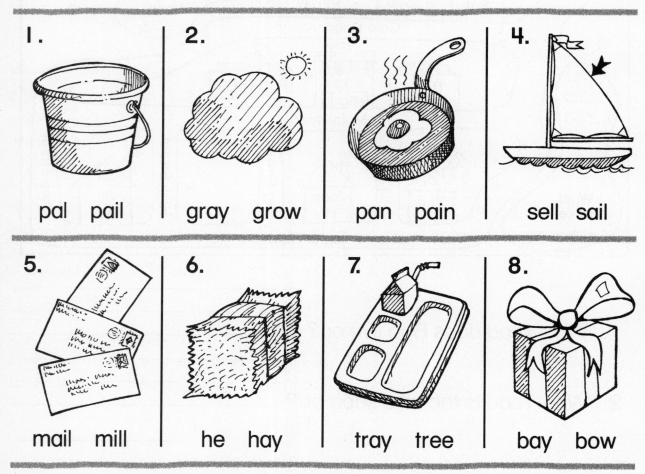

| 1. | 2. | 3. | 4. |
|---|---|---|---|
| pal pail | gray grow | pan pain | sell sail |
| **5.** | **6.** | **7.** | **8.** |
| mail mill | he hay | tray tree | bay bow |

**Find** the word that has the same **long a** sound as .
**Mark** the ⬭ to show your answer.

9. ⬭ rap
⬭ clap
⬭ clay

10. ⬭ nap
⬭ neat
⬭ nail

**Notes for Home:** Your child reviewed words in which the long *a* sound is spelled *ai* and *ay*.
***Home Activity:*** Ask your child to think of a rhyming word for each long *a* word on this page.

Name ______________________________

**Look** at each word. **Say** it.
**Listen** for the **long i** sound in  .

| | **Write** each word. | **Check** it. |
|---|---|---|
| 1. lie | | |
| 2. pie | | |
| 3. tie | | |
| 4. night | | |
| 5. light | | |
| 6. right | | |

## Word Wall Words

**Write** each word.

| | | |
|---|---|---|
| 7. been | | |
| 8. found | | |

**Notes for Home:** Your child spelled words with the long *i* sound spelled *ie* and *igh* and two frequently used words: *been, found.* ***Home Activity:*** Work with your child to write a story that includes the spelling words and is about getting lost in a bakery.

Name ______________________________

**Pick** the best adjective from the box to finish each sentence. **Write** it on the line.

| soft | clean | wet | old | full |
|---|---|---|---|---|

1. This is a ______________ box.

2. This is an ______________ home.

3. This kitten is ______________ .

4. The ______________ dog shakes.

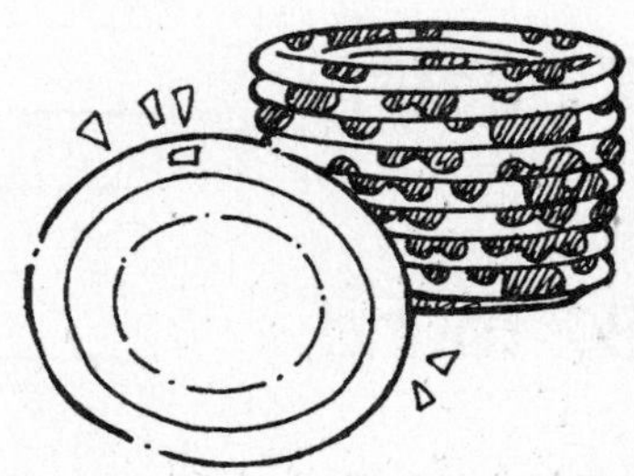

5. I need a ______________ dish to use.

**Notes for Home:** Your child used adjectives that tell what kind of object something is, such as *full box* or *wet dog*. ***Home Activity:*** Play *I Spy* with your child. Encourage your child to describe an object using adjectives for kind, and see if you can guess what object he or she is talking about.

Name ______________________________

# Part 1: Vocabulary

**Read** each sentence.
**Mark** the ⬭ for the word that fits.

1. Have you ______ to the sea?

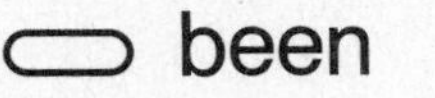
⬭ been

⬭ found
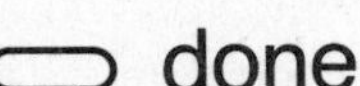
⬭ done

2. Dean and Pam run ______ .

⬭ lost
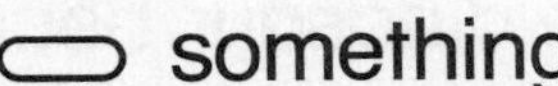
⬭ something

⬭ together

3. Pam was the ______ one in the water.

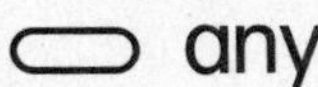
⬭ any

⬭ first
⬭ together

4. Dean ______ a pretty shell.

⬭ said

⬭ found

⬭ went

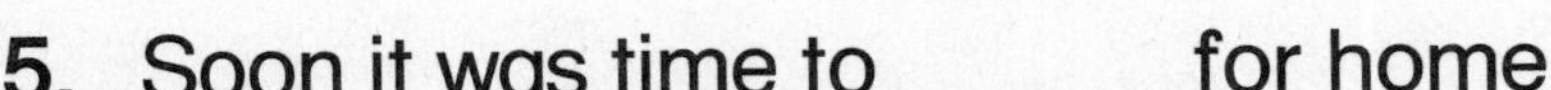
5. Soon it was time to ______ for home.

⬭ start
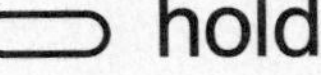
⬭ hold
⬭ bring

Name ______________________



# Part 2: Comprehension

**Read** each question.
**Mark** the ⬭ for the answer.

6. The teacher wants everyone to
   - ⬭ stay together.
   - ⬭ get lost.
   - ⬭ see the dinosaur.

7. Why does Jim go with Danny?
   - ⬭ He does not hear the teacher.
   - ⬭ He wants to see a dinosaur.
   - ⬭ The teacher tells him to go.

8. Jim runs away from the dinosaur because he
   - ⬭ wants to eat hot dogs.
   - ⬭ is scared.
   - ⬭ does not want to get lost.

9. Jim is brave when he
   - ⬭ sees the dinosaur.
   - ⬭ goes to find his teacher.
   - ⬭ eats a hot dog.

10. How does Jim find his teacher?
    - ⬭ He asks the whale for help.
    - ⬭ The penguins tell him what to do.
    - ⬭ He looks in many rooms.

STOP

Name ______________________

**Write** the contraction for each pair of words.

1. I + am = ______

2. you + will = ______

3. is + not = ______

4. they + are = ______

5. could + not = ______

6. she + had = ______

7. do + not = ______

8. would + not = ______

**Find** the contraction.
**Mark** the ⬭ to show your answer.

9. ⬭ it's
⬭ hits
⬭ its

10. ⬭ were
⬭ we're
⬭ worry

**Notes for Home:** Your child reviewed contractions—words made up of two words and an apostrophe. ***Home Activity:*** Write the words *it, is, did, not, I, am, we,* and *are* on separate index cards. Ask your child to see how many different contractions he or she can form.

Name ______________________



lie pie tie night light right

**Write** three words from the box that rhyme with **my**.

1. ______ 2. ______ 3. ______

**Write** three words from the box that rhyme with **fight**.

4. ______ 5. ______ 6. ______

**Pick** a word from the box to finish each sentence.
**Write** it on the line.

7. I won't tell a ______ .

8. I ate the ______ .

**Pick** a word from the box to finish each sentence.
**Write** it on the line.

been found

9. I have ______ at Fred's shop.

10. I ______ two cats there!

**Notes for Home:** Your child spelled words with the long *i* sound spelled *ie* and *igh*. ***Home Activity:*** Ask your child to make up a silly song using the spelling words. Work together to write the words to the song when it's finished.

Name ____________________



RETEACHING

This mop is **wet**.

The **happy** pup jumps.

An **adjective** can tell what kind.

**Read** each sentence.
**Circle** the adjective or adjectives.

1. The hat is old.

2. Nan gets a new hat.

3. The new hat is pretty.

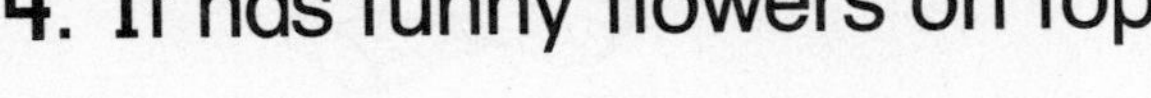

4. It has funny flowers on top.

5. Now Nan is happy!

**Notes for Home:** Your child identified adjectives that tell what kind. ***Home Activity:*** Together, make up a story about an imaginary place. Have your child use adjectives to describe what kinds of things someone visiting the place might see.

Name ______________________________

**Read** each sentence.
**Choose** the correct adjective in ( ).
**Write** it on the line.

1. I like to pet the (soft/hard) rabbit.

2. The children are (sad/happy).

3. The (fast/slow) snail is moving.

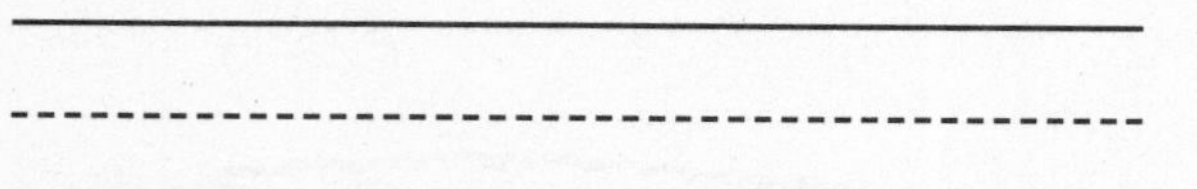

4. This duck was very (bad/good)!

5. Don't touch the (hot/cold) fire!

6. That is a (long/sad) bat.

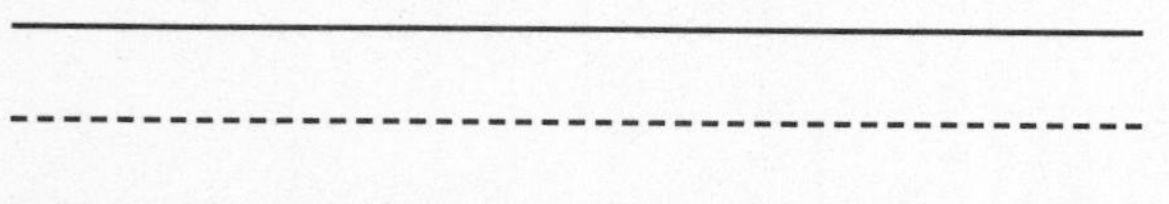

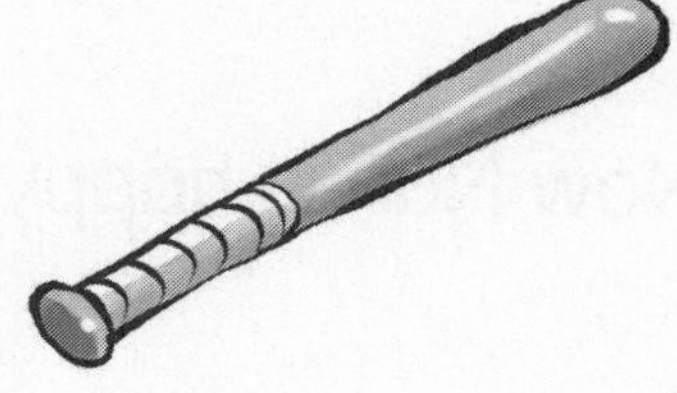

**Notes for Home:** Your child identified appropriate adjectives—words that describe—in sentences. ***Home Activity:*** Put three objects on a table. (For example: apple, orange, banana) Have your child use adjectives in sentences to describe what kinds of objects they are.

**You are your child's first and best teacher!**

**Here are ways to help your child practice skills while having fun!**

**Day 1** Work with your child to think of pairs of words that have the long *e* and long *i* vowel sounds of *y*, such as *pretty city; funny baby; shy fly;* or *dry sky*.

**Day 2** Make up a simple crossword or word search puzzle using the following words that the children are learning to read: *animals, even, heard, most,* and *their.*

**Day 3** Read a paragraph from a children's story or magazine article to your child. Ask him or her to tell you what the main idea of the paragraph is.

**Day 4** Ask your child to choose a topic he or she is interested in, such as a favorite animal or sports figure, and to present an oral report about that topic to the family. Encourage your child to speak clearly.

**Day 5** Play "I Spy" with your child using number adjectives. For example, you might see two books and say *I spy some books. Tell me how many.* Your child must then name and spell the appropriate number *(two)*.

**Read with your child EVERY DAY!**



(fold here)

# Family Times

**Chompy's Afternoon** **Dinosaur Babies**

### I'm a Baby Dinosaur

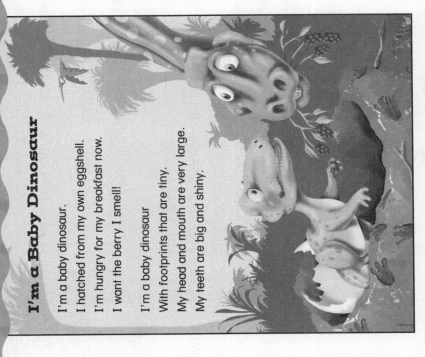

I'm a baby dinosaur.
I hatched from my own eggshell.
I'm hungry for my breakfast now.
I want the berry I smell!

I'm a baby dinosaur
With footprints that are tiny.
My head and mouth are very large.
My teeth are big and shiny.

This rhyme includes words your child is working with in school: words with *y* that represent the long *e* sound *(hungry)* and the long *i* sound *(my)* as well as compound words *(eggshell)*. Read "I'm a Baby Dinosaur" with your child. Sort all the words with *y* into two groups according to the two different vowel sounds.

Name: ____________________

# Compound Treasures

**Materials** paper, marker, scissors, paper clip, pencil, 1 button per player

## Game Directions

1. Make a simple spinner as shown.
2. Players place buttons on Start, take turns spinning, and move the number of spaces shown.
3. When a player lands on a picture square, he or she must say the compound word that names the picture. Answers are shown below.
4. The first player to reach the end wins!

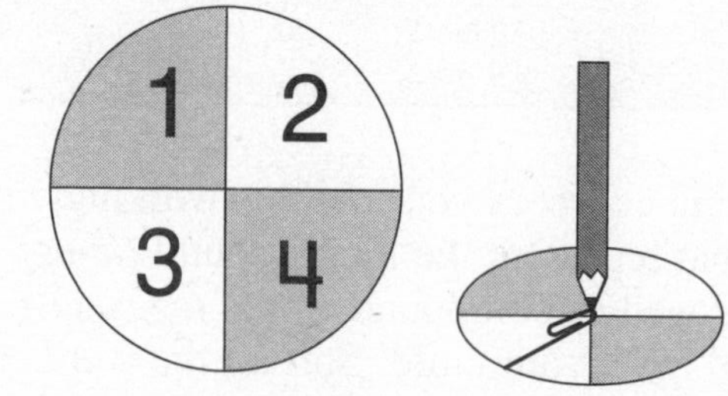


Answers (in order): football, eggshell, raincoat, cowboy, footprint, cupcake

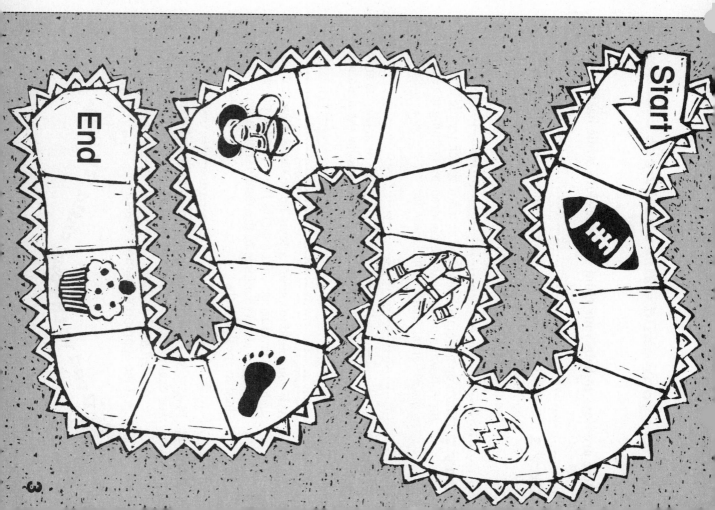



Start

End

Name ______________________________

**Write** a word from the box to match each picture.
**Circle** the word if it ends like **baby.**
**Underline** the word if it ends like **cry.**

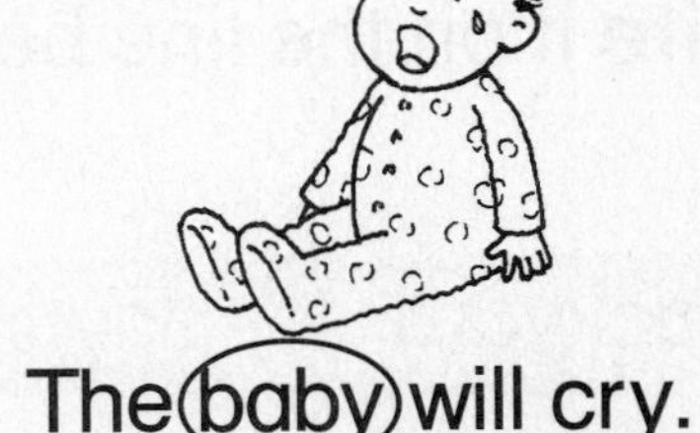

The baby will cry.

| bunny | fly | puppy |
|---|---|---|
| city | fry | silly |

1. 
______________

2. 
______________

3. 
______________

4. 
______________

5. 
______________

6. 
______________

**Draw** a picture of each word.

7. berry

8. sky

**Notes for Home:** Your child practiced reading words with the vowel sounds of *y* heard in *baby* or *cry*. ***Home Activity:*** Encourage your child to draw pictures of things that have the vowel sound of *y* in their names. Ask your child to label the pictures.

Name ______________________

**Pick** a word from the box to finish each sentence.
**Write** it on the line below the sentence.

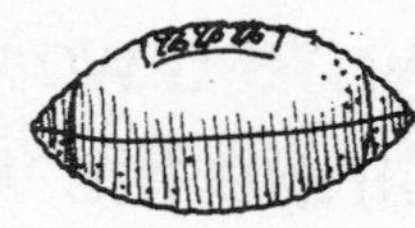

**football**

| backyard | daytime | eggshell | footprint | haircut |
|---|---|---|---|---|

1. I sat in the ______ of my home.

______________________

2. I painted the ______ .

______________________

3. ______ is a good time to play.

______________________

4. Mr. Green gave Bill a ______ .

______________________

5. I saw a ______ in the mud.

______________________

**Notes for Home:** Your child identified and wrote compound words—longer words formed by joining two smaller words. ***Home Activity:*** Encourage your child to make up sentences using the compound words from the box above.

Name ______________________________

**Pick** a word from the box to finish each sentence.
**Write** it on the line.

| animals | even | heard | most | their |
|---|---|---|---|---|

1. Last night I ____________________ something outside.

2. I know that ____________________ live in our backyard.

3. ____________________ of them come out at night.

4. I can ____________________ see them if I look outside.

5. I see ____________________ faces looking at me!

**Notes for Home:** This week your child is learning to read the words *animals, even, heard, most,* and *their.* ***Home Activity:*** Work with your child to write a story using these new words. Help your child read the story to you when he or she is done.

Name ______________________________

**Read** each story.
**Circle** the words that tell what the story is about.
**Draw** a picture to show what the story is about.

1. Jen feeds her cat.
She takes care of her cat.
She pets her cat.

cats and dogs
food
Jen and her cat

2.

3. Mike and Todd are friends.
They play ball.
They go to the beach.

friends
baseball
the beach

4.

**Write** a title for this story.

5. Len looks on the shelf.
He looks in the box.
He looks for his cap in many places.

______________________________

**Notes for Home:** Your child identified the main idea in a story. ***Home Activity:*** Read a story with your child. Encourage him or her to tell you what the story is all about.

Name ______________________

Some **adjectives** tell how many. __two__ tops

**Look** at the picture.
**Pick** a word from the box to finish each sentence.
**Write** it on the line.

| one | two | three | four | five |
|---|---|---|---|---|

1. There are ______________ balls in the box.

2. I see ______________ toy cats on the floor.

3. The girl is spinning ______________ top.

4. There are ______________ boxes of games.

5. The man stands by ______________ dolls.

**Notes for Home:** Your child wrote adjectives that tell how many. ***Home Activity:*** Take a walk with your child. Count objects you see on the way and encourage your child to spell the word for each number.

Name ______________________

**Pick** a word from the box to finish each sentence.
**Write** it on the line.

animals even heard heavy most their

1. Many ______________ live on my dad's ranch.

2. I ______________ the sheep say "baa."

3. ______________ of our sheep are black.

4. We cut ______________ hair twice a year.

5. The big sheep are ______________ .

6. Some are ______________ as heavy as my dad.

**Notes for Home:** Your child completed a story using words learned this week.
***Home Activity:*** Encourage your child to write a poem or song using as many of these words as possible.

Name ________________________________

pie

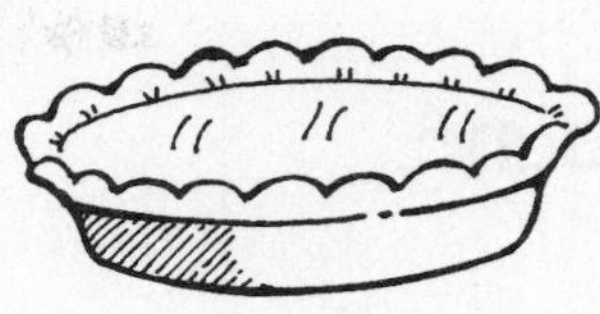

knight

**Circle** the word for each picture.

| 1. | 2. | 3. | 4. |
|---|---|---|---|
| 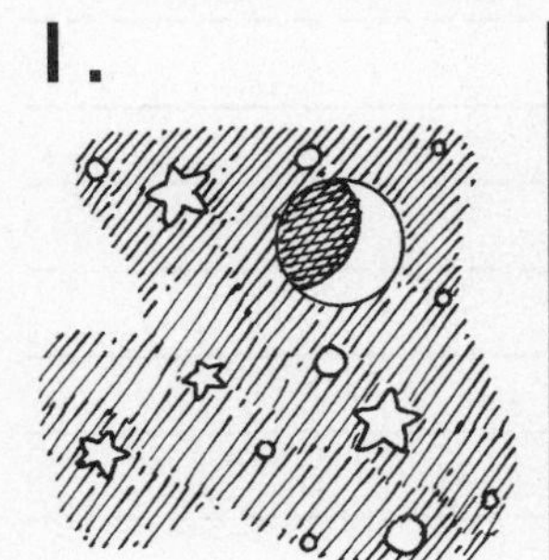 | 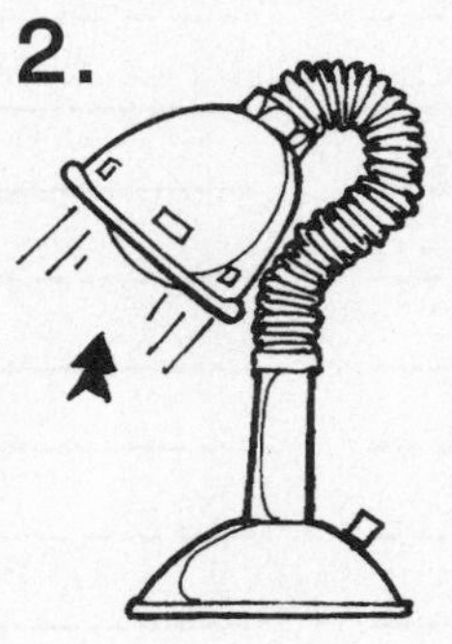 |  |  |
| night note | let light | tie tea | fig fight |

| 5. | 6. | 7. | 8. |
|---|---|---|---|
| 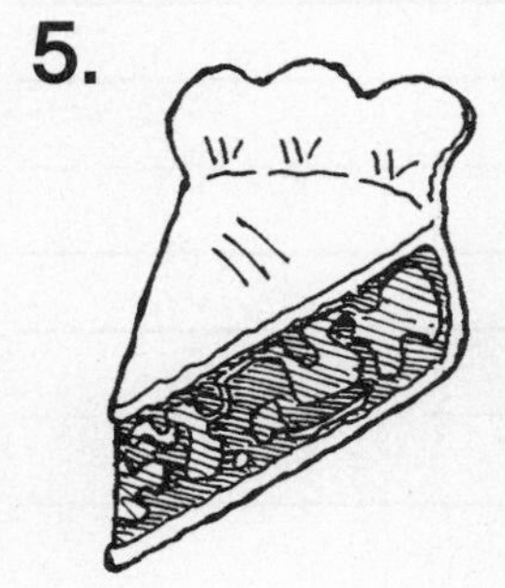 |  |  |  |
| pea pie | high hay | sit sigh | tights toads |

**Find** the word that has the same **long i** sound as 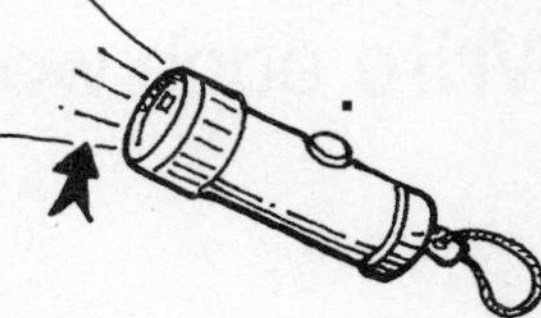.
**Mark** the ⬭ to show your answer.

9. ⬭ lit
⬭ lie
⬭ lift

10. ⬭ mitt
⬭ might
⬭ mill

**Notes for Home:** Your child reviewed words in which the long *i* sound is spelled *igh* and *ie* as in *knight* and *pie*. ***Home Activity:*** Encourage your child to create a poem or song using rhyming *igh* and *ie* words.

Name ______________________

**Look** at each word. **Say** it.
**Listen** for the **long e** or **long i** sound.

| | **Write** each word. | **Check** it. |
|---|---|---|
| 1. baby | | |
| 2. funny | | |
| 3. many | | |
| 4. my | | |
| 5. why | | |
| 6. fly | | |

## Word Wall Words

**Write** each word.

| | | |
|---|---|---|
| 7. even | | |
| 8. most | | |

**Notes for Home:** Your child spelled words in which *y* represents either a long *e* or a long *i* vowel sound, as well as two frequently used words: *even, most.* ***Home Activity:*** Have your child write and sort the words into long *e* words, long *i* words, and Word Wall Words.

Name ______________________________

**Pick** the adjective from the box that tells how many.
**Write** it on the line.
**Draw** a line from the group of words to the picture it matches.

one two three four

1. ______________ dolls

5. 

2. ______________ dog

6. 

3. ______________ boxes

7. 

4. ______________ dishes

8. 

**Draw** a picture about six mice.
**Write** a sentence that tells about your picture.

9.

10. ______________________________________________

**Notes for Home:** Your child used adjectives that describe numbers. ***Home Activity:*** Write the numbers 1–10 on a sheet of paper. Ask your child to write the word for each number, then draw a picture to match that number, such as a picture of two cats to go with the number *two*.

Name ______________________



# Test-Taking Tips

1. Write your name on the test.
2. Read each question twice.
3. Read all the answer choices for the question.
4. Mark your answer carefully.
5. Check your answer.

Name ______________________________



# Part 1: Vocabulary

**Read** each sentence.

**Mark** the ⬭ for the word that fits.

1. Sam likes ______.

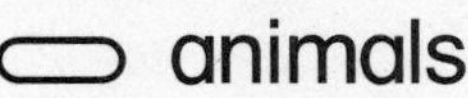 

⬭ animals ⬭ found ⬭ think

2. He ______ likes bugs!

⬭ around ⬭ together ⬭ even

3. One day he ______ some ducks.

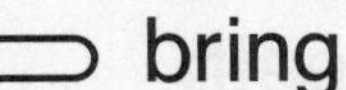

⬭ show ⬭ bring ⬭ heard

4. ______ ducks live by the water.

⬭ Most ⬭ About ⬭ When

5. Sam found ______ nest.

⬭ as ⬭ their ⬭ more

Name ______________________________

## Part 2: Comprehension

**Read** each sentence.
**Mark** the ⬭ for the answer.

**6.** Dinosaur hunters can
- ⬭ hear baby dinosaurs.
- ⬭ see dinosaur mothers.
- ⬭ find dinosaur eggs.

**7.** What did some baby dinosaurs eat?
- ⬭ bugs
- ⬭ milk
- ⬭ hot dogs

**8.** Some big dinosaurs stayed around the baby dinosaurs to
- ⬭ keep the little ones safe.
- ⬭ tell a story.
- ⬭ go to sleep.

**9.** How were baby dinosaurs like you when you were a baby?
- ⬭ They were born with teeth.
- ⬭ They came out of eggs.
- ⬭ They started growing.

**10.** What is *Dinosaur Babies* about?
- ⬭ animals of long ago
- ⬭ how to eat eggs
- ⬭ funny tails

Name ______________________________

**Add -ed** and **-ing** to each word.
**Write** the new word on the line.

| Word | | Add -ed | | Add -ing |
|---|---|---|---|---|
| help | 1. | ______________ | 2. | ______________ |
| jog | 3. | ______________ | 4. | ______________ |
| mix | 5. | ______________ | 6. | ______________ |
| hop | 7. | ______________ | 8. | ______________ |

**Find** the word that changes its spelling before adding **-ed** or **-ing**.
**Mark** the ⬭ to show your answer.

9. ⬭ stop
   ⬭ sail
   ⬭ talk

10. ⬭ play
    ⬭ snap
    ⬭ ask

**Notes for Home:** Your child added *-ed* and *-ing* to verbs, doubling the consonant as needed. ***Home Activity:*** Have your child read aloud the words with *-ed* and *-ing* endings. Talk about whether the spelling changed before the endings were added.

Name ______________________

baby funny many my why fly

**Write** three words from the box that have the **long e** sound.

1. ____________ 2. ____________ 3. ____________

**Write** three words from the box that have the **long i** sound.

4. ____________ 5. ____________ 6. ____________

**Pick** a word from the box to match each clue.
**Write** it in the puzzle.

7. go in plane

8. a lot

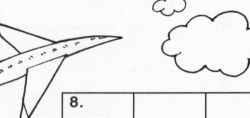

**Pick** a word from the box to finish each sentence.
**Write** it on the line.

even most

9. I did ____________ of my tasks.

10. I ____________ made my bed!

**Notes for Home:** Your child spelled words in which *y* represents either a long *e* or a long *i* vowel sound, as well as two frequently used words: *even, most.* ***Home Activity:*** Challenge your child to write other long *e* and long *i* words with *y*.

Name ______________________________

**three** balls

Some **adjectives** tell how many.

**Draw** a line from the adjective to the picture.

1. **five** bees 

2. **one** sun 

3. **three** birds 

4. **ten** trees 

5. **six** flowers 

6. **two** houses 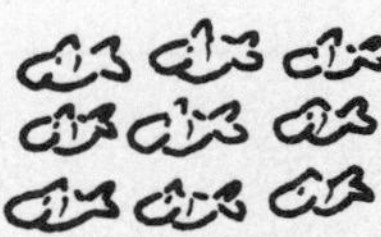

7. **seven** dolls 

8. **nine** fish 

9. **four** bicycles 

10. **eight** wagons 

**Notes for Home:** Your child identified adjectives that tell how many. ***Home Activity:*** Have your child draw a picture of groups of things. Then have him or her count items in the drawing and label the drawing with number words.

Name ______________________________

**Answer** each question.
**Write** the number word.

1. How many cats are by the door?

______________________________

2. How many frogs jump?

______________________________

3. How many birds are in the tree?

______________________________

4. How many dogs have nothing to do?

______________________________

**Notes for Home:** Your child wrote adjectives that tell how many. ***Home Activity:*** Write two questions for your child that will require numbers as answers. *(How many clocks are in our home?)* Have your child write each answer in a complete sentence.

**You are your child's first and best teacher!**

**Here are ways to help your child practice skills while having fun!**

**Day 1** Work with your child to write notes to friends using as many *ew* and *ue* words as possible. Some words that might be used are: *stew, chew, blew, new, flew, clue,* and *glue.*

**Day 2** Help your child write sentences using at least two of the following words in each sentence: *because, better, give, people,* or *put.*

**Day 3** Read a story or watch a favorite TV show or video with your child. Encourage your child to tell what happened (effect) and why it happened (cause).

**Day 4** Your child is learning to work in small groups. Invite a few friends or family members to join you and your child in a project, such as making cookies or painting pictures.

**Day 5** Help your child find information about a topic of interest. Then encourage him or her to write a paragraph explaining what he or she has learned about that topic.

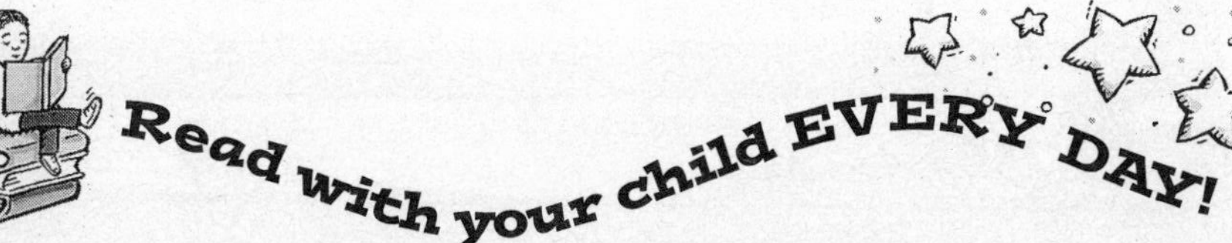
Read with your child EVERY DAY!

(fold here)

# Family Times

**The True Story of Abbie Burgess** — **The Bravest Cat!**

**Bluey and Dewey**

Bluey is a bluebird.
One day he crashes down.
Dewey dashes over
And looks with a frown.

Up in the branches
Bluey hurt his wing.
Dewey helps Bluey
And fixes him a sling.

Dewey teaches Bluey
To fly away.
He wishes he'll see Bluey
On another day.

This rhyme includes words your child is working with in school: words with *ew* and *ue (Dewey, Bluey)* and words that end in *-es (teaches, branches)*. Read "Bluey and Dewey" together. Help your child act out the rhyme.

Name: ____________________

# Mix and Match Plurals

**Materials** index cards

**Game Directions**

1. Write the pairs of words shown on page 3 on separate index cards.
2. Mix the cards. Divide them among 2 or 4 players.
3. Players place their cards in a stack and begin flipping over the cards one at a time so all players can see the cards.
4. When a player sees any singular / plural match, he or she yells "Match!" and gets to keep that pair.
5. Play until all matches have been made. The player with the most matches wins!

| | |
|---|---|
| box | boxes |
| fox | foxes |
| dish | dishes |
| coach | coaches |
| watch | watches |
| batch | batches |
| wish | wishes |
| crash | crashes |
| ash | ashes |
| peach | peaches |

Name ______________________________

**Read** the name of each child below.
**Pick** words from the box with vowel sounds that are spelled the same.
**Write** the words on the lines.

n**ew**s

gl**ue**

| blue | chew | clue | few | glue | grew | knew | true |
|---|---|---|---|---|---|---|---|

**Sue**

1. ______________
2. ______________
3. ______________
4. ______________

**Stewart**

5. ______________
6. ______________
7. ______________
8. ______________

**Notes for Home:** Your child practiced writing words with the vowel patterns *ew* and *ue*.
***Home Activity:*** Help your child think of other ways to spell the sound made by *ew* and *ue*.

Name ______________________

**Add -es** to the word in ( ) to finish each sentence.
**Write** the new word on the line.

box<u>es</u>

She wash<u>es</u> the windows

(fox)

1. Look at those ______________ !

(dish)

2. Hand me four ______________ .

(bus)

3. They took two ______________ .

(pass)

4. He ______________ the ball.

(catch)

5. She ______________ the ball.

**Notes for Home:** Your child practiced writing verbs and plural nouns that end in *-es*. ***Home Activity:*** Write two nouns for your child. Ask your child to point out which ones take *-es* to form a plural. (Nouns that end in *s, ss, sh, ch,* and *x* use *-es* when made plural.)

Name ______________________________

**Pick** a word from the box to finish each sentence.
**Write** it on the line.

| because | better | give | people | put |
|---|---|---|---|---|

1. I like to ride my bike ____________ it is fun.

2. Some ____________ like skating.

3. I like riding ____________ than skating.

4. I ____________ my baby sister a ride!

5. I always ____________ my bike away.

**Notes for Home:** This week your child is learning to read the words *because, better, give, people*, and *put*. ***Home Activity:*** Write each word on a separate slip of paper. Put the slips of paper in a bowl or hat. Ask your child to pick one word and use it in a sentence.

Name ________________________________

**Draw** a line to match what happens with why it happens.

| | What Happens | Why It Happens |
|---|---|---|
| 1. |  |  |
| 2. |  |  |
| 3. |  |  |
| 4. |  |  |
| 5. |  |  |

**Notes for Home:** Your child identified what happens (effect) and why it happens (cause). ***Home Activity:*** While watching a television show, encourage your child to identify what happens and why.

Name ______________________________

An **adjective** tells more about a person, place, or thing.
**Cute** tells more about Mary's cat.

Mary has a <u>**cute**</u> cat.

**Pick** a word from the box that helps each sentence tell more.
**Write** it on the line.

| black | hot | tall | three | wet |
|---|---|---|---|---|

1. Dad sips a ______________ drink.

2. Tom is a ______________ man.

3. I have a ______________ cat.

4. I have ______________ sisters.

5. Take off your ______________ coat.

**Notes for Home:** Your child used adjectives to improve sentences. ***Home Activity:*** Make up simple sentences for your child. Encourage your child to add adjectives to make each sentence more interesting.

Name ______________________



**Pick** a word from the box to finish each sentence.
**Write** it on the line.

| because | better | burns | give | people | put |
|---|---|---|---|---|---|

1. My dog barks ______________ there is a fire!

2. His barking wakes up the sleeping ______________.

3. The firefighters ______________ the fire out.

4. My dog has ______________ on his feet.

5. I will ______________ my dog a big hug.

6. That will make him feel ______________.

**Notes for Home:** Your child used words learned this week to finish a story. ***Home Activity:*** Take turns reading each word from the box aloud and using it in a sentence.

Name ______________________________

fry 

baby 

**Circle** the word for each picture.

1.  many man
2.  sit city
3.  lock lucky
4.  carry care
5.  funny fry
6.  cry crib
7.  flea fly
8.  sky skate

**Find** the word where **y** does **not** have the same sound as the other two words.
**Mark** the ⬭ to show your answer.

9. ⬭ my
⬭ many
⬭ Mary

10. ⬭ why
⬭ spy
⬭ lady

**Notes for Home:** Your child reviewed the vowel sounds of *y*—the long *e* sound in *baby* and the long *i* sound in *fry*. ***Home Activity:*** Work with your child to write two word lists—one of words in which *y* represents the long *e* sound and one in which it represents the long *i* sound.

Name ______________________



**Look** at each word. **Say** it.
**Listen** for the vowel sound.

| | **Write** each word. | **Check** it. |
|---|---|---|
| 1. new | | |
| 2. grew | | |
| 3. drew | | |
| 4. blue | | |
| 5. true | | |
| 6. glue | | |

## Word Wall Words

**Write** each word.

| | | |
|---|---|---|
| 7. give | | |
| 8. put | | |

**Notes for Home:** Your child spelled words with *ew* and *ue* that stand for the same vowel sound, as well as two frequently used words: *give, put.* ***Home Activity:*** Encourage your child to draw pictures for some of the spelling words. Help your child label each picture.

Name ______________________________

Add adjectives to tell more about a person, place, or thing.

Jan has a dog.   Jan has a **small** dog.

---

What word describes the animal best?
**Circle** a word to finish each sentence.
**Write** it on the line.

old  bushy  new

1. The pup has a ________________ tail.

long  sweet  nice

2. What ________________ legs the spider has!

square  shy  best

3. The ________________ mice hide in their cage.

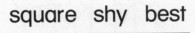

fast  fine  lazy

4. The ________________ cat sleeps all day.

---

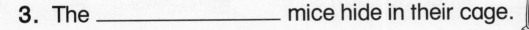

**Write** about a frog.
**Use** an adjective to describe it.

5. ________________________________________

**Notes for Home:** Your child used adjectives (words that describe a person, place, or thing) to improve sentences. ***Home Activity:*** Write some simple sentences for your child. *(I saw a cow.)* Invite your child to improve the sentences with one or more adjectives. *(I saw a big, fat cow.)*

Name ______________________________

**Look** at the picture.
**Circle** the adjective that tells more about the picture.

new old

1. The ______ home was on fire.

strong weak

2. A ______ cat walked out.

striped spotted

3. It was carrying a ______ kitten.

little huge

4. The ______ kitten was now safe.

**Write** a sentence about the cat in the picture.
**Use** an adjective from the box.

big brave older glad

5. ______________________________________________

**Notes for Home:** Your child used adjectives to make sentences more descriptive. ***Home Activity:*** Say a simple sentence naming an object around you *(I see a tree.)*. Encourage your child to improve your sentence by adding adjectives to it *(I see a tall, green tree.)*.

Name ______________________________

# Part 1: Vocabulary

**Read** each sentence.
**Mark** the ⬭ for the word that fits.

1. Some ______ saw a fire.
   - ⬭ please
   - ⬭ every
   - ⬭ people

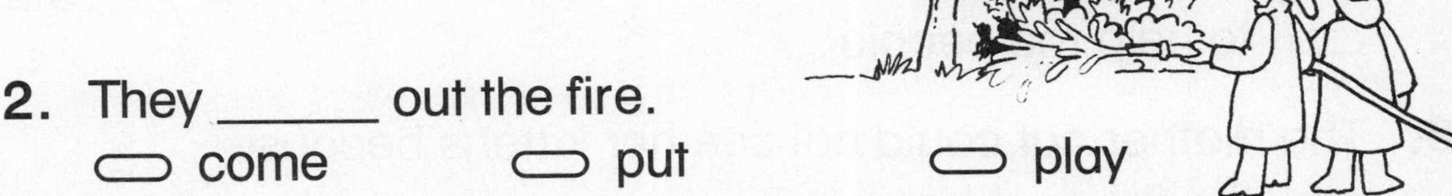

2. They ______ out the fire.
   - ⬭ come
   - ⬭ put
   - ⬭ play

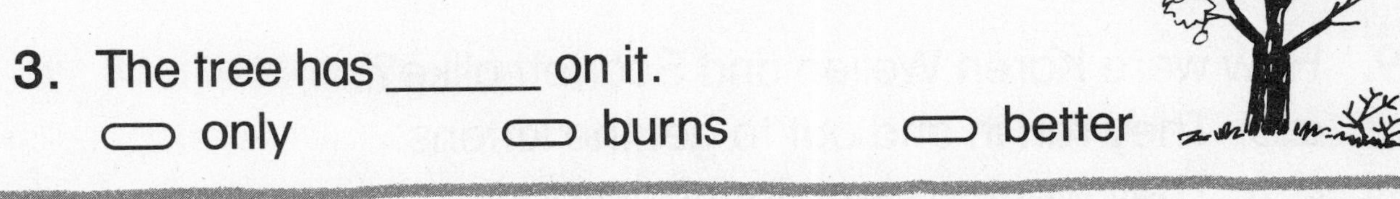

3. The tree has ______ on it.
   - ⬭ only
   - ⬭ burns
   - ⬭ better

4. It will not get ______ .
   - ⬭ around
   - ⬭ better
   - ⬭ because

5. The man will ______ us a new tree.
   - ⬭ give
   - ⬭ put
   - ⬭ sing

GO ON

Name ___________________________



## Part 2: Comprehension

**Read** each question.

**Mark** the ⬭ for the answer.

6. What building was on fire?
   - ⬭ a shop
   - ⬭ a garage
   - ⬭ a hospital

7. Why did the cat run into the fire?
   - ⬭ to put the fire out
   - ⬭ to get her kittens
   - ⬭ to help the people

8. The mother cat could not see her kittens because
   - ⬭ the fire hurt her eyes.
   - ⬭ a man took the kittens away.
   - ⬭ the kittens were in a box.

9. How were Karen Wellen and Scarlett alike?
   - ⬭ They ran in and out to get the kittens.
   - ⬭ They went to sleep in the garage.
   - ⬭ They took a long time to get better.

10. *The Bravest Cat!* tells about a
    - ⬭ real cat.
    - ⬭ cat that sings.
    - ⬭ funny cat.

Name ______________________________

lung 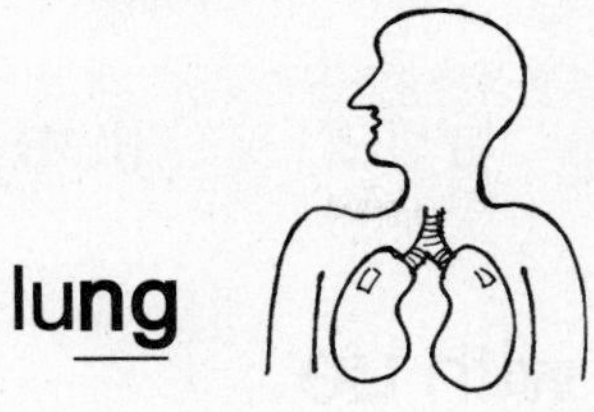

bank 

**Circle** the word for each picture.

| 1. | 2. | 3. | 4. |
|---|---|---|---|
| tank tan | rink ring | fang fan | skunk skate |

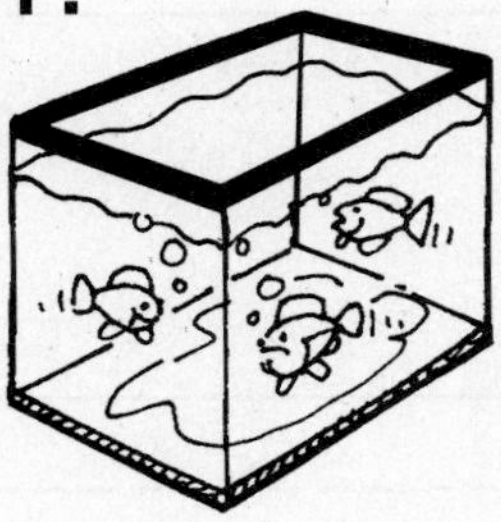

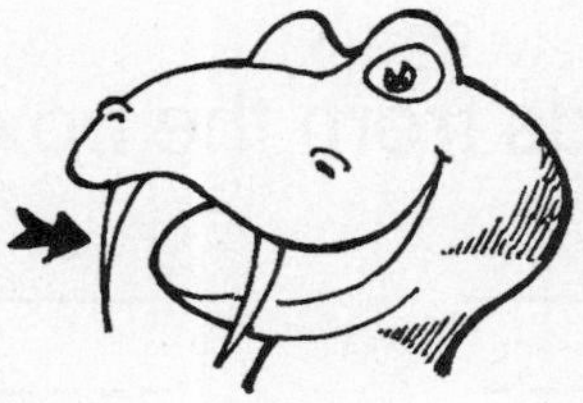

| 5. | 6. | 7. | 8. |
|---|---|---|---|
| drip drink | sign sing | hand hung | kin ink |

**Find** the word that has the same ending sound as .
**Mark** the ⊂⊃ to show your answer.

9. ⊂⊃ sand
⊂⊃ sang
⊂⊃ sank

10. ⊂⊃ train
⊂⊃ think
⊂⊃ thing

**Notes for Home:** Your child reviewed words that end with *-ng* and *-nk*. ***Home Activity:*** Say one of the words with *-ing* or *-nk* on this page and ask your child to think of a word that rhymes with it. Then have your child think of a word for you to rhyme.

Name ______________________

new grew drew blue true glue

**Write** three words from the box that end with **ue**.

1. ____________ 2. ____________ 3. ____________

**Write** three words from the box that end with **ew**.

4. ____________ 5. ____________ 6. ____________

**Write** the words from the box that tell something that happened in the past.

7. ____________ 8. ____________

**Pick** a word from the box to finish each sentence.
**Write** it on the line.

give put

9. ____________ me the cat.

10. I will ____________ him in his bed.

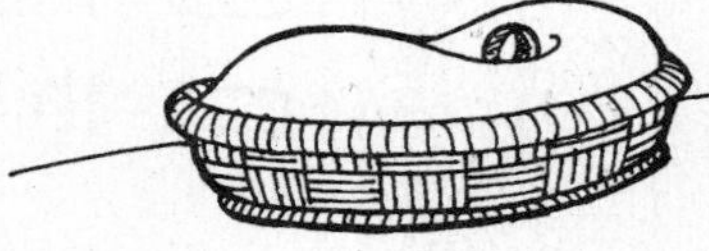

**Notes for Home:** Your child spelled words with *ew* and *ue* that stand for the same vowel sound, as well as two frequently used words: *give, put. **Home Activity:*** Work with your child to write the spelling words in alphabetical order.

Name ______________________

The **fat** pig eats food.

An **adjective** tells more about a person, place, or thing.

**Read** each sentence.
**Write** the adjective in each sentence.

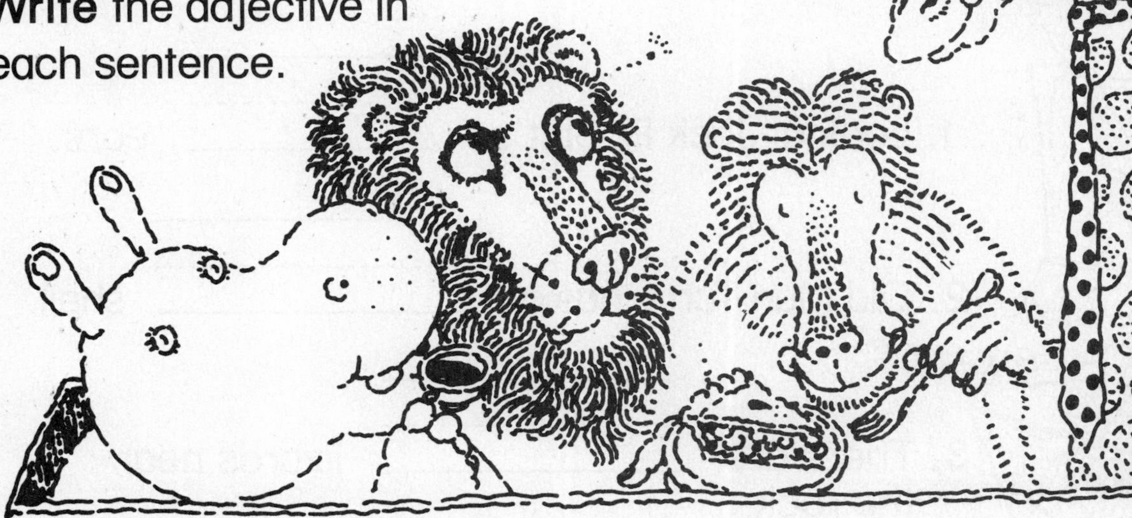

1. A tall giraffe wears a tie.
______________________

2. A big baboon eats a pie.
______________________

3. A lion scares a tiny flea.
______________________

4. A wet hippo drinks tea.
______________________

**Notes for Home:** Your child wrote adjectives—words that describe. ***Home Activity:*** Ask your child to use adjectives to describe things he or she saw at school today.

Name ______________________________

**Finish** the caption for each picture.
**Write** the best adjective to complete each sentence.

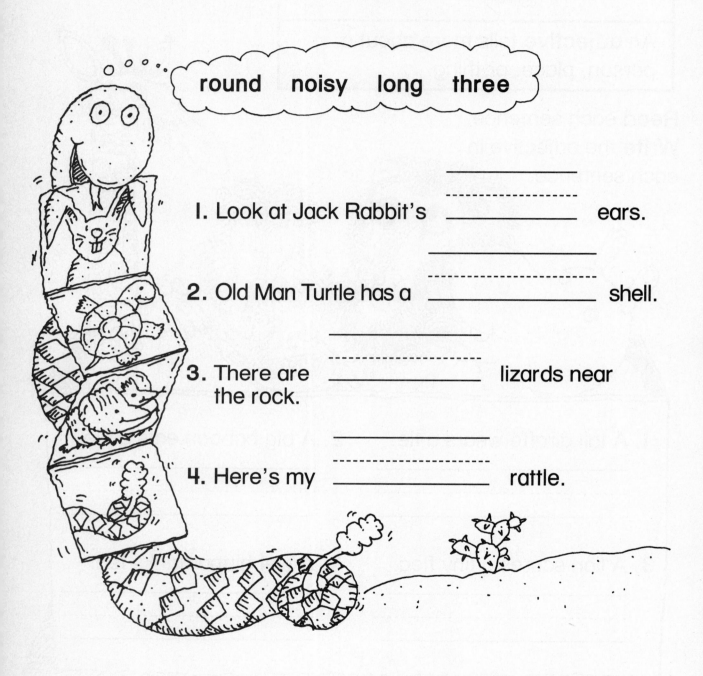

round noisy long three

1. Look at Jack Rabbit's ______________ ears.

2. Old Man Turtle has a ______________ shell.

3. There are ______________ lizards near the rock.

4. Here's my ______________ rattle.

**Notes for Home:** Your child wrote adjectives in sentences. ***Home Activity:*** Have your child draw himself or herself. Then have him or her use adjectives to write a description of the drawing.

Name ______________________________

**Correct** each sentence.
**Write** it on the line.
Hint: Each sentence should begin with a capital letter.
It should end with a . or ? .

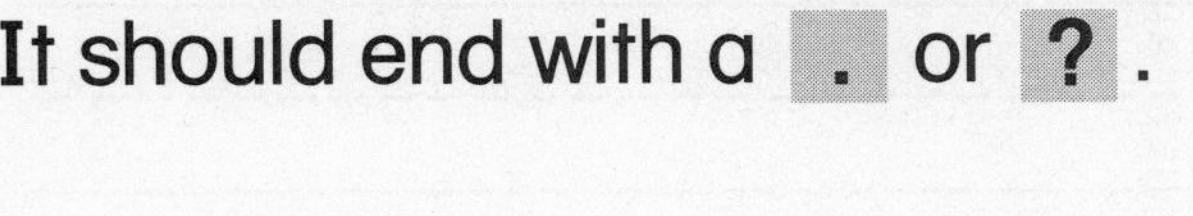

1. do goats make good pets

______________________________

2. we had a goat named Jo

______________________________

3. it liked to come inside

______________________________

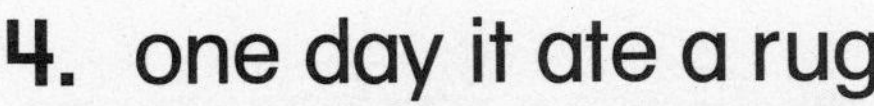

4. one day it ate a rug

______________________________

5. why do goats like rugs

______________________________

**Notes for Home:** Your child corrected sentences using capital letters and end marks. ***Home Activity:*** Help your child find out about a favorite animal. Invite your child to write a short report on that animal. Make sure that sentences are written correctly.

Name

I read

It was about

Words I Can Now Read and Write

**You are your child's first and best teacher!**

**Here are ways to help your child practice skills while having fun!**

**Day 1** Take turns naming places you could travel to that have the same vowel sound heard in *car*. You could travel to the *park*, the *market*, a *garden*, a *farm*, and so on.

**Day 2** Your child is learning to read these words: *much, shall, these, wish,* and *work.* Ask him or her to finish the sentence: *I shall…* using each of the four other words.

**Day 3** On separate index cards, write or draw three daily events. *(We ate breakfast. We woke up. We went to the park.)* Ask your child to put these events in the correct order.

**Day 4** Your child is learning to use complete sentences when speaking. Ask your child to use sentences when telling about his or her day.

**Day 5** Write a short story. Make deliberate punctuation errors and include sentence fragments such as *My sister and I.* or *Went to the beach.* Have your child find and correct the errors.

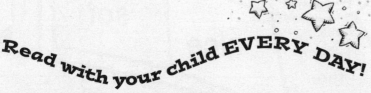

**Read with your child EVERY DAY!**

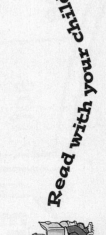

(fold here)

# Family Times

**Bluebirds in the Garden** **The Garden**

**My Garden**

I have a large garden.
It's in my backyard.
I work very quickly.
I work very hard.

My garden grows slowly.
I work until dark.
My dog barks so loudly.
My dog's name is Clark.

At night Clark will take charge.
Clark does his own part.
He watches my garden.
Clark is really smart.

This rhyme includes words your child is working with in school: words with *ar* where the letter *r* changes the sound of the vowel *(large)* and words that end with *-ly (quickly)*. Give your child directions on how to sing "My Garden" using words ending in *-ly*. For example: *Sing this part quietly.*

Name: ______________________

# Add the Suffix

**Materials** 1 coin, 1 button per player

**Game Directions**

1. Players place buttons on Start.
2. Players take turns flipping the coin to see how many spaces to move—one for heads, two for tails.
3. For each space landed on, the player reads the word shown and then writes the word with the suffix *-ly* added.
4. Play stops when someone reaches the End. The player with the most *-ly* words wins.

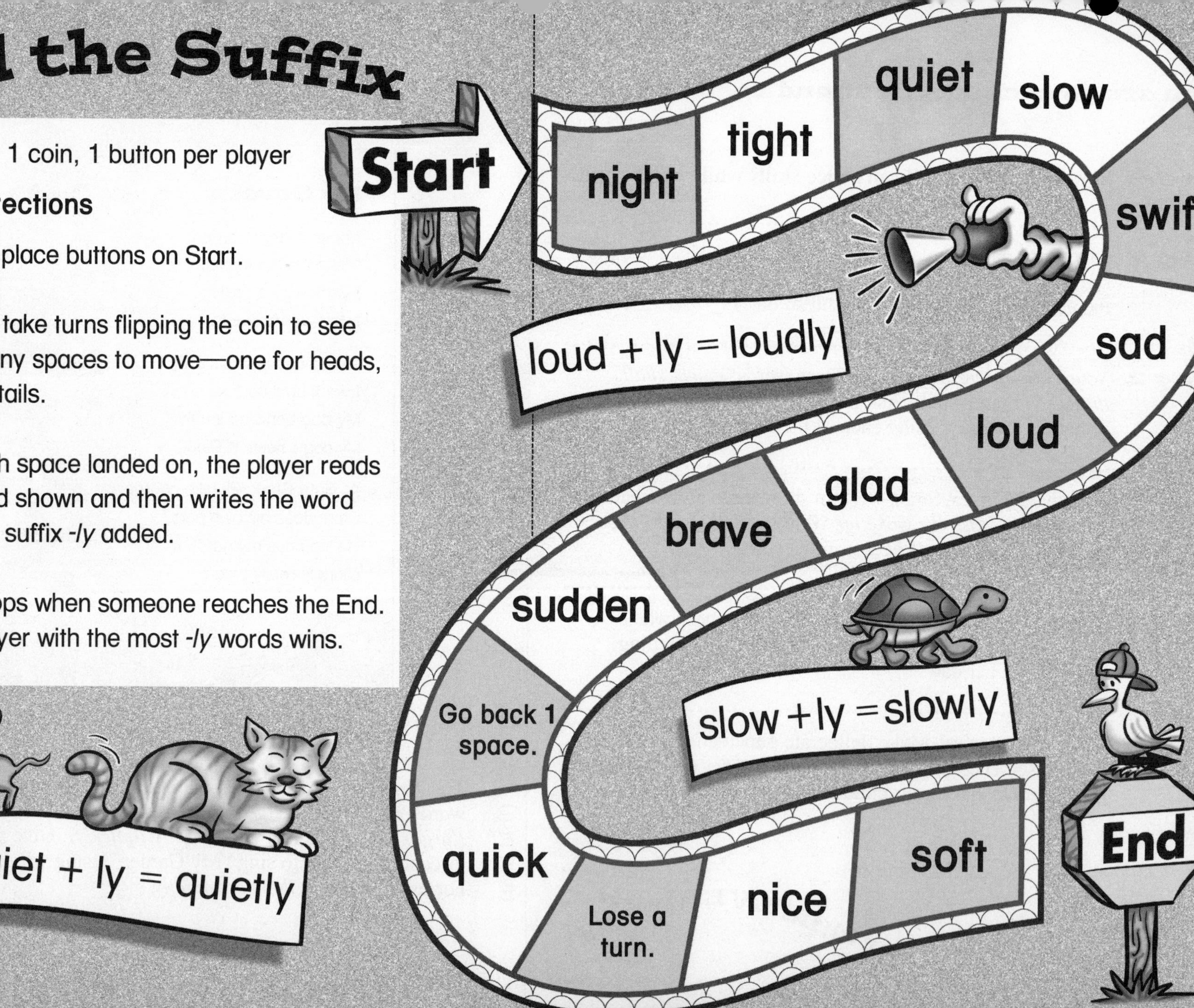

Name ______________________________

**Circle** a word to finish each sentence.
**Write** it on the line.

garden

farm frame

1. We went to a ______________ .

band barn

2. I saw a big ______________ .

yard yarn

3. I saw a garden in the ______________ .

dark duck

4. It was getting ______________ .

car crate

5. So we got in the ______________ .

**Notes for Home:** Your child read and wrote words with *ar* where the letter *r* changes the vowel sound. ***Home Activity:*** Work with your child to say words that rhyme with *car, farm,* and *art.*

Name ______________________________

**Add -ly** to the word in ( ).
**Write** the new word on the line.

sweet + -ly = sweet<u>ly</u>

(loud)

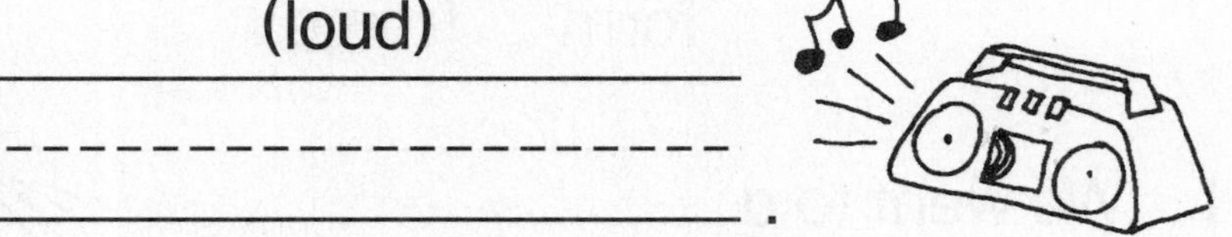

1. The tape played ______________________.

(slow)

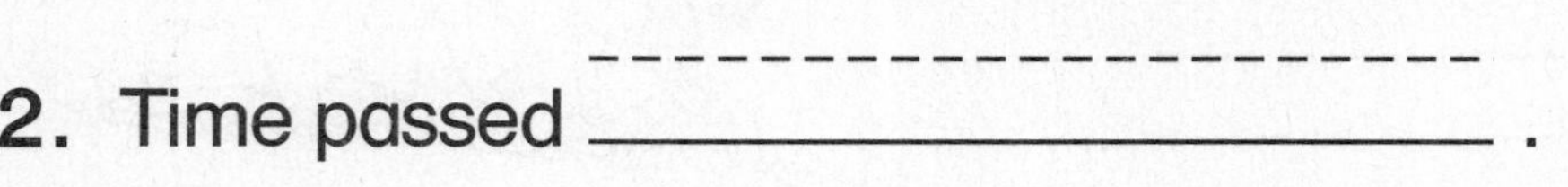

2. Time passed ______________________.

(sudden)

3. The rain came ______________________.

(quick)

4. We ran ______________________.

(safe)

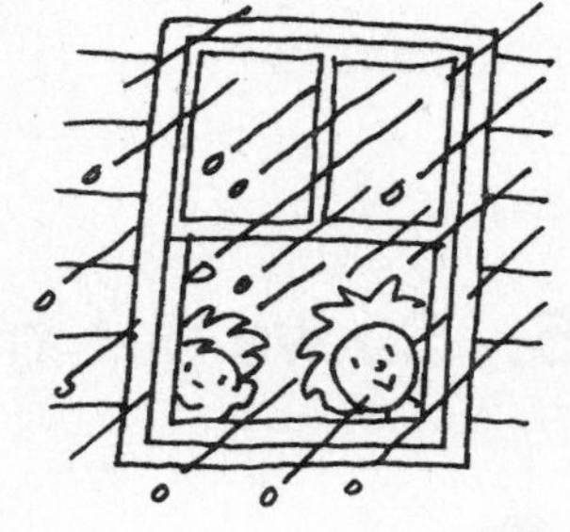

5. We got home ______________________.

**Notes for Home:** Your child added *-ly* to words. ***Home Activity:*** Ask your child to give you instructions using words with the *-ly* suffix *(Clap loudly. Talk softly. Walk quickly.)*. Follow your child's instructions.

Name ______________________

**Pick** a word from the box to finish each sentence.
**Write** it on the line.

| much | shall | these | wish | work |
|---|---|---|---|---|

1. I ______________ I had a plant.

2. How ______________ is this one?

3. Mom can pay ______________ men.

4. I ______________ take it home.

5. I will ______________ to make it grow.

**Notes for Home:** This week your child is learning to read the words *much, shall, these, wish,* and *work.* ***Home Activity:*** Write these words on slips of paper. Have your child pick a word and use it in a sentence.

Name ______________________

**Write** a number in each box to show the right order.

**Look** at each picture.
**Draw** what will happen next.

4.

5.

**Notes for Home:** Your child put a series of events in order and drew pictures to show what event will happen next. ***Home Activity:*** Have your child tell you about something that happened today. Be sure your child tells the events in order. Ask leading questions, such as *What happened first?*

Name ______________________________

A **sentence** tells a complete idea.
A sentence begins with a **capital letter**.
**Questions** end with a **?**.
**Telling sentences** end with a **.** .

The dog plays.

**Circle** each complete sentence.
**Write** it correctly on the line.
Hint: Some groups of words are **not** complete sentences.
Do **not** circle them.

1. my class is fun ______________________________

2. in the water ______________________________

3. who are you ______________________________

4. my friends and I ______________________________

5. we play games ______________________________

**Notes for Home:** Your child identified complete sentences and used capital letters and end marks to write them. ***Home Activity:*** Play a clapping game. Ask your child to clap once if you say a sentence fragment *(to the store)*, and twice if you say a complete sentence *(We went to school.)*.

Name ______________________________

**Pick** a word from the box to match each clue.
**Write** it on the line.

| ground | much | shall | these | wish | work |
|---|---|---|---|---|---|

1. do a job

2. hope

3. a lot

4. rhymes with *knees*

5. rhymes with *round*

6. almost the same as *will*

**Notes for Home:** Your child used words learned this week to match clues. ***Home Activity:*** Make up some rhymes with your child using these words. For example: *Look what I found upon the ground.*

Name ______________________________

**Circle** the word for each picture.

toad

blow

1.

wins window

2.

snap snow

3.
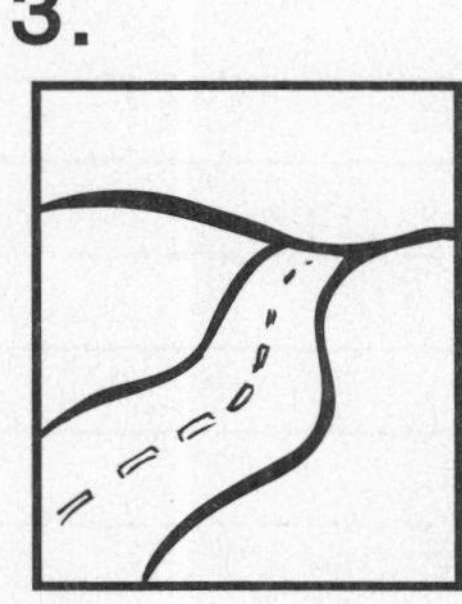
road read

4.

boat beat

5.

crow crew

6.

bee bow

7.

coat cost

8.
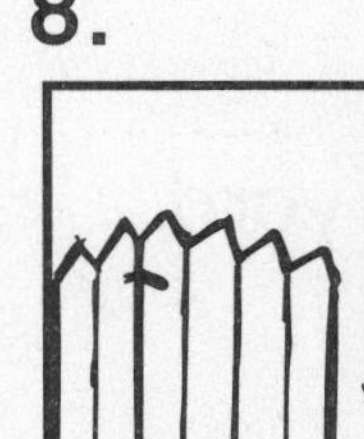
goat gate

**Find** the word that has the same **long o** sound as .
**Mark** the ⬭ to show your answer.

9. ⬭ got
⬭ goal
⬭ good

10. ⬭ low
⬭ lost
⬭ look

**Notes for Home:** Your child reviewed words in which the long *o* sound is spelled *oa* and *ow*, as in *toad* and *blow*. ***Home Activity:*** Together, list as many words with the long *o* sound in their names as possible. Then ask your child to sort the words by their spellings.

Name ______________________

**Look** at each word. **Say** it.
**Listen** for the vowel sound in  .

| | **Write** each word. | **Check** it. |
|---|---|---|
| 1. far | | |
| 2. car | | |
| 3. star | | |
| 4. dark | | |
| 5. yard | | |
| 6. start | | |

## Word Wall Words

**Write** each word.

| | | |
|---|---|---|
| 7. work | | |
| 8. these | | |

**Notes for Home:** Your child spelled words with *ar* in which the letter *r* changes the sound of the vowel *a* and two frequently used words: *work, these.* ***Home Activity:*** Work with your child to make up a poem using some of the spelling words.

Name ______________________



**Read** each group of words.
**Write S** if the words make a complete sentence.
**Write N** if the words do **not** make a complete sentence.

______ 1. The flowers grew.

______ 2. Grew very tall.

______ 3. Did you see my flowers?

**Write** each sentence correctly on the line.
**Begin** each sentence with a capital letter.
**Add** a  or **?** at the end.

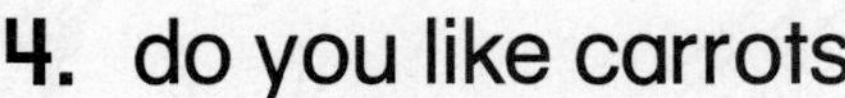

4. do you like carrots

______________________________________

5. we like eating carrots

______________________________________

**Notes for Home:** Your child identified and wrote complete sentences. ***Home Activity:*** Help your child write a letter to a friend. Remind your child to use complete sentences, capital letters, and proper end marks.

Name ______________________

# Test-Taking Tips

1. Write your name on the test.

2. Read each question twice.

3. Read all the answer choices for the question.

4. Mark your answer carefully.

5. Check your answer.

Name ______________________________

## Part 1: Vocabulary

**Read** each sentence.
**Mark** the ⬭ for the word that fits.

1. ______ dogs like to play.

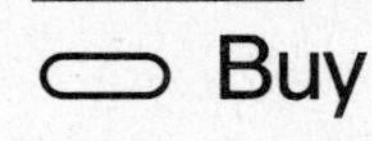 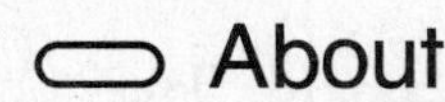 

⬭ Buy ⬭ About ⬭ These

2. This dog eats too ______ .

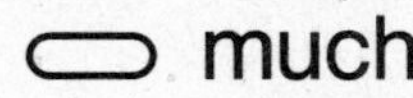 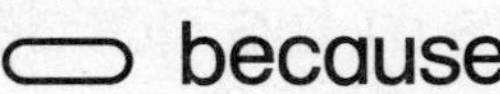 

⬭ much ⬭ because ⬭ old

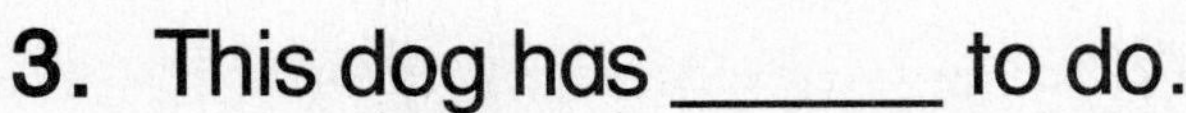

3. This dog has ______ to do.

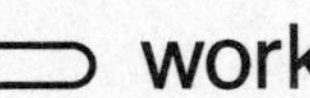 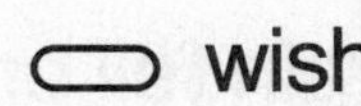

⬭ these ⬭ work ⬭ wish

4. This dog sleeps on the ______ .

⬭ ground ⬭ animals ⬭ together

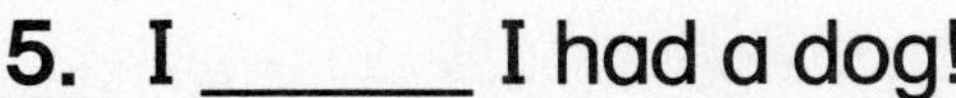

5. I ______ I had a dog!

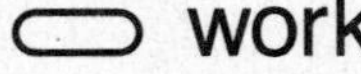 

⬭ shall ⬭ work ⬭ wish

Name ______________________________

## Part 2: Comprehension

**Read** each question.
**Mark** the ⬭ for the answer.

6. Toad wanted to have
   - ⬭ some work.
   - ⬭ a friend.
   - ⬭ a garden.

7. Right after Toad planted seeds, he
   - ⬭ went out to his garden with candles.
   - ⬭ told the seeds to start growing.
   - ⬭ played music for his seeds.

8. Why did Toad sing songs in his garden?
   - ⬭ He wanted to be like Frog.
   - ⬭ He wanted to make up a new song.
   - ⬭ He wanted to help the seeds.

9. What helped the seeds grow?
   - ⬭ The rain fell on them.
   - ⬭ Toad told them stories.
   - ⬭ Toad fell asleep.

10. Why is this story funny?
    - ⬭ Frog gives Toad some seeds.
    - ⬭ Toad thinks his seeds are afraid to grow.
    - ⬭ The seeds start to grow.

Name ______________________

beach

watch

brush

moth

**Circle** the word for each picture.

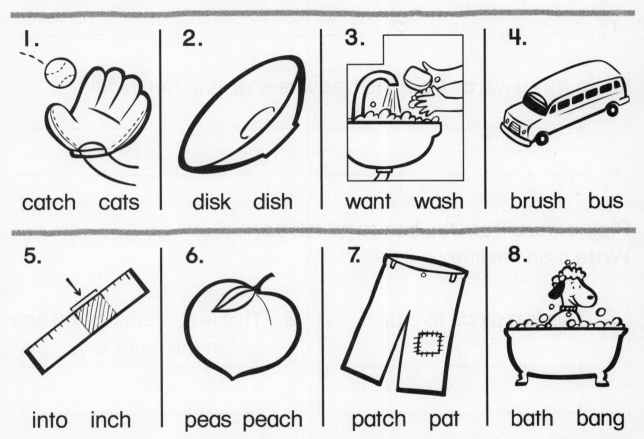

| 1. | 2. | 3. | 4. |
|---|---|---|---|
| catch cats | disk dish | want wash | brush bus |
| **5.** | **6.** | **7.** | **8.** |
| into inch | peas peach | patch pat | bath bang |

**Find** the word that has the same ending sound as the picture.
**Mark** the ⬭ to show your answer.

9. ⬭ watch
⬭ fish
⬭ flag

10. ⬭ bag
⬭ tent
⬭ teeth

**Notes for Home:** Your child read words ending with *ch, tch, sh,* and *th.* ***Home Activity:*** Help your child find items in the house that end with one of these sounds, such as *brush* and *couch*. Together, draw pictures of these items and label them.

Name ______________________

far car star dark yard start

**Write** three words from the box that rhyme with **bar**.

1. ____________ 2. ____________ 3. ____________

**Write** three words from the box where **ar** is in the middle.

4. ____________ 5. ____________ 6. ____________

**Pick** a word from the box to match each clue.
**Write** it on the line.

7. This is a place to play.

____________

8. This is something you can see in the night sky.

____________

**Pick** a word from the box to match each clue.
**Write** it on the line.

work these

9. rhymes with *knees* ____________

10. do a job ____________

**Notes for Home:** Your child spelled words with *ar* in which the letter *r* changes the sound of the vowel *a* and two frequently used words: *work, these.* ***Home Activity:*** Say each spelling word, and then use it in a sentence. Repeat the word and have your child write it.

Name ______________________



**RETEACHING**

A **sentence** tells a complete idea.
It begins with a **capital letter.**
**Questions** end with a **?**.
**Statements** end with a **.**.

**Circle** each group of words that makes a complete thought.
**Write** each sentence correctly on the line.
Remember to use a capital letter and an end mark for each sentence.

1. we will run

______________________

2. can I play

______________________

3. can Ted come

______________________

4. are no balls

______________________

5. is there a bat

______________________

**Notes for Home:** Your child correctly wrote statements and questions. ***Home Activity:*** Have your child explain rules for writing statements and questions correctly.

Name ______________________________

**Read** each group of words.
**Circle** each group of words that makes a complete sentence.

1. Are apples.
2. Lunch is good.
3. Can I eat too?
4. Is hungry.
5. Did Dad make it?
6. I helped cook lunch.

**Change** each telling sentence into an asking sentence.

It is four o'clock. Is it four o'clock?

7. There are apples.

______________________________

8. This is for me.

______________________________

**Notes for Home:** Your child correctly identified complete sentences. ***Home Activity:*** Say three questions to your child. Have him or her write them. Then help your child turn each question into a statement.

**You are your child's first and best teacher!**

**Here are ways to help your child practice skills while having fun!**

**Day 1** With your child, make up a story about a storm. Try to use as many words with the same vowel sound heard in *storm* as you can, such as *for, before, story,* or *tore.*

**Day 2** Your child is learning to read these words: *before, cold, full, off,* and *would.* Write questions for your child using these words. The questions can be silly or serious. Help your child read and answer each question.

**Day 3** Read a story with your child. Then discuss with your child what the theme of the story is. (The theme is the big idea of a story, for example, *Honesty is the best policy.)*

**Day 4** Your child is learning to listen to messages. Take turns giving and writing messages—one of you says a message that the other one writes down.

**Day 5** Read a story with your child. Ask your child to tell you whether he or she liked the story. Encourage your child to give examples of things he or she liked or didn't like about the story.

**Read with your child EVERY DAY!**



(fold here)

# Family Times

**Jordan Makes a New Friend** **Ice-Cold Birthday**

### A Stormy Morning

On this morning, it will rain.
A storm is coming now.
We'll stay inside. We'll have fun.
Just let me tell you how.

We'll write a story that is short.
We'll have some milk and popcorn.
We'll paint a picture of a horse.
We'll play my shiny horn.

When the storm has moved away
After all this fun,
We will have played and laughed a lot.
We'll go outside and run.

This rhyme includes words your child is working with in school: words with *or* where the letter *r* changes the vowel sound *(storm)* and words ending in *-ed* and *-ing.* Chant "A Stormy Morning" with your child. With your child, talk about things that he or she could do on a rainy day.

Name: ______________________

# End the Verb

**Materials** 1 button per player, index cards

**Game Directions**

1. Write the word endings below on three index cards. Players take turns choosing one of the word endings and tossing a button on the gameboard.

2. Player adds the chosen ending to the word landed on and spells the new word. A correct spelling earns 1 point.

3. The first player to get 10 points wins!

**Word Endings**

-s or -es

-ed

-ing

sled + ing = sledding



| | | |
|---|---|---|
| sled | bake | snow |
| spill | come | happen |
| start | play | rain |
| need | show | smile |

Name ______________________

**Circle** a word to finish each sentence.
**Write** it on the line.

horn

stare store

1. We went to the ______________ .

corn can

2. We got some ______________ .

storm start

3. Then a ______________ came.

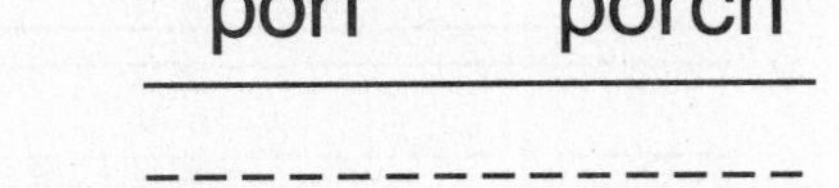

port porch

4. We ran for the ______________ .

for far

5. It rained ______________ two days.

**Notes for Home:** This week your child is learning to read words with *or* that have the same sound heard in *horn*. ***Home Activity:*** Work with your child to see how many words you can come up with to rhyme with *corn, score,* and *short.*

Name ______________________________

| | | |
|---|---|---|
| run**s** | rain**ed** | com**ing** |
| wash**es** | bak**ed** | napp**ing** |

**Add** the ending.
**Write** the new word on the line.

| | Word | | Ending | New Word |
|---|---|---|---|---|
| 1. | start | + | -ed | |
| 2. | bake | + | -ing | |
| 3. | teach | + | -es | |
| 4. | spill | + | -ed | |
| 5. | save | + | -ed | |
| 6. | blow | + | -ing | |
| 7. | mix | + | -es | |
| 8. | make | + | -ing | |
| 9. | rain | + | -s | |
| 10. | happen | + | -ed | |

**Notes for Home:** Your child added *-s, -es, -ed,* and *-ing* to verbs. ***Home Activity:*** Write a few of the new words above on slips of paper. Have your child choose a word and act it out or use it in a sentence.

Name ______________________________

**Pick** a word from the box to finish each sentence.
**Write** it on the line.

| before | cold | full | off | would |
|---|---|---|---|---|

1. It is very ________________ out.

2. I wish it ________________ snow.

3. We need snow ________________ we can sled.

4. Now the yard is ________________ of snow.

5. We will not take ________________ our hats!

**Notes for Home:** This week your child is learning to read the words *before, cold, full, off,* and *would.* ***Home Activity:*** Help your child write a winter story using these words.

Name ______________________________

**Read** the story.

## The Party

John went to a party.
He had fun playing games.
He liked eating cake.
He laughed and joked a lot.
John had a good time.

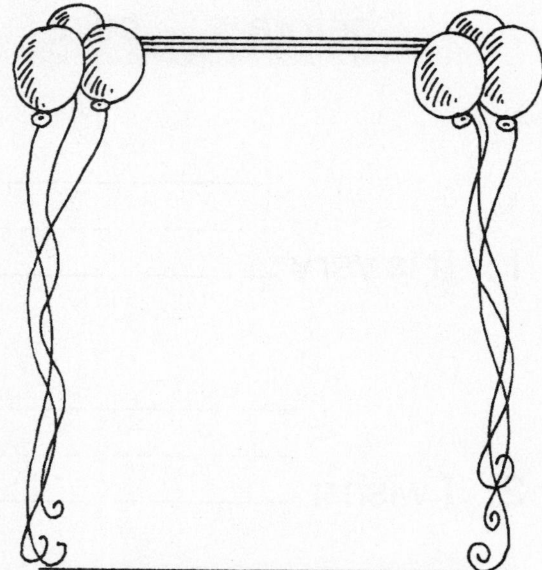

1. **Circle** the sentence that tells the big idea of the story.
2. **Draw** a picture in the box to show the big idea.

**Read** the big idea below.

3. **Draw** a picture in the box to show the big idea.
4. **Write** a title for your picture.

**Big Idea:**
It is great to have a friend.

______________________________________________

**Notes for Home:** Your child identified the theme, or the big idea of a story. ***Home Activity:*** Read a story to your child. Ask your child what the big idea of the story is. Encourage your child to think about how events in the story might be like his or her own life.

Name ______________________________

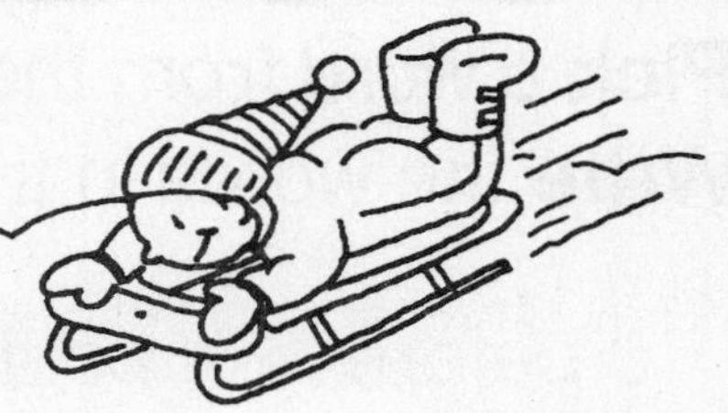

An **exclamation** tells about strong feelings.
It begins with a capital letter.
It ends with a **!** .

This is so much fun!

**Read** each sentence.
**Circle** each sentence that is an exclamation.

1. There was one foot of snow!

2. Do you know what we did?

3. We had a snow party!

4. All my friends came over.

**Write** a sentence that is an exclamation.

5. ______________________________

______________________________

**Notes for Home:** Your child identified and wrote exclamatory sentences *(This food is great!)*. ***Home Activity:*** Discuss with your child something fun that you did together. Ask your child to write some exclamatory sentences about that time.

Name ______________________________

**Pick** a word from the box to match each clue.
**Write** the words in the puzzles.

| before | cold | full | off | would | wrote |
|---|---|---|---|---|---|

1. ______ you like to come to my party?
2. not after
3.

4. not on
5. not empty
6. not hot

**Notes for Home:** Your child used words learned this week to solve a puzzle. ***Home Activity:*** Help your child write a poem using some of these words above.

Name ______________________________



**Circle** the word for each picture.

farm

1. 
arm aim

2. 
band barn

3. 
care car

4. 
jar jam

5. 
duck dark

6. 
party paint

7. 
cart cork

8. 
cord card

**Find** the word that rhymes with ☆.
**Mark** the ⬭ to show your answer.

9. ⬭ farm
⬭ far
⬭ for

10. ⬭ tar
⬭ thorn
⬭ trap

**Notes for Home:** Your child read words with *ar* that have the vowel sound heard in *farm*. ***Home Activity:*** Ask your child to make up a story about a car trip. Encourage your child to use words with *ar* that have the same vowel sound as *car*.

Name ______________________________

**Look** at each word. **Say** it.
**Listen** for the vowel sound in  .

| | **Write** each word. | **Check** it. |
|---|---|---|
| 1. or | | |
| 2. for | | |
| 3. fork | | |
| 4. born | | |
| 5. short | | |
| 6. torn | | |

# Word Wall Words

**Write** each word.

| | | |
|---|---|---|
| 7. cold | | |
| 8. would | | |

**Notes for Home:** Your child spelled words with *or* that have the vowel sound heard in *storm* and two frequently used words: *cold, would.* ***Home Activity:*** Work with your child to write these spelling words in alphabetical order.

Name ______________________

**Write** each sentence correctly.
**Begin** each sentence with a capital letter.
**Add** a **!** at the end.

1. my room is a mess

2. this pie is good

3. he runs very fast

4. we love our pet

**Draw** a picture for one of the sentences above.

5.

**Notes for Home:** Your child wrote exclamations—sentences that express strong feelings. ***Home Activity:*** Take turns saying sentences that express strong feelings. Encourage your child to speak with emotion.

Name ______________________________

# Test-Taking Tips

1. Write your name on the test.

2. Read each question twice.

3. Read all the answer choices for the question.

4. Mark your answer carefully.

5. Check your answer.

Name ______________________________

# Part 1: Vocabulary

**Read** each sentence.
**Mark** the ⬭ for the word that fits.

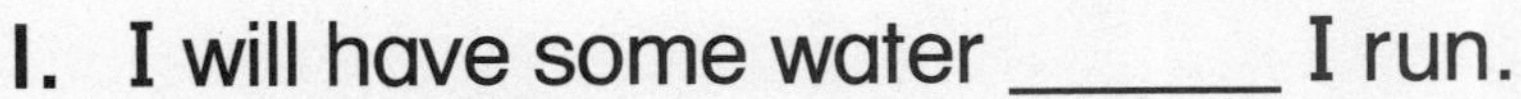

1. I will have some water ______ I run.

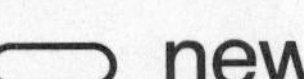

⬭ before ⬭ new ⬭ around

2. Jack ______ like some water too.

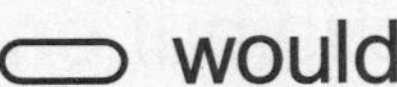

⬭ bring ⬭ would ⬭ think

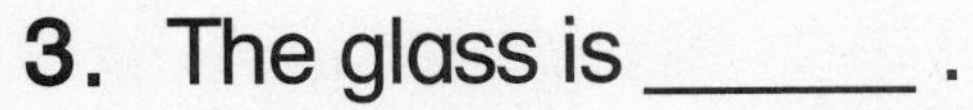

3. The glass is ______ .

⬭ when ⬭ full ⬭ off

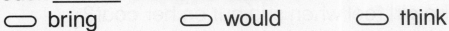

4. I shut ______ the water.

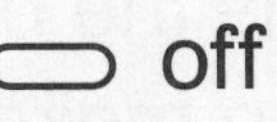

⬭ before ⬭ four ⬭ off

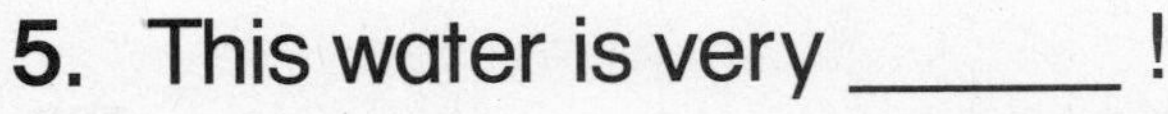

5. This water is very ______ !

⬭ cold ⬭ would ⬭ old

GO ON

Name ______________________



# Part 2: Comprehension

**Read** each question.
**Mark** the ⬭ for the answer.

6. On the day of the girl's birthday,
   - ⬭ she broke her arm.
   - ⬭ she spilled green paint.
   - ⬭ it was snowing.

7. Why did the birthday cake stop baking?
   - ⬭ No one came to the party.
   - ⬭ The power was out.
   - ⬭ It was cold out.

8. How did the girl feel when she put on her coat?
   - ⬭ sad
   - ⬭ happy
   - ⬭ sleepy

9. What did Mom do?
   - ⬭ She made a flag.
   - ⬭ She told a story.
   - ⬭ She made a pancake.

10. This story seems to say that
    - ⬭ a sled is the best thing to get.
    - ⬭ you can make your own fun.
    - ⬭ every day is like a birthday.

STOP

Name ________________________________

**Pick** a word from the box to finish each compound word.
**Write** it on the line.
**Draw** a line to the picture it matches.

flashlight

| brush | cakes | coat | man |
|---|---|---|---|

1. pan________________

5.

2. paint________________

6.

3. rain________________

7.

4. snow________________

8.

---

**Find** the compound word.
**Mark** the ⊂⊃ to show your answer.

9. ⊂⊃ playing
⊂⊃ everything
⊂⊃ walking

10. ⊂⊃ mitten
⊂⊃ marching
⊂⊃ maybe

**Notes for Home:** Your child reviewed compound words—words formed by joining two or more other words. ***Home Activity:*** Walk around the house with your child and help him or her write down as many things as you see that are compound words (*toothbrush, dishwasher, hairbrush*).

Name ______________________

or for fork born short torn

**Write** two words from the box that rhyme with **corn**.

1. ______________ 2. ______________

**Write** two words from the box that rhyme with **more**.

3. ______________ 4. ______________

**Pick** a word from the box to finish each sentence.
**Write** it on the line.

5. I have a ______________ stack of pancakes.

6. I eat them with a ______________ .

**Pick** a word from the box to match each clue.
**Write** it on the line.

cold would

7. not hot ______________

8. sounds like *wood* ______________

**Notes for Home:** Your child spelled words with *or* that have the same vowel sound as *f<u>or</u>k* and two frequently used words: *cold, would.* ***Home Activity:*** Challenge your child to use each spelling word in a written sentence. Then have your child read each sentence aloud.

Name ______________________________

RETEACHING

An **exclamation** is a sentence that shows strong feeling.
It begins with a capital letter.
It ends with **!**.

**I'm so scared!**

**Read** each sentence.
**Write** the exclamation on the line.

1. I need some help. Help me!

2. I'm having a great time! This is fun.

3. Leave me alone! Please leave.

4. I feel good. I'm so happy!

5. Look out! You should be careful.

**Notes for Home:** Your child identified and wrote exclamations—sentences that show strong feeling. ***Home Activity:*** Ask your child to write short sentences that show strong, happy feelings and that end with exclamation marks (*!*).

Name ________________________________

**Look** at each picture.
**Write** an exclamation about it.

1.

2.

3.

4.

5.

**Notes for Home:** Your child wrote exclamations—sentences that express strong feeling. ***Home Activity:*** Write an exclamation and have your child act it out. Then change roles.

**You *are* your child's first *and* best teacher!**

**Here are ways to help your child practice skills while having fun!**

**Day 1** Write *her, bird,* and *turtle* on a sheet of paper. Help your child list other words with this vowel sound spelled *er, ir,* and *ur (fern, shirt, hurt).*

**Day 2** Ask your child to draw a picture that shows different animal homes and then write about the picture using any of these words: *each, once, other, under,* and *which.*

**Day 3** Watch a TV show or movie with your child. Ask your child to tell you how a character feels based on the way the character acts or talks.

**Day 4** Your child is learning to write commands, such as *Sit down.* Take turns giving and following commands.

**Day 5** Children enjoy acting out the stories they hear. When you find a book with strong story action, invite your child to act it out as you read.

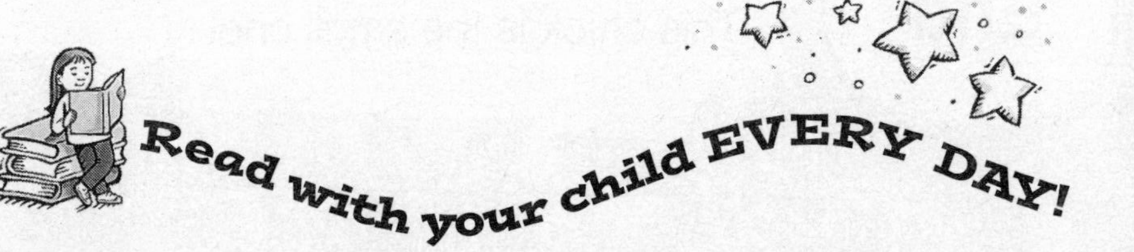
Read with your child EVERY DAY!

(fold here)

# Family Times

**Show Time: Your First Play** **Do You Live in a Nest?**

### Our First-Grade Play

Will you join our first-grade play?
You can dance and twirl.
You'll wear a purple shirt or skirt
Like every boy and girl.

The turkeys are the biggest birds.
They burst out from their cage.
Smaller birds and turtles too
Will chirp or whirl on stage.

This rhyme includes words your child is working with in school: words with *ir* and *ur* that have the same vowel sound *(first, burst)* and words with the comparative endings *-er* and *-est (smaller, biggest).* Read "Our First-Grade Play" with your child. Together, find words that have the same vowel sound as *first.*

Name: ______________________

# Fair to Compare

**Materials** paper, scissors, marker, bag, 1 button per player

**Game Directions**

**1.** Copy the sentences shown. Cut apart each sentence and put it in a bag.

**2.** Players place buttons on Start and take turns drawing sentences from bag.

**3.** Players must add either the *-er* or *-est* ending to the underlined word so it makes sense in the sentence. Answers are shown below.

**4.** A player who answers correctly may move his or her button to the next space. The first player to reach the end wins!

**Answers (in order): harder, tallest, smaller, nicest, softer, hotter, coldest, smoother, smallest**

Start

This test was hard than the last one.

The man was the tall I've ever seen.

An ant is small than a dog.

I have the nice friend of all.

My cat's fur is soft than a feather.

Today is hot than yesterday.

This is the cold day ever.

This rock is smooth than that rock.

This chick is the small one.

End

Name ______________________

**Pick** the letters from the box to finish each word.
**Write** the letters on the line.

er ir ur

turtle

1. p ______ se

2. f ______ st

3. f ______ n

4. d ______ t

5. sk ______ t

6. h ______

7. b ______ d

8. t ______ key

9. cl ______ k

10. n ______ se

**Notes for Home:** Your child wrote words in which the letters *er, ir,* and *ur* represent the same vowel sound heard in *her*, *shirt*, and *turtle*. ***Home Activity:*** Make a list of the words with *er, ir,* and *ur* that have this vowel sound. Ask your child to sort the words by their spelling.

Name ______________________________

**Circle** the word for each picture.

small

small<u>**er**</u>

small<u>**est**</u>

1.
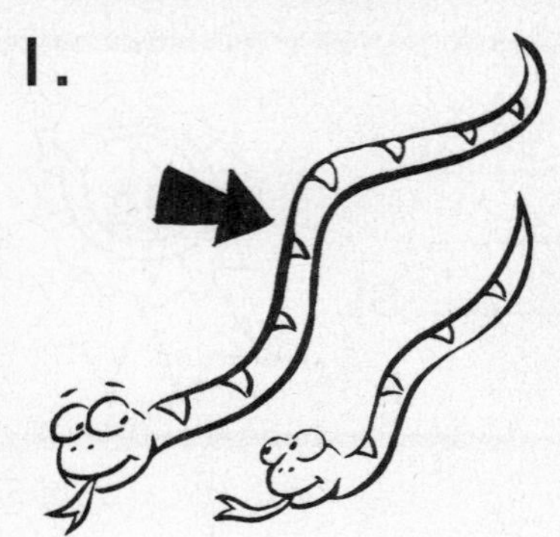
longer longest

2.

warmer warmest

3.

slower slowest

4.

lower lowest

5.

taller tallest

6.

higher highest

**Write -er** or **-est** to finish the word in each sentence.

7. The little bird has the small __________ nest.

8. The big bird sings a sweet __________ song than the little bird.

**Notes for Home:** Your child identified the comparative endings *-er* and *-est* as in *small<u>er</u>* and *small<u>est</u>*. ***Home Activity:*** Compare different animals with your child. Use *-er* when comparing two animals. Use *-est* when comparing more than two.

Name ________________________________

**Pick** a word from the box to finish each sentence.
**Write** it on the line.

| each | once | other | under | which |
|---|---|---|---|---|

1. ______________ animal has a home.

2. I ______________ saw a bird in her nest.

3. Some animals live ______________ a log.

4. ______________ animals live in barns.

5. ______________ home do you live in?

**Notes for Home:** This week your child is learning to read the words *each, once, other, under,* and *which*. ***Home Activity:*** Write each of these words on a slip of paper. Hold each slip up for your child and ask him or her to read the word aloud to you.

Name ______________________

**Look** at each picture.
**Write** a sentence that tells what happened.

1.

______________________________________________

2.

______________________________________________

3.

______________________________________________

4.

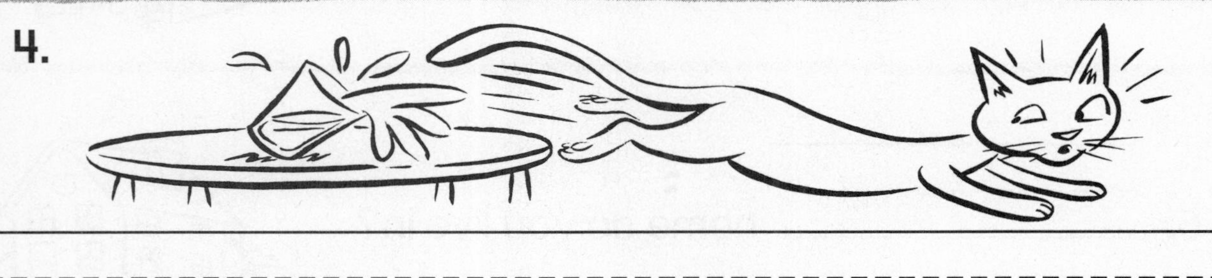

______________________________________________

**Notes for Home:** Your child drew conclusions from pictures. ***Home Activity:*** Look at a storybook with your child. Cover up the words with a slip of paper. Invite your child to tell you about the story using only the illustrations.

Name ______________________________

A **command** is a sentence that tells you to do something.
A command ends with a **.** .

Shut the door.

Please take off your boots.

**Circle** each sentence that is a command.

1. Do you live here?
2. Please come in.
3. Please sit down.
4. This is a great play!
5. I like to be in plays.
6. Which bird sings sweetest?
7. Stay here.
8. Open your book.

**Write** two commands.

9. ______________________________

10. ______________________________

**Notes for Home:** Your child identified and wrote commands. ***Home Activity:*** Have your child pretend he or she is the director of a play. Ask your child to give stage directions in the form of commands. For example: *Move to the right.*

Name ________________________________

**Pick** a word from the box to match each clue.
**Write** the words in the puzzles.

| each | great | once | other | under | which |
|---|---|---|---|---|---|

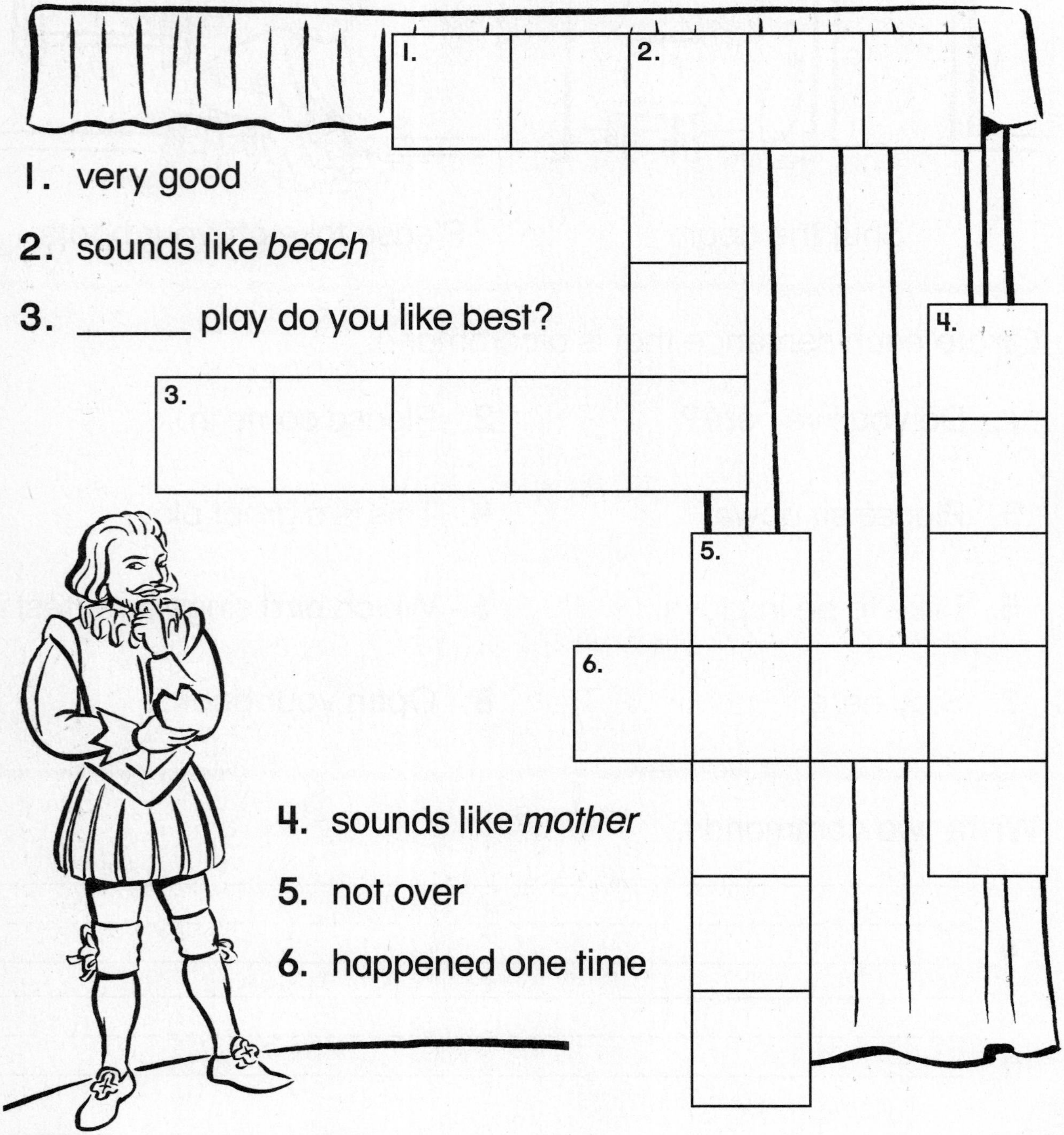

1. very good
2. sounds like *beach*
3. ______ play do you like best?

4. sounds like *mother*
5. not over
6. happened one time

**Notes for Home:** Your child solved puzzles using words he or she learned this week. ***Home Activity:*** Work with your child to write a short play. Try to use as many of the words from the box as possible. Together, act out what you wrote.

Name ________________________________

**Read** the chart.
**Use** it to answer each question.

| Tickets | |
|---|---|
| Monday | 𝍸 |
| Tuesday | IIII |
| Wednesday | III |
| Thursday | II |
| Friday | 𝍸 I |

𝍸 = 5

1. On which day did the students sell 5 tickets?

2. Did the students sell more tickets on Monday or Friday?

3. On which day were the fewest tickets sold?

4. How many tickets were sold on Wednesday and Thursday?

**Notes for Home:** Your child used a chart to find information and answer questions.
***Home Activity:*** Together, create a chart showing chores that family members do at home.

Name ______________________________

**Say** the word for each picture.
**Circle** the word that has the same vowel sound as the picture.

| 1. | 2. | 3. | 4. |
|---|---|---|---|
| cart cork | born burn | shirt tore | car store |

| 5. | 6. | 7. | 8. |
|---|---|---|---|
| fort first | share short | more most | fork farm |

**Find** the word that has the same middle sound as .
**Mark** the ⬭ to show your answer.

9. ⬭ porch
⬭ perch
⬭ part

10. ⬭ such
⬭ shut
⬭ shore

**Notes for Home:** Your child reviewed words spelled with *or* as in *storm*. ***Home Activity:*** Help your child make up a story using words with this vowel sound, such as *unicorn, horn, stork, popcorn,* or *boring*. Then have your child illustrate his or her story.

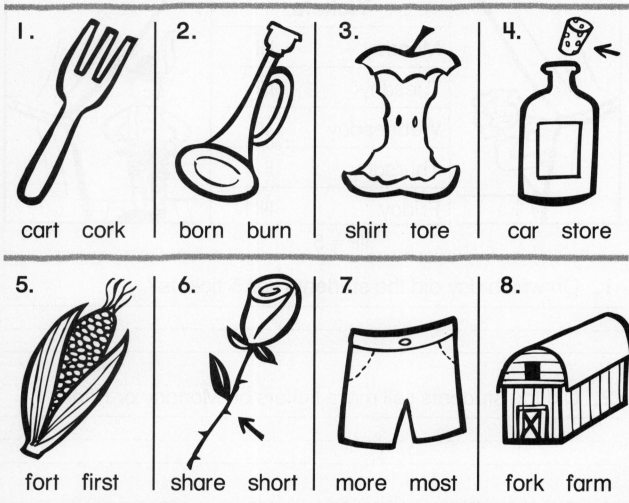

Name ____________________

**Look** at each word. **Say** it.
**Listen** for the vowel sound in  .

| | **Write** each word. | **Check** it. |
|---|---|---|
| 1. her | | |
| 2. turn | | |
| 3. hurt | | |
| 4. girl | | |
| 5. first | | |
| 6. bird | | |

## Word Wall Words

**Write** each word.

| | | |
|---|---|---|
| 7. once | | |
| 8. which | | |

**Notes for Home:** Your child spelled words with *er, ir,* and *ur* that have the same vowel sound *(her, girl, hurt)* and two frequently used words: *once, which.* ***Home Activity:*** Say each spelling word. Have your child use it in a sentence. Then have your child write it down.

Name ______________________________

**Read** each sentence.
**Circle** each sentence that is a command.

1. I got the starring part in a play!
2. Do you want to come?
3. Please come at two.
4. Sit in the front row.
5. Bring all your friends.
6. Watch for the big dog.
7. That dog will be me!

**Write** three sentences that are commands.

8. ______________________________

9. ______________________________

10. ______________________________

**Notes for Home:** Your child identified and wrote commands (For example: *Bring me that bag.*). ***Home Activity:*** Play a version of "Simon Says" where your child follows the directions *only* if you give him or her a command. Then change roles.

Name ______________________________

# Part 1: Vocabulary

**Read** each sentence.

**Mark** the ⬭ for the word that fits.

1. ______ nest is for me?

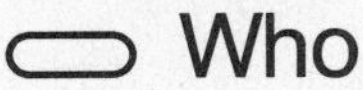

⬭ Who ⬭ Before ⬭ Which

2. Cat sleeps _____ the bed.

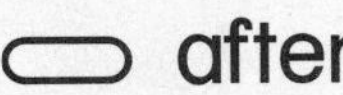

⬭ under ⬭ after ⬭ much

3. Ben rides the bus _____ day.

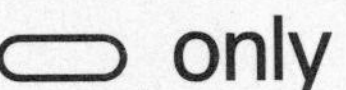

⬭ each ⬭ only ⬭ these

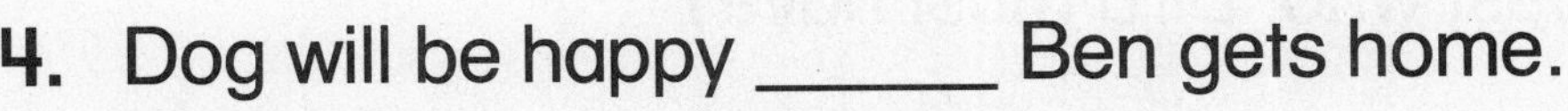

4. Dog will be happy ______ Ben gets home.

⬭ which ⬭ once ⬭ each

5. This one is for you. The ______ one is for me.

⬭ under ⬭ off ⬭ other

GO ON

Name ______________________________



# Part 2: Comprehension

**Read** each question.
**Mark** the ⬭ for the answer.

6. Who is coming to visit?
   - ⬭ Frog
   - ⬭ Bird
   - ⬭ Cat

7. Frog lives by the
   - ⬭ water.
   - ⬭ rock.
   - ⬭ tree.

8. What is in Horse's barn?
   - ⬭ bones
   - ⬭ hay
   - ⬭ rocks

9. Bird is the only one who
   - ⬭ runs.
   - ⬭ eats.
   - ⬭ sings.

10. Who knows best what Bird must have?
    - ⬭ Cricket
    - ⬭ Lion
    - ⬭ Turtle

STOP

Name ______________________



**Add -s** or **-es** to each verb.
**Write** the new verb on the line.

1. play ____________
2. fix ____________
3. rain ____________
4. kiss ____________
5. wish ____________
6. ask ____________

**Add -ed** and **-ing** to each verb.
**Write** the new verbs on the lines.

| | Add -ed | Add -ing |
|---|---|---|
| 7. jump | | |
| 8. bake | | |
| 9. start | | |
| 10. stop | | |

**Notes for Home:** Your child reviewed words that end in *-s, -es, -ed,* and *-ing*. ***Home Activity:*** Help your child list verbs. Ask him or her to change the verbs by adding *-s, -es, -ed,* or *-ing*. Discuss how the spelling, sound, and meaning of a word changes when the endings are added.

Name ______________________

her turn hurt girl first bird

**Write** three words from the box that are spelled with **ir**.

1. ____________ 2. ____________ 3. ____________

**Write** two words from the box that are spelled with **ur**.

4. ____________ 5. ____________

**Write** the word from the box that is spelled with **er**.

6. ____________

**Write** the word from the box that is the opposite of each word.

7. boy ____________ 8. last ____________

**Pick** a word from the box to finish each sentence.
**Write** it on the line.

once which

9. ____________ I was in a play.

10. ____________ play were you in?

**Notes for Home:** Your child spelled words with *er, ir,* and *ur* that have the same vowel sound *(her, girl, hurt)* and two frequently used words: *once, which*. ***Home Activity:*** Say each spelling word. Have your child use it in a sentence. Then have your child write it down.

Name ______________________________

RETEACHING

**Go to bed.**

One kind of sentence is called a **command**.
A **command** tells someone to do something.
It ends with a **.**.

**Draw** a picture for each command.

**1.** Eat your dinner.

**2.** Please come here.

**3.** Get in line.

**4.** Please read this book to me.

---

**Write** a command.
**Draw** a picture of it.

**5.** ______________________________

______________________________

______________________________

**Notes for Home:** Your child showed understanding of commands by illustrating them. ***Home Activity:*** Have your child write commands that lead to a treasure. *(Take ten steps. Open the cupboard. Look on the shelf. Find the cookie.)*

Name ______________________________

**Draw** a line under each command.

1. Please come here.
2. Are you happy today?
3. When are we going?
4. Help me with this.
5. You are my friend.
6. Put on your coat.
7. Turn off the light.
8. What time is it?
9. Tell me what time it is.

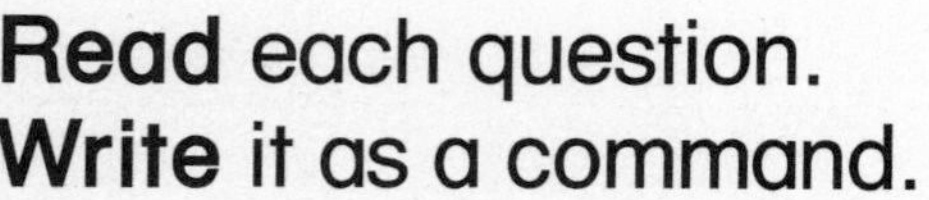

**Read** each question.
**Write** it as a command.

10. Will you play ball?

______________________________

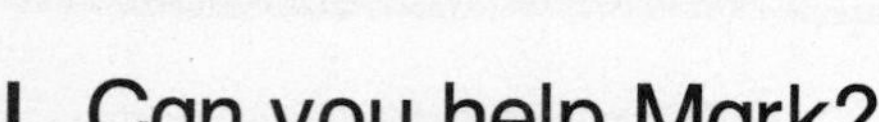

11. Can you help Mark?

______________________________

12. Will you go there?

______________________________

**Notes for Home:** Your child identified and wrote commands. ***Home Activity:*** Have your child make up an imaginary pet. Then help him or her write commands for the pet. *(Come here. Eat your carrots.)*

**You *are* your child's first *and* best teacher!**

**Here are ways to help your child practice skills while having fun!**

**Day 1** Play a clapping game with your child. Take turns saying two-syllable words, such as *paper, poster,* and *funny,* clapping once for each syllable.

**Day 2** Your child is learning to read these words: *along, goes, great, idea,* and *pull.* Encourage your child to make up a simple poem using as many of these words as possible.

**Day 3** When reading with your child, ask him or her to retell the story in simple terms. Ask helpful questions, such as: *What happened at the beginning? What happened in the middle? What happened at the end?*

**Day 4** Your child is learning to express an opinion and to persuade other people. Have your child think of a product he or she likes, such as a kind of juice or a breakfast cereal, and try to convince you to use it.

**Day 5** Read a story together and look for the pronouns *I, we, you, he, she, it,* or *they.* Challenge your child to tell you the character or thing each pronoun represents.

**Read with your child EVERY DAY!**



(fold here)

# Family Times

**What's New in Mrs. Powell's Class?** **Fox on Stage**

### You Will See

Now it's time to see our play.
It begins at noon today.
You will come in and sit down.
You will never want to frown.
You will see a funny clown.
You will see an owl that's brown.

You will see a shiny crown.
You will see a yellow gown.
You will see a jolly cow.
You will hear a cat meow.
You will see us take a bow.
You will clap and then say, "Wow!"

This rhyme includes words your child is working with in school: words spelled with *ow* that have the same vowel sound as *clown* and two-syllable words with one or two consonants in the middle, such as *today*. Help your child draw pictures of the things to see that are listed in the rhyme.

Name: ______________________

# Clown Goes to Town

**Materials** 1 coin, 1 button per player, paper, pencil

**Game Directions**

**1.** Place buttons on Start.

**2.** Players take turns flipping the coin to see how many spaces to move—one space for heads, two for tails.

**3.** Player must say a word beginning with the consonant or consonants on the space that has the same vowel sound as *clown*. Use a word only once. Make a list to keep track.

**4.** The first player to reach the end wins!

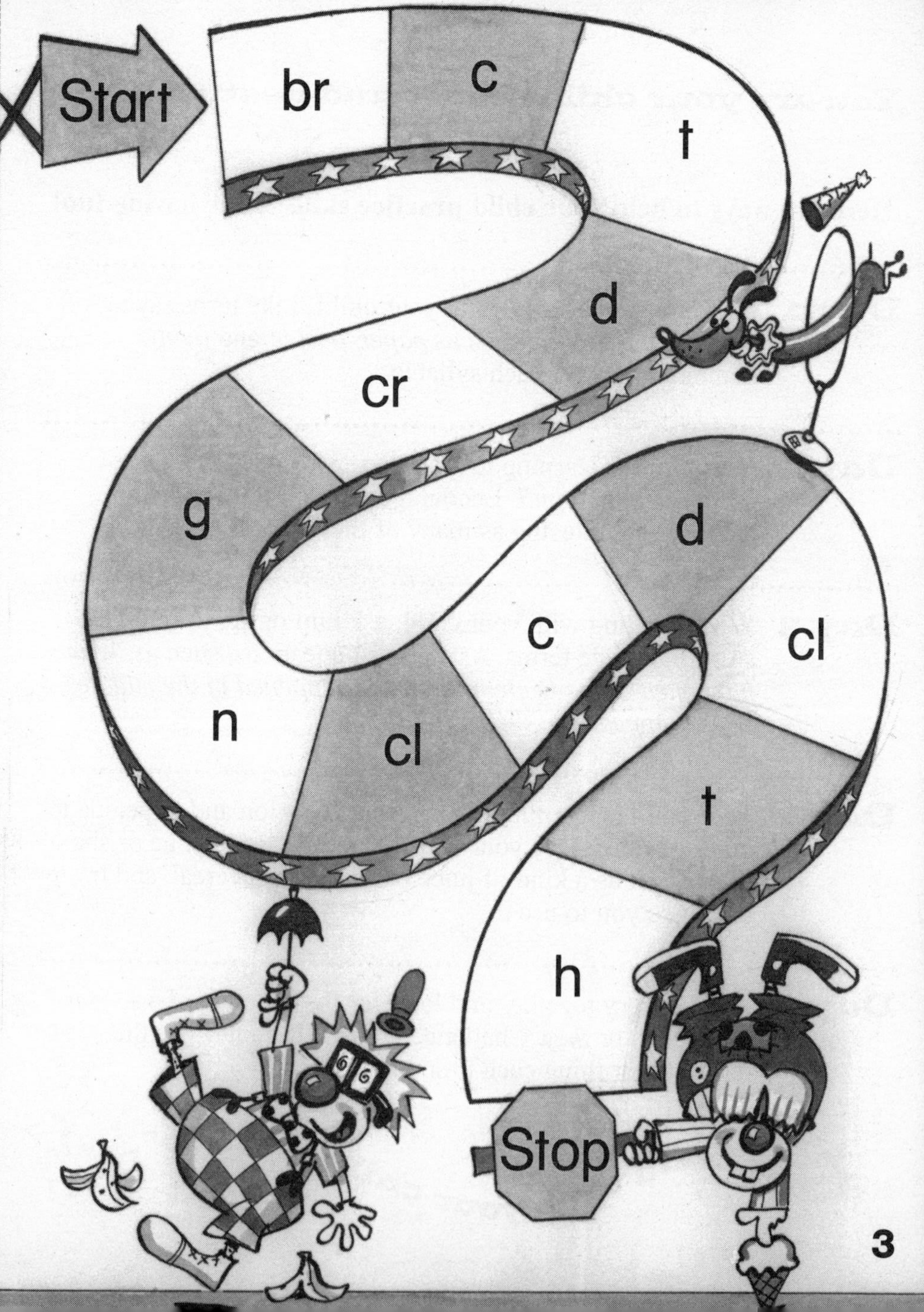

Start → br → c → t → d → cr → g → n → cl → c → d → cl → t → h → Stop

Name ______________________

**Pick** a word from the box to match each picture.
**Write** it on the line.

cr**ow**n

| clown | cow | flower | owl | towel | town |
|---|---|---|---|---|---|

1. ______________________

2. ______________________

3. ______________________

4. ______________________

5. ______________________

6. ______________________

**Notes for Home:** Your child read and wrote words with *ow* that have the vowel sound heard in *crown.* ***Home Activity:*** Encourage your child to think of other words with *ow* that rhyme with *cow* and *brown.*

Name ____________________

**Say** the word for each picture.
**Write** the letters to finish each word.

rabbit

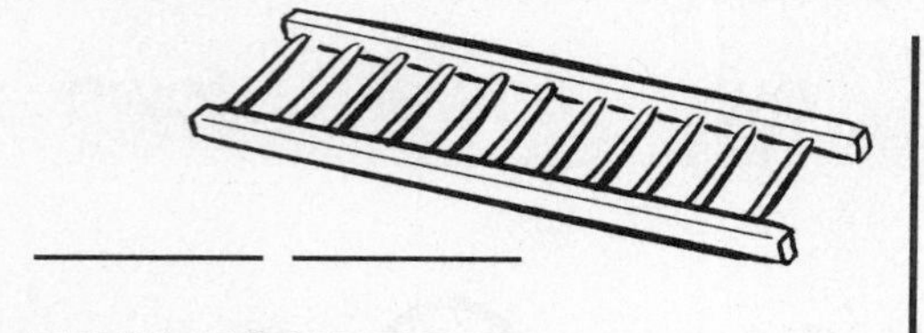

1. la ____ ____ er

2. pa ____ er

3. zi ____ ____ er

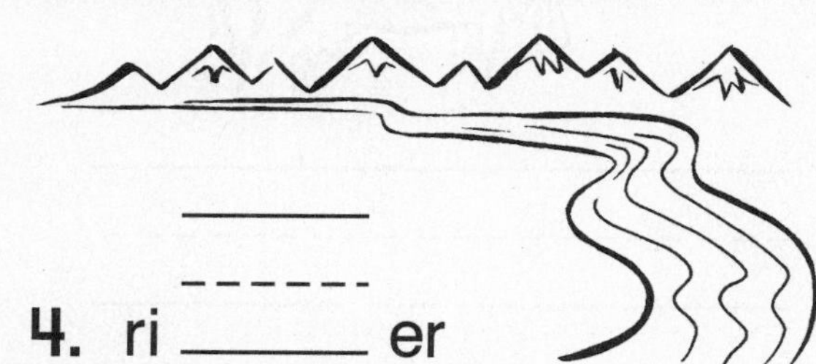

4. ri ____ er

**Put** the two parts together to make a word.
**Write** the word on the line.

5. mum • my

____________________

6. nev • er

____________________

7. be • gan

____________________

8. for • got

____________________

**Notes for Home:** Your child practiced reading and writing two-syllable words. ***Home Activity:*** Look in your refrigerator. Name different items in the refrigerator. Decide whether each name has one syllable or more than one syllable.

Name ______________________

**Pick** a word from the box to finish each sentence.
**Write** it on the line.

| along | goes | great | idea | pull |
|---|---|---|---|---|

1. We have a ______________ big dog.

2. He ______________ outside to play.

3. We run ______________ the fence.

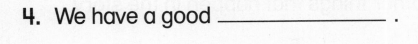

4. We have a good ______________ .

5. He can ______________ the wagon.

**Notes for Home:** This week your child is learning to read the words *along, goes, great, idea,* and *pull*. ***Home Activity:*** Help your child write sentences that contain each of these words. Ask your child to draw pictures showing what happens in each sentence.

Name ______________________________

**Read** the story.
**Look** at the pictures.

## Cat and Fox Make Muffins

Cat and Fox want muffins.
First they get what they need.
They mix it all together.
They put the mix in a muffin pan.
Then they bake the muffins.

Soon the muffins are done.
They are very hot and sweet.
Cat and Fox put jam on them.
They eat two muffins each.
There are two muffins left.

**Write** 1, 2, 3 in the pictures to tell what happens in the beginning, middle, and end.

1. ☐
2. ☐
3. ☐

**Draw** pictures of two other things that happen in the story.

4.

5.

**Notes for Home:** Your child identified and drew pictures of important story events. ***Home Activity:*** Ask your child to tell you a short version of a favorite story. Remind him or her to include all the important parts of the plot and tell them in order.

Name ______________________________

A **pronoun** is a word that can take the place of a noun.
These words are pronouns: **I, we, you, he, she, it, they.**

**Tom and Mike** like school. **They** like school.

**Read** each sentence.
**Circle** the pronoun that replaces the underlined words.

1. My dogs and I play. We They

2. The ball goes up. It She

3. My mom and dad play too. She They

4. My dad throws the ball. He She

5. My mom catches it. She It

**Notes for Home:** Your child used personal pronouns—*I, we, you, he, she, it,* and *they*—to replace the subject in sentences. ***Home Activity:*** Make up a few simple sentences that begin with nouns , such as *Jill went to the store.* Ask your child to replace the noun with a pronoun.

Name ______________________________

**Pick** a word from the box to match each clue.
**Write** the words in the puzzles.

| along | folks | goes | great | idea | pull |
|---|---|---|---|---|---|

1. rhymes with *strong*
2. very good
3. something you think of

4. people
5. not push
6. not comes.

**Notes for Home:** Your child solved puzzles using words learned this week. ***Home Activity:*** Together, write a story about a great idea. Use as many of the listed words as possible. Help your child to read the story aloud.

Name ____________________

her

bird

curtain

**Say** the word for each picture.
**Circle** the word that has the same vowel sound as the picture.

1. third short
2. clerk cork
3. dart dirt
4. star stir
5. barn surf
6. her harm
7. forest girl
8. turn track

**Find** the word that has the same vowel sound as .
**Mark** the ⊂⊃ to show your answer.

9. ⊂⊃ turkey
   ⊂⊃ basket
   ⊂⊃ target

10. ⊂⊃ brand
    ⊂⊃ burn
    ⊂⊃ card

**Notes for Home:** Your child reviewed words spelled with *er, ir,* and *ur* that have the same vowel sound *(her, bird, curtain)*. ***Home Activity:*** Help your child make up rhymes using words with this vowel sound and these spellings *(You can't wear that shirt. It is covered in dirt!)*.

Name ______________________________

**Look** at each word. **Say** it.
**Listen** for the **vowel** sound in  .

| | **Write** each word. | **Check** it. |
|---|---|---|
| 1. how | | |
| 2. now | | |
| 3. town | | |
| 4. down | | |
| 5. brown | | |
| 6. clown | | |

# Word Wall Words

**Write** each word.

| | | |
|---|---|---|
| 7. pull | | |
| 8. goes | | |

**Notes for Home:** Your child spelled words with *ow* with the vowel sound heard in <u>owl</u> and two frequently used words: *pull, goes*. ***Home Activity:*** Work with your child to make up nonsense rhyming sentences with these sounds, such as: *How now, brown cow?*

Name ______________________________

**Read** each sentence.
**Pick** a pronoun from the box to replace the underlined words.
**Write** it on the line.

he it she they we

______________ 1. Bob and I put on a play.

______________ 2. John and Amy came to see us.

______________ 3. John sat on a bench.

______________ 4. Amy sat next to him.

______________ 5. The play was funny.

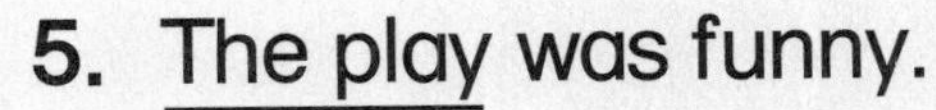

**Notes for Home:** Your child replaced nouns with pronouns in sentences. ***Home Activity:*** Read a story with your child. Point out the pronouns and ask your child what person, place, or thing each pronoun represents.

Name ___________________________



# Test-Taking Tips

1. Write your name on the test.

2. Read each question twice.

3. Read all the answer choices for the question.

4. Mark your answer carefully.

5. Check your answer.

Name ______________________________

# Part 1: Vocabulary

**Read** each sentence.
**Mark** the ⬭ for the word that fits.

1. Emma has an ______ .

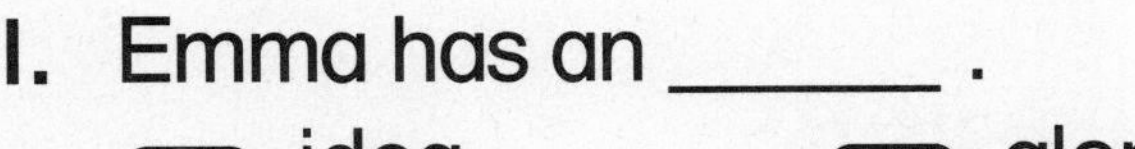

⬭ idea  ⬭ along  ⬭ any

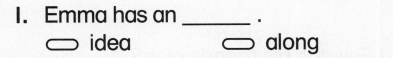

2. She ties a rope ______ the tree's side.

⬭ when  ⬭ any  ⬭ along

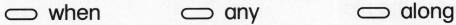

3. "______ on the rope," says Emma.

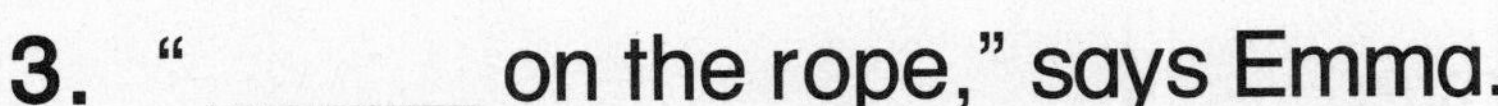

⬭ Sing  ⬭ Pull  ⬭ Jump

4. The basket ______ up.

⬭ buys  ⬭ goes  ⬭ puts

5. What a ______ plan!

⬭ new  ⬭ right  ⬭ great

GO ON

Name ______________________________



# Part 2: Comprehension

**Read** each question.

**Mark** the ⬭ for the answer.

6. What were Fox and his friends doing at first?
   - ⬭ just lying around
   - ⬭ putting on a play
   - ⬭ watching TV

7. What kind of play did Fox and his friends plan?
   - ⬭ a funny play
   - ⬭ a long play
   - ⬭ a scary play

8. At the end of the play,
   - ⬭ Dexter crashed into the set.
   - ⬭ the curtain came down.
   - ⬭ Fox's costume fell apart in the rain.

9. When the show was over,
   - ⬭ Fox got all wet.
   - ⬭ people said the show was very funny.
   - ⬭ Carmen went to buy a new car.

10. Why did Fox start to plan a new show?
    - ⬭ People liked his first show.
    - ⬭ Dexter asked him to.
    - ⬭ His TV was still broken.

STOP

Name ______________________________

**Look** at each picture.
**Add 's** to a word to tell who owns something.
**Write** the new word on the line.

1.

________________ mug

2.
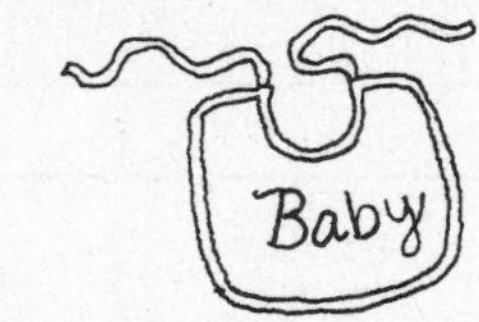


________________ bib

3.

________________ room

4.

________________ chair

5.

________________ ball

6.

________________ dish

**Find** the words that tell who owns something.
**Mark** the ⬭ to show your answer.

7. ⬭ Mom gems
⬭ Mom's gems
⬭ Moms gems

8. ⬭ Dad tie
⬭ Dads tie
⬭ Dad's tie

**Notes for Home:** Your child used *'s* to tell who owns something. ***Home Activity:*** Draw pictures with your child of objects that someone in your family owns. Help your child label each picture, such as *the cat's dish* or *the baby's crib.*

Name ______________________



how now town down brown clown

**Write** the words from the box that rhyme with **cow**.

1. ______________ 2. ______________

**Write** the words from the box that rhyme with **crown**.

3. ______________ 4. ______________

5. ______________ 6. ______________

**Pick** a word from the box to match each clue.
**Write** it on the line.

7. not up ______________

8. It's smaller than a city. ______________

**Pick** a word from the box to finish each sentence.
**Write** it on the line.

pull goes

9. You must ______________ the rope down.

10. Now the curtain ______________ up.

**Notes for Home:** Your child spelled words with *ow* that have the vowel sound heard in *cl*<u>*ow*</u>*n* and spelled two frequently used words: *pull, goes*. ***Home Activity:*** Say each spelling word, and then use it in a sentence. Repeat the word, and have your child write it.

Name ______________________________

**RETEACHING**

**The mother** cooks breakfast.
**She** cooks breakfast.

**The boy** eats an apple.
**He** eats an apple.

**The glass** holds water.
**It** holds water.

**He, she, it, I, we, you,** and **they** can take the place of nouns. They are called **pronouns.**

**Draw** a line to connect sentences that have matching meanings.

| | |
|---|---|
| 1. The boys read a book. | He hears the story. |
| 2. The book is very big. | They read a book. |
| 3. A man hears the story. | It is very big. |
| 4. My sister and I clean. | We clean. |
| 5. A car comes. | She says hello. |
| 6. The girl says hello. | It comes. |

**Notes for Home:** Your child identified sentences with pronouns. ***Home Activity:*** Read a sentence from a story to your child. *(The rabbit hopped away.)* Have him or her replace a noun in the sentence with a pronoun, and say the new sentence. *(It hopped away.)*

Name ______________________________

**Circle** the correct word in each box.
**Write** it in each sentence.

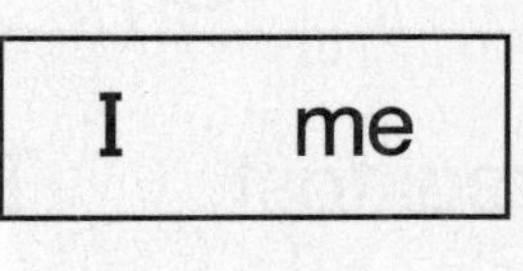


I. Sally sees Mrs. Bear and __________.

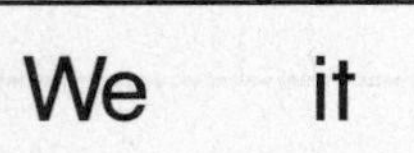


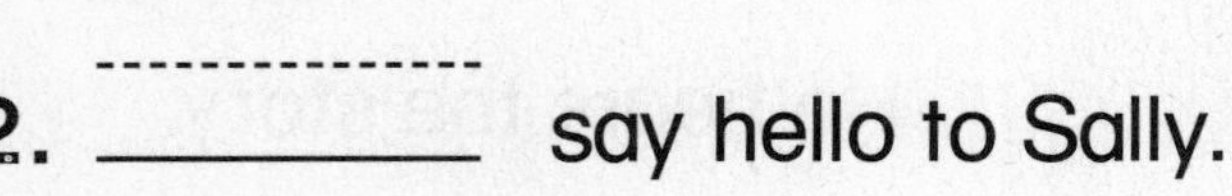

2. __________ say hello to Sally.

It They

3. ______ is big and dark.

**Notes for Home:** Your child wrote pronouns in sentences. ***Home Activity:*** Have your child write a short poem about two animals or people. Challenge him or her to use pronouns in the poem.

**You are your child's first and best teacher!**

**Here are ways to help your child practice skills while having fun!**

**Day 1** Your child is learning to read two-syllable words. Challenge your child to name a one-syllable word and a two-syllable word that both begin with the same letter, such as *camp* and *camper.*

**Day 2** Your child is learning to read these words: *almost, knew, picture, thought,* and *took.* Encourage your child to make up a story using as many of these words as possible.

**Day 3** When reading with your child, ask him or her to tell you the big idea of the story. Ask your child if the characters are like any real people you both know.

**Day 4** Your child is learning to give directions. Ask your child to explain to you how to play a favorite game. If you already know how to play the game, pretend you don't.

**Day 5** Your child is learning to write about pictures. Select a family photograph that your child likes and ask him or her to write a story about it.

**Read with your child EVERY DAY!**



(fold here)

# Family Times

**Doggy Art** **The Snow Glory**

## A Surprise for Molly

Can you come to my house in the ground?
My little house is cozy and round.

There will be so many friends around.
So come right over. Don't make a sound.

It is Molly's party. She's a mouse.
We'll have balloons and crouch in my house.

When she comes inside, we'll start to rise.
We'll jump right out and shout, "Surprise!"

This rhyme includes words your child is working with in school: words with *ou* that have the same vowel sound as *house* and two-syllable words with one or two consonants in the middle *(many, Molly)*. Sing "A Surprise for Molly" with your child. Together, find all the two-syllable words in the rhyme.

Name: ______________________

# Shout It Out!

**Materials** 1 button per player, paper, pencil

**Game Directions**

1. Take turns tossing a button on the gameboard and naming words spelled with *ou* that rhyme with the word landed on.

2. Players earn 1 point for each rhyming word named. Do not use a word more than once. Make a list to keep track.

3. The first player to earn 10 points wins!



| | |
|---|---|
| sound | scout |
| mouse | loud |
| ground | shout |
| house | cloud |

Name ______________________________

**Read** each sentence.
**Circle** the word that has the same vowel sound as **mouth.**

mouth

1. Tim went out to play.

2. Lee rolled the ball on the ground.

3. Tim kicked it hard and started to shout.

4. He ran all around the bases.

5. Tim was very proud!

**Notes for Home:** Your child identified words with the same vowel sound as *mouth*. ***Home Activity:*** Ask your child to write a short poem using words that rhyme with *out* and *round.*

Name ________________________________

**Circle** a word to match each picture.

flower 

1.  petal / peanut

2.  hamper / hammer

3.   whiter / whisper

4. 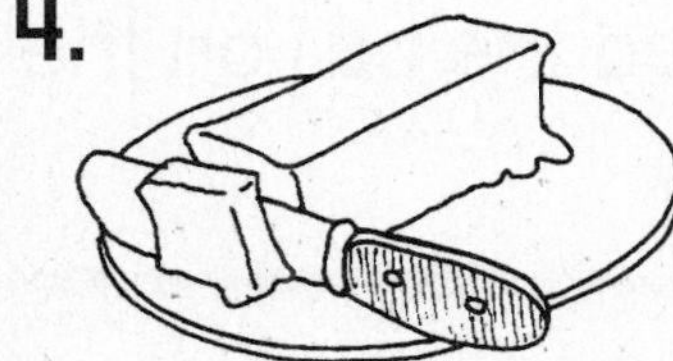 brother / butter

5. 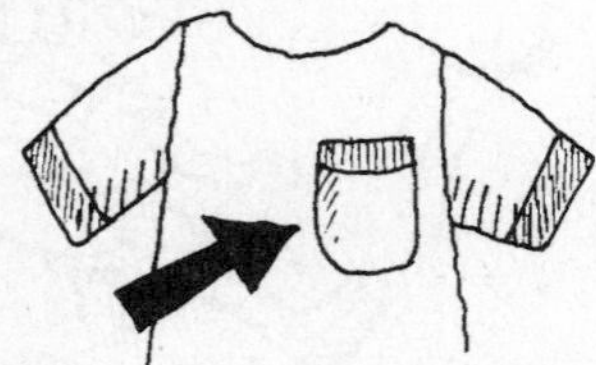 popcorn / pocket

6. 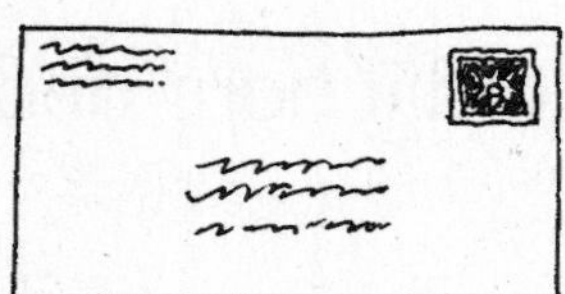 ladder / letter

7.  collar / color

8.  kitten / kitchen

9. 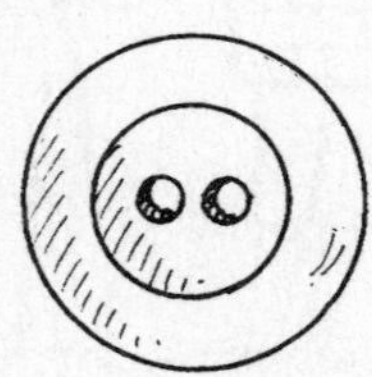 button / butter

10.  water / wagon

**Notes for Home:** Your child read two-syllable words. ***Home Activity:*** Point out two-syllable words in advertisements and help your child read them. Encourage your child to sound out each syllable.

Name ______________________



**Pick** a word from the box to finish each sentence.
**Write** it on the line.

| almost | knew | picture | thought | took |
|---|---|---|---|---|

1. I wanted to draw a ______________ of my cat.

2. I ______________ about it all day.

3. Then I ______________ how I would draw it.

4. Now I am ______________ done.

5. It ______________ a long time.

**Notes for Home:** This week your child is learning to read the words *almost, knew, picture, thought,* and *took.* ***Home Activity:*** Ask your child to write a letter to a friend using as many of these words as possible.

Name ________________________________

**Read** the story.
**Draw** a picture of the big idea of the story.

## Kelly and Anna

Kelly was sad.
She saw her friend Anna.
Anna was sad too.
So Kelly gave Anna a flower.
Anna felt better.
Kelly did too.

1.

2. What is the big idea of the story? Circle your answer.

People like flowers.

People feel better if they do something nice.

**Think** about the last time you made someone feel better.
**Draw** a picture that shows what you did.

3.

**Notes for Home:** Your child identified the theme, or the big idea, in a story. ***Home Activity:*** Tell your child a story about a childhood event. Then, discuss the big idea of the story. Invite your child to tell you about a similar experience.

Name ______________________________

Use these **pronouns** in the **naming part** of a sentence.

**I he she we they**

Use these **pronouns** in the **action part** of a sentence.

**me him her us them**

She saw us.

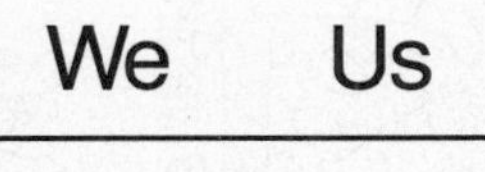

**Circle** a pronoun to finish the sentence.
**Write** the pronoun on the line.

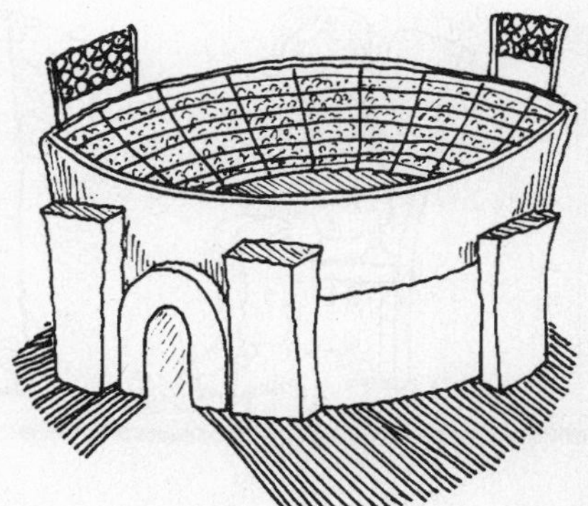

We Us

1. ____________ went to a ball game.

we us

2. My dad took ____________ .

He Him

3. ____________ carried my sister!

I Me

4. ____________ carried a team flag.

They Them

5. ____________ won the game!

**Notes for Home:** Your child used the pronouns *I, me, he, him, she, her, we, us, they,* and *them* to complete sentences. ***Home Activity:*** Read a story with your child. Ask your child to point out and read aloud the pronouns.

Name ______________________

**Pick** a word from the box that means the opposite.
**Write** it on the line.

| almost | knew | picture | stood | thought | took |
|---|---|---|---|---|---|

**1.** sat ______________

**2.** gave ______________

**Pick** a word from the box to match each clue.
**Write** it on the line.

**3.** You can find *most* hidden here. ______________

**4.** It sounds like *new*. ______________

**5.** It is what you think. ______________

**6.** You may see this in a book. ______________

**Notes for Home:** Your child found words that mean the opposite and answered clues. ***Home Activity:*** Take turns saying a word and giving a word that means the opposite.

Name ______________________________

**Circle** the word for each picture.

S<u>ue</u> gr<u>ew</u> this flower.

1. blew black
2. flow flew
3. glue glow
4. chew chick
5. clap clue
6. stew stop
7. crew crown
8. news now

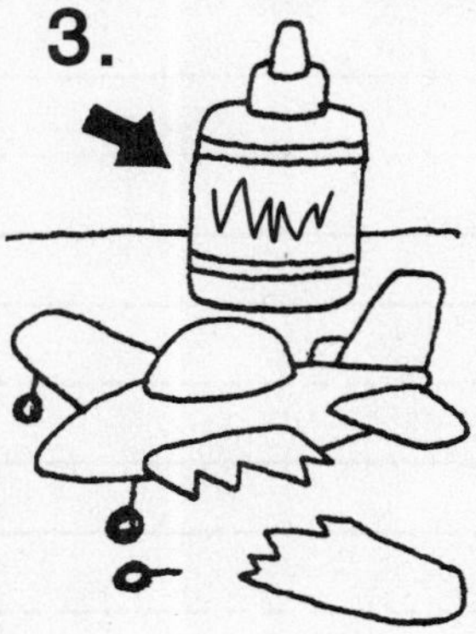

**Find** the word that has the same vowel sound as **grew**.
**Mark** the ⊂⊃ to show your answer.

9. ⊂⊃ few
⊂⊃ feel
⊂⊃ flow

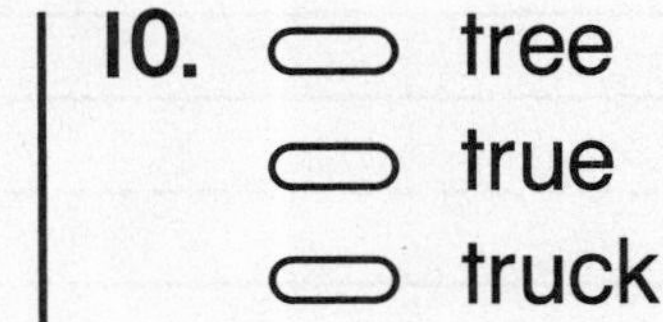

10. ⊂⊃ tree
⊂⊃ true
⊂⊃ truck

**Notes for Home:** Your child practiced reading words with *ew* and *ue (S<u>ue</u>, gr<u>ew</u>)*.
***Home Activity:*** Work with your child to make up silly rhyming pairs that contain this vowel sound and these spellings, such as *blue stew* or *new glue*.

Name ______________________________



**Look** at each word. **Say** it.
**Listen** for the middle consonant sound.

| | **Write** each word. | **Check** it. |
| --- | --- | --- |
| 1. pretty | | |
| 2. happy | | |
| 3. little | | |
| 4. kitten | | |
| 5. puppy | | |
| 6. better | | |

## Word Wall Words

**Write** each word.

| | | |
| --- | --- | --- |
| 7. took | | |
| 8. almost | | |

**Notes for Home:** Your child spelled words with double consonants in the middle *(pretty)* and two frequently used words: *took, almost.* ***Home Activity:*** Look at storybooks, food packages, or magazines for words with double consonants. Make a list of the words you find.

Name ______________________

**Circle** a pronoun to finish each sentence.
**Write** it on the line.

Us We

1. ______________ went to the park.

we us

2. My puppy came with ______________ .

Her She

3. ______________ showed the puppy the flowers.

they them

4. Nell and I picked ______________ .

he him

5. But ______________ thinks flowers are good to eat!

**Notes for Home:** Your child wrote subject and object pronouns to complete sentences (*We saw them at the beach*). ***Home Activity:*** Take turns using these pronouns in sentences: *I, me, he, him, she, her, we, us, they,* and *them.*

Name ______________________________



# Test-Taking Tips

1. Write your name on the test.

2. Read each question twice.

3. Read all the answer choices for the question.

4. Mark your answer carefully.

5. Check your answer.

Name ______________________________

# Part 1: Vocabulary

**Read** each sentence.
**Mark** the ⬭ for the word that fits.

1. Rosa was making a pretty ______ .

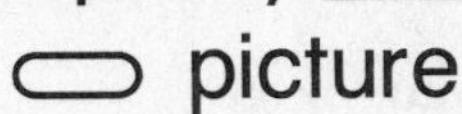

⬭ ground ⬭ picture ⬭ answer

2. Rosa ______ what she wanted.

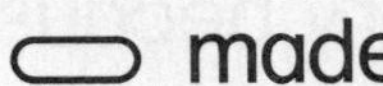

⬭ went ⬭ made ⬭ knew

3. She can ______ reach the can.

⬭ almost ⬭ right ⬭ around

4. She ______ of a way to get it.

⬭ thought ⬭ laughed ⬭ took

5. Then she ______ it down.

⬭ found ⬭ lost ⬭ took

GO ON

Name ______________________________

# Part 2: Comprehension

**Read** each sentence.
**Mark** the ⬭ for the answer.

6. When the snow went away, Henry wanted to
   - ⬭ get a new pet.
   - ⬭ ride his bike.
   - ⬭ plant some seeds.

7. When Henry found a flower, he
   - ⬭ told his mother about it.
   - ⬭ took it inside.
   - ⬭ walked on it.

8. Henry wanted the snow glory because it was
   - ⬭ not growing in the yard.
   - ⬭ as white as the snow.
   - ⬭ so pretty.

9. The snow glory ended up
   - ⬭ in Mudge's belly.
   - ⬭ in the ground.
   - ⬭ in the jar.

10. This story seems to say that
    - ⬭ Mudge is a bad dog.
    - ⬭ snow is better than mud.
    - ⬭ no one owns the flowers.

STOP

Name ______________________________

**Circle** the word for each picture.

tall taller tallest

1.

fatter fattest

2.

thinner thinnest

3.

younger youngest

4.

older oldest

5.

smaller smallest

6.

colder coldest

**Find** the word that could be used to compare **two** things.
**Mark** the ⬭ to show your answer.

7.  warm
 warmer
⬭ warmest

8.  loud
⬭ louder
⬭ loudest

**Notes for Home:** Your child reviewed words with the comparative endings *-er* and *-est.*
***Home Activity:*** With your child, look at family photos or photos in a magazine. Ask your child to compare people or objects in the photos using words with *-er* and *-est* endings.

Name ________________________________

pretty happy little kitten puppy better

**Write** four words from the box that have the letters **tt**.

1. ____________________ 2. ____________________

3. ____________________ 4. ____________________

**Write** two words from the box that have the letters **pp**.

5. ____________________ 6. ____________________

**Pick** a word from the box to match each clue.
**Write** it on the line.

7. a baby cat ____________________

8. not big ____________________

**Pick** a word from the box to finish each sentence.
**Write** it on the line.

took almost

9. The dog ____________________ ate the flower.

10. The boy ____________________ it away from the dog.

**Notes for Home:** Your child practiced spelling words with double consonants in the middle *(pretty)* and two frequently-used words: *took, almost*. ***Home Activity:*** Together, make up a story about a kitten and a puppy using these spelling words. Help your child write the story.

Name ______________________________

**RETEACHING**

A **pronoun** can take the place of some words in a sentence.
**I, he, she, we,** and **they** are used in the **naming part** of a sentence.
**Me, him, her, us,** and **them** are used in the action part of the sentence.

**We** take **them**.

**Read** each sentence.
**Choose** a pronoun to replace each underlined group of words.
**Write** the pronoun on the line.

1. Sarah and I are going to begin a play. ______________

2. The play is about my brother. ______________

3. My brother is funny. ______________

4. My parents are going to watch. ______________

5. The play is for my parents. ______________

**Notes for Home:** Your child wrote personal pronouns correctly. ***Home Activity:*** Look at pictures of people from magazines with your child. Have your child describe the pictures, using personal pronouns in sentences.

Name ______________________

**Read** each sentence.
**Circle** the correct word in ( ).
**Write** it on the line.

---

1. (I/me) got a snake today. __________

2. A man told (I/me) about the snake. __________

3. (We/It) looked at the snake. __________

4. The snake looked at (her/us). __________

5. I gave water to (it/me). __________

**Notes for Home:** Your child wrote personal pronouns that fit in sentences. ***Home Activity:*** Together, find personal pronouns in a favorite story. Then have your child make up new sentences, using the personal pronouns from the story.

## You *are* your child's first *and* best teacher!

**Here are ways to help your child practice skills while having fun!**

**Day 1** With your child, look through a challenging story or children's magazine. Find words with two or more syllables. Help your child read them by sounding out each syllable.

**Day 2** Your child is learning to read these words: *always, boy, move, open,* and *school.* Have your child make up a story about a new child at school using these words.

**Day 3** Ask you child to imagine that you are packing for a family trip. Tell your child what you are packing *(suntan oil, blankets, towels, swim fins).* Ask your child to figure out where you are going *(to the beach or the pool).*

**Day 4** If you hear incorrect grammar, ask your child to think about what he or she said to prompt a correction. Ask: *Does that sound right to you?*

**Day 5** Look through a favorite storybook with your child. Ask your child to point out all the nouns that show just one person, place, or thing. Challenge your child to change each noun to make it show more than one.

**Read with your child EVERY DAY!**



(fold here)

# Family Times

**I'll Join You** **Leon and Bob**

### Troy and Roy

My name is Troy.
I pretended all day.
I acted like a cowboy.
I galloped away!

I rounded up the cattle.
I bundled some hay.
I asked my friend Roy
If he wanted to play.

"Oh boy!" said Roy
As he joined in with me.
We planted in the soil.
We snacked by a tree.

This rhyme includes words your child is working with in school: words with *oi* and *oy* that have the same vowel sound *(soil, boy)* and words with more than one syllable *(cowboy, acted)*. Read "Troy and Roy" with your child. Work together to find all the words with more than one syllable.

Name: ____________________

# Make Some Noise

**Materials** 1 coin, 1 button per player

**Game Directions**

1. Players place buttons on Start.

2. Players take turns flipping the coin and moving one space for heads or two for tails.

3. A player reads the word on the space aloud. If the word contains the vowel sound heard in *n<u>oi</u>se* or *b<u>oy</u>*, the player may flip and move again.

4. The first player to reach the end wins!

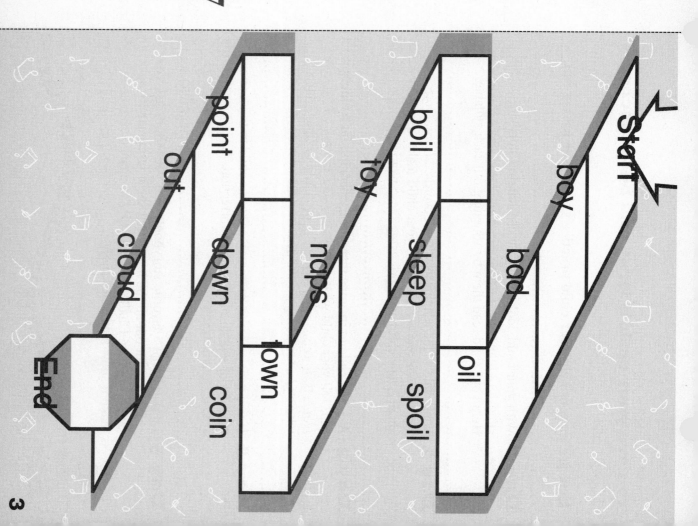

Start

boy

bad

oil

spoil

sleep

boil

toy

naps

town

coin

down

point

out

cloud

End

Name ______________________________

**Circle** the word for each picture.

The b<u>oy</u> makes a n<u>oi</u>se.

1. 
tie toy

2. 
soil sail

3. 
joy jay

4. 
bays boys

5. 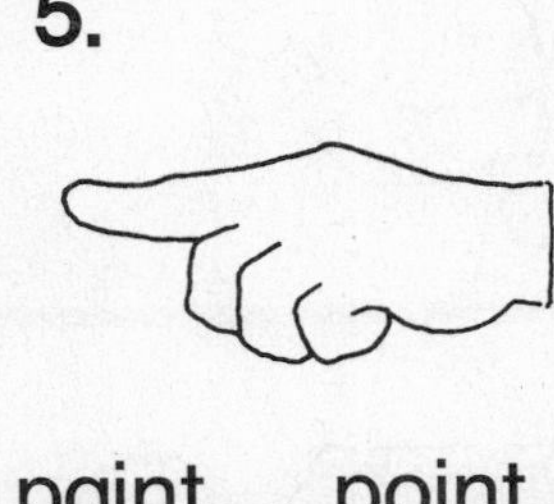
paint point

6. 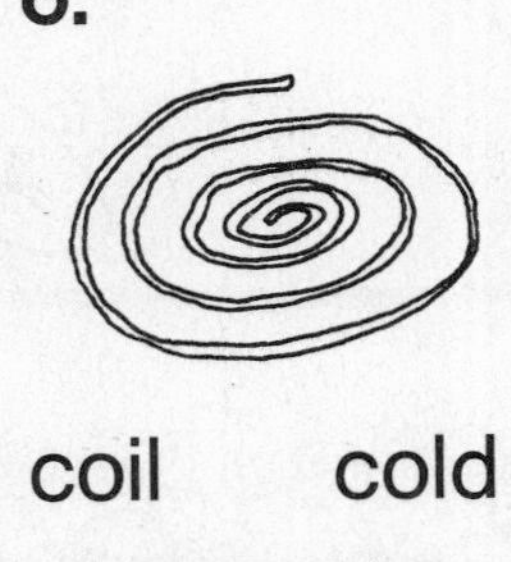
coil cold

7. 
oil owl

8. 
boil ball

**Draw** a picture for each word.

9. coin

10. toys

**Notes for Home:** Your child practiced reading words with *oi* and *oy (coin, boy)*. ***Home Activity:*** Write the words above with *oi* and *oy* on slips of paper. Have your child pick a word and use it in a sentence.

Name ______________________________

**Circle** a word in ( ) to finish each sentence.

**walking**

1. Bob ate his (broken / breakfast).

2. He (grabbed / graded) his hat.

3. He went (outer / outside) .

4. He (walked / watched) to the bus stop.

5. He (waited / wanted) for the bus.

**Notes for Home:** Your child read words with more than one syllable. ***Home Activity:*** When you read longer words with your child, encourage him or her to sound out the smaller, more familiar word parts.

Name ______________________________

**Pick** a word from the box to finish each sentence.
**Write** it on the line.

| always | boy | move | open | school |
|---|---|---|---|---|

1. We will ______________ soon.

2. I will go to a new ______________ .

3. I met a nice ______________ .

4. He let me ______________ his pet's box.

5. Now I hope we ______________ live here.

**Notes for Home:** This week your child is learning to read the words *always, boy, move, open,* and *school.* ***Home Activity:*** Write these words on slips of paper. Have your child pick a word and read it aloud.

Name ______________________________

**Circle** the sentence that tells about the picture.

1.

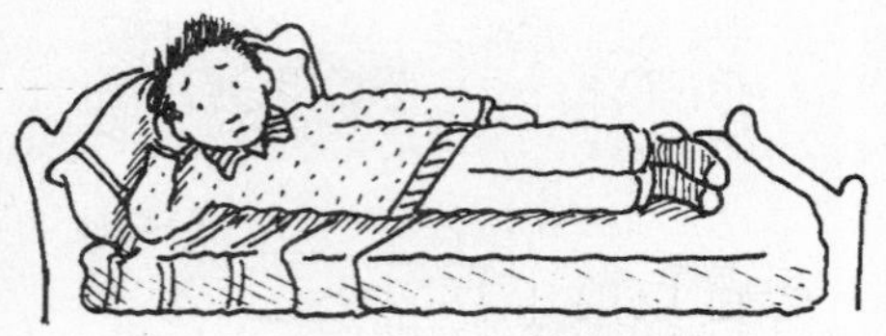

The boy is happy.
The boy is sad.

2.

The boys are lonely.
The boys are happy.

3.

It is summer.
It is winter.

4.

The girls went swimming.
The girls went to school.

**Read** the sentences.
**Write** an answer to the question.

Mom threw the ball to Sue.
Sue ran to catch the ball.
"Nice catch," said Mom.
She and Sue smiled at each other.

5. How does Sue feel?

______________________________

**Notes for Home:** Your child drew conclusions using picture and word clues. ***Home Activity:*** Look at pictures of your family with your child. Ask questions, such as: *"What are we doing here? How do you think this person is feeling?"*

Name ______________________________

**Add -s** or **-es** to most nouns to show more than one.

cat<u>s</u>

watch<u>es</u>

**Add -s** or **-es** to each word.
**Write** the new word on the line.
**Draw** a picture of the word.

1. ball + -s

2.

3. dress + -es

4.

5. box + -es

6.

7. bus + -es

8.

9. star + -s

10.

**Notes for Home:** Your child added *-s* and *-es* to singular nouns to make them plural. ***Home Activity:*** Look through a catalog or magazine with your child. Take turns naming pictures that show more than one item. Help your child write some of these plural nouns.

Name ______________________

**Pick** a word from the box to match each clue.
**Write** it on the line.

| always | army | boy | move | open | school |
|---|---|---|---|---|---|

1. go to a new place

2. not closed

3. not a girl

4. not sometimes

5.

6.

**Notes for Home:** Your child used clues to write words learned this week. ***Home Activity:*** Make up new clues for the words on this page. Ask your child to identify the words. Challenge your child to think of some clues too.

Name ______________________________

**Circle** the word for each picture.

cr<u>ow</u>n  h<u>ou</u>se

1. 
floor  flower

2. 
couch  crush

3. 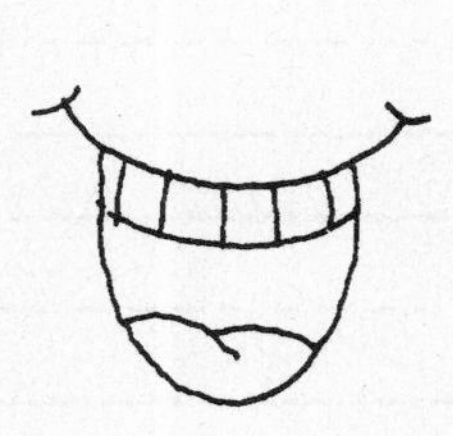
month  mouth

4. 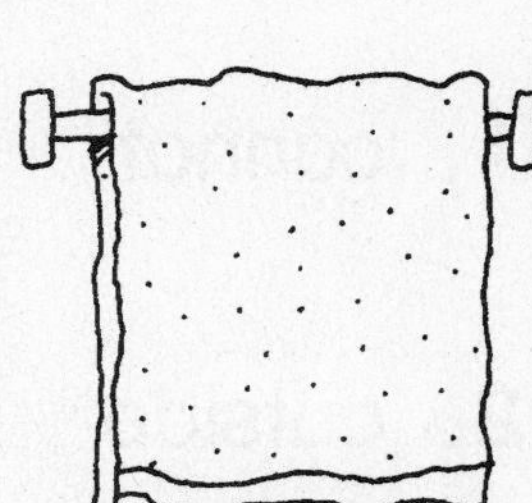
tile  towel

5. 
mouse  mess

6. 
chew  cow

7. 
clown  clean

8. 
owl  oil

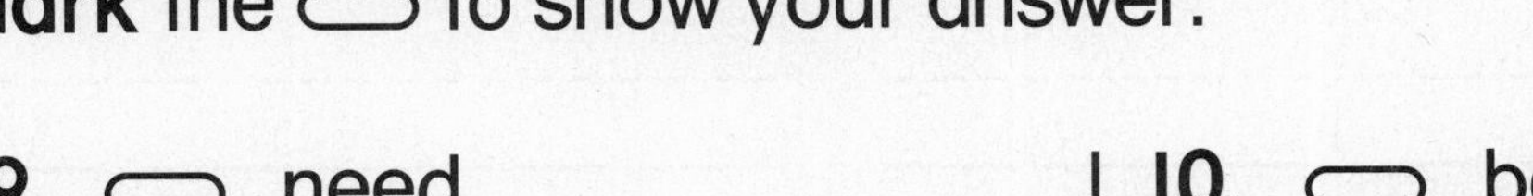

**Find** the word that has the same vowel sound as [cloud].
**Mark** the ⬭ to show your answer.

9. ⬭ need
⬭ hide
⬭ hound

10. ⬭ been
⬭ brown
⬭ brain

**Notes for Home:** Your child reviewed words with the vowel sound heard in *cr<u>ow</u>n* and *h<u>ou</u>se*. ***Home Activity:*** Make up the first line of a rhyme. It should end with a word with this vowel sound. Ask your child to make up the second line that ends with a rhyming word.

Name ______________________

**Look** at each word. **Say** it.
**Look** for two words in each compound word.

| | **Write** each word. | **Check** it. |
|---|---|---|
| 1. cannot | | |
| 2. outside | | |
| 3. grandma | | |
| 4. something | | |
| 5. popcorn | | |
| 6. tiptoe | | |

## Word Wall Words

**Write** each word.

| | | |
|---|---|---|
| 7. school | | |
| 8. always | | |

**Notes for Home:** Your child spelled compound words, such as *popcorn,* and two frequently-used words: *school, always*. ***Home Activity:*** Say each compound word aloud. Have your child identify the two words that make up each word.

Name ______________________________

Make sure every sentence is complete.

**Not a sentence:** The big yellow cat.
**Sentence:** The big yellow cat hissed at me.

**Add** a word or words to make each sentence complete.
**Write** it on the line.

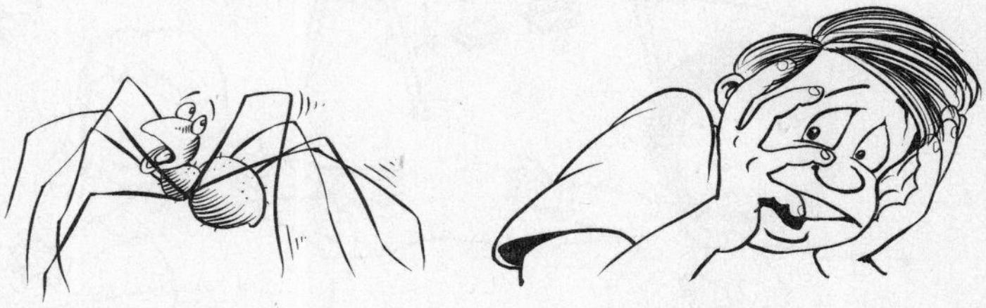

1. Huge spiders.

______________________________

2. You ugly bug.

______________________________

3. Ran on its long legs.

______________________________

4. Scared of me too.

______________________________

**Write** a complete sentence about something that scares you.

5. ______________________________

**Notes for Home:** Your child corrected incomplete sentences. ***Home Activity:*** Encourage your child to write some sentences about a time when he or she felt scared or frightened. Check that your child has formed complete sentences.

Name ______________________

**Read** each sentence.
**Add -s** or **-es** to the word in ( ) to show more than one.
**Write** the new word on the line to finish each sentence.

1. I have two ______________ . (friend)

2. One wears ______________ . (glass)

3. The other wears two ______________ in her hair. (bow)

4. We all wear ______________ . (dress)

5. We like to play ______________ . (game)

**Notes for Home:** Your child wrote plurals ending with *-s* and *-es*. ***Home Activity:*** Look at newspaper or magazine ads with your child and point out the plurals. Talk about which words have just *-s* added to the singular noun *(tire, tires)* and which have *-es (box, boxes)*.

Name ______________________________

# Part I: Vocabulary

**Read** each sentence.
**Mark** the ⬭ for the word that fits.

1. This ______ is Ray.

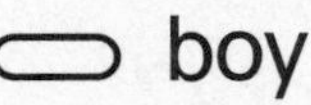 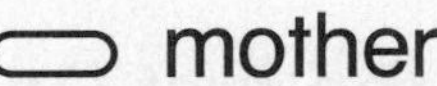

⬭ boy ⬭ mother ⬭ school

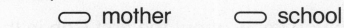

2. Ray will ______ to a new house.

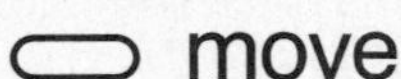

⬭ make ⬭ move ⬭ open

3. It is time to ______ the boxes.

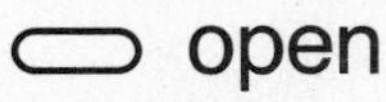 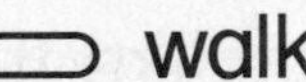

⬭ open ⬭ walk ⬭ think

4. This is Ray's new ______ .

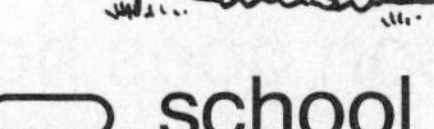

⬭ cold ⬭ idea ⬭ school

5. His friend ______ walks there with him.

⬭ very ⬭ always ⬭ about

Name ______________________________



# Part 2: Comprehension

**Read** each question.
**Mark** the ⬭ for the answer.

6. Where was Leon's dad?
   - ⬭ in town
   - ⬭ in the army
   - ⬭ at home

7. What do you know about the first Bob in this story?
   - ⬭ He is not real.
   - ⬭ He runs a lot.
   - ⬭ He can sing.

8. You can tell that Leon is
   - ⬭ sad because his dad is away.
   - ⬭ happy because he likes his new home.
   - ⬭ mad because his mom can't take him to school.

9. Why did Leon keep thinking about the new boy?
   - ⬭ He had never seen a boy like that.
   - ⬭ He did not like the new boy.
   - ⬭ He wanted the boy to be a friend.

10. How does the story end?
    - ⬭ Leon goes home.
    - ⬭ Leon has a new friend.
    - ⬭ Leon knows two boys named Bob.

Name ______________________________

**Read** each sentence.
**Add -ly** to the word in the ( ) to tell how something happened.
**Write** the new word on the line to finish each sentence.

1. The music started ______________________ . (sudden)

2. The drummer played ______________________ . (loud)

3. The band marched ______________________ . (quick)

4. The float moved ______________________ . (slow)

5. The girl sang ______________________ . (sweet)

**Notes for Home:** Your child reviewed words with the suffix *-ly*. ***Home Activity:*** Have your child give you directions using words with *-ly*. *(Clap your hands softly. Turn around quickly.)* Follow your child's instructions.

Name ______________________

cannot outside grandma something popcorn tiptoe

**Add** a word to each word below to make a word from the box.
**Write** the compound word on the line.

1. some ______________
2. toe ______________
3. not ______________
4. out ______________
5. grand ______________
6. pop ______________

**Pick** a word from the box to match each clue.
**Write** it on the line.

7. a place to go ______________
8. something to eat ______________

**Pick** a word from the box to finish each sentence.
**Write** it on the line.

school always

9. I go to ______________ .

10. I ______________ have fun there.

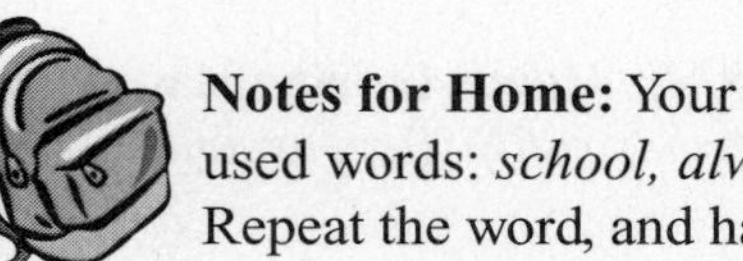

**Notes for Home:** Your child spelled compound words, such as *popcorn,* and two frequently used words: *school, always.* ***Home Activity:*** Say each spelling word, and use it in a sentence. Repeat the word, and have your child write it.

Name ______________________



RETEACHING

one bow

two bows

An **-s** makes a noun mean more than one.

Pretend that you need to buy more than one of each item listed. **Write** the correct noun.

# Shopping List

candle

1. ______________________

cupcake

2. ______________________

egg

3. ______________________

present

4. ______________________

card

5. ______________________

**Notes for Home:** Your child wrote plural forms of nouns. ***Home Activity:*** Have your child make a list of things two people might need if they were to go on a trip to a cold place. Remind your child to use plural forms of nouns.

Name ______________________________



**Look** for each musical instrument.
**Write** the number and naming word to complete each sentence.

drum drums

1. I spy ______________________.

bell bells

2. I spy ______________________.

guitars guitar

3. I spy ______________________.

shaker shakers

4. I spy ______________________.

**Notes for Home:** Your child wrote plural forms of nouns in sentences. ***Home Activity:*** Together, write a story about plants and animals. Challenge your child to use plural nouns in two sentences.

Name ______________________________

**Correct** each sentence.
**Write** it on the line.
Hint: Check the spelling of words that mean more than one.

1. I play with my friendes.

2. We roar like liones.

3. We hide in the bushs.

4. Boxs make great cars.

5. Sheets make good tentes.

**Notes for Home:** Your child corrected the spelling of plural nouns (words that show more than one). ***Home Activity:*** Read a story with your child. Later, point out some singular nouns from the story you read. Have your child change each noun to its plural form by adding *-s* or *-es*.

Name

I read

It was about

## Words I Can Now Read and Write

Name ______________________________

I read ______________________________

______________________________

It was about

Name

I read

It was about

Name ______________________________

# Words I Can Now Read and Write

**Directions:** Use the tables below to find the percentage score for the total number correct out of the total number of items. The last entry in each table shows the total number of items.

| Number Correct | 1 | 2 |
|---|---|---|
| Percentage Score | 50% | 100% |

| Number Correct | 1 | 2 | 3 |
|---|---|---|---|
| Percentage Score | 33% | 66% | 100% |

| Number Correct | 1 | 2 | 3 | 4 |
|---|---|---|---|---|
| Percentage Score | 25% | 50% | 75% | 100% |

| Number Correct | 1 | 2 | 3 | 4 | 5 |
|---|---|---|---|---|---|
| Percentage Score | 20% | 40% | 60% | 80% | 100% |

| Number Correct | 1 | 2 | 3 | 4 | 5 | 6 |
|---|---|---|---|---|---|---|
| Percentage Score | 17% | 33% | 50% | 66% | 83% | 100% |

| Number Correct | 1 | 2 | 3 | 4 | 5 | 6 | 7 |
|---|---|---|---|---|---|---|---|
| Percentage Score | 14% | 29% | 43% | 57% | 71% | 86% | 100% |

| Number Correct | 1 | 2 | 3 | 4 | 5 | 6 | 7 | 8 |
|---|---|---|---|---|---|---|---|---|
| Percentage Score | 13% | 25% | 38% | 50% | 63% | 75% | 88% | 100% |

| Number Correct | 1 | 2 | 3 | 4 | 5 | 6 | 7 | 8 | 9 |
|---|---|---|---|---|---|---|---|---|---|
| Percentage Score | 11% | 22% | 33% | 44% | 56% | 67% | 78% | 89% | 100% |

| Number Correct | 1 | 2 | 3 | 4 | 5 | 6 | 7 | 8 | 9 | 10 |
|---|---|---|---|---|---|---|---|---|---|---|
| Percentage Score | 10% | 20% | 30% | 40% | 50% | 60% | 70% | 80% | 90% | 100% |

| Number Correct | 1 | 2 | 3 | 4 | 5 | 6 | 7 | 8 | 9 | 10 | 11 | 12 | 13 | 14 | 15 |
|---|---|---|---|---|---|---|---|---|---|---|---|---|---|---|---|
| Percentage Score | 7% | 13% | 20% | 27% | 33% | 40% | 47% | 53% | 60% | 67% | 73% | 80% | 87% | 93% | 100% |

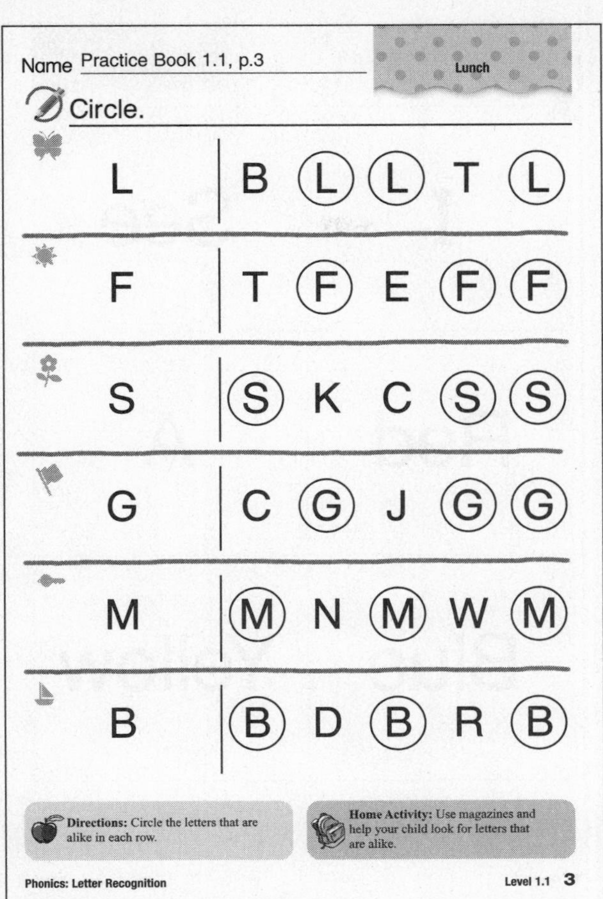

Name Practice Book 1.1, p.3

Lunch

Circle.

| | |
|---|---|
| L | B (L) (L) T (L) |
| F | T (F) E (F) (F) |
| S | (S) K C (S) (S) |
| G | C (G) J (G) (G) |
| M | (M) N (M) W (M) |
| B | (B) D (B) R (B) |

**Directions:** Circle the letters that are alike in each row.

**Home Activity:** Use magazines and help your child look for letters that are alike.

Phonics: Letter Recognition Level 1.1 3

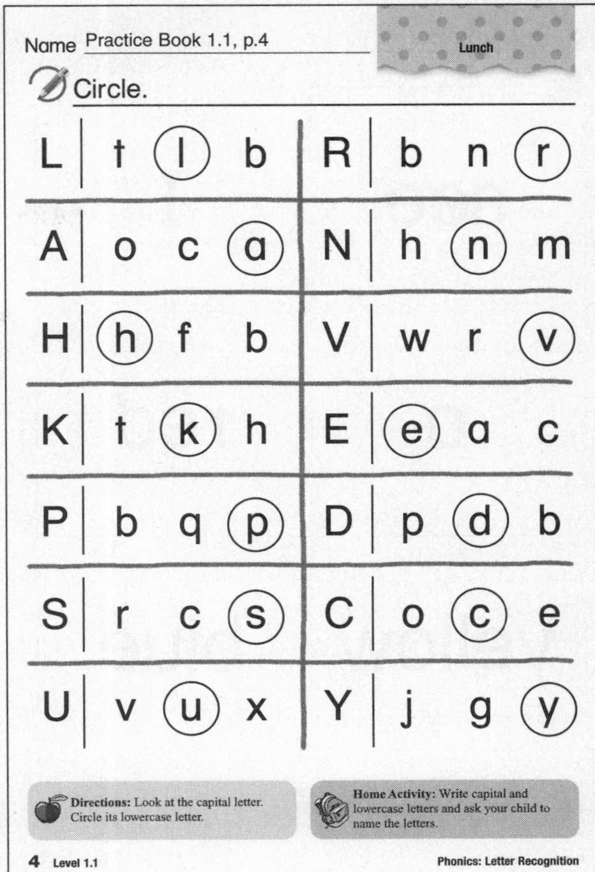

Name Practice Book 1.1, p.4

Lunch

Circle.

| | | | |
|---|---|---|---|
| L | t (l) b | R | b n (r) |
| A | o c (a) | N | h (n) m |
| H | (h) f b | V | w r (v) |
| K | t (k) h | E | (e) a c |
| P | b q (p) | D | p (d) b |
| S | r c (s) | C | o (c) e |
| U | v (u) x | Y | j g (y) |

**Directions:** Look at the capital letter. Circle its lowercase letter.

**Home Activity:** Write capital and lowercase letters and ask your child to name the letters.

4 Level 1.1 Phonics: Letter Recognition

Name Practice Book 1.1, p.5

Lunch

Color.

**Directions:** Color the picture that tells what will happen next.

**Home Activity:** Show pictures and have your child predict what might happen next.

Comprehension: Predicting Level 1.1 5

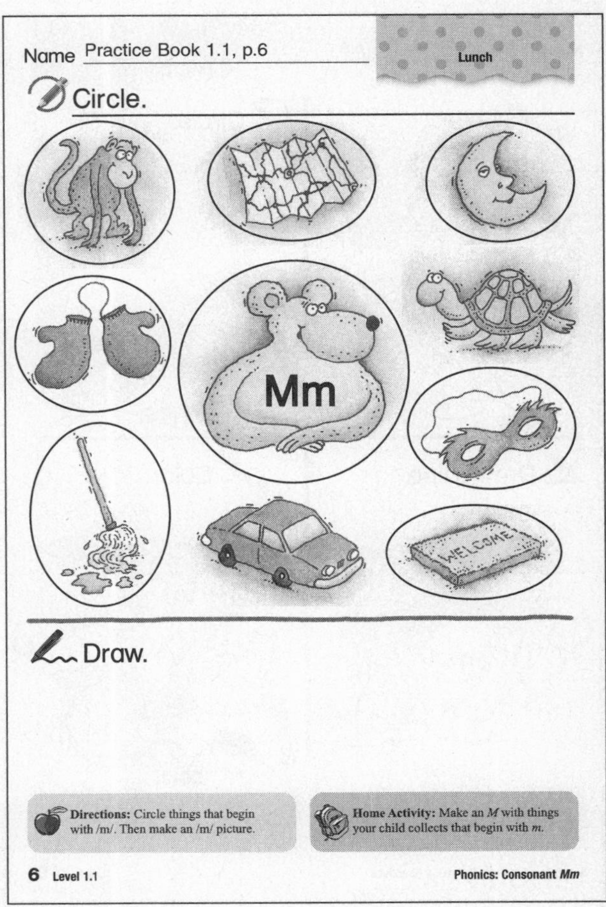

Name Practice Book 1.1, p.6

Lunch

Circle.



Draw.

**Directions:** Circle things that begin with /m/. Then make an /m/ picture.

**Home Activity:** Make an *M* with things your child collects that begin with *m*.

6 Level 1.1 Phonics: Consonant *Mm*

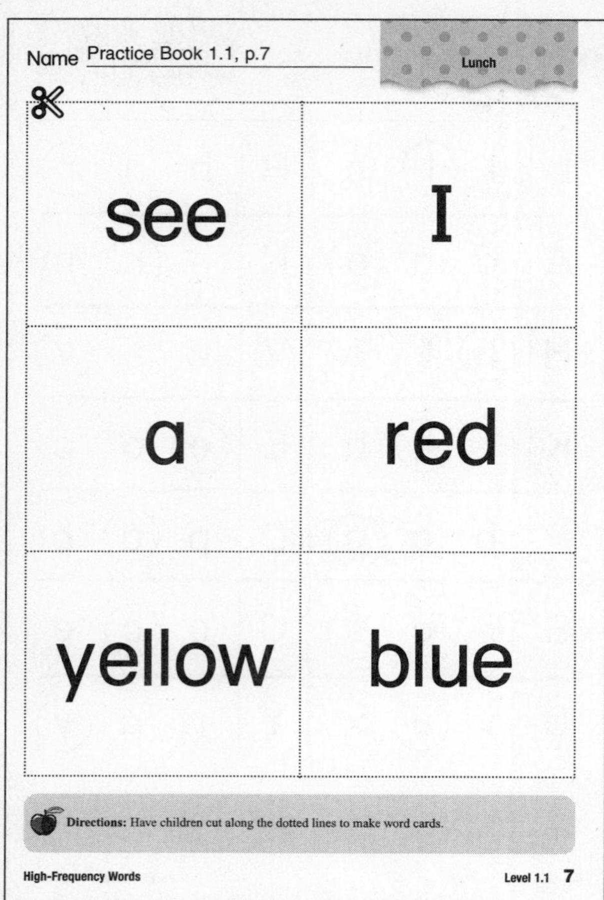
Name Practice Book 1.1, p.7
Lunch
see
I
a
red
yellow
blue
Directions: Have children cut along the dotted lines to make word cards.
High-Frequency Words
Level 1.1 7

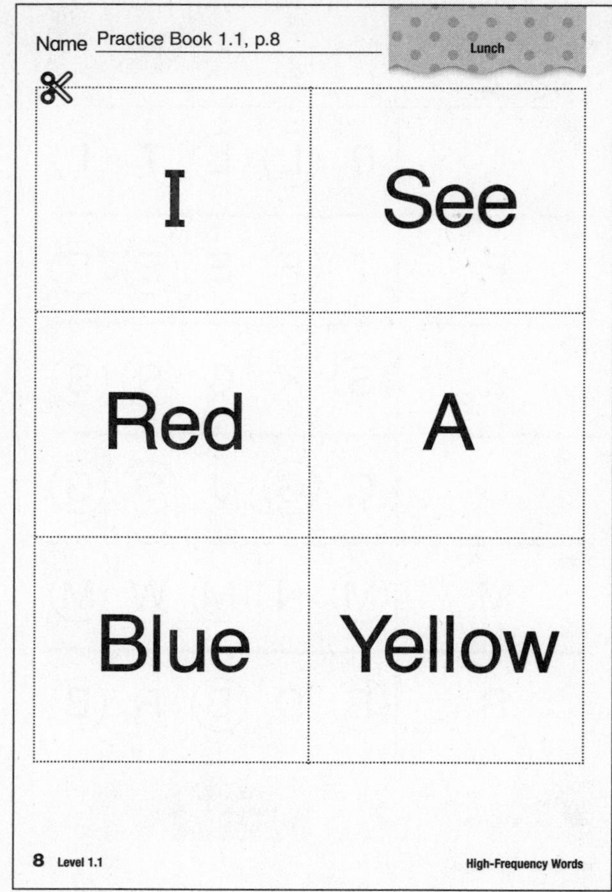
Name Practice Book 1.1, p.8
Lunch
I
See
Red
A
Blue
Yellow
8 Level 1.1
High-Frequency Words

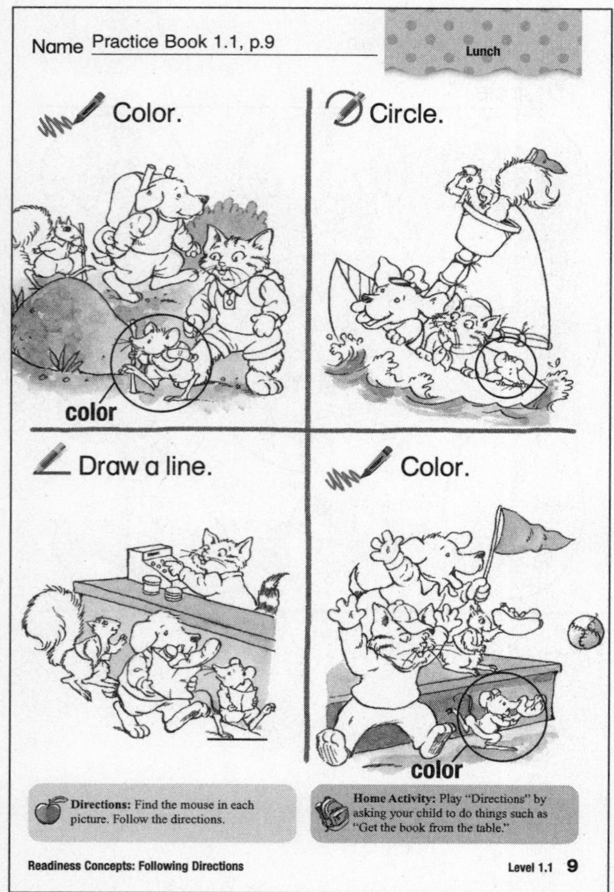
Name Practice Book 1.1, p.9
Lunch
Color.
Circle.
color
Draw a line.
Color.
color
Directions: Find the mouse in each picture. Follow the directions.
Home Activity: Play "Directions" by asking your child to do things such as "Get the book from the table."
Readiness Concepts: Following Directions
Level 1.1 9

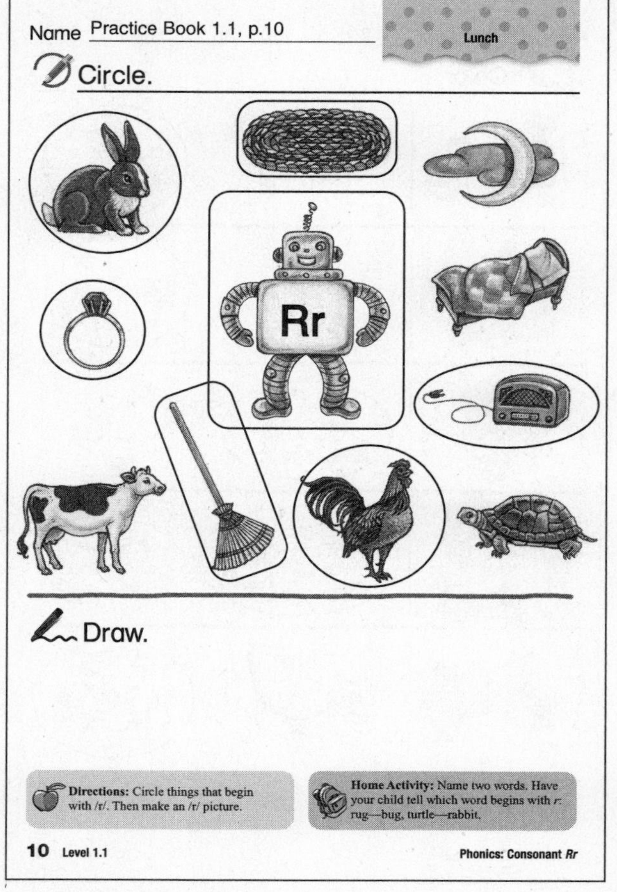
Name Practice Book 1.1, p.10
Lunch
Circle.
Rr
Draw.
Directions: Circle things that begin with /r/. Then make an /r/ picture.
Home Activity: Name two words. Have your child tell which word begins with r: rug—bug, turtle—rabbit.
10 Level 1.1
Phonics: Consonant Rr

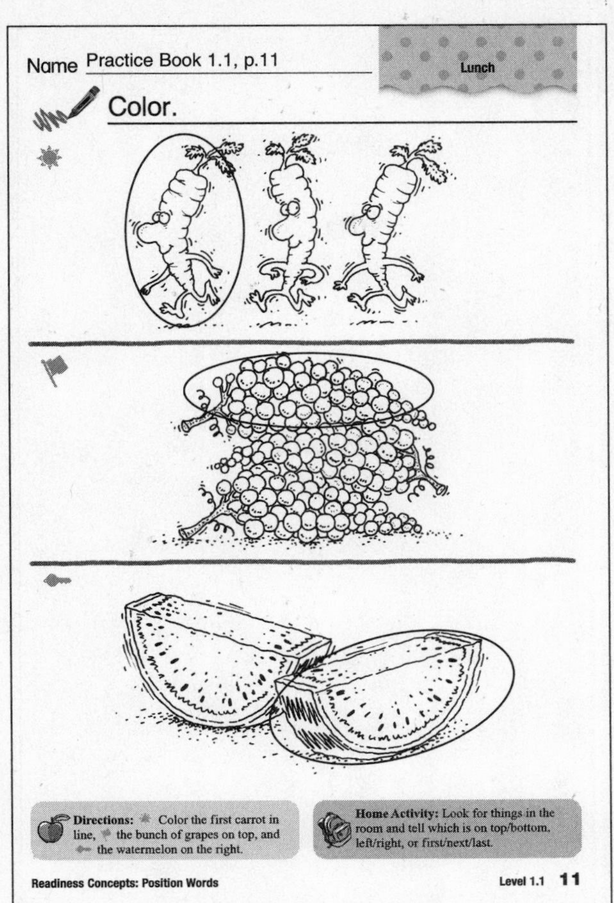

Name Practice Book 1.1, p.11

Lunch

Color.

Directions: Color the first carrot in line, the bunch of grapes on top, and the watermelon on the right.

Home Activity: Look for things in the room and tell which is on top/bottom, left/right, or first/next/last.

Readiness Concepts: Position Words

Level 1.1 11

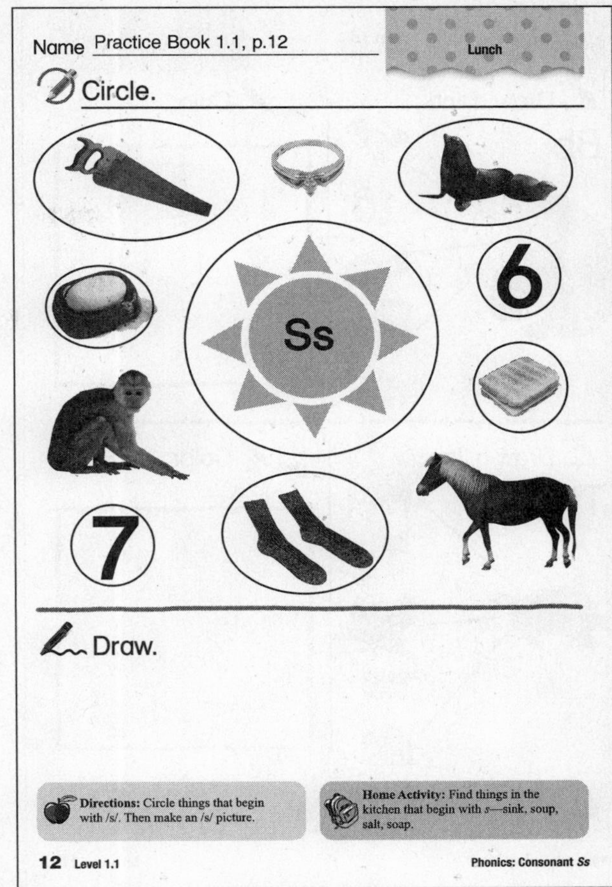

Name Practice Book 1.1, p.12

Lunch

Circle.



Draw.

Directions: Circle things that begin with /s/. Then make an /s/ picture.

Home Activity: Find things in the kitchen that begin with *s*—sink, soup, salt, soap.

12 Level 1.1

Phonics: Consonant *Ss*

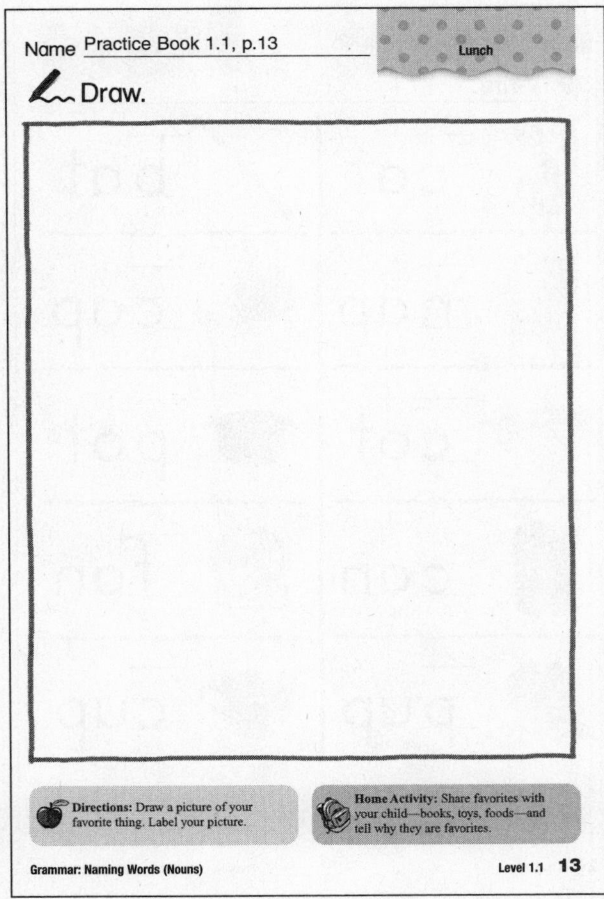

Name Practice Book 1.1, p.13

Lunch

Draw.

Directions: Draw a picture of your favorite thing. Label your picture.

Home Activity: Share favorites with your child—books, toys, foods—and tell why they are favorites.

Grammar: Naming Words (Nouns)

Level 1.1 13

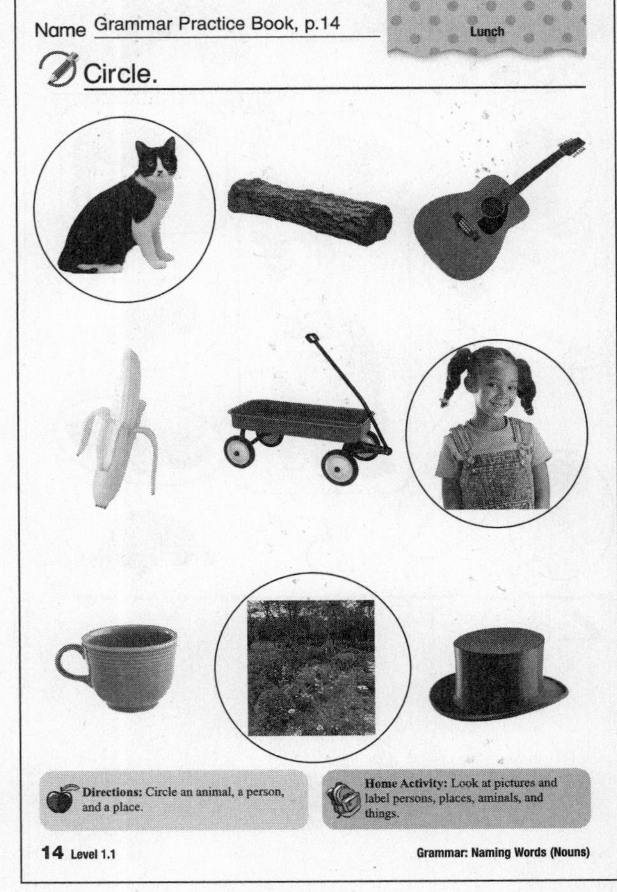

Name Grammar Practice Book, p.14

Lunch

Circle.

Directions: Circle an animal, a person, and a place.

Home Activity: Look at pictures and label persons, places, aminals, and things.

14 Level 1.1

Grammar: Naming Words (Nouns)

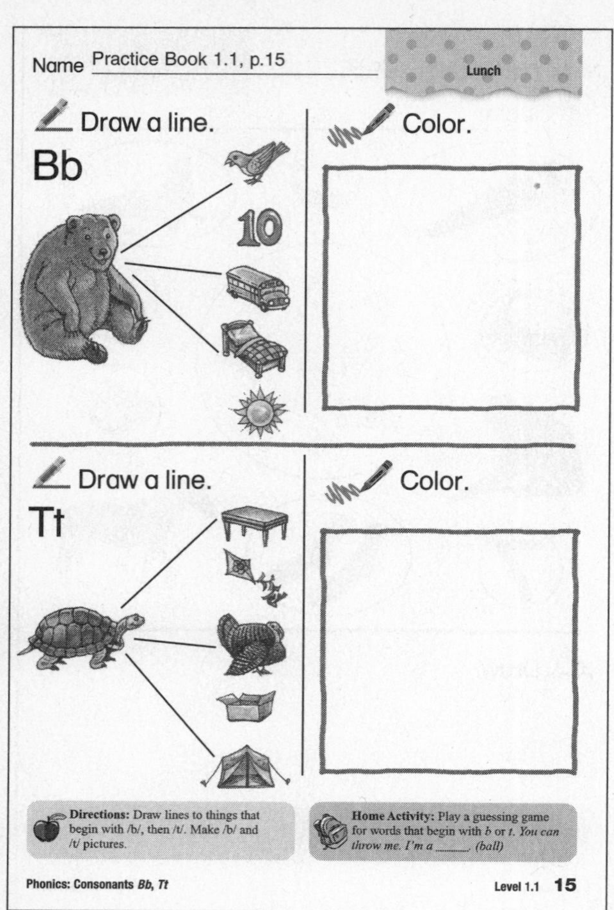
Name Practice Book 1.1, p.15
Lunch
Draw a line.
Bb
10
Color.
Draw a line.
Tt
Color.
Directions: Draw lines to things that begin with /b/, then /t/. Make /b/ and /t/ pictures.
Home Activity: Play a guessing game for words that begin with b or t. You can throw me. I'm a ______. (ball)
Phonics: Consonants Bb, Tt
Level 1.1 15

Blank
Page

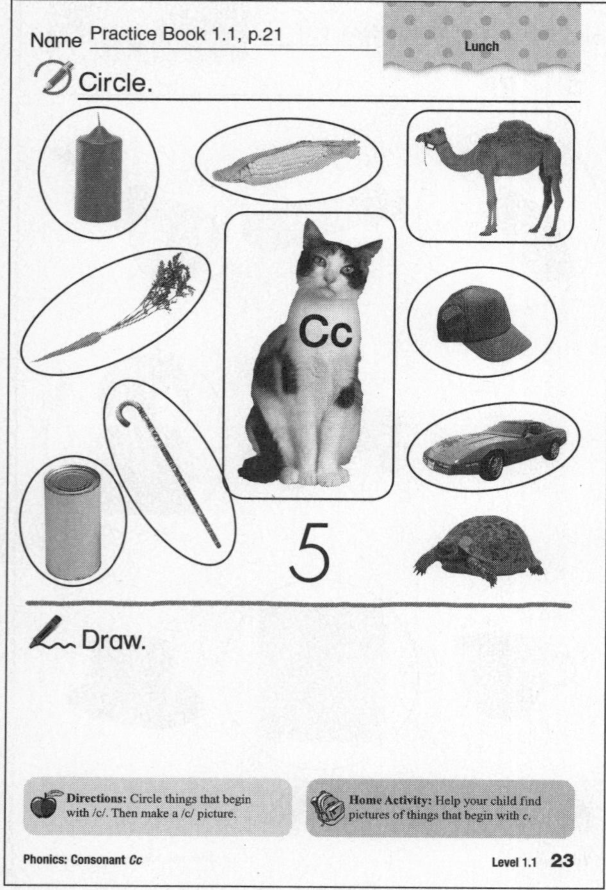
Name Practice Book 1.1, p.21
Lunch
Circle.
Cc
5
Draw.
Directions: Circle things that begin with /c/. Then make a /c/ picture.
Home Activity: Help your child find pictures of things that begin with c.
Phonics: Consonant Cc
Level 1.1 23

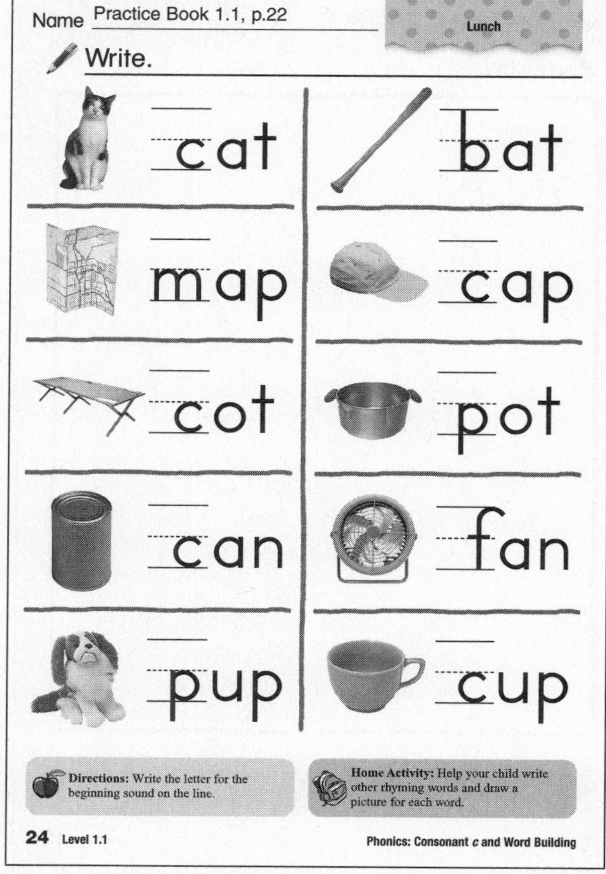
Name Practice Book 1.1, p.22
Lunch
Write.
cat
bat
map
cap
cot
pot
can
fan
pup
cup
Directions: Write the letter for the beginning sound on the line.
Home Activity: Help your child write other rhyming words and draw a picture for each word.
24 Level 1.1
Phonics: Consonant c and Word Building

Name Practice Book 1.1, p.23
Lunch
Color.
Directions: Color the picture that belongs in each group.
Home Activity: Help your child name words that belong in groups such as toys, foods, colors, and animals.
Comprehension: Classifying
Level 1.1 25

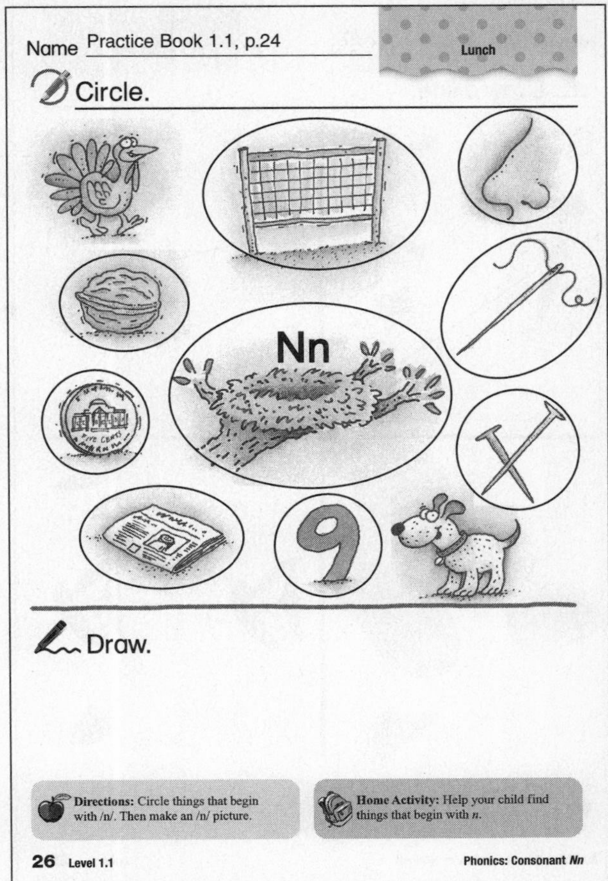
Name Practice Book 1.1, p.24
Lunch
Circle.
Nn
Draw.
Directions: Circle things that begin with /n/. Then make an /n/ picture.
Home Activity: Help your child find things that begin with n.
26 Level 1.1
Phonics: Consonant Nn

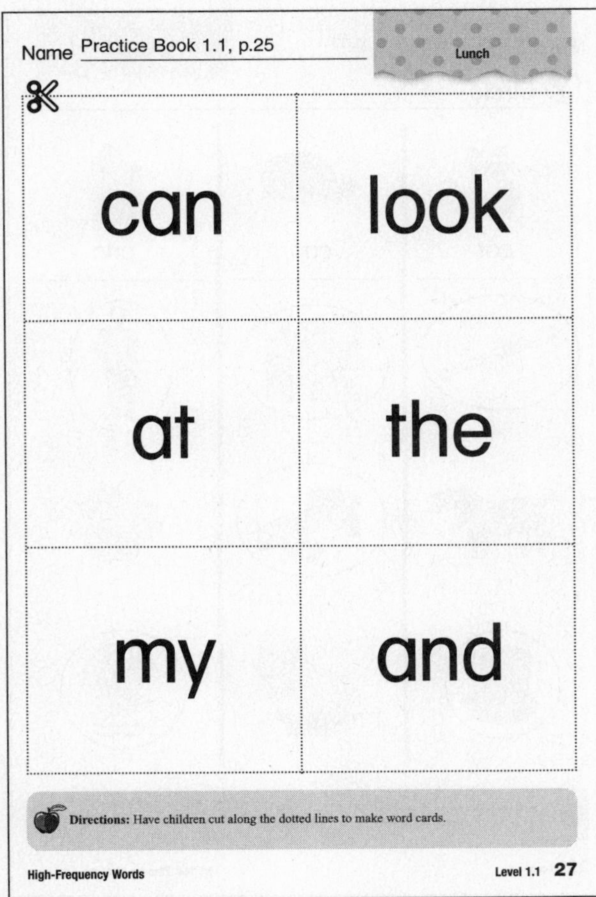
Name Practice Book 1.1, p.25
Lunch
can
look
at
the
my
and
Directions: Have children cut along the dotted lines to make word cards.
High-Frequency Words
Level 1.1 27

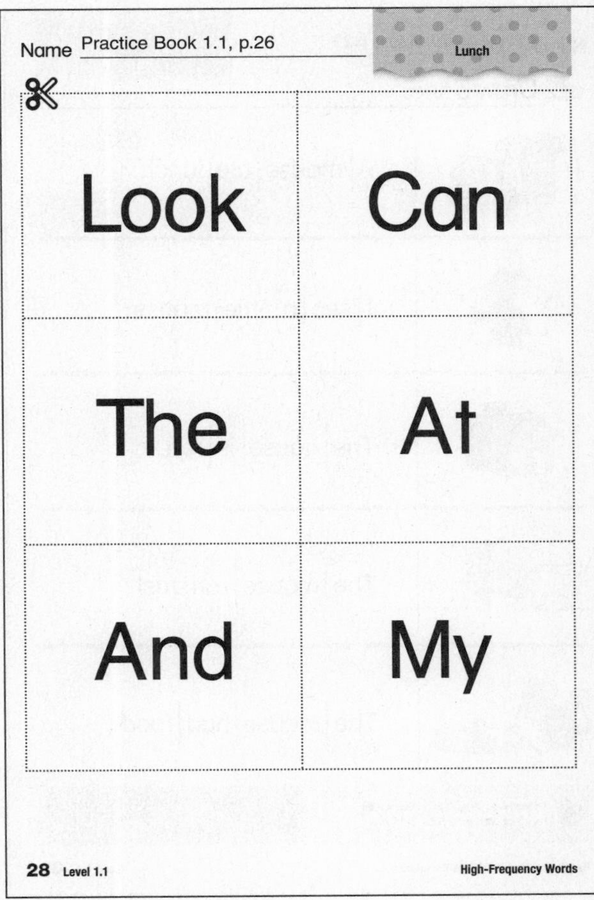
Name Practice Book 1.1, p.26
Lunch
Look
Can
The
At
And
My
28 Level 1.1
High-Frequency Words

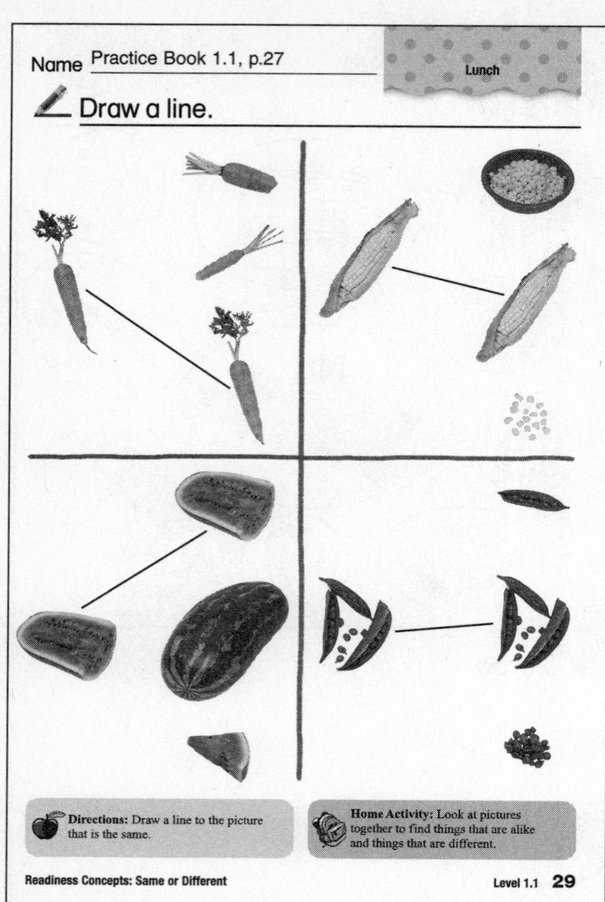

Name Practice Book 1.1, p.27

Lunch

Draw a line.

**Directions:** Draw a line to the picture that is the same.

**Home Activity:** Look at pictures together to find things that are alike and things that are different.

Readiness Concepts: Same or Different

Level 1.1 29

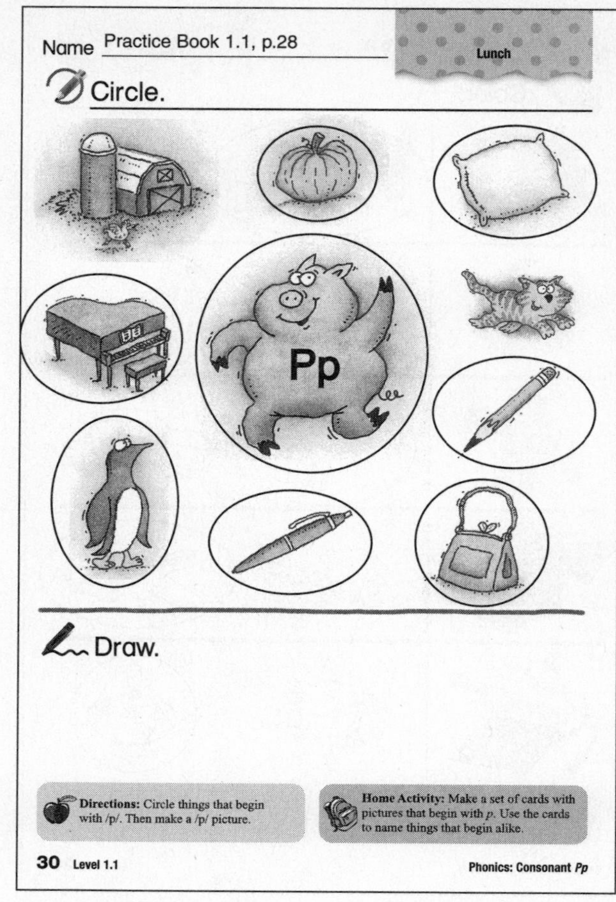

Name Practice Book 1.1, p.28

Lunch

Circle.



Draw.

**Directions:** Circle things that begin with /p/. Then make a /p/ picture.

**Home Activity:** Make a set of cards with pictures that begin with *p*. Use the cards to name things that begin alike.

30 Level 1.1

Phonics: Consonant *Pp*

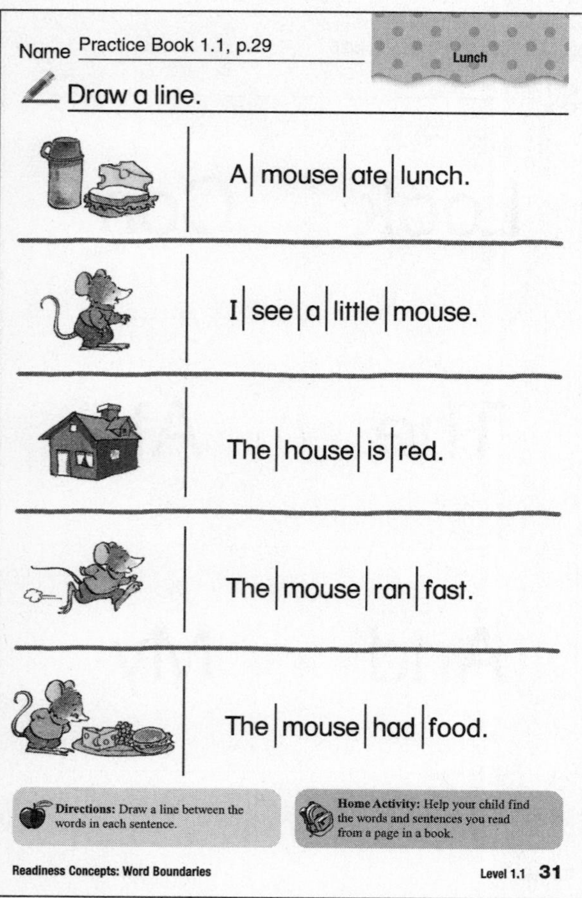

Name Practice Book 1.1, p.29

Lunch

Draw a line.

A | mouse | ate | lunch.

I | see | a | little | mouse.

The | house | is | red.

The | mouse | ran | fast.

The | mouse | had | food.

**Directions:** Draw a line between the words in each sentence.

**Home Activity:** Help your child find the words and sentences you read from a page in a book.

Readiness Concepts: Word Boundaries

Level 1.1 31

Name Practice Book 1.1, p.30

Lunch

Circle.

| cat | cap | can |
|---|---|---|

**Directions:** In each column, circle the pictures whose names rhyme.

**Home Activity:** Have your child say the rhyming words and use each word in a sentence.

32 Level 1.1

Phonics: Phonograms *-an, -ap, -at*

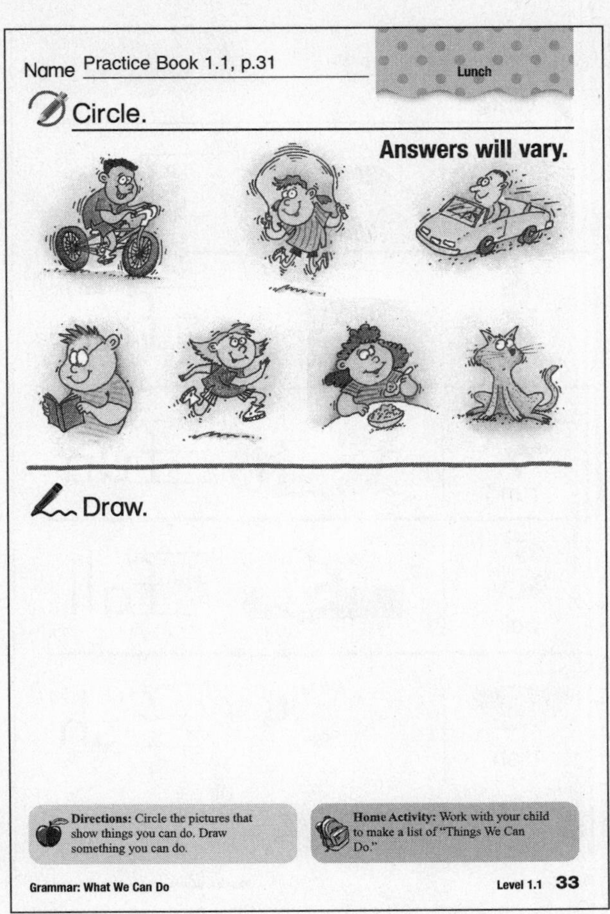
Name Practice Book 1.1, p.31
Lunch
Circle.
Answers will vary.
Draw.
Directions: Circle the pictures that show things you can do. Draw something you can do.
Home Activity: Work with your child to make a list of "Things We Can Do."
Grammar: What We Can Do
Level 1.1 33

Name Grammar Practice Book, p.2
Lunch
Circle.
Directions: Circle three things you can do.
Home Activity: Ask your child to tell about his or her favorite activity.
34 Level 1.1
Grammar: What We Can Do

Name Practice Book 1.1, p.32
Lunch
Write.
can
cat
man
WELCOME
mat
pan
bat
fan
hat
van
rat
Directions: Write the letter for the beginning sound to make rhyming words.
Home Activity: Make word cards and practice reading the words.
Phonics: Phonograms -an, -at
Level 1.1 35

Blank
Page

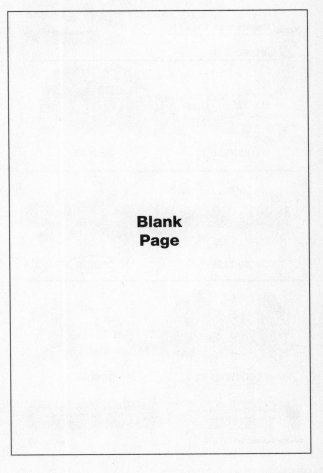

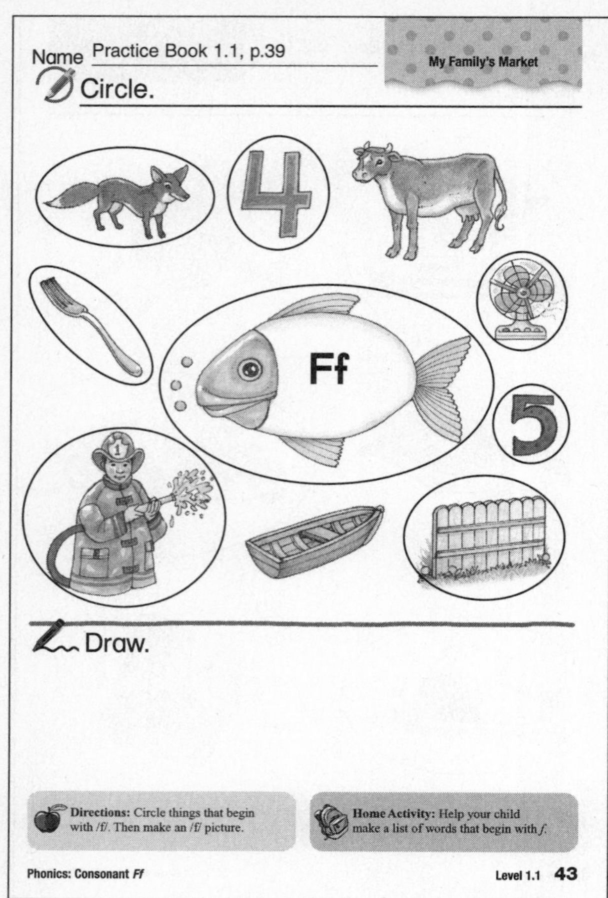
Name Practice Book 1.1, p.39
My Family's Market
Circle.
Ff
Draw.
Directions: Circle things that begin with /f/. Then make an /f/ picture.
Home Activity: Help your child make a list of words that begin with f.
Phonics: Consonant Ff
Level 1.1 43

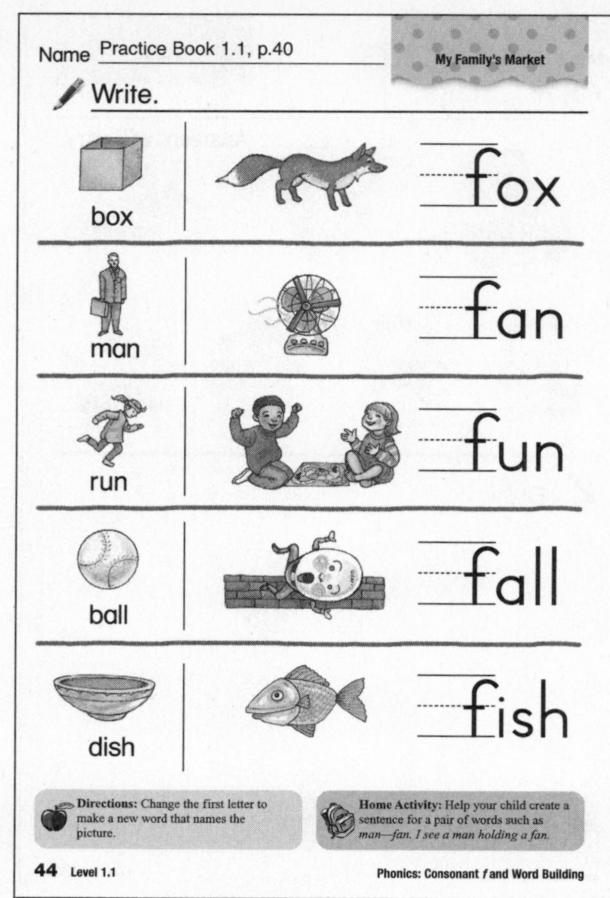
Name Practice Book 1.1, p.40
My Family's Market
Write.
box
fox
man
fan
run
fun
ball
fall
dish
fish
Directions: Change the first letter to make a new word that names the picture.
Home Activity: Help your child create a sentence for a pair of words such as man—fan. I see a man holding a fan.
44 Level 1.1
Phonics: Consonant f and Word Building

Name Practice Book 1.1, p.41
My Family's Market
Circle.
animals
people
animals
people
animals
people
Directions: Circle the word that tells what the picture is all about.
Home Activity: Show pictures to your child and have your child tell what the picture is all about (the main idea).
Comprehension: Main Idea
Level 1.1 45

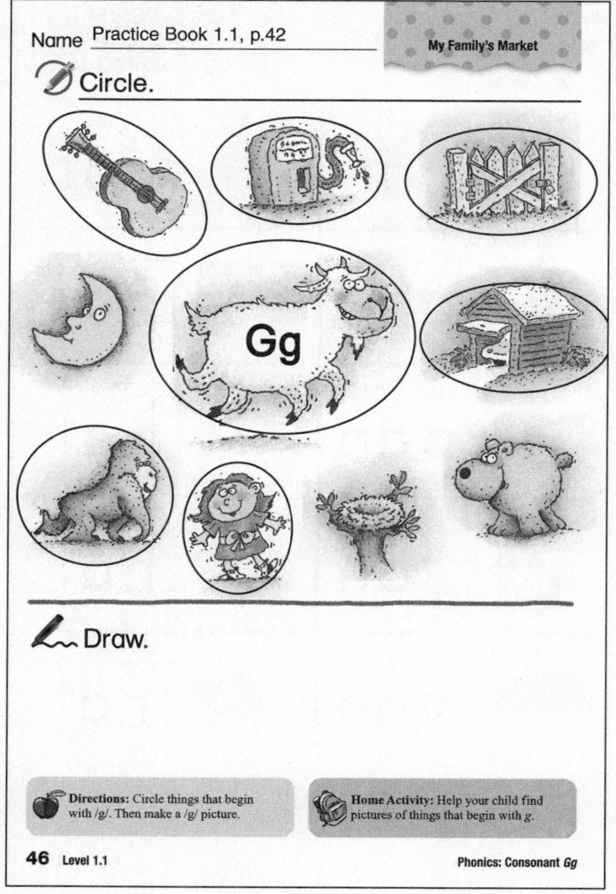
Name Practice Book 1.1, p.42
My Family's Market
Circle.
Gg
Draw.
Directions: Circle things that begin with /g/. Then make a /g/ picture.
Home Activity: Help your child find pictures of things that begin with g.
46 Level 1.1
Phonics: Consonant Gg

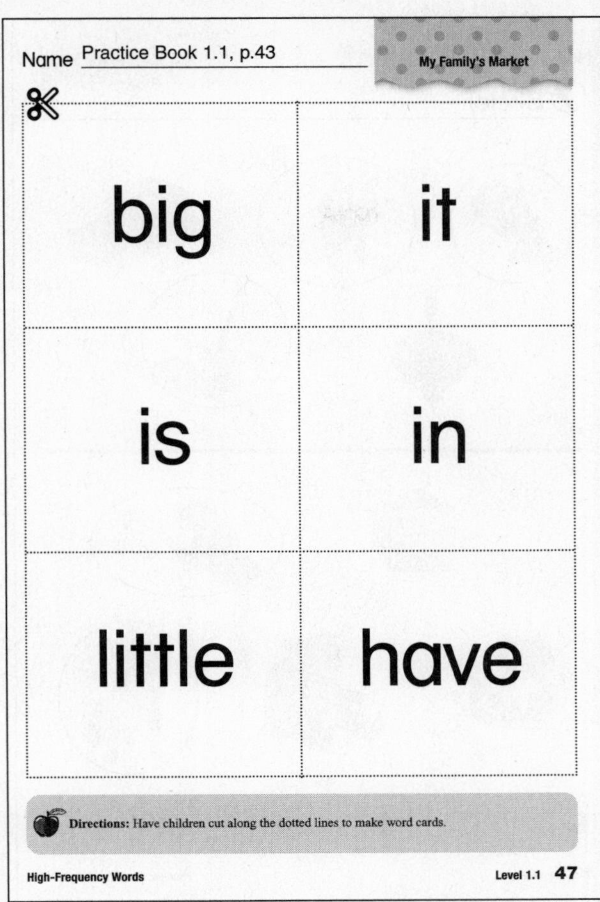
Name Practice Book 1.1, p.43
My Family's Market
big
it
is
in
little
have
Directions: Have children cut along the dotted lines to make word cards.
High-Frequency Words
Level 1.1 47

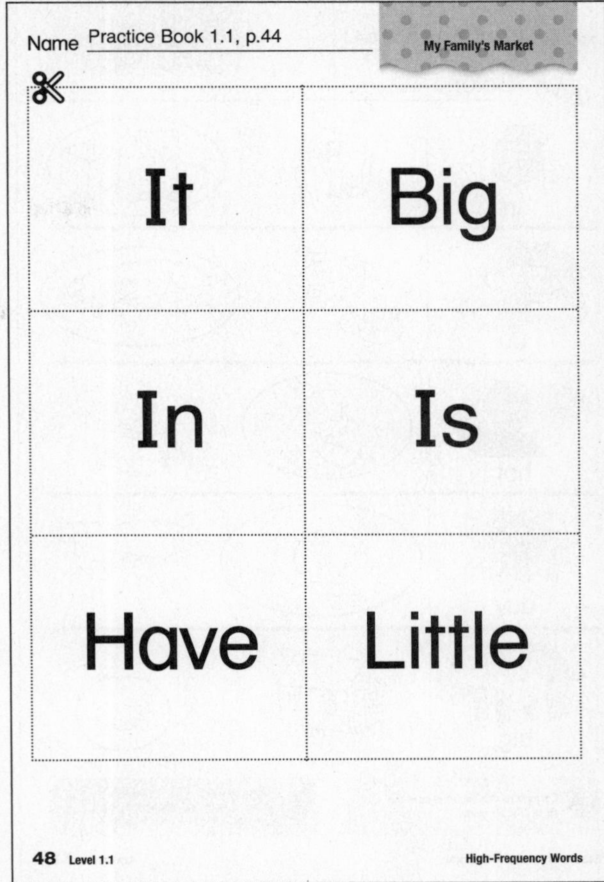
Name Practice Book 1.1, p.44
My Family's Market
It
Big
In
Is
Have
Little
48 Level 1.1
High-Frequency Words

Name Practice Book 1.1, p.45
My Family's Market
Draw a line.
10
STOP
Directions: Draw lines to the pictures that rhyme.
Home Activity: Have your child name a rhyming word for words such as ball, fish, car, hot, cold, book, rake, boat, pin, pet.
Readiness Concepts: Rhyme
Level 1.1 49

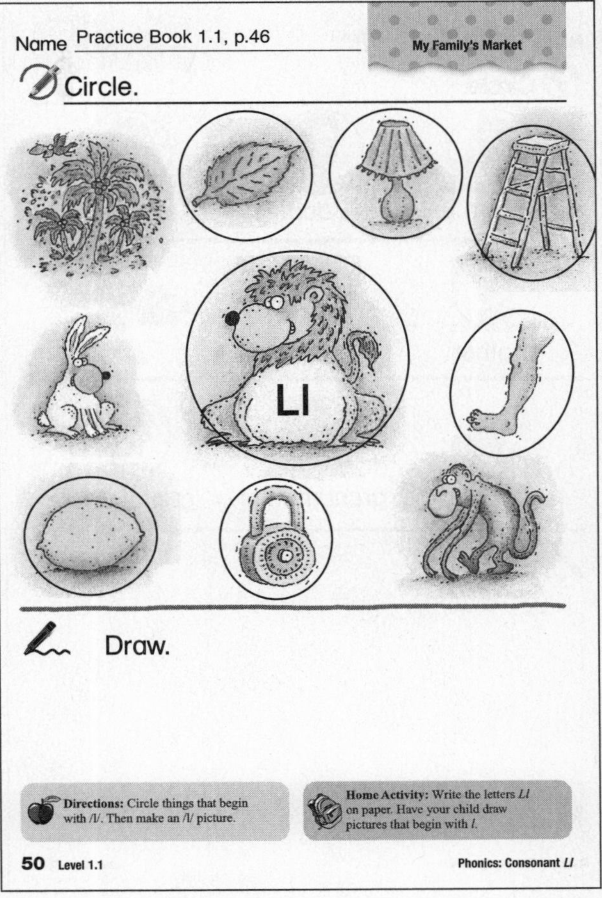
Name Practice Book 1.1, p.46
My Family's Market
Circle.
Ll
Draw.
Directions: Circle things that begin with /l/. Then make an /l/ picture.
Home Activity: Write the letters Ll on paper. Have your child draw pictures that begin with l.
50 Level 1.1
Phonics: Consonant Ll

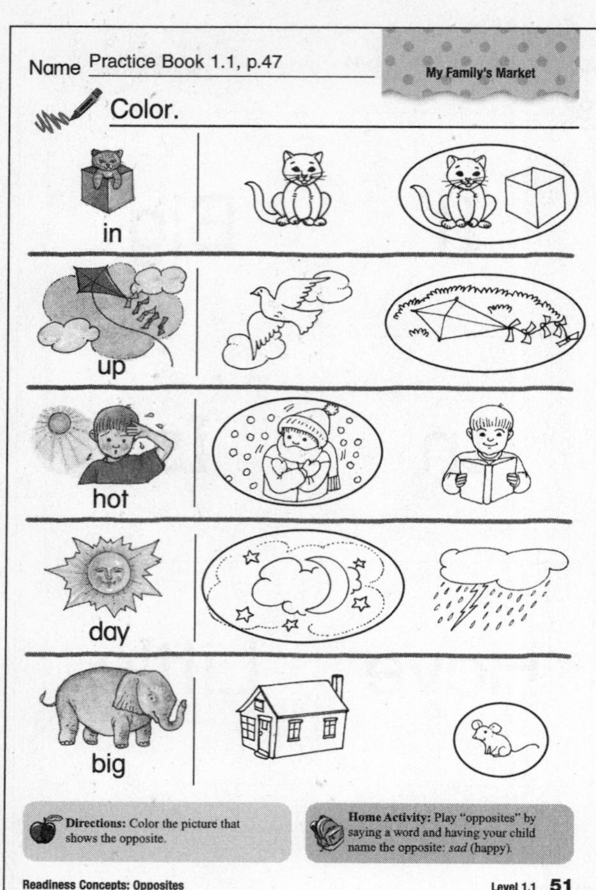

Name Practice Book 1.1, p.47

My Family's Market

Color.

in

up

hot

day

big

**Directions:** Color the picture that shows the opposite.

**Home Activity:** Play "opposites" by saying a word and having your child name the opposite: *sad* (happy).

Readiness Concepts: Opposites

Level 1.1 51

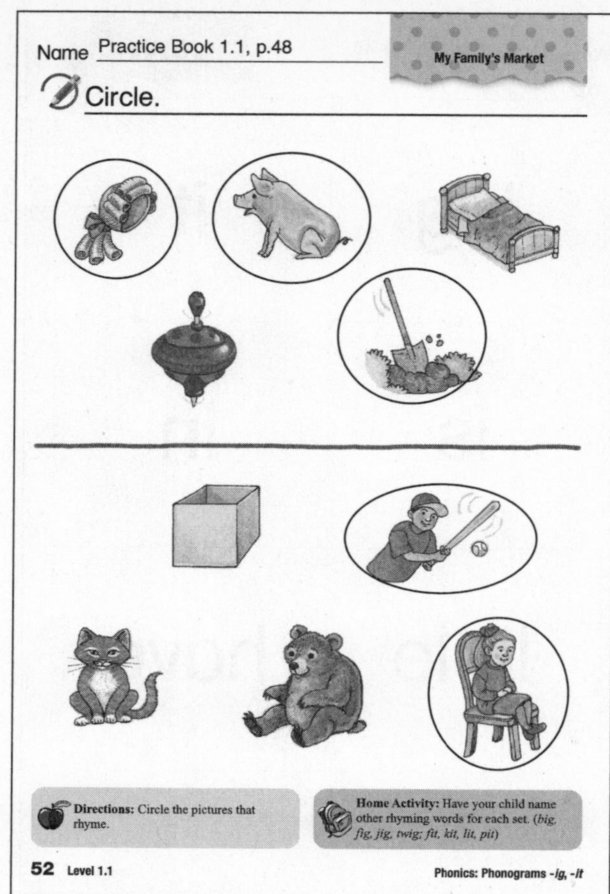

Name Practice Book 1.1, p.48

My Family's Market

Circle.

**Directions:** Circle the pictures that rhyme.

**Home Activity:** Have your child name other rhyming words for each set. (*big, fig, jig, twig; fit, kit, lit, pit*)

52 Level 1.1

Phonics: Phonograms *-ig, -it*

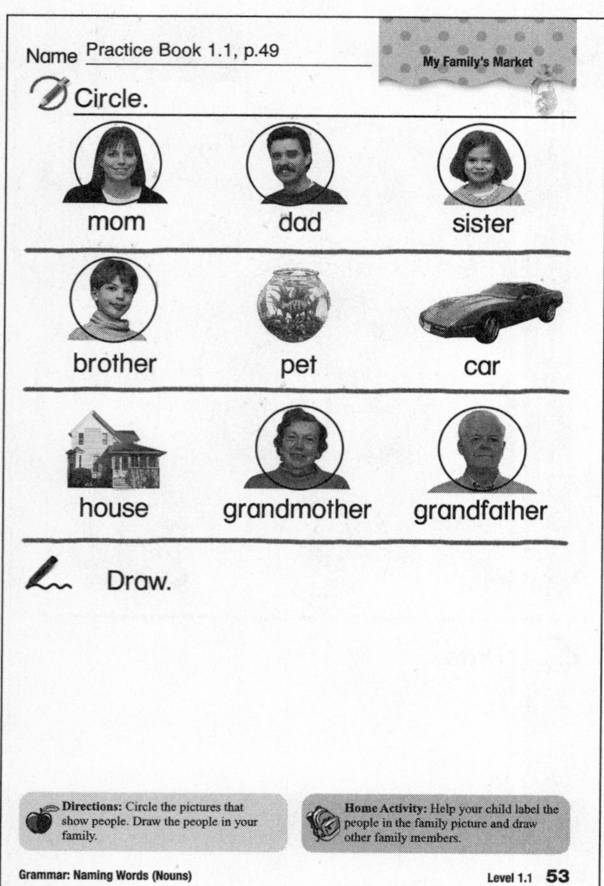

Name Practice Book 1.1, p.49

My Family's Market

Circle.

mom dad sister

brother pet car

house grandmother grandfather

Draw.

**Directions:** Circle the pictures that show people. Draw the people in your family.

**Home Activity:** Help your child label the people in the family picture and draw other family members.

Grammar: Naming Words (Nouns)

Level 1.1 53

Name Grammar Practice Book, p.3

My Family's Market

Circle.

**Directions:** Circle the person in each row.

**Home Activity:** Have your child draw and label a picture of himself or herself playing with friends.

54 Level 1.1

Grammar: Naming Words (Nouns)

Name Practice Book 1.1, p.50
My Family's Market
Circle.
pig
wig
sit
lit
dig
pig
bit
hit
big
dig
kit
bit
fig
wig
fit
lit
Directions: Circle the word that names the picture.
Home Activity: Make word cards for words that rhyme with win and will.
Phonics: Phonograms -ig, -it
Level 1.1 55

Blank
Page

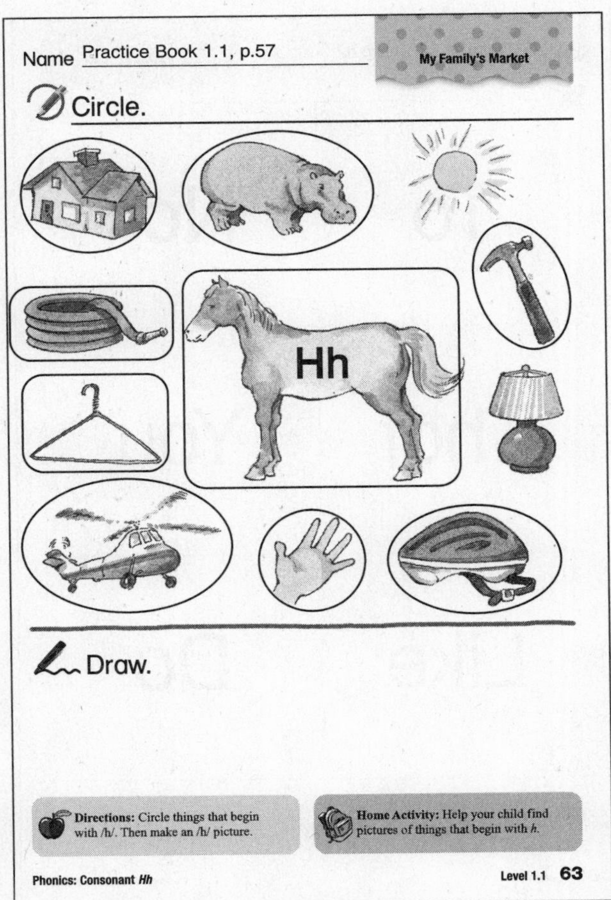
Name Practice Book 1.1, p.57
My Family's Market
Circle.
Hh
Draw.
Directions: Circle things that begin with /h/. Then make an /h/ picture.
Home Activity: Help your child find pictures of things that begin with h.
Phonics: Consonant Hh
Level 1.1 63

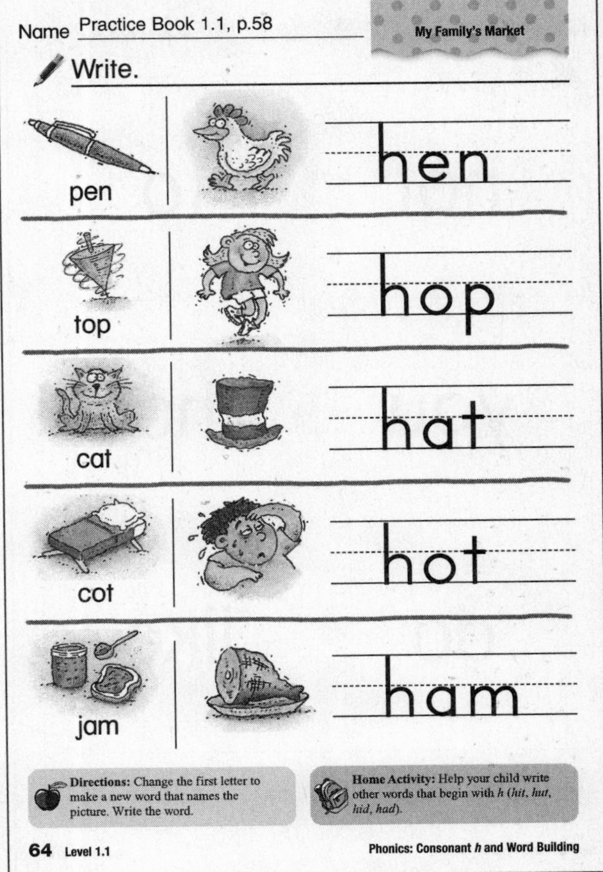
Name Practice Book 1.1, p.58
My Family's Market
Write.
pen
hen
top
hop
cat
hat
cot
hot
jam
ham
Directions: Change the first letter to make a new word that names the picture. Write the word.
Home Activity: Help your child write other words that begin with h (hit, hut, hid, had).
64 Level 1.1
Phonics: Consonant h and Word Building

Name Practice Book 1.1, p.59

My Family's Market

Circle.

**Directions:** Circle the picture that shows something make-believe.

**Home Activity:** Have your child tell you why each picture on the page is real or make-believe.

Comprehension: Fact/Fantasy

Level 1.1 65

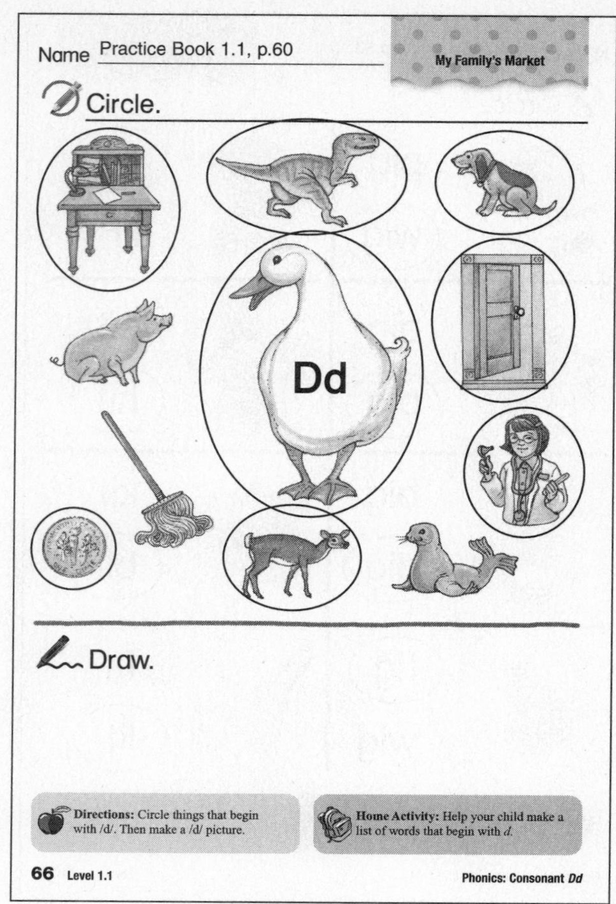
Name Practice Book 1.1, p.60

My Family's Market

Circle.



Draw.

**Directions:** Circle things that begin with /d/. Then make a /d/ picture.

**Home Activity:** Help your child make a list of words that begin with *d*.

66 Level 1.1

Phonics: Consonant *Dd*

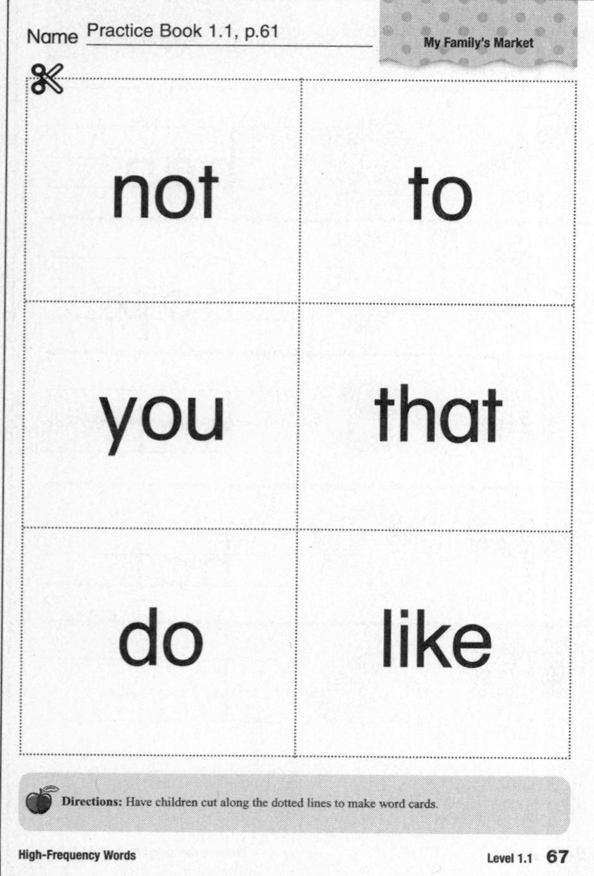
Name Practice Book 1.1, p.61

My Family's Market

| not | to |
|---|---|
| you | that |
| do | like |

**Directions:** Have children cut along the dotted lines to make word cards.

High-Frequency Words

Level 1.1 67

Name Practice Book 1.1, p.62

My Family's Market

| To | Not |
|---|---|
| That | You |
| Like | Do |

68 Level 1.1

High-Frequency Words

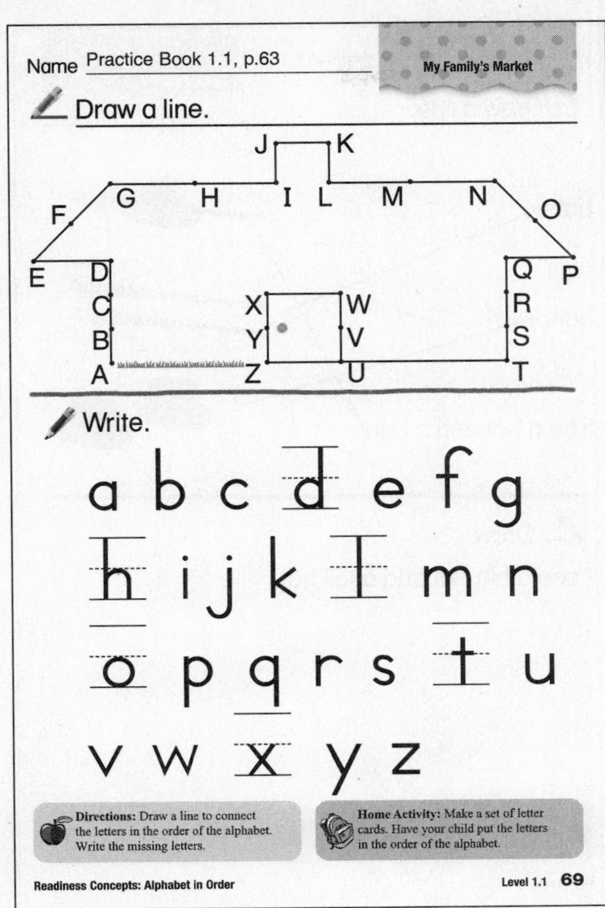
Name Practice Book 1.1, p.63

My Family's Market

Draw a line.



Write.

a b c d e f g
h i j k l m n
o p q r s t u
v w x y z

**Directions:** Draw a line to connect the letters in the order of the alphabet. Write the missing letters.

**Home Activity:** Make a set of letter cards. Have your child put the letters in the order of the alphabet.

Readiness Concepts: Alphabet in Order

Level 1.1 69

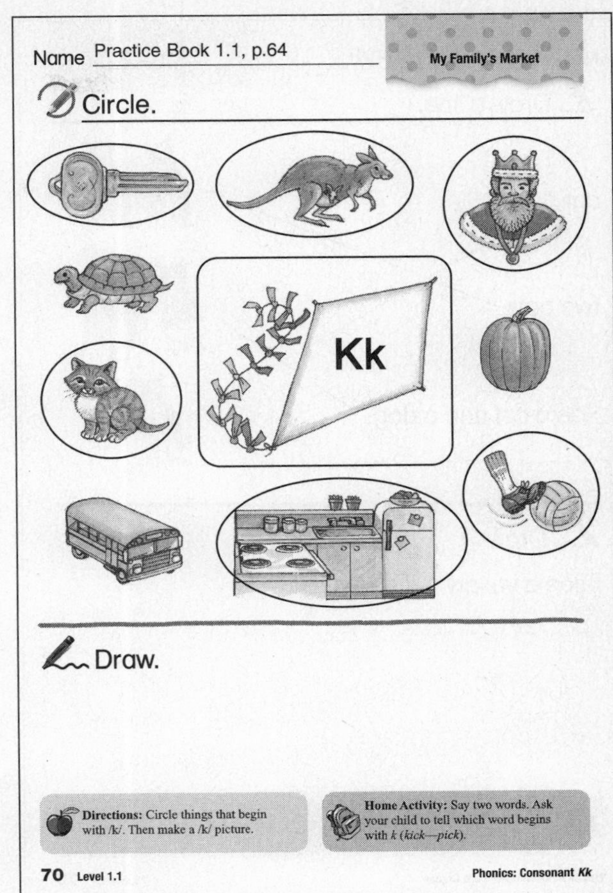
Name Practice Book 1.1, p.64

My Family's Market

Circle.



Draw.

**Directions:** Circle things that begin with /k/. Then make a /k/ picture.

**Home Activity:** Say two words. Ask your child to tell which word begins with *k* (*kick—pick*).

70 Level 1.1

Phonics: Consonant *Kk*

Name Practice Book 1.1, p.65

My Family's Market

Color.

Write.

Circle.

| H | b | F | (H) |
|---|---|---|---|
| M | (M) | n | N |

| K | B | (K) | t |
|---|---|---|---|
| D | P | b | (D) |

**Directions:** Color the make-believe picture. Write your name. Circle the matching letters.

**Home Activity:** Give directions like the ones on the page and have your child follow the directions.

Readiness Concepts: Following Directions

Level 1.1 71

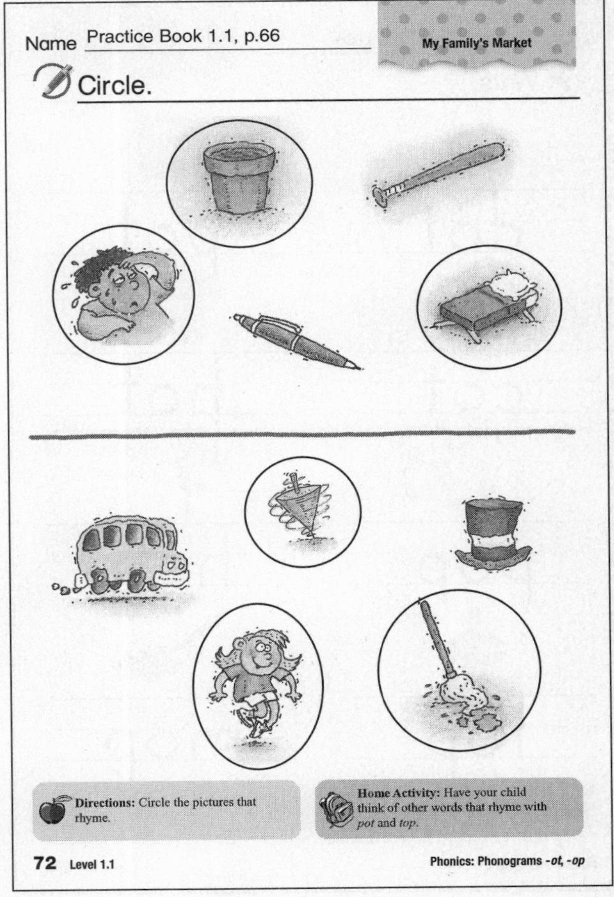
Name Practice Book 1.1, p.66

My Family's Market

Circle.

**Directions:** Circle the pictures that rhyme.

**Home Activity:** Have your child think of other words that rhyme with *pot* and *top*.

72 Level 1.1

Phonics: Phonograms *-ot, -op*

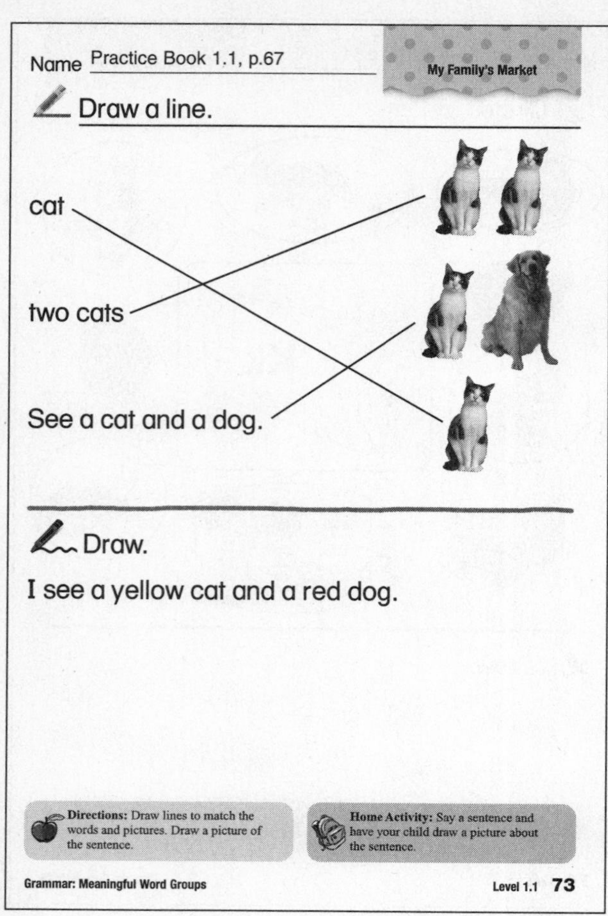

Name Practice Book 1.1, p.67
My Family's Market
Draw a line.
cat
two cats
See a cat and a dog.
Draw.
I see a yellow cat and a red dog.
Directions: Draw lines to match the words and pictures. Draw a picture of the sentence.
Home Activity: Say a sentence and have your child draw a picture about the sentence.
Grammar: Meaningful Word Groups
Level 1.1 73


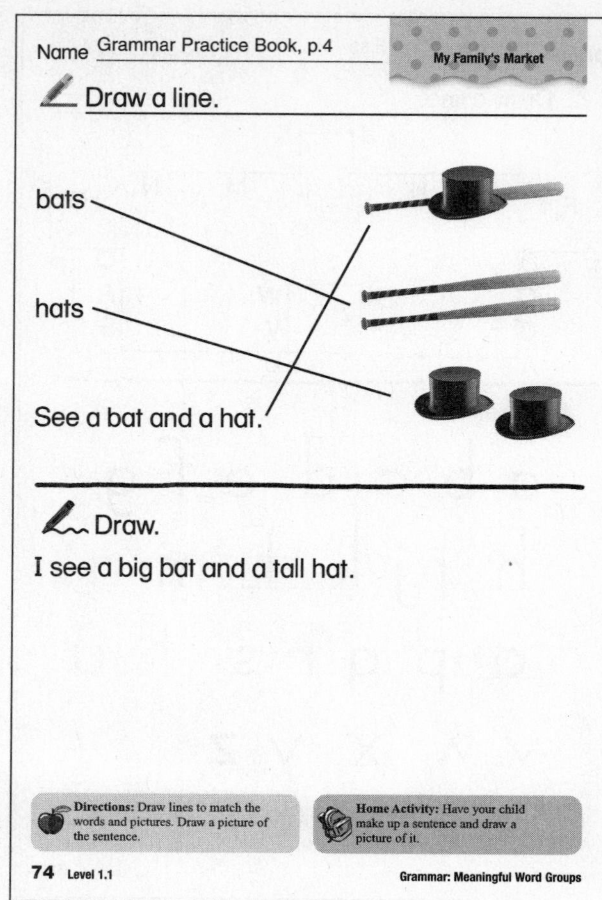

Name Grammar Practice Book, p.4
My Family's Market
Draw a line.
bats
hats
See a bat and a hat.
Draw.
I see a big bat and a tall hat.
Directions: Draw lines to match the words and pictures. Draw a picture of the sentence.
Home Activity: Have your child make up a sentence and draw a picture of it.
74 Level 1.1
Grammar: Meaningful Word Groups


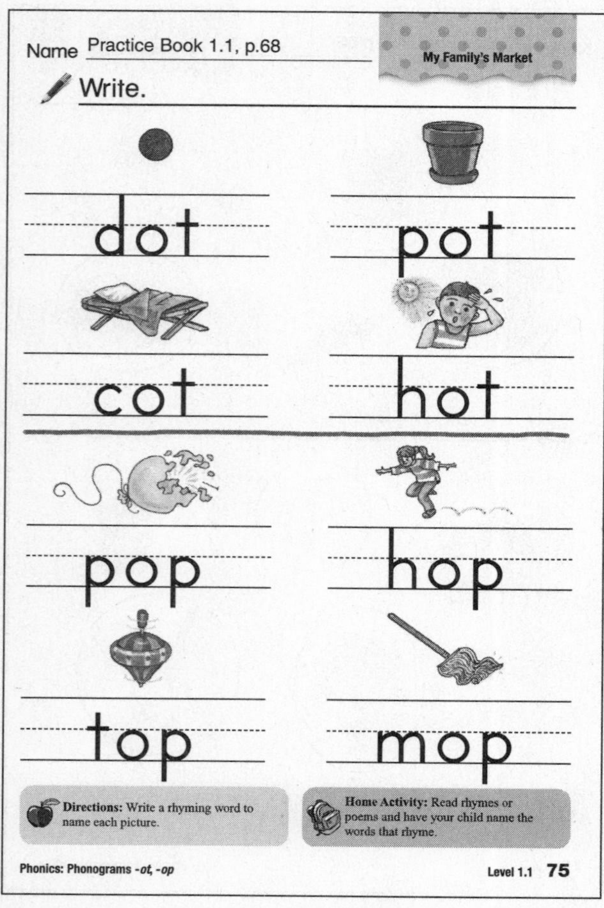

Name Practice Book 1.1, p.68
My Family's Market
Write.
dot
pot
cot
hot
pop
hop
top
mop
Directions: Write a rhyming word to name each picture.
Home Activity: Read rhymes or poems and have your child name the words that rhyme.
Phonics: Phonograms -ot, -op
Level 1.1 75


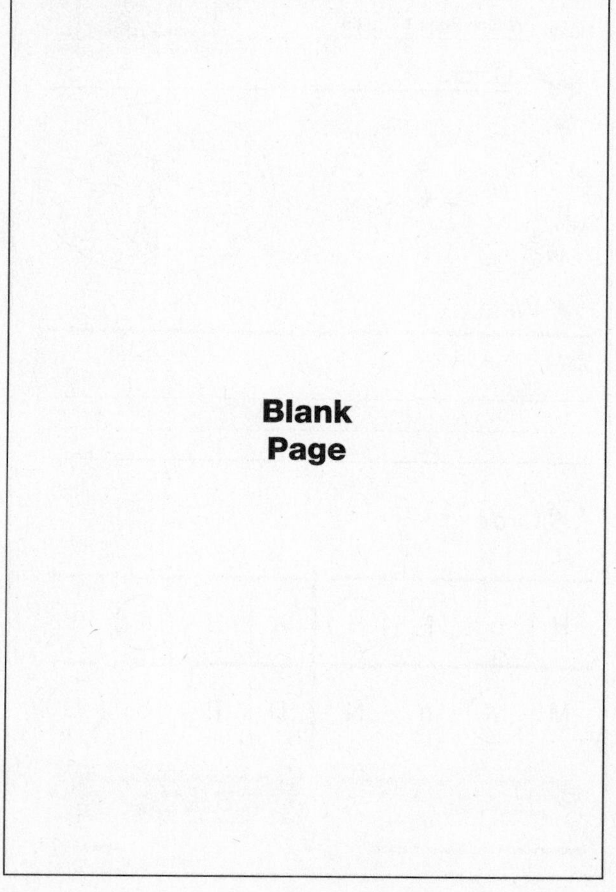

Blank
Page

Name Practice Book 1.1, p.75
Tumble Bumble
Circle.
Jj
Draw.
Directions: Circle things that begin with /j/. Then make a /j/ picture.
Home Activity: Help your child find things around the house that begin with *j*.
Phonics: Consonant *Jj*
Level 1.1 83

Name Practice Book 1.1, p.76
Tumble Bumble
Write.
net
jet
ham
jam
car
jar
bug
jug
log
jog
Directions: Change the first letter to make a new word that names the picture. Write the word.
Home Activity: Ask your child to read the rhyming words and use each word in a sentence.
84 Level 1.1
Phonics: Consonant *j* and Word Building

Name Practice Book 1.1, p.77
Tumble Bumble
Write.
3 1 2
2 3 1
2 1 3
2 3 1
Directions: Number the pictures 1, 2, and 3 to tell the order that things happened.
Home Activity: Read a story and ask your child to retell the story.
Comprehension: Sequence
Level 1.1 85

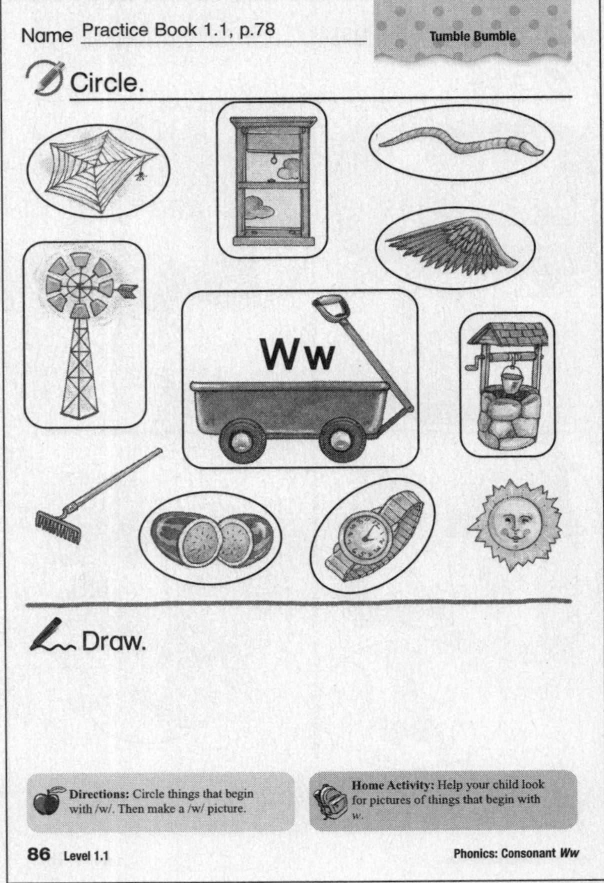
Name Practice Book 1.1, p.78
Tumble Bumble
Circle.
Ww
Draw.
Directions: Circle things that begin with /w/. Then make a /w/ picture.
Home Activity: Help your child look for pictures of things that begin with *w*.
86 Level 1.1
Phonics: Consonant *Ww*

Name Practice Book 1.1, p.79
Tumble Bumble
get
what
we
one
two
three
Directions: Have children cut along the dotted lines to make word cards.
High-Frequency Words
Level 1.1 87

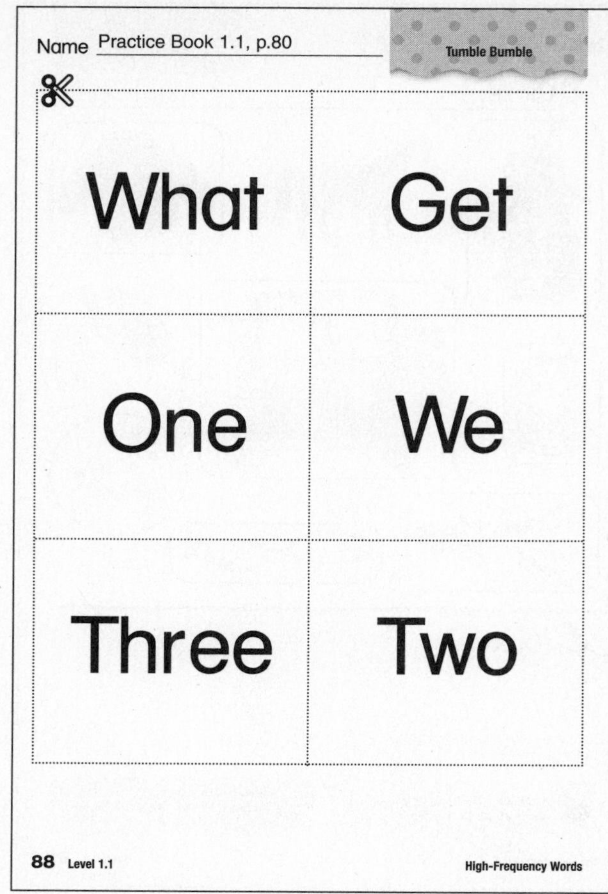
Name Practice Book 1.1, p.80
Tumble Bumble
What
Get
One
We
Three
Two
88 Level 1.1
High-Frequency Words

Name Practice Book 1.1, p.81
Tumble Bumble
Circle.
Directions: Circle the two things in each picture whose names rhyme.
Home Activity: Ask your child to name the rhyming pictures and give other rhyming words.
Readiness Concepts: Rhyme
Level 1.1 89

Name Practice Book 1.1, p.82
Tumble Bumble
Circle.
Vv
Draw.
Directions: Circle things that begin with /v/. Then make a /v/ picture.
Home Activity: Help your child make a list of words that begin with v.
90 Level 1.1
Phonics: Consonant Vv

Name Practice Book 1.1, p.83
Tumble Bumble
Write.
We get one.
We get
one.
I have two.
I have
two.
We have three.
We have
three.
Directions: Write each word used in the sentence.
Home Activity: Read the sentences together. Have your child copy each sentence.
Readiness Concepts: Divide Sentences into Words
Level 1.1 91

Name Practice Book 1.1, p.84
Tumble Bumble
Write.
net vet pet
pen hen ten
Directions: Write the letter to make each rhyming word.
Home Activity: Help your child use the words to make rhymes: Jack and Jill had a pet. They took it to a vet.
92 Level 1.1
Phonics: Phonograms -et, -en

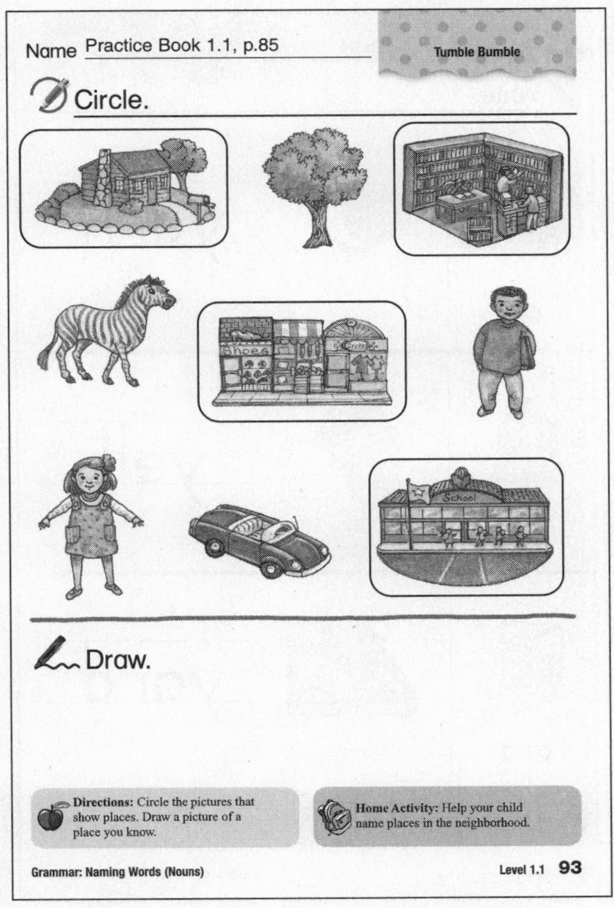
Name Practice Book 1.1, p.85
Tumble Bumble
Circle.
Draw.
Directions: Circle the pictures that show places. Draw a picture of a place you know.
Home Activity: Help your child name places in the neighborhood.
Grammar: Naming Words (Nouns)
Level 1.1 93

Name Grammar Practice Book, p.5
Tumble Bumble
Circle.
Directions: Circle the pictures of places.
Home Activity: Help your child label places in pictures.
94 Level 1.1
Grammar: Naming Words (Nouns)

Name Practice Book 1.1, p.86

Tumble Bumble

Write.

pet wet

net jet

pen ten

hen men

**Directions:** Write a rhyming word to name each picture.

**Home Activity:** Ask your child to make other rhyming words for each set. (*bet, set, let, vet; then, when, den*)

Phonics: Phonograms *-et, -en* Level 1.1 95

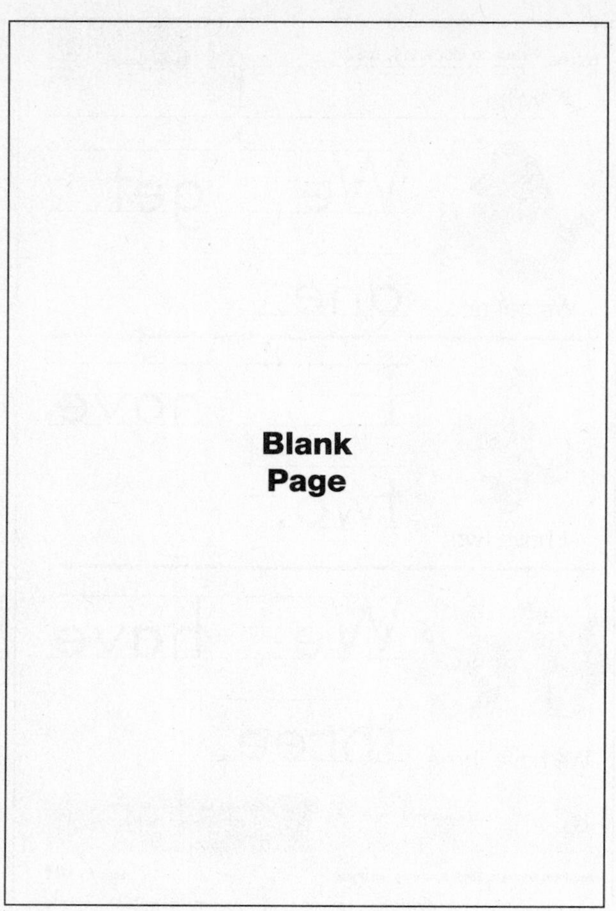
Blank Page

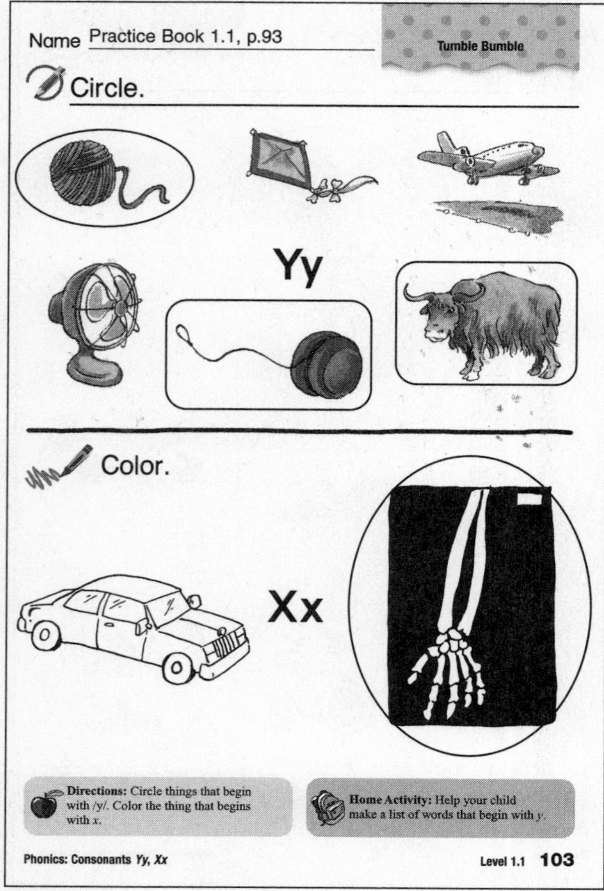
Name Practice Book 1.1, p.93

Tumble Bumble

Circle.

Yy

Color.

Xx

**Directions:** Circle things that begin with /y/. Color the thing that begins with *x*.

**Home Activity:** Help your child make a list of words that begin with *y*.

Phonics: Consonants *Yy, Xx* Level 1.1 103

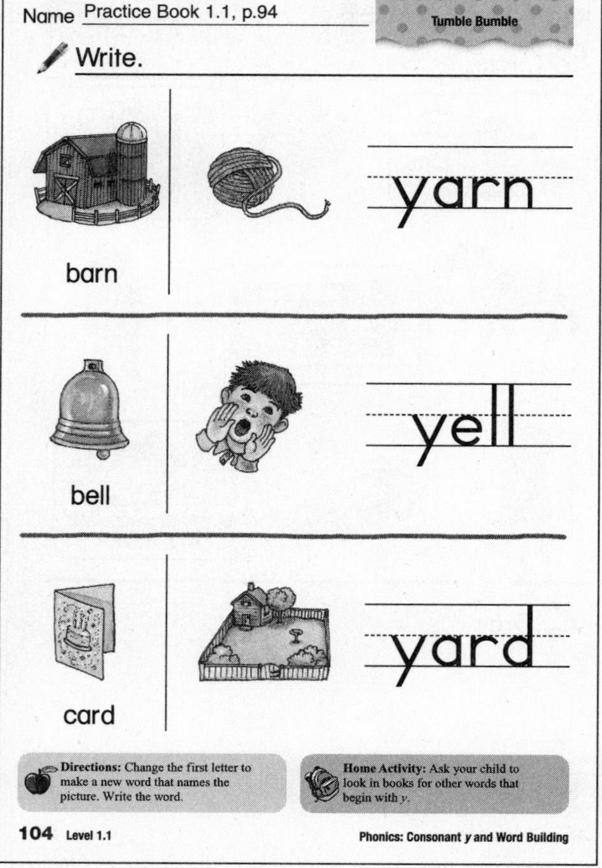
Name Practice Book 1.1, p.94

Tumble Bumble

Write.

barn yarn

bell yell

card yard

**Directions:** Change the first letter to make a new word that names the picture. Write the word.

**Home Activity:** Ask your child to look in books for other words that begin with *y*.

104 Level 1.1 Phonics: Consonant *y* and Word Building

Name Practice Book 1.1, p.95
Tumble Bumble
Draw.
Directions: Draw something that happened in Tumble Bumble.
Home Activity: Have your child tell you the story in the book Tumble Bumble.
Comprehension: Recall/Retell
Level 1.1 105

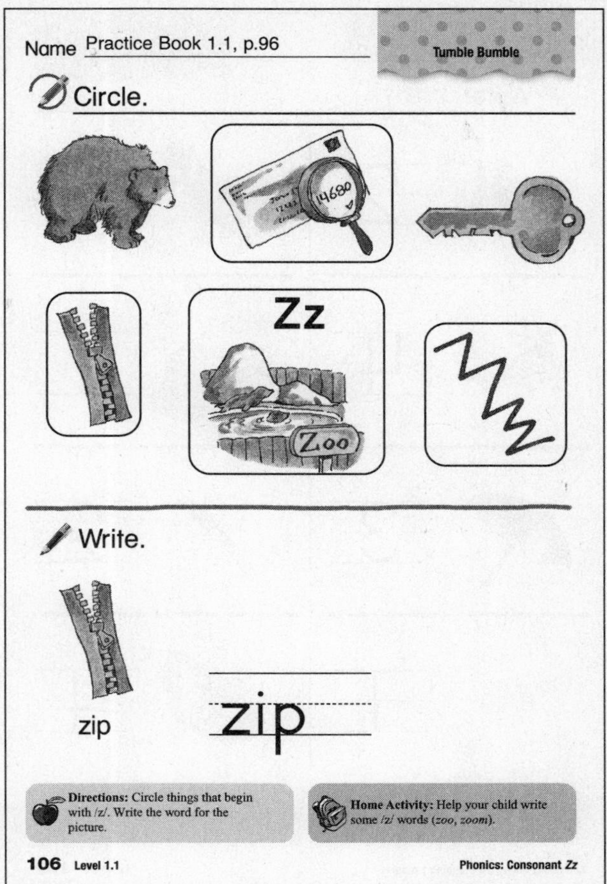
Name Practice Book 1.1, p.96
Tumble Bumble
Circle.
Zz
Zoo
Write.
zip
zip
Directions: Circle things that begin with /z/. Write the word for the picture.
Home Activity: Help your child write some /z/ words (zoo, zoom).
106 Level 1.1
Phonics: Consonant Zz

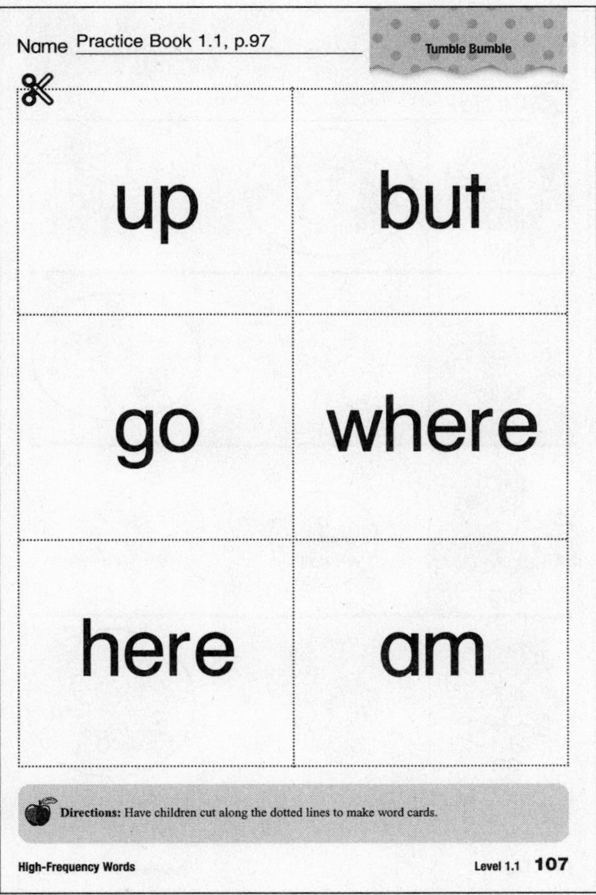
Name Practice Book 1.1, p.97
Tumble Bumble
up
but
go
where
here
am
Directions: Have children cut along the dotted lines to make word cards.
High-Frequency Words
Level 1.1 107

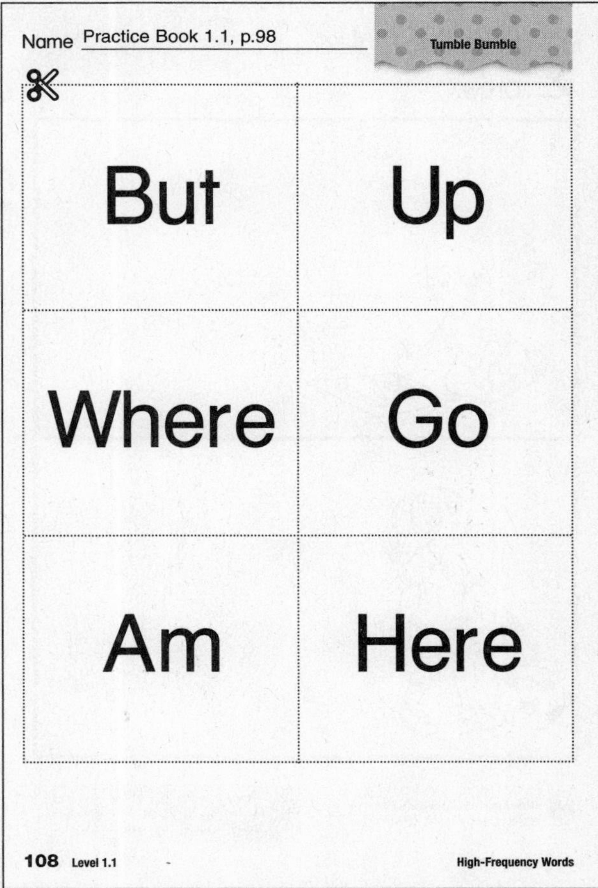
Name Practice Book 1.1, p.98
Tumble Bumble
But
Up
Where
Go
Am
Here
108 Level 1.1
High-Frequency Words

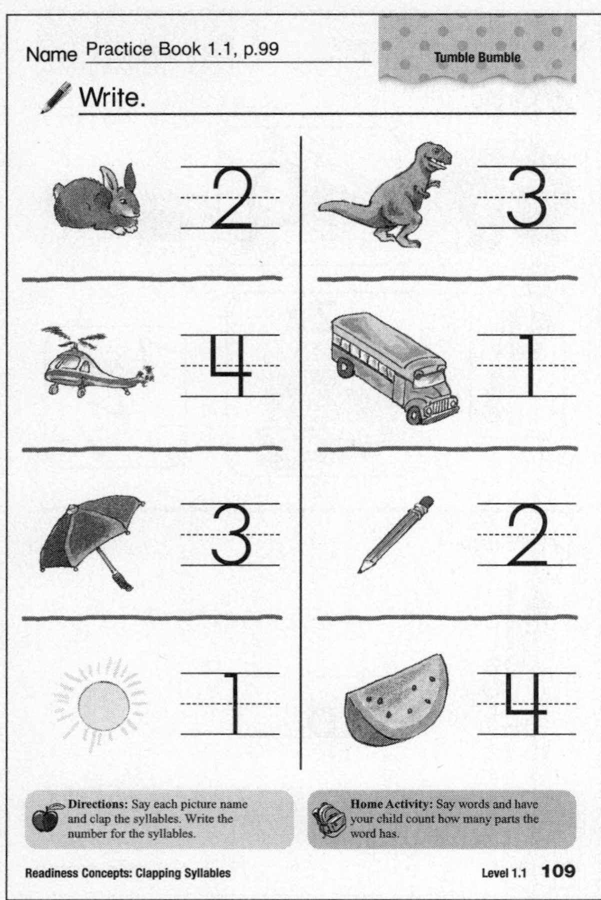
Name Practice Book 1.1, p.99
Tumble Bumble
Write.
2
3
4
1
3
2
1
4
Directions: Say each picture name and clap the syllables. Write the number for the syllables.
Home Activity: Say words and have your child count how many parts the word has.
Readiness Concepts: Clapping Syllables
Level 1.1 109

Name Practice Book 1.1, p.100
Tumble Bumble
Circle.
qu
Draw.
Directions: Circle things that begin with qu /kw/. Then make a /qu/ picture.
Home Activity: Say two words. Ask your child to tell which word begins with qu (quit/hit, pack/quack, pick/quick).
110 Level 1.1
Phonics: Consonant Qu, qu

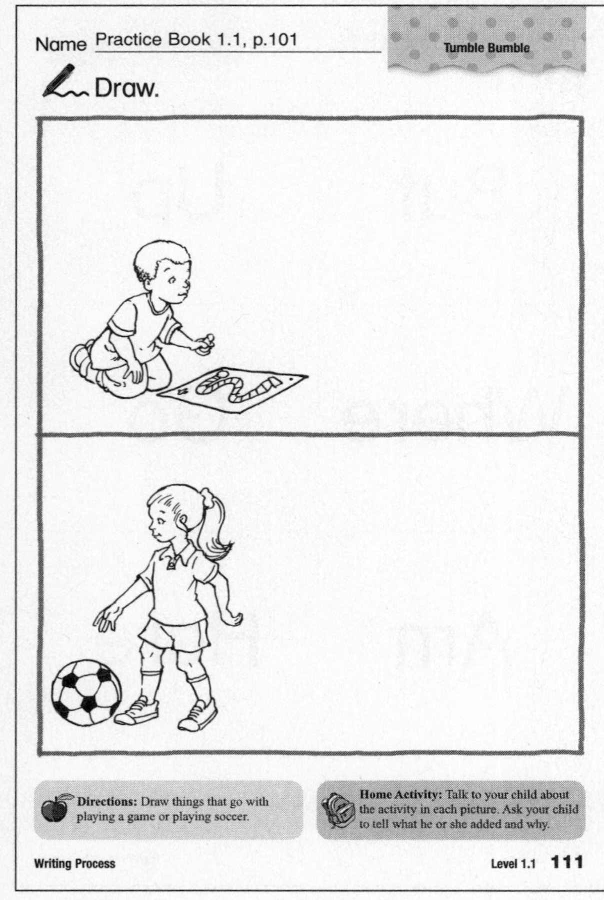
Name Practice Book 1.1, p.101
Tumble Bumble
Draw.
Directions: Draw things that go with playing a game or playing soccer.
Home Activity: Talk to your child about the activity in each picture. Ask your child to tell what he or she added and why.
Writing Process
Level 1.1 111

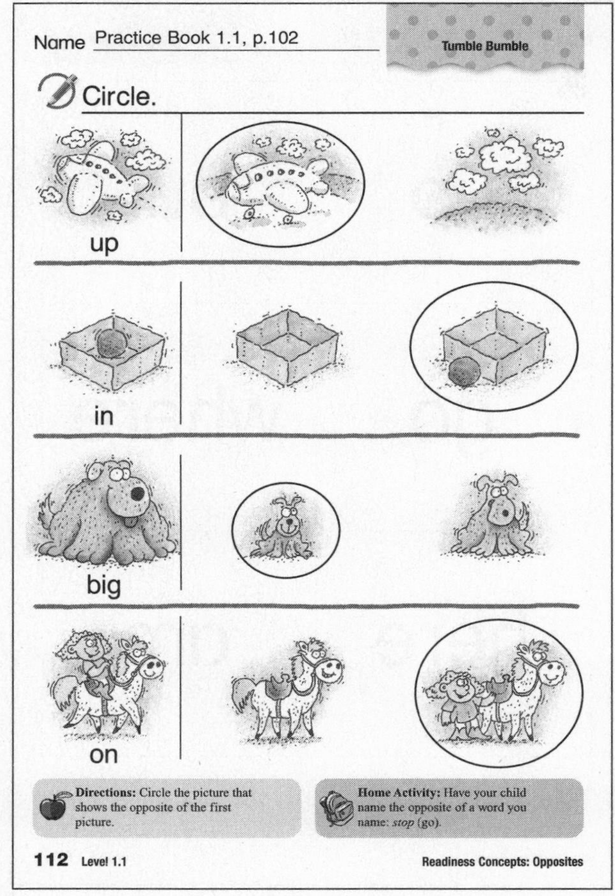
Name Practice Book 1.1, p.102
Tumble Bumble
Circle.
up
in
big
on
Directions: Circle the picture that shows the opposite of the first picture.
Home Activity: Have your child name the opposite of a word you name: stop (go).
112 Level 1.1
Readiness Concepts: Opposites

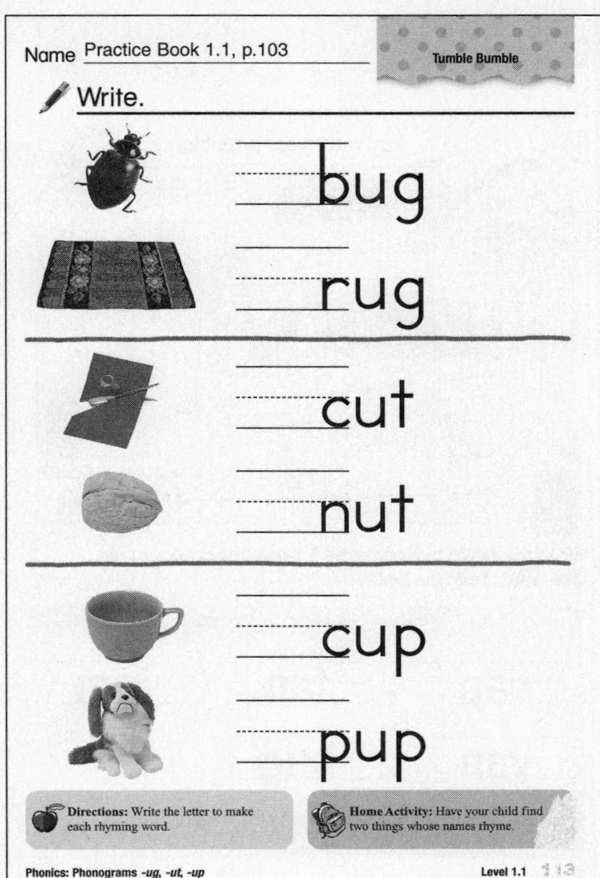
Name Practice Book 1.1, p.103
Tumble Bumble
Write.
bug
rug
cut
nut
cup
pup
Directions: Write the letter to make each rhyming word.
Home Activity: Have your child find two things whose names rhyme.
Phonics: Phonograms -ug, -ut, -up
Level 1.1 113

Name Practice Book 1.1, p.104
Tumble Bumble
Circle and write.
hug
bug
tug
rug
bug
rug
cut
nut
pup
cup
nut
cup
Directions: Circle the word that names the picture. Write the word.
Home Activity: Read the pair of words in each box and make sentences using both of the words.
114 Level 1.1
Phonics: Phonograms -ug, -ut, -up

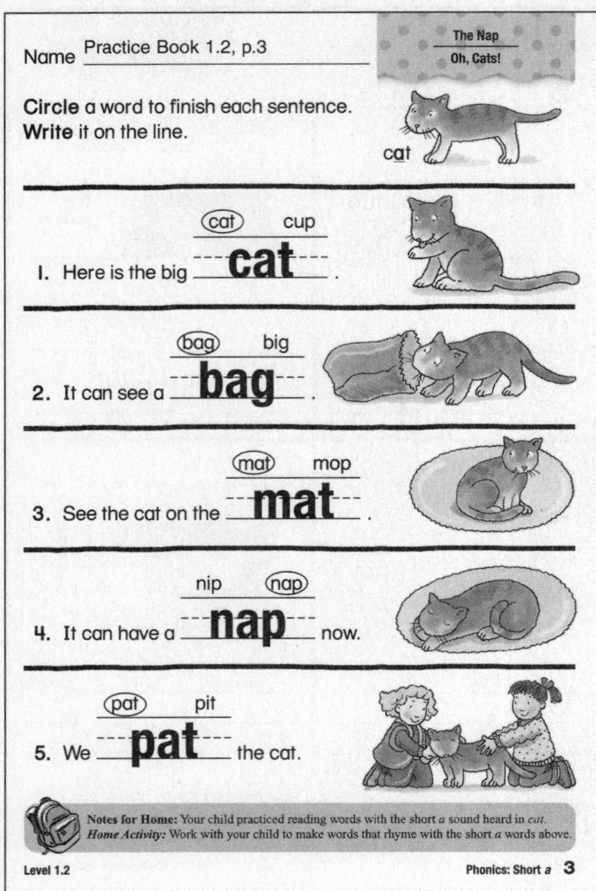

Name Practice Book 1.2, p.3

The Nap
Oh, Cats!

**Circle** a word to finish each sentence.
**Write** it on the line.

cat

1. Here is the big **cat** . (cat) cup
2. It can see a **bag** . (bag) big
3. See the cat on the **mat** . (mat) mop
4. It can have a **nap** now. nip (nap)
5. We **pat** the cat. (pat) pit

**Notes for Home:** Your child practiced reading words with the short *a* sound heard in *cat*. *Home Activity:* Work with your child to make words that rhyme with the short *a* words above.

Level 1.2 Phonics: Short *a* 3

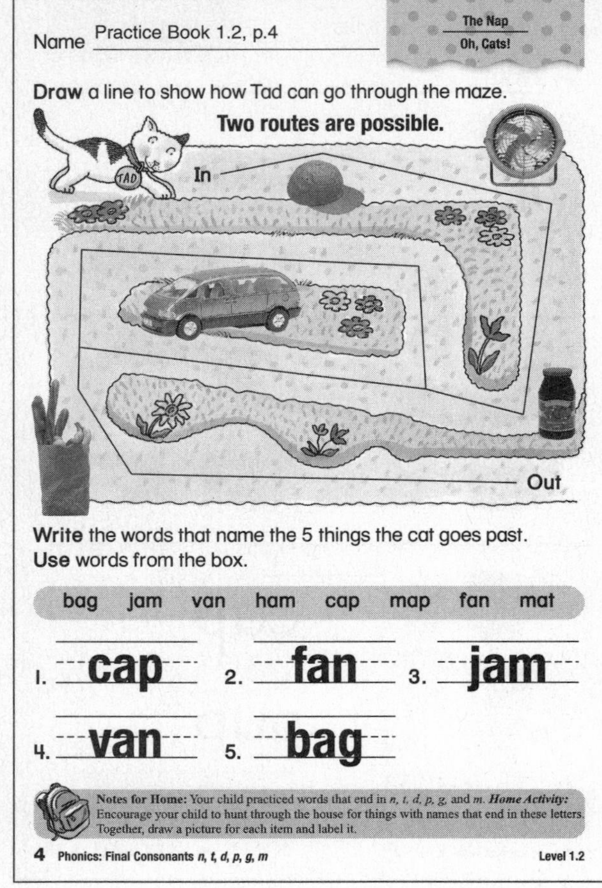

Name Practice Book 1.2, p.4

The Nap
Oh, Cats!

**Draw** a line to show how Tad can go through the maze.

**Two routes are possible.**



**Write** the words that name the 5 things the cat goes past.
**Use** words from the box.

bag jam van ham cap map fan mat

1. **cap**
2. **fan**
3. **jam**
4. **van**
5. **bag**

**Notes for Home:** Your child practiced words that end in *n, t, d, p, g,* and *m*. *Home Activity:* Encourage your child to hunt through the house for things with names that end in these letters. Together, draw a picture for each item and label it.

4 Phonics: Final Consonants *n, t, d, p, g, m* Level 1.2

Name Practice Book 1.2, p.5

The Nap
Oh, Cats!

**Pick** a word from the box to finish each sentence.
**Write** it on the line.

away come down no will

1. No, Nan. I **will** not get up.
2. **No** , Pam. Do not get up here.
3. Go **away** , you two!
4. Get **down** , Nan!
5. Nan and Pam, **come** here and see.

**Notes for Home:** This week your child is learning to read the words *away, come, down, no* and *will*. *Home Activity:* As you read with your child, encourage him or her to point out these words in print.

Level 1.2 High-Frequency Words 5

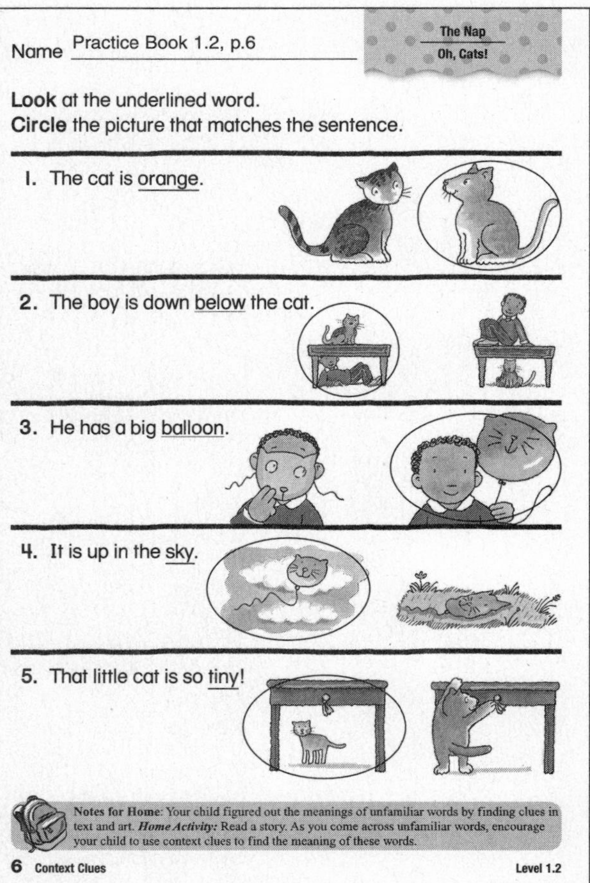

Name Practice Book 1.2, p.6

The Nap
Oh, Cats!

**Look** at the underlined word.
**Circle** the picture that matches the sentence.

1. The cat is orange.
2. The boy is down below the cat.
3. He has a big balloon.
4. It is up in the sky.
5. That little cat is so tiny!

**Notes for Home:** Your child figured out the meanings of unfamiliar words by finding clues in text and art. *Home Activity:* Read a story. As you come across unfamiliar words, encourage your child to use context clues to find the meaning of these words.

6 Context Clues Level 1.2

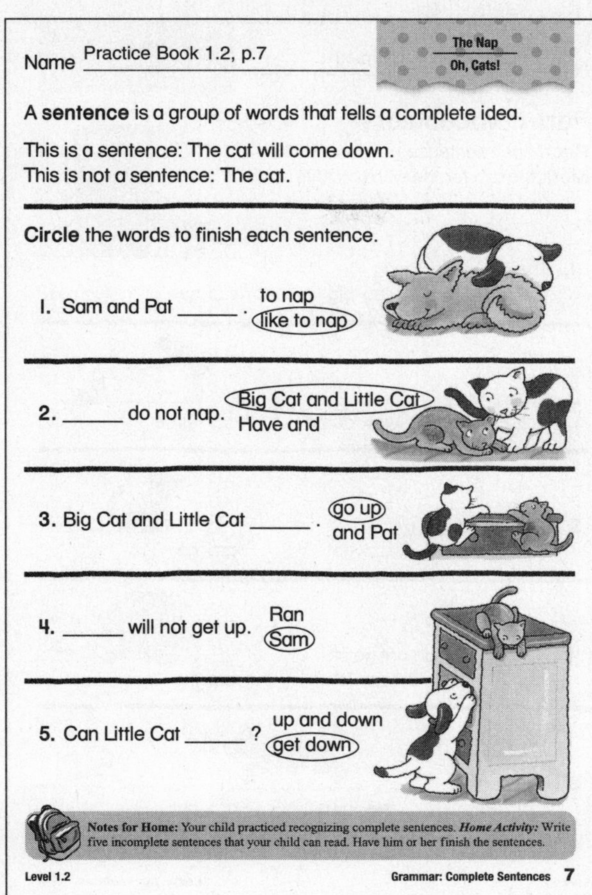
Name Practice Book 1.2, p.7

The Nap
Oh, Cats!

A **sentence** is a group of words that tells a complete idea.

This is a sentence: The cat will come down.
This is not a sentence: The cat.

**Circle** the words to finish each sentence.

1. Sam and Pat ______ . to nap / (like to nap)
2. ______ do not nap. (Big Cat and Little Cat) / Have and
3. Big Cat and Little Cat ______ . (go up) / and Pat
4. ______ will not get up. Ran / (Sam)
5. Can Little Cat ______ ? up and down / (get down)

**Notes for Home:** Your child practiced recognizing complete sentences. *Home Activity:* Write five incomplete sentences that your child can read. Have him or her finish the sentences.

Level 1.2 Grammar: Complete Sentences 7

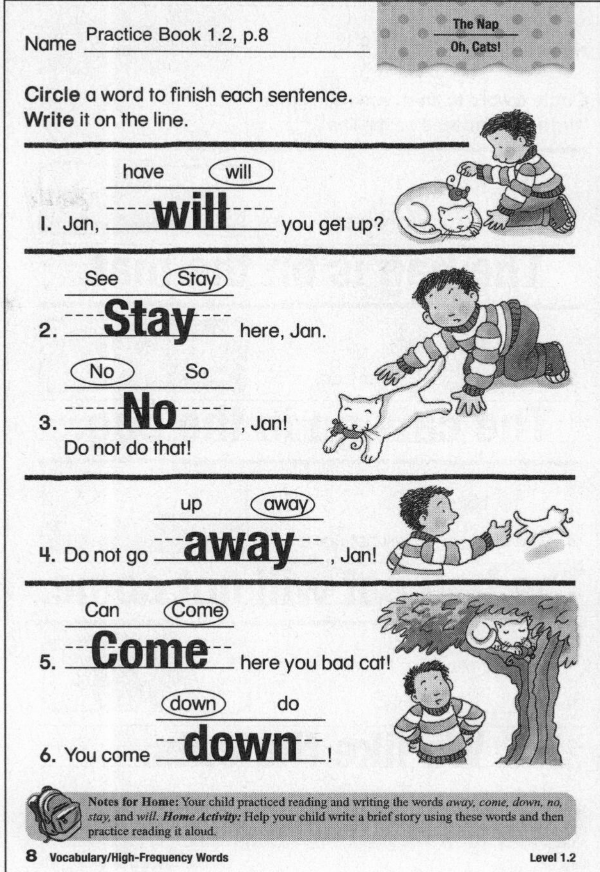
Name Practice Book 1.2, p.8

The Nap
Oh, Cats!

**Circle** a word to finish each sentence.
**Write** it on the line.

1. Jan, **will** you get up? have / (will)
2. **Stay** here, Jan. See / (Stay)
3. **No**, Jan! Do not do that! (No) / So
4. Do not go **away**, Jan! up / (away)
5. **Come** here you bad cat! Can / (Come)
6. You come **down**! (down) / do

**Notes for Home:** Your child practiced reading and writing the words *away, come, down, no, stay,* and *will. Home Activity:* Help your child write a brief story using these words and then practice reading it aloud.

8 Vocabulary/High-Frequency Words Level 1.2

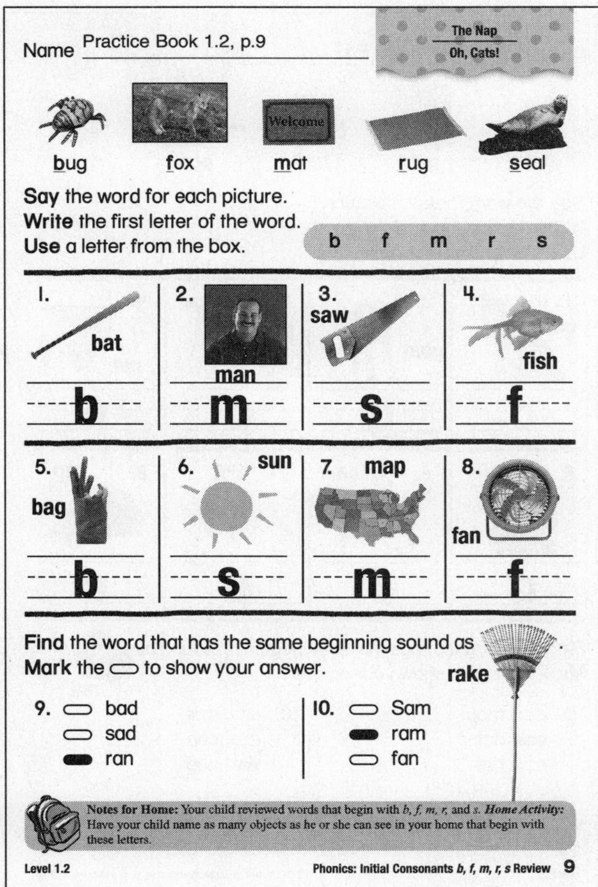
Name Practice Book 1.2, p.9

The Nap
Oh, Cats!

bug fox mat rug seal

Welcome

**Say** the word for each picture.
**Write** the first letter of the word.
**Use** a letter from the box.

b f m r s

1. bat **b**
2. man **m**
3. saw **s**
4. fish **f**
5. bag **b**
6. sun **s**
7. map **m**
8. fan **f**

**Find** the word that has the same beginning sound as rake.
**Mark** the ⬭ to show your answer.

9. ⬭ bad ⬭ sad ⬬ ran
10. ⬭ Sam ⬬ ram ⬭ fan

**Notes for Home:** Your child reviewed words that begin with *b, f, m, r,* and *s. Home Activity:* Have your child name as many objects as he or she can see in your home that begin with these letters.

Level 1.2 Phonics: Initial Consonants *b, f, m, r, s* Review 9

Name Practice Book 1.2, p.10

The Nap
Oh, Cats!

**Look** at each word. **Say** it.
**Listen** for the middle and ending sounds in **bat** and **fan**.

| | **Write** each word. | **Check** it. |
|---|---|---|
| 1. at | at | at |
| 2. sat | sat | sat |
| 3. cat | cat | cat |
| 4. an | an | an |
| 5. ran | ran | ran |
| 6. man | man | man |

## Word Wall Words

**Write** each word.

| | | |
|---|---|---|
| 7. will | will | will |
| 8. no | no | no |

**Notes for Home:** Your child spelled words that end with *-at* and *-an* and two frequently used words: *will, no. Home Activity:* Ask your child to draw different pictures showing a man and a cat. Challenge your child to use these spelling words to label the pictures.

10 Spelling: Word Families *-at* and *-an* Level 1.2

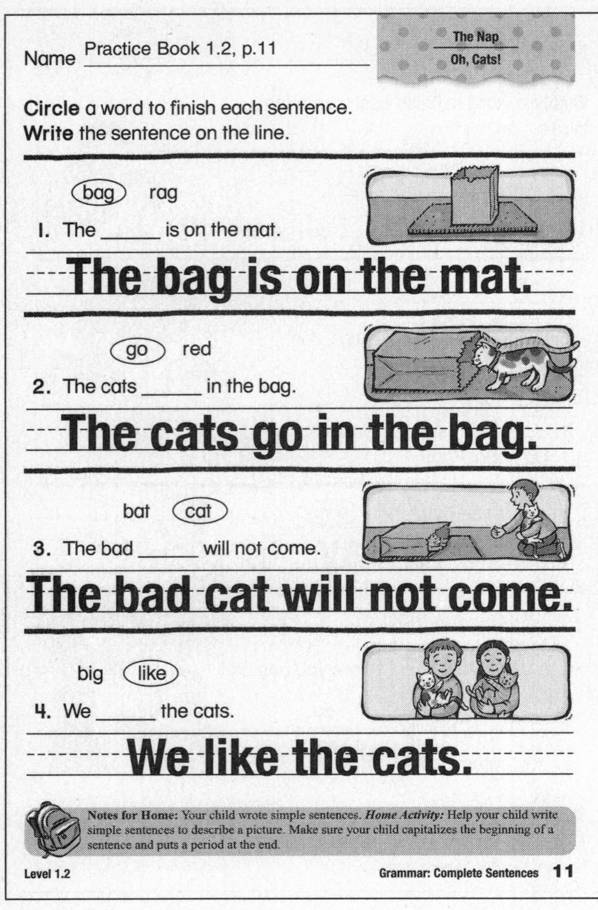
Name Practice Book 1.2, p.11

The Nap
Oh, Cats!

**Circle** a word to finish each sentence.
**Write** the sentence on the line.

(bag) rag
1. The ____ is on the mat.
**The bag is on the mat.**

(go) red
2. The cats ____ in the bag.
**The cats go in the bag.**

bat (cat)
3. The bad ____ will not come.
**The bad cat will not come.**

big (like)
4. We ____ the cats.
**We like the cats.**

**Notes for Home:** Your child wrote simple sentences. *Home Activity:* Help your child write simple sentences to describe a picture. Make sure your child capitalizes the beginning of a sentence and puts a period at the end.

Level 1.2 Grammar: Complete Sentences 11

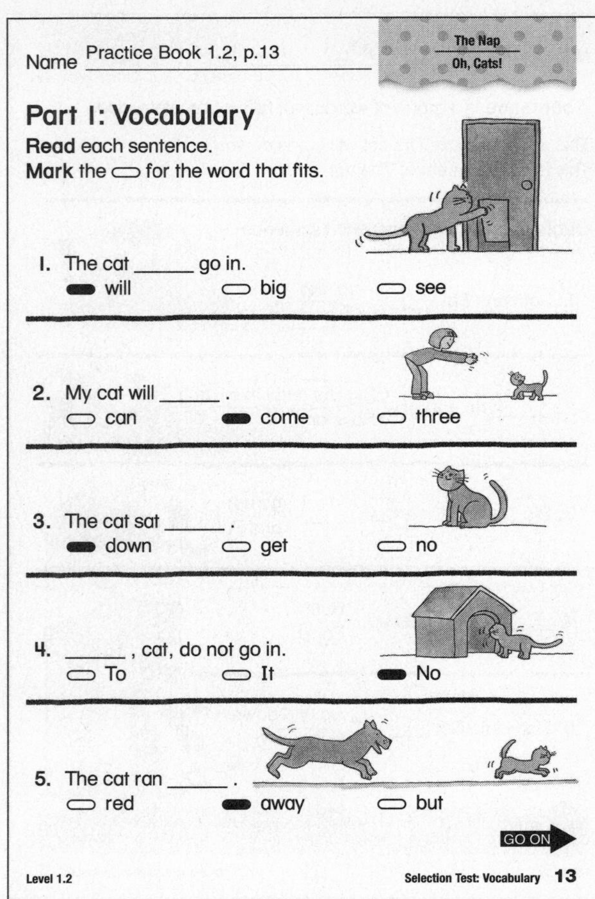
Name Practice Book 1.2, p.13

The Nap
Oh, Cats!

## Part 1: Vocabulary

**Read** each sentence.
**Mark** the ⬭ for the word that fits.

1. The cat ____ go in.
   - ● will
   - ○ big
   - ○ see

2. My cat will ____ .
   - ○ can
   - ● come
   - ○ three

3. The cat sat ____ .
   - ● down
   - ○ get
   - ○ no

4. ____ , cat, do not go in.
   - ○ To
   - ○ It
   - ● No

5. The cat ran ____ .
   - ○ red
   - ● away
   - ○ but

GO ON

Level 1.2 Selection Test: Vocabulary 13

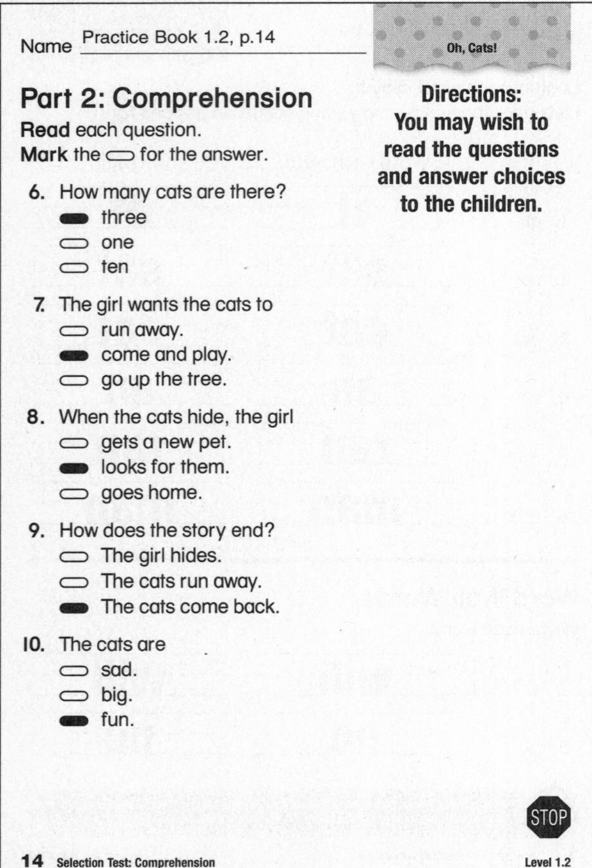
Name Practice Book 1.2, p.14

Oh, Cats!

## Part 2: Comprehension

**Read** each question.
**Mark** the ⬭ for the answer.

**Directions: You may wish to read the questions and answer choices to the children.**

6. How many cats are there?
   - ● three
   - ○ one
   - ○ ten

7. The girl wants the cats to
   - ○ run away.
   - ● come and play.
   - ○ go up the tree.

8. When the cats hide, the girl
   - ○ gets a new pet.
   - ● looks for them.
   - ○ goes home.

9. How does the story end?
   - ○ The girl hides.
   - ○ The cats run away.
   - ● The cats come back.

10. The cats are
    - ○ sad.
    - ○ big.
    - ● fun.

STOP

14 Selection Test: Comprehension Level 1.2

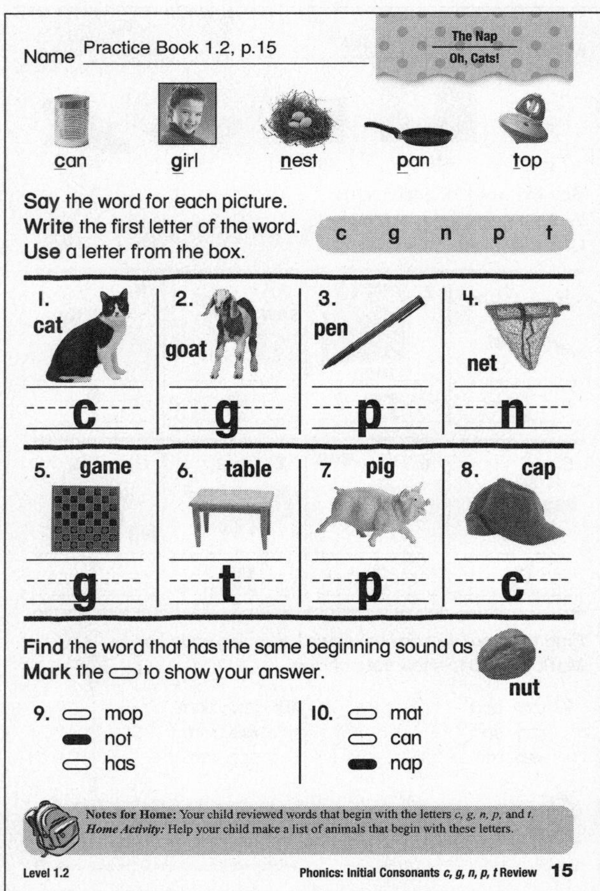
Name Practice Book 1.2, p.15

The Nap
Oh, Cats!

can girl nest pan top

**Say** the word for each picture.
**Write** the first letter of the word.
**Use** a letter from the box.

c g n p t

| 1. cat | 2. goat | 3. pen | 4. net |
|---|---|---|---|
| **c** | **g** | **p** | **n** |
| **5. game** | **6. table** | **7. pig** | **8. cap** |
| **g** | **t** | **p** | **c** |

**Find** the word that has the same beginning sound as (nut).
**Mark** the ⬭ to show your answer.

9.
- ○ mop
- ● not
- ○ has

10.
- ○ mat
- ○ can
- ● nap

**Notes for Home:** Your child reviewed words that begin with the letters *c, g, n, p,* and *t.* *Home Activity:* Help your child make a list of animals that begin with these letters.

Level 1.2 Phonics: Initial Consonants *c, g, n, p, t* Review 15

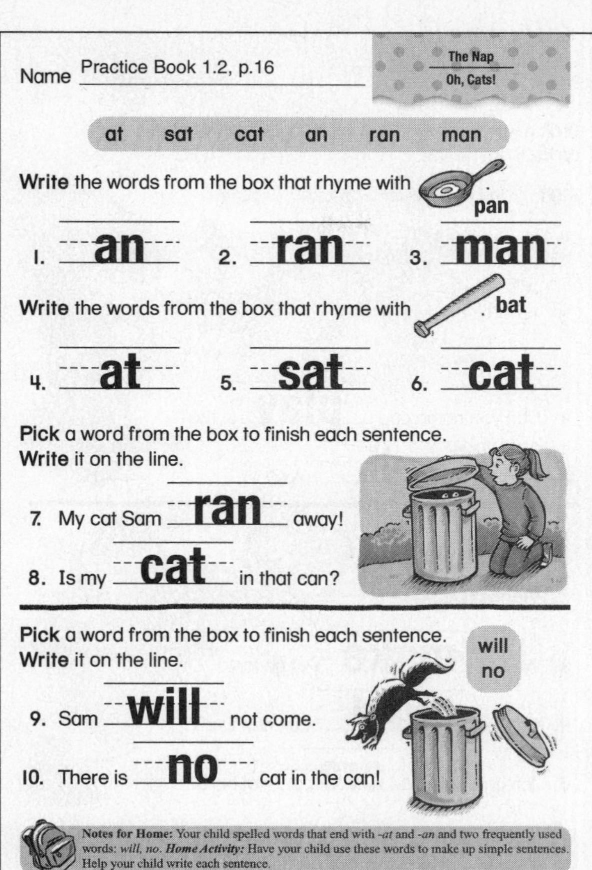
Name Practice Book 1.2, p.16
The Nap
Oh, Cats!
at sat cat an ran man
Write the words from the box that rhyme with pan.
1. an 2. ran 3. man
Write the words from the box that rhyme with bat.
4. at 5. sat 6. cat
Pick a word from the box to finish each sentence.
Write it on the line.
7. My cat Sam ran away!
8. Is my cat in that can?
Pick a word from the box to finish each sentence.
Write it on the line.
will
no
9. Sam will not come.
10. There is no cat in the can!
Notes for Home: Your child spelled words that end with -at and -an and two frequently used words: will, no. Home Activity: Have your child use these words to make up simple sentences. Help your child write each sentence.
16 Spelling: Word Families -at and -an
Level 1.2

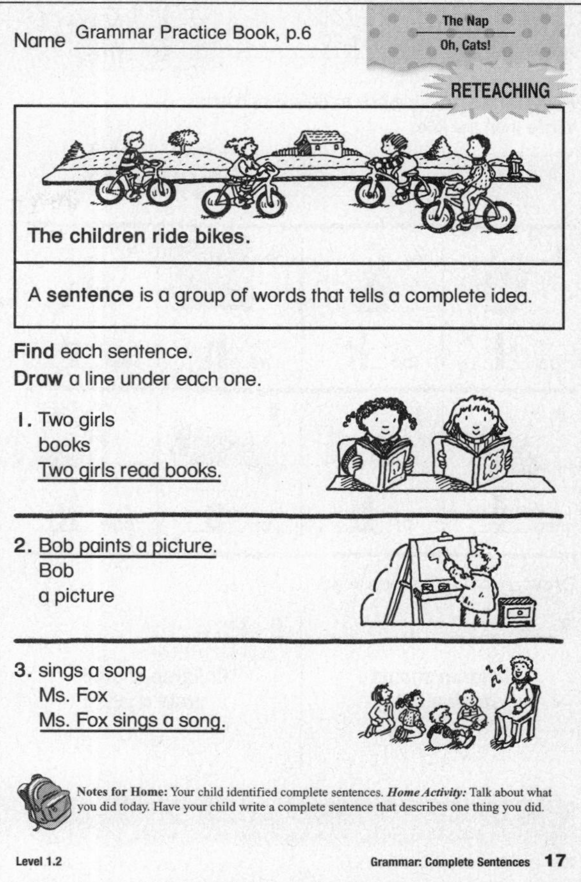
Name Grammar Practice Book, p.6
The Nap
Oh, Cats!
RETEACHING
The children ride bikes.
A sentence is a group of words that tells a complete idea.
Find each sentence.
Draw a line under each one.
1. Two girls
books
Two girls read books.
2. Bob paints a picture.
Bob
a picture
3. sings a song
Ms. Fox
Ms. Fox sings a song.
Notes for Home: Your child identified complete sentences. Home Activity: Talk about what you did today. Have your child write a complete sentence that describes one thing you did.
Level 1.2
Grammar: Complete Sentences 17

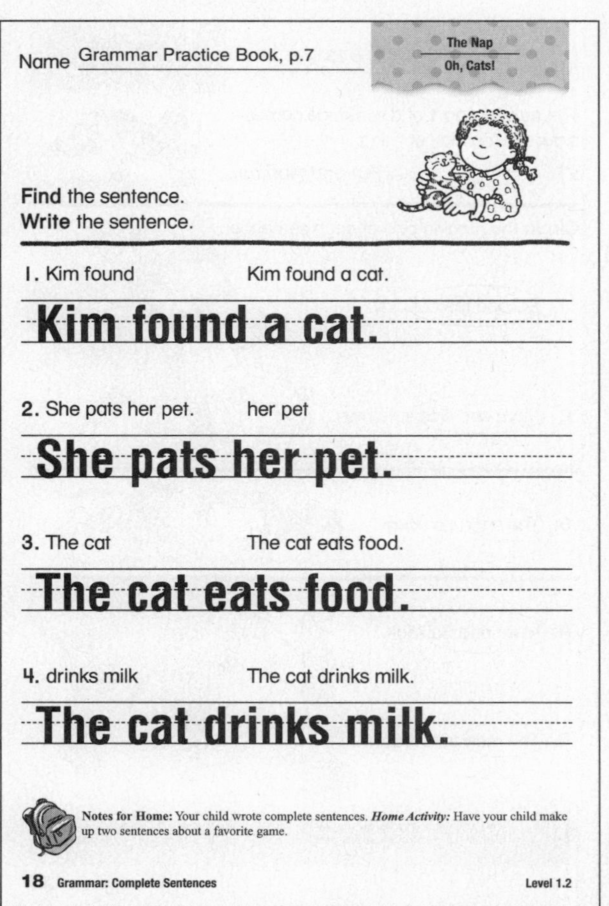
Name Grammar Practice Book, p.7
The Nap
Oh, Cats!
Find the sentence.
Write the sentence.
1. Kim found Kim found a cat.
Kim found a cat.
2. She pats her pet. her pet
She pats her pet.
3. The cat The cat eats food.
The cat eats food.
4. drinks milk The cat drinks milk.
The cat drinks milk.
Notes for Home: Your child wrote complete sentences. Home Activity: Have your child make up two sentences about a favorite game.
18 Grammar: Complete Sentences
Level 1.2

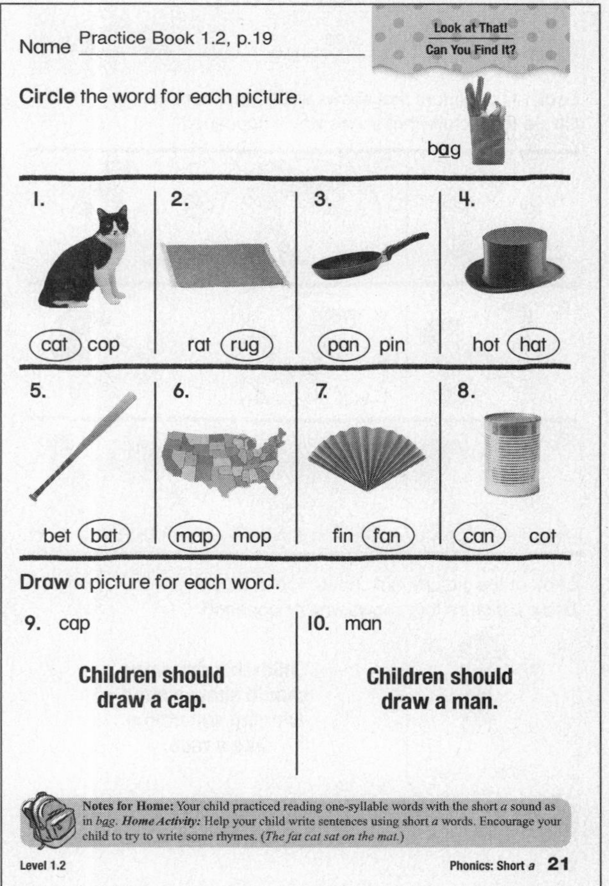
Name Practice Book 1.2, p.19
Look at That!
Can You Find It?
Circle the word for each picture.
bag
1. cat cop
2. rat rug
3. pan pin
4. hot hat
5. bet bat
6. map mop
7. fin fan
8. can cot
Draw a picture for each word.
9. cap
Children should draw a cap.
10. man
Children should draw a man.
Notes for Home: Your child practiced reading one-syllable words with the short a sound as in bag. Home Activity: Help your child write sentences using short a words. Encourage your child to try to write some rhymes. (The fat cat sat on the mat.)
Level 1.2
Phonics: Short a 21

Name Practice Book 1.2, p.20

Look at That! Can You Find It?

**Pick** a letter from the box to finish each word.
**Write** it on the line.

b k s r f l

snail

1. pai **l**
2. loc **k**
3. we **b**
4. sta **r**
5. lea **f**
6. tu **b**
7. bu **s**
8. boo **k**

**Draw** a picture for each word.

9. car

**Children should draw a car.**

10. jar

**Children should draw a jar.**

**Notes for Home:** Your child is learning to read words that end with the letters *b, k, s, r, f,* and *l.* ***Home Activity:*** Go on a "Last Letter Hunt" around your home with your child. Together make a list of all the things you can find whose names end with *b, k, s, r, f,* or *l.*

22 Phonics: Final Consonants *b, k, s, r, f, l* Level 1.2

Name Practice Book 1.2, p.21

Look at That! Can You Find It?

**Pick** a word from the box to finish each sentence.
**Write** it on the line.

all are find make play

1. Can you come and **play** tag?
2. Will you **all** play?
3. We will **make** Pat go look.
4. Can Pat **find** Jan and Dan?
5. Jan and Dan **are** not here!

**Notes for Home:** This week your child is learning to read the words *all, are, find, make,* and *play.* ***Home Activity:*** Write these words on cards. Take turns drawing two cards. Try to use both words in one sentence. Help your child write his or her sentences.

Level 1.2 High-Frequency Words 23

Name Practice Book 1.2, p.22

Look at That! Can You Find It?

**Look** at the picture that shows what happened.
**Circle** the picture that shows why it happened.

1.

2.

3.

**Look** at the picture that shows what happened.
**Draw** a picture that shows why it happened.

4.

**Children's drawings should show a child winning something like a race.**

**Notes for Home:** Your child learned about cause (why something happens) and effect (what happens). ***Home Activity:*** Give your child some causes and challenge him or her to guess what might happen. (For example: *It was raining, and Nan does not have a coat. Nan will get wet.*)

24 Cause and Effect Level 1.2

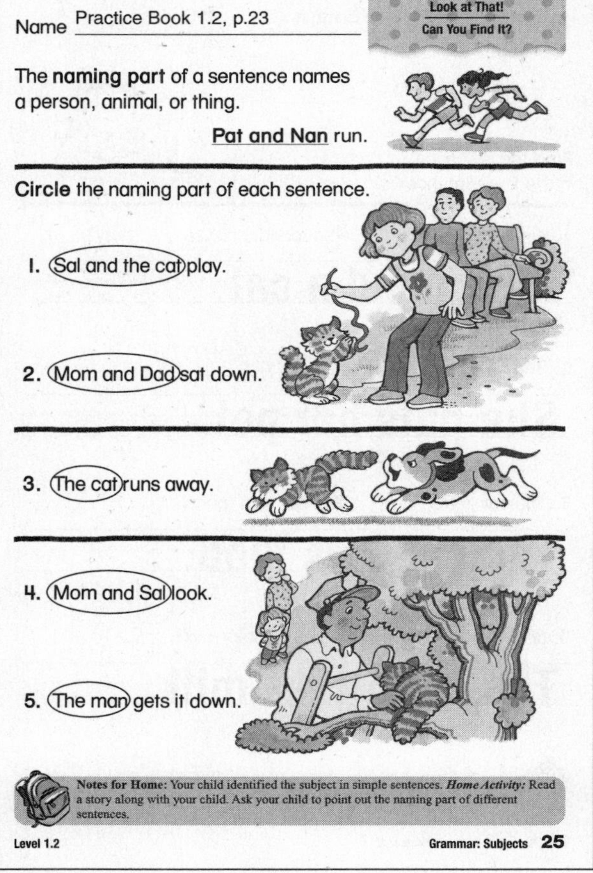

Name Practice Book 1.2, p.23

Look at That! Can You Find It?

The **naming part** of a sentence names a person, animal, or thing.

**Pat and Nan** run.

**Circle** the naming part of each sentence.

1. (Sal and the cat) play.
2. (Mom and Dad) sat down.
3. (The cat) runs away.
4. (Mom and Sal) look.
5. (The man) gets it down.

**Notes for Home:** Your child identified the subject in simple sentences. ***Home Activity:*** Read a story along with your child. Ask your child to point out the naming part of different sentences.

Level 1.2 Grammar: Subjects 25

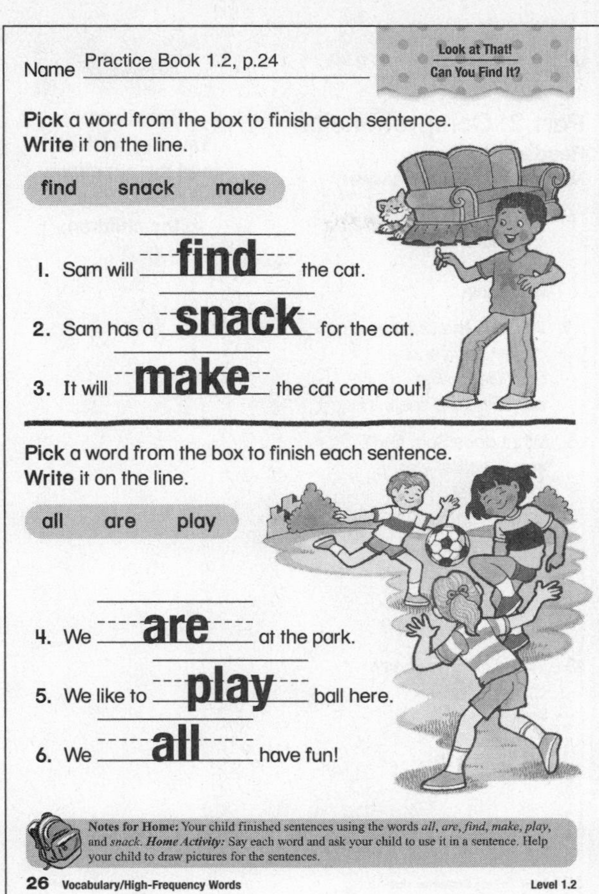
Name Practice Book 1.2, p.24
Look at That! Can You Find It?
Pick a word from the box to finish each sentence.
Write it on the line.
find snack make
1. Sam will find the cat.
2. Sam has a snack for the cat.
3. It will make the cat come out!
Pick a word from the box to finish each sentence.
Write it on the line.
all are play
4. We are at the park.
5. We like to play ball here.
6. We all have fun!
Notes for Home: Your child finished sentences using the words all, are, find, make, play, and snack. Home Activity: Say each word and ask your child to use it in a sentence. Help your child to draw pictures for the sentences.
26 Vocabulary/High-Frequency Words Level 1.2

Name Practice Book 1.2, p.25
Look at That! Can You Find It?
doll hat jam kite lock
Say the word for each picture.
Write the first letter of the word.
Use a letter from the box.
d h j k l
1. dog d
2. jar j
3. horse h
4. duck d
5. hen h
6. key k
7. log l
8. kitten k
Find the word that has the same beginning sound as the picture.
Mark the ⬭ to show your answer.
9. lion: dad, lap, had
10. kangaroo: jet, king, Dan
Notes for Home: Your child reviewed words that begin with the letters d, h, j, k, and l. Home Activity: Help your child make a list of people's names that begin with these sounds.
Level 1.2 Phonics: Initial Consonants d, h, j, k, l Review 27

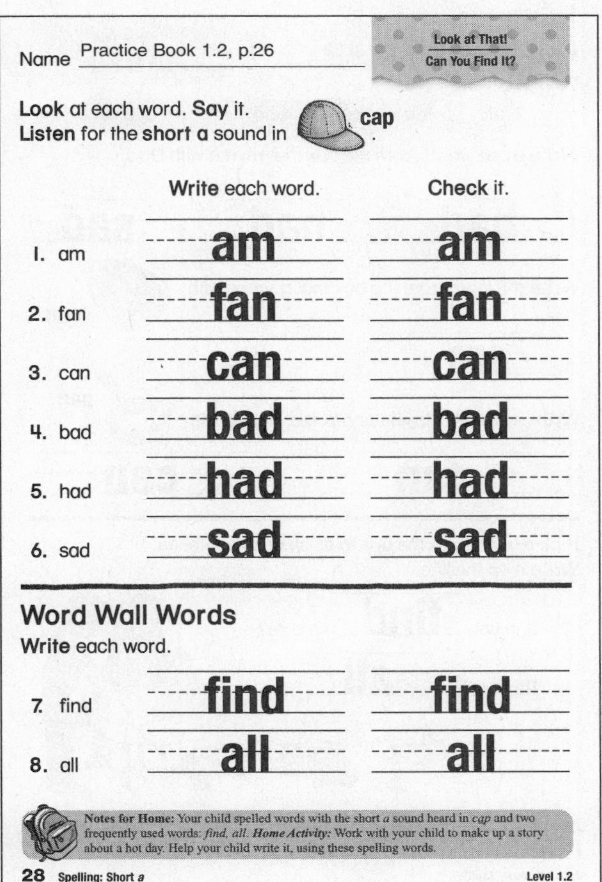
Name Practice Book 1.2, p.26
Look at That! Can You Find It?
Look at each word. Say it.
Listen for the short a sound in cap.
Write each word. Check it.
1. am am am
2. fan fan fan
3. can can can
4. bad bad bad
5. had had had
6. sad sad sad
Word Wall Words
Write each word.
7. find find find
8. all all all
Notes for Home: Your child spelled words with the short a sound heard in cap and two frequently used words: find, all. Home Activity: Work with your child to make up a story about a hot day. Help your child write it, using these spelling words.
28 Spelling: Short a Level 1.2

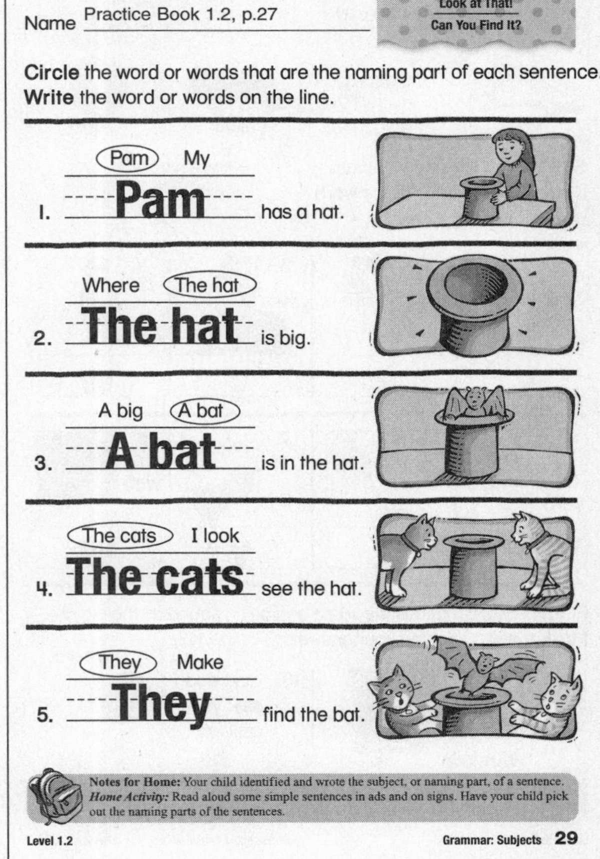
Name Practice Book 1.2, p.27
Look at That! Can You Find It?
Circle the word or words that are the naming part of each sentence.
Write the word or words on the line.
1. Pam My — Pam has a hat.
2. Where The hat — The hat is big.
3. A big A bat — A bat is in the hat.
4. The cats I look — The cats see the hat.
5. They Make — They find the bat.
Notes for Home: Your child identified and wrote the subject, or naming part, of a sentence. Home Activity: Read aloud some simple sentences in ads and on signs. Have your child pick out the naming parts of the sentences.
Level 1.2 Grammar: Subjects 29

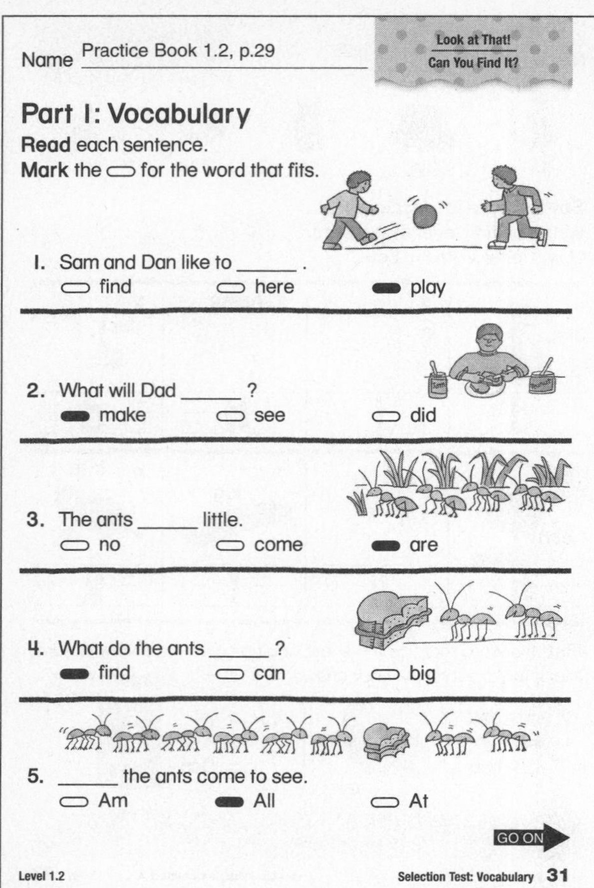

Look at That!
Can You Find It?

Name Practice Book 1.2, p.29

## Part 1: Vocabulary

**Read** each sentence.
**Mark** the ⬭ for the word that fits.

1. Sam and Dan like to _____ .
   ⬭ find ⬭ here ⬬ play

2. What will Dad _____ ?
   ⬬ make ⬭ see ⬭ did

3. The ants _____ little.
   ⬭ no ⬭ come ⬬ are

4. What do the ants _____ ?
   ⬬ find ⬭ can ⬭ big

5. _____ the ants come to see.
   ⬭ Am ⬬ All ⬭ At

GO ON

Level 1.2 Selection Test: Vocabulary 31

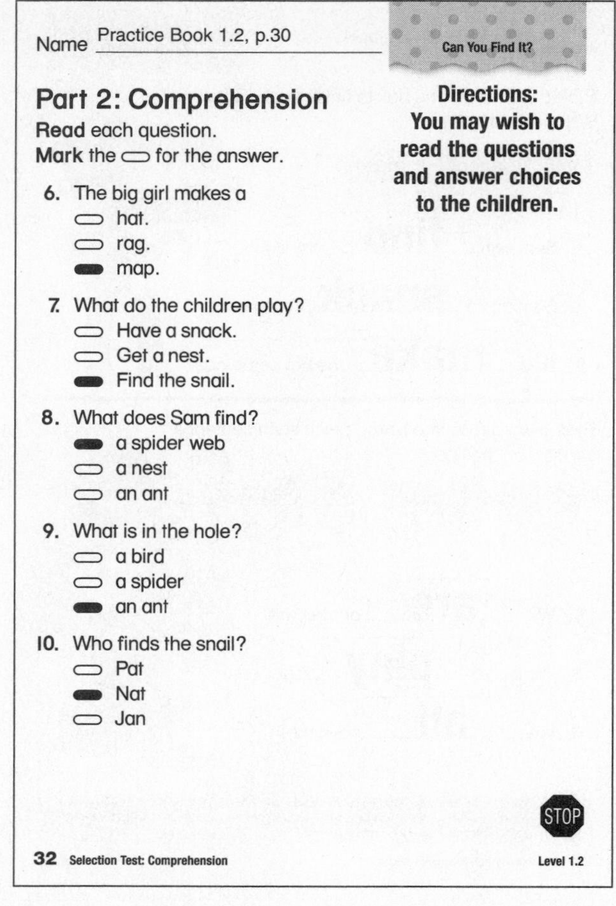

Can You Find It?

Name Practice Book 1.2, p.30

## Part 2: Comprehension

**Read** each question.
**Mark** the ⬭ for the answer.

**Directions: You may wish to read the questions and answer choices to the children.**

6. The big girl makes a
   ⬭ hat.
   ⬭ rag.
   ⬬ map.

7. What do the children play?
   ⬭ Have a snack.
   ⬭ Get a nest.
   ⬬ Find the snail.

8. What does Sam find?
   ⬬ a spider web
   ⬭ a nest
   ⬭ an ant

9. What is in the hole?
   ⬭ a bird
   ⬭ a spider
   ⬬ an ant

10. Who finds the snail?
    ⬭ Pat
    ⬬ Nat
    ⬭ Jan

STOP

32 Selection Test: Comprehension Level 1.2

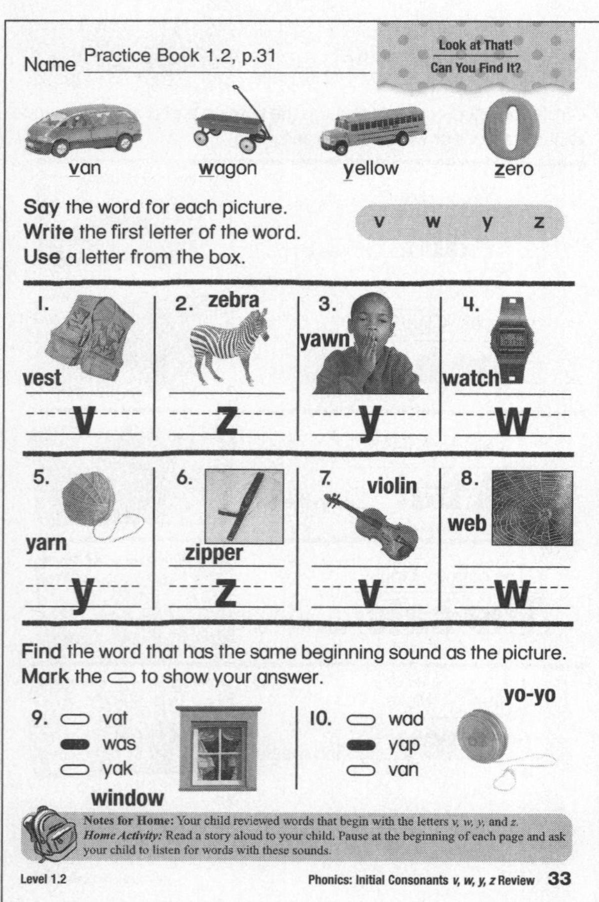

Look at That!
Can You Find It?

Name Practice Book 1.2, p.31

van wagon yellow zero

**Say** the word for each picture.
**Write** the first letter of the word.
**Use** a letter from the box.

v w y z

1. vest — v
2. zebra — z
3. yawn — y
4. watch — w
5. yarn — y
6. zipper — z
7. violin — v
8. web — w

**Find** the word that has the same beginning sound as the picture.
**Mark** the ⬭ to show your answer.

9. ⬭ vat ⬬ was ⬭ yak — window
10. ⬭ wad ⬬ yap ⬭ van — yo-yo

**Notes for Home:** Your child reviewed words that begin with the letters *v, w, y,* and *z.* ***Home Activity:*** Read a story aloud to your child. Pause at the beginning of each page and ask your child to listen for words with these sounds.

Level 1.2 Phonics: Initial Consonants *v, w, y, z* Review 33

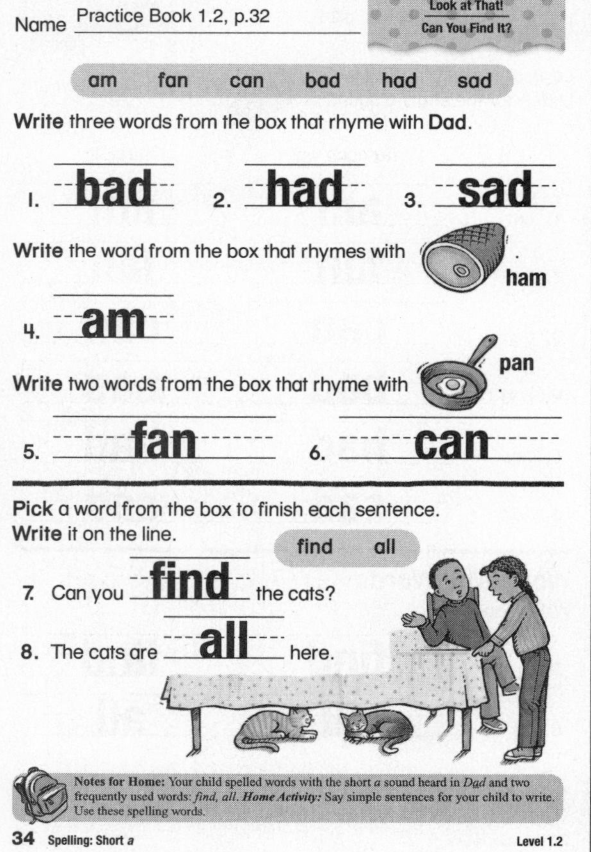

Look at That!
Can You Find It?

Name Practice Book 1.2, p.32

am fan can bad had sad

**Write** three words from the box that rhyme with **Dad**.

1. bad 2. had 3. sad

**Write** the word from the box that rhymes with ham.

4. am

**Write** two words from the box that rhyme with pan.

5. fan 6. can

**Pick** a word from the box to finish each sentence.
**Write** it on the line.

find all

7. Can you find the cats?
8. The cats are all here.

**Notes for Home:** Your child spelled words with the short *a* sound heard in *Dad* and two frequently used words: *find, all.* ***Home Activity:*** Say simple sentences for your child to write. Use these spelling words.

34 Spelling: Short *a* Level 1.2

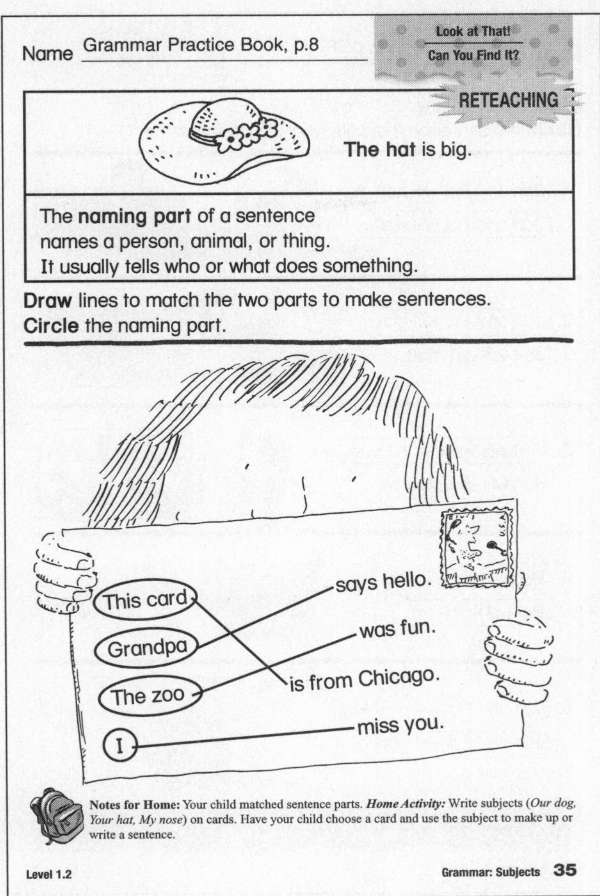
Name Grammar Practice Book, p.8

Look at That!
Can You Find It?

RETEACHING

The **hat** is big.

The **naming part** of a sentence
names a person, animal, or thing.
It usually tells who or what does something.

**Draw** lines to match the two parts to make sentences.
**Circle** the naming part.

This card — is from Chicago.
Grandpa — says hello.
The zoo — was fun.
I — miss you.

**Notes for Home:** Your child matched sentence parts. ***Home Activity:*** Write subjects (*Our dog, Your hat, My nose*) on cards. Have your child choose a card and use the subject to make up or write a sentence.

Level 1.2 Grammar: Subjects 35

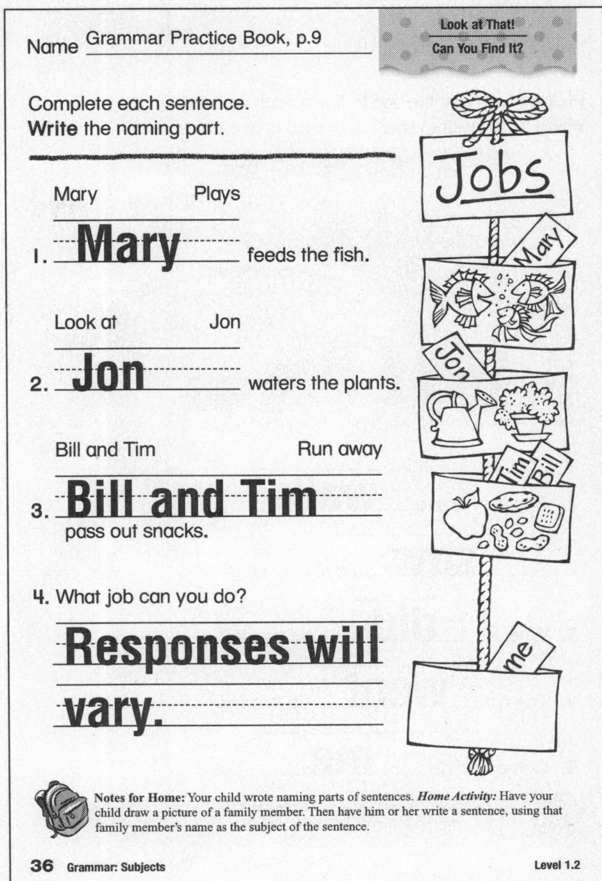
Name Grammar Practice Book, p.9

Look at That!
Can You Find It?

Complete each sentence.
**Write** the naming part.



Mary Plays

1. **Mary** feeds the fish.

Look at Jon

2. **Jon** waters the plants.

Bill and Tim Run away

3. **Bill and Tim** pass out snacks.

4. What job can you do?

**Responses will vary.**

**Notes for Home:** Your child wrote naming parts of sentences. ***Home Activity:*** Have your child draw a picture of a family member. Then have him or her write a sentence, using that family member's name as the subject of the sentence.

36 Grammar: Subjects Level 1.2

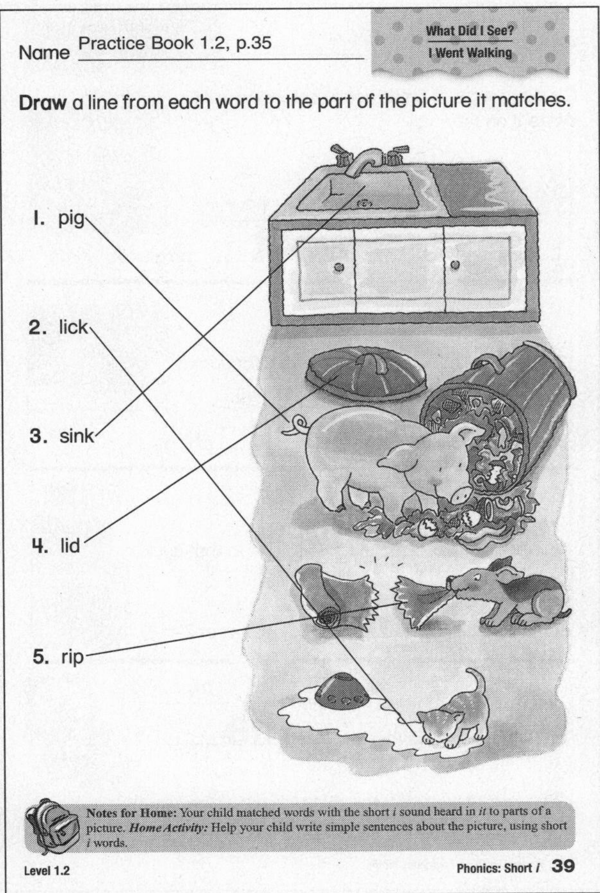
Name Practice Book 1.2, p.35

What Did I See?
I Went Walking

**Draw** a line from each word to the part of the picture it matches.

1. pig
2. lick
3. sink
4. lid
5. rip

**Notes for Home:** Your child matched words with the short *i* sound heard in *it* to parts of a picture. ***Home Activity:*** Help your child write simple sentences about the picture, using short *i* words.

Level 1.2 Phonics: Short *i* 39

Name Practice Book 1.2, p.36

What Did I See?
I Went Walking

**Circle** a word that ends like **black** to finish each sentence.
**Write** it on the line.

black

(Jack) Nan

1. Here is **Jack**.

pal (duck)

2. Zack is his **duck**.

bag (sack)

3. What is in the **sack**?

(Zack) Kim

4. Oh, **Zack**, do not do that!

(sick) sad

5. Zack is **sick**.

**Notes for Home:** Your child practiced reading and writing words that end in *-ck*. ***Home Activity:*** Help your child write and read words that rhyme with the words ending in *-ck*, such as *sack* and *back*.

40 Phonics: Final *-ck* Level 1.2

Name Practice Book 1.2, p.37

What Did I See?
I Went Walking

**Pick** a word from the box to finish each sentence.
**Write** it on the line. Use each word only once.

did me saw walk went

1. Sal and I like to **walk**.
2. Sal **saw** a big, fat cat.
3. Where **did** the cat go?
4. The cat **went** up and hid.
5. Come back to **me**, Sal!

**Notes for Home:** This week your child is learning to read the words *did, me, saw, walk,* and *went.* ***Home Activity:*** Work with your child to use these words to write about a walk you have taken.

Level 1.2 High-Frequency Words 41

Name Practice Book 1.2, p.38

What Did I See?
I Went Walking

**Look** at the picture.
**Circle** the sentence that tells what will happen next.

1. Jan and Pal will nap.
   (Jan and Pal will walk.)
2. (Jan and Pal will play.)
   Jan will get mad.
3. (Jan will walk to the van.)
   Jan will sit in the van.
4. Pal will sit on it.
   (Pal will lick it up.)
5. Jan and Pal will play tag.
   (Jan and Pal will go in.)

**Notes for Home:** Your child used picture clues to make predictions about what event will happen next. ***Home Activity:*** As you read a story to your child, pause to ask your child what he or she thinks will happen next in the story. Discuss why your child thinks so.

42 Predicting Level 1.2

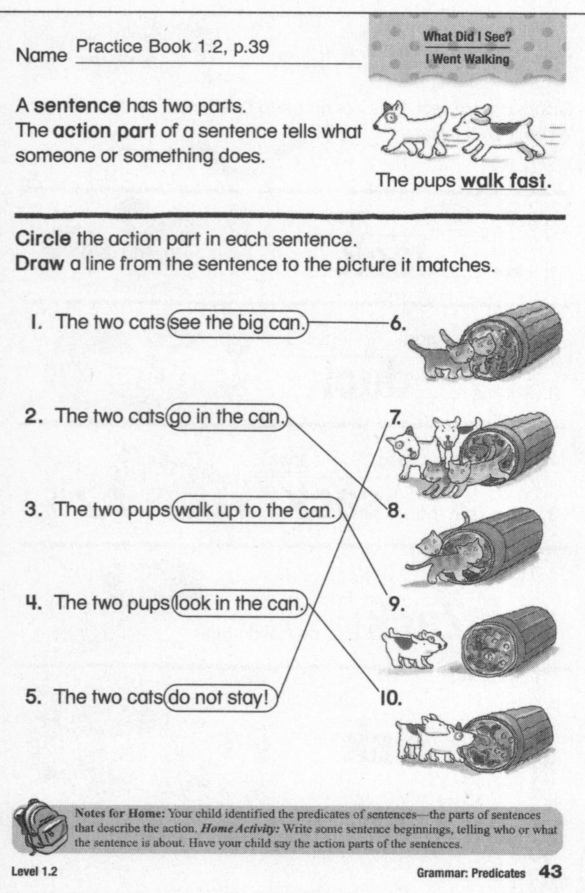
Name Practice Book 1.2, p.39

What Did I See?
I Went Walking

A **sentence** has two parts.
The **action part** of a sentence tells what someone or something does.

The pups **walk fast**.

**Circle** the action part in each sentence.
**Draw** a line from the sentence to the picture it matches.

1. The two cats (see the big can.) — 6.
2. The two cats (go in the can.) — 8.
3. The two pups (walk up to the can.) — 9.
4. The two pups (look in the can.) — 10.
5. The two cats (do not stay!) — 7.

**Notes for Home:** Your child identified the predicates of sentences—the parts of sentences that describe the action. ***Home Activity:*** Write some sentence beginnings, telling who or what the sentence is about. Have your child say the action parts of the sentences.

Level 1.2 Grammar: Predicates 43

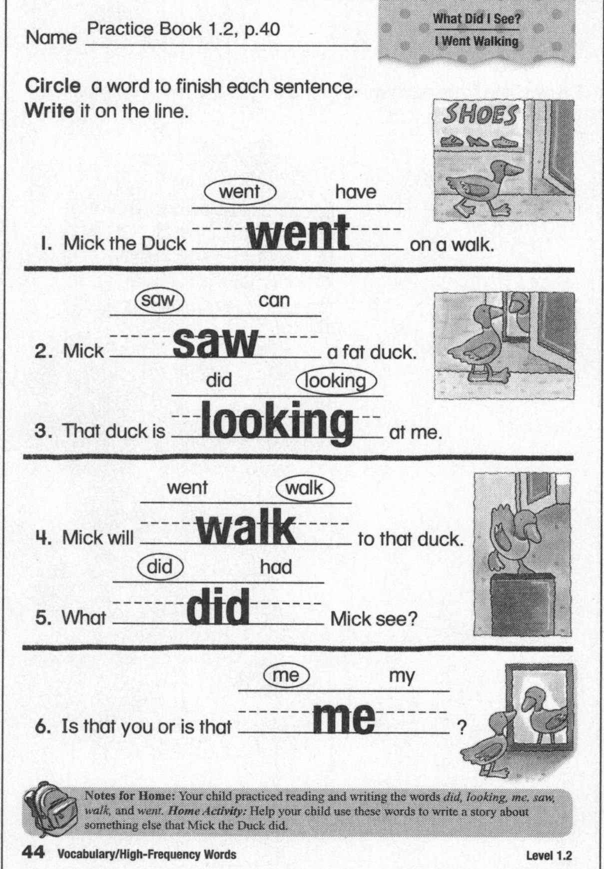
Name Practice Book 1.2, p.40

What Did I See?
I Went Walking

**Circle** a word to finish each sentence.
**Write** it on the line.



1. (went) have — Mick the Duck **went** on a walk.
2. (saw) can — Mick **saw** a fat duck.
3. did (looking) — That duck is **looking** at me.
4. went (walk) — Mick will **walk** to that duck.
5. (did) had — What **did** Mick see?
6. (me) my — Is that you or is that **me**?

**Notes for Home:** Your child practiced reading and writing the words *did, looking, me, saw, walk,* and *went.* ***Home Activity:*** Help your child use these words to write a story about something else that Mick the Duck did.

44 Vocabulary/High-Frequency Words Level 1.2

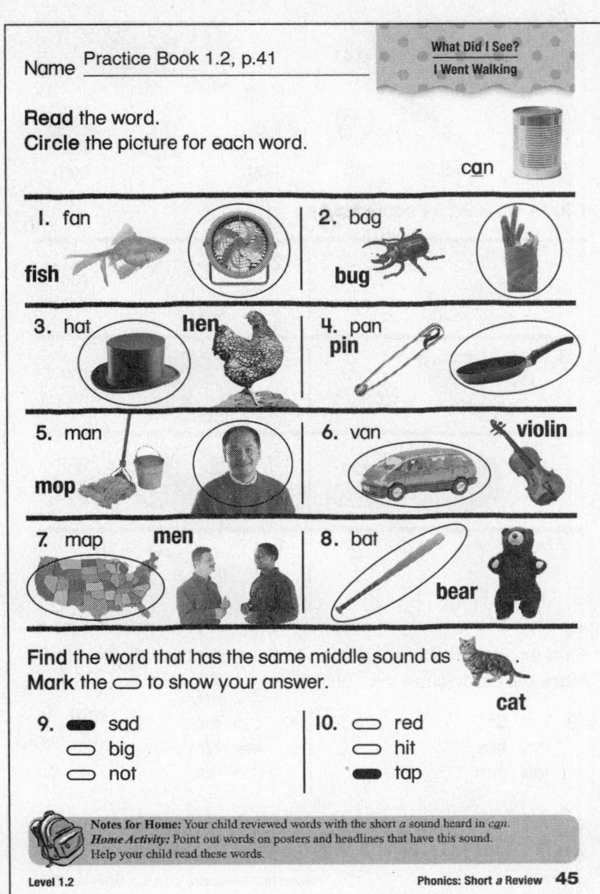

Name Practice Book 1.2, p.41

What Did I See?
I Went Walking

**Read** the word.
**Circle** the picture for each word.

can

1. fan — fish
2. bag — bug
3. hat — hen
4. pan — pin
5. man — mop
6. van — violin
7. map — men
8. bat — bear

**Find** the word that has the same middle sound as cat.
**Mark** the ⬭ to show your answer.

9. ⬬ sad ⬭ big ⬭ not

10. ⬭ red ⬭ hit ⬬ tap

**Notes for Home:** Your child reviewed words with the short *a* sound heard in *can*. ***Home Activity:*** Point out words on posters and headlines that have this sound. Help your child read these words.

Level 1.2 — Phonics: Short *a* Review 45

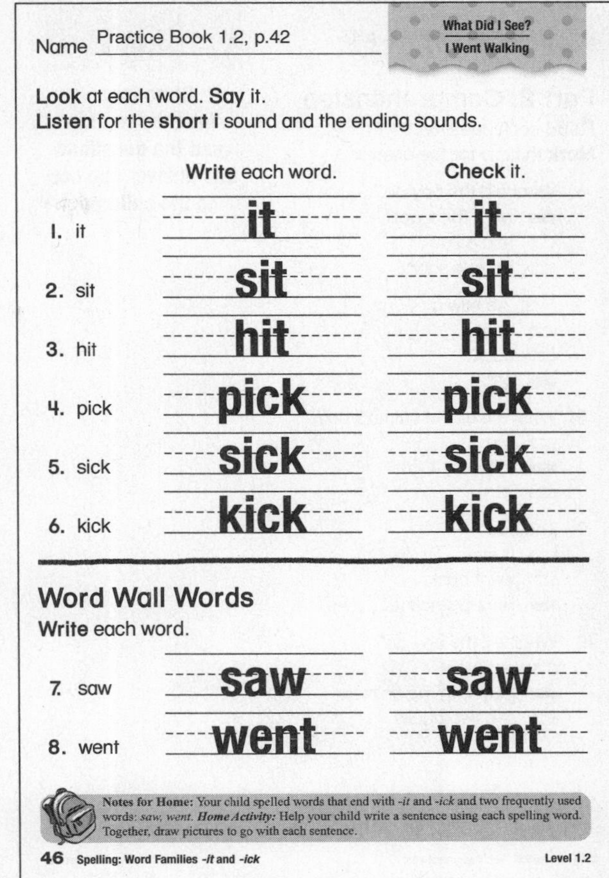

Name Practice Book 1.2, p.42

What Did I See?
I Went Walking

**Look** at each word. **Say** it.
**Listen** for the **short i** sound and the ending sounds.

| | **Write** each word. | **Check** it. |
|---|---|---|
| 1. it | it | it |
| 2. sit | sit | sit |
| 3. hit | hit | hit |
| 4. pick | pick | pick |
| 5. sick | sick | sick |
| 6. kick | kick | kick |

**Word Wall Words**
**Write** each word.

| | | |
|---|---|---|
| 7. saw | saw | saw |
| 8. went | went | went |

**Notes for Home:** Your child spelled words that end with *-it* and *-ick* and two frequently used words: *saw, went.* ***Home Activity:*** Help your child write a sentence using each spelling word. Together, draw pictures to go with each sentence.

46 Spelling: Word Families *-it* and *-ick* — Level 1.2

Name Practice Book 1.2, p.43

What Did I See?
I Went Walking

**Circle** the word that is the action part of each sentence.
**Write** it on the line.

two (see)

1. The pigs **see** a big rip.

(walk) no

2. The pink pigs **walk** in.

**Match** the naming part with the action part to make a sentence that makes sense.
**Write** the sentence on the line.

**Answers may appear in any order.**

| | |
|---|---|
| My dad | is in the jar. |
| The cat | has a van. |
| The jam | naps in my lap. |

3. **My dad has a van.**
4. **The cat naps in my lap.**
5. **The jam is in the jar.**

**Notes for Home:** Your child identified predicates—the parts of sentences that describe what a person or thing does. ***Home Activity:*** Read a story with your child. As you read, cover the predicates of some sentences. Ask your child to think of a way to complete each sentence.

Level 1.2 — Grammar: Predicates 47

Name Practice Book 1.2, p.44

What Did I See?
I Went Walking

## Part 1: Vocabulary

**Read** each sentence.
**Mark** the ⬭ for the word that fits.

1. The boy _____ up.
⬭ find ⬭ away ⬬ went

2. The boy _____ the cats.
⬭ make ⬬ saw ⬭ walk

3. The dog will come to _____ .
⬬ me ⬭ did ⬭ down

4. See me _____ !
⬭ make ⬬ walk ⬭ find

5. What _____ I find?
⬭ went ⬭ all ⬬ did

GO ON

Level 1.2 — Selection Test: Vocabulary 49

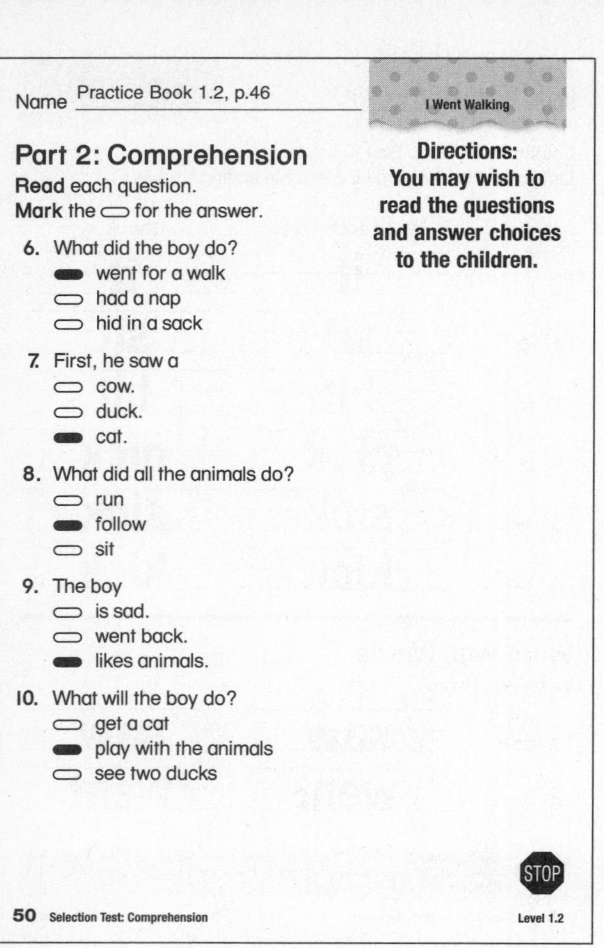

I Went Walking

Name Practice Book 1.2, p.46

## Part 2: Comprehension

**Directions: You may wish to read the questions and answer choices to the children.**

**Read** each question.
**Mark** the ⬭ for the answer.

6. What did the boy do?
   - ⬬ went for a walk
   - ⬭ had a nap
   - ⬭ hid in a sack
7. First, he saw a
   - ⬭ cow.
   - ⬭ duck.
   - ⬬ cat.
8. What did all the animals do?
   - ⬭ run
   - ⬬ follow
   - ⬭ sit
9. The boy
   - ⬭ is sad.
   - ⬭ went back.
   - ⬬ likes animals.
10. What will the boy do?
    - ⬭ get a cat
    - ⬬ play with the animals
    - ⬭ see two ducks

STOP

50 Selection Test: Comprehension Level 1.2

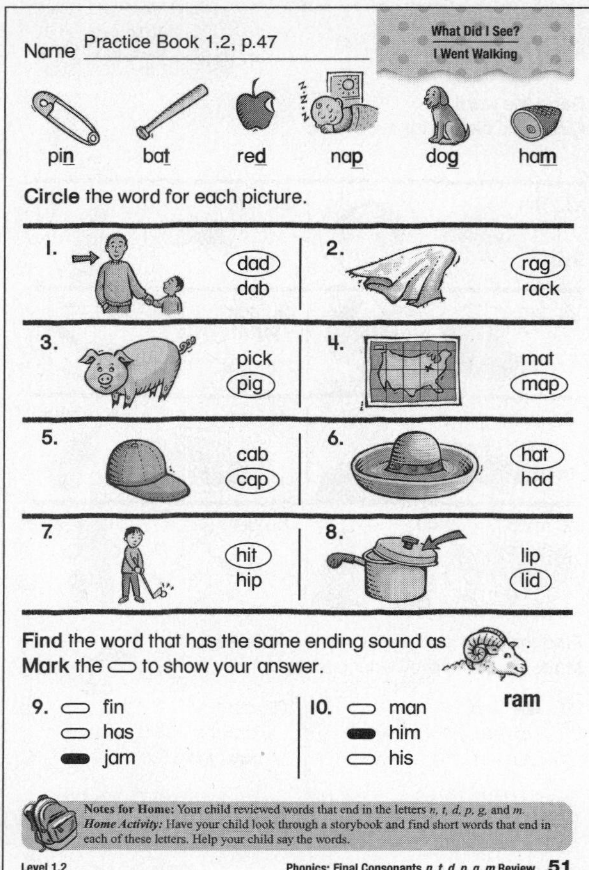

What Did I See?
I Went Walking

Name Practice Book 1.2, p.47

pin bat red nap dog ham

**Circle** the word for each picture.

| | | | |
|---|---|---|---|
| 1. | (dad) dab | 2. | (rag) rack |
| 3. | pick (pig) | 4. | mat (map) |
| 5. | cab (cap) | 6. | (hat) had |
| 7. | (hit) hip | 8. | lip (lid) |

**Find** the word that has the same ending sound as ram.
**Mark** the ⬭ to show your answer.

9. ⬭ fin ⬭ has ⬬ jam

10. ⬭ man ⬬ him ⬭ his

**Notes for Home:** Your child reviewed words that end in the letters *n, t, d, p, g,* and *m.* ***Home Activity:*** Have your child look through a storybook and find short words that end in each of these letters. Help your child say the words.

Level 1.2 Phonics: Final Consonants *n, t, d, p, g, m* Review 51

What Did I See?
I Went Walking

Name Practice Book 1.2, p.48

it sit hit pick sick kick

**Write** three words from the box that rhyme with [mitt].

1. it 2. sit 3. hit

**Write** three words from the box that rhyme with [lick].

4. pick 5. sick 6. kick

**Write** two words from the box to tell what the hippo is doing.

7. sit
8. kick

**Pick** a word from the box to finish each sentence.
**Write** it on the line.

saw went

9. I saw you!

10. Dan went away.

**Notes for Home:** Your child spelled words that end with *-it* and *-ick* and two frequently used words: *saw, went.* ***Home Activity:*** Have your child use these spelling words and others like them to write a story about a pig.

52 Spelling: Word Families *-it* and *-ick* Level 1.2

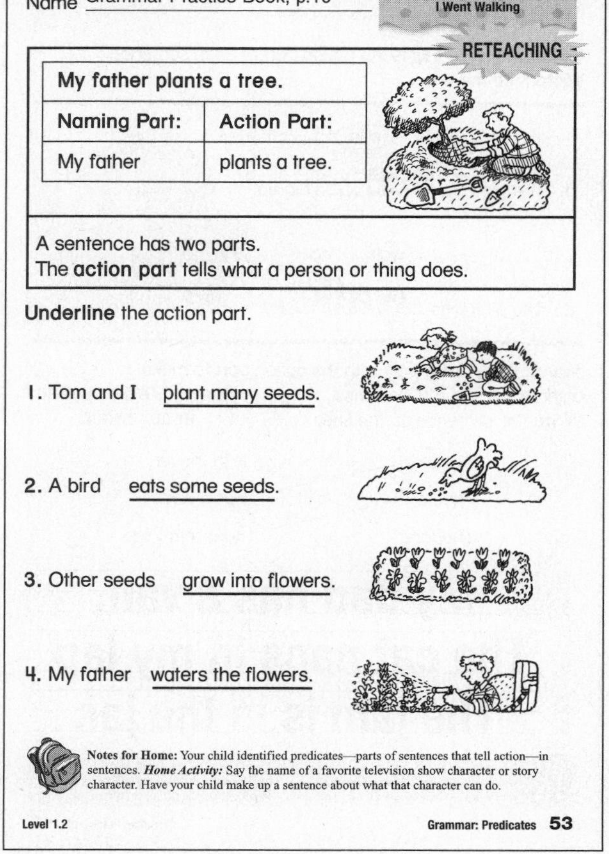

What Did I See?
I Went Walking

Name Grammar Practice Book, p.10

RETEACHING

| My father plants a tree. | |
|---|---|
| **Naming Part:** | **Action Part:** |
| My father | plants a tree. |

A sentence has two parts.
The **action part** tells what a person or thing does.

**Underline** the action part.

1. Tom and I plant many seeds.
2. A bird eats some seeds.
3. Other seeds grow into flowers.
4. My father waters the flowers.

**Notes for Home:** Your child identified predicates—parts of sentences that tell action—in sentences. ***Home Activity:*** Say the name of a favorite television show character or story character. Have your child make up a sentence about what that character can do.

Level 1.2 Grammar: Predicates 53

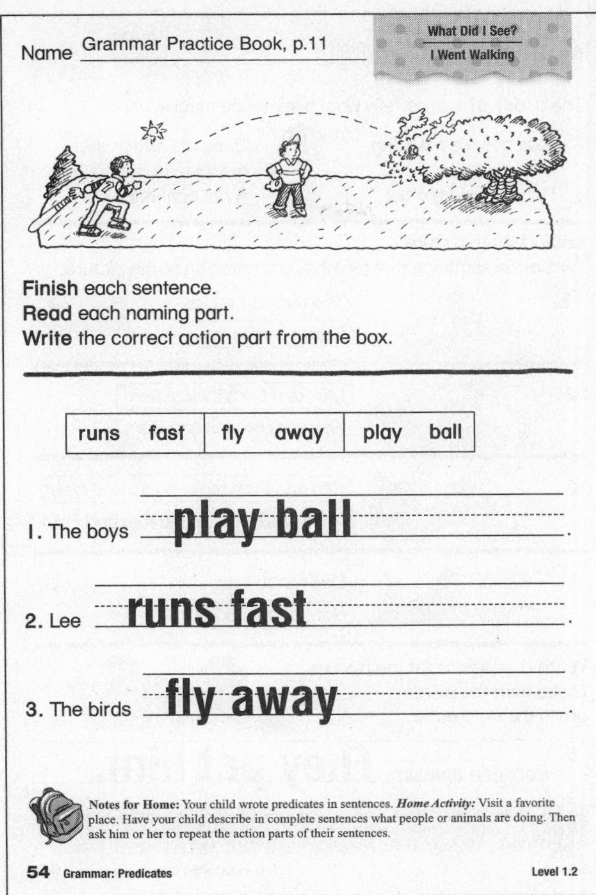
Name Grammar Practice Book, p.11

What Did I See?
I Went Walking

Finish each sentence.
Read each naming part.
Write the correct action part from the box.

| runs fast | fly away | play ball |
|---|---|---|

1. The boys play ball.
2. Lee runs fast.
3. The birds fly away.

**Notes for Home:** Your child wrote predicates in sentences. *Home Activity:* Visit a favorite place. Have your child describe in complete sentences what people or animals are doing. Then ask him or her to repeat the action parts of their sentences.

54 Grammar: Predicates Level 1.2

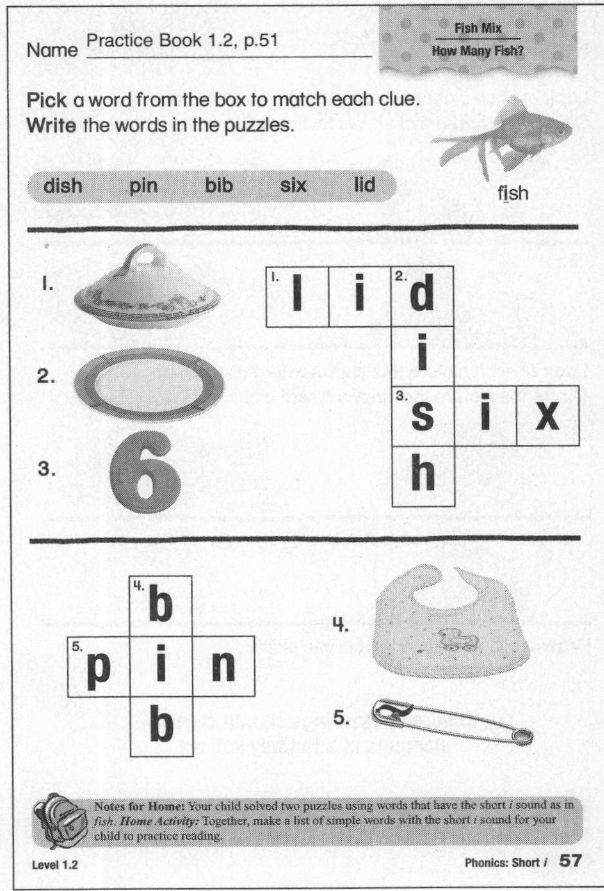
Name Practice Book 1.2, p.51

Fish Mix
How Many Fish?

Pick a word from the box to match each clue.
Write the words in the puzzles.

dish pin bib six lid

fish

1. lid
2. dish
3. six
4. bib
5. pin

**Notes for Home:** Your child solved two puzzles using words that have the short *i* sound as in *fish*. *Home Activity:* Together, make a list of simple words with the short *i* sound for your child to practice reading.

Level 1.2 Phonics: Short *i* 57

Name Practice Book 1.2, p.52

Fish Mix
How Many Fish?

Circle a word to finish each sentence.
Write it on the line.

six

1. The fish are in a bag. (box / bag)
2. I have six fish. (six / two)
3. I mix up the fish. (mix / make)
4. Can you fix it? (fit / fix)
5. Get me the red box. (back / box)

**Notes for Home:** Your child practiced reading words that end with *-x*. *Home Activity:* On cards, write *box, fix, mix,* and *six*. Show each card to your child to give him or her practice reading these words.

58 Phonics: Final *-x* Level 1.2

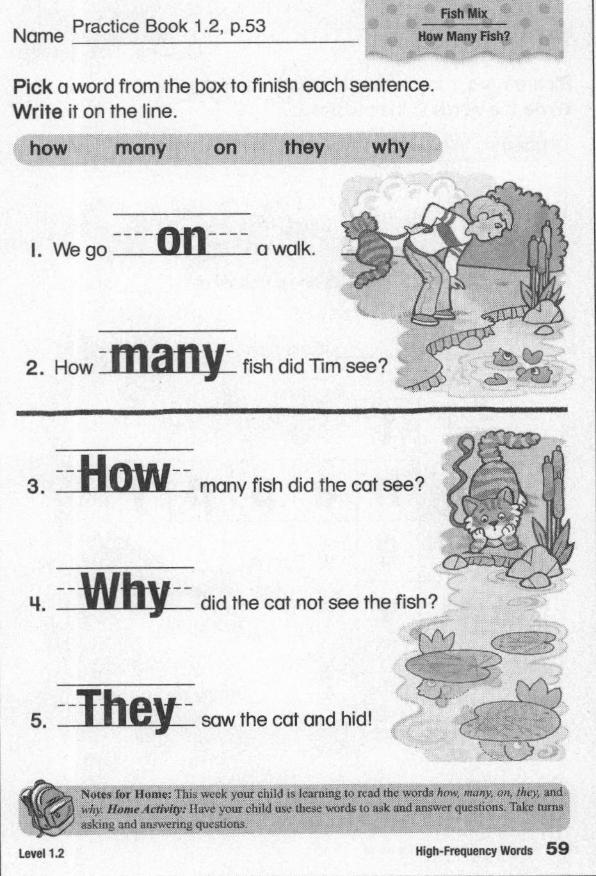
Name Practice Book 1.2, p.53

Fish Mix
How Many Fish?

Pick a word from the box to finish each sentence.
Write it on the line.

how many on they why

1. We go on a walk.
2. How many fish did Tim see?
3. How many fish did the cat see?
4. Why did the cat not see the fish?
5. They saw the cat and hid!

**Notes for Home:** This week your child is learning to read the words *how, many, on, they,* and *why*. *Home Activity:* Have your child use these words to ask and answer questions. Take turns asking and answering questions.

Level 1.2 High-Frequency Words 59

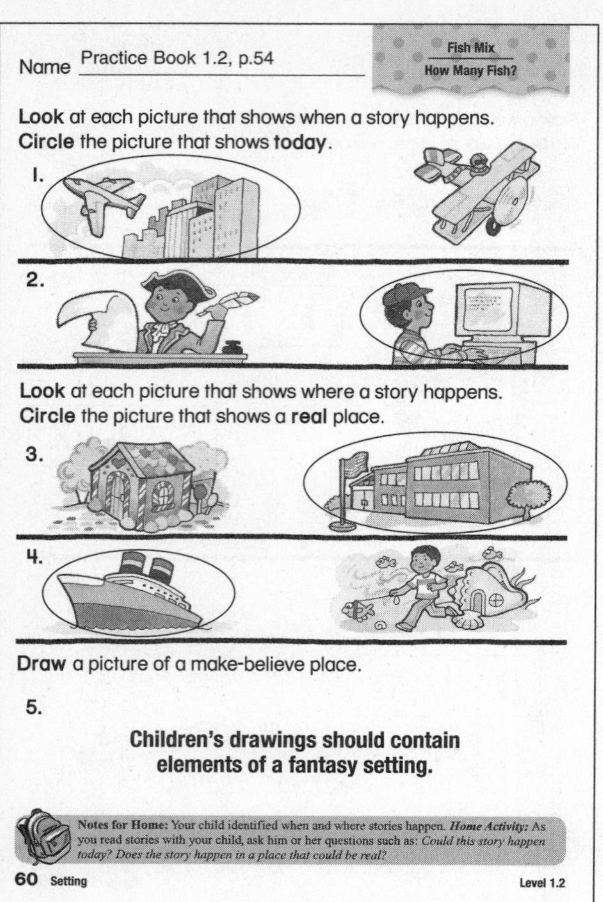
Name Practice Book 1.2, p.54

Fish Mix
How Many Fish?

**Look** at each picture that shows when a story happens.
**Circle** the picture that shows **today**.

1.

2.

**Look** at each picture that shows where a story happens.
**Circle** the picture that shows a **real** place.

3.

4.

**Draw** a picture of a make-believe place.

5.

**Children's drawings should contain elements of a fantasy setting.**

**Notes for Home:** Your child identified when and where stories happen. *Home Activity:* As you read stories with your child, ask him or her questions such as: *Could this story happen today? Does the story happen in a place that could be real?*

60 Setting Level 1.2

Name Practice Book 1.2, p.55

Fish Mix
How Many Fish?

The **order of words** tells what a sentence means.

Matches the meaning of the picture:
Dan can make a hat.

Does not match the meaning of the picture:
A hat can make Dan.

**Look** at each picture.
**Circle** the sentence that matches the meaning of the picture.

1. The rock is on Dan.
(Dan is on the rock.)

2. (Max and Sam look at fish.)
Fish look at Max and Sam.

3. (Kim and Pam make a fish and a cat.)
A fish and a cat make Kim and Pam.

4. Dad ran to Nan.
(Nan ran to Dad.)

**Write** a sentence for the picture.
**Make** sure the words are in the right order.

5. **Possible answer: They pet him.**

**Notes for Home:** Your child practiced using words in sentences in an order that makes sense for each picture. *Home Activity:* On strips of paper, write simple sentences your child can read. Cut them up and have him or her reassemble the words into a sentence that makes sense.

Level 1.2 Grammar: Word Order (in Sentences) 61

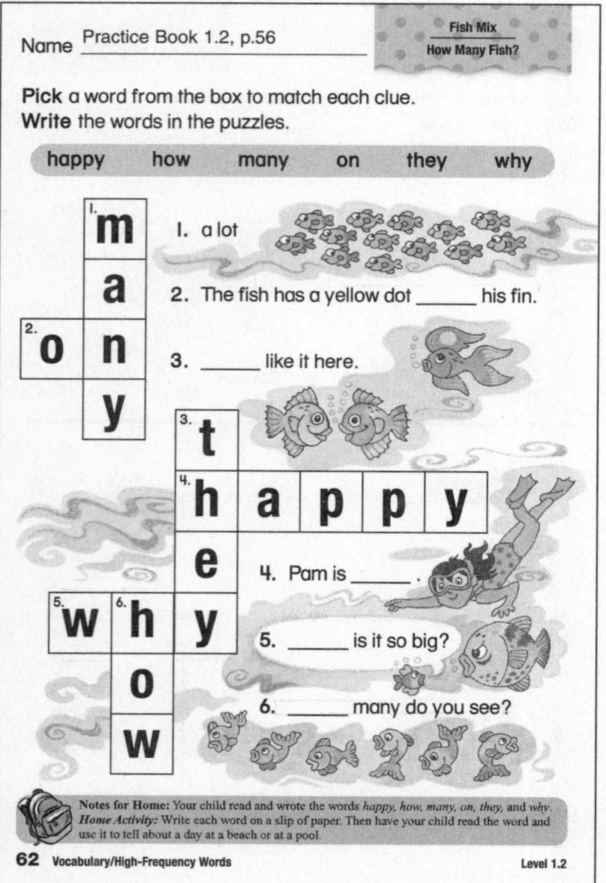
Name Practice Book 1.2, p.56

Fish Mix
How Many Fish?

**Pick** a word from the box to match each clue.
**Write** the words in the puzzles.

happy how many on they why

1. a lot — **many**

2. The fish has a yellow dot ______ his fin. — **on**

3. ______ like it here. — **they**

4. Pam is ______. — **happy**

5. ______ is it so big? — **why**

6. ______ many do you see? — **how**

**Notes for Home:** Your child read and wrote the words *happy, how, many, on, they,* and *why*. *Home Activity:* Write each word on a slip of paper. Then have your child read the word and use it to tell about a day at a beach or at a pool.

62 Vocabulary/High-Frequency Words Level 1.2

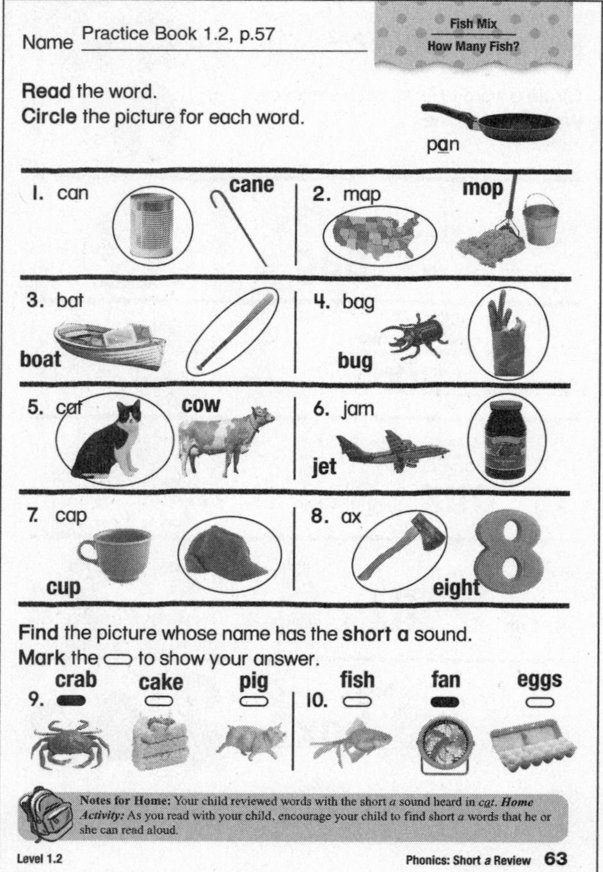
Name Practice Book 1.2, p.57

Fish Mix
How Many Fish?

**Read** the word.
**Circle** the picture for each word.

pan

1. can — cane
2. map — mop
3. bat — boat
4. bag — bug
5. cat — cow
6. jam — jet
7. cap — cup
8. ax — eight

**Find** the picture whose name has the **short a** sound.
**Mark** the ⊂⊃ to show your answer.

9. crab (marked) cake pig
10. fish fan (marked) eggs

**Notes for Home:** Your child reviewed words with the short *a* sound heard in *cat*. *Home Activity:* As you read with your child, encourage your child to find short *a* words that he or she can read aloud.

Level 1.2 Phonics: Short *a* Review 63

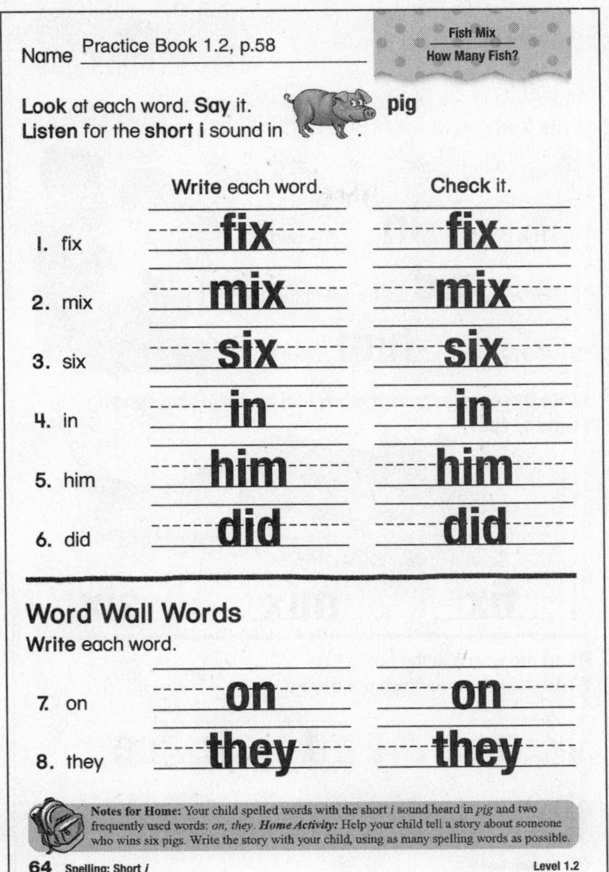
Name Practice Book 1.2, p.58

Fish Mix
How Many Fish?

**Look** at each word. **Say** it.
**Listen** for the **short i** sound in pig.

| | Write each word. | Check it. |
|---|---|---|
| 1. fix | fix | fix |
| 2. mix | mix | mix |
| 3. six | six | six |
| 4. in | in | in |
| 5. him | him | him |
| 6. did | did | did |

**Word Wall Words**
**Write** each word.

| | | |
|---|---|---|
| 7. on | on | on |
| 8. they | they | they |

**Notes for Home:** Your child spelled words with the short *i* sound heard in *pig* and two frequently used words: *on, they. Home Activity:* Help your child tell a story about someone who wins six pigs. Write the story with your child, using as many spelling words as possible.

64 Spelling: Short *i* Level 1.2

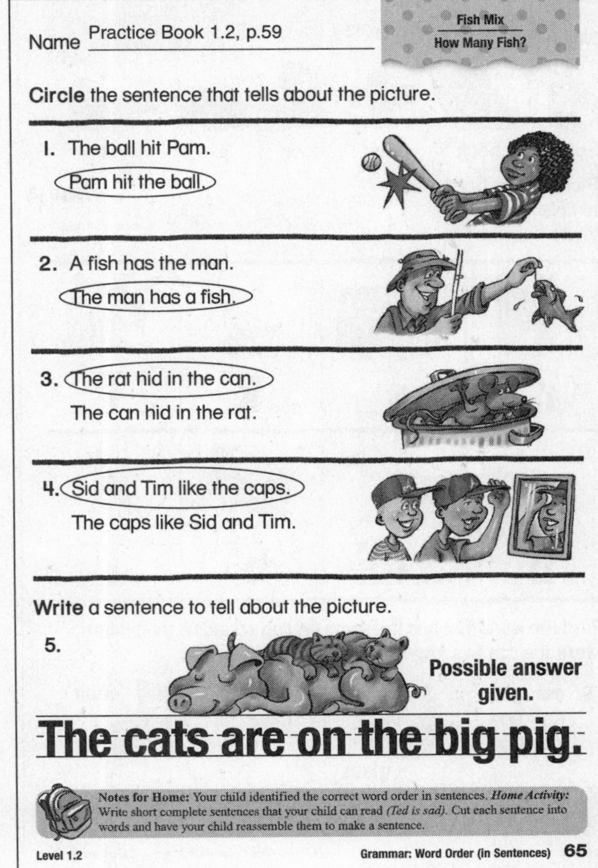
Name Practice Book 1.2, p.59

Fish Mix
How Many Fish?

**Circle** the sentence that tells about the picture.

1. The ball hit Pam.
   (Pam hit the ball.)
2. A fish has the man.
   (The man has a fish.)
3. (The rat hid in the can.)
   The can hid in the rat.
4. (Sid and Tim like the caps.)
   The caps like Sid and Tim.

**Write** a sentence to tell about the picture.

5. Possible answer given.
   **The cats are on the big pig.**

**Notes for Home:** Your child identified the correct word order in sentences. *Home Activity:* Write short complete sentences that your child can read *(Ted is sad).* Cut each sentence into words and have your child reassemble them to make a sentence.

Level 1.2 Grammar: Word Order (in Sentences) 65

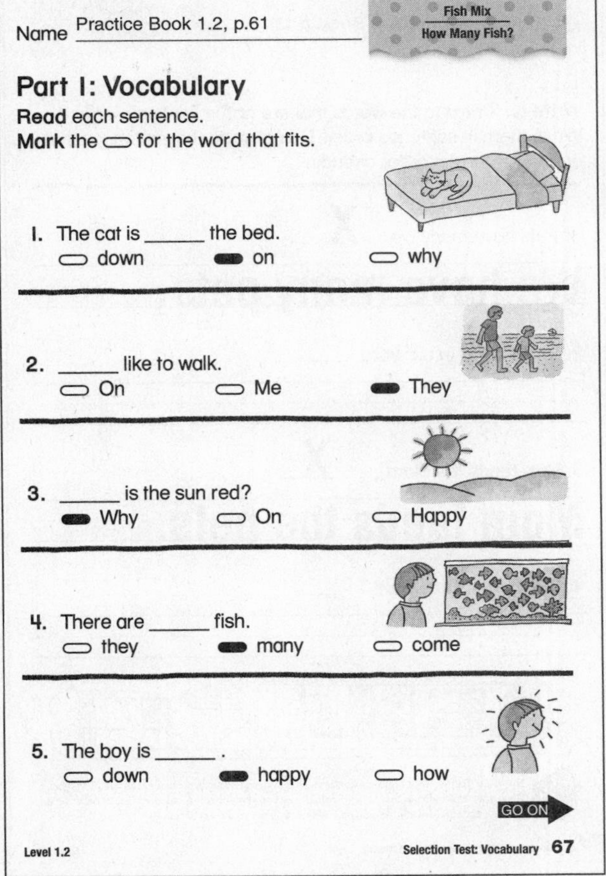
Name Practice Book 1.2, p.61

Fish Mix
How Many Fish?

**Part 1: Vocabulary**
**Read** each sentence.
**Mark** the ⬭ for the word that fits.

1. The cat is ______ the bed.
   ⬭ down ⬬ on ⬭ why
2. ______ like to walk.
   ⬭ On ⬭ Me ⬬ They
3. ______ is the sun red?
   ⬬ Why ⬭ On ⬭ Happy
4. There are ______ fish.
   ⬭ they ⬬ many ⬭ come
5. The boy is ______ .
   ⬭ down ⬬ happy ⬭ how

GO ON

Level 1.2 Selection Test: Vocabulary 67

Name Practice Book 1.2, p.62

How Many Fish?

## Part 2: Comprehension

**Read** each question.
**Mark** the ⬭ for the answer.

**Directions: You may wish to read the questions and answer choices to the children.**

6. How many fish are in this story?
   ⬭ two
   ⬬ six
   ⬭ ten
7. The fish live in a
   ⬭ sink.
   ⬭ pail.
   ⬬ bay.
8. The pail is
   ⬭ yellow.
   ⬭ blue.
   ⬬ red.
9. One yellow fish
   ⬭ hid in a can.
   ⬭ had a wish.
   ⬬ lost its way.
10. The yellow fish was happy to
    ⬭ stay lost.
    ⬭ go to the sink.
    ⬬ get away.

STOP

68 Selection Test: Comprehension Level 1.2

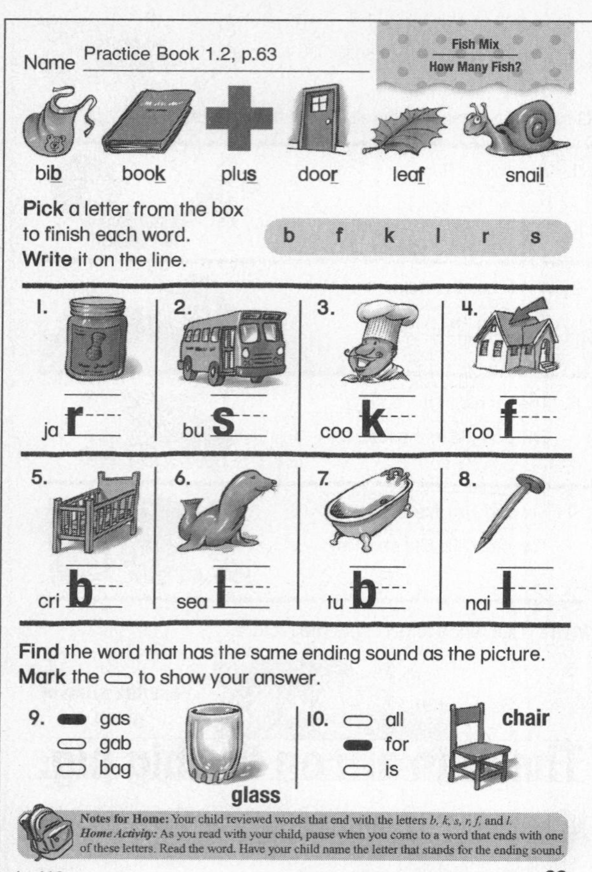

Name Practice Book 1.2, p.63

**Fish Mix**
**How Many Fish?**

bib book plus door leaf snail

**Pick** a letter from the box to finish each word.
**Write** it on the line.

b f k l r s

1. ja **r**
2. bu **s**
3. coo **k**
4. roo **f**
5. cri **b**
6. sea **l**
7. tu **b**
8. nai **l**

**Find** the word that has the same ending sound as the picture.
**Mark** the ⬭ to show your answer.

9. ● gas ○ gab ○ bag — glass
10. ○ all ● for ○ is — chair

**Notes for Home:** Your child reviewed words that end with the letters *b, k, s, r, f,* and *l.* *Home Activity:* As you read with your child, pause when you come to a word that ends with one of these letters. Read the word. Have your child name the letter that stands for the ending sound.

Level 1.2 — Phonics: Final Consonants *b, k, s, r, f, l* Review 69

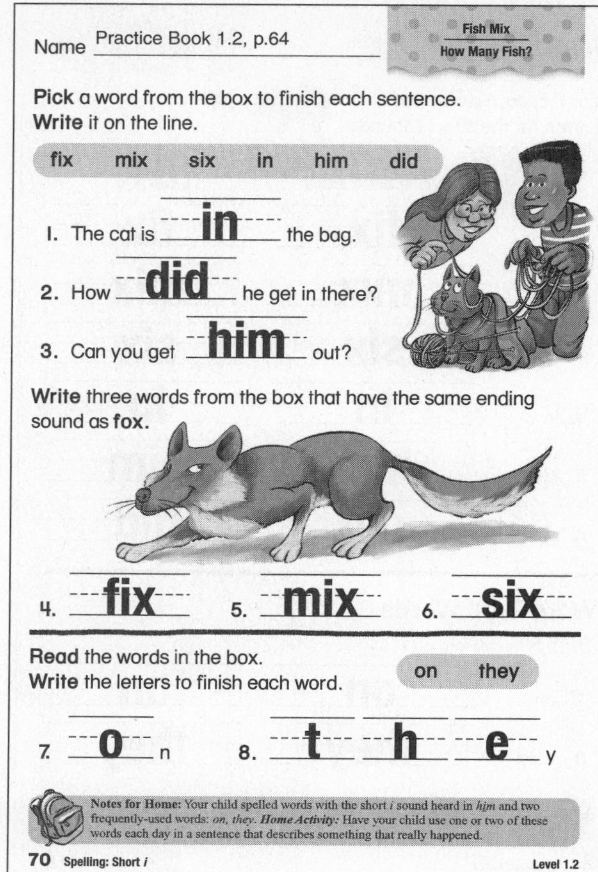

Name Practice Book 1.2, p.64

**Fish Mix**
**How Many Fish?**

**Pick** a word from the box to finish each sentence.
**Write** it on the line.

fix mix six in him did

1. The cat is **in** the bag.
2. How **did** he get in there?
3. Can you get **him** out?

**Write** three words from the box that have the same ending sound as **fox.**

4. **fix** 5. **mix** 6. **six**

**Read** the words in the box.
**Write** the letters to finish each word.

on they

7. **o** n
8. **t h e** y

**Notes for Home:** Your child spelled words with the short *i* sound heard in *him* and two frequently-used words: *on, they.* *Home Activity:* Have your child use one or two of these words each day in a sentence that describes something that really happened.

70 Spelling: Short *i* — Level 1.2

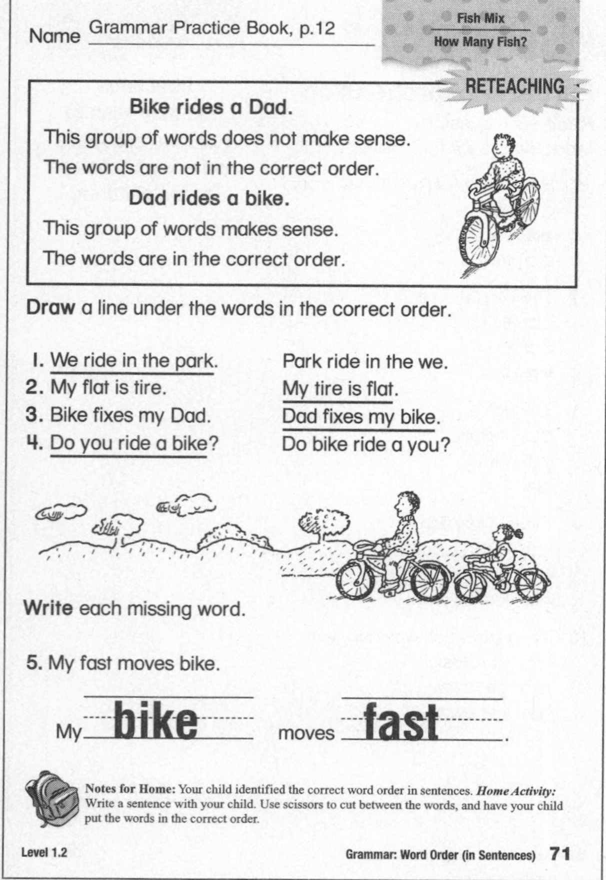

Name Grammar Practice Book, p.12

**Fish Mix**
**How Many Fish?**

**RETEACHING**

**Bike rides a Dad.**
This group of words does not make sense.
The words are not in the correct order.
**Dad rides a bike.**
This group of words makes sense.
The words are in the correct order.

**Draw** a line under the words in the correct order.

1. <u>We ride in the park.</u> Park ride in the we.
2. My flat is tire. <u>My tire is flat.</u>
3. Bike fixes my Dad. <u>Dad fixes my bike.</u>
4. <u>Do you ride a bike?</u> Do bike ride a you?

**Write** each missing word.

5. My fast moves bike.

My **bike** moves **fast**.

**Notes for Home:** Your child identified the correct word order in sentences. *Home Activity:* Write a sentence with your child. Use scissors to cut between the words, and have your child put the words in the correct order.

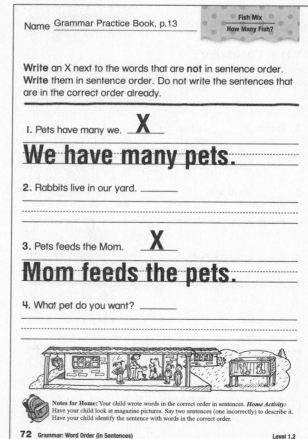

Level 1.2 — Grammar: Word Order (in Sentences) 71

Name Grammar Practice Book, p.13

**Fish Mix**
**How Many Fish?**

**Write** an X next to the words that are **not** in sentence order.
**Write** them in sentence order. Do not write the sentences that are in the correct order already.

1. Pets have many we. **X**

**We have many pets.**

2. Rabbits live in our yard. _____

3. Pets feeds the Mom. **X**

**Mom feeds the pets.**

4. What pet do you want? _____

**Notes for Home:** Your child wrote words in the correct order in sentences. *Home Activity:* Have your child look at magazine pictures. Say two sentences (one incorrectly) to describe it. Have your child identify the sentence with words in the correct order.

72 Grammar: Word Order (in Sentences) — Level 1.2

Jog, Frog, Jog
Tadpole to Frog

Name Practice Book 1.2, p.67

**Say** the word for each picture.
**Circle** the picture if the word has the **short o** sound in **top.**

top

1. frog
2. bat
3. dog
4. log
5. cap
6. box
7. clock
8. pot
9. stop
10. boat
11. nose
12. lock
13. sock
14. knot
15. duck

**Notes for Home:** Your child identified words that contain the short *o* sound in *top. Home Activity:* Encourage your child to use any of the short *o* words pictured above in sentences. Challenge your child to think of other short *o* words.

Level 1.2 Phonics: Short o 75

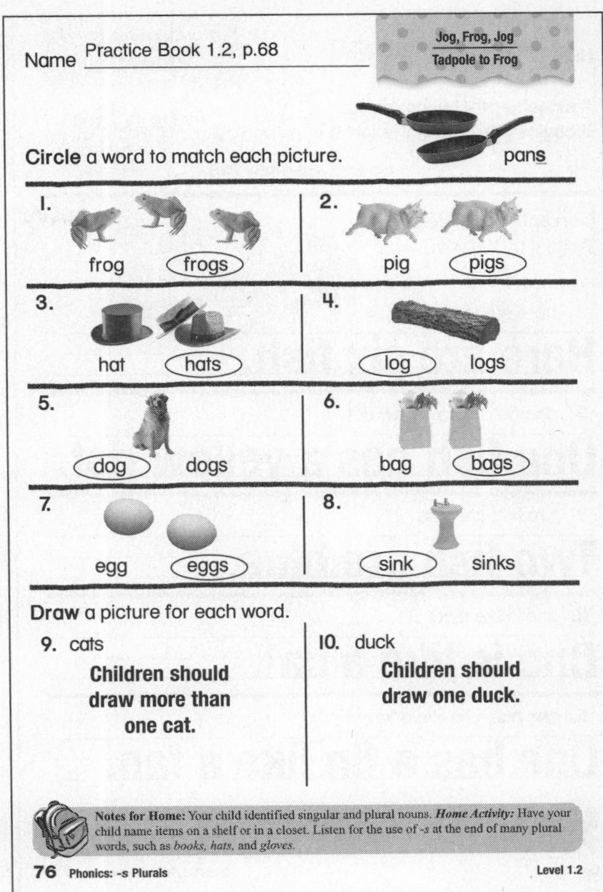
Jog, Frog, Jog
Tadpole to Frog

Name Practice Book 1.2, p.68

**Circle** a word to match each picture.

pans

1. frog frogs
2. pig pigs
3. hat hats
4. log logs
5. dog dogs
6. bag bags
7. egg eggs
8. sink sinks

**Draw** a picture for each word.

9. cats
**Children should draw more than one cat.**

10. duck
**Children should draw one duck.**

**Notes for Home:** Your child identified singular and plural nouns. *Home Activity:* Have your child name items on a shelf or in a closet. Listen for the use of *-s* at the end of many plural words, such as *books, hats,* and *gloves.*

76 Phonics: -s Plurals Level 1.2

Jog, Frog, Jog
Tadpole to Frog

Name Practice Book 1.2, p.69

**Circle** a word to finish each sentence.
**Write** it on the line.

1. What a lot of **water** is in there! water many
2. Look at **this** big fish! they this
3. **Does** he like it in there? Has Does
4. What will **he** do now? he has
5. See him go **into** the big rocks. into up

**Notes for Home:** This week your child is learning to read the words *does, he, into, this,* and *water. Home Activity:* Help your child make up sentences that contain these words. Draw pictures to match each sentence.

Level 1.2 High-Frequency Words 77

Jog, Frog, Jog
Tadpole to Frog

Name Practice Book 1.2, p.70

**Circle** the four books that may tell you about something real.

1. Frogs
2. Bob the Frog
3. Planes
4. Plants
5. Pinky Pig
6. Cary Car's Big Day
7. Space Travel
8. A Dog's Tale

**Think** of a book that tells you about something real.
**Write** its name on the line.
**Draw** a picture in the box that shows what the book is about.

9.

10. **Children's titles and illustrations should indicate nonfiction books.**

**Notes for Home:** Your child has learned to tell what a book might be about by figuring out why it was written. *Home Activity:* As you read various materials with your child, ask what he or she thinks each is about and why the author wrote it.

78 Author's Purpose Level 1.2

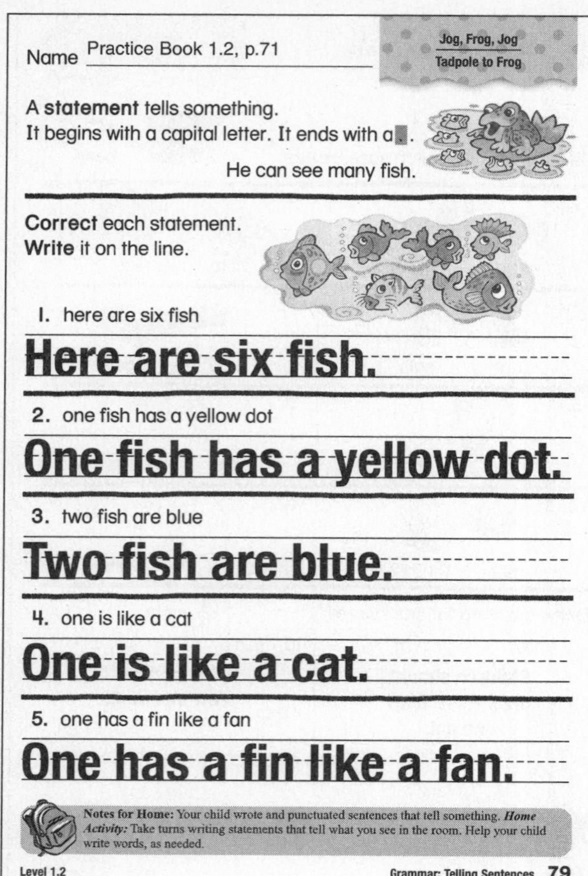

Name Practice Book 1.2, p.71

Jog, Frog, Jog
Tadpole to Frog

A **statement** tells something.
It begins with a capital letter. It ends with a .

He can see many fish.

**Correct** each statement.
**Write** it on the line.

1. here are six fish
Here are six fish.

2. one fish has a yellow dot
One fish has a yellow dot.

3. two fish are blue
Two fish are blue.

4. one is like a cat
One is like a cat.

5. one has a fin like a fan
One has a fin like a fan.

**Notes for Home:** Your child wrote and punctuated sentences that tell something. ***Home Activity:*** Take turns writing statements that tell what you see in the room. Help your child write words, as needed.

Level 1.2 Grammar: Telling Sentences 79

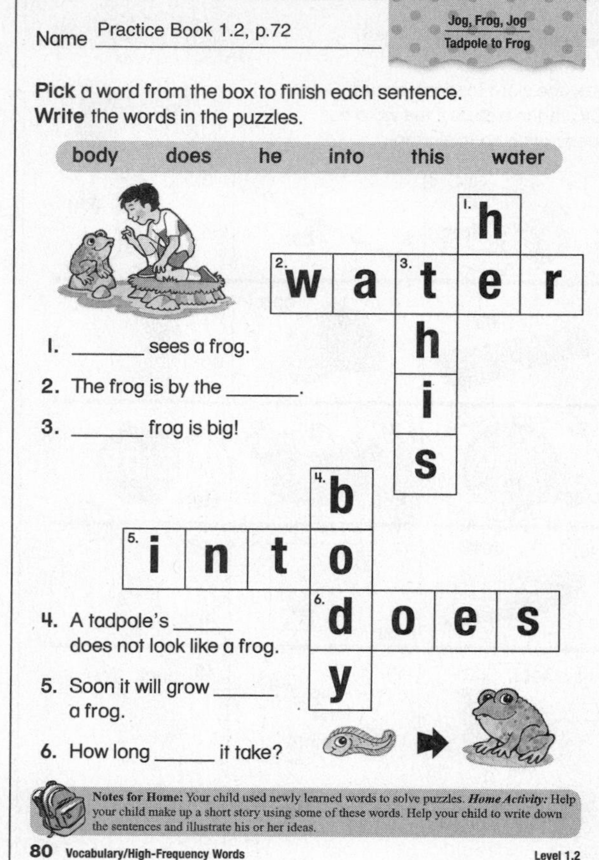

Name Practice Book 1.2, p.72

Jog, Frog, Jog
Tadpole to Frog

**Pick** a word from the box to finish each sentence.
**Write** the words in the puzzles.

body does he into this water

1. ______ sees a frog.
2. The frog is by the ______.
3. ______ frog is big!
4. A tadpole's ______ does not look like a frog.
5. Soon it will grow ______ a frog.
6. How long ______ it take?

Puzzle answers: 1. he 2. water 3. this 4. body 5. into 6. does

**Notes for Home:** Your child used newly learned words to solve puzzles. ***Home Activity:*** Help your child make up a short story using some of these words. Help your child to write down the sentences and illustrate his or her ideas.

80 Vocabulary/High-Frequency Words Level 1.2

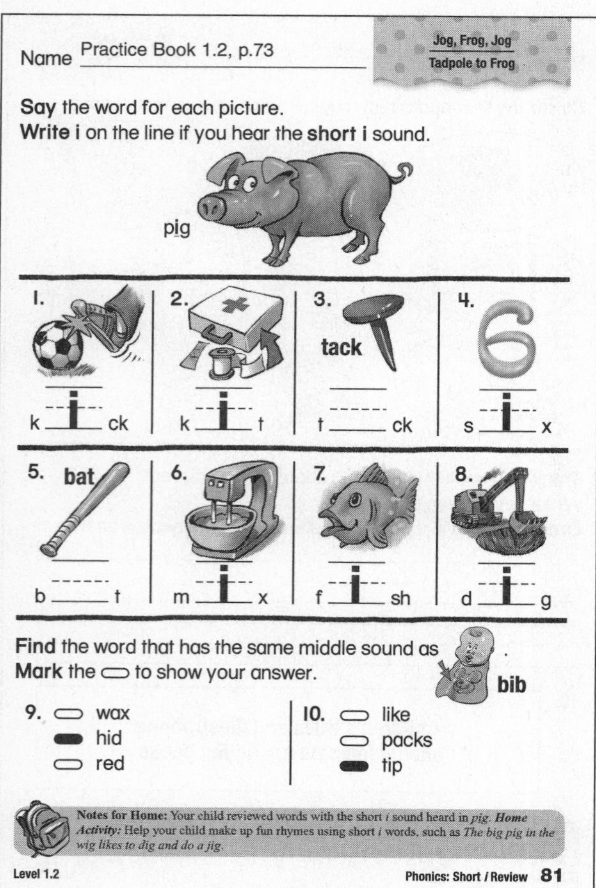

Name Practice Book 1.2, p.73

Jog, Frog, Jog
Tadpole to Frog

**Say** the word for each picture.
**Write i** on the line if you hear the **short i** sound.

pig

1. k i ck
2. k i t
3. tack — t ___ ck
4. s i x
5. bat — b ___ t
6. m i x
7. f i sh
8. d i g

**Find** the word that has the same middle sound as bib.
**Mark** the ⊂⊃ to show your answer.

9. ○ wax ● hid ○ red
10. ○ like ○ packs ● tip

**Notes for Home:** Your child reviewed words with the short *i* sound heard in *pig*. ***Home Activity:*** Help your child make up fun rhymes using short *i* words, such as *The big pig in the wig likes to dig and do a jig.*

Level 1.2 Phonics: Short *i* Review 81

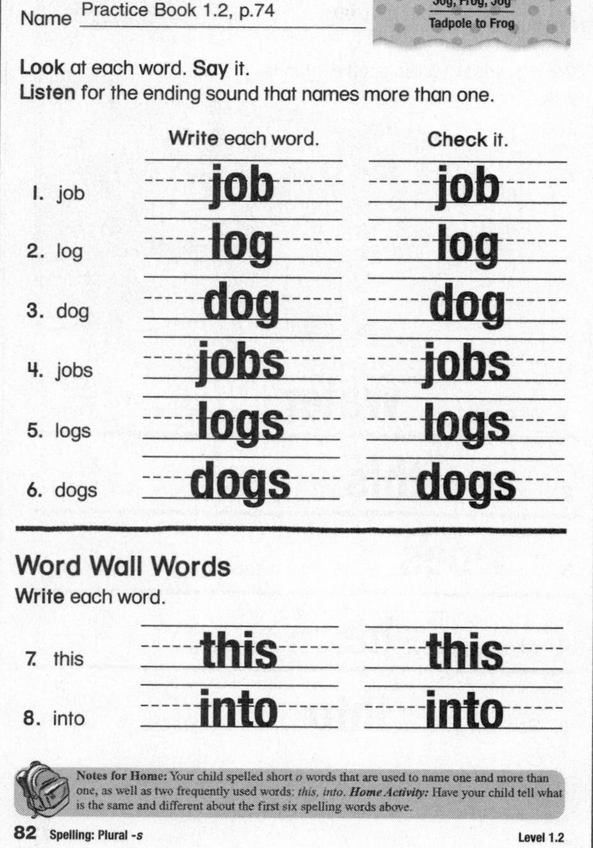

Name Practice Book 1.2, p.74

Jog, Frog, Jog
Tadpole to Frog

**Look** at each word. **Say** it.
**Listen** for the ending sound that names more than one.

| | **Write** each word. | **Check** it. |
|---|---|---|
| 1. job | job | job |
| 2. log | log | log |
| 3. dog | dog | dog |
| 4. jobs | jobs | jobs |
| 5. logs | logs | logs |
| 6. dogs | dogs | dogs |

**Word Wall Words**
**Write** each word.

| | | |
|---|---|---|
| 7. this | this | this |
| 8. into | into | into |

**Notes for Home:** Your child spelled short *o* words that are used to name one and more than one, as well as two frequently used words: *this, into.* ***Home Activity:*** Have your child tell what is the same and different about the first six spelling words above.

82 Spelling: Plural *-s* Level 1.2

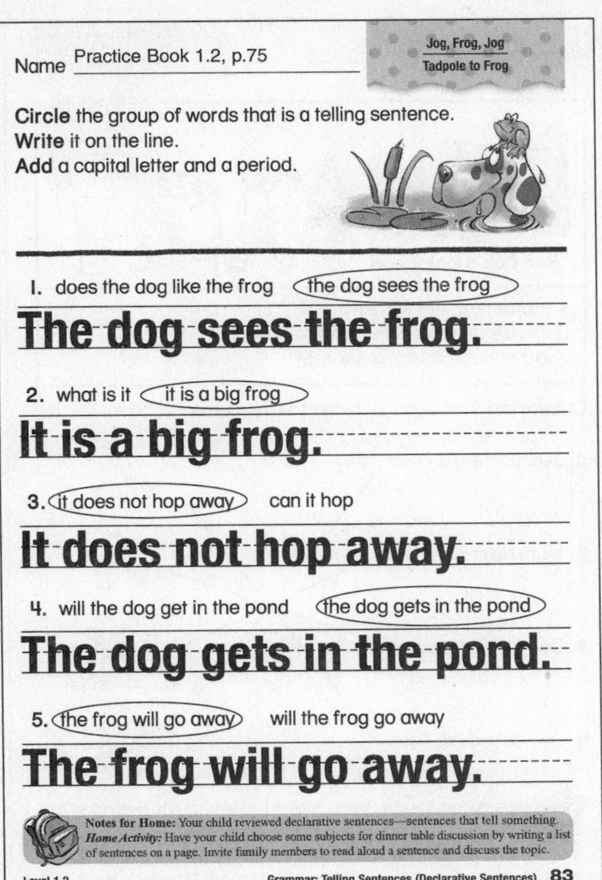

Jog, Frog, Jog
Tadpole to Frog

Name Practice Book 1.2, p.75

**Circle** the group of words that is a telling sentence.
**Write** it on the line.
**Add** a capital letter and a period.

1. does the dog like the frog (the dog sees the frog)

The dog sees the frog.

2. what is it (it is a big frog)

It is a big frog.

3. (it does not hop away) can it hop

It does not hop away.

4. will the dog get in the pond (the dog gets in the pond)

The dog gets in the pond.

5. (the frog will go away) will the frog go away

The frog will go away.

**Notes for Home:** Your child reviewed declarative sentences—sentences that tell something. ***Home Activity:*** Have your child choose some subjects for dinner table discussion by writing a list of sentences on a page. Invite family members to read aloud a sentence and discuss the topic.

Level 1.2 Grammar: Telling Sentences (Declarative Sentences) 83

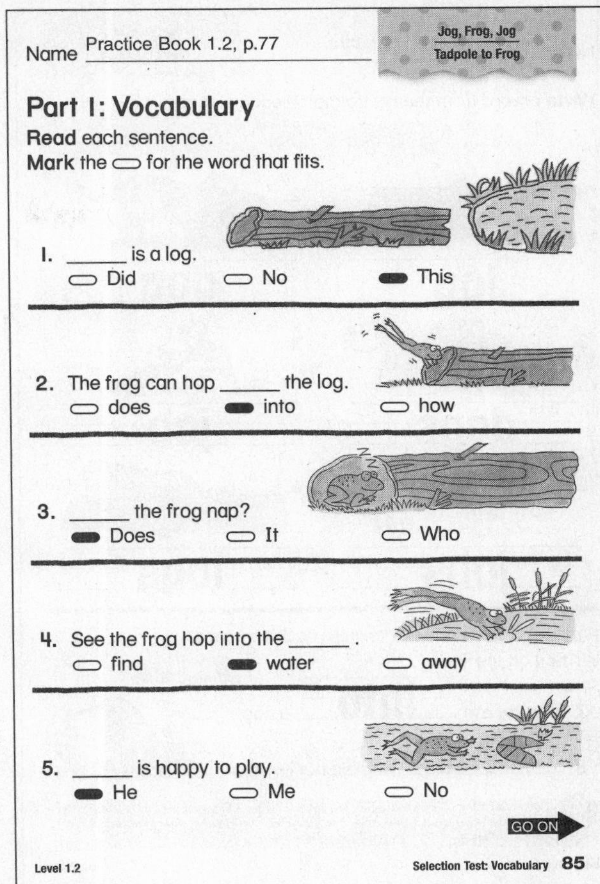

Jog, Frog, Jog
Tadpole to Frog

Name Practice Book 1.2, p.77

## Part 1: Vocabulary

**Read** each sentence.
**Mark** the ⬭ for the word that fits.

1. _____ is a log.
   - ⬭ Did
   - ⬭ No
   - ⬬ This

2. The frog can hop _____ the log.
   - ⬭ does
   - ⬬ into
   - ⬭ how

3. _____ the frog nap?
   - ⬬ Does
   - ⬭ It
   - ⬭ Who

4. See the frog hop into the _____.
   - ⬭ find
   - ⬬ water
   - ⬭ away

5. _____ is happy to play.
   - ⬬ He
   - ⬭ Me
   - ⬭ No

GO ON

Level 1.2 Selection Test: Vocabulary 85

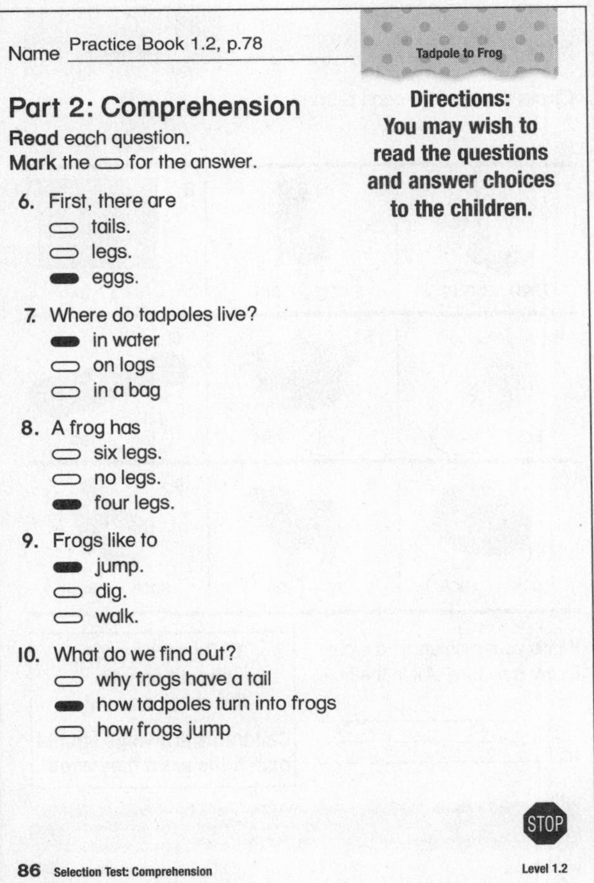

Tadpole to Frog

Name Practice Book 1.2, p.78

## Part 2: Comprehension

**Read** each question.
**Mark** the ⬭ for the answer.

**Directions: You may wish to read the questions and answer choices to the children.**

6. First, there are
   - ⬭ tails.
   - ⬭ legs.
   - ⬬ eggs.

7. Where do tadpoles live?
   - ⬬ in water
   - ⬭ on logs
   - ⬭ in a bag

8. A frog has
   - ⬭ six legs.
   - ⬭ no legs.
   - ⬬ four legs.

9. Frogs like to
   - ⬬ jump.
   - ⬭ dig.
   - ⬭ walk.

10. What do we find out?
    - ⬭ why frogs have a tail
    - ⬬ how tadpoles turn into frogs
    - ⬭ how frogs jump

STOP

86 Selection Test: Comprehension Level 1.2

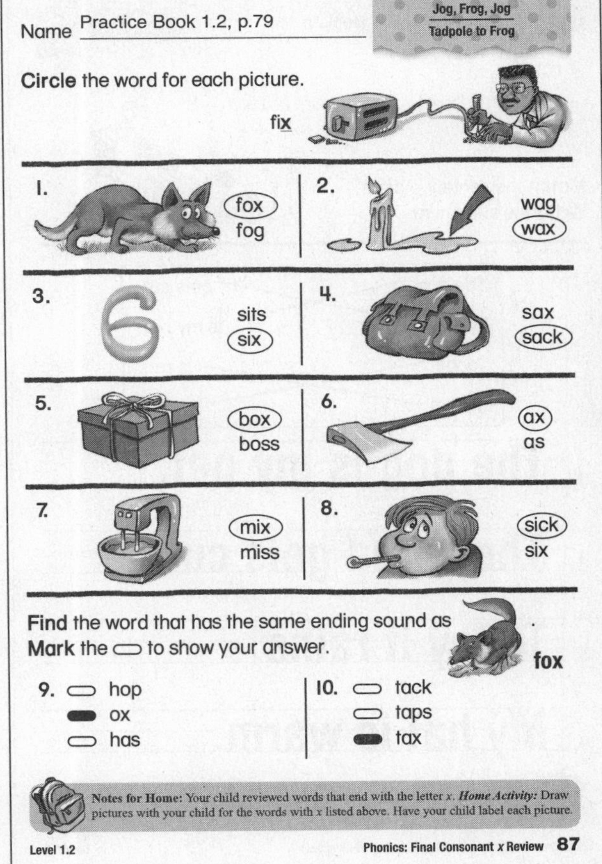

Jog, Frog, Jog
Tadpole to Frog

Name Practice Book 1.2, p.79

**Circle** the word for each picture.

fix

1. (fox) fog
2. wag (wax)
3. sits (six)
4. sax (sack)
5. (box) boss
6. (ax) as
7. (mix) miss
8. (sick) six

**Find** the word that has the same ending sound as fox.
**Mark** the ⬭ to show your answer.

9. 
   - ⬭ hop
   - ⬬ ox
   - ⬭ has

10. 
    - ⬭ tack
    - ⬭ taps
    - ⬬ tax

**Notes for Home:** Your child reviewed words that end with the letter *x*. ***Home Activity:*** Draw pictures with your child for the words with *x* listed above. Have your child label each picture.

Level 1.2 Phonics: Final Consonant *x* Review 87

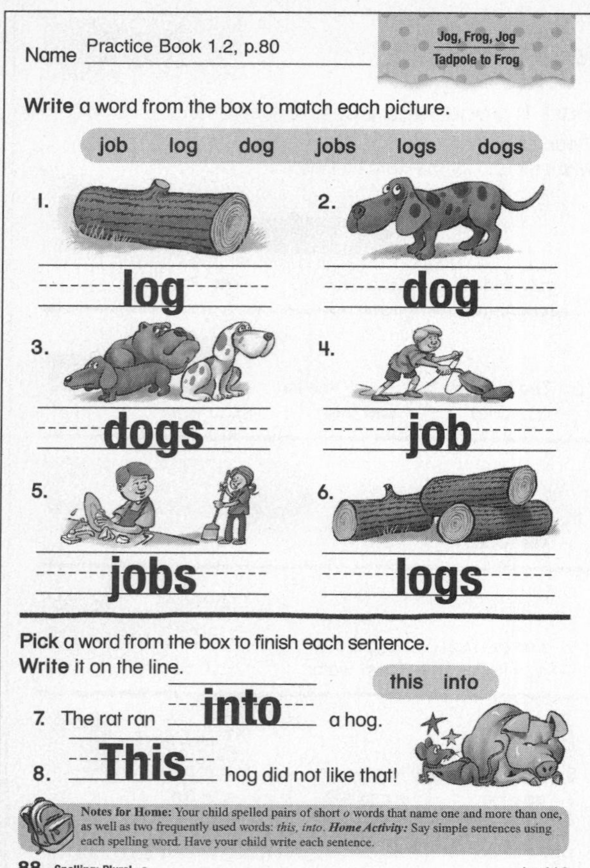

Name Practice Book 1.2, p.80

Jog, Frog, Jog
Tadpole to Frog

**Write** a word from the box to match each picture.

job log dog jobs logs dogs

1. log
2. dog
3. dogs
4. job
5. jobs
6. logs

**Pick** a word from the box to finish each sentence.
**Write** it on the line.

this into

7. The rat ran into a hog.
8. This hog did not like that!

**Notes for Home:** Your child spelled pairs of short *o* words that name one and more than one, as well as two frequently used words: *this, into.* ***Home Activity:*** Say simple sentences using each spelling word. Have your child write each sentence.

88 Spelling: Plural *-s* Level 1.2

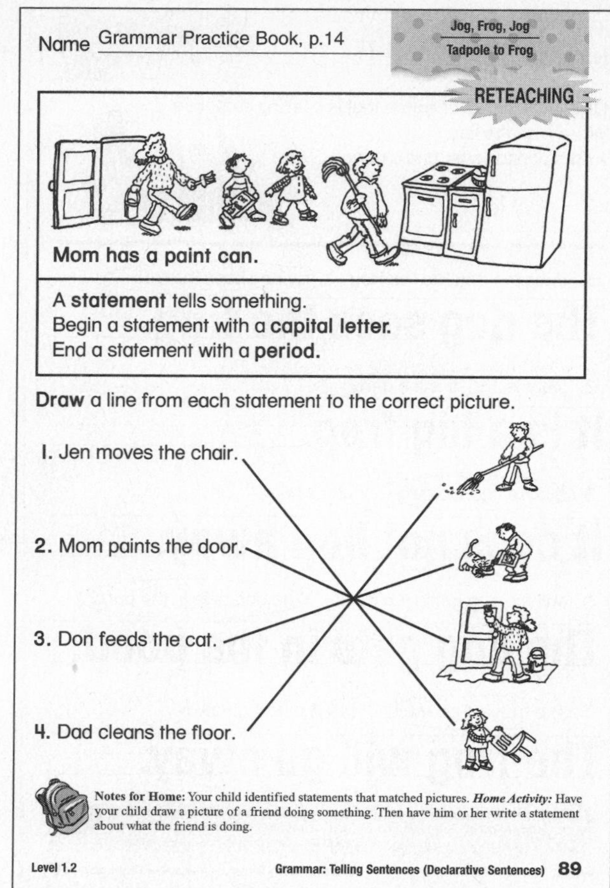

Name Grammar Practice Book, p.14

Jog, Frog, Jog
Tadpole to Frog

RETEACHING

**Mom has a paint can.**

A **statement** tells something.
Begin a statement with a **capital letter.**
End a statement with a **period.**

**Draw** a line from each statement to the correct picture.

1. Jen moves the chair.
2. Mom paints the door.
3. Don feeds the cat.
4. Dad cleans the floor.

**Notes for Home:** Your child identified statements that matched pictures. ***Home Activity:*** Have your child draw a picture of a friend doing something. Then have him or her write a statement about what the friend is doing.

Level 1.2 Grammar: Telling Sentences (Declarative Sentences) 89

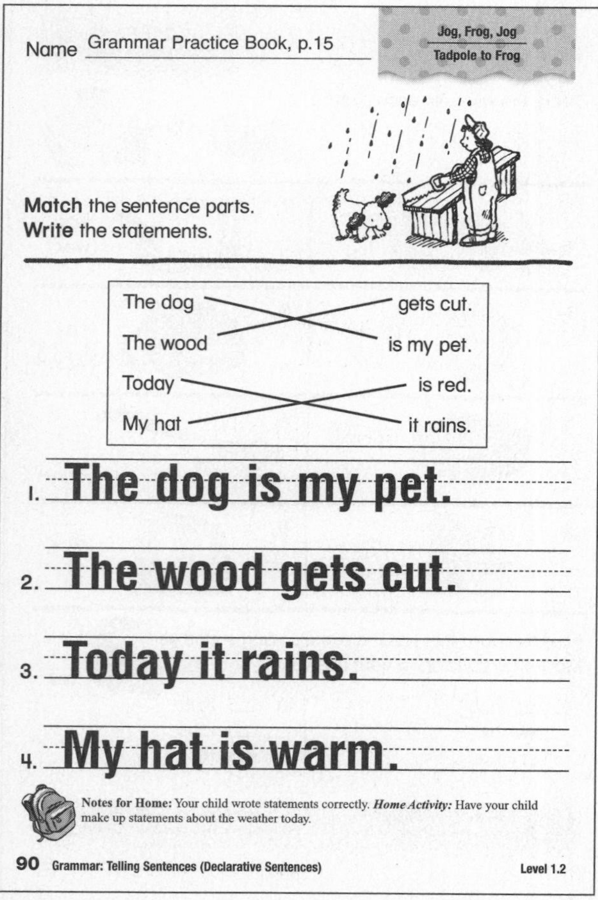

Name Grammar Practice Book, p.15

Jog, Frog, Jog
Tadpole to Frog

**Match** the sentence parts.
**Write** the statements.

| | |
|---|---|
| The dog | gets cut. |
| The wood | is my pet. |
| Today | is red. |
| My hat | it rains. |

1. The dog is my pet.
2. The wood gets cut.
3. Today it rains.
4. My hat is warm.

**Notes for Home:** Your child wrote statements correctly. ***Home Activity:*** Have your child make up statements about the weather today.

90 Grammar: Telling Sentences (Declarative Sentences) Level 1.2

Name Practice Book 1.2, p.83

A Big Job
Sweet Potato Pie

**Circle** the word for each picture.

top

1. map (mop)
2. (dog) dig
3. (fox) fix
4. lick (lock)
5. (pot) pit
6. (log) leg
7. rack (rock)
8. ax (ox)
9. sack (sock)

**Write** your own **short o** word.
**Draw** a picture of it in the box.

10.

**Children's words should contain the short *o* sound.**
**Children's drawings should match the word they wrote.**

**Notes for Home:** Your child practiced reading words with the short *o* sound as in *top.* ***Home Activity:*** Write the endings *-ock, -od, -og, -op, -ot,* and *-ox* on slips of paper. Have your child use different beginning letters to write words with these endings.

Level 1.2 Phonics: Short *o* 93

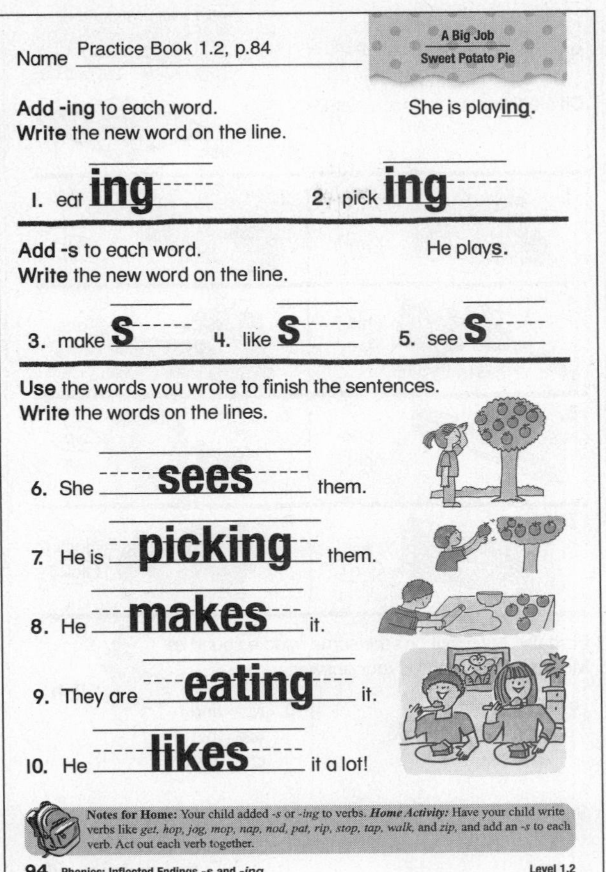

A Big Job
Sweet Potato Pie

Name Practice Book 1.2, p.84

**Add -ing** to each word. She is play**ing**.
**Write** the new word on the line.

1. eat **ing** 2. pick **ing**

**Add -s** to each word. He play**s**.
**Write** the new word on the line.

3. make **s** 4. like **s** 5. see **s**

**Use** the words you wrote to finish the sentences.
**Write** the words on the lines.

6. She **sees** them.
7. He is **picking** them.
8. He **makes** it.
9. They are **eating** it.
10. He **likes** it a lot!

**Notes for Home:** Your child added *-s* or *-ing* to verbs. ***Home Activity:*** Have your child write verbs like *get, hop, jog, mop, nap, nod, pat, rip, stop, tap, walk,* and *zip,* and add an *-s* to each verb. Act out each verb together.

94 Phonics: Inflected Endings -s and -*ing* Level 1.2

A Big Job
Sweet Potato Pie

Name Practice Book 1.2, p.85

**Pick** a word from the box to finish each sentence.
**Write** it on the line.

by eat sing stop them

1. We **stop** walking.
2. We sit **by** the water.
3. I **eat** two yams.
4. I like **them** hot!
5. They like to **sing**.

**Notes for Home:** This week your child is learning to read the words *by, eat, sing, stop,* and *them.* ***Home Activity:*** Encourage your child to use these words to make up a story about a person or animal that cannot sing. Help your child write the story and read it aloud.

Level 1.2 High-Frequency Words 95

A Big Job
Sweet Potato Pie

Name Practice Book 1.2, p.86

**Look** at the first picture.
**Circle** the picture that shows what made this happen.

1.
2.
3.
4.

**Look** at the picture. **Draw** what happened first.

5. **The drawing should show an event that would cause the children to get wet, such as a rainstorm.**

**Notes for Home:** Your child identified causes (why something happens) and effects (what happens). ***Home Activity:*** Call your child's attention to causes and effects by asking questions such as: *What do you think made that happen? What would happen if . . .?*

96 Cause and Effect Level 1.2

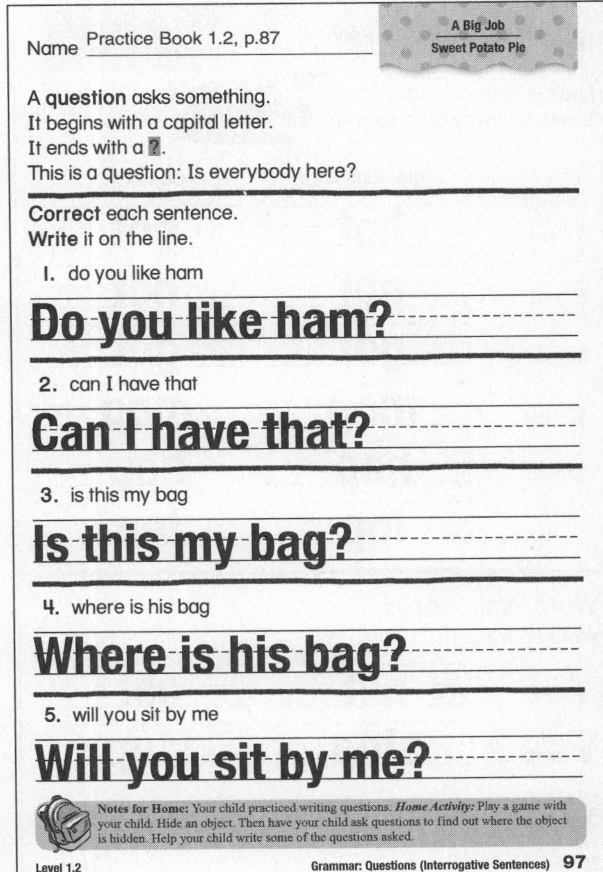

A Big Job
Sweet Potato Pie

Name Practice Book 1.2, p.87

A **question** asks something.
It begins with a capital letter.
It ends with a ?.
This is a question: Is everybody here?

**Correct** each sentence.
**Write** it on the line.

1. do you like ham
**Do you like ham?**
2. can I have that
**Can I have that?**
3. is this my bag
**Is this my bag?**
4. where is his bag
**Where is his bag?**
5. will you sit by me
**Will you sit by me?**

**Notes for Home:** Your child practiced writing questions. ***Home Activity:*** Play a game with your child. Hide an object. Then have your child ask questions to find out where the object is hidden. Help your child write some of the questions asked.

Level 1.2 Grammar: Questions (Interrogative Sentences) 97

Name Practice Book 1.2, p.88

A Big Job
Sweet Potato Pie

**Pick** a word from the box to finish each sentence.
**Write** it on the line.

by eat sing stop them

1. Sit **by** me.
2. Do you like **them** ?
3. Will you **eat** that?
4. No! Sam, **stop** that!
5. It likes to **sing** .

**Notes for Home:** Your child practiced using the words *by, eat, sing, stop,* and *them.* ***Home Activity:*** Help your child use these words to write a story about a family party.

98 Vocabulary/High-Frequency Words Level 1.2

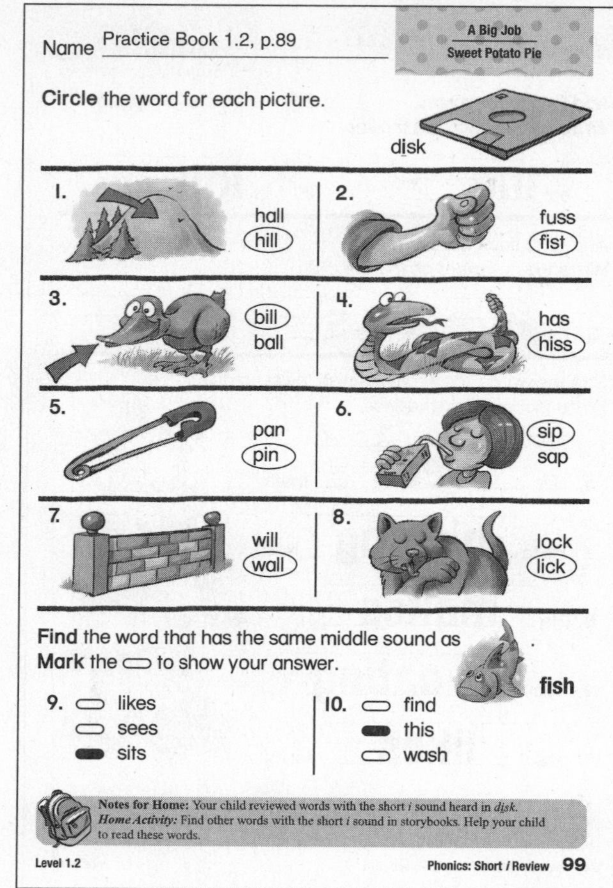

Name Practice Book 1.2, p.89

A Big Job
Sweet Potato Pie

**Circle** the word for each picture.

d**i**sk

1. hall (hill)
2. fuss (fist)
3. (bill) ball
4. has (hiss)
5. pan (pin)
6. (sip) sap
7. will (wall)
8. lock (lick)

**Find** the word that has the same middle sound as fish.
**Mark** the ⬭ to show your answer.

9. ⬭ likes ⬭ sees ⬬ sits
10. ⬭ find ⬬ this ⬭ wash

**Notes for Home:** Your child reviewed words with the short *i* sound heard in *disk.* ***Home Activity:*** Find other words with the short *i* sound in storybooks. Help your child to read these words.

Level 1.2 Phonics: Short *i* Review 99

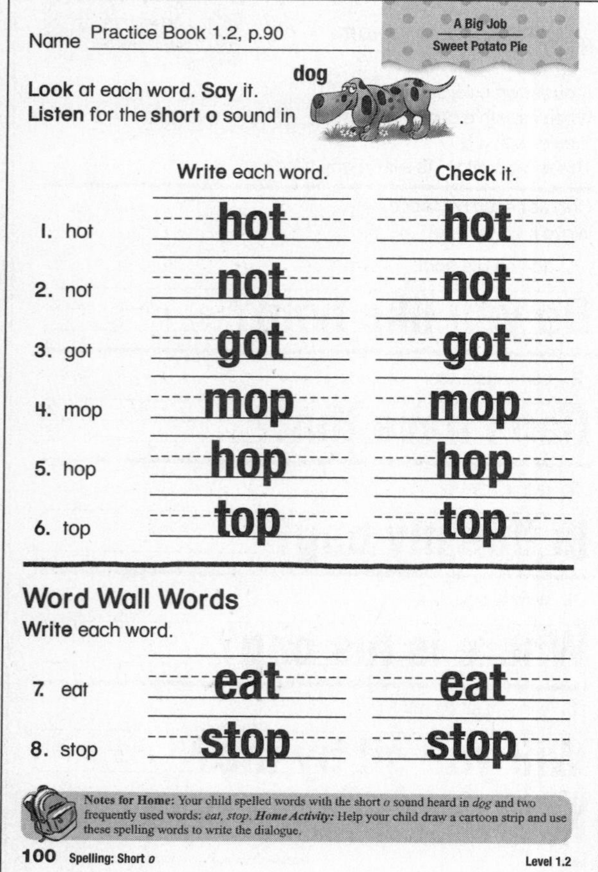

Name Practice Book 1.2, p.90

A Big Job
Sweet Potato Pie

**Look** at each word. **Say** it.
**Listen** for the **short o** sound in dog.

| | **Write** each word. | **Check** it. |
|---|---|---|
| 1. hot | hot | hot |
| 2. not | not | not |
| 3. got | got | got |
| 4. mop | mop | mop |
| 5. hop | hop | hop |
| 6. top | top | top |

**Word Wall Words**
**Write** each word.

| | | |
|---|---|---|
| 7. eat | eat | eat |
| 8. stop | stop | stop |

**Notes for Home:** Your child spelled words with the short *o* sound heard in *dog* and two frequently used words: *eat, stop.* ***Home Activity:*** Help your child draw a cartoon strip and use these spelling words to write the dialogue.

100 Spelling: Short *o* Level 1.2

Name Practice Book 1.2, p.91

A Big Job
Sweet Potato Pie

Add words to tell more about something.
Nan likes to eat fish.
Nan likes to eat big fish.

What would make each sentence better?
**Pick** a word from the box to finish each sentence.
**Write** it on the line. Use each word only once.
**Possible answers given.**

red hot little many

1. Jill likes to eat **red** jam.
2. Bob likes to eat **many** nuts.
3. I like to eat **hot** ham.
4. My cat likes to eat **little** fish!

**Write** a sentence about what you like to eat. **Possible answer given.**

5. **I like big, hot buns and jam.**

**Notes for Home:** Your child added details to simple sentences to make them more interesting. ***Home Activity:*** Write some simple sentences about favorite foods for your child. Work with your child to add interesting details to each sentence.

Level 1.2 Writing Process: Revise 101

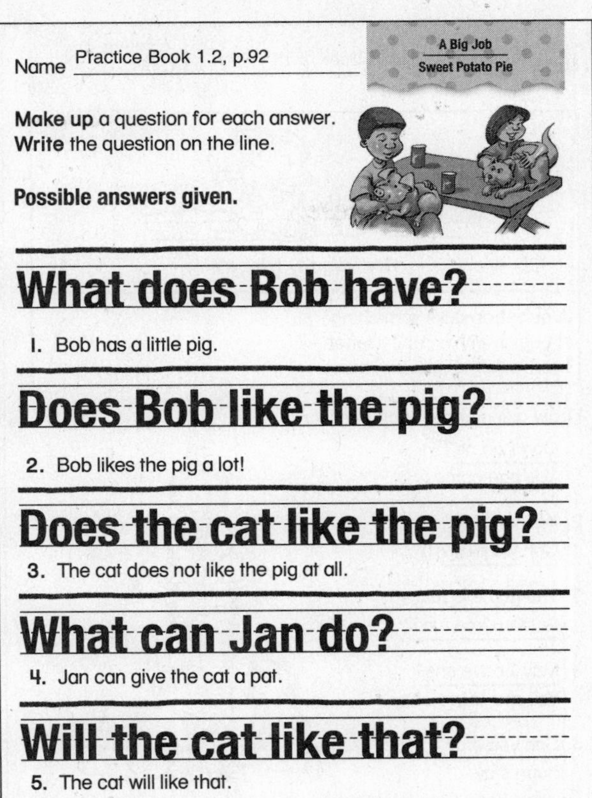

Name Practice Book 1.2, p.92

A Big Job
Sweet Potato Pie

**Make up** a question for each answer.
**Write** the question on the line.

**Possible answers given.**

What does Bob have?

1. Bob has a little pig.

Does Bob like the pig?

2. Bob likes the pig a lot!

Does the cat like the pig?

3. The cat does not like the pig at all.

What can Jan do?

4. Jan can give the cat a pat.

Will the cat like that?

5. The cat will like that.

**Notes for Home:** Your child wrote questions. ***Home Activity:*** Have your child use the words *how, what,* and *where* to write questions to ask you. Help your child with spelling as needed. Check to be sure your child uses a question mark at the end of each sentence.

102 Grammar: Questions (Interrogative Sentences) Level 1.2

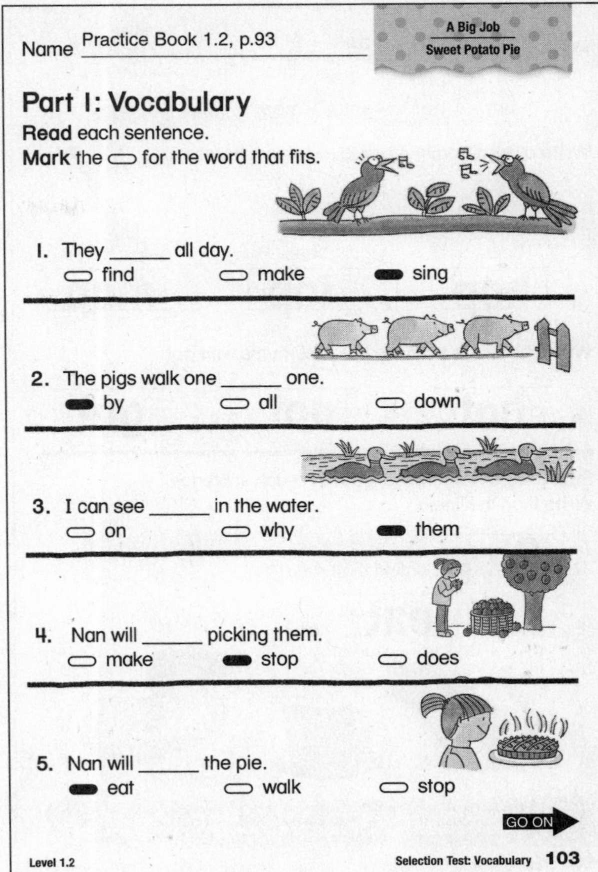

Name Practice Book 1.2, p.93

A Big Job
Sweet Potato Pie

## Part 1: Vocabulary

**Read** each sentence.
**Mark** the ⬭ for the word that fits.

1. They _____ all day.
   - ⬭ find
   - ⬭ make
   - ⬬ sing

2. The pigs walk one _____ one.
   - ⬬ by
   - ⬭ all
   - ⬭ down

3. I can see _____ in the water.
   - ⬭ on
   - ⬭ why
   - ⬬ them

4. Nan will _____ picking them.
   - ⬭ make
   - ⬬ stop
   - ⬭ does

5. Nan will _____ the pie.
   - ⬬ eat
   - ⬭ walk
   - ⬭ stop

GO ON

Level 1.2 Selection Test: Vocabulary 103

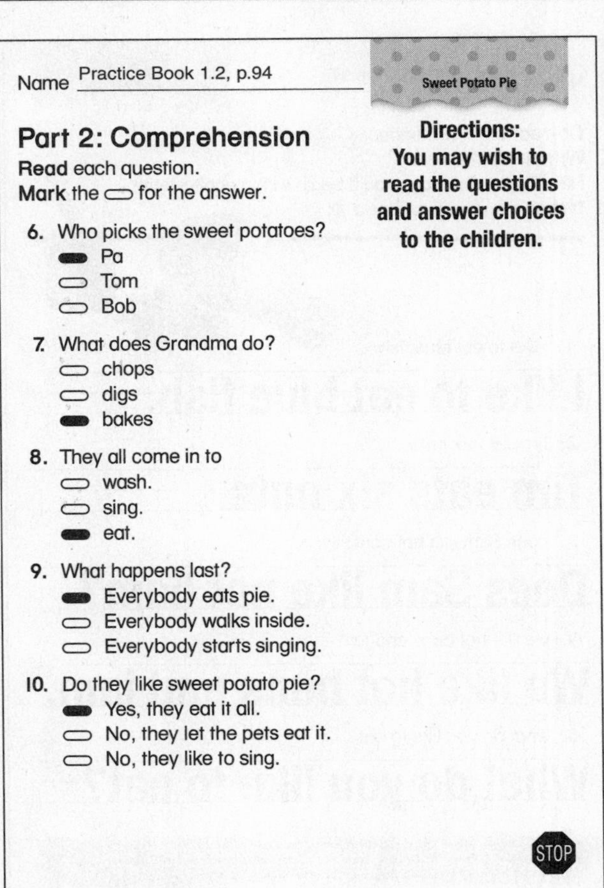

Name Practice Book 1.2, p.94

Sweet Potato Pie

## Part 2: Comprehension

**Read** each question.
**Mark** the ⬭ for the answer.

**Directions: You may wish to read the questions and answer choices to the children.**

6. Who picks the sweet potatoes?
   - ⬬ Pa
   - ⬭ Tom
   - ⬭ Bob

7. What does Grandma do?
   - ⬭ chops
   - ⬭ digs
   - ⬬ bakes

8. They all come in to
   - ⬭ wash.
   - ⬭ sing.
   - ⬬ eat.

9. What happens last?
   - ⬬ Everybody eats pie.
   - ⬭ Everybody walks inside.
   - ⬭ Everybody starts singing.

10. Do they like sweet potato pie?
    - ⬬ Yes, they eat it all.
    - ⬭ No, they let the pets eat it.
    - ⬭ No, they like to sing.

STOP

104 Selection Test: Comprehension Level 1.2

Name Practice Book 1.2, p.95

A Big Job
Sweet Potato Pie

**Circle** the word for each picture.

backpack

1. (rack) rats
2. robs (rock)
3. kiss (kick)
4. bags (back)
5. pick (pig)
6. look (lock)
7. (lick) lock
8. (sock) stop

**Find** the word that has the same ending sound as clock.
**Mark** the ⬭ to show your answer.

9. 
   - ⬭ dogs
   - ⬬ dock
   - ⬭ dots

10. 
    - ⬬ tick
    - ⬭ this
    - ⬭ wish

**Notes for Home:** Your child reviewed words that end with *-ck*. ***Home Activity:*** Help your child write words that end in *-ck*. Then use them to make up nonsense rhymes together (For example: *On top of the rocks stood a goat in pink socks.*).

Level 1.2 Phonics: Final -ck Review 105

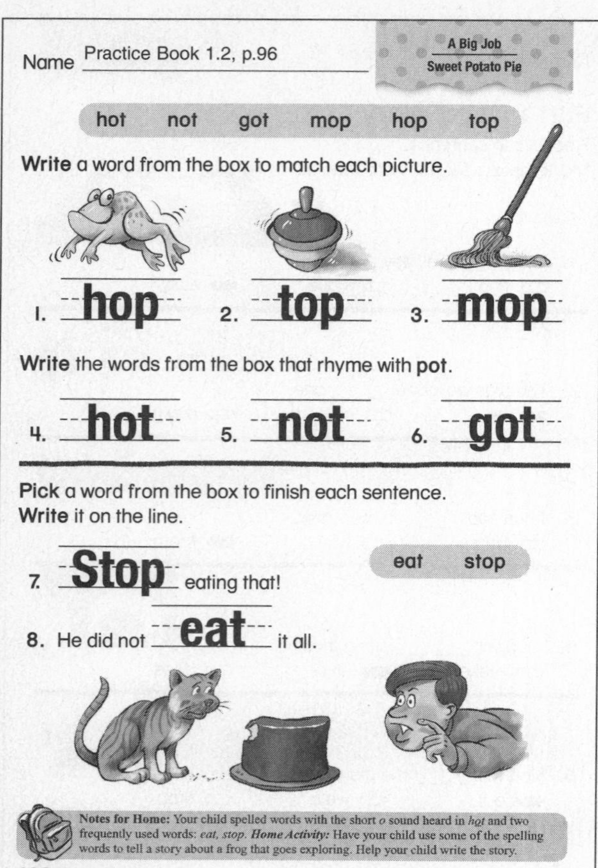

Name Practice Book 1.2, p.96

A Big Job
Sweet Potato Pie

hot not got mop hop top

**Write** a word from the box to match each picture.

1. hop 2. top 3. mop

**Write** the words from the box that rhyme with **pot**.

4. hot 5. not 6. got

**Pick** a word from the box to finish each sentence.
**Write** it on the line.

eat stop

7. Stop eating that!

8. He did not eat it all.

**Notes for Home:** Your child spelled words with the short *o* sound heard in *hot* and two frequently used words: *eat, stop.* ***Home Activity:*** Have your child use some of the spelling words to tell a story about a frog that goes exploring. Help your child write the story.

106 Spelling: Short *o* Level 1.2

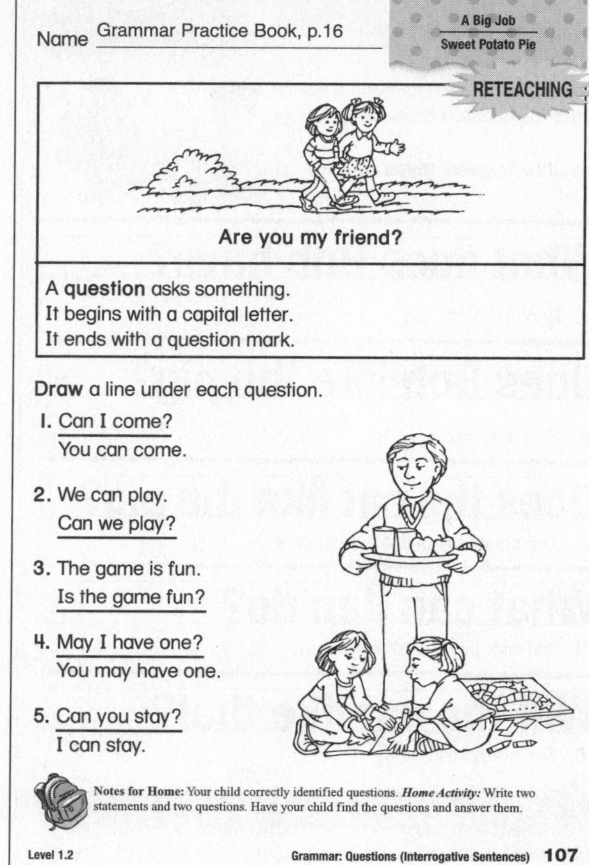

Name Grammar Practice Book, p.16

A Big Job
Sweet Potato Pie

RETEACHING

Are you my friend?

A **question** asks something.
It begins with a capital letter.
It ends with a question mark.

**Draw** a line under each question.

1. Can I come?
You can come.
2. We can play.
Can we play?
3. The game is fun.
Is the game fun?
4. May I have one?
You may have one.
5. Can you stay?
I can stay.

**Notes for Home:** Your child correctly identified questions. ***Home Activity:*** Write two statements and two questions. Have your child find the questions and answer them.

Level 1.2 Grammar: Questions (Interrogative Sentences) 107

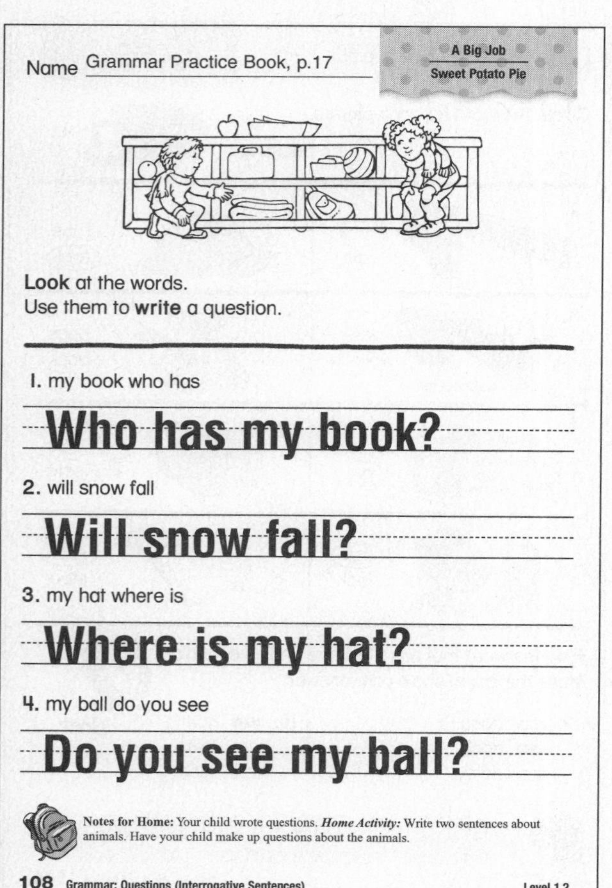

Name Grammar Practice Book, p.17

A Big Job
Sweet Potato Pie

**Look** at the words.
Use them to **write** a question.

1. my book who has
Who has my book?
2. will snow fall
Will snow fall?
3. my hat where is
Where is my hat?
4. my ball do you see
Do you see my ball?

**Notes for Home:** Your child wrote questions. ***Home Activity:*** Write two sentences about animals. Have your child make up questions about the animals.

108 Grammar: Questions (Interrogative Sentences) Level 1.2

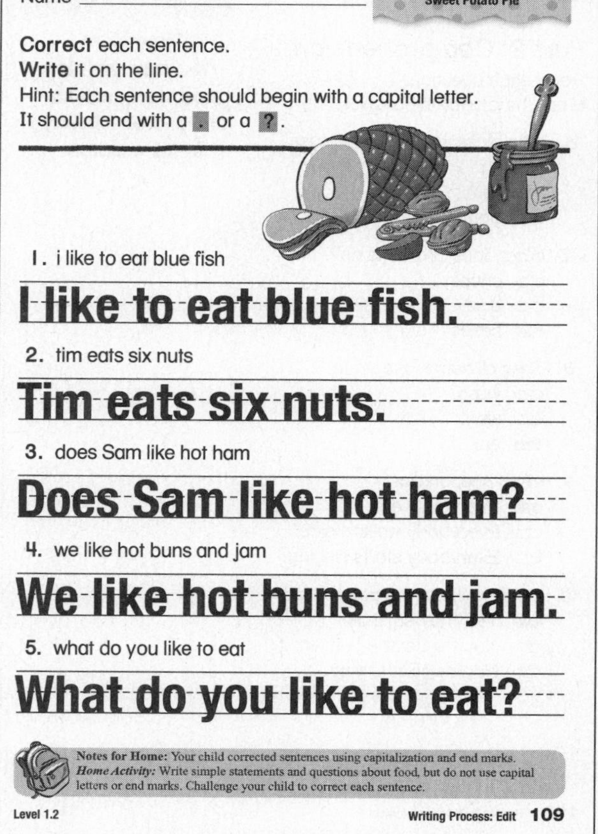

Name Practice Book 1.2, p.97

A Big Job
Sweet Potato Pie

**Correct** each sentence.
**Write** it on the line.
Hint: Each sentence should begin with a capital letter.
It should end with a . or a ?.

1. i like to eat blue fish
I like to eat blue fish.
2. tim eats six nuts
Tim eats six nuts.
3. does Sam like hot ham
Does Sam like hot ham?
4. we like hot buns and jam
We like hot buns and jam.
5. what do you like to eat
What do you like to eat?

**Notes for Home:** Your child corrected sentences using capitalization and end marks. ***Home Activity:*** Write simple statements and questions about food, but do not use capital letters or end marks. Challenge your child to correct each sentence.

Level 1.2 Writing Process: Edit 109

The Big Mess
The Little Red Hen
Name Practice Book 1.3, p.3
Circle a word to finish each sentence.
Write it on the line.
hen
1. The hen is in the pen . (pen) pan
2. Ken likes to pet the hen. pot (pet)
3. What is in the bag ? (bag) beg
4. The hen wants to be fed . (fed) fan
5. The hen makes a mess . miss (mess)
Notes for Home: Your child practiced reading and writing words with the short e sound heard in hen. Home Activity: Work with your child to make a list of all the words on this page with a short e.
Level 1.3
Phonics: Short e 3

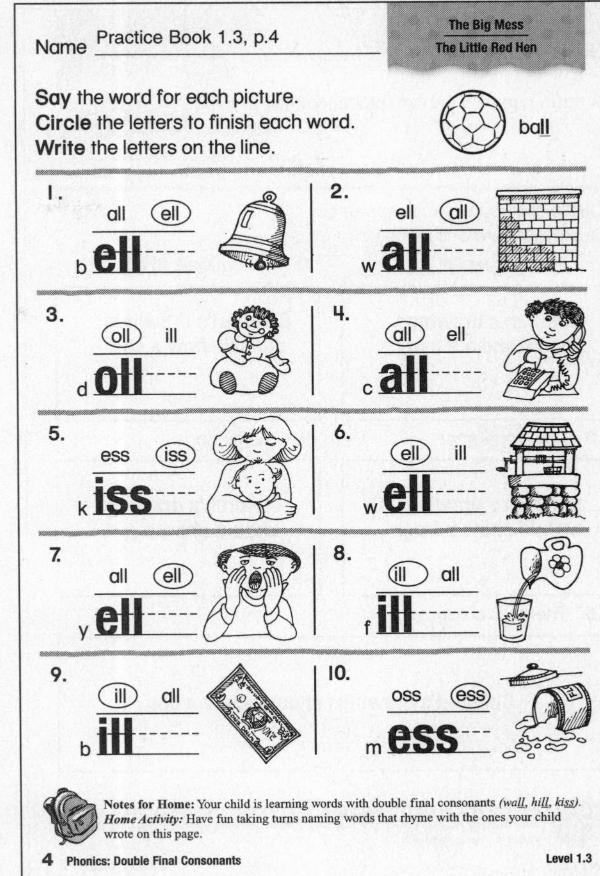
The Big Mess
The Little Red Hen
Name Practice Book 1.3, p.4
Say the word for each picture.
Circle the letters to finish each word.
Write the letters on the line.
ball
1. all (ell) b ell
2. ell (all) w all
3. (oll) ill d oll
4. (all) ell c all
5. ess (iss) k iss
6. (ell) ill w ell
7. all (ell) y ell
8. (ill) all f ill
9. (ill) all b ill
10. oss (ess) m ess
Notes for Home: Your child is learning words with double final consonants (wall, hill, kiss). Home Activity: Have fun taking turns naming words that rhyme with the ones your child wrote on this page.
4 Phonics: Double Final Consonants
Level 1.3

The Big Mess
The Little Red Hen
Name Practice Book 1.3, p.5
Pick a word from the box to finish each sentence.
Write it on the line.
help now said so who
1. Who can get the cat?
2. Ben can help the cat get down.
3. Who can help them now ?
4. "Go find Dad!" Ben said to Nan.
5. He is here!
So now we can get down.
Notes for Home: This week your child is learning to read the words help, now, said, so, and who. Home Activity: Ask your child to use each word in a spoken sentence.
Level 1.3
High-Frequency Words 5

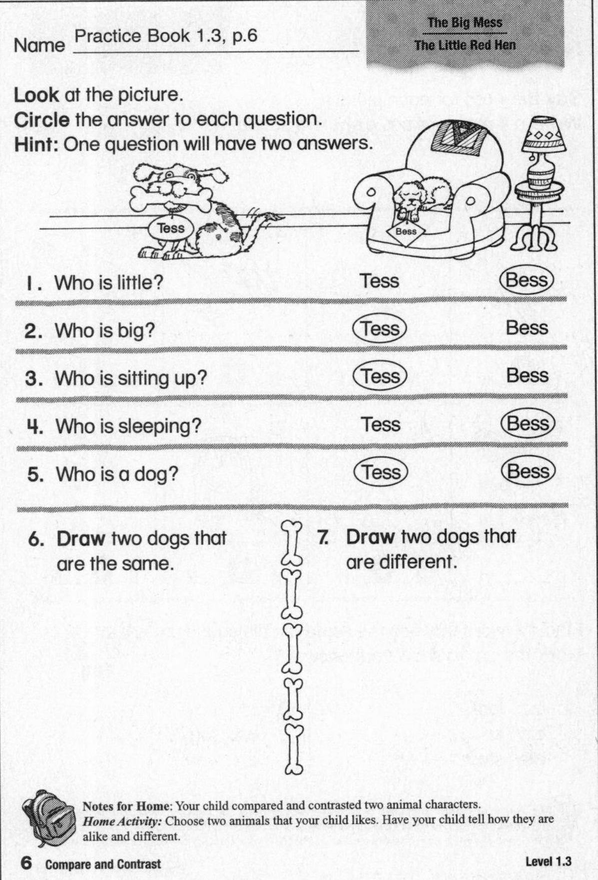
The Big Mess
The Little Red Hen
Name Practice Book 1.3, p.6
Look at the picture.
Circle the answer to each question.
Hint: One question will have two answers.
Tess
Bess
1. Who is little? Tess (Bess)
2. Who is big? (Tess) Bess
3. Who is sitting up? (Tess) Bess
4. Who is sleeping? Tess (Bess)
5. Who is a dog? (Tess) (Bess)
6. Draw two dogs that are the same.
7. Draw two dogs that are different.
Notes for Home: Your child compared and contrasted two animal characters. Home Activity: Choose two animals that your child likes. Have your child tell how they are alike and different.
6 Compare and Contrast
Level 1.3

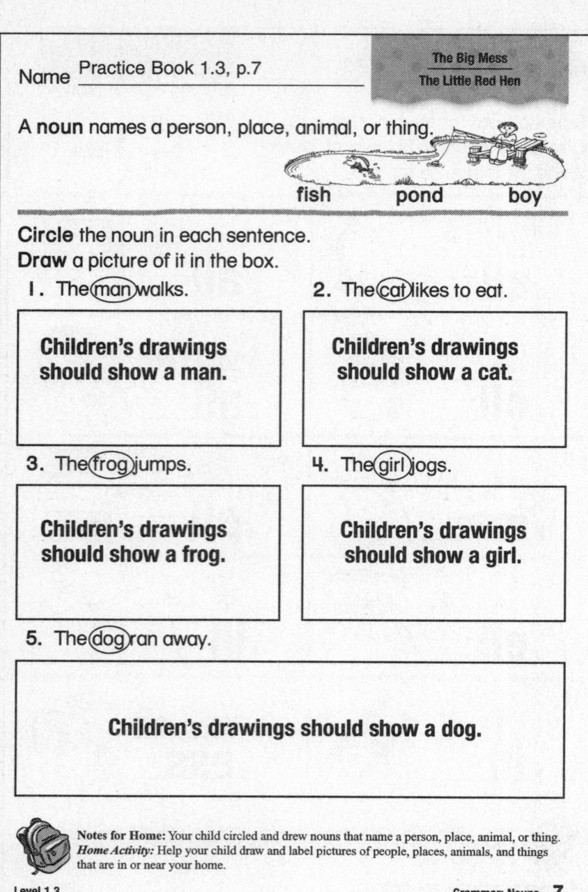
Name Practice Book 1.3, p.7

The Big Mess
The Little Red Hen

A **noun** names a person, place, animal, or thing.

fish pond boy

**Circle** the noun in each sentence.
**Draw** a picture of it in the box.

1. The (man) walks.
2. The (cat) likes to eat.

**Children's drawings should show a man.**

**Children's drawings should show a cat.**

3. The (frog) jumps.
4. The (girl) jogs.

**Children's drawings should show a frog.**

**Children's drawings should show a girl.**

5. The (dog) ran away.

**Children's drawings should show a dog.**

**Notes for Home:** Your child circled and drew nouns that name a person, place, animal, or thing. ***Home Activity:*** Help your child draw and label pictures of people, places, animals, and things that are in or near your home.

Level 1.3 Grammar: Nouns 7

Name Practice Book 1.3, p.8

The Big Mess
The Little Red Hen

**Pick** a word from the box to finish each sentence.
**Write** it on the line.

help now said so want who

1. "I need **help**!" said Tim.
2. "I need it **now**!"
3. "**Who** will help me?"

4. "I **want** to help you," said Dan.
5. "**So** do I," said Jan.
6. "We all want to help," they **said**.

**Notes for Home:** Your child read and wrote the words *help, now, said, so, want,* and *who* to complete sentences. ***Home Activity:*** Ask your child to use each vocabulary word in a short sentence. Work together to write each sentence.

8 Vocabulary/High-Frequency Words Level 1.3

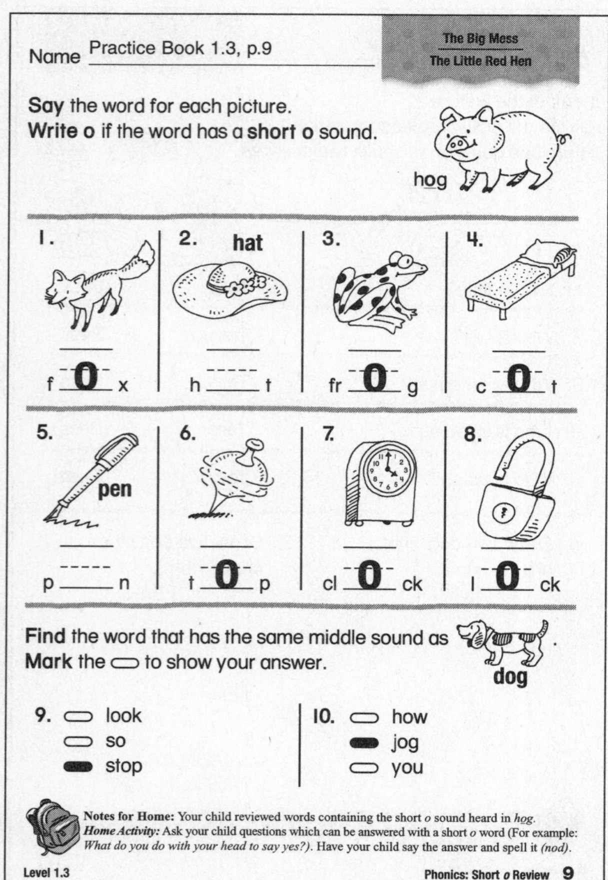
Name Practice Book 1.3, p.9

The Big Mess
The Little Red Hen

**Say** the word for each picture.
**Write o** if the word has a **short o** sound.

hog

1. f **o** x
2. hat — h ___ t
3. fr **o** g
4. c **o** t
5. pen — p ___ n
6. t **o** p
7. cl **o** ck
8. l **o** ck

**Find** the word that has the same middle sound as dog.
**Mark** the ⬭ to show your answer.

9. ⬭ look ⬭ so ⬬ stop
10. ⬭ how ⬬ jog ⬭ you

**Notes for Home:** Your child reviewed words containing the short *o* sound heard in *hog.* ***Home Activity:*** Ask your child questions which can be answered with a short *o* word (For example: *What do you do with your head to say yes?*). Have your child say the answer and spell it *(nod).*

Level 1.3 Phonics: Short *o* Review 9

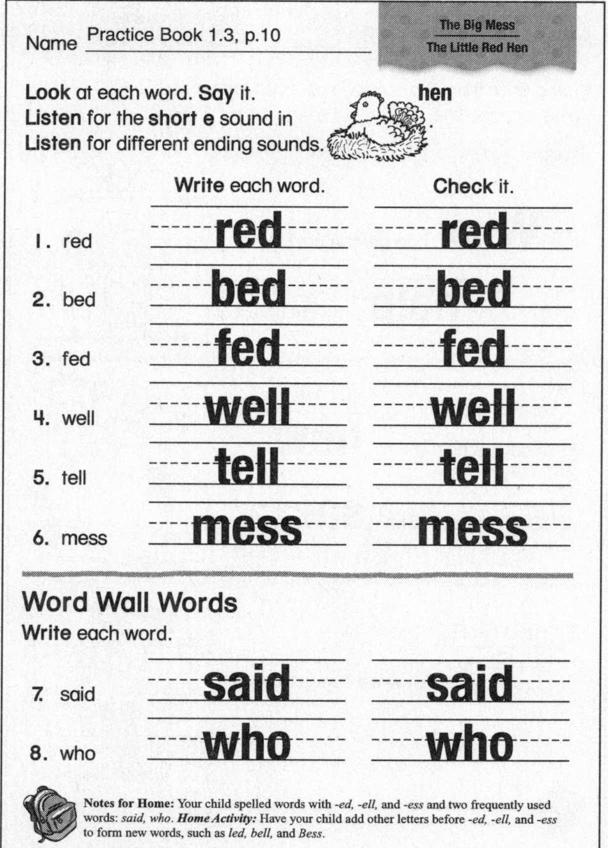
Name Practice Book 1.3, p.10

The Big Mess
The Little Red Hen

**Look** at each word. **Say** it.
**Listen** for the **short e** sound in hen.
**Listen** for different ending sounds.

| | Write each word. | Check it. |
|---|---|---|
| 1. red | **red** | **red** |
| 2. bed | **bed** | **bed** |
| 3. fed | **fed** | **fed** |
| 4. well | **well** | **well** |
| 5. tell | **tell** | **tell** |
| 6. mess | **mess** | **mess** |

## Word Wall Words

Write each word.

| | | |
|---|---|---|
| 7. said | **said** | **said** |
| 8. who | **who** | **who** |

**Notes for Home:** Your child spelled words with *-ed, -ell,* and *-ess* and two frequently used words: *said, who.* ***Home Activity:*** Have your child add other letters before *-ed, -ell,* and *-ess* to form new words, such as *led, bell,* and *Bess.*

10 Spelling: Word Families *-ed, -ell,* and *-ess* Level 1.3

Name Practice Book 1.3, p.11

The Big Mess
The Little Red Hen

**Circle** the noun that matches each picture.

1. many little (fish) — fish
2. (hog) fat sit — hog
3. hot (pans) three — pans
4. (hen) eat peck — hen

**Write** a noun to go with each picture. **Possible answers given.**

5. bed
6. box
7. cat
8. pot

**Notes for Home:** Your child reviewed nouns—words that name people, places, animals, or things. *Home Activity:* Read a story book with your child and look for words that are nouns. Then ask your child to use those nouns in new sentences.

Level 1.3 Grammar: Nouns 11

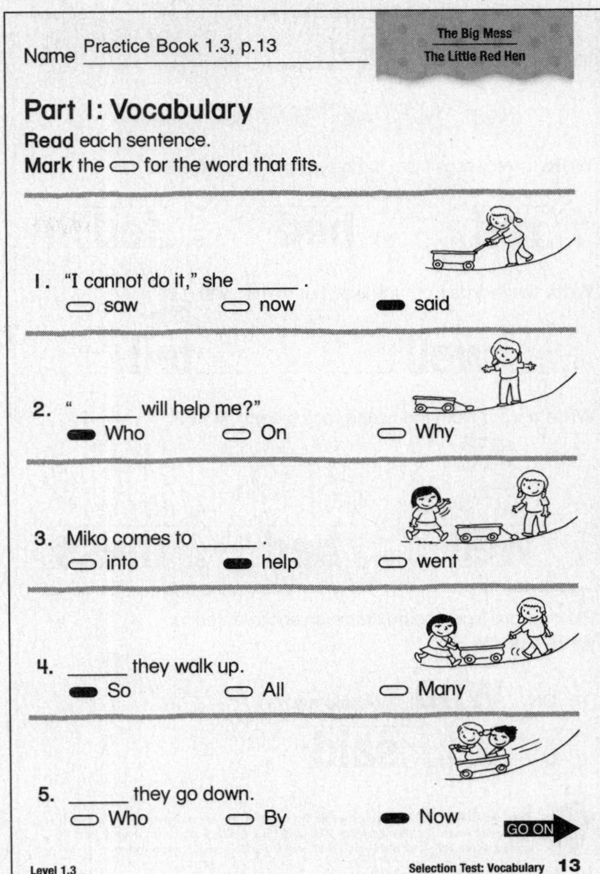

Name Practice Book 1.3, p.13

The Big Mess
The Little Red Hen

**Part 1: Vocabulary**

**Read** each sentence.
**Mark** the ⬭ for the word that fits.

1. "I cannot do it," she _____.
⬭ saw ⬭ now ⬬ said

2. "_____ will help me?"
⬬ Who ⬭ On ⬭ Why

3. Miko comes to _____.
⬭ into ⬬ help ⬭ went

4. _____ they walk up.
⬬ So ⬭ All ⬭ Many

5. _____ they go down.
⬭ Who ⬭ By ⬬ Now

GO ON

Level 1.3 Selection Test: Vocabulary 13

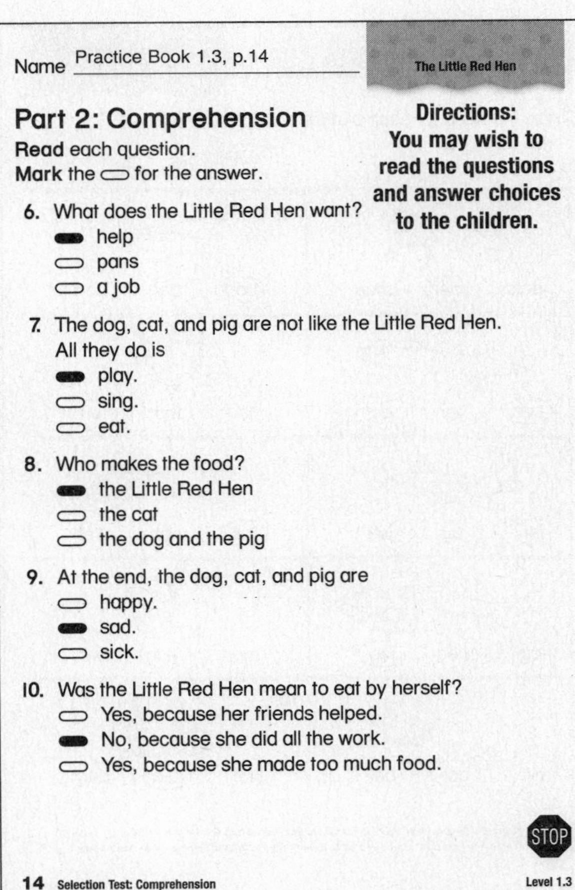

Name Practice Book 1.3, p.14

The Little Red Hen

**Part 2: Comprehension**

**Read** each question.
**Mark** the ⬭ for the answer.

**Directions: You may wish to read the questions and answer choices to the children.**

6. What does the Little Red Hen want?
⬬ help
⬭ pans
⬭ a job

7. The dog, cat, and pig are not like the Little Red Hen. All they do is
⬬ play.
⬭ sing.
⬭ eat.

8. Who makes the food?
⬬ the Little Red Hen
⬭ the cat
⬭ the dog and the pig

9. At the end, the dog, cat, and pig are
⬭ happy.
⬬ sad.
⬭ sick.

10. Was the Little Red Hen mean to eat by herself?
⬭ Yes, because her friends helped.
⬬ No, because she did all the work.
⬭ Yes, because she made too much food.

STOP

14 Selection Test: Comprehension Level 1.3

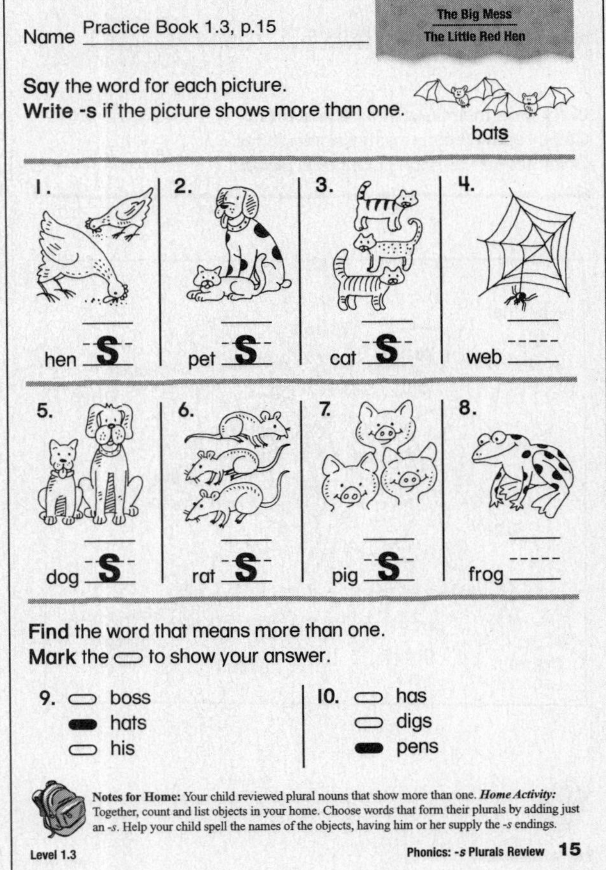

Name Practice Book 1.3, p.15

The Big Mess
The Little Red Hen

**Say** the word for each picture.
**Write -s** if the picture shows more than one.

bats

1. hen s
2. pet s
3. cat s
4. web
5. dog s
6. rat s
7. pig s
8. frog

**Find** the word that means more than one.
**Mark** the ⬭ to show your answer.

9. ⬭ boss
⬬ hats
⬭ his

10. ⬭ has
⬭ digs
⬬ pens

**Notes for Home:** Your child reviewed plural nouns that show more than one. *Home Activity:* Together, count and list objects in your home. Choose words that form their plurals by adding just an *-s*. Help your child spell the names of the objects, having him or her supply the *-s* endings.

Level 1.3 Phonics: *-s* Plurals Review 15

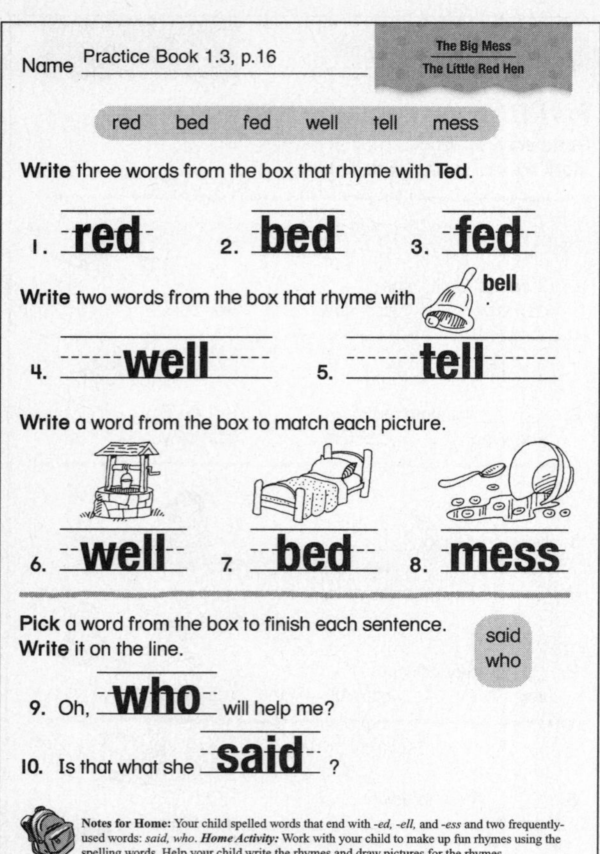

Name Practice Book 1.3, p.16

The Big Mess
The Little Red Hen

red bed fed well tell mess

**Write** three words from the box that rhyme with **Ted**.

1. red 2. bed 3. fed

**Write** two words from the box that rhyme with bell.

4. well 5. tell

**Write** a word from the box to match each picture.

6. well 7. bed 8. mess

**Pick** a word from the box to finish each sentence.
**Write** it on the line.

said
who

9. Oh, who will help me?

10. Is that what she said ?

**Notes for Home:** Your child spelled words that end with *-ed, -ell,* and *-ess* and two frequently-used words: *said, who.* ***Home Activity:*** Work with your child to make up fun rhymes using the spelling words. Help your child write the rhymes and draw pictures for the rhymes.

16 Spelling: Word Families *-ed, -ell,* and *-ess* Level 1.3

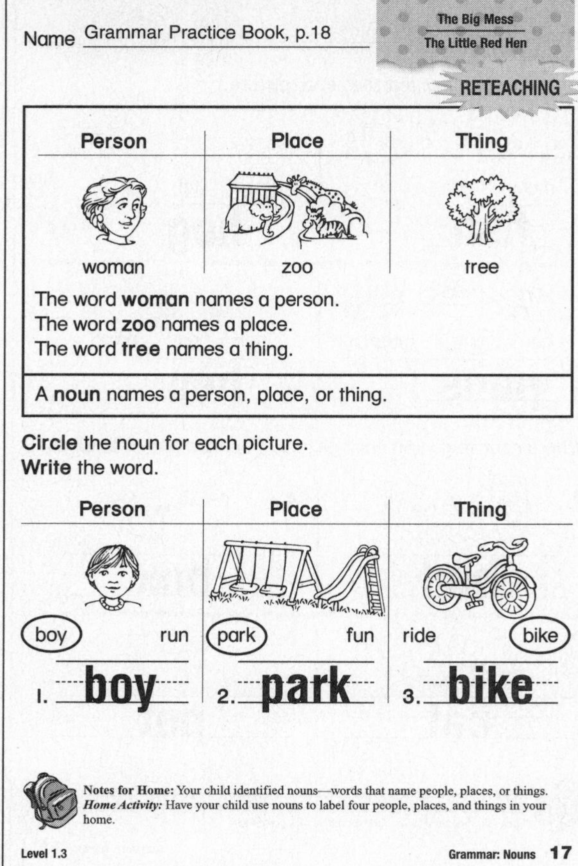

Name Grammar Practice Book, p.18

The Big Mess
The Little Red Hen

RETEACHING

| Person | Place | Thing |
|---|---|---|
| woman | zoo | tree |

The word **woman** names a person.
The word **zoo** names a place.
The word **tree** names a thing.

A **noun** names a person, place, or thing.

**Circle** the noun for each picture.
**Write** the word.

| Person | Place | Thing |
|---|---|---|
| (boy) run | (park) fun | ride (bike) |
| 1. boy | 2. park | 3. bike |

**Notes for Home:** Your child identified nouns—words that name people, places, or things. ***Home Activity:*** Have your child use nouns to label four people, places, and things in your home.

Level 1.3 Grammar: Nouns 17

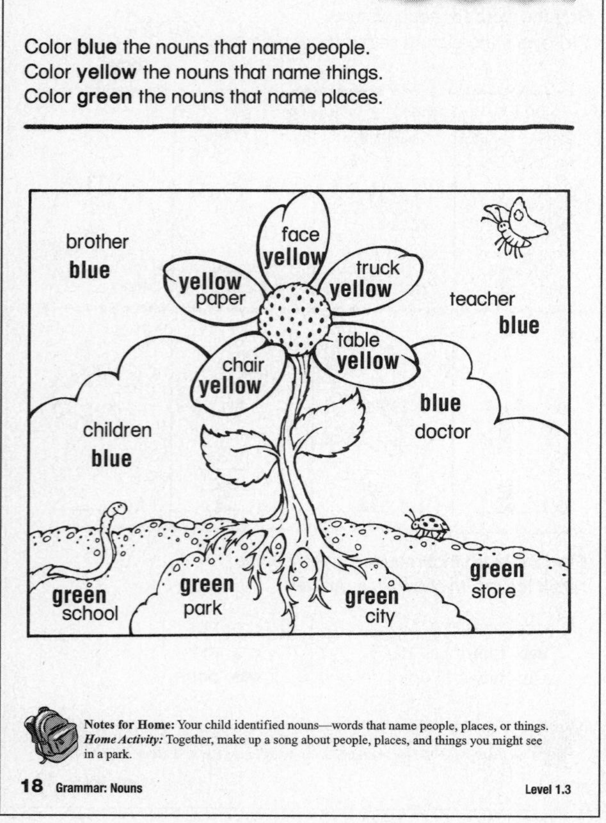

Name Grammar Practice Book, p.19

The Big Mess
The Little Red Hen

Color **blue** the nouns that name people.
Color **yellow** the nouns that name things.
Color **green** the nouns that name places.



**Notes for Home:** Your child identified nouns—words that name people, places, or things. ***Home Activity:*** Together, make up a song about people, places, and things you might see in a park.

18 Grammar: Nouns Level 1.3

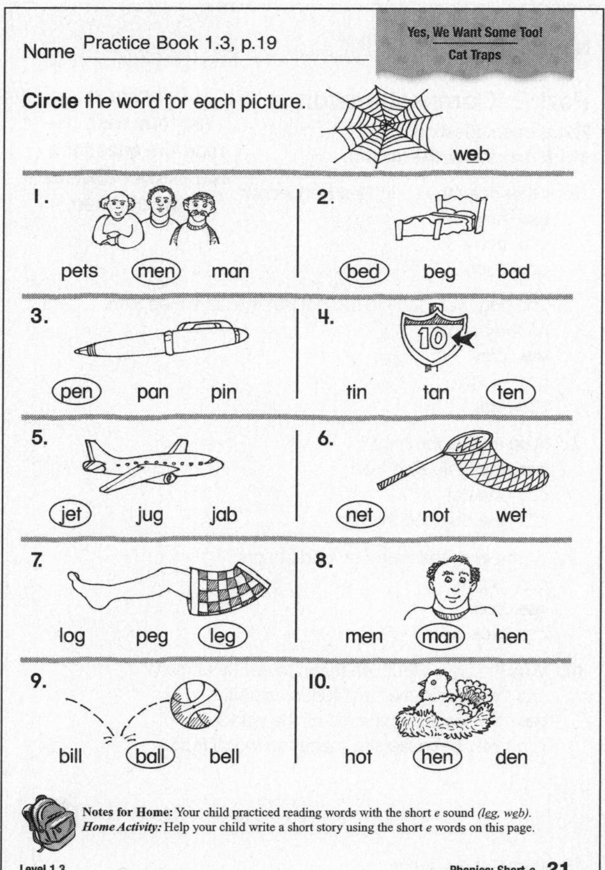

Name Practice Book 1.3, p.19

Yes, We Want Some Too!
Cat Traps

**Circle** the word for each picture.

web

1. pets (men) man
2. (bed) beg bad
3. (pen) pan pin
4. tin tan (ten)
5. (jet) jug jab
6. (net) not wet
7. log peg (leg)
8. men (man) hen
9. bill (ball) bell
10. hot (hen) den

**Notes for Home:** Your child practiced reading words with the short *e* sound *(leg, web).* ***Home Activity:*** Help your child write a short story using the short *e* words on this page.

Level 1.3 Phonics: Short *e* 21

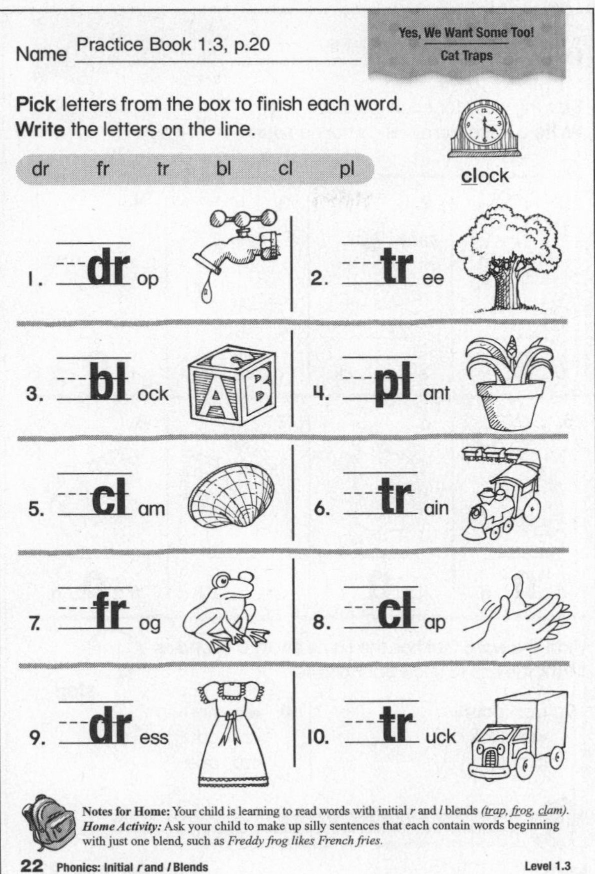

Yes, We Want Some Too!
Cat Traps

Name Practice Book 1.3, p.20

**Pick** letters from the box to finish each word.
**Write** the letters on the line.

dr fr tr bl cl pl

clock

1. dr op
2. tr ee
3. bl ock
4. pl ant
5. cl am
6. tr ain
7. fr og
8. cl ap
9. dr ess
10. tr uck

**Notes for Home:** Your child is learning to read words with initial *r* and *l* blends (*trap, frog, clam*). ***Home Activity:*** Ask your child to make up silly sentences that each contain words beginning with just one blend, such as *Freddy frog likes French fries.*

22 Phonics: Initial *r* and *l* Blends Level 1.3

Yes, We Want Some Too!
Cat Traps

Name Practice Book 1.3, p.21

**Pick** a word from the box to finish each sentence.
**Write** it on the line. Use each word only once.

for good some too want

1. Do you want to eat?
2. Yes, I want some food.
3. Here is some food for you.
4. That looks good.
5. I will eat some too.

**Notes for Home:** This week your child is learning to read the words *for, good, some, too,* and *want.* ***Home Activity:*** Get puppets or use washable markers to draw a face on closed fingers for puppets. Use the puppets to have a dialogue with your child using these new words.

Level 1.3 High-Frequency Words 23

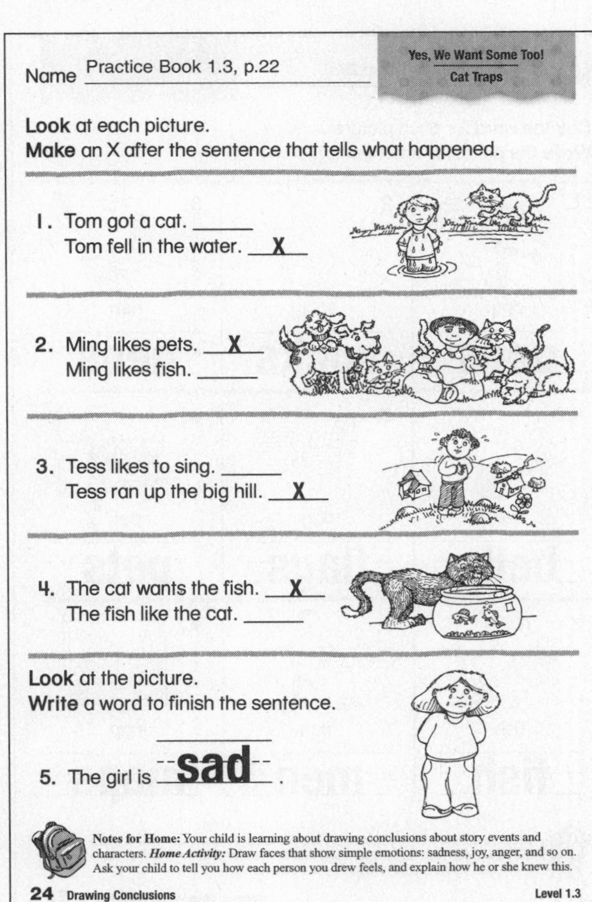

Yes, We Want Some Too!
Cat Traps

Name Practice Book 1.3, p.22

**Look** at each picture.
**Make** an X after the sentence that tells what happened.

1. Tom got a cat. ____
Tom fell in the water. X

2. Ming likes pets. X
Ming likes fish. ____

3. Tess likes to sing. ____
Tess ran up the big hill. X

4. The cat wants the fish. X
The fish like the cat. ____

**Look** at the picture.
**Write** a word to finish the sentence.

5. The girl is sad.

**Notes for Home:** Your child is learning about drawing conclusions about story events and characters. ***Home Activity:*** Draw faces that show simple emotions: sadness, joy, anger, and so on. Ask your child to tell you how each person you drew feels, and explain how he or she knew this.

24 Drawing Conclusions Level 1.3

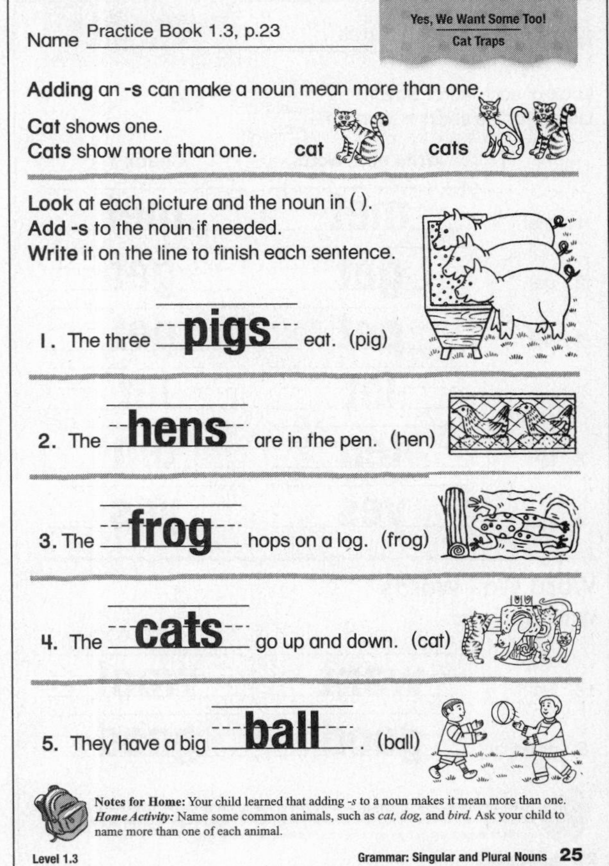

Yes, We Want Some Too!
Cat Traps

Name Practice Book 1.3, p.23

**Adding** an **-s** can make a noun mean more than one.

**Cat** shows one.
**Cats** show more than one. **cat** **cats**

**Look** at each picture and the noun in ( ).
**Add -s** to the noun if needed.
**Write** it on the line to finish each sentence.

1. The three pigs eat. (pig)
2. The hens are in the pen. (hen)
3. The frog hops on a log. (frog)
4. The cats go up and down. (cat)
5. They have a big ball. (ball)

**Notes for Home:** Your child learned that adding *-s* to a noun makes it mean more than one. ***Home Activity:*** Name some common animals, such as *cat, dog,* and *bird.* Ask your child to name more than one of each animal.

Level 1.3 Grammar: Singular and Plural Nouns 25

Name Practice Book 1.3, p.24

Yes, We Want Some Too!
Cat Traps

**Pick** a word from the box to finish each sentence.
**Write** it in the puzzle.

for good meow some too want

1. The fish is ______ the cat.
2. "______!" said the cat.
3. I will give the cat ______ of the fish.

1. for
2. meow
3. some

4. I ______ to play!
5. He likes to play ______!
6. We will have a ______ time.

4. want
5. too
6. good

Notes for Home: Your child solved puzzles using the words *for, good, meow, some, too,* and *want.* ***Home Activity:*** Say each word and ask your child to use it in a sentence. Help your child write each sentence.

26 Vocabulary/High-Frequency Words Level 1.3

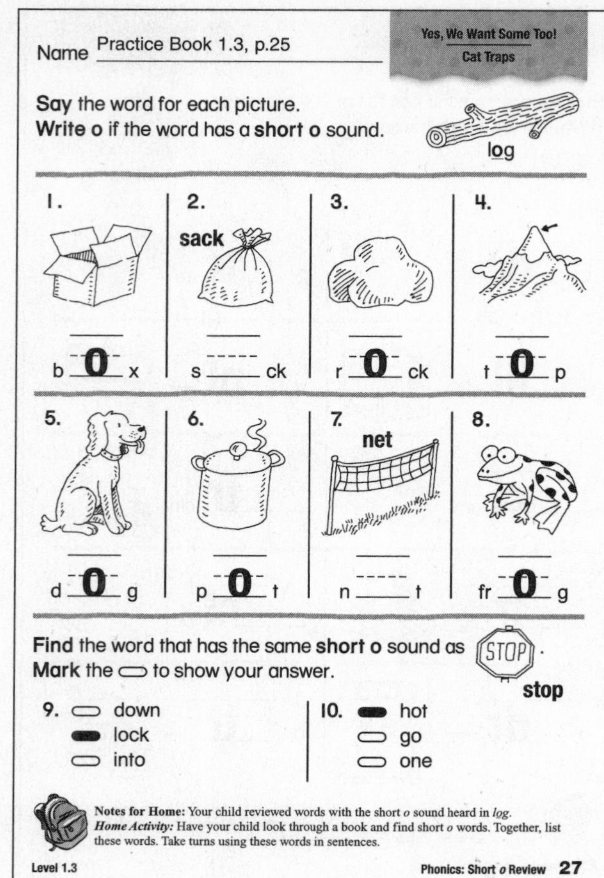

Name Practice Book 1.3, p.25

Yes, We Want Some Too!
Cat Traps

**Say** the word for each picture.
**Write o** if the word has a **short o** sound.

log

1. b o x
2. sack s ___ ck
3. r o ck
4. t o p
5. d o g
6. p o t
7. net n ___ t
8. fr o g

**Find** the word that has the same **short o** sound as stop. **Mark** the ⬭ to show your answer.

9. ⬭ down
   ⬬ lock
   ⬭ into

10. ⬬ hot
    ⬭ go
    ⬭ one

Notes for Home: Your child reviewed words with the short *o* sound heard in *log.* ***Home Activity:*** Have your child look through a book and find short *o* words. Together, list these words. Take turns using these words in sentences.

Level 1.3 Phonics: Short *o* Review 27

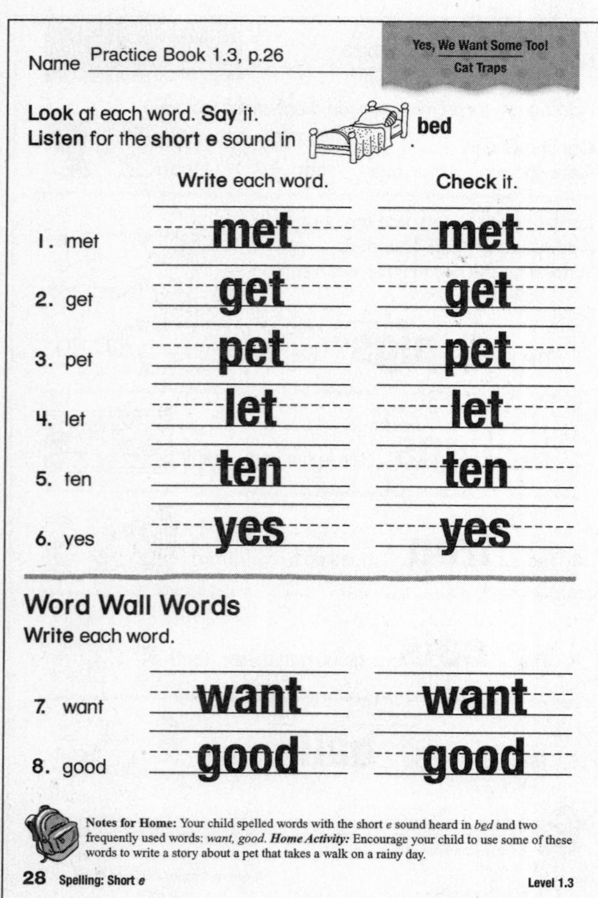

Name Practice Book 1.3, p.26

Yes, We Want Some Too!
Cat Traps

**Look** at each word. **Say** it.
**Listen** for the **short e** sound in bed.

| | Write each word. | Check it. |
|---|---|---|
| 1. met | met | met |
| 2. get | get | get |
| 3. pet | pet | pet |
| 4. let | let | let |
| 5. ten | ten | ten |
| 6. yes | yes | yes |

**Word Wall Words**
**Write** each word.

| | | |
|---|---|---|
| 7. want | want | want |
| 8. good | good | good |

Notes for Home: Your child spelled words with the short *e* sound heard in *bed* and two frequently used words: *want, good.* ***Home Activity:*** Encourage your child to use some of these words to write a story about a pet that takes a walk on a rainy day.

28 Spelling: Short *e* Level 1.3

Name Practice Book 1.3, p.27

Yes, We Want Some Too!
Cat Traps

**Say** the word for each picture.
**Write** the plural for each word.

1. dog — dogs
2. sock — socks
3. hen — hens
4. bell — bells
5. flag — flags
6. pet — pets
7. fish — fish
8. man — men
9. map — maps

Notes for Home: Your child reviewed nouns that become plural when just *-s* is added and irregular plurals like *men* and *fish.* ***Home Activity:*** Look at a picture book with your child. List several nouns. Include both singular and plural nouns.

Level 1.3 Grammar: Singular and Plural Nouns 29

Name Practice Book 1.3, p.29

Yes, We Want Some Too!
Cat Traps

## Part 1: Vocabulary

**Read** each sentence.
**Mark** the ⬭ for the word that fits.

1. The cats ______ to eat.
   - ⬭ make
   - ⬬ want
   - ⬭ sing
2. The cats get ______ chow.
   - ⬭ on
   - ⬬ some
   - ⬭ into
3. Now they meow ______ more.
   - ⬭ how
   - ⬭ away
   - ⬬ for
4. The chow was ______ .
   - ⬬ good
   - ⬭ them
   - ⬭ happy
5. This cat is ______ fat!
   - ⬭ all
   - ⬭ by
   - ⬬ too

GO ON

Level 1.3 Selection Test: Vocabulary 31

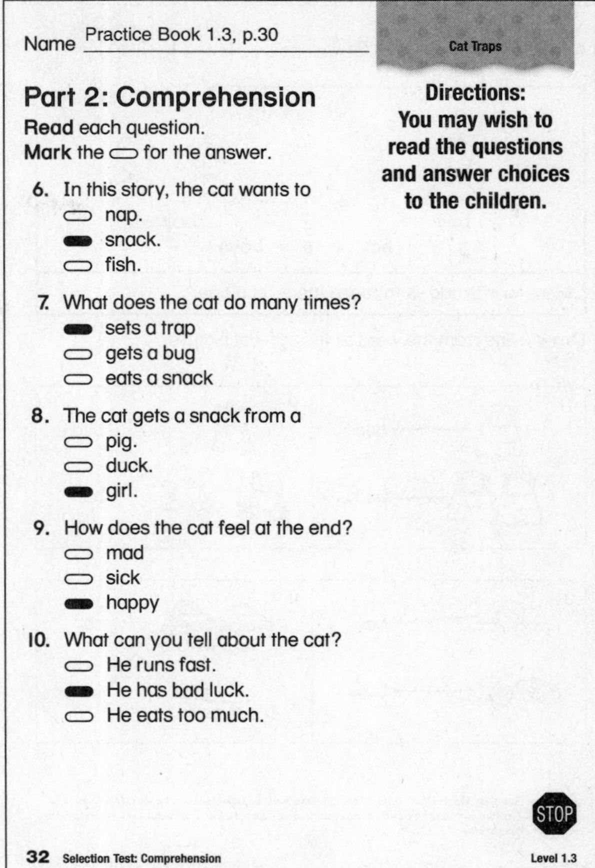

Name Practice Book 1.3, p.30

Cat Traps

## Part 2: Comprehension

**Read** each question.
**Mark** the ⬭ for the answer.

**Directions: You may wish to read the questions and answer choices to the children.**

6. In this story, the cat wants to
   - ⬭ nap.
   - ⬬ snack.
   - ⬭ fish.
7. What does the cat do many times?
   - ⬬ sets a trap
   - ⬭ gets a bug
   - ⬭ eats a snack
8. The cat gets a snack from a
   - ⬭ pig.
   - ⬭ duck.
   - ⬬ girl.
9. How does the cat feel at the end?
   - ⬭ mad
   - ⬭ sick
   - ⬬ happy
10. What can you tell about the cat?
    - ⬭ He runs fast.
    - ⬬ He has bad luck.
    - ⬭ He eats too much.

STOP

32 Selection Test: Comprehension Level 1.3

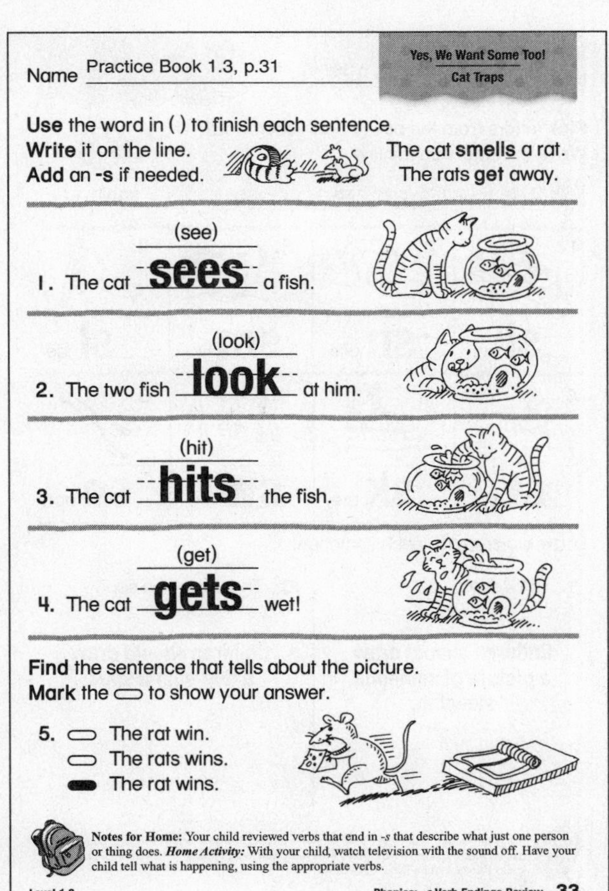

Name Practice Book 1.3, p.31

Yes, We Want Some Too!
Cat Traps

**Use** the word in ( ) to finish each sentence.
**Write** it on the line.
**Add** an **-s** if needed.

The cat **smells** a rat.
The rats **get** away.

1. (see) The cat **sees** a fish.
2. (look) The two fish **look** at him.
3. (hit) The cat **hits** the fish.
4. (get) The cat **gets** wet!

**Find** the sentence that tells about the picture.
**Mark** the ⬭ to show your answer.

5. 
   - ⬭ The rat win.
   - ⬭ The rats wins.
   - ⬬ The rat wins.

**Notes for Home:** Your child reviewed verbs that end in *-s* that describe what just one person or thing does. ***Home Activity:*** With your child, watch television with the sound off. Have your child tell what is happening, using the appropriate verbs.

Level 1.3 Phonics: -s Verb Endings Review 33

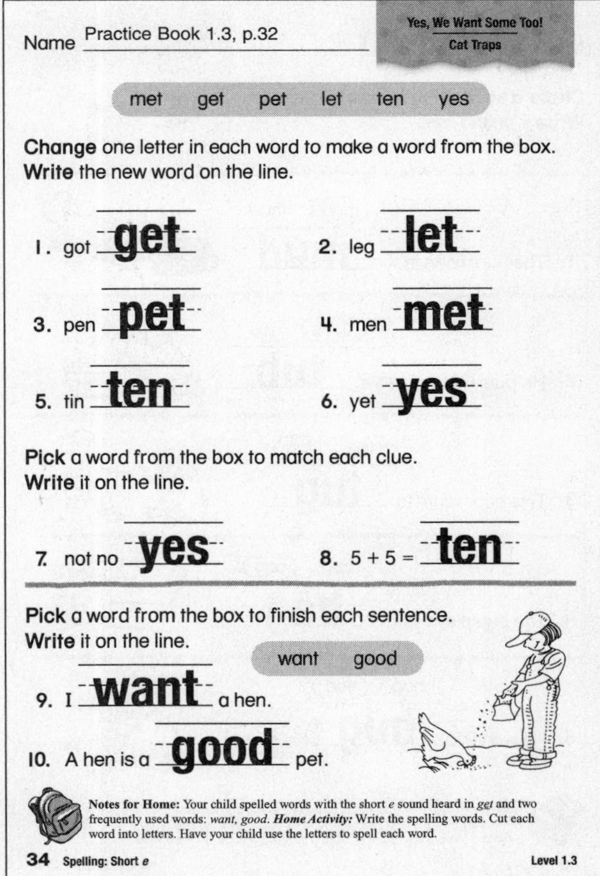

Name Practice Book 1.3, p.32

Yes, We Want Some Too!
Cat Traps

met get pet let ten yes

**Change** one letter in each word to make a word from the box.
**Write** the new word on the line.

1. got **get**
2. leg **let**
3. pen **pet**
4. men **met**
5. tin **ten**
6. yet **yes**

**Pick** a word from the box to match each clue.
**Write** it on the line.

7. not no **yes**
8. 5 + 5 = **ten**

**Pick** a word from the box to finish each sentence.
**Write** it on the line.

want good

9. I **want** a hen.
10. A hen is a **good** pet.

**Notes for Home:** Your child spelled words with the short *e* sound heard in *get* and two frequently used words: *want, good.* ***Home Activity:*** Write the spelling words. Cut each word into letters. Have your child use the letters to spell each word.

34 Spelling: Short *e* Level 1.3

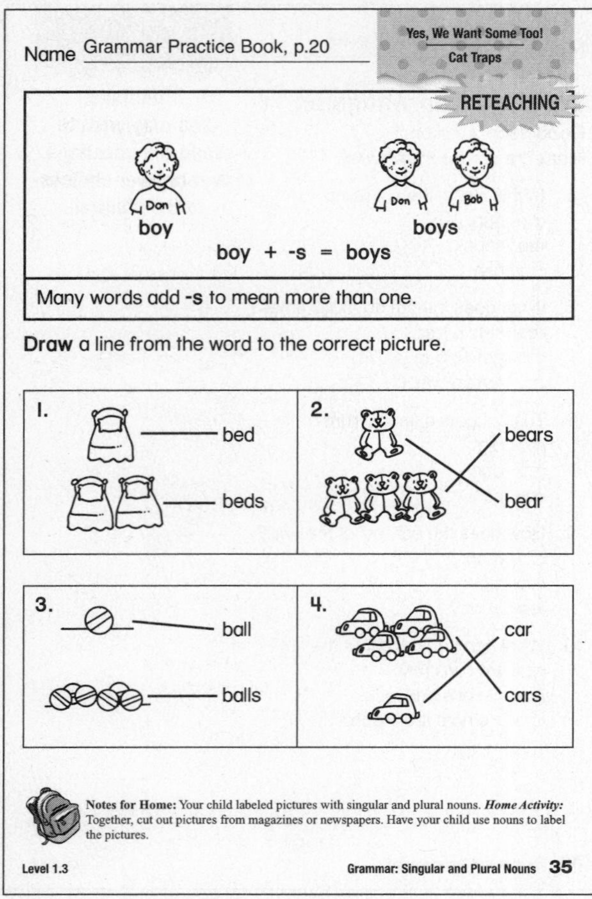

Name Grammar Practice Book, p.20

Yes, We Want Some Too!
Cat Traps

RETEACHING

boy

boys

boy + -s = boys

Many words add **-s** to mean more than one.

**Draw** a line from the word to the correct picture.

| 1. bed / beds | 2. bears / bear |
|---|---|
| 3. ball / balls | 4. car / cars |

**Notes for Home:** Your child labeled pictures with singular and plural nouns. ***Home Activity:*** Together, cut out pictures from magazines or newspapers. Have your child use nouns to label the pictures.

Level 1.3 Grammar: Singular and Plural Nouns 35

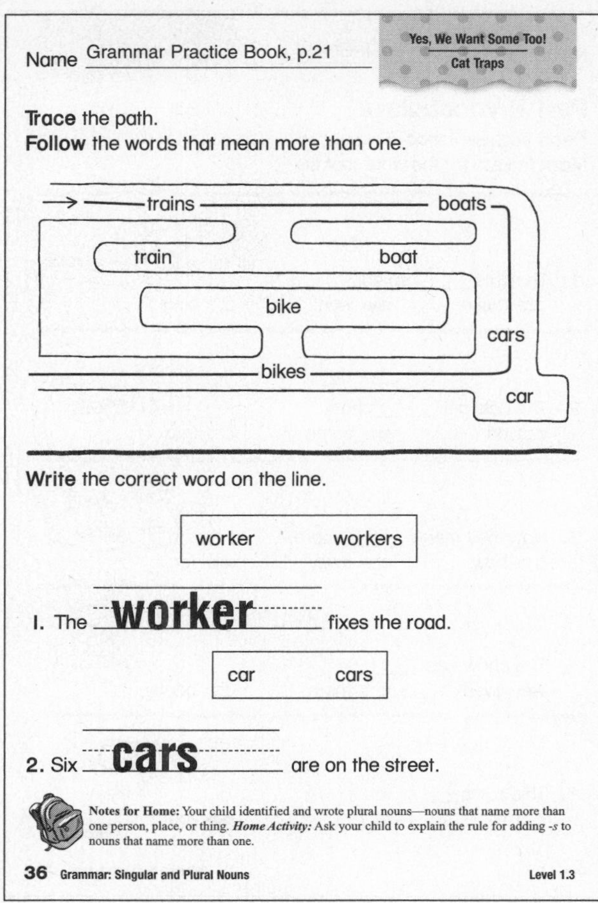

Name Grammar Practice Book, p.21

Yes, We Want Some Too!
Cat Traps

**Trace** the path.
**Follow** the words that mean more than one.

trains boats train boat bike cars bikes car

**Write** the correct word on the line.

worker workers

1. The **worker** fixes the road.

car cars

2. Six **cars** are on the street.

**Notes for Home:** Your child identified and wrote plural nouns—nouns that name more than one person, place, or thing. ***Home Activity:*** Ask your child to explain the rule for adding *-s* to nouns that name more than one.

36 Grammar: Singular and Plural Nouns Level 1.3

Name Practice Book 1.3, p.35

My Buddy, Stan
Biscuit

**Circle** a word to finish each sentence.
**Write** it on the line.

pup

1. mud mad — The pup walks in the **mud**.
2. tub tab — He puts the pup in the **tub**.
3. tag tug — This pup wants to **tug**.
4. bug bag — The pup plays with a **bag**.
5. hog hug — He wants to **hug** his pup.

**Notes for Home:** Your child practiced reading words with the short *u* sound heard in *pup*. ***Home Activity:*** Work with your child to write a story using as many of the short *u* words listed above as possible. Draw pictures to go along with the story you write.

Level 1.3 Phonics: Short *u* 39

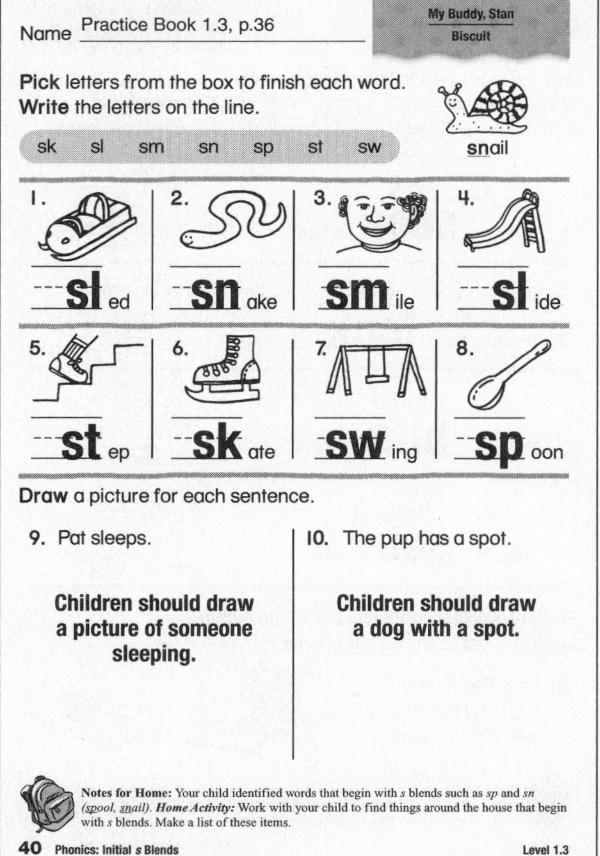

Name Practice Book 1.3, p.36

My Buddy, Stan
Biscuit

**Pick** letters from the box to finish each word.
**Write** the letters on the line.

sk sl sm sn sp st sw

snail

| 1. **sl**ed | 2. **sn**ake | 3. **sm**ile | 4. **sl**ide |
|---|---|---|---|
| 5. **st**ep | 6. **sk**ate | 7. **sw**ing | 8. **sp**oon |

**Draw** a picture for each sentence.

9. Pat sleeps.

**Children should draw a picture of someone sleeping.**

10. The pup has a spot.

**Children should draw a dog with a spot.**

**Notes for Home:** Your child identified words that begin with *s* blends such as *sp* and *sn* (*spool, snail*). ***Home Activity:*** Work with your child to find things around the house that begin with *s* blends. Make a list of these items.

40 Phonics: Initial *s* Blends Level 1.3

Name Practice Book 1.3, p.37

My Buddy, Stan
Biscuit

**Pick** a word from the box to finish each sentence.
**Write** it on the line. Use each word only once.

jump more sleep time with

1. It is **time** for bed.
2. Tim wants to **sleep** .
3. The pup wants to **jump** .
4. The pup gets one **more** hug.
5. The pup will sleep **with** Tim.

**Notes for Home:** This week your child is learning to read the words *jump, more, sleep, time,* and *with. **Home Activity:*** Together with your child, write a short poem about a new puppy. Use as many of the words on this page as possible.

Level 1.3 High-Frequency Words 41

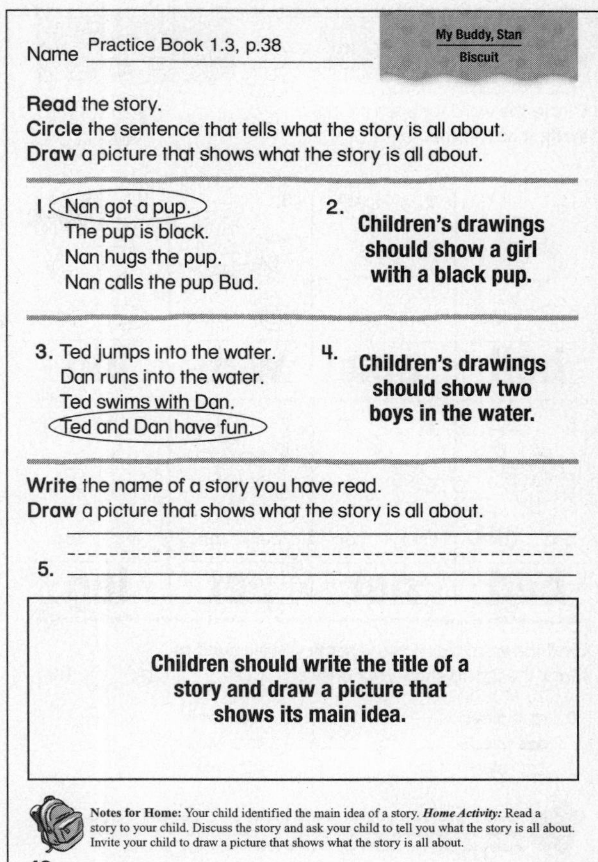

Name Practice Book 1.3, p.38

My Buddy, Stan
Biscuit

**Read** the story.
**Circle** the sentence that tells what the story is all about.
**Draw** a picture that shows what the story is all about.

1. (Nan got a pup.)
The pup is black.
Nan hugs the pup.
Nan calls the pup Bud.

2. **Children's drawings should show a girl with a black pup.**

3. Ted jumps into the water.
Dan runs into the water.
Ted swims with Dan.
(Ted and Dan have fun.)

4. **Children's drawings should show two boys in the water.**

**Write** the name of a story you have read.
**Draw** a picture that shows what the story is all about.

5.

**Children should write the title of a story and draw a picture that shows its main idea.**

**Notes for Home:** Your child identified the main idea of a story. ***Home Activity:*** Read a story to your child. Discuss the story and ask your child to tell you what the story is all about. Invite your child to draw a picture that shows what the story is all about.

42 Main Idea Level 1.3

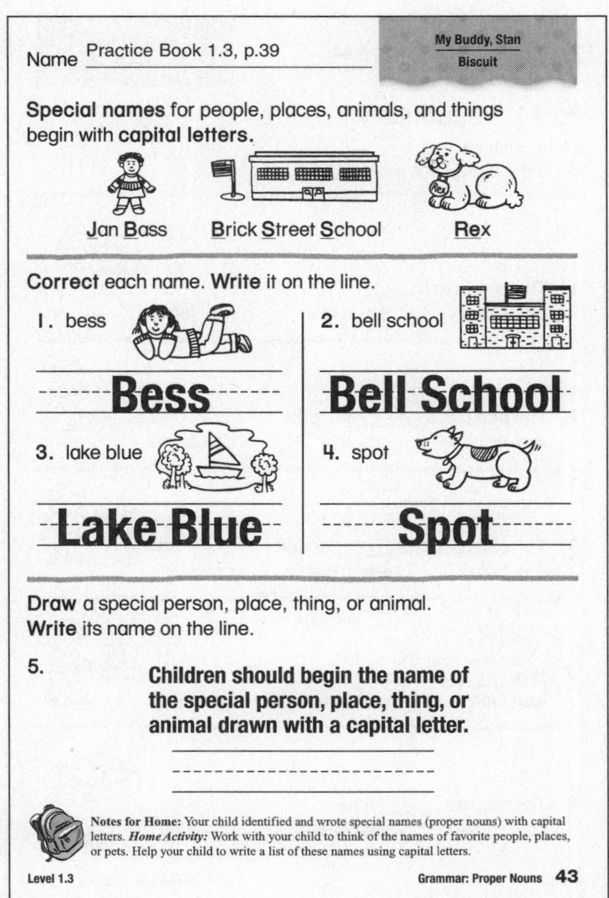

Name Practice Book 1.3, p.39

My Buddy, Stan
Biscuit

**Special names** for people, places, animals, and things begin with **capital letters.**

Jan Bass Brick Street School Rex

**Correct** each name. **Write** it on the line.

1. bess **Bess**
2. bell school **Bell School**
3. lake blue **Lake Blue**
4. spot **Spot**

**Draw** a special person, place, thing, or animal.
**Write** its name on the line.

5. **Children should begin the name of the special person, place, thing, or animal drawn with a capital letter.**

**Notes for Home:** Your child identified and wrote special names (proper nouns) with capital letters. ***Home Activity:*** Work with your child to think of the names of favorite people, places, or pets. Help your child to write a list of these names using capital letters.

Level 1.3 Grammar: Proper Nouns 43

Name Practice Book 1.3, p.40

My Buddy, Stan
Biscuit

**Pick** a word from the box to match each clue.
**Write** the words in the puzzles.

hear jump more sleep time with

1. **jump**
2. The pup wants one ______ hug. **more**
3. **sleep**
4. Can I go ______ you? **with**
5. It is ______ for bed. **time**
6. **hear**

**Notes for Home:** Your child completed puzzles using words that he or she learned to read this week. ***Home Activity:*** Work with your child to write sentences using these words. Have him or her read the sentences aloud to you.

44 Vocabulary/High-Frequency Words Level 1.3

Name Practice Book 1.3, p.41

My Buddy, Stan
Biscuit

**Circle** the word for each picture.
**Write** it on the line.

vet

1. (bell) bill — **bell**
2. pin (pen) — **pen**
3. (web) won — **web**
4. (jug) jet — **jug**
5. bad (bed) — **bed**
6. (net) not — **net**
7. (pet) pit — **pet**
8. (leg) log — **leg**

**Find** the word that has the same vowel sound as hen
**Mark** the ⊂⊃ to show your answer.

9. ⊂⊃ sleep ● sled ⊂⊃ slap

10. ● well ⊂⊃ wall ⊂⊃ we

**Notes for Home:** Your child reviewed words with the short *e* sound heard in *vet*. ***Home Activity:*** Help your child write a silly poem in which all the rhyming words have the short *e* sound. Encourage your child to read the poem aloud to other family members.

Level 1.3 Phonics: Short *e* Review 45

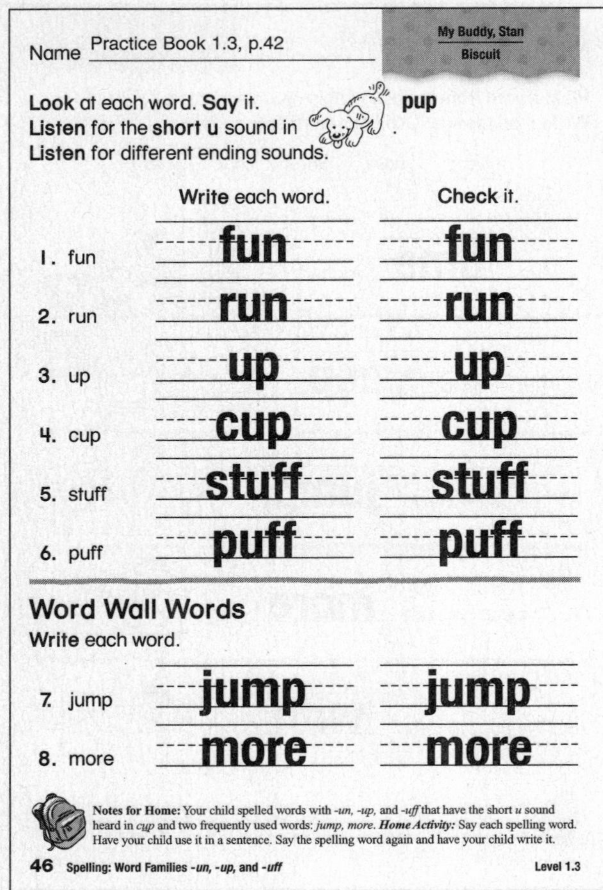

Name Practice Book 1.3, p.42

My Buddy, Stan
Biscuit

**Look** at each word. **Say** it.
**Listen** for the **short u** sound in pup.
**Listen** for different ending sounds.

| | Write each word. | Check it. |
|---|---|---|
| 1. fun | fun | fun |
| 2. run | run | run |
| 3. up | up | up |
| 4. cup | cup | cup |
| 5. stuff | stuff | stuff |
| 6. puff | puff | puff |

**Word Wall Words**
**Write** each word.

| | | |
|---|---|---|
| 7. jump | jump | jump |
| 8. more | more | more |

**Notes for Home:** Your child spelled words with *-un, -up,* and *-uff* that have the short *u* sound heard in *cup* and two frequently used words: *jump, more.* ***Home Activity:*** Say each spelling word. Have your child use it in a sentence. Say the spelling word again and have your child write it.

46 Spelling: Word Families *-un, -up,* and *-uff* Level 1.3

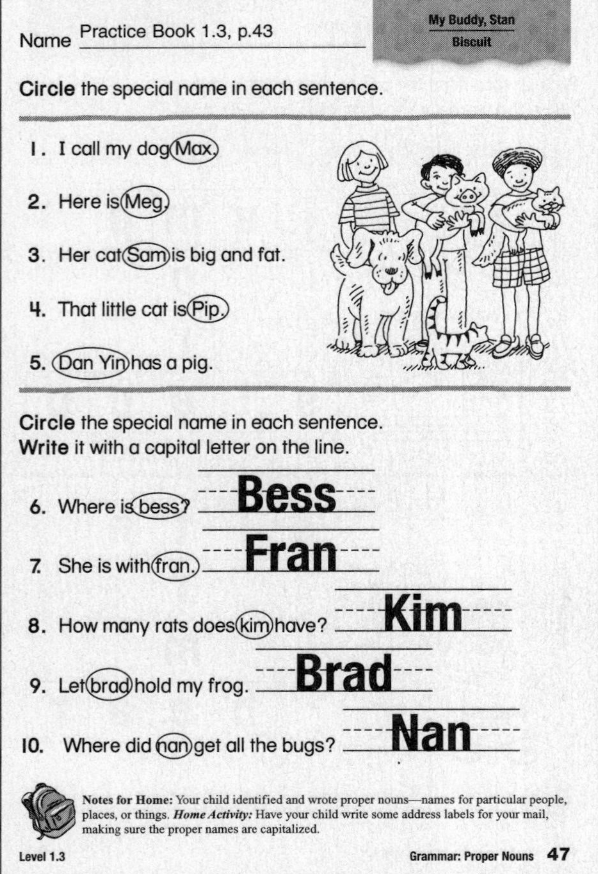

Name Practice Book 1.3, p.43

My Buddy, Stan
Biscuit

**Circle** the special name in each sentence.

1. I call my dog (Max).
2. Here is (Meg).
3. Her cat (Sam) is big and fat.
4. That little cat is (Pip).
5. (Dan Yin) has a pig.

**Circle** the special name in each sentence.
**Write** it with a capital letter on the line.

6. Where is (bess)? **Bess**
7. She is with (fran). **Fran**
8. How many rats does (kim) have? **Kim**
9. Let (brad) hold my frog. **Brad**
10. Where did (nan) get all the bugs? **Nan**

**Notes for Home:** Your child identified and wrote proper nouns—names for particular people, places, or things. ***Home Activity:*** Have your child write some address labels for your mail, making sure the proper names are capitalized.

Level 1.3 Grammar: Proper Nouns 47

Name Practice Book 1.3, p.44

My Buddy, Stan
Biscuit

**Part 1: Vocabulary**
**Read** each sentence.
**Mark** the ⊂⊃ for the word that fits.

1. The pup likes to ______ .
⊂⊃ more ⊂⊃ make ● jump

2. The pup plays ______ the girl.
● with ⊂⊃ this ⊂⊃ some

3. The pup gets one ______ snack.
⊂⊃ help ● more ⊂⊃ now

4. It is ______ for bed.
● time ⊂⊃ jump ⊂⊃ sleep

5. The pup will ______ now.
⊂⊃ some ● sleep ⊂⊃ time

GO ON

Level 1.3 Selection Test: Vocabulary 49

Name Practice Book 1.3, p.46

Biscuit

## Part 2: Comprehension

**Read** each question.
**Mark** the ⬭ for the answer.

**Directions: You may wish to read the questions and answer choices to the children.**

6. What is it time for Biscuit to do?
   - ⬭ play
   - ⬭ eat
   - ⬬ sleep
7. Biscuit does not go to bed. Biscuit wants to
   - ⬭ eat.
   - ⬬ hear a story.
   - ⬭ kiss a doll.
8. How is Biscuit like a baby?
   - ⬭ He can say "Woof."
   - ⬭ He can sing.
   - ⬬ He likes hugs.
9. How does the story end?
   - ⬭ The girl plays.
   - ⬬ Biscuit sleeps.
   - ⬭ Biscuit runs away.
10. What is a good name for this story?
    - ⬭ "A Happy Girl"
    - ⬬ "Time for Bed"
    - ⬭ "One More Walk"

STOP

50 Selection Test: Comprehension Level 1.3

Name Practice Book 1.3, p.47

My Buddy, Stan
Biscuit

**Circle** the word for each picture.
**Write** it on the line.

doll

| 1. | 2. | 3. | 4. |
| --- | --- | --- | --- |
| (puff) pull | snip (sniff) | stuns (stuff) | miss (mitt) |
| puff | sniff | stuff | mitt |

| 5. | 6. | 7. | 8. |
| --- | --- | --- | --- |
| (kiss) kick | bat (ball) | tops (toss) | (buzz) bull |
| kiss | ball | toss | buzz |

**Find** the word that has the same ending sound as well.
**Mark** the ⬭ to show your answer.

9. ⬭ vet
   ⬬ still
   ⬭ walk

10. ⬬ smell
    ⬭ black
    ⬭ yellow

**Notes for Home:** Your child reviewed words that have double final consonants such as *doll.* ***Home Activity:*** Have your child collect words like these from signs and stories and then write the found words in lists. Invite him or her to keep a separate list for each letter pair.

Level 1.3 Phonics: Double Final Consonants Review 51

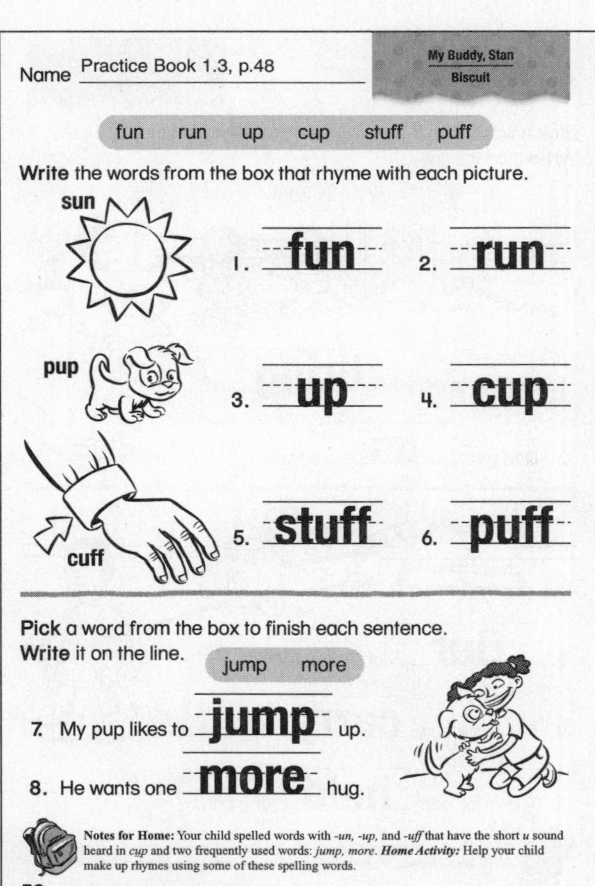
Name Practice Book 1.3, p.48

My Buddy, Stan
Biscuit

fun run up cup stuff puff

**Write** the words from the box that rhyme with each picture.

sun
1. fun 2. run

pup
3. up 4. cup

cuff
5. stuff 6. puff

**Pick** a word from the box to finish each sentence.
**Write** it on the line.

jump more

7. My pup likes to jump up.
8. He wants one more hug.

**Notes for Home:** Your child spelled words with *-un, -up,* and *-uff* that have the short *u* sound heard in *cup* and two frequently used words: *jump, more.* ***Home Activity:*** Help your child make up rhymes using some of these spelling words.

52 Spelling: Word Families *-un, -up,* and *-uff* Level 1.3

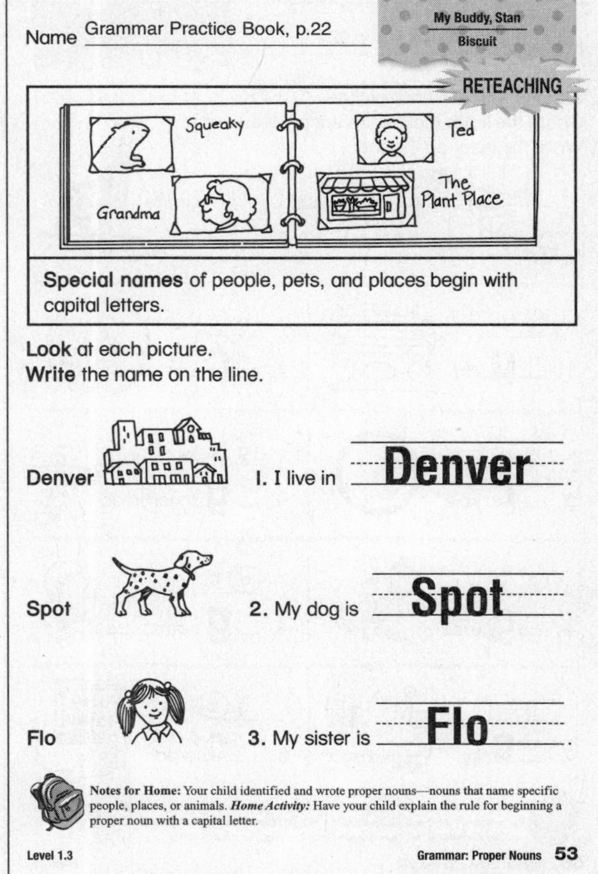
Name Grammar Practice Book, p.22

My Buddy, Stan
Biscuit

RETEACHING



**Special names** of people, pets, and places begin with capital letters.

**Look** at each picture.
**Write** the name on the line.

Denver 1. I live in Denver.

Spot 2. My dog is Spot.

Flo 3. My sister is Flo.

**Notes for Home:** Your child identified and wrote proper nouns—nouns that name specific people, places, or animals. ***Home Activity:*** Have your child explain the rule for beginning a proper noun with a capital letter.

Level 1.3 Grammar: Proper Nouns 53

My Buddy, Stan / Biscuit

Name Grammar Practice Book, p.23

**Circle** the special name in each box.
**Write** one special name in each sentence.

| boy | (Bob) | town | (Salem) |
|---|---|---|---|
| (Fluffy) | cat | (Aunt Kate) | woman |

1. **Bob** sits on a chair.

2. **Fluffy** runs around the house.

3. They live in **Salem**.

**Notes for Home:** Your child identified and wrote proper nouns. ***Home Activity:*** Have your child draw a picture of family members. Have him or her use proper nouns to label the drawing. Make sure your child uses capital letters to write proper nouns.

54 Grammar: Proper Nouns Level 1.3

Trucks / Communities

Name Practice Book 1.3, p.51

**Circle** a word to finish each sentence.
**Write** it on the line.

duck

1. Here is the **bus**. (bun bat (bus))

2. Rob sees the ducks **tug**. (hug (tug) tag)

3. Rob sees the ducks **run**. ((run) ran rip)

4. One duck fell in the **mud**. (mad (mud) bud)

5. Now the ducks have **fun**! (fan fin (fun))

**Notes for Home:** Your child practiced reading and writing words with the short *u* sound heard in *bug* and *duck*. ***Home Activity:*** Work together to write a poem using as many of the short *u* words shown above as you can.

Level 1.3 Phonics: Short *u* 57

Trucks / Communities

Name Practice Book 1.3, p.52

**Say** the word for each picture.
**Circle** the letter that begins each word.
**Write** the letter on the line.

circus giraffe

1. ((g) c) **g** ym
2. (g (c)) **c** ent
3. (g (c)) **c** ircle
4. ((g) c) **g** ingerbread
5. ((g) c) **g** erbil
6. ((g) c) **g** erms
7. (g (c)) **c** ity
8. (g (c)) **c** ereal



**Notes for Home:** Your child practiced writing words that begin with *c* and *g* that stand for the /s/ sound in *circus* and the /j/ sound in *giraffe*. ***Home Activity:*** Ask your child to say the *c* /s/ and *g* /j/ words on this page out loud, emphasizing the initial sounds.

58 Phonics: Initial *c* /s/ and *g* /j/ Level 1.3

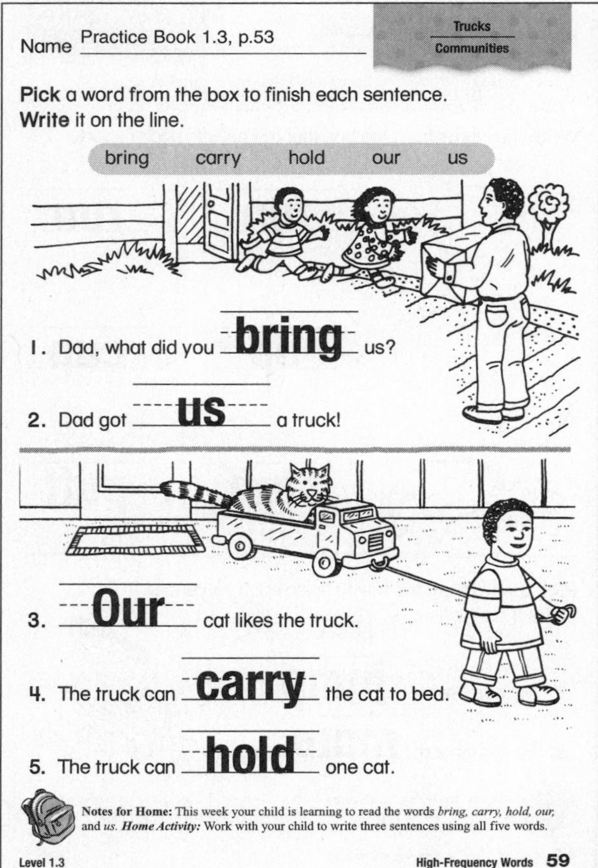

Trucks / Communities

Name Practice Book 1.3, p.53

**Pick** a word from the box to finish each sentence.
**Write** it on the line.

bring carry hold our us

1. Dad, what did you **bring** us?

2. Dad got **us** a truck!

3. **Our** cat likes the truck.

4. The truck can **carry** the cat to bed.

5. The truck can **hold** one cat.

**Notes for Home:** This week your child is learning to read the words *bring, carry, hold, our,* and *us*. ***Home Activity:*** Work with your child to write three sentences using all five words.

Level 1.3 High-Frequency Words 59

Name Practice Book 1.3, p.54

Trucks
Communities

**Look** at the pictures. **Read** the sentence.
**Circle** the word in ( ) that tells how the objects are alike.

fish cat pup

1. A fish, a cat, and a pup are all (pets, red).

cup tub glass

2. A cup, a tub, and a glass all hold (frogs, water).

bus truck van

3. You (skip, go) in a bus, a truck, and a van.

bat ball block

4. You (play, sing) with a bat, a ball, and a block.

ham plum nut

5. You (eat, walk) a ham, a plum, and a nut.

**Notes for Home:** Your child is learning about classifying—grouping things belonging together. *Home Activity:* Draw three smiling faces and one sad one. Ask your child which one does not belong and why.

60 Classifying Level 1.3

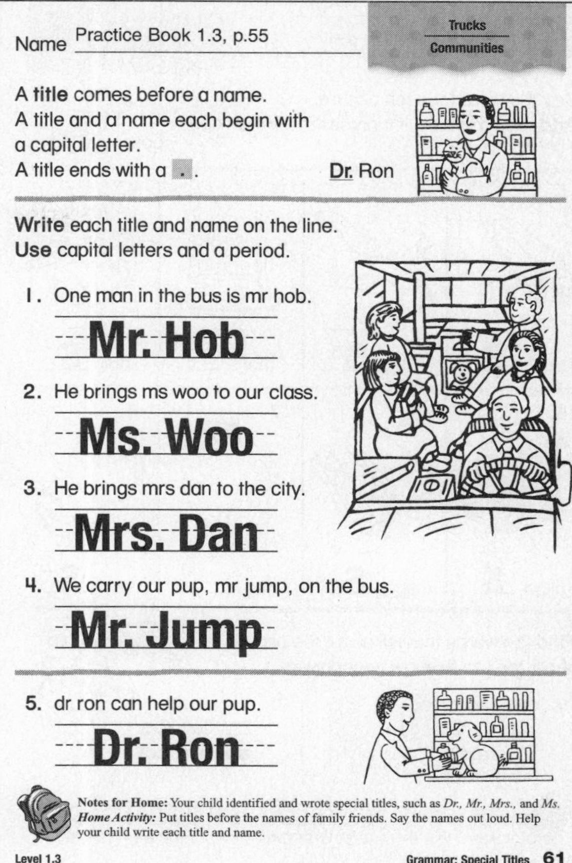

Name Practice Book 1.3, p.55

Trucks
Communities

A **title** comes before a name.
A title and a name each begin with a capital letter.
A title ends with a **.**

Dr. Ron

**Write** each title and name on the line.
**Use** capital letters and a period.

1. One man in the bus is mr hob.

**Mr. Hob**

2. He brings ms woo to our class.

**Ms. Woo**

3. He brings mrs dan to the city.

**Mrs. Dan**

4. We carry our pup, mr jump, on the bus.

**Mr. Jump**

5. dr ron can help our pup.

**Dr. Ron**

**Notes for Home:** Your child identified and wrote special titles, such as *Dr., Mr., Mrs.,* and *Ms. Home Activity:* Put titles before the names of family friends. Say the names out loud. Help your child write each title and name.

Level 1.3 Grammar: Special Titles 61

Name Practice Book 1.3, p.56

Trucks
Communities

**Pick** the word from the box to finish each sentence.
**Write** it on the line. Use each word only once.

bring build carry hold our us

1. Look at **us** go.
2. We are in **our** van.
3. Dad will **bring** us to the water.
4. We **carry** a cup, a ball, and a truck.
5. The cup can **hold** water.
6. We play and **build** a city.

**Notes for Home:** Your child used newly learned words to fill in the blanks in a story. *Home Activity:* Say each vocabulary word aloud, and have your child write it down.

62 Vocabulary/High-Frequency Words Level 1.3

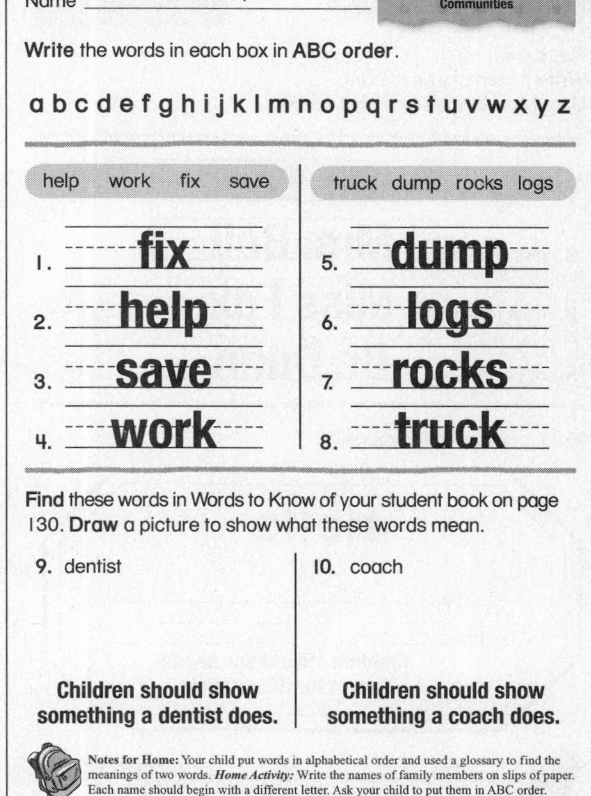

Name Practice Book 1.3, p.57

Trucks
Communities

**Write** the words in each box in **ABC order**.

a b c d e f g h i j k l m n o p q r s t u v w x y z

help work fix save

1. **fix**
2. **help**
3. **save**
4. **work**

truck dump rocks logs

5. **dump**
6. **logs**
7. **rocks**
8. **truck**

**Find** these words in Words to Know of your student book on page 130. **Draw** a picture to show what these words mean.

9. dentist

**Children should show something a dentist does.**

10. coach

**Children should show something a coach does.**

**Notes for Home:** Your child put words in alphabetical order and used a glossary to find the meanings of two words. *Home Activity:* Write the names of family members on slips of paper. Each name should begin with a different letter. Ask your child to put them in ABC order.

Level 1.3 Research and Study Skills: Alphabetical Order/Glossary 63

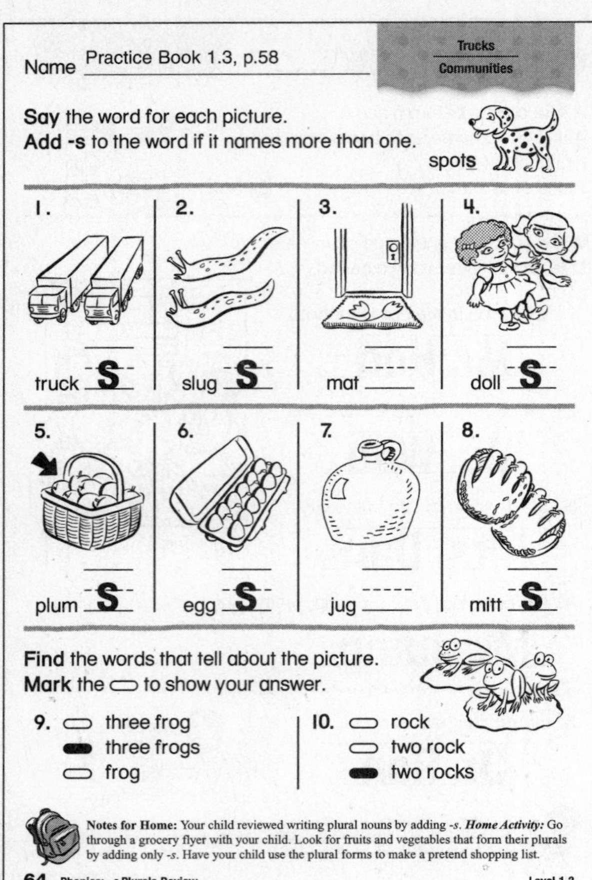
Name Practice Book 1.3, p.58

Trucks
Communities

**Say** the word for each picture.
**Add -s** to the word if it names more than one.

spots

1. truck **s**
2. slug **s**
3. mat
4. doll **s**
5. plum **s**
6. egg **s**
7. jug
8. mitt **s**

**Find** the words that tell about the picture.
**Mark** the ⬭ to show your answer.

9. ⬭ three frog
   ⬬ three frogs
   ⬭ frog

10. ⬭ rock
    ⬭ two rock
    ⬬ two rocks

**Notes for Home:** Your child reviewed writing plural nouns by adding *-s*. ***Home Activity:*** Go through a grocery flyer with your child. Look for fruits and vegetables that form their plurals by adding only *-s*. Have your child use the plural forms to make a pretend shopping list.

64 Phonics: *-s* Plurals Review Level 1.3

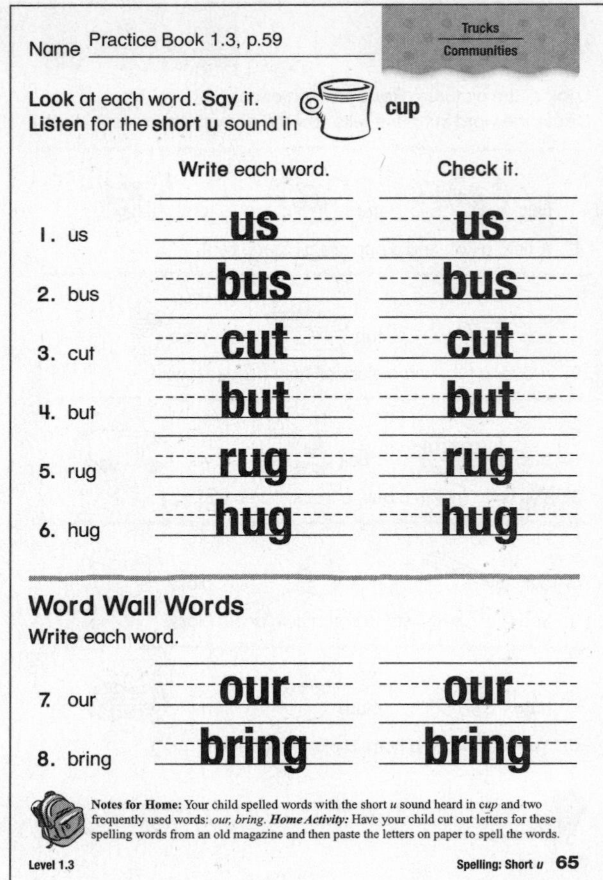
Name Practice Book 1.3, p.59

Trucks
Communities

**Look** at each word. **Say** it.
**Listen** for the **short u** sound in cup.

| | Write each word. | Check it. |
|---|---|---|
| 1. us | us | us |
| 2. bus | bus | bus |
| 3. cut | cut | cut |
| 4. but | but | but |
| 5. rug | rug | rug |
| 6. hug | hug | hug |

**Word Wall Words**
**Write** each word.

| | | |
|---|---|---|
| 7. our | our | our |
| 8. bring | bring | bring |

**Notes for Home:** Your child spelled words with the short *u* sound heard in *cup* and two frequently used words: *our, bring*. ***Home Activity:*** Have your child cut out letters for these spelling words from an old magazine and then paste the letters on paper to spell the words.

Level 1.3 Spelling: Short *u* 65

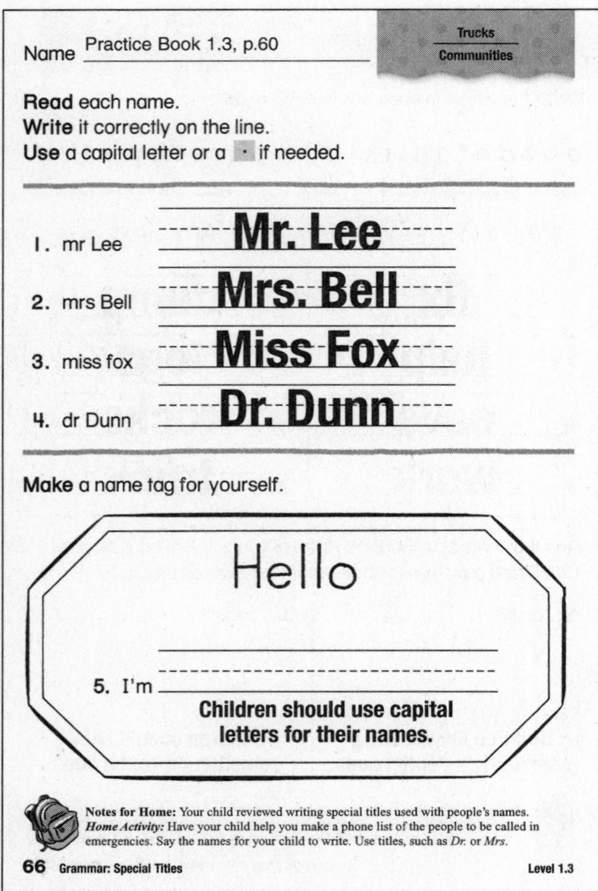
Name Practice Book 1.3, p.60

Trucks
Communities

**Read** each name.
**Write** it correctly on the line.
**Use** a capital letter or a . if needed.

1. mr Lee **Mr. Lee**
2. mrs Bell **Mrs. Bell**
3. miss fox **Miss Fox**
4. dr Dunn **Dr. Dunn**

**Make** a name tag for yourself.

Hello

5. I'm

**Children should use capital letters for their names.**

**Notes for Home:** Your child reviewed writing special titles used with people's names. ***Home Activity:*** Have your child help you make a phone list of the people to be called in emergencies. Say the names for your child to write. Use titles, such as *Dr.* or *Mrs.*

66 Grammar: Special Titles Level 1.3

Name Practice Book 1.3, p.61

Trucks
Communities

## Part 1: Vocabulary

**Read** each sentence.
**Mark** the ⬭ for the word that fits.

1. This is ____ mom.
   ⬭ and ⬬ our ⬭ many

2. Mom will go with ____ .
   ⬭ all ⬭ by ⬬ us

3. She can ____ the bag.
   ⬭ stop ⬬ carry ⬭ come

4. I will ____ the door.
   ⬭ play ⬭ make ⬬ hold

5. Sal will ____ a bag in for Mom.
   ⬬ bring ⬭ sing ⬭ find

GO ON

Level 1.3 Selection Test: Vocabulary 67

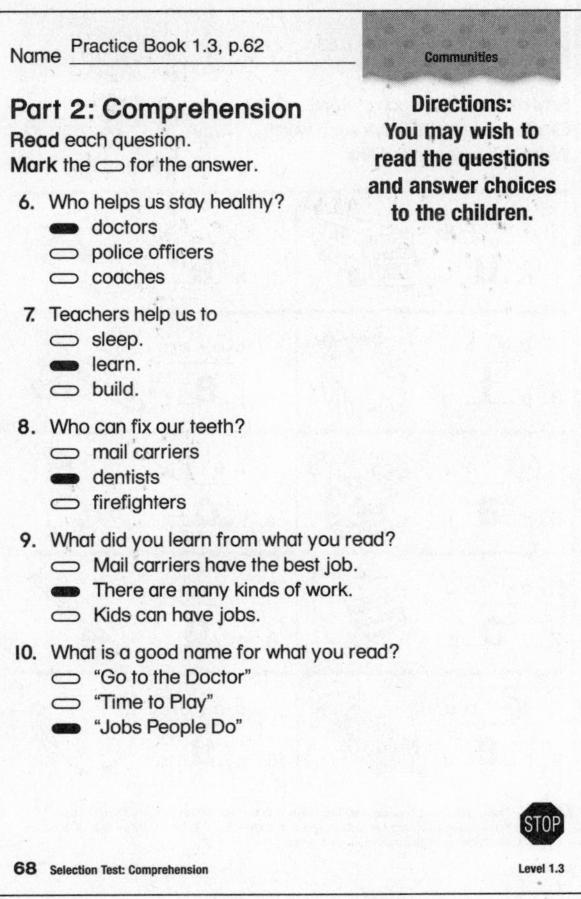
Name Practice Book 1.3, p.62

Communities

## Part 2: Comprehension

**Read** each question.
**Mark** the ⬭ for the answer.

**Directions: You may wish to read the questions and answer choices to the children.**

6. Who helps us stay healthy?
   - ⬬ doctors
   - ⬭ police officers
   - ⬭ coaches

7. Teachers help us to
   - ⬭ sleep.
   - ⬬ learn.
   - ⬭ build.

8. Who can fix our teeth?
   - ⬭ mail carriers
   - ⬬ dentists
   - ⬭ firefighters

9. What did you learn from what you read?
   - ⬭ Mail carriers have the best job.
   - ⬬ There are many kinds of work.
   - ⬭ Kids can have jobs.

10. What is a good name for what you read?
    - ⬭ "Go to the Doctor"
    - ⬭ "Time to Play"
    - ⬬ "Jobs People Do"

STOP

68 Selection Test: Comprehension Level 1.3

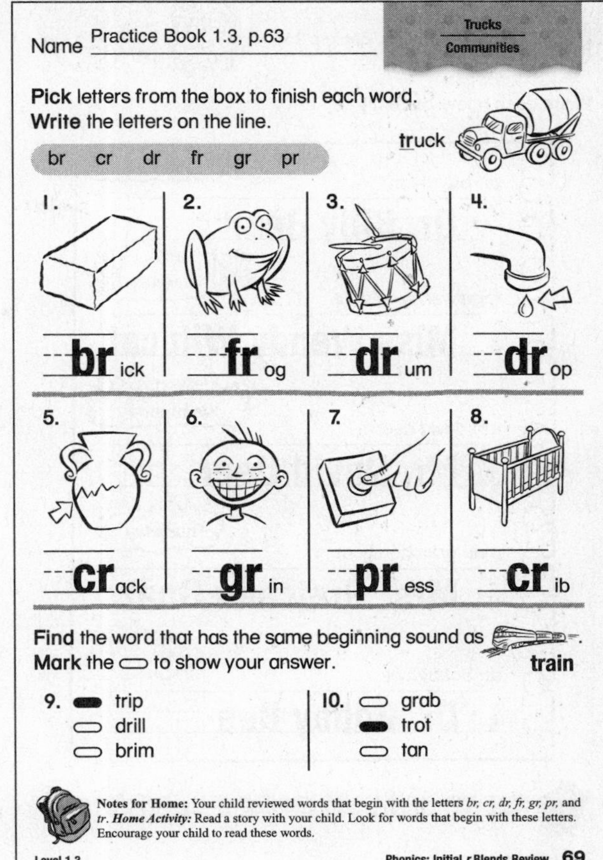
Name Practice Book 1.3, p.63

Trucks / Communities

**Pick** letters from the box to finish each word.
**Write** the letters on the line.

truck

br cr dr fr gr pr

| 1. | 2. | 3. | 4. |
|---|---|---|---|
| **br** ick | **fr** og | **dr** um | **dr** op |

| 5. | 6. | 7. | 8. |
|---|---|---|---|
| **cr** ack | **gr** in | **pr** ess | **cr** ib |

**Find** the word that has the same beginning sound as train.
**Mark** the ⬭ to show your answer.

9. ⬬ trip ⬭ drill ⬭ brim

10. ⬭ grab ⬬ trot ⬭ tan

**Notes for Home:** Your child reviewed words that begin with the letters *br, cr, dr, fr, gr, pr,* and *tr*. ***Home Activity:*** Read a story with your child. Look for words that begin with these letters. Encourage your child to read these words.

Level 1.3 Phonics: Initial *r* Blends Review 69

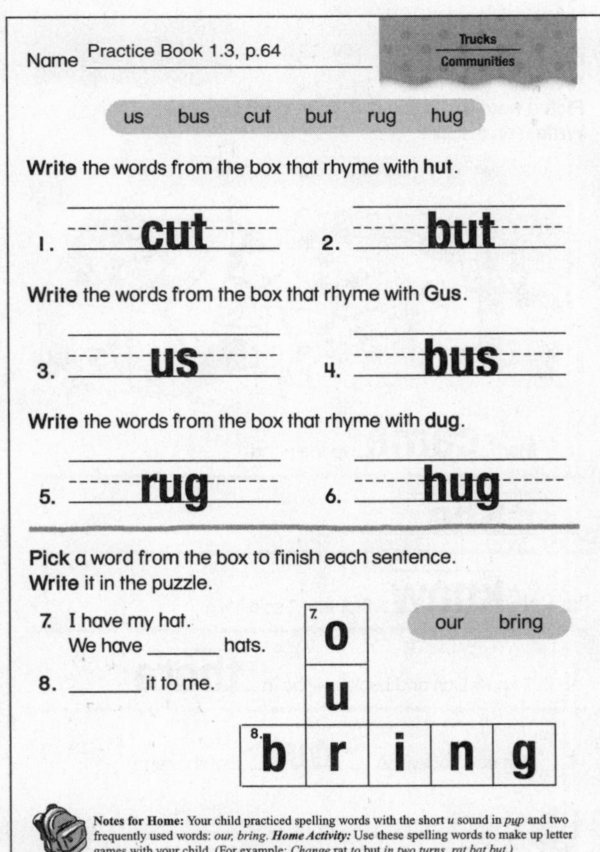
Name Practice Book 1.3, p.64

Trucks / Communities

us bus cut but rug hug

**Write** the words from the box that rhyme with **hut**.

1. **cut** 2. **but**

**Write** the words from the box that rhyme with **Gus**.

3. **us** 4. **bus**

**Write** the words from the box that rhyme with **dug**.

5. **rug** 6. **hug**

**Pick** a word from the box to finish each sentence.
**Write** it in the puzzle.

our bring

7. I have my hat. We have _______ hats.

8. _______ it to me.

7. o u r (down); 8. b r i n g (across)

**Notes for Home:** Your child practiced spelling words with the short *u* sound in *pup* and two frequently used words: *our, bring*. ***Home Activity:*** Use these spelling words to make up letter games with your child. (For example: *Change* rat *to* but *in two turns. rat bat but.)*

70 Spelling: Short *u* Level 1.3

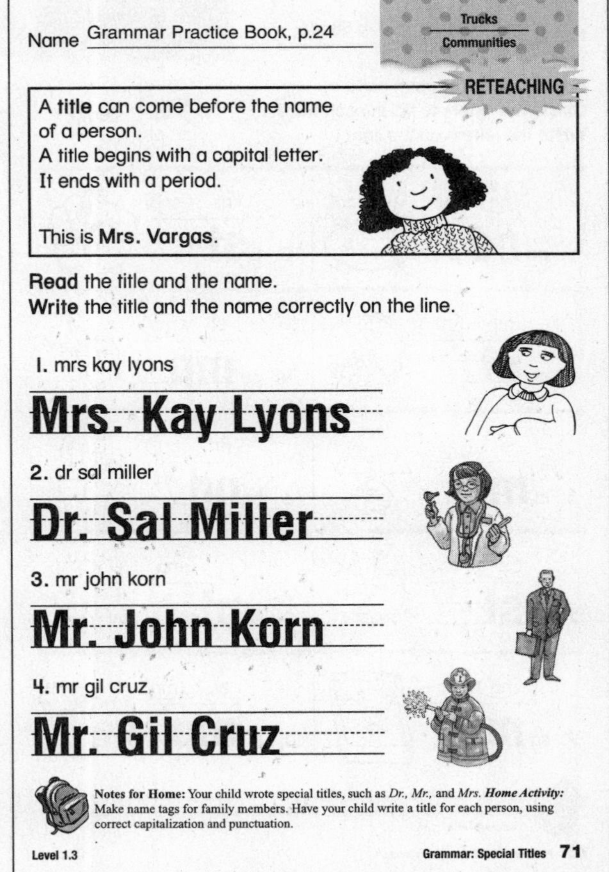
Name Grammar Practice Book, p.24

Trucks / Communities

RETEACHING

A **title** can come before the name of a person.
A title begins with a capital letter.
It ends with a period.

This is **Mrs. Vargas.**

**Read** the title and the name.
**Write** the title and the name correctly on the line.

1. mrs kay lyons
   **Mrs. Kay Lyons**
2. dr sal miller
   **Dr. Sal Miller**
3. mr john korn
   **Mr. John Korn**
4. mr gil cruz
   **Mr. Gil Cruz**

**Notes for Home:** Your child wrote special titles, such as *Dr., Mr.,* and *Mrs.* ***Home Activity:*** Make name tags for family members. Have your child write a title for each person, using correct capitalization and punctuation.

Level 1.3 Grammar: Special Titles 71

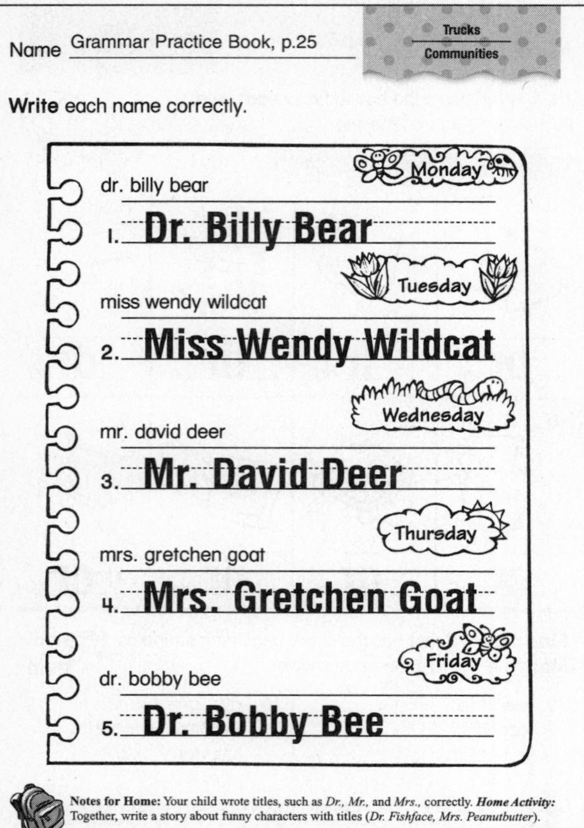

Name Grammar Practice Book, p.25

Trucks
Communities

**Write** each name correctly.



dr. billy bear

1. Dr. Billy Bear

miss wendy wildcat

2. Miss Wendy Wildcat

mr. david deer

3. Mr. David Deer

mrs. gretchen goat

4. Mrs. Gretchen Goat

dr. bobby bee

5. Dr. Bobby Bee

**Notes for Home:** Your child wrote titles, such as *Dr., Mr.,* and *Mrs.,* correctly. ***Home Activity:*** Together, write a story about funny characters with titles (*Dr. Fishface, Mrs. Peanutbutter*).

72 Grammar: Special Titles Level 1.3

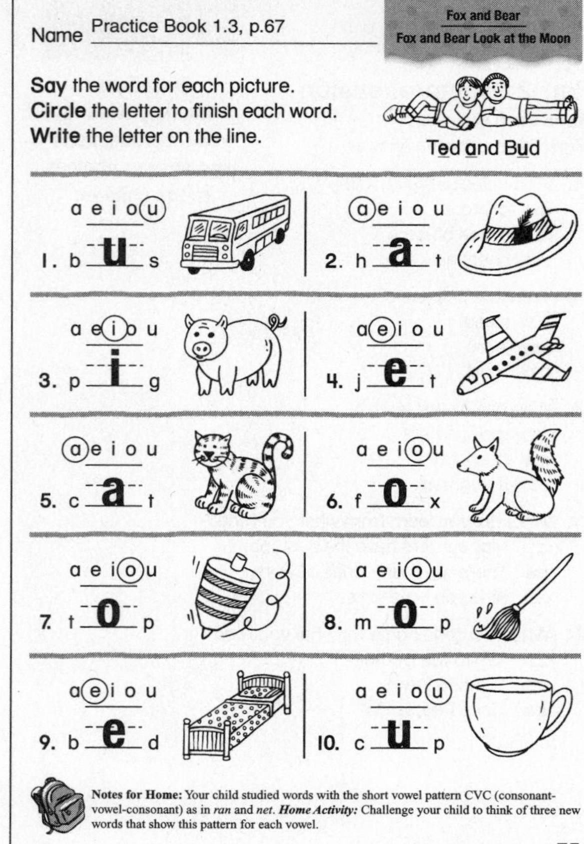

Name Practice Book 1.3, p.67

Fox and Bear
Fox and Bear Look at the Moon

**Say** the word for each picture.
**Circle** the letter to finish each word.
**Write** the letter on the line.

Ted and Bud

1. a e i o (u) — b u s
2. (a) e i o u — h a t
3. a e (i) o u — p i g
4. a (e) i o u — j e t
5. (a) e i o u — c a t
6. a e i (o) u — f o x
7. a e i (o) u — t o p
8. a e i (o) u — m o p
9. a (e) i o u — b e d
10. a e i o (u) — c u p

**Notes for Home:** Your child studied words with the short vowel pattern CVC (consonant-vowel-consonant) as in *ran* and *net*. ***Home Activity:*** Challenge your child to think of three new words that show this pattern for each vowel.

Level 1.3 Phonics: Short Vowel Pattern CVC 75

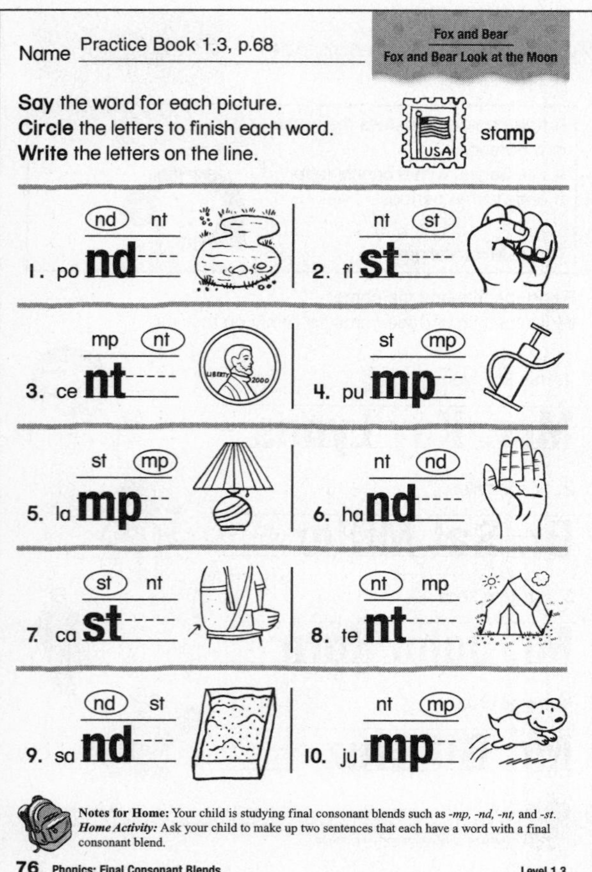

Name Practice Book 1.3, p.68

Fox and Bear
Fox and Bear Look at the Moon

**Say** the word for each picture.
**Circle** the letters to finish each word.
**Write** the letters on the line.



stamp

1. (nd) nt — po nd
2. nt (st) — fi st
3. mp (nt) — ce nt
4. st (mp) — pu mp
5. st (mp) — la mp
6. nt (nd) — ha nd
7. (st) nt — ca st
8. (nt) mp — te nt
9. (nd) st — sa nd
10. nt (mp) — ju mp

**Notes for Home:** Your child is studying final consonant blends such as *-mp, -nd, -nt,* and *-st.* ***Home Activity:*** Ask your child to make up two sentences that each have a word with a final consonant blend.

76 Phonics: Final Consonant Blends Level 1.3

Name Practice Book 1.3, p.69

Fox and Bear
Fox and Bear Look at the Moon

**Pick** a word from the box to finish each sentence.
**Write** it on the line.

came know out she there

1. Meg came to the pond.
2. She saw a tent.
3. "I know that tent," said Meg.
4. "I know Dan and Lucky will be in there."
5. Dan and Lucky ran out of the tent!

**Notes for Home:** This week your child is learning to read the words *came, know, out, she,* and *there.* ***Home Activity:*** On a piece of paper, write the first and last letters of each word. Say each word aloud and ask your child to fill in the middle letter or letters.

Level 1.3 High-Frequency Words 77

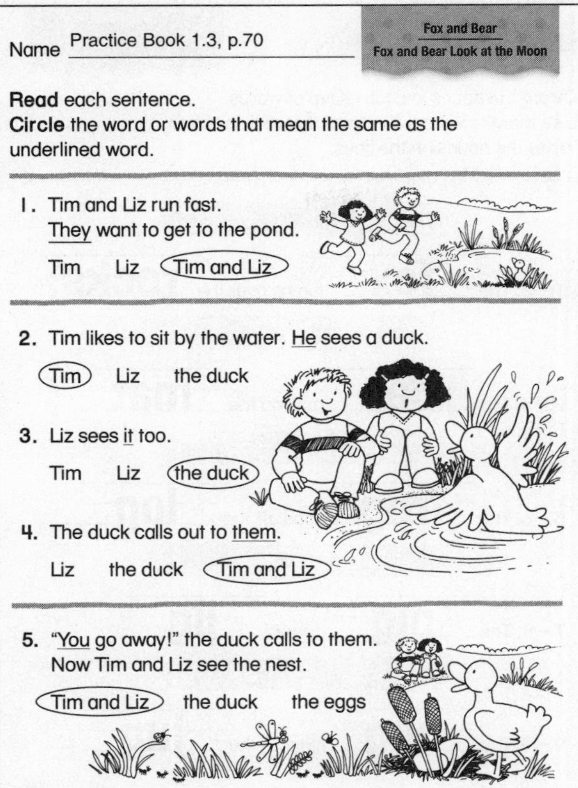
Name Practice Book 1.3, p.70

Fox and Bear
Fox and Bear Look at the Moon

**Read** each sentence.
**Circle** the word or words that mean the same as the underlined word.

1. Tim and Liz run fast.
They want to get to the pond.
Tim Liz (Tim and Liz)

2. Tim likes to sit by the water. He sees a duck.
(Tim) Liz the duck

3. Liz sees it too.
Tim Liz (the duck)

4. The duck calls out to them.
Liz the duck (Tim and Liz)

5. "You go away!" the duck calls to them.
Now Tim and Liz see the nest.
(Tim and Liz) the duck the eggs

**Notes for Home:** Your child used words and pictures to identify the person or thing that each pronoun represents. ***Home Activity:*** Read the above sentences with your child. Discuss the clues he or she used to figure out each answer.

78 Context Clues Level 1.3

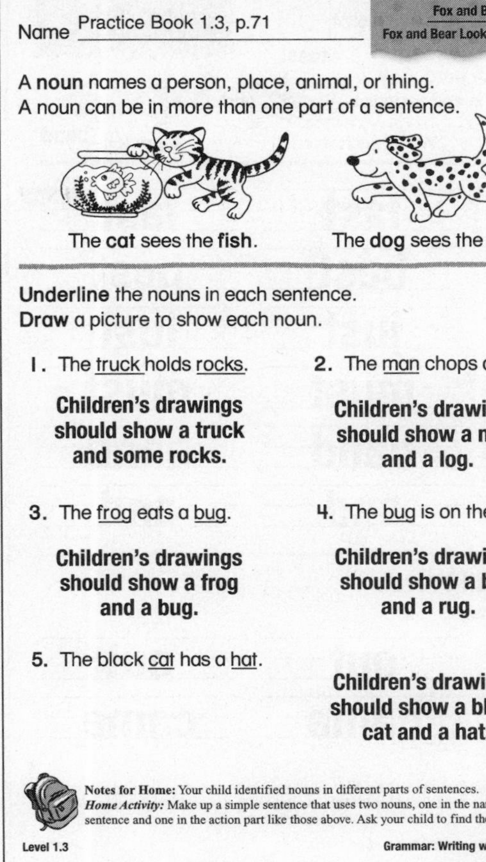
Name Practice Book 1.3, p.71

Fox and Bear
Fox and Bear Look at the Moon

A **noun** names a person, place, animal, or thing.
A noun can be in more than one part of a sentence.

The **cat** sees the **fish**.
The **dog** sees the **cat**!

**Underline** the nouns in each sentence.
**Draw** a picture to show each noun.

1. The truck holds rocks.
**Children's drawings should show a truck and some rocks.**

2. The man chops a log.
**Children's drawings should show a man and a log.**

3. The frog eats a bug.
**Children's drawings should show a frog and a bug.**

4. The bug is on the rug.
**Children's drawings should show a bug and a rug.**

5. The black cat has a hat.
**Children's drawings should show a black cat and a hat.**

**Notes for Home:** Your child identified nouns in different parts of sentences. ***Home Activity:*** Make up a simple sentence that uses two nouns, one in the naming part of the sentence and one in the action part like those above. Ask your child to find the nouns.

Level 1.3 Grammar: Writing with Nouns 79

Name Practice Book 1.3, p.74

Fox and Bear
Fox and Bear Look at the Moon

**Pick** a word from the box to finish each sentence.
**Write** it in the puzzle.

came know out she there

1. Do you ______ what is in the box?
2. The frog hops ______ of the box!
3. The frog does not like it in ______.
4. The frog ______ from the pond.
5. ______ wants to go back to her pond.

1. know
2. out
3. there
4. came
5. she

**Notes for Home:** Your child used newly learned vocabulary words to complete the crossword puzzle. ***Home Activity:*** Say each word from the box aloud, and ask your child to tell you what it means or use it in a sentence.

80 Vocabulary/High-Frequency Words Level 1.3

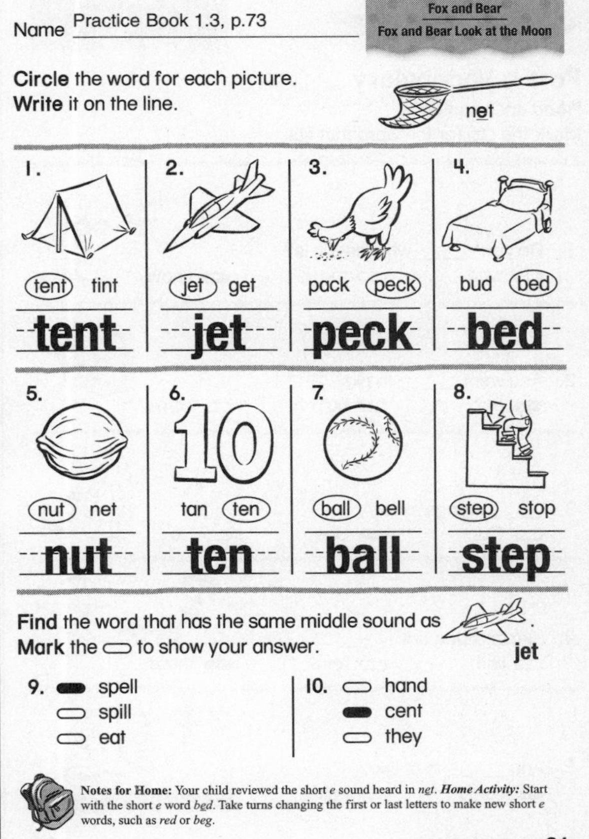
Name Practice Book 1.3, p.73

Fox and Bear
Fox and Bear Look at the Moon

**Circle** the word for each picture.
**Write** it on the line.

net

1. (tent) tint — tent
2. (jet) get — jet
3. pack (peck) — peck
4. bud (bed) — bed
5. (nut) net — nut
6. tan (ten) — ten
7. (ball) bell — ball
8. (step) stop — step

**Find** the word that has the same middle sound as jet.
**Mark** the ⊂⊃ to show your answer.

9. ● spell ○ spill ○ eat
10. ○ hand ● cent ○ they

**Notes for Home:** Your child reviewed the short *e* sound heard in *net*. ***Home Activity:*** Start with the short *e* word *bed*. Take turns changing the first or last letters to make new short *e* words, such as *red* or *beg*.

Level 1.3 Phonics: Short *e* Review 81

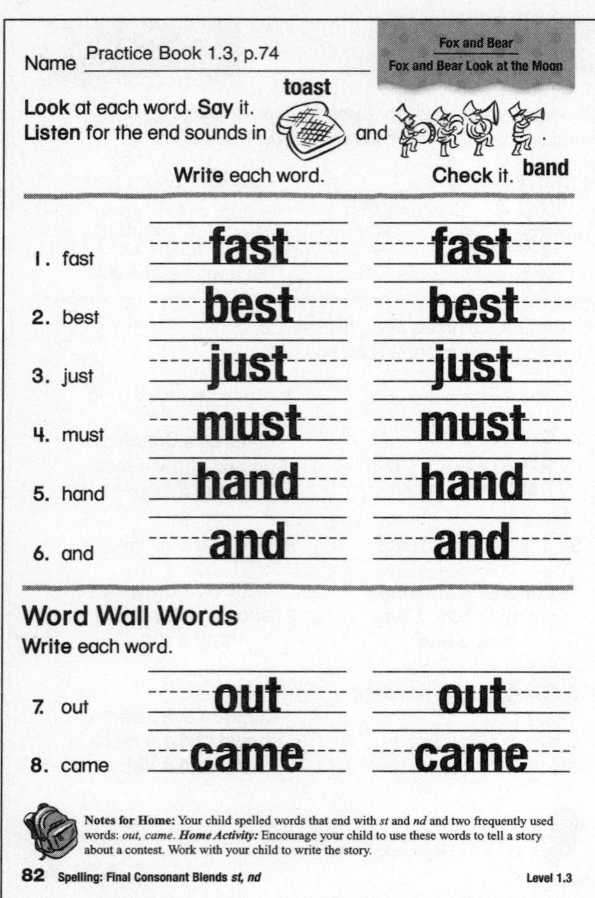

Name Practice Book 1.3, p.74

Fox and Bear
Fox and Bear Look at the Moon

**Look** at each word. **Say** it.
**Listen** for the end sounds in toast and band.

**Write** each word. **Check** it.

| | Write each word. | Check it. |
|---|---|---|
| 1. fast | fast | fast |
| 2. best | best | best |
| 3. just | just | just |
| 4. must | must | must |
| 5. hand | hand | hand |
| 6. and | and | and |

## Word Wall Words

**Write** each word.

| | | |
|---|---|---|
| 7. out | out | out |
| 8. came | came | came |

**Notes for Home:** Your child spelled words that end with *st* and *nd* and two frequently used words: *out, came.* ***Home Activity:*** Encourage your child to use these words to tell a story about a contest. Work with your child to write the story.

82 Spelling: Final Consonant Blends *st, nd* Level 1.3

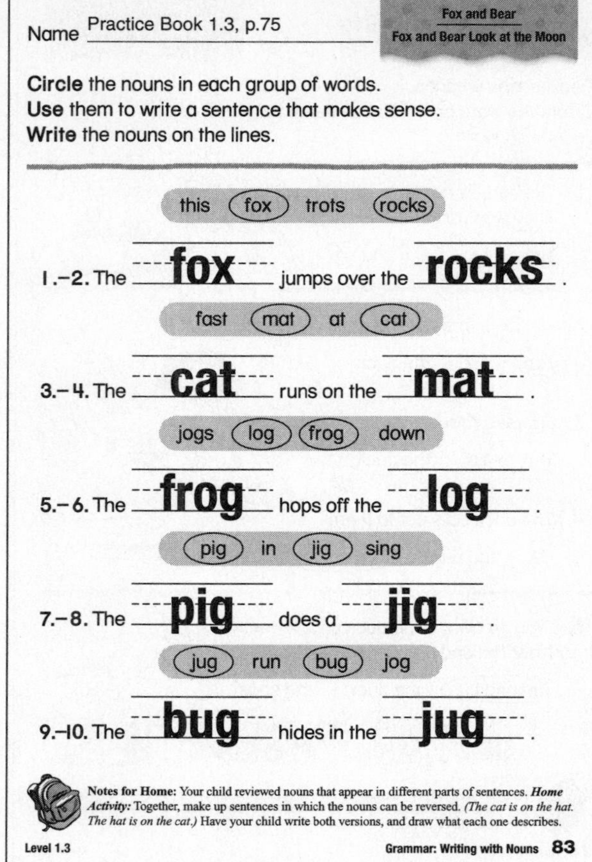

Name Practice Book 1.3, p.75

Fox and Bear
Fox and Bear Look at the Moon

**Circle** the nouns in each group of words.
**Use** them to write a sentence that makes sense.
**Write** the nouns on the lines.

this (fox) trots (rocks)

1.–2. The fox jumps over the rocks.

fast (mat) at (cat)

3.–4. The cat runs on the mat.

jogs (log) (frog) down

5.–6. The frog hops off the log.

(pig) in (jig) sing

7.–8. The pig does a jig.

(jug) run (bug) jog

9.–10. The bug hides in the jug.

**Notes for Home:** Your child reviewed nouns that appear in different parts of sentences. ***Home Activity:*** Together, make up sentences in which the nouns can be reversed. *(The cat is on the hat. The hat is on the cat.)* Have your child write both versions, and draw what each one describes.

Level 1.3 Grammar: Writing with Nouns 83

Name Practice Book 1.3, p.77

Fox and Bear
Fox and Bear Look at the Moon

## Part 1: Vocabulary

**Read** each sentence.
**Mark** the ⬭ for the word that fits.

1. Do you _____ what time it is?
   ⬭ who ⬭ too ⬬ know

2. Ana went _____ to play.
   ⬬ out ⬭ help ⬭ some

3. _____ brings a ball.
   ⬭ Our ⬬ She ⬭ So

4. Kim and Dan are _____ .
   ⬭ with ⬭ for ⬬ there

5. Ana _____ in at two.
   ⬬ came ⬭ hold ⬭ know

GO ON

Level 1.3 Selection Test: Vocabulary 85

Name Practice Book 1.3, p.78

Fox and Bear Look at the Moon

## Part 2: Comprehension

**Read** each sentence.
**Mark** the ⬭ for the answer.

**Directions: You may wish to read the questions and answer choices to the children.**

6. To Fox and Bear, the moon looked
   ⬭ sad.
   ⬭ red.
   ⬬ fat.

7. As Bear sat and sat, Fox
   ⬬ went to sleep.
   ⬭ jumped in.
   ⬭ played.

8. "She looked at the moon." Who is she?
   ⬭ Fox
   ⬬ Bear
   ⬭ Cat

9. When the moon was gone, where did it go?
   ⬭ in the water
   ⬬ behind a cloud
   ⬭ by the tree

10. What did Bear do at the end?
   ⬭ Bear got the moon out.
   ⬬ Bear gave Fox a pat.
   ⬭ Bear had a nap.

STOP

86 Selection Test: Comprehension Level 1.3

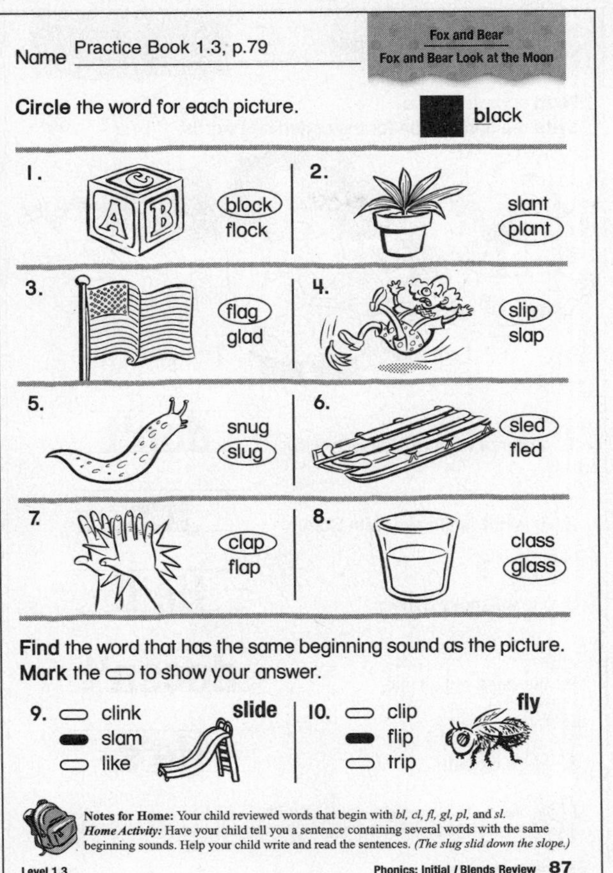
Name Practice Book 1.3, p.79

Fox and Bear
Fox and Bear Look at the Moon

**Circle** the word for each picture. black

1. block flock (circled: block)
2. slant plant (circled: plant)
3. flag glad (circled: flag)
4. slip slap (circled: slip)
5. snug slug (circled: slug)
6. sled fled (circled: sled)
7. clap flap (circled: clap)
8. class glass (circled: glass)

**Find** the word that has the same beginning sound as the picture.
**Mark** the ⊂⊃ to show your answer.

9. slide — clink, slam (marked), like
10. fly — clip, flip (marked), trip

**Notes for Home:** Your child reviewed words that begin with *bl, cl, fl, gl, pl,* and *sl.* ***Home Activity:*** Have your child tell you a sentence containing several words with the same beginning sounds. Help your child write and read the sentences. *(The slug slid down the slope.)*

Level 1.3 Phonics: Initial / Blends Review 87

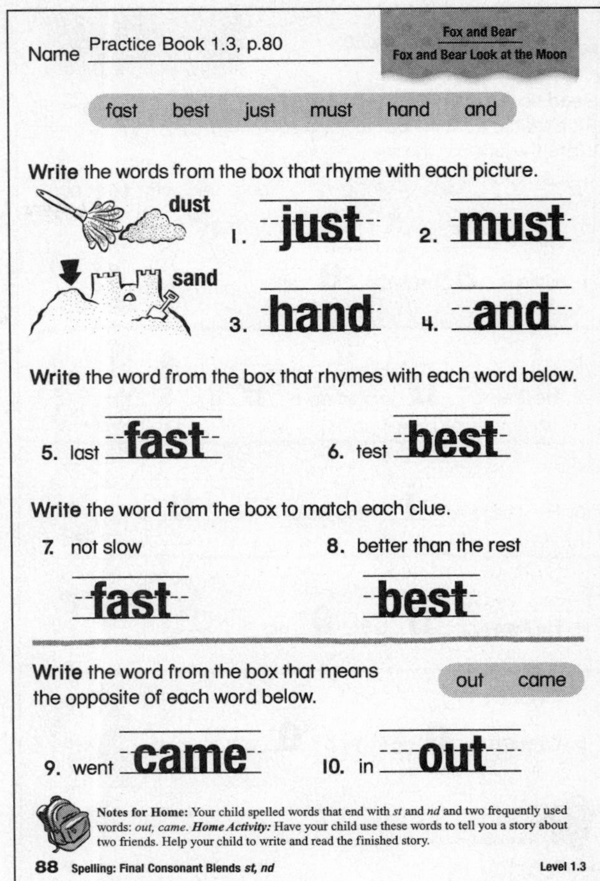
Name Practice Book 1.3, p.80

Fox and Bear
Fox and Bear Look at the Moon

fast best just must hand and

**Write** the words from the box that rhyme with each picture.

dust
1. just 2. must

sand
3. hand 4. and

**Write** the word from the box that rhymes with each word below.

5. last fast 6. test best

**Write** the word from the box to match each clue.

7. not slow 8. better than the rest

fast best

**Write** the word from the box that means the opposite of each word below.

out came

9. went came 10. in out

**Notes for Home:** Your child spelled words that end with *st* and *nd* and two frequently used words: *out, came.* ***Home Activity:*** Have your child use these words to tell you a story about two friends. Help your child to write and read the finished story.

88 Spelling: Final Consonant Blends *st, nd* Level 1.3

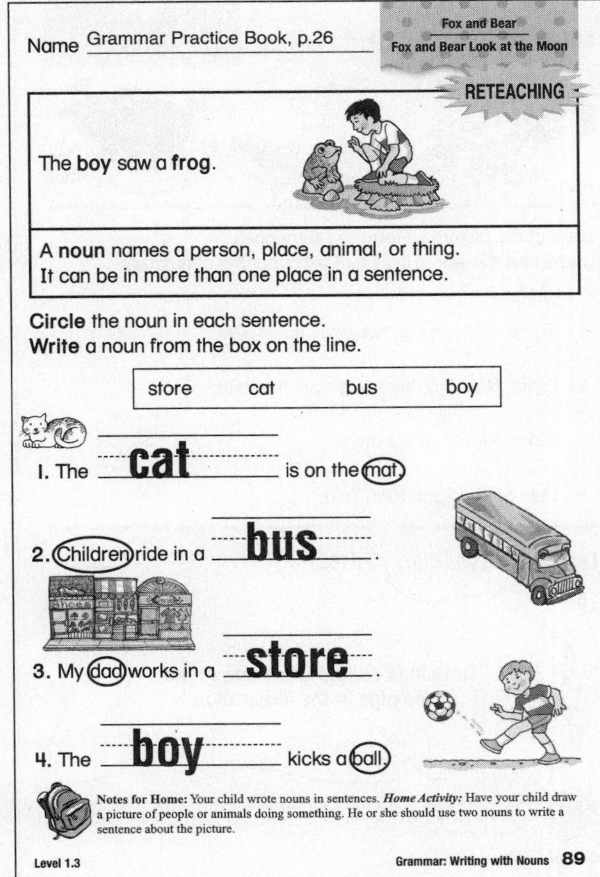
Name Grammar Practice Book, p.26

Fox and Bear
Fox and Bear Look at the Moon

RETEACHING

The **boy** saw a **frog**.

A **noun** names a person, place, animal, or thing.
It can be in more than one place in a sentence.

**Circle** the noun in each sentence.
**Write** a noun from the box on the line.

store cat bus boy

1. The cat is on the (mat).
2. (Children) ride in a bus.
3. My (dad) works in a store.
4. The boy kicks a (ball).

**Notes for Home:** Your child wrote nouns in sentences. ***Home Activity:*** Have your child draw a picture of people or animals doing something. He or she should use two nouns to write a sentence about the picture.

Level 1.3 Grammar: Writing with Nouns 89

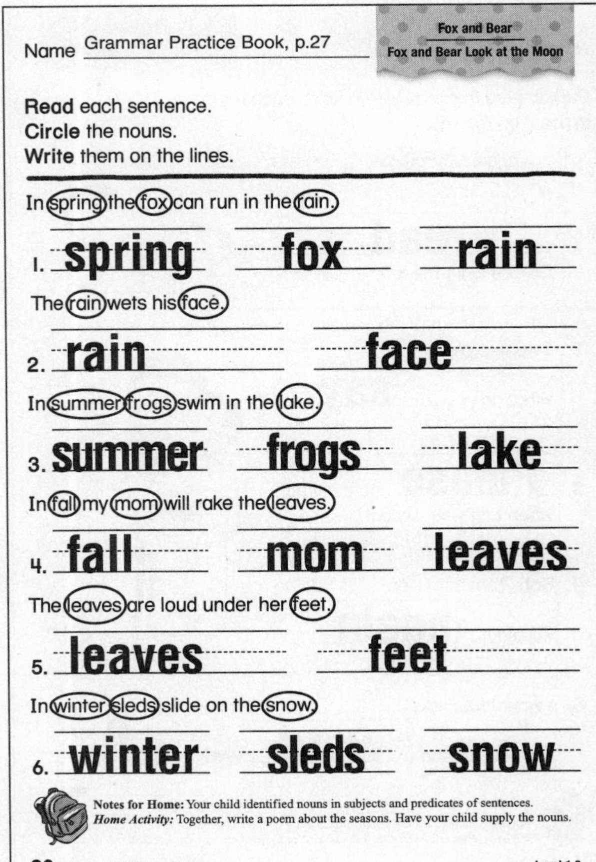
Name Grammar Practice Book, p.27

Fox and Bear
Fox and Bear Look at the Moon

**Read** each sentence.
**Circle** the nouns.
**Write** them on the lines.

In (spring) the (fox) can run in the (rain).
1. spring fox rain

The (rain) wets his (face).
2. rain face

In (summer) (frogs) swim in the (lake).
3. summer frogs lake

In (fall) my (mom) will rake the (leaves).
4. fall mom leaves

The (leaves) are loud under her (feet).
5. leaves feet

In (winter) (sleds) slide on the (snow).
6. winter sleds snow

**Notes for Home:** Your child identified nouns in subjects and predicates of sentences. ***Home Activity:*** Together, write a poem about the seasons. Have your child supply the nouns.

90 Grammar: Writing with Nouns Level 1.3

I Can Read
Lilly Reads

Name Practice Book 1.3, p.83

**Read** each sentence.
**Pick** a letter from the box to finish each word.
**Write** the letter on the line.

a e i o u

bag beg big bog bug

1. Little S **a** m is a p **e** st!

2. He likes to j **u** mp on my b **e** d.

3. He likes to sp **i** ll the water in the c **u** p.

4. He likes to h **u** g fr **o** gs.

5. Why is a fr **o** g in my b **o** x?

**Notes for Home:** Your child wrote words with the short vowel pattern CVC (Consonant-Vowel-Consonant), such as *big* and *bag*. ***Home Activity:*** Challenge your child to write five new sentences with words that have the short vowel pattern CVC.

Level 1.3 Phonics: Short Vowel Pattern CVC 93

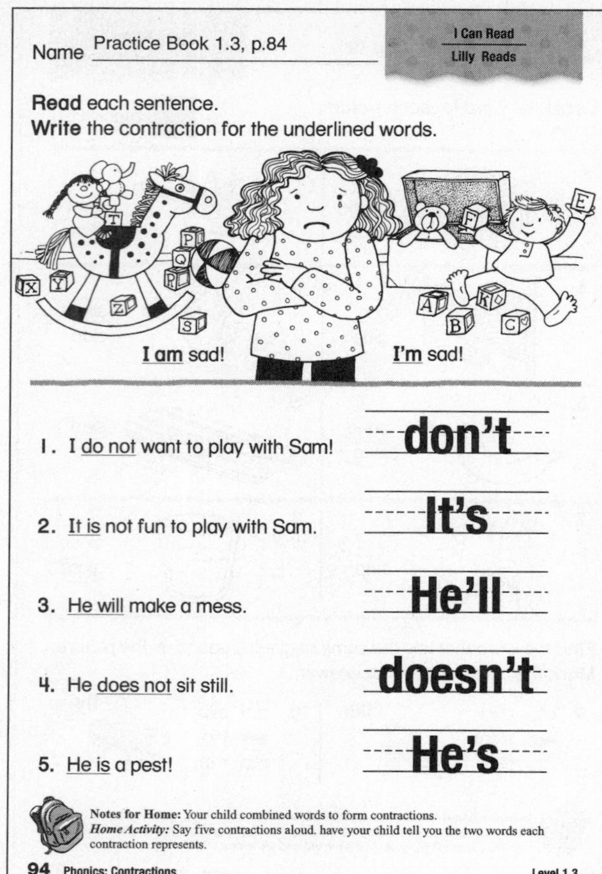

I Can Read
Lilly Reads

Name Practice Book 1.3, p.84

**Read** each sentence.
**Write** the contraction for the underlined words.



1. I do not want to play with Sam! **don't**
2. It is not fun to play with Sam. **It's**
3. He will make a mess. **He'll**
4. He does not sit still. **doesn't**
5. He is a pest! **He's**

**Notes for Home:** Your child combined words to form contractions. ***Home Activity:*** Say five contractions aloud. have your child tell you the two words each contraction represents.

94 Phonics: Contractions Level 1.3

I Can Read
Lilly Reads

Name Practice Book 1.3, p.85

**Pick** a word from the box to finish each rhyme.
**Write** it on the line.

again please read say word

1. I can **read** to you.
Do you want me to?

2. I want to play.
What do you **say**?

3. **Please** hold my hat,
when I hit with the bat.

4. Bob, Tom, and Ben,
will play **again**.

5. I want that dress.
Will you say the **word** *yes*?

**Notes for Home:** This week your child is learning to read the words *again, please, read, say,* and *word.* ***Home Activity:*** Ask your child to use these words to make up additional rhymes.

Level 1.3 High-Frequency Words 95

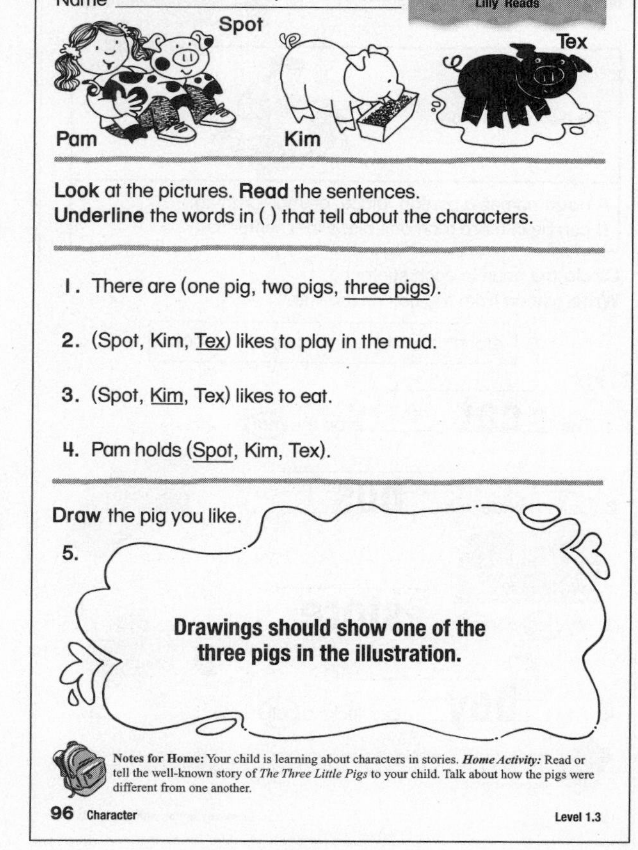

I Can Read
Lilly Reads

Name Practice Book 1.3, p.86



**Look** at the pictures. **Read** the sentences.
**Underline** the words in ( ) that tell about the characters.

1. There are (one pig, two pigs, three pigs).
2. (Spot, Kim, Tex) likes to play in the mud.
3. (Spot, Kim, Tex) likes to eat.
4. Pam holds (Spot, Kim, Tex).

**Draw** the pig you like.

5. **Drawings should show one of the three pigs in the illustration.**

**Notes for Home:** Your child is learning about characters in stories. ***Home Activity:*** Read or tell the well-known story of *The Three Little Pigs* to your child. Talk about how the pigs were different from one another.

96 Character Level 1.3

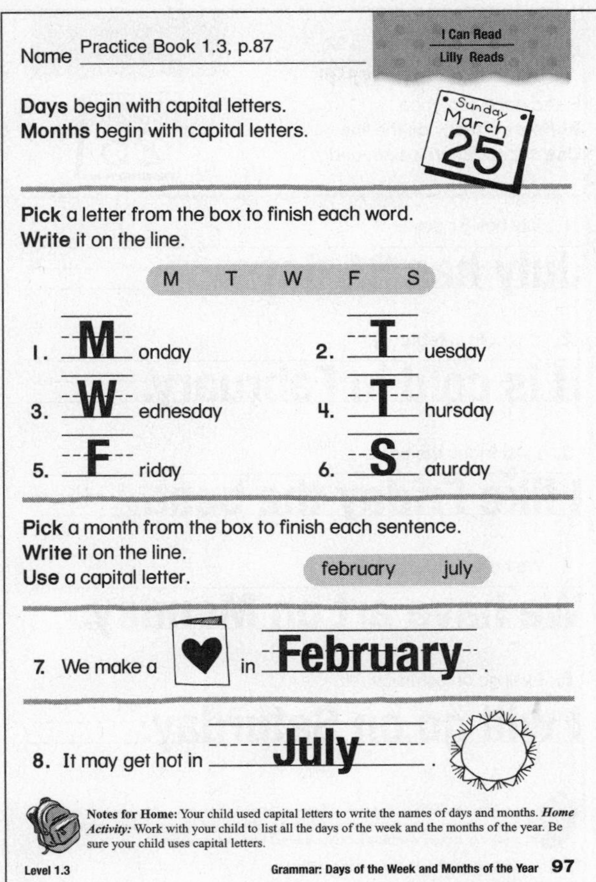

Name Practice Book 1.3, p.87

I Can Read
Lilly Reads

**Days** begin with capital letters.
**Months** begin with capital letters.

**Pick** a letter from the box to finish each word.
**Write** it on the line.

M T W F S

1. **M**onday
2. **T**uesday
3. **W**ednesday
4. **T**hursday
5. **F**riday
6. **S**aturday

**Pick** a month from the box to finish each sentence.
**Write** it on the line.
**Use** a capital letter.

february july

7. We make a ♥ in **February**.
8. It may get hot in **July**.

**Notes for Home:** Your child used capital letters to write the names of days and months. ***Home Activity:*** Work with your child to list all the days of the week and the months of the year. Be sure your child uses capital letters.

Level 1.3 Grammar: Days of the Week and Months of the Year 97

Name Practice Book 1.3, p.88

I Can Read
Lilly Reads

**Pick** a word from the box to finish each sentence.
**Write** it on the line. Use each word only once.

again please read say word

1. "I want Peg to **read** to us," said Tim.
2. "Will you read us this story **again**?" said Tim.
3. "Do **say** yes," said Bess.
4. "Say one more **word**," said Peg.
5. "**Please**!" said Tim and Bess.

**Notes for Home:** Your child worked with the new vocabulary words *again, please, read, say,* and *word.* ***Home Activity:*** Say each word and ask your child to write it and then use it in a sentence.

98 Vocabulary/High-Frequency Words Level 1.3

Name Practice Book 1.3, p.89

I Can Read
Lilly Reads

**Circle** the picture for each word.

sun

1. nut — knot
2. cut — cat
3. bug — bag
4. gum — game
5. fun — fan
6. truck — train
7. mutt — mitt
8. cub — cab

**Find** the word that has the same middle sound as rug.
**Mark** the ⬭ to show your answer.

9. ⬭ you ● jump ⬭ blue
10. ⬭ look ⬭ our ● puff

**Notes for Home:** Your child reviewed words that have the short *u* sound heard in *sun.* ***Home Activity:*** Challenge your child to write as many words as he or she can with one of these endings: *-uff, -ug, -um, -ump,* and *-ut.*

Level 1.3 Phonics: Short *u* Review 99

Name Practice Book 1.3, p.90

I Can Read
Lilly Reads

**Look** at each word. **Say** it.
**Listen** for the beginning sounds and short vowel sounds of each word.

| | Write each word. | Check it. |
|---|---|---|
| 1. clap | clap | clap |
| 2. sled | sled | sled |
| 3. trip | trip | trip |
| 4. spot | spot | spot |
| 5. drop | drop | drop |
| 6. drum | drum | drum |

## Word Wall Words

**Write** each word.

| | | |
|---|---|---|
| 7. read | read | read |
| 8. please | please | please |

**Notes for Home:** Your child spelled words with short vowel sounds that begin with a consonant blend (*clap*), and two frequently used words: *read, please.* ***Home Activity:*** Say each spelling word aloud. Have your child spell the word and use it in a sentence.

100 Spelling: Short Vowels with Initial Blends Level 1.3

Name Practice Book 1.3, p.91

I Can Read
Lilly Reads

Leave out sentences that do not belong.

I like dogs.
~~My cat is brown.~~
My dog is big.

**Circle** four sentences to tell about a pond.

1. (I like to go to the little pond.)
2. (I read my book beside the water.)
3. It was hot on Friday.
4. (I can smell the damp mud by the water.)
5. (I see two green frogs jump into the water.)
6. I will not let my dog play inside.

**Write** a sentence about a pond. **Possible answer given.**

7. **The frogs go plop into the pond.**

**Notes for Home:** Your child identified sentences that do not belong in a group. ***Home Activity:*** Tell a short story to your child. Make up one or two sentences that do not belong with the rest. Ask your child to tell you which sentences do not belong and to explain why.

Level 1.3 Writing Process: Revise 101

Name Practice Book 1.3, p.92

I Can Read
Lilly Reads

Monday
March
25

**Read** each sentence.
**Write** it correctly on the line.
**Use** capital letters as needed.

1. july has 31 days.
**July has 31 days.**

2. It is cold in february.
**It is cold in February.**

3. I like friday the best.
**I like Friday the best.**

4. We have art on monday.
**We have art on Monday.**

5. I will go on saturday.
**I will go on Saturday.**

**Notes for Home:** Your child wrote the days of the week and months of the year with capital letters. ***Home Activity:*** Have your child look at a calendar and list special days your family celebrates. Be sure your child uses capital letters wherever appropriate.

102 Grammar: Days of the Week and Months of the Year Level 1.3

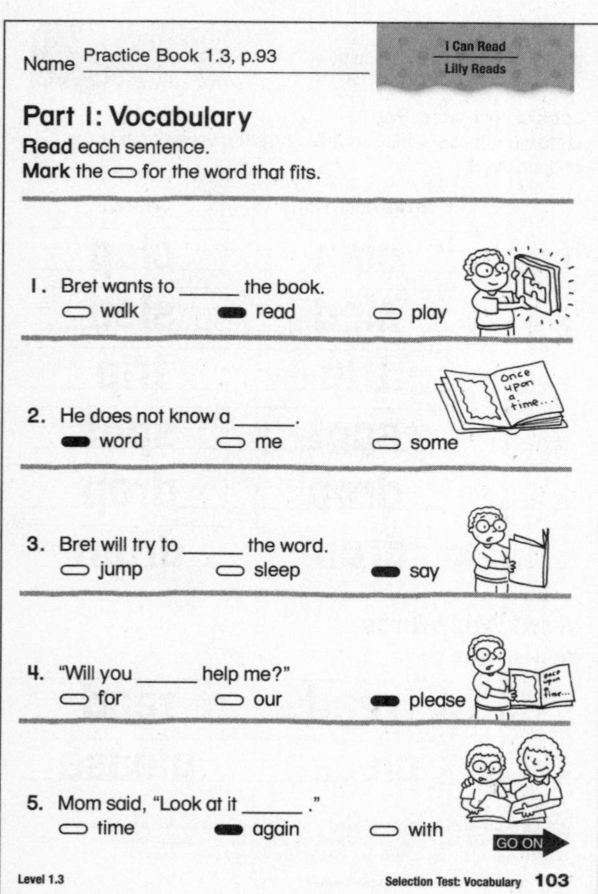

Name Practice Book 1.3, p.93

I Can Read
Lilly Reads

## Part 1: Vocabulary

**Read** each sentence.
**Mark** the ○ for the word that fits.

1. Bret wants to ____ the book.
○ walk ● read ○ play

2. He does not know a ____.
● word ○ me ○ some

3. Bret will try to ____ the word.
○ jump ○ sleep ● say

4. "Will you ____ help me?"
○ for ○ our ● please

5. Mom said, "Look at it ____."
○ time ● again ○ with

GO ON

Level 1.3 Selection Test: Vocabulary 103

Name Practice Book 1.3, p.94

Lilly Reads

## Part 2: Comprehension

**Read** each question.
**Mark** the ○ for the answer.

**Directions: You may wish to read the questions and answer choices to the children.**

6. Mrs. Woo asks Lilly to
○ find a list.
● read a page.
○ sit up tall.

7. Why did Lilly stop?
○ She got to the end.
○ She wanted to play.
● She did not know a word.

8. What can you tell about Willy?
● He wants to read.
○ He is Lilly's best pal.
○ He knows an elf.

9. How did Lilly feel at the end?
○ mad
● happy
○ sad

10. Did Mrs. Woo help Lilly?
○ Yes, she let Lilly rest.
○ No, she let Willy read.
● Yes, she said for Lilly to try again.

STOP

104 Selection Test: Comprehension Level 1.3

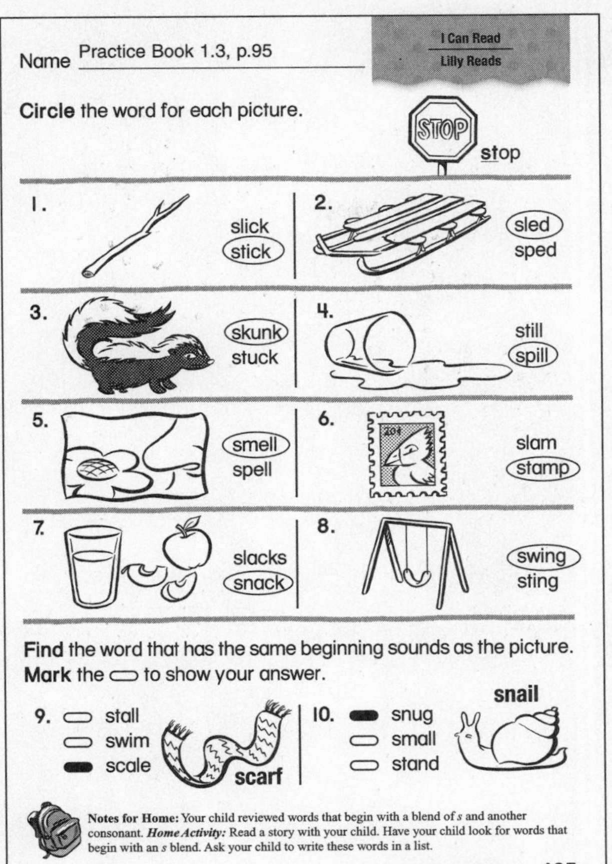

Name Practice Book 1.3, p.95

I Can Read
Lilly Reads

**Circle** the word for each picture.

STOP stop

1. slick / (stick)
2. (sled) / sped
3. (skunk) / stuck
4. still / (spill)
5. (smell) / spell
6. slam / (stamp)
7. slacks / (snack)
8. (swing) / sting

**Find** the word that has the same beginning sounds as the picture.
**Mark** the ⊂⊃ to show your answer.

9. ⊂⊃ stall ⊂⊃ swim ● scale — scarf
10. ● snug ⊂⊃ small ⊂⊃ stand — snail

**Notes for Home:** Your child reviewed words that begin with a blend of *s* and another consonant. ***Home Activity:*** Read a story with your child. Have your child look for words that begin with an *s* blend. Ask your child to write these words in a list.

Level 1.3 Phonics: Initial *s* Blends Review 105

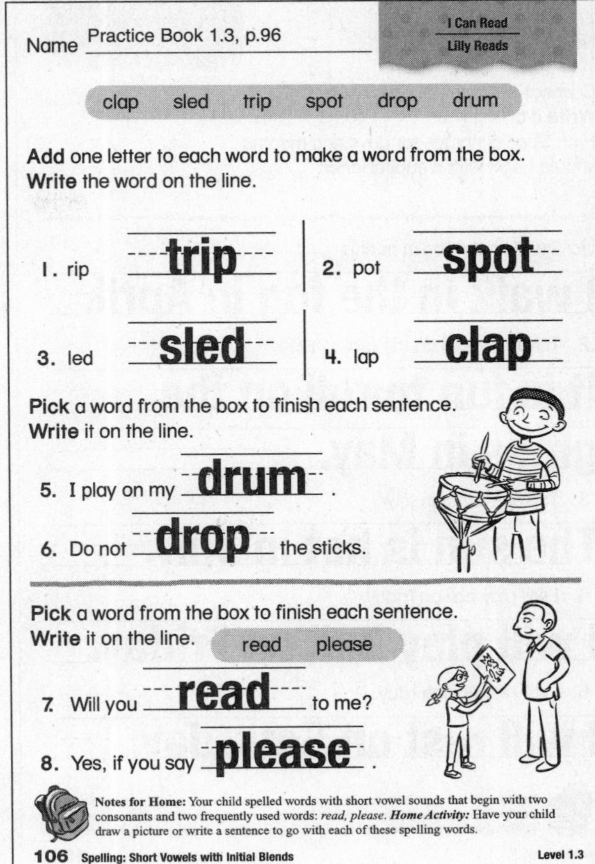

Name Practice Book 1.3, p.96

I Can Read
Lilly Reads

clap sled trip spot drop drum

**Add** one letter to each word to make a word from the box.
**Write** the word on the line.

1. rip **trip**
2. pot **spot**
3. led **sled**
4. lap **clap**

**Pick** a word from the box to finish each sentence.
**Write** it on the line.

5. I play on my **drum**.
6. Do not **drop** the sticks.

**Pick** a word from the box to finish each sentence.
**Write** it on the line.

read please

7. Will you **read** to me?
8. Yes, if you say **please**.

**Notes for Home:** Your child spelled words with short vowel sounds that begin with two consonants and two frequently used words: *read, please.* ***Home Activity:*** Have your child draw a picture or write a sentence to go with each of these spelling words.

106 Spelling: Short Vowels with Initial Blends Level 1.3

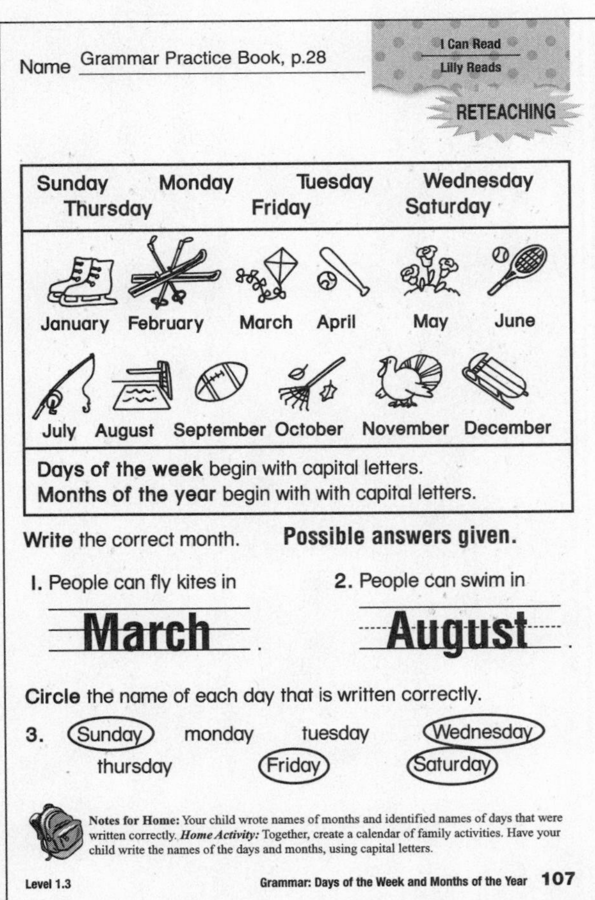

Name Grammar Practice Book, p.28

I Can Read
Lilly Reads

RETEACHING

Sunday Monday Tuesday Wednesday
Thursday Friday Saturday

January February March April May June
July August September October November December

**Days of the week** begin with capital letters.
**Months of the year** begin with with capital letters.

**Write** the correct month. **Possible answers given.**

1. People can fly kites in **March**.
2. People can swim in **August**.

**Circle** the name of each day that is written correctly.

3. (Sunday) monday tuesday (Wednesday) thursday (Friday) (Saturday)

**Notes for Home:** Your child wrote names of months and identified names of days that were written correctly. ***Home Activity:*** Together, create a calendar of family activities. Have your child write the names of the days and months, using capital letters.

Level 1.3 Grammar: Days of the Week and Months of the Year 107

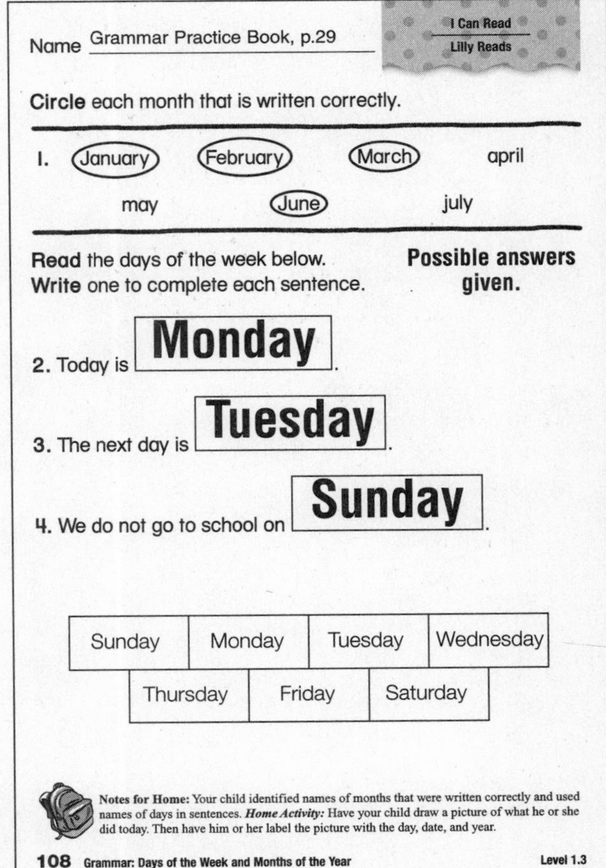

Name Grammar Practice Book, p.29

I Can Read
Lilly Reads

**Circle** each month that is written correctly.

1. (January) (February) (March) april may (June) july

**Read** the days of the week below.
**Write** one to complete each sentence. **Possible answers given.**

2. Today is **Monday**.
3. The next day is **Tuesday**.
4. We do not go to school on **Sunday**.

| Sunday | Monday | Tuesday | Wednesday |
|---|---|---|---|
| Thursday | Friday | Saturday | |

**Notes for Home:** Your child identified names of months that were written correctly and used names of days in sentences. ***Home Activity:*** Have your child draw a picture of what he or she did today. Then have him or her label the picture with the day, date, and year.

108 Grammar: Days of the Week and Months of the Year Level 1.3

Name Practice Book 1.3, p.97

I Can Read
Lilly Reads

**Correct** each sentence.
**Write** it on the line.
Hint: Special names for days and months should begin with a capital letter.

1. I walk in the fog in april.

**I walk in the fog in April.**

2. It is fun to roll on the grass in may.

**It is fun to roll on the grass in May.**

3. The sun is hot in july.

**The sun is hot in July.**

4. I will play ball on friday.

**I will play ball on Friday.**

5. I will rest on saturday.

**I will rest on Saturday.**

**Notes for Home:** Your child identified and capitalized proper nouns for days of the week and months of the year in sentences. ***Home Activity:*** Help your child make a calendar. Check that all days, months, and holidays are capitalized. Together, fill in special events and holidays.

Level 1.3 Writing Process: Edit 109

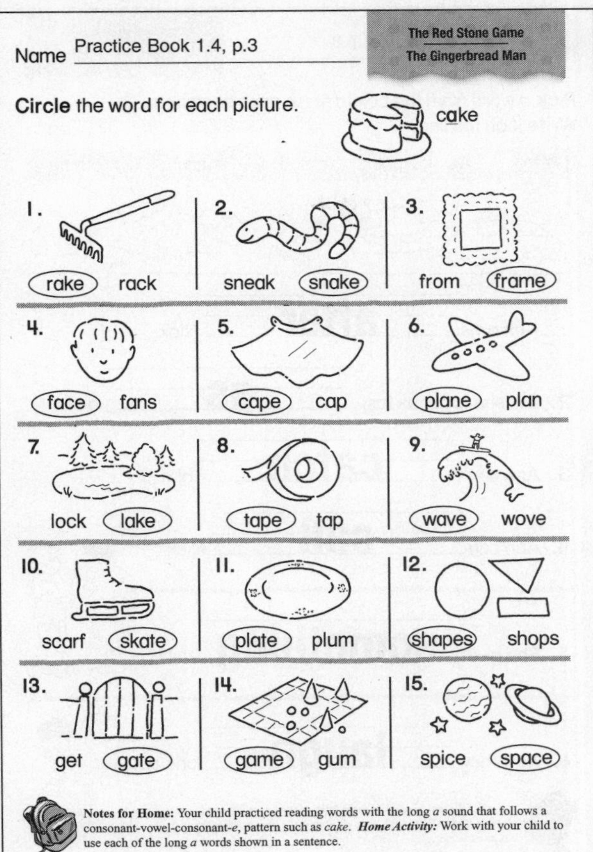
Name Practice Book 1.4, p.3

The Red Stone Game
The Gingerbread Man

**Circle** the word for each picture.

cake

| 1. rake (circled) rack | 2. sneak snake (circled) | 3. from frame (circled) |
|---|---|---|
| 4. face (circled) fans | 5. cape (circled) cap | 6. plane (circled) plan |
| 7. lock lake (circled) | 8. tape (circled) tap | 9. wave (circled) wove |
| 10. scarf skate (circled) | 11. plate (circled) plum | 12. shapes (circled) shops |
| 13. get gate (circled) | 14. game (circled) gum | 15. spice space (circled) |

**Notes for Home:** Your child practiced reading words with the long *a* sound that follows a consonant-vowel-consonant-*e*, pattern such as *cake*. ***Home Activity:*** Work with your child to use each of the long *a* words shown in a sentence.

Level 1.4 Phonics: Long *a* (CVC*e*) 3

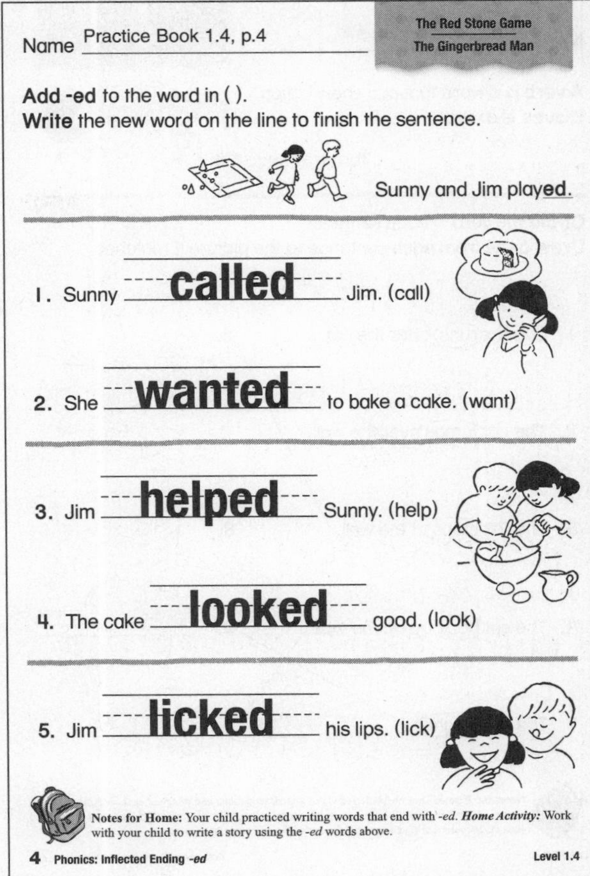
Name Practice Book 1.4, p.4

The Red Stone Game
The Gingerbread Man

**Add -ed** to the word in ( ).
**Write** the new word on the line to finish the sentence.

Sunny and Jim play**ed**.

1. Sunny **called** Jim. (call)

2. She **wanted** to bake a cake. (want)

3. Jim **helped** Sunny. (help)

4. The cake **looked** good. (look)

5. Jim **licked** his lips. (lick)

**Notes for Home:** Your child practiced writing words that end with *-ed*. ***Home Activity:*** Work with your child to write a story using the *-ed* words above.

4 Phonics: Inflected Ending *-ed* Level 1.4

Name Practice Book 1.4, p.5

The Red Stone Game
The Gingerbread Man

**Read** each sentence.
**Circle** the picture that tells about the sentence.

after as call laugh something

1. Sam gave a call to Jane.

2. He ran after Jane.

3. Sam gave something to Jane.

4. Jane wanted to laugh.

5. It looked the same as Jane.

**Notes for Home:** This week your child learned to read the words *after, as, call, laugh,* and *something.* ***Home Activity:*** Write each word in a simple sentence. Ask your child to read the sentences to you.

Level 1.4 High-Frequency Words 5

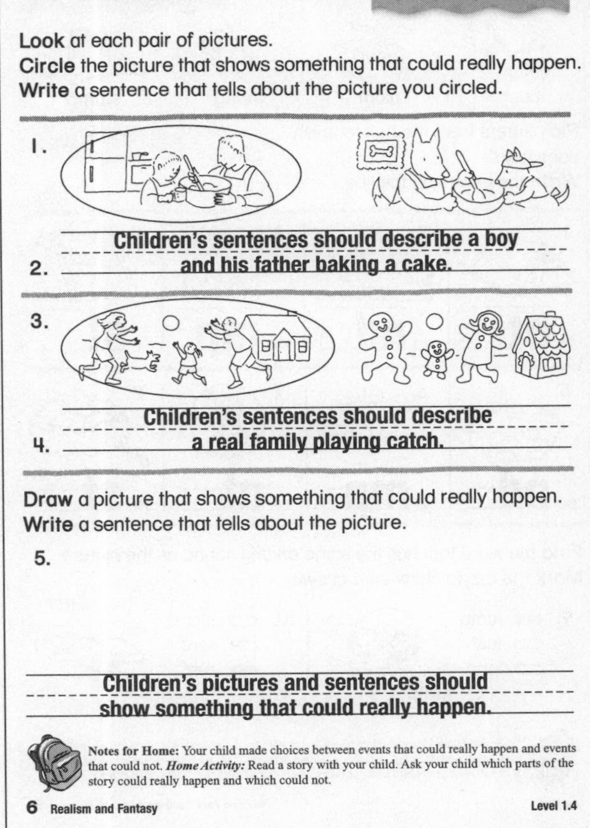
Name Practice Book 1.4, p.6

The Red Stone Game
The Gingerbread Man

**Look** at each pair of pictures.
**Circle** the picture that shows something that could really happen.
**Write** a sentence that tells about the picture you circled.

1.

2. **Children's sentences should describe a boy and his father baking a cake.**

3.

4. **Children's sentences should describe a real family playing catch.**

**Draw** a picture that shows something that could really happen.
**Write** a sentence that tells about the picture.

5.

**Children's pictures and sentences should show something that could really happen.**

**Notes for Home:** Your child made choices between events that could really happen and events that could not. ***Home Activity:*** Read a story with your child. Ask your child which parts of the story could really happen and which could not.

6 Realism and Fantasy Level 1.4

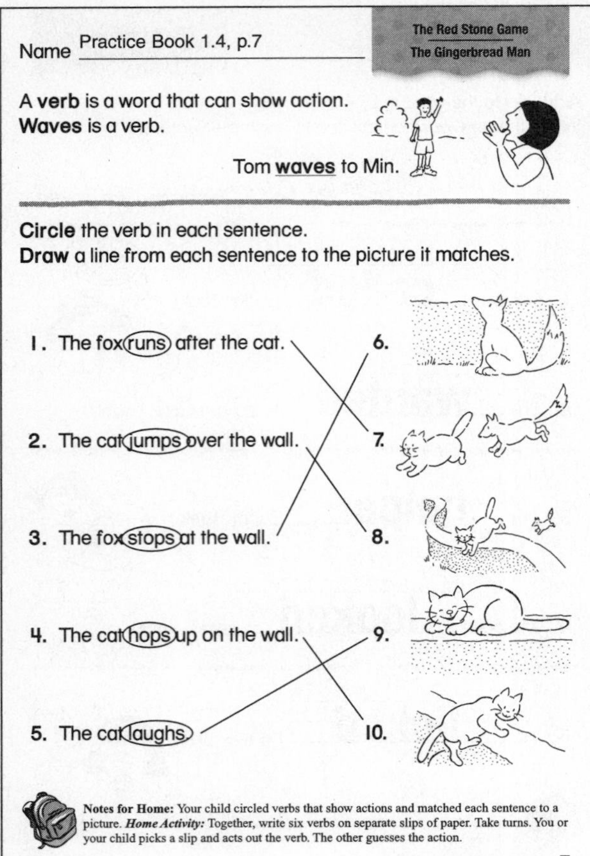

The Red Stone Game
The Gingerbread Man

Name Practice Book 1.4, p.7

A **verb** is a word that can show action.
**Waves** is a verb.

Tom **waves** to Min.

**Circle** the verb in each sentence.
**Draw** a line from each sentence to the picture it matches.

1. The fox (runs) after the cat. — 7.
2. The cat (jumps) over the wall. — 8.
3. The fox (stops) at the wall. — 6.
4. The cat (hops) up on the wall. — 10.
5. The cat (laughs). — 9.

**Notes for Home:** Your child circled verbs that show actions and matched each sentence to a picture. *Home Activity:* Together, write six verbs on separate slips of paper. Take turns. You or your child picks a slip and acts out the verb. The other guesses the action.

Level 1.4 Grammar: Verbs (Action Words) 7

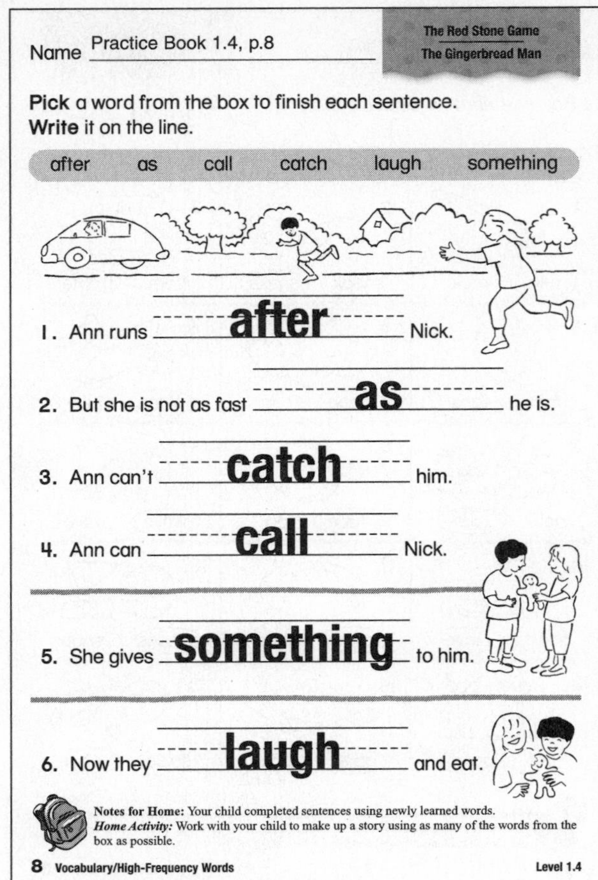

The Red Stone Game
The Gingerbread Man

Name Practice Book 1.4, p.8

**Pick** a word from the box to finish each sentence.
**Write** it on the line.

after as call catch laugh something

1. Ann runs **after** Nick.
2. But she is not as fast **as** he is.
3. Ann can't **catch** him.
4. Ann can **call** Nick.
5. She gives **something** to him.
6. Now they **laugh** and eat.

**Notes for Home:** Your child completed sentences using newly learned words. *Home Activity:* Work with your child to make up a story using as many of the words from the box as possible.

8 Vocabulary/High-Frequency Words Level 1.4

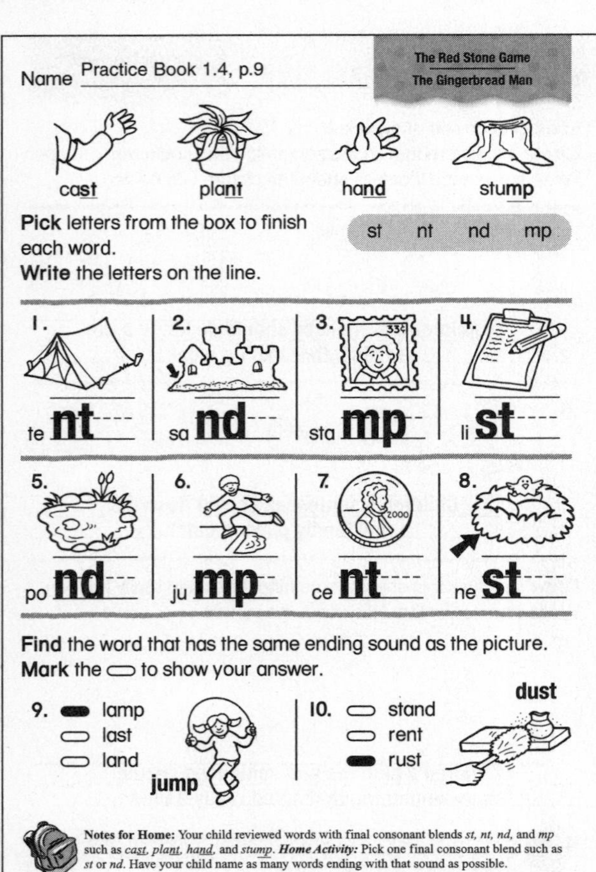

The Red Stone Game
The Gingerbread Man

Name Practice Book 1.4, p.9

cast plant hand stump

**Pick** letters from the box to finish each word.
**Write** the letters on the line.

st nt nd mp

1. te **nt**
2. sa **nd**
3. sta **mp**
4. li **st**
5. po **nd**
6. ju **mp**
7. ce **nt**
8. ne **st**

**Find** the word that has the same ending sound as the picture.
**Mark** the ⬭ to show your answer.

9. (jump) ● lamp ○ last ○ land
10. (dust) ○ stand ○ rent ● rust

**Notes for Home:** Your child reviewed words with final consonant blends *st, nt, nd,* and *mp* such as *cast, plant, hand,* and *stump.* *Home Activity:* Pick one final consonant blend such as *st* or *nd.* Have your child name as many words ending with that sound as possible.

Level 1.4 Phonics: Final Consonant Blends Review 9

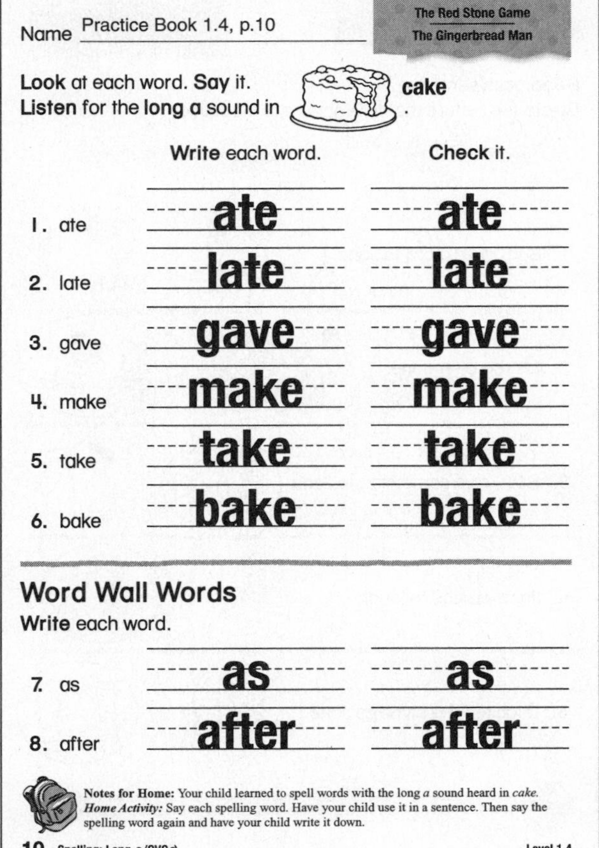

The Red Stone Game
The Gingerbread Man

Name Practice Book 1.4, p.10

**Look** at each word. **Say** it.
**Listen** for the **long a** sound in cake.

| | Write each word. | Check it. |
|---|---|---|
| 1. ate | ate | ate |
| 2. late | late | late |
| 3. gave | gave | gave |
| 4. make | make | make |
| 5. take | take | take |
| 6. bake | bake | bake |

**Word Wall Words**
**Write** each word.

| | | |
|---|---|---|
| 7. as | as | as |
| 8. after | after | after |

**Notes for Home:** Your child learned to spell words with the long *a* sound heard in *cake.* *Home Activity:* Say each spelling word. Have your child use it in a sentence. Then say the spelling word again and have your child write it down.

10 Spelling: Long *a* (CVC*e*) Level 1.4

Name Practice Book 1.4, p.11

The Red Stone Game
The Gingerbread Man

**Read** the sentence.
**Underline** the verb.
**Write** the verb on the line.

1. Dan bakes a cake.
**bakes**

2. Mom eats the cake.
**eats**

3. Dan calls Dad.
**calls**

4. Dad runs home fast.
**runs**

5. Dad asks for more!
**asks**

**Notes for Home:** Your child identified and wrote verbs—words that show action. *Home Activity:* Read a story with your child. Ask your child to point out the verbs in the sentences. Later, make a list of some of the action words and take turns acting them out.

Level 1.4 Grammar: Verbs (Action Words) 11

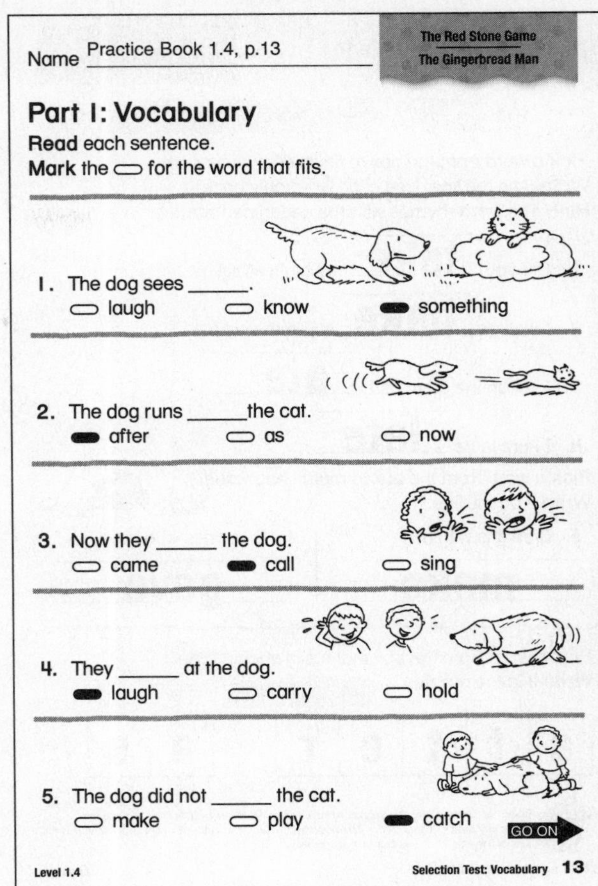

Name Practice Book 1.4, p.13

The Red Stone Game
The Gingerbread Man

## Part 1: Vocabulary

**Read** each sentence.
**Mark** the ⬭ for the word that fits.

1. The dog sees ______.
⬭ laugh ⬭ know ⬬ something

2. The dog runs ______ the cat.
⬬ after ⬭ as ⬭ now

3. Now they ______ the dog.
⬭ came ⬬ call ⬭ sing

4. They ______ at the dog.
⬬ laugh ⬭ carry ⬭ hold

5. The dog did not ______ the cat.
⬭ make ⬭ play ⬬ catch

GO ON

Level 1.4 Selection Test: Vocabulary 13

Name Practice Book 1.4, p.14

The Gingerbread Man

## Part 2: Comprehension

**Read** each question.
**Mark** the ⬭ for the answer.

**Directions: You may wish to read the questions and answer choices to the children.**

6. Who makes the Gingerbread Man?
⬭ the man
⬬ the woman
⬭ the girl

7. What does the Gingerbread Man do first?
⬬ runs from the farm
⬭ sees some water
⬭ takes a ride

8. Why does the Gingerbread Man laugh?
⬬ No one can catch him.
⬭ He wants to get wet.
⬭ The fox is funny.

9. What does the Gingerbread Man think the fox will do?
⬭ eat him up
⬬ help him
⬭ bring him water

10. What part of the story could be real?
⬭ A gingerbread man runs away.
⬭ A fox talks to a gingerbread man.
⬬ A boy wants to eat a gingerbread man.

STOP

14 Selection Test: Comprehension Level 1.4

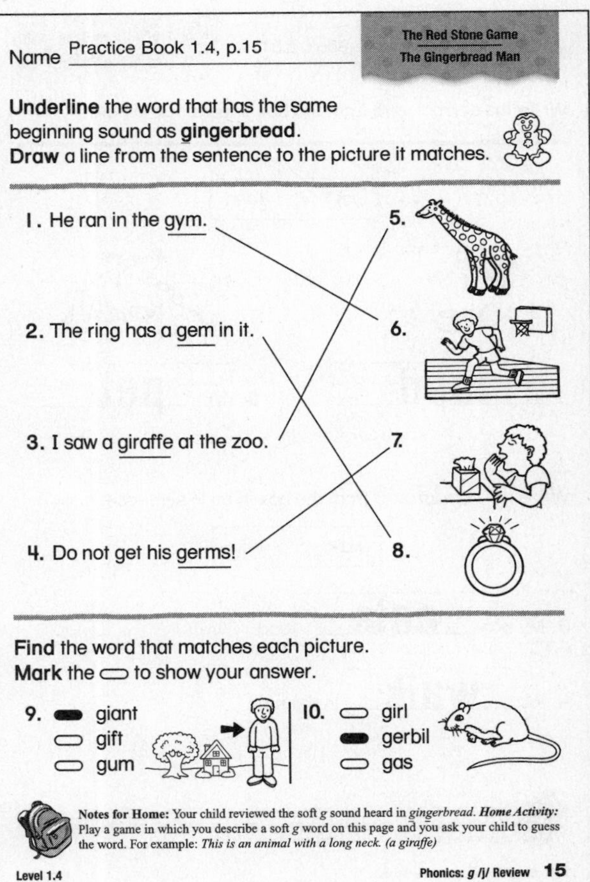

Name Practice Book 1.4, p.15

The Red Stone Game
The Gingerbread Man

**Underline** the word that has the same beginning sound as **gingerbread**.
**Draw** a line from the sentence to the picture it matches.

1. He ran in the gym.
2. The ring has a gem in it.
3. I saw a giraffe at the zoo.
4. Do not get his germs!

5.
6.
7.
8.

**Find** the word that matches each picture.
**Mark** the ⬭ to show your answer.

9. ⬬ giant ⬭ gift ⬭ gum

10. ⬭ girl ⬬ gerbil ⬭ gas

**Notes for Home:** Your child reviewed the soft *g* sound heard in *gingerbread*. *Home Activity:* Play a game in which you describe a soft *g* word on this page and you ask your child to guess the word. For example: *This is an animal with a long neck. (a giraffe)*

Level 1.4 Phonics: *g* /j/ Review 15

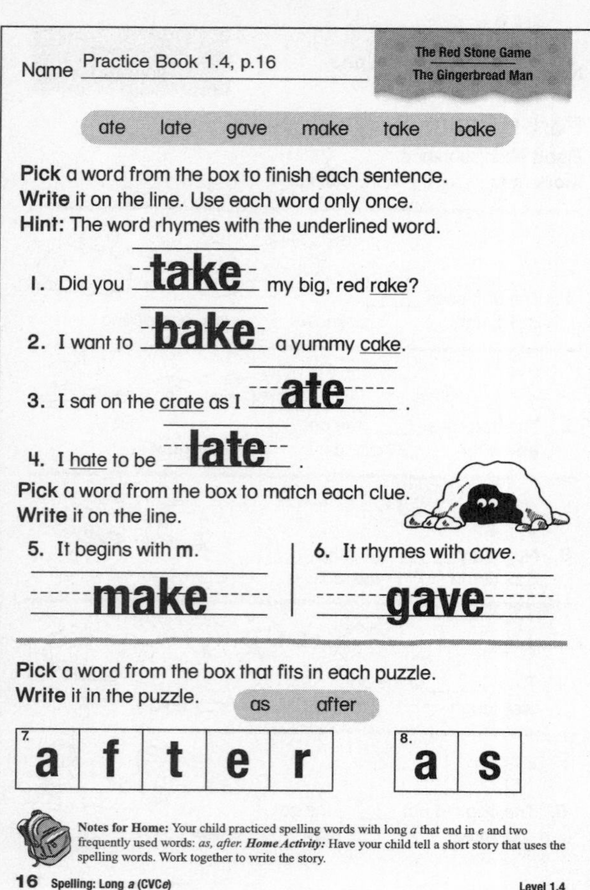

The Red Stone Game
The Gingerbread Man

Name Practice Book 1.4, p.16

ate late gave make take bake

**Pick** a word from the box to finish each sentence.
**Write** it on the line. Use each word only once.
**Hint:** The word rhymes with the underlined word.

1. Did you **take** my big, red rake?
2. I want to **bake** a yummy cake.
3. I sat on the crate as I **ate**.
4. I hate to be **late**.

**Pick** a word from the box to match each clue.
**Write** it on the line.

5. It begins with **m**. **make**
6. It rhymes with *cave*. **gave**

**Pick** a word from the box that fits in each puzzle.
**Write** it in the puzzle.

as after

7. a f t e r
8. a s

**Notes for Home:** Your child practiced spelling words with long *a* that end in *e* and two frequently used words: *as, after. **Home Activity:*** Have your child tell a short story that uses the spelling words. Work together to write the story.

16 Spelling: Long *a* (CVC*e*) Level 1.4

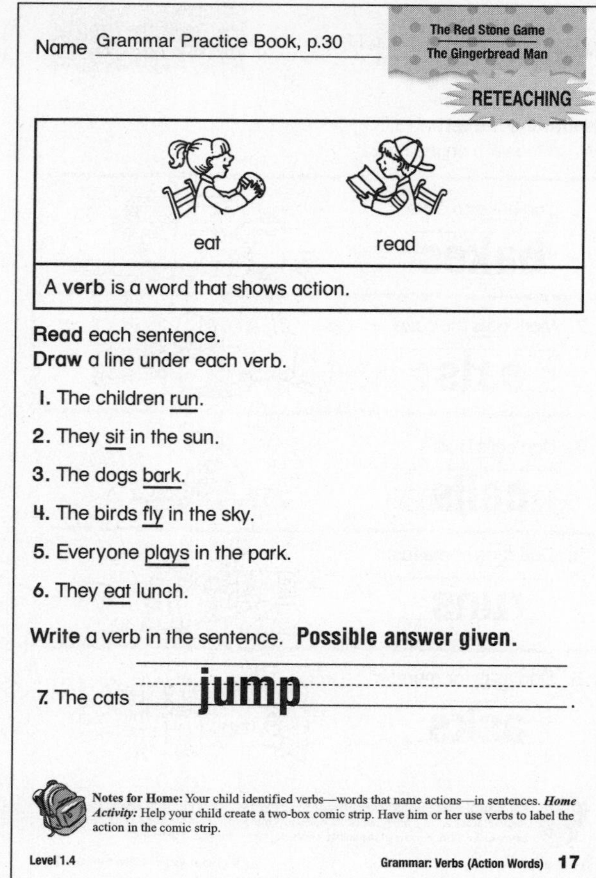

The Red Stone Game
The Gingerbread Man
RETEACHING

Name Grammar Practice Book, p.30

eat read

A **verb** is a word that shows action.

**Read** each sentence.
**Draw** a line under each verb.

1. The children run.
2. They sit in the sun.
3. The dogs bark.
4. The birds fly in the sky.
5. Everyone plays in the park.
6. They eat lunch.

**Write** a verb in the sentence. **Possible answer given.**

7. The cats **jump**.

**Notes for Home:** Your child identified verbs—words that name actions—in sentences. ***Home Activity:*** Help your child create a two-box comic strip. Have him or her use verbs to label the action in the comic strip.

Level 1.4 Grammar: Verbs (Action Words) 17

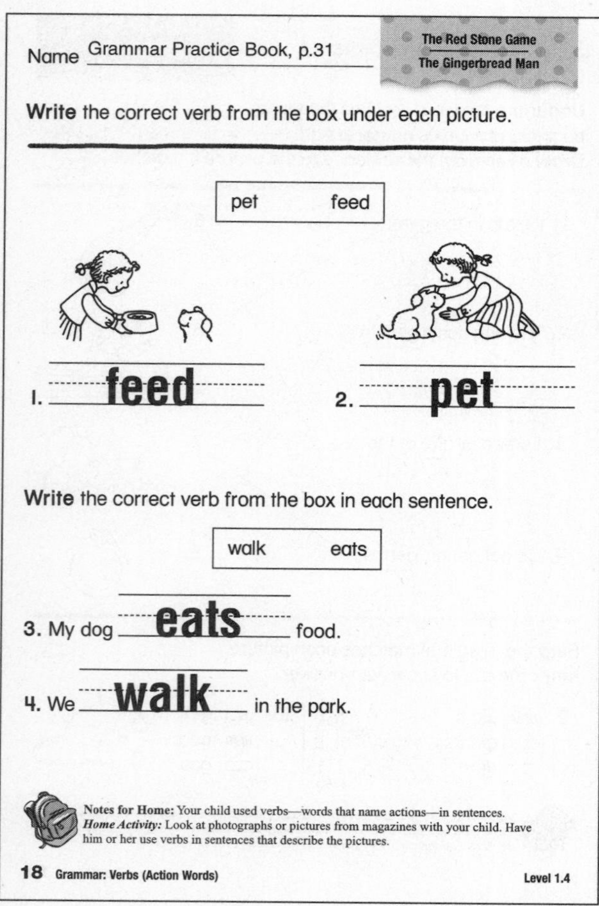

The Red Stone Game
The Gingerbread Man

Name Grammar Practice Book, p.31

**Write** the correct verb from the box under each picture.

pet feed

1. **feed**
2. **pet**

**Write** the correct verb from the box in each sentence.

walk eats

3. My dog **eats** food.
4. We **walk** in the park.

**Notes for Home:** Your child used verbs—words that name actions—in sentences. ***Home Activity:*** Look at photographs or pictures from magazines with your child. Have him or her use verbs in sentences that describe the pictures.

18 Grammar: Verbs (Action Words) Level 1.4

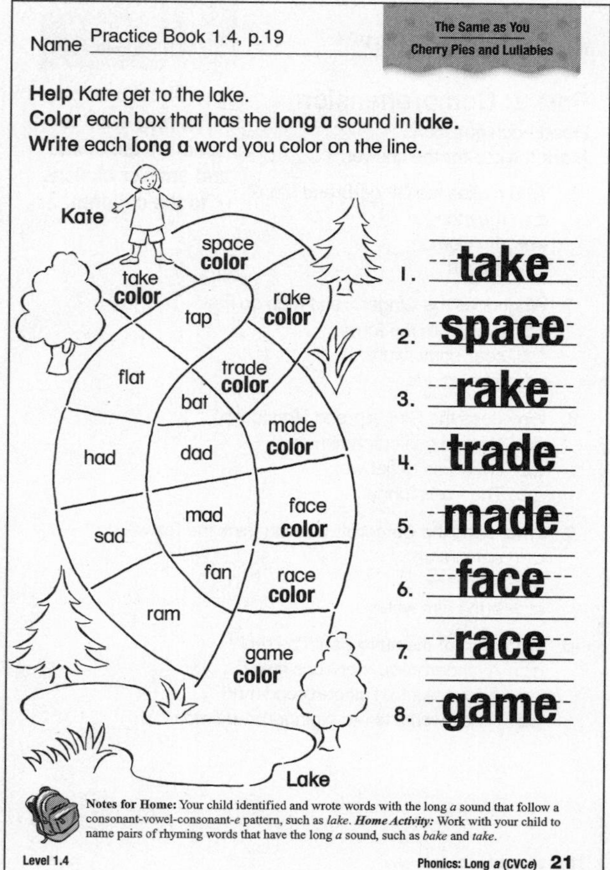

The Same as You
Cherry Pies and Lullabies

Name Practice Book 1.4, p.19

**Help** Kate get to the lake.
**Color** each box that has the **long a** sound in **lake.**
**Write** each **long a** word you color on the line.



1. **take**
2. **space**
3. **rake**
4. **trade**
5. **made**
6. **face**
7. **race**
8. **game**

**Notes for Home:** Your child identified and wrote words with the long *a* sound that follow a consonant-vowel-consonant-*e* pattern, such as *lake. **Home Activity:*** Work with your child to name pairs of rhyming words that have the long *a* sound, such as *bake* and *take*.

Level 1.4 Phonics: Long *a* (CVC*e*) 21

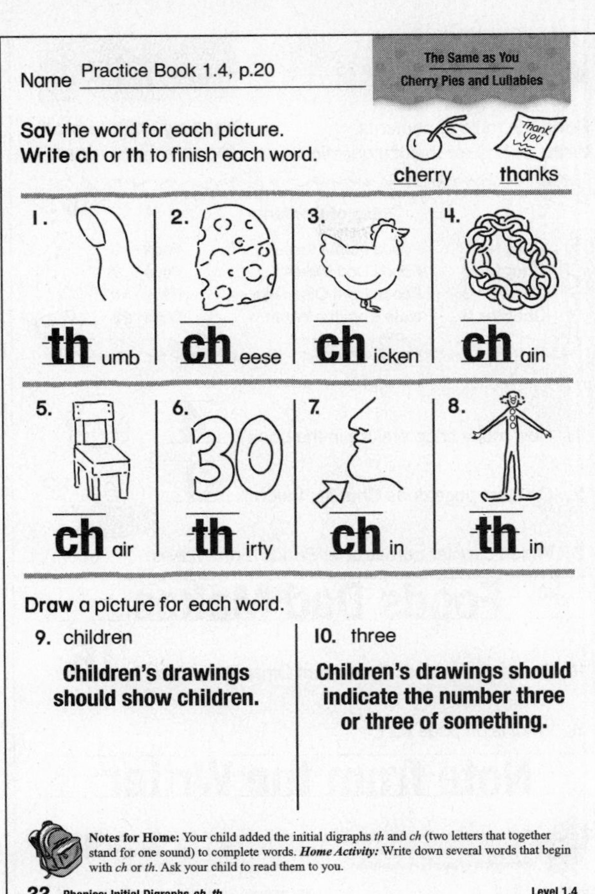
Name Practice Book 1.4, p.20

The Same as You
Cherry Pies and Lullabies

**Say** the word for each picture.
**Write ch** or **th** to finish each word.

cherry thanks

1. **th** umb
2. **ch** eese
3. **ch** icken
4. **ch** ain
5. **ch** air
6. **th** irty
7. **ch** in
8. **th** in

**Draw** a picture for each word.

9. children

**Children's drawings should show children.**

10. three

**Children's drawings should indicate the number three or three of something.**

**Notes for Home:** Your child added the initial digraphs *th* and *ch* (two letters that together stand for one sound) to complete words. ***Home Activity:*** Write down several words that begin with *ch* or *th*. Ask your child to read them to you.

22 Phonics: Initial Digraphs *ch, th* Level 1.4

Name Practice Book 1.4, p.21

The Same as You
Cherry Pies and Lullabies

**Pick** a word from the box to finish each sentence.
**Write** it on the line.

every made mother of was

1. My mother **made** me a doll.
2. The doll was made **of** rags.
3. It **was** soft.
4. Now my **mother** sings.
5. She sings to us **every** time we go to bed.

**Notes for Home:** This week your child learned to read the words *every, made, mother, of,* and *was*. ***Home Activity:*** Help your child write or tell you sentences that include these words.

Level 1.4 High-Frequency Words 23

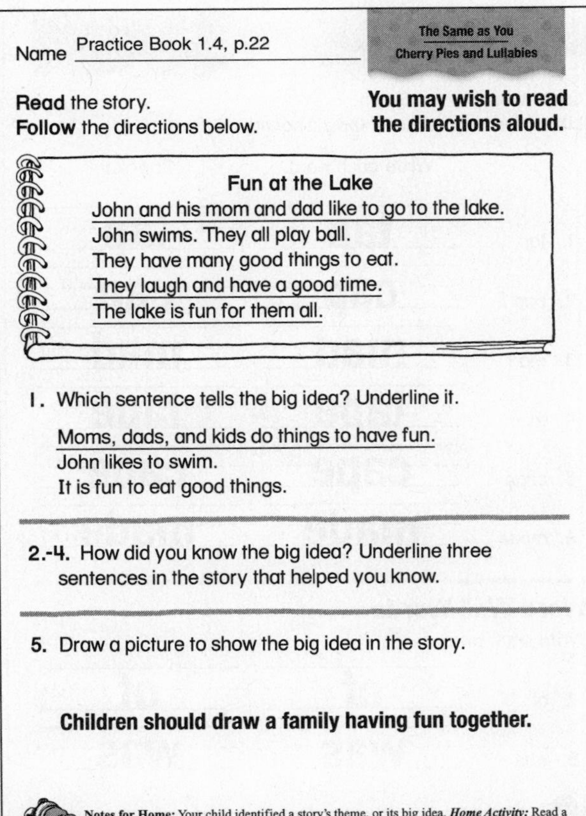
Name Practice Book 1.4, p.22

The Same as You
Cherry Pies and Lullabies

**Read** the story.
**Follow** the directions below.

**You may wish to read the directions aloud.**

Fun at the Lake

John and his mom and dad like to go to the lake.
John swims. They all play ball.
They have many good things to eat.
They laugh and have a good time.
The lake is fun for them all.

1. Which sentence tells the big idea? Underline it.

Moms, dads, and kids do things to have fun.
John likes to swim.
It is fun to eat good things.

2.-4. How did you know the big idea? Underline three sentences in the story that helped you know.

5. Draw a picture to show the big idea in the story.

**Children should draw a family having fun together.**

**Notes for Home:** Your child identified a story's theme, or its big idea. ***Home Activity:*** Read a story with your child. Discuss the story's big idea. Help your child connect this idea to something in his or her own life.

24 Theme Level 1.4

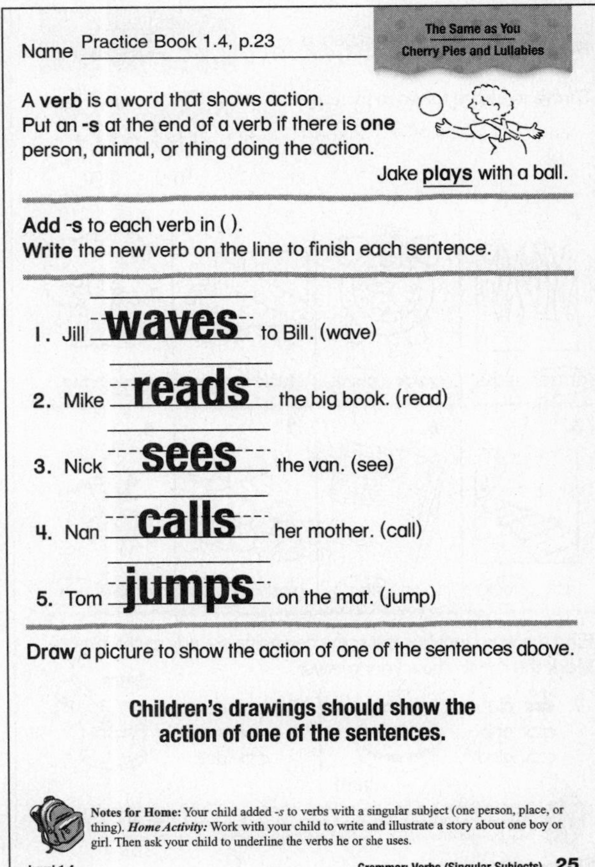
Name Practice Book 1.4, p.23

The Same as You
Cherry Pies and Lullabies

A **verb** is a word that shows action.
Put an **-s** at the end of a verb if there is **one** person, animal, or thing doing the action.

Jake plays with a ball.

**Add -s** to each verb in ( ).
**Write** the new verb on the line to finish each sentence.

1. Jill **waves** to Bill. (wave)
2. Mike **reads** the big book. (read)
3. Nick **sees** the van. (see)
4. Nan **calls** her mother. (call)
5. Tom **jumps** on the mat. (jump)

**Draw** a picture to show the action of one of the sentences above.

**Children's drawings should show the action of one of the sentences.**

**Notes for Home:** Your child added *-s* to verbs with a singular subject (one person, place, or thing). ***Home Activity:*** Work with your child to write and illustrate a story about one boy or girl. Then ask your child to underline the verbs he or she uses.

Level 1.4 Grammar: Verbs (Singular Subjects) 25

The Same as You
Cherry Pies and Lullabies

Name Practice Book 1.4, p.24

**Pick** a word from the box to finish each sentence.
**Write** it on the line.

every made mother of was

1. My **mother** likes to bake.
2. This is one **of** her cakes.
3. **Every** cake she bakes is good!
4. Once she **made** a pink cake.
5. It **was** good.

**Notes for Home:** Your child completed sentences using words that he or she learned this week. ***Home Activity:*** Recall with your child a time when the two of you baked or cooked together. Work together to write sentences about it using as many of these words as possible.

26 Vocabulary/High-Frequency Words Level 1.4

The Same as You
Cherry Pies and Lullabies

Name Practice Book 1.4, p.25

**Read** the table of contents.
**Write** an answer to each question.

**You may wish to read the questions aloud.**

Table of Contents

| | | | |
|---|---|---|---|
| Chapter 1 | Foods Mom Makes | Page | 3 |
| Chapter 2 | Foods Dad Makes | Page | 9 |
| Chapter 3 | Foods from Other Places | Page | 16 |
| Chapter 4 | Note from the Writer | Page | 22 |

1. How many chapters are in the book? **4**
2. On what page does Chapter 1 start? **3**
3. Which chapter comes after Foods Mom Makes?
**Foods Dad Makes**
4. On what page does Foods from Other Places start? **16**
5. What is on page 22?
**Note from the Writer**

**Notes for Home:** Your child read a table of contents. ***Home Activity:*** Before you read a chapter book to your child, look at the table of contents together. Talk about the different chapter titles, the number of pages per chapter, and anything else listed in the table of contents.

Level 1.4 Research and Study Skills: Table of Contents 27

The Same as You
Cherry Pies and Lullabies

Name Practice Book 1.4, p.26

**Circle** the word for each picture.

frog clap

1. (grass) glass
2. crack (clock)
3. tuck (truck)
4. (tree) tee
5. tack (track)
6. fog (flag)
7. glad (grapes)
8. crab (claw)

**Find** the word that has the same beginning sounds as the picture.
**Mark** the ⬭ to show your answer.

9. ● club ⬭ crib ⬭ glad — clam
10. ⬭ dump ● dress ⬭ doll — drum

**Notes for Home:** Your child reviewed words with initial *r* and *l* blends, such as *frog* and *clap*. ***Home Activity:*** Help your child make flashcards for words with these blends. He or she can write the word on one side of a card and draw a picture to illustrate it on the other side.

28 Phonics: Initial *r* and *l* Blends Review Level 1.4

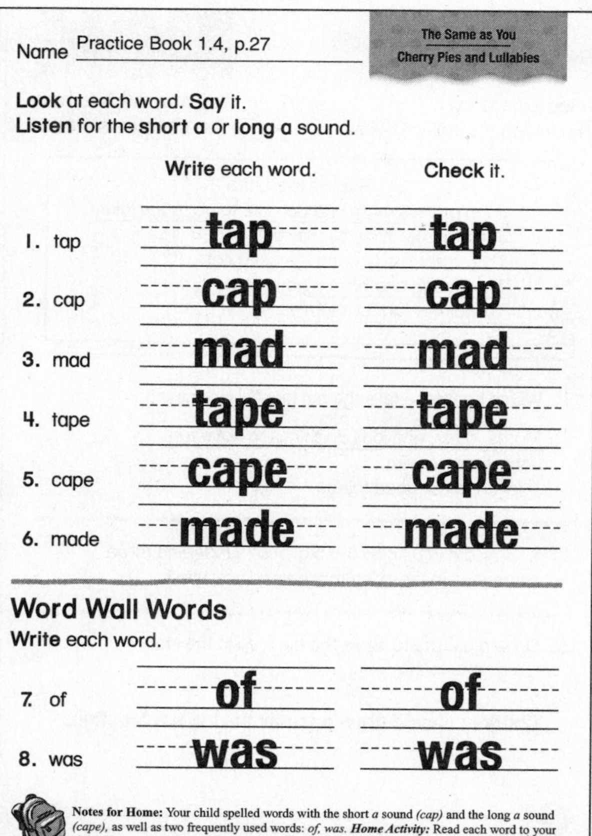

The Same as You
Cherry Pies and Lullabies

Name Practice Book 1.4, p.27

**Look** at each word. **Say** it.
**Listen** for the **short *a*** or **long *a*** sound.

| | Write each word. | Check it. |
|---|---|---|
| 1. tap | **tap** | **tap** |
| 2. cap | **cap** | **cap** |
| 3. mad | **mad** | **mad** |
| 4. tape | **tape** | **tape** |
| 5. cape | **cape** | **cape** |
| 6. made | **made** | **made** |

**Word Wall Words**
**Write** each word.

| | | |
|---|---|---|
| 7. of | **of** | **of** |
| 8. was | **was** | **was** |

**Notes for Home:** Your child spelled words with the short *a* sound *(cap)* and the long *a* sound *(cape)*, as well as two frequently used words: *of, was.* ***Home Activity:*** Read each word to your child. Have your child sort the words into short *a* words, long *a* words, and Word Wall Words.

Level 1.4 Spelling: Long *a* / Short *a* 29

Name Practice Book 1.4, p.28

The Same as You
Cherry Pies and Lullabies

**Circle** the verb that tells what one person or animal does.
**Write** the verb on the line to finish each sentence.

1. Mom **reads** a book. (reads circled / read)
2. Dad **sings** a song. (sing / sings circled)
3. Sally **sleeps** in her bed. (sleep / sleeps circled)
4. Skip **sits** by the bed. (sits circled / sit)
5. Fluff **naps** on the bed. (nap / naps circled)

**Notes for Home:** Your child chose verbs to show the action of one person or animal. *Home Activity:* Have your child say a sentence about each of your family members. Ask your child to identify the verbs he or she uses in each sentence.

30 Grammar: Verbs (Singular Subjects) Level 1.4

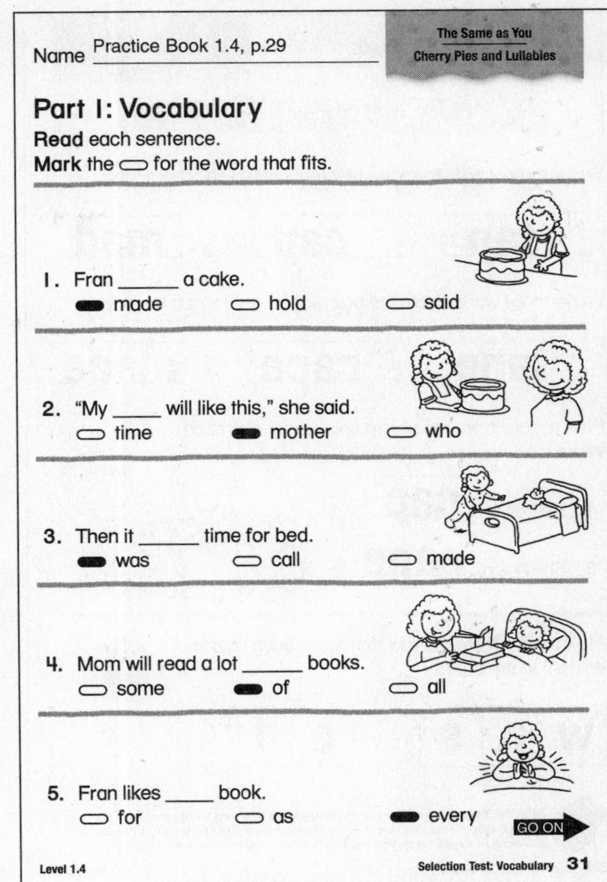

Name Practice Book 1.4, p.29

The Same as You
Cherry Pies and Lullabies

## Part 1: Vocabulary

**Read** each sentence.
**Mark** the ⬭ for the word that fits.

1. Fran ____ a cake.
   - ● made
   - ⬭ hold
   - ⬭ said
2. "My ____ will like this," she said.
   - ⬭ time
   - ● mother
   - ⬭ who
3. Then it ____ time for bed.
   - ● was
   - ⬭ call
   - ⬭ made
4. Mom will read a lot ____ books.
   - ⬭ some
   - ● of
   - ⬭ all
5. Fran likes ____ book.
   - ⬭ for
   - ⬭ as
   - ● every

GO ON

Level 1.4 Selection Test: Vocabulary 31

Name Practice Book 1.4, p.30

Cherry Pies and Lullabies

## Part 2: Comprehension

**Read** each question.
**Mark** the ⬭ for the answer.

**Directions: You may wish to read the questions and answer choices to the children.**

6. What does the grandmother bake?
   - ● cherry pie
   - ⬭ hot dogs
   - ⬭ plum pie
7. Who made a crown of flowers for the girl?
   - ⬭ her great-grandmother
   - ⬭ her grandmother
   - ● her mother
8. Why does the mother give the girl a quilt?
   - ⬭ The girl asks for one.
   - ● The mother had one when she was small.
   - ⬭ The grandmother tells the mother to.
9. Every woman in this story
   - ● has a little girl.
   - ⬭ plants flowers.
   - ⬭ bakes all day.
10. In this story, every woman
    - ● does the same things in her own way.
    - ⬭ has the same crown of flowers.
    - ⬭ lives in the same place.

STOP

32 Selection Test: Comprehension Level 1.4

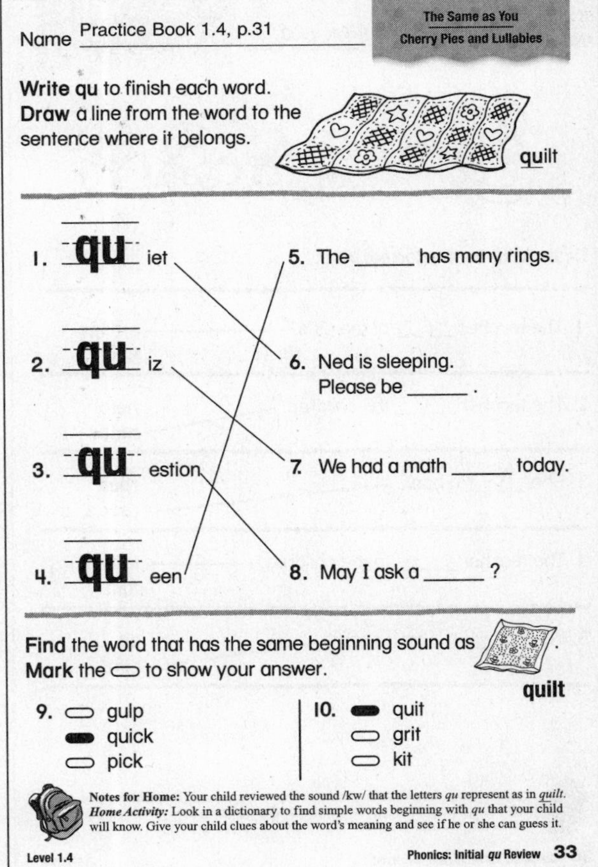

Name Practice Book 1.4, p.31

The Same as You
Cherry Pies and Lullabies

**Write qu** to finish each word.
**Draw** a line from the word to the sentence where it belongs.

quilt

1. **qu**iet — 6
2. **qu**iz — 7
3. **qu**estion — 8
4. **qu**een — 5

5. The ____ has many rings.
6. Ned is sleeping. Please be ____.
7. We had a math ____ today.
8. May I ask a ____ ?

**Find** the word that has the same beginning sound as quilt.
**Mark** the ⬭ to show your answer.

9. 
   - ⬭ gulp
   - ● quick
   - ⬭ pick
10. 
    - ● quit
    - ⬭ grit
    - ⬭ kit

**Notes for Home:** Your child reviewed the sound /kw/ that the letters *qu* represent as in *quilt*. *Home Activity:* Look in a dictionary to find simple words beginning with *qu* that your child will know. Give your child clues about the word's meaning and see if he or she can guess it.

Level 1.4 Phonics: Initial *qu* Review 33

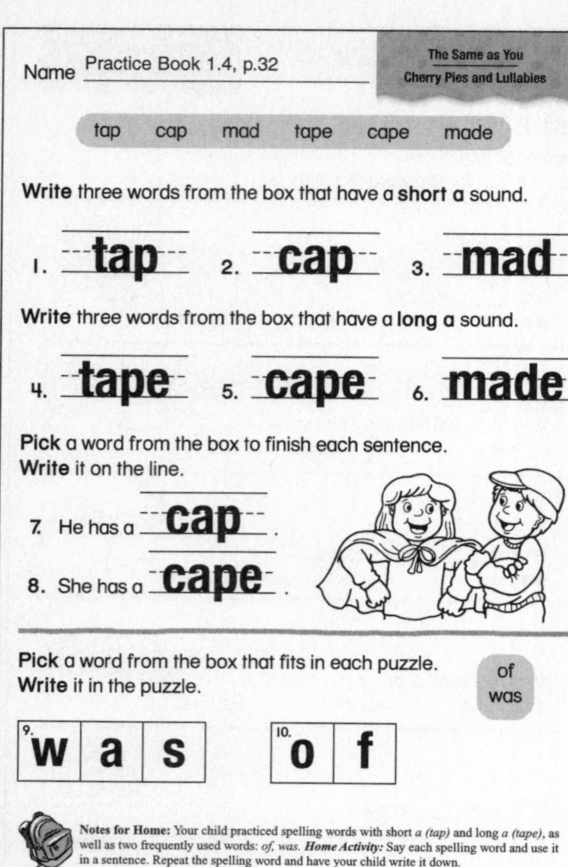

Name Practice Book 1.4, p.32

The Same as You
Cherry Pies and Lullabies

tap cap mad tape cape made

**Write** three words from the box that have a **short a** sound.

1. tap 2. cap 3. mad

**Write** three words from the box that have a **long a** sound.

4. tape 5. cape 6. made

**Pick** a word from the box to finish each sentence.
**Write** it on the line.

7. He has a cap.

8. She has a cape.

**Pick** a word from the box that fits in each puzzle.
**Write** it in the puzzle.

of
was

9. w a s

10. o f

**Notes for Home:** Your child practiced spelling words with short *a (tap)* and long *a (tape)*, as well as two frequently used words: *of, was*. ***Home Activity:*** Say each spelling word and use it in a sentence. Repeat the spelling word and have your child write it down.

34 Spelling: Long *a* / Short *a* Level 1.4

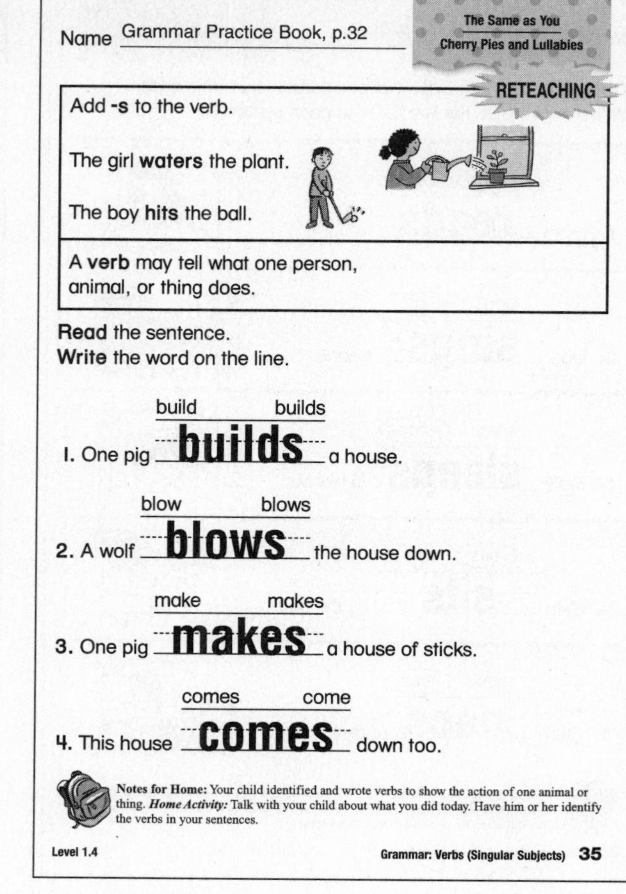

Name Grammar Practice Book, p.32

The Same as You
Cherry Pies and Lullabies

RETEACHING

Add **-s** to the verb.

The girl **waters** the plant.

The boy **hits** the ball.

A **verb** may tell what one person, animal, or thing does.

**Read** the sentence.
**Write** the word on the line.

build builds
1. One pig builds a house.

blow blows
2. A wolf blows the house down.

make makes
3. One pig makes a house of sticks.

comes come
4. This house comes down too.

**Notes for Home:** Your child identified and wrote verbs to show the action of one animal or thing. ***Home Activity:*** Talk with your child about what you did today. Have him or her identify the verbs in your sentences.

Level 1.4 Grammar: Verbs (Singular Subjects) 35

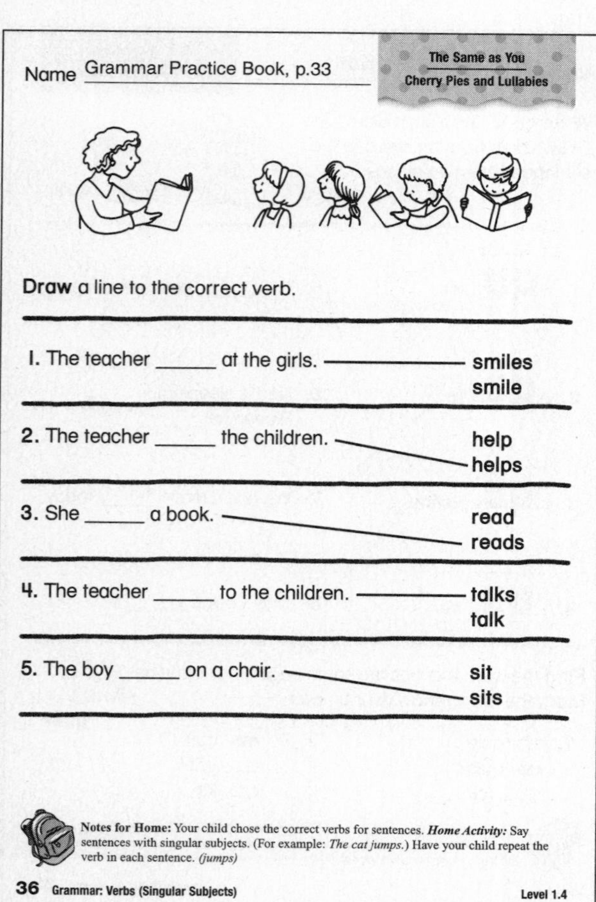

Name Grammar Practice Book, p.33

The Same as You
Cherry Pies and Lullabies

**Draw** a line to the correct verb.

1. The teacher ______ at the girls. — smiles / smile

2. The teacher ______ the children. — help / helps

3. She ______ a book. — read / reads

4. The teacher ______ to the children. — talks / talk

5. The boy ______ on a chair. — sit / sits

**Notes for Home:** Your child chose the correct verbs for sentences. ***Home Activity:*** Say sentences with singular subjects. (For example: *The cat jumps.*) Have your child repeat the verb in each sentence. *(jumps)*

36 Grammar: Verbs (Singular Subjects) Level 1.4

Name Practice Book 1.4, p.35

Rose and Grandma
Our Family Get-Together

**Pick** the word with the **long o** sound to finish each sentence.
**Write** it on the line.

rope

home hot
1. Ben walked home.

bone boss
2. Pug wants a bone.

stop stone
3. Hal picks up a stone.

joke job
4. I told my best joke.

not nose
5. Sal bumped her nose.

**Notes for Home:** Your child identified and wrote words with the long *o* sound that follow the pattern consonant-vowel-consonant-*e* (CVC*e*) as in *rope*. ***Home Activity:*** Work with your child to write a story using as many long *o* words that follow the CVC*e* pattern as possible.

Level 1.4 Phonics: Long *o* (CVC*e*) 39

Rose and Grandma
Our Family Get-Together

Name Practice Book 1.4, p.36

**Say** the word for each picture.
**Write sh** or **wh** to finish each word.

**sh**irt **wh**eat

1. **sh**op
2. **sh**ip
3. **wh**eel
4. **wh**ale
5. **wh**isper
6. **sh**oe
7. **wh**iskers
8. **sh**eep
9. **wh**istle
10. **sh**ell

**Notes for Home:** Your child identified words that begin with *sh* and *wh* as in *shirt* and *wheat*. ***Home Activity:*** Write a list of words that begin with *sh* and *wh*. Help your child read the words aloud and draw pictures of them.

40 Phonics: Initial Digraphs *sh, wh* Level 1.4

Rose and Grandma
Our Family Get-Together

Name Practice Book 1.4, p.37

**Pick** a word from the box to finish each sentence.
**Write** it on the line.

father going has thank very

1. Jim walks with his **father**.
2. They are **going** to see Grandma.
3. Jim **has** a cake for her.
4. He wants to **thank** her for the game she gave him.
5. He likes the game **very** much.

**Notes for Home:** This week your child is learning to read the words *father, going, has, thank,* and *very*. ***Home Activity:*** Write simple sentences with these words. Help your child read the sentences aloud. Have your child point to the words he or she knows as you read.

Level 1.4 High-Frequency Words 41

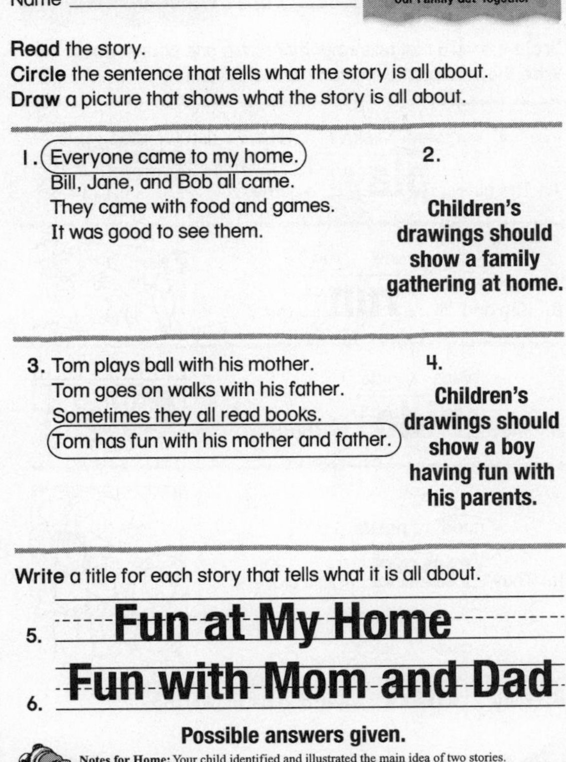

Rose and Grandma
Our Family Get-Together

Name Practice Book 1.4, p.38

**Read** the story.
**Circle** the sentence that tells what the story is all about.
**Draw** a picture that shows what the story is all about.

1. (Everyone came to my home.) Bill, Jane, and Bob all came. They came with food and games. It was good to see them.

2. **Children's drawings should show a family gathering at home.**

3. Tom plays ball with his mother. Tom goes on walks with his father. Sometimes they all read books. (Tom has fun with his mother and father.)

4. **Children's drawings should show a boy having fun with his parents.**

**Write** a title for each story that tells what it is all about.

5. **Fun at My Home**
6. **Fun with Mom and Dad**

**Possible answers given.**

**Notes for Home:** Your child identified and illustrated the main idea of two stories. ***Home Activity:*** Invite your child to name his or her favorite story. Then ask your child to tell you in a sentence or two what the story is all about.

42 Main Idea Level 1.4

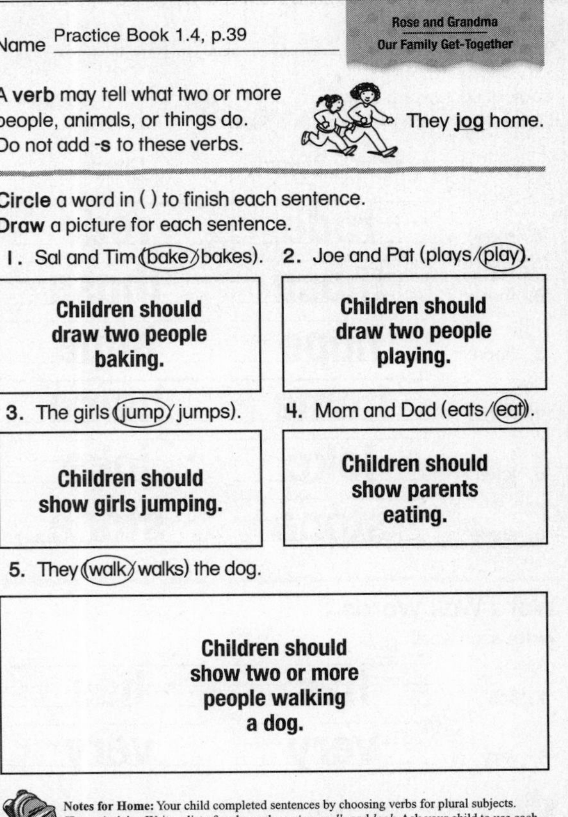

Rose and Grandma
Our Family Get-Together

Name Practice Book 1.4, p.39

A **verb** may tell what two or more people, animals, or things do. Do not add **-s** to these verbs.

They <u>jog</u> home.

**Circle** a word in ( ) to finish each sentence.
**Draw** a picture for each sentence.

1. Sal and Tim ((bake)/bakes). **Children should draw two people baking.**
2. Joe and Pat (plays/(play)). **Children should draw two people playing.**
3. The girls ((jump)/jumps). **Children should show girls jumping.**
4. Mom and Dad (eats/(eat)). **Children should show parents eating.**
5. They ((walk)/walks) the dog. **Children should show two or more people walking a dog.**

**Notes for Home:** Your child completed sentences by choosing verbs for plural subjects. ***Home Activity:*** Write a list of verbs such as *sing, walk,* and *look*. Ask your child to use each verb in a sentence that tells about more than one person doing the action.

Level 1.4 Grammar: Verbs (Plural Subjects) 43

Name Practice Book 1.4, p.40

Rose and Grandma
Our Family Get-Together

**Pick** a word from the box to finish each sentence.
**Write** it on the line. Use each word only once.

cousins father going has thank very

1. Her **father** and mother took Jill on a trip.
2. They went to see all of her **cousins**.
3. She **has** a lot to tell them.
4. Jill had a **very** good time.
5. She is **going** to see them again.
6. Jill calls to **thank** them for the fun day.

**Notes for Home:** Your child completed sentences using words that he or she learned this week. ***Home Activity:*** Work with your child to write a story about a family gathering using as many of these words as possible.

44 Vocabulary/High-Frequency Words Level 1.4

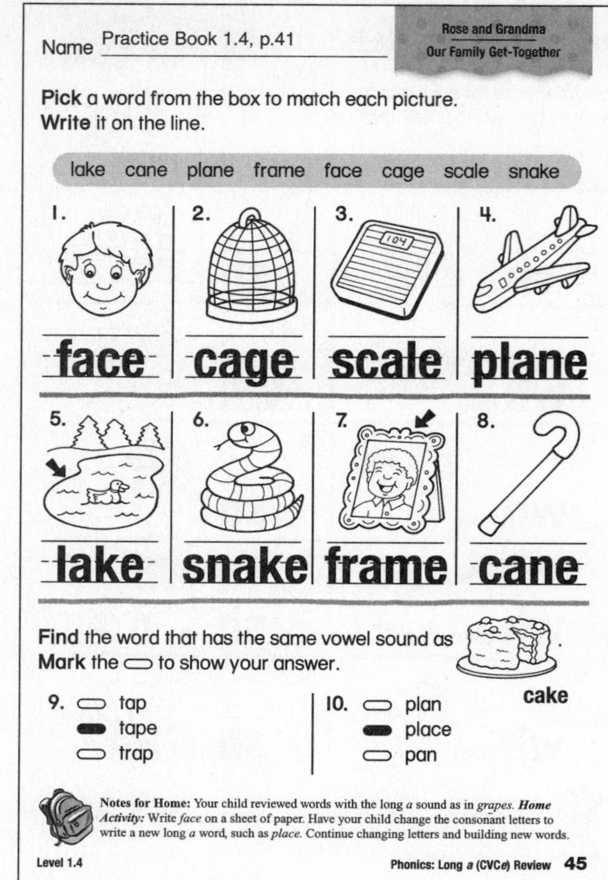

Name Practice Book 1.4, p.41

Rose and Grandma
Our Family Get-Together

**Pick** a word from the box to match each picture.
**Write** it on the line.

lake cane plane frame face cage scale snake

1. **face** 2. **cage** 3. **scale** 4. **plane**
5. **lake** 6. **snake** 7. **frame** 8. **cane**

**Find** the word that has the same vowel sound as cake.
**Mark** the ⊂⊃ to show your answer.

9. ⊂⊃ tap
   ● tape
   ⊂⊃ trap

10. ⊂⊃ plan
   ● place
   ⊂⊃ pan

**Notes for Home:** Your child reviewed words with the long *a* sound as in *grapes.* ***Home Activity:*** Write *face* on a sheet of paper. Have your child change the consonant letters to write a new long *a* word, such as *place.* Continue changing letters and building new words.

Level 1.4 Phonics: Long *a* (CVC*e*) Review 45

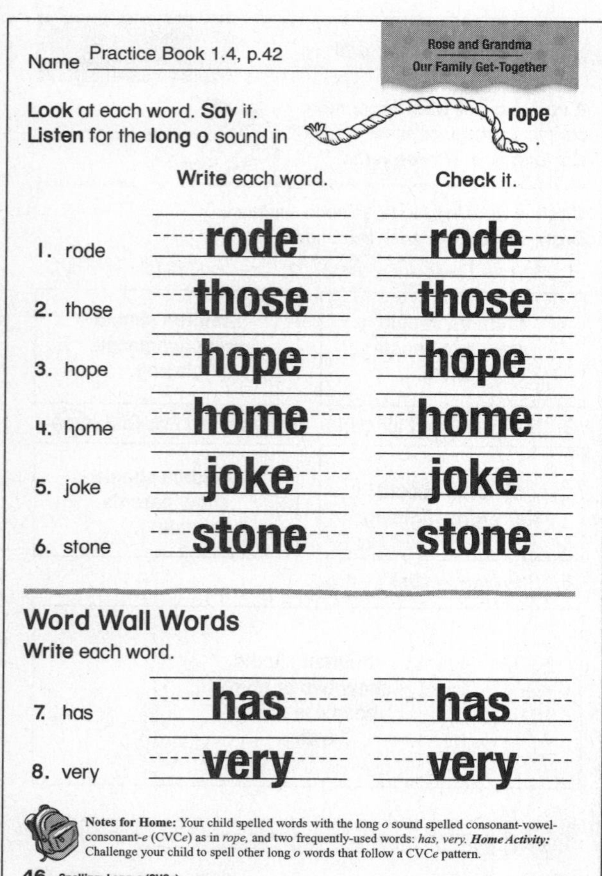

Name Practice Book 1.4, p.42

Rose and Grandma
Our Family Get-Together

**Look** at each word. **Say** it.
**Listen** for the **long o** sound in rope.

| | **Write** each word. | **Check** it. |
|---|---|---|
| 1. rode | rode | rode |
| 2. those | those | those |
| 3. hope | hope | hope |
| 4. home | home | home |
| 5. joke | joke | joke |
| 6. stone | stone | stone |

## Word Wall Words

**Write** each word.

| | | |
|---|---|---|
| 7. has | has | has |
| 8. very | very | very |

**Notes for Home:** Your child spelled words with the long *o* sound spelled consonant-vowel-consonant-*e* (CVC*e*) as in *rope,* and two frequently-used words: *has, very.* ***Home Activity:*** Challenge your child to spell other long *o* words that follow a CVC*e* pattern.

46 Spelling: Long *o* (CVC*e*) Level 1.4

Name Practice Book 1.4, p.43

Rose and Grandma
Our Family Get-Together

**Circle** the verb that tells what more than one person does.
**Write** the verb on the line to finish each sentence.

1. (play) plays — The girls **play** a game.
2. runs (run) — Kim and Jill **run** away.
3. hides (hide) — They **hide** in a bush.
4. (need) needs — They **need** more players.
5. asks (ask) — They **ask** Ken and Bill to play too.

**Notes for Home:** Your child chose verbs to show the action of two or more people. ***Home Activity:*** Have your child tell you a story about the children in his or her class. Encourage your child to use plural subjects (two or more people) as he or she tells the story.

Level 1.4 Grammar: Verbs (Plural Subjects) 47

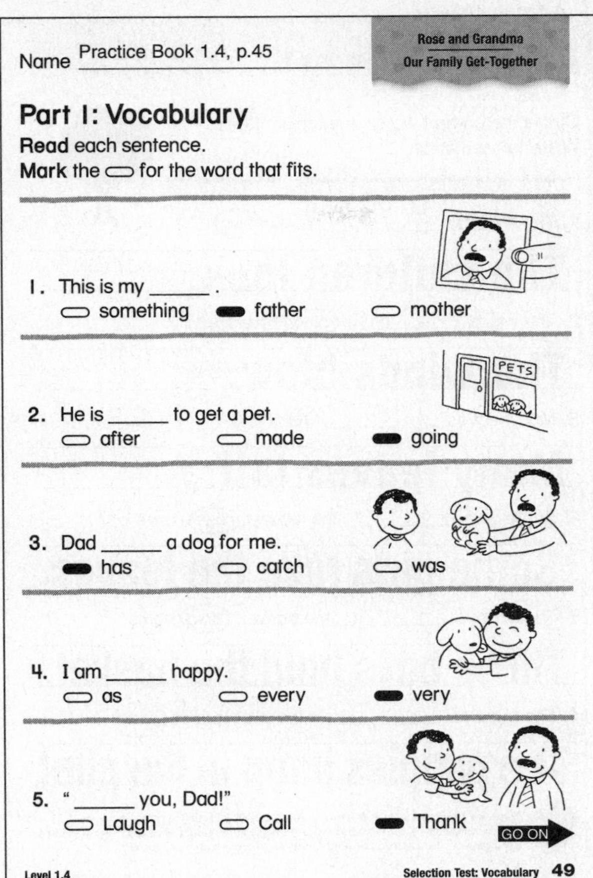
Name Practice Book 1.4, p.45

Rose and Grandma
Our Family Get-Together

## Part 1: Vocabulary

**Read** each sentence.
**Mark** the ⬭ for the word that fits.

1. This is my ______.
   - something
   - father (marked)
   - mother

2. He is ______ to get a pet.
   - after
   - made
   - going (marked)

3. Dad ______ a dog for me.
   - has (marked)
   - catch
   - was

4. I am ______ happy.
   - as
   - every
   - very (marked)

5. "______ you, Dad!"
   - Laugh
   - Call
   - Thank (marked)



Level 1.4 Selection Test: Vocabulary 49

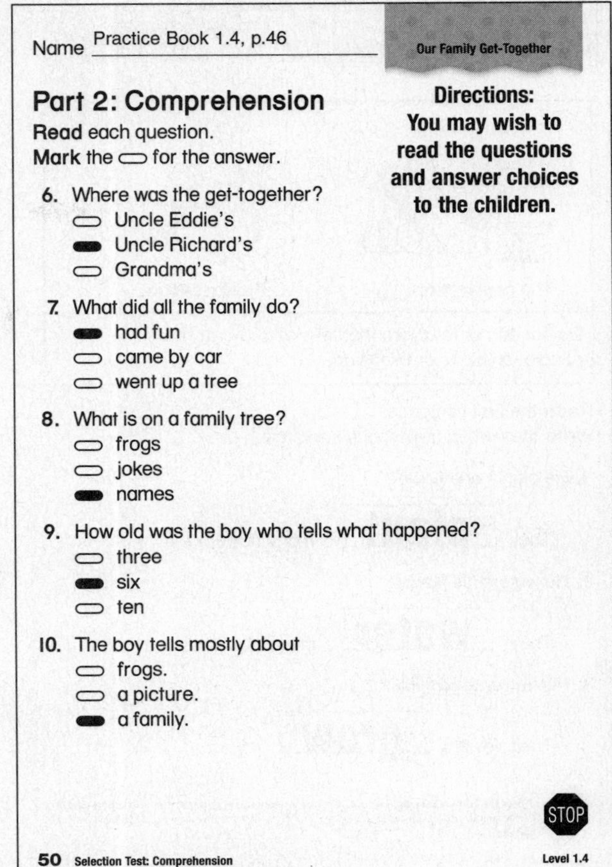
Name Practice Book 1.4, p.46

Our Family Get-Together

## Part 2: Comprehension

**Read** each question.
**Mark** the ⬭ for the answer.

**Directions: You may wish to read the questions and answer choices to the children.**

6. Where was the get-together?
   - Uncle Eddie's
   - Uncle Richard's (marked)
   - Grandma's

7. What did all the family do?
   - had fun (marked)
   - came by car
   - went up a tree

8. What is on a family tree?
   - frogs
   - jokes
   - names (marked)

9. How old was the boy who tells what happened?
   - three
   - six (marked)
   - ten

10. The boy tells mostly about
    - frogs.
    - a picture.
    - a family. (marked)



50 Selection Test: Comprehension Level 1.4

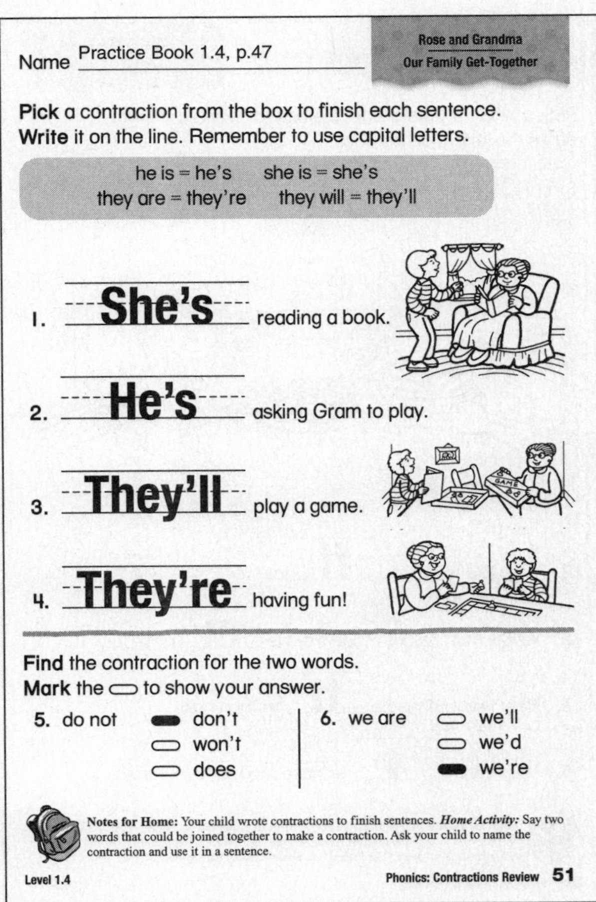
Name Practice Book 1.4, p.47

Rose and Grandma
Our Family Get-Together

**Pick** a contraction from the box to finish each sentence.
**Write** it on the line. Remember to use capital letters.

he is = he's　she is = she's
they are = they're　they will = they'll

1. She's reading a book.
2. He's asking Gram to play.
3. They'll play a game.
4. They're having fun!

**Find** the contraction for the two words.
**Mark** the ⬭ to show your answer.

5. do not
   - don't (marked)
   - won't
   - does

6. we are
   - we'll
   - we'd
   - we're (marked)

**Notes for Home:** Your child wrote contractions to finish sentences. ***Home Activity:*** Say two words that could be joined together to make a contraction. Ask your child to name the contraction and use it in a sentence.

Level 1.4 Phonics: Contractions Review 51

Name Practice Book 1.4, p.48

Rose and Grandma
Our Family Get-Together

**Say** the word for each picture.
**Pick** a word from the box that rhymes with it.
**Write** the word on the line.

rode　those　hope　home　joke　stone

1. rope — hope
2. bone — stone
3. smoke — joke
4. hose — those
5. toad — rode
6. comb — home

**Put** the letters in the correct order to make a word from the box.
**Write** it on the line.

has　very

7. sha — has
8. yvre — very

**Notes for Home:** Your child spelled words with long *o* that follow a consonant-vowel-consonant-*e* pattern *(rope)* and two frequently used words: *has, very.* ***Home Activity:*** Write *rope*. Have your child tell what letters to change to form different spelling words, such as *hope*.

52 Spelling: Long *o* (CVCe) Level 1.4

Name Grammar Practice Book, p.34

Rose and Grandma
Our Family Get-Together

RETEACHING

The people **work**. Two foxes **run**.

Do not add **-s** to a verb that tells what two or more people, animals, or things do.

**Read** the first sentence.
**Write** the verb in the second sentence.

1. He plants one flower.

They **plant** many flowers.

2. He waters his flower.

They **water** their flowers.

3. His flower grows tall.

Their flowers **grow** tall.

**Notes for Home:** Your child identified verbs in sentences with plural subjects. ***Home Activity:*** Write plural subjects on cards. *(The dogs, The pigs)* Have your child write a sentence for each subject.



Name Grammar Practice Book, p.35

Rose and Grandma
Our Family Get-Together

**Circle** the correct word for each sentence.
**Write** the sentence.

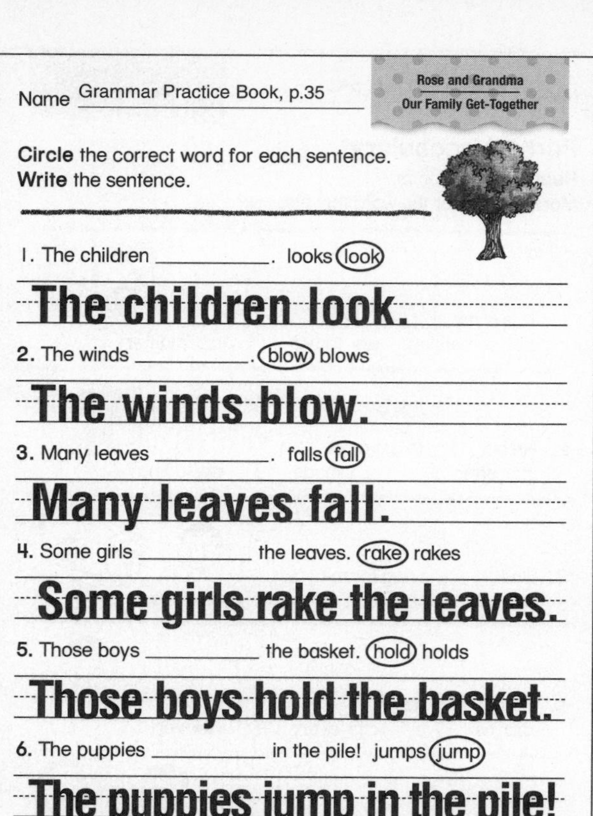

1. The children ______. looks (look)

**The children look.**

2. The winds ______. (blow) blows

**The winds blow.**

3. Many leaves ______. falls (fall)

**Many leaves fall.**

4. Some girls ______ the leaves. (rake) rakes

**Some girls rake the leaves.**

5. Those boys ______ the basket. (hold) holds

**Those boys hold the basket.**

6. The puppies ______ in the pile! jumps (jump)

**The puppies jump in the pile!**

**Notes for Home:** Your child identified verbs that show the action of two or more people, animals, or things. ***Home Activity:*** Look at photographs of groups of people. Have your child say a sentence that describes what the people are doing in each photograph.



Name Practice Book 1.4, p.51

The Rolling Rice Cake
The Rat and the Cat

**Pick** a word from the box to match each picture.
**Write** the word on the line.
**Circle** each picture whose name has the **long i** sound.

| bike | dime | fire | line |
|---|---|---|---|
| mice | pig | six | slide |

kite

1. **dime**
2. **bike**
3. **six**
4. **mice**
5. **line**
6. **pig**
7. **fire**
8. **slide**

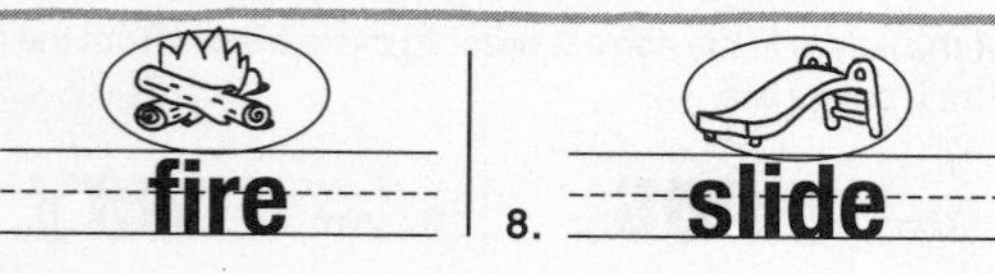

**Notes for Home:** Your child practiced reading words with the long *i* sound that follow a consonant-vowel-consonant-*e* pattern such as *kite*. ***Home Activity:*** Work with your child to write a story using as many of the long *i* words listed above as possible.



Name Practice Book 1.4, p.52

The Rolling Rice Cake
The Rat and the Cat

**Pick** a letter or letters from the box to finish each word.
**Write** the letters on the lines.

ff m tt pp v

water butter

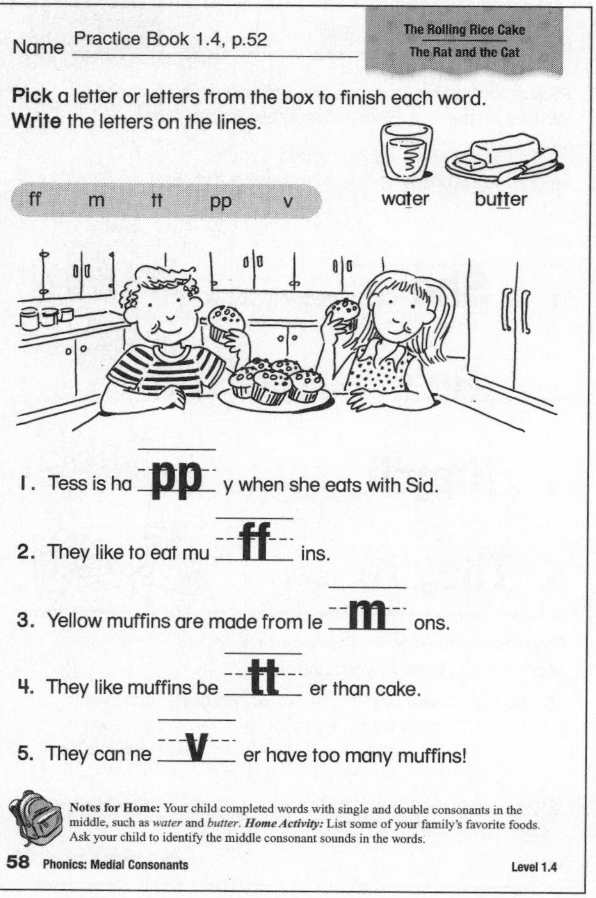

1. Tess is ha **pp** y when she eats with Sid.
2. They like to eat mu **ff** ins.
3. Yellow muffins are made from le **m** ons.
4. They like muffins be **tt** er than cake.
5. They can ne **v** er have too many muffins!

**Notes for Home:** Your child completed words with single and double consonants in the middle, such as *water* and *butter*. ***Home Activity:*** List some of your family's favorite foods. Ask your child to identify the middle consonant sounds in the words.

Name Practice Book 1.4, p.53

The Rolling Rice Cake
The Rat and the Cat

**Pick** a word from the box to finish each sentence.
**Write** it on the line.

be friend pretty soon your

1. Sal is my best **friend**.
2. She has a **pretty** doll.
3. This hat is for **your** doll.
4. It will be dark **soon**.
5. Then it will **be** time to go.

**Notes for Home:** This week your child learned to read the words *be, friend, pretty, soon,* and *your. Home Activity:* Write these words on slips of paper and have your child practice reading each word you show.

Level 1.4 High-Frequency Words 59

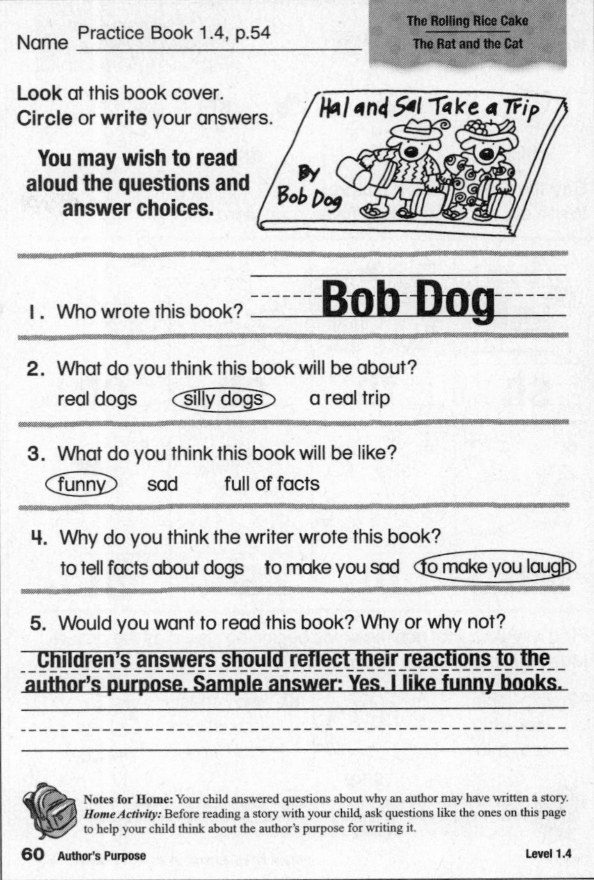

Name Practice Book 1.4, p.54

The Rolling Rice Cake
The Rat and the Cat

**Look** at this book cover.
**Circle** or **write** your answers.

**You may wish to read aloud the questions and answer choices.**



1. Who wrote this book? **Bob Dog**
2. What do you think this book will be about?
   real dogs (silly dogs) a real trip
3. What do you think this book will be like?
   (funny) sad full of facts
4. Why do you think the writer wrote this book?
   to tell facts about dogs to make you sad (to make you laugh)
5. Would you want to read this book? Why or why not?
   **Children's answers should reflect their reactions to the author's purpose. Sample answer: Yes. I like funny books.**

**Notes for Home:** Your child answered questions about why an author may have written a story. *Home Activity:* Before reading a story with your child, ask questions like the ones on this page to help your child think about the author's purpose for writing it.

60 Author's Purpose Level 1.4

Name Practice Book 1.4, p.55

The Rolling Rice Cake
The Rat and the Cat

**Verbs** can tell about action that takes place now.

Today Mom and I cook dinner.

**Verbs** can tell about action that happened in the past.
Add **-ed** to these verbs.

Yesterday Dad and Sam cooked dinner.

**Look** at the picture.
**Circle** the sentence that tells when the action happened.

1. (We fix the bike.)
   We fixed the bike.
2. We bake a cake.
   (We baked a cake.)
3. (Ted and Ned jump on the bed.)
   Ted and Ned jumped on the bed.
4. Pat and Jane water the plants.
   (Pat and Jane watered the plants.)

**Draw** a picture about the sentence.

5. Tim and Nan play in the sandbox.

**Children's drawings should show a boy and a girl playing in a sandbox**

**Notes for Home:** Your child used pictures to distinguish between present and past tense verbs in sentences. *Home Activity:* Write *bake, baked, mix,* and *mixed*. Work with your child to think of a sentence for each word.

Level 1.4 Grammar: Now and in the Past 61

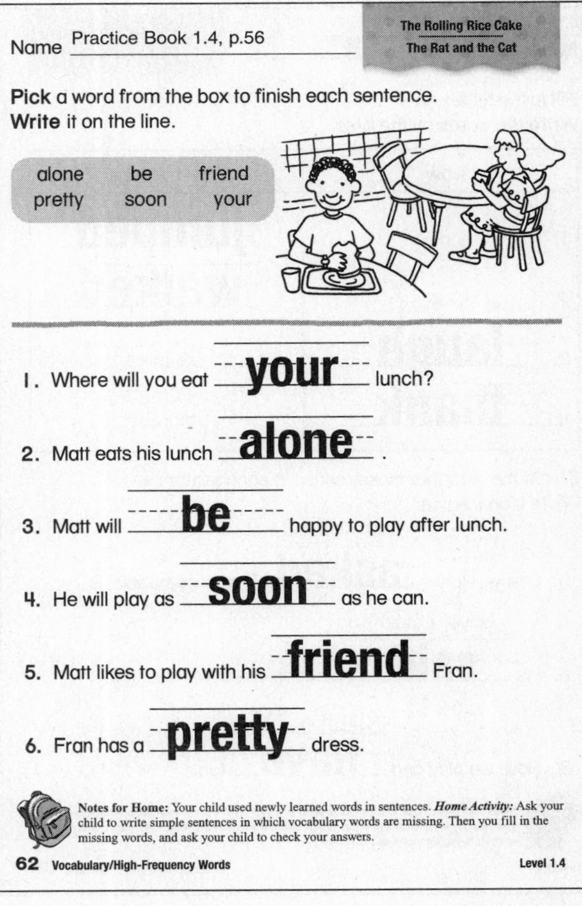

Name Practice Book 1.4, p.56

The Rolling Rice Cake
The Rat and the Cat

**Pick** a word from the box to finish each sentence.
**Write** it on the line.

alone be friend pretty soon your

1. Where will you eat **your** lunch?
2. Matt eats his lunch **alone**.
3. Matt will **be** happy to play after lunch.
4. He will play as **soon** as he can.
5. Matt likes to play with his **friend** Fran.
6. Fran has a **pretty** dress.

**Notes for Home:** Your child used newly learned words in sentences. *Home Activity:* Ask your child to write simple sentences in which vocabulary words are missing. Then you fill in the missing words, and ask your child to check your answers.

62 Vocabulary/High-Frequency Words Level 1.4

Name Practice Book 1.4, p.57

The Rolling Rice Cake
The Rat and the Cat

chick ship thorn whip

**Say** the word for each picture.
**Write ch, sh, th,** or **wh** to finish each word.

1. sh op
2. th in
3. ch ips
4. ch eck
5. wh ale
6. th ink
7. sh irt
8. th umb

**Find** the word that has the same beginning sound as the picture.
**Mark** the ⬭ to show your answer.

9. ⬭ chin ⬬ shin ⬭ thin — ship
10. ⬬ chest ⬭ shorts ⬭ why — cheese

**Notes for Home:** Your child reviewed words that begin with *ch, sh, th,* and *wh.* *Home Activity:* Choose one of these letter combinations. Take turns with your child naming as many words beginning with that sound as you can.

Level 1.4 Phonics: Initial Digraphs *ch, sh, th, wh* Review 63

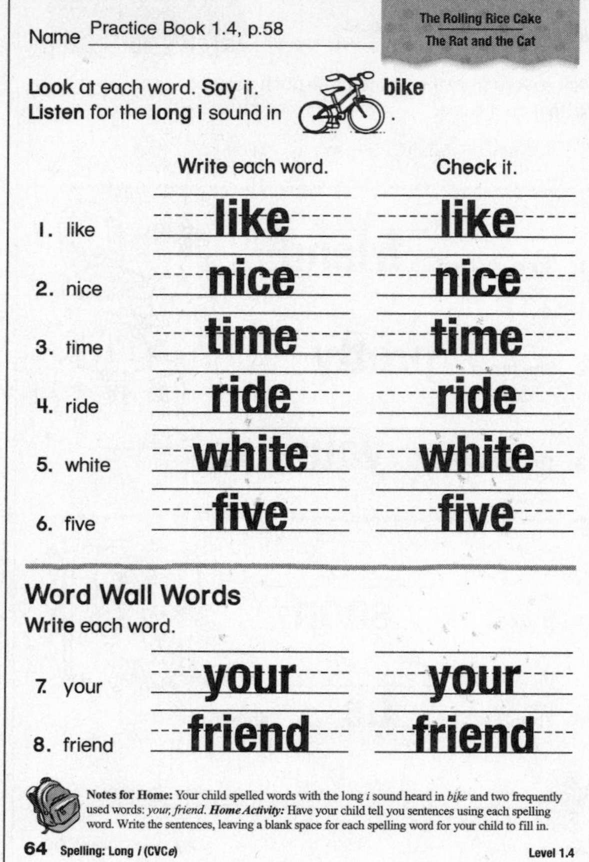

Name Practice Book 1.4, p.58

The Rolling Rice Cake
The Rat and the Cat

**Look** at each word. **Say** it.
**Listen** for the **long i** sound in bike.

| | Write each word. | Check it. |
|---|---|---|
| 1. like | like | like |
| 2. nice | nice | nice |
| 3. time | time | time |
| 4. ride | ride | ride |
| 5. white | white | white |
| 6. five | five | five |

**Word Wall Words**
**Write** each word.

| | | |
|---|---|---|
| 7. your | your | your |
| 8. friend | friend | friend |

**Notes for Home:** Your child spelled words with the long *i* sound heard in *bike* and two frequently used words: *your, friend.* ***Home Activity:*** Have your child tell you sentences using each spelling word. Write the sentences, leaving a blank space for each spelling word for your child to fill in.

64 Spelling: Long *i* (CVC*e*) Level 1.4

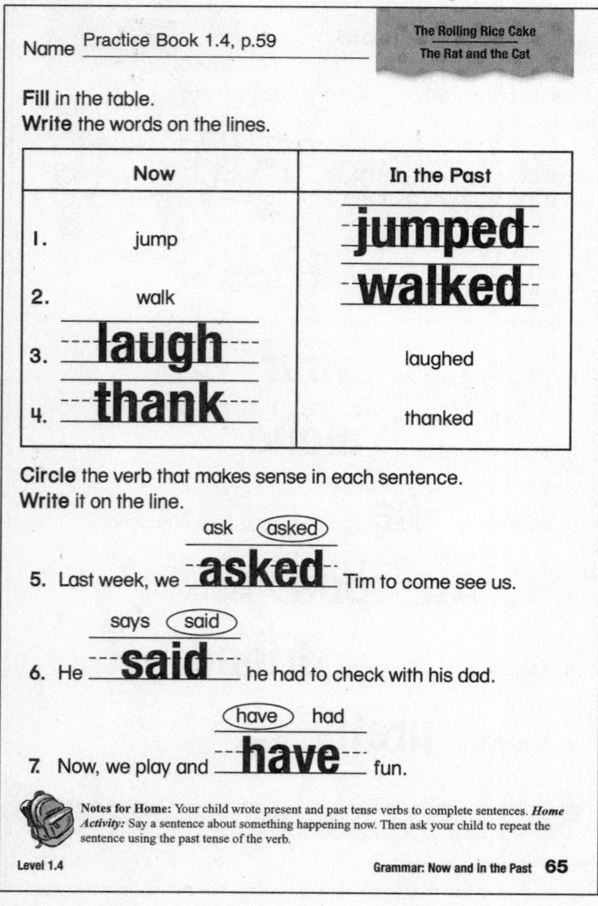

Name Practice Book 1.4, p.59

The Rolling Rice Cake
The Rat and the Cat

**Fill** in the table.
**Write** the words on the lines.

| | Now | In the Past |
|---|---|---|
| 1. | jump | jumped |
| 2. | walk | walked |
| 3. | laugh | laughed |
| 4. | thank | thanked |

**Circle** the verb that makes sense in each sentence.
**Write** it on the line.

5. Last week, we asked Tim to come see us. (ask / (asked))
6. He said he had to check with his dad. (says / (said))
7. Now, we play and have fun. ((have) / had)

**Notes for Home:** Your child wrote present and past tense verbs to complete sentences. *Home Activity:* Say a sentence about something happening now. Then ask your child to repeat the sentence using the past tense of the verb.

Level 1.4 Grammar: Now and in the Past 65

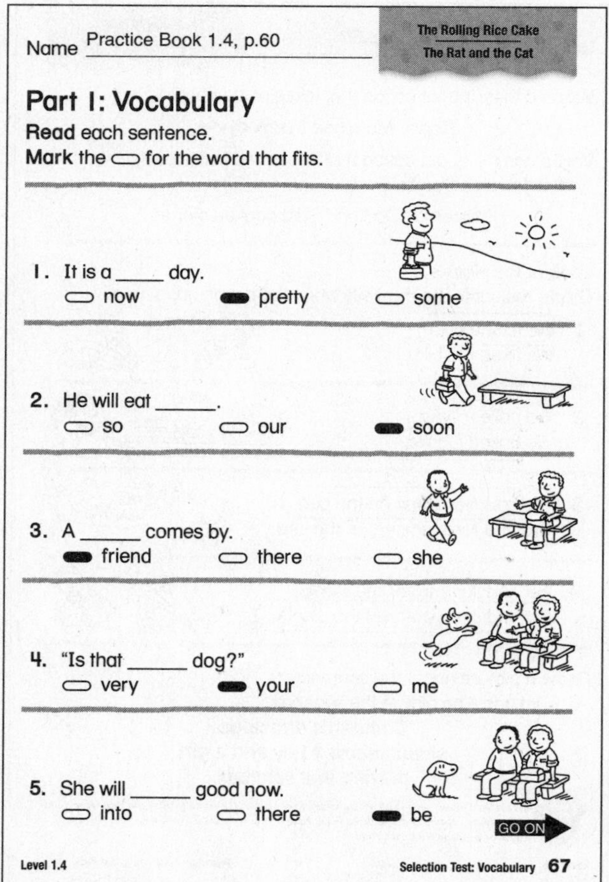

Name Practice Book 1.4, p.60

The Rolling Rice Cake
The Rat and the Cat

**Part 1: Vocabulary**
**Read** each sentence.
**Mark** the ⬭ for the word that fits.

1. It is a _____ day.
⬭ now ⬬ pretty ⬭ some

2. He will eat _____.
⬭ so ⬭ our ⬬ soon

3. A _____ comes by.
⬬ friend ⬭ there ⬭ she

4. "Is that _____ dog?"
⬭ very ⬬ your ⬭ me

5. She will _____ good now.
⬭ into ⬭ there ⬬ be

GO ON

Level 1.4 Selection Test: Vocabulary 67

Name Practice Book 1.4, p.62

The Rat and the Cat

## Part 2: Comprehension

**Read** each question.
**Mark** the ⬭ for the answer.

**Directions: You may wish to read the questions and answer choices to the children.**

6. The rat first sees the cat in
   - ⬬ a shop.
   - ⬭ a box.
   - ⬭ his home.
7. The rat wants the cat to
   - ⬭ do some tricks.
   - ⬬ be his friend.
   - ⬭ catch fish for him.
8. The man thinks the cat will
   - ⬭ run away from the rat.
   - ⬬ eat the rat.
   - ⬭ have fun with the rat.
9. What part of this story could be real?
   - ⬭ A rat has a cat for a pet.
   - ⬭ A cat talks.
   - ⬬ A man has a shop.
10. At the end, this story
    - ⬭ makes you sad.
    - ⬭ sings a song.
    - ⬬ has a surprise.

STOP

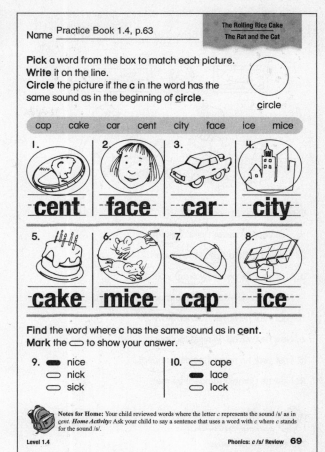



Name Practice Book 1.4, p.63

The Rolling Rice Cake
The Rat and the Cat

**Pick** a word from the box to match each picture.
**Write** it on the line.
**Circle** the picture if the **c** in the word has the same sound as in the beginning of **circle**.

circle

cap cake car cent city face ice mice

1. cent 2. face 3. car 4. city
5. cake 6. mice 7. cap 8. ice

**Find** the word where **c** has the same sound as in **cent**.
**Mark** the ⬭ to show your answer.

9. ⬬ nice ⬭ nick ⬭ sick
10. ⬭ cape ⬬ lace ⬭ lock

**Notes for Home:** Your child reviewed words where the letter *c* represents the sound /s/ as in *cent*. ***Home Activity:*** Ask your child to say a sentence that uses a word with *c* where *c* stands for the sound /s/.



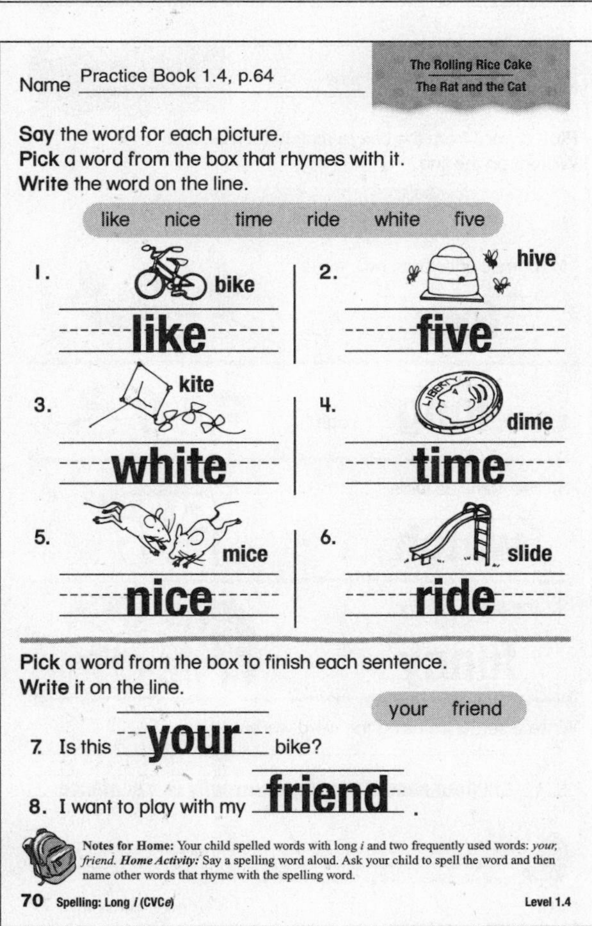

Name Practice Book 1.4, p.64

The Rolling Rice Cake
The Rat and the Cat

**Say** the word for each picture.
**Pick** a word from the box that rhymes with it.
**Write** the word on the line.

like nice time ride white five

1. bike — like
2. hive — five
3. kite — white
4. dime — time
5. mice — nice
6. slide — ride

**Pick** a word from the box to finish each sentence.
**Write** it on the line.

your friend

7. Is this your bike?
8. I want to play with my friend.

**Notes for Home:** Your child spelled words with long *i* and two frequently used words: *your, friend.* ***Home Activity:*** Say a spelling word aloud. Ask your child to spell the word and then name other words that rhyme with the spelling word.



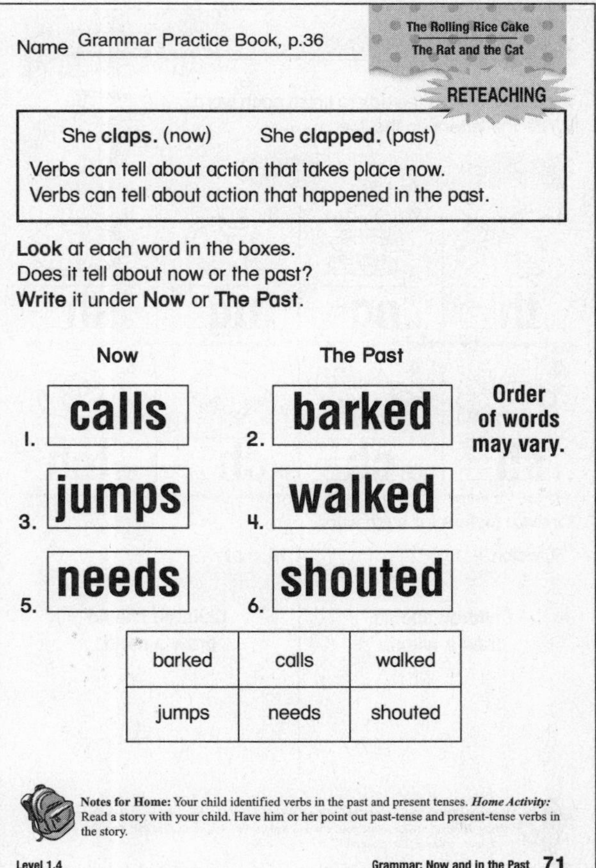

Name Grammar Practice Book, p.36

The Rolling Rice Cake
The Rat and the Cat

RETEACHING

She **claps.** (now) She **clapped.** (past)
Verbs can tell about action that takes place now.
Verbs can tell about action that happened in the past.

**Look** at each word in the boxes.
Does it tell about now or the past?
**Write** it under **Now** or **The Past**.

| Now | The Past |
|---|---|
| 1. calls | 2. barked |
| 3. jumps | 4. walked |
| 5. needs | 6. shouted |

**Order of words may vary.**

| barked | calls | walked |
|---|---|---|
| jumps | needs | shouted |

**Notes for Home:** Your child identified verbs in the past and present tenses. ***Home Activity:*** Read a story with your child. Have him or her point out past-tense and present-tense verbs in the story.

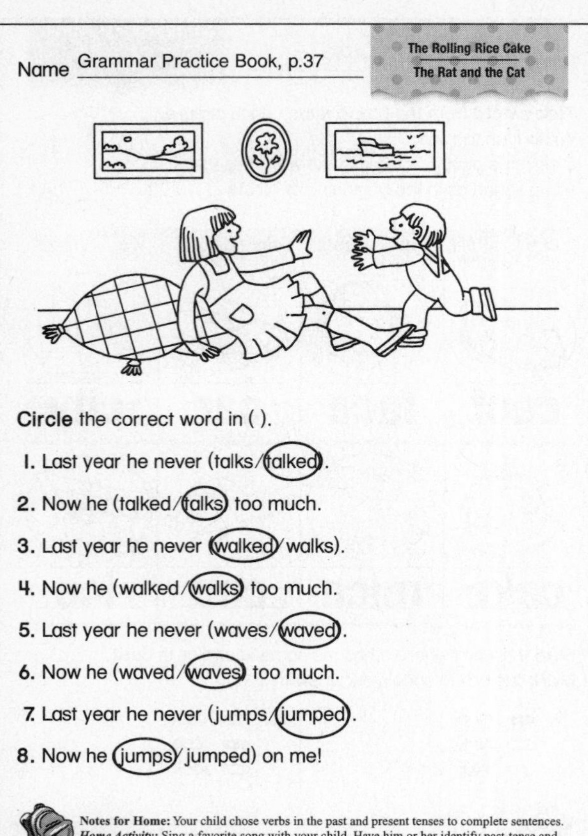
Name Grammar Practice Book, p.37

The Rolling Rice Cake
The Rat and the Cat

Circle the correct word in ( ).

1. Last year he never (talks/talked).
2. Now he (talked/talks) too much.
3. Last year he never (walked/walks).
4. Now he (walked/walks) too much.
5. Last year he never (waves/waved).
6. Now he (waved/waves) too much.
7. Last year he never (jumps/jumped).
8. Now he (jumps/jumped) on me!

**Notes for Home:** Your child chose verbs in the past and present tenses to complete sentences. ***Home Activity:*** Sing a favorite song with your child. Have him or her identify past-tense and present-tense verbs in the song.

72 Grammar: Now and in the Past Level 1.4

Name Practice Book 1.4, p.67

June and the Mule: A Tall Tale
Slim, Luke, and the Mules

**Look** at each picture.
**Circle** the word to finish each sentence.
**Write** it on the line.

mule

flute flop flood
1. Mike plays the **flute**.

tune tub tube
2. I filled the **tub**.

team tan tune
3. Do you like that **tune**?

cute can cut
4. My cat is very **cute**.

cub cube cab
5. This is an ice **cube**.

**Notes for Home:** Your child practiced reading words with the long *u* sound that follow a consonant-vowel-consonant-*e* pattern, such as *mule*. ***Home Activity:*** Work with your child to think of pairs of rhyming words that have the long *u* sound.

Level 1.4 Phonics: Long *u* (CVC*e*) 75

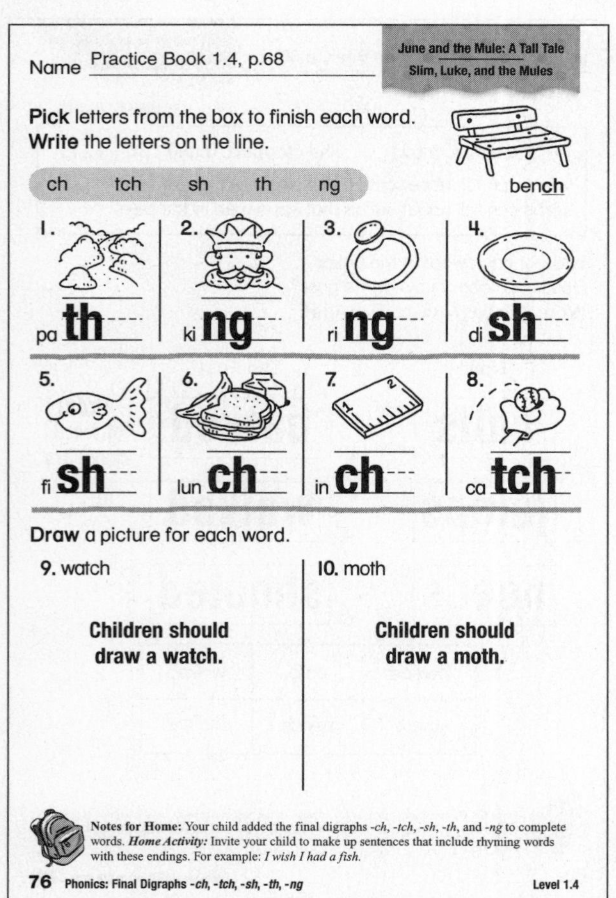
Name Practice Book 1.4, p.68

June and the Mule: A Tall Tale
Slim, Luke, and the Mules

**Pick** letters from the box to finish each word.
**Write** the letters on the line.

ch tch sh th ng

bench

1. pa**th**
2. ki**ng**
3. ri**ng**
4. di**sh**
5. fi**sh**
6. lun**ch**
7. in**ch**
8. ca**tch**

**Draw** a picture for each word.

9. watch
**Children should draw a watch.**

10. moth
**Children should draw a moth.**

**Notes for Home:** Your child added the final digraphs *-ch, -tch, -sh, -th*, and *-ng* to complete words. ***Home Activity:*** Invite your child to make up sentences that include rhyming words with these endings. For example: *I wish I had a fish.*

76 Phonics: Final Digraphs *-ch, -tch, -sh, -th, -ng* Level 1.4

Name Practice Book 1.4, p.69

June and the Mule: A Tall Tale
Slim, Luke, and the Mules

**Pick** a word from the box to match each clue.
**Write** it on the line.

four funny long watch

1. comes after one, two, three
**four**

2. a **long** rope

3. the same as *look*
**watch**

4. the same as *silly*
**funny**

**Write** a sentence using the word *were*.

5. **Children should use *were* correctly in a sentence.**

**Notes for Home:** This week your child learned to read the words *four, funny, long, watch*, and *were*. ***Home Activity:*** Challenge your child to use as many of the vocabulary words as possible in one silly sentence, such as *I watched four long, funny clowns.*

Level 1.4 High-Frequency Words 77

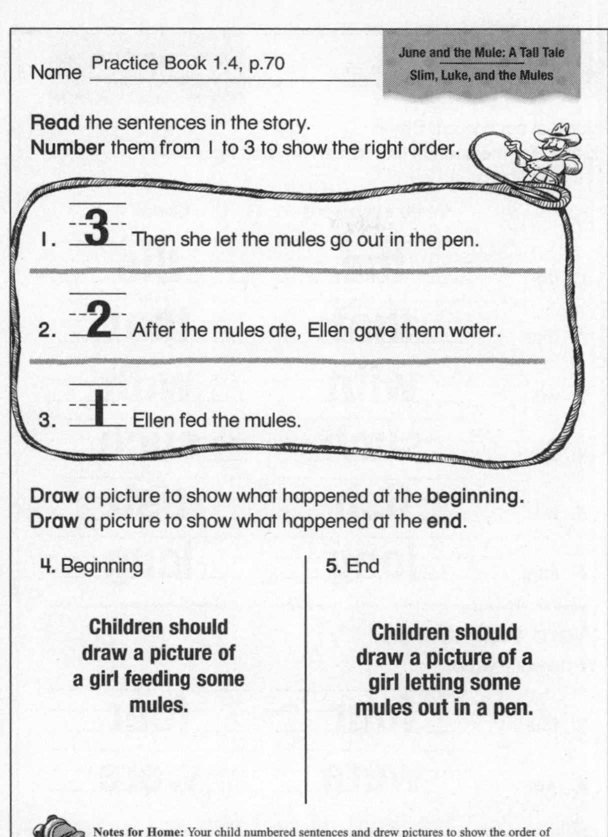

June and the Mule: A Tall Tale
Slim, Luke, and the Mules

Name Practice Book 1.4, p.70

**Read** the sentences in the story.
**Number** them from 1 to 3 to show the right order.

1. **3** Then she let the mules go out in the pen.
2. **2** After the mules ate, Ellen gave them water.
3. **1** Ellen fed the mules.

**Draw** a picture to show what happened at the **beginning**.
**Draw** a picture to show what happened at the **end**.

| 4. Beginning | 5. End |
| --- | --- |
| **Children should draw a picture of a girl feeding some mules.** | **Children should draw a picture of a girl letting some mules out in a pen.** |

**Notes for Home:** Your child numbered sentences and drew pictures to show the order of events in a story. ***Home Activity:*** Together, write a four-sentence story, with each sentence on a separate strip of paper. Help your child put the sentences in the correct order.

78 Plot Level 1.4

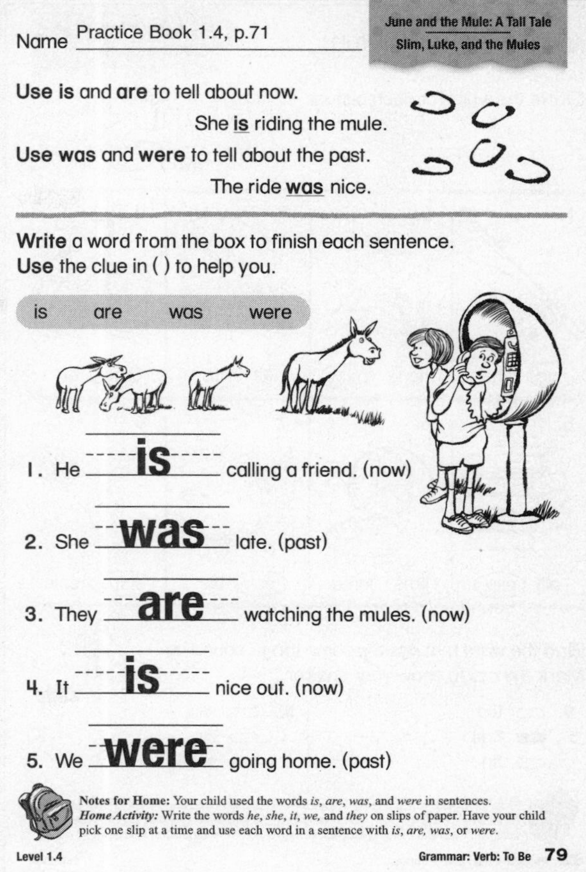

June and the Mule: A Tall Tale
Slim, Luke, and the Mules

Name Practice Book 1.4, p.71

**Use is** and **are** to tell about now.
She is riding the mule.
**Use was** and **were** to tell about the past.
The ride **was** nice.

**Write** a word from the box to finish each sentence.
**Use** the clue in ( ) to help you.

is are was were

1. He **is** calling a friend. (now)
2. She **was** late. (past)
3. They **are** watching the mules. (now)
4. It **is** nice out. (now)
5. We **were** going home. (past)

**Notes for Home:** Your child used the words *is, are, was,* and *were* in sentences. ***Home Activity:*** Write the words *he, she, it, we,* and *they* on slips of paper. Have your child pick one slip at a time and use each word in a sentence with *is, are, was,* or *were.*

Level 1.4 Grammar: Verb: To Be 79

June and the Mule: A Tall Tale
Slim, Luke, and the Mules

Name Practice Book 1.4, p.72

**Pick** a word from the box to finish each sentence.
**Write** it on the line.

count four funny long watch were

1. We **were** going to see the mules.
2. It is a **long** walk to the pen.
3. We like to **watch** the mules.
4. Sam will **count** how many mules are there.
5. There are **four** mules in the pen.
6. I laugh at the **funny** mule.

**Notes for Home:** Your child completed sentences using words learned this week. ***Home Activity:*** Work with your child to write a story using as many of these words as possible.

80 Vocabulary/High-Frequency Words Level 1.4

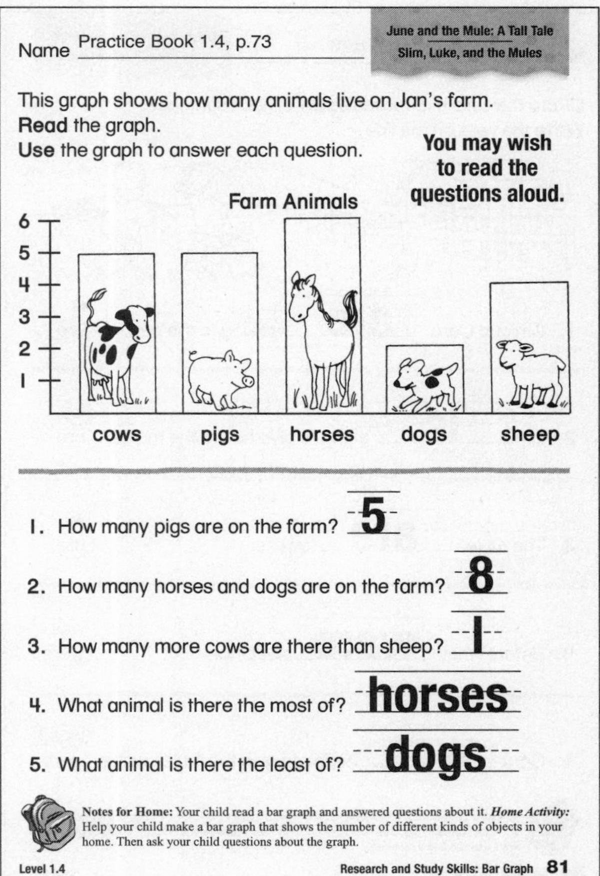

June and the Mule: A Tall Tale
Slim, Luke, and the Mules

Name Practice Book 1.4, p.73

This graph shows how many animals live on Jan's farm.
**Read** the graph.
**Use** the graph to answer each question.

**You may wish to read the questions aloud.**



1. How many pigs are on the farm? **5**
2. How many horses and dogs are on the farm? **8**
3. How many more cows are there than sheep? **1**
4. What animal is there the most of? **horses**
5. What animal is there the least of? **dogs**

**Notes for Home:** Your child read a bar graph and answered questions about it. ***Home Activity:*** Help your child make a bar graph that shows the number of different kinds of objects in your home. Then ask your child questions about the graph.

Level 1.4 Research and Study Skills: Bar Graph 81

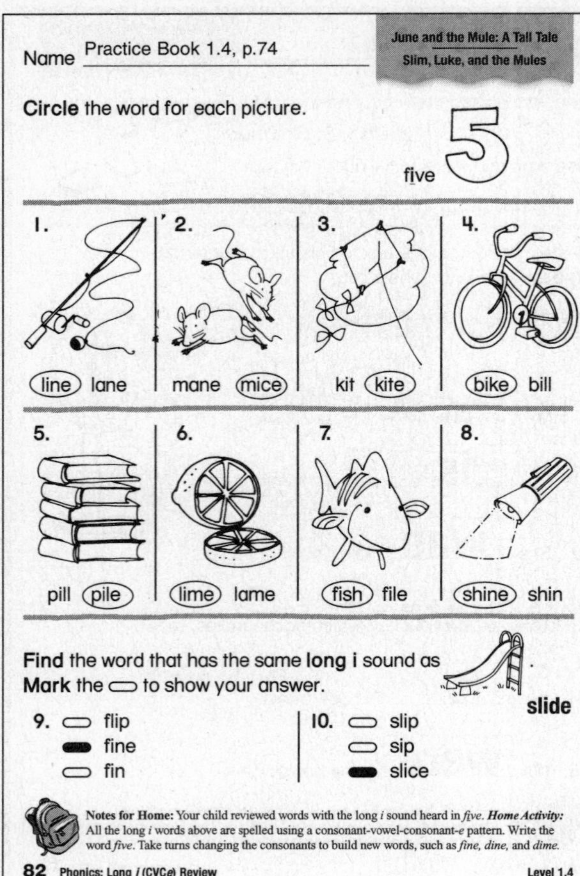

Name Practice Book 1.4, p.74

June and the Mule: A Tall Tale
Slim, Luke, and the Mules

**Circle** the word for each picture.

five 5

1. (line) lane
2. mane (mice)
3. kit (kite)
4. (bike) bill
5. pill (pile)
6. (lime) lame
7. (fish) file
8. (shine) shin

**Find** the word that has the same **long i** sound as slide.
**Mark** the ⬭ to show your answer.

9. ⬭ flip
 ⬬ fine
 ⬭ fin

10. ⬭ slip
 ⬭ sip
 ⬬ slice

**Notes for Home:** Your child reviewed words with the long *i* sound heard in *five*. ***Home Activity:*** All the long *i* words above are spelled using a consonant-vowel-consonant-*e* pattern. Write the word *five*. Take turns changing the consonants to build new words, such as *fine, dine,* and *dime.*

82 Phonics: Long *i* (CVC*e*) Review Level 1.4

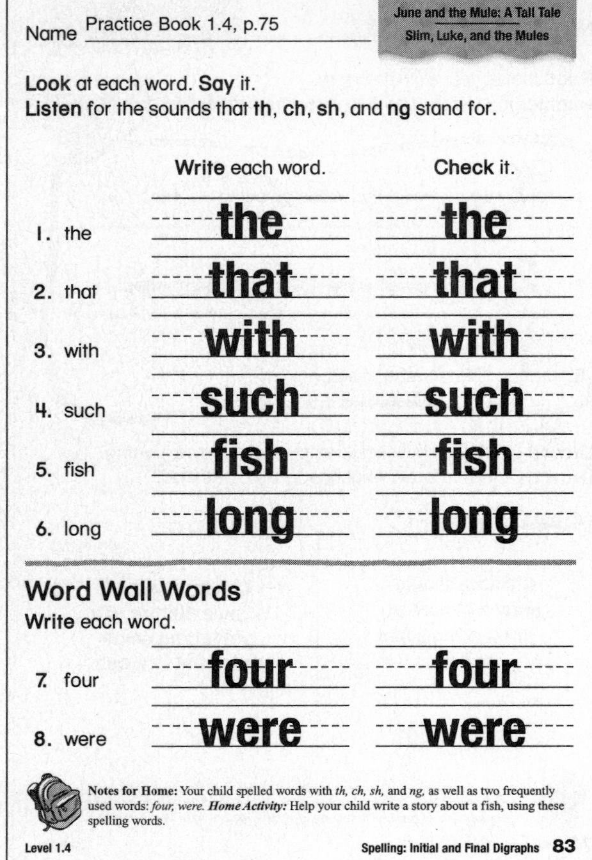

Name Practice Book 1.4, p.75

June and the Mule: A Tall Tale
Slim, Luke, and the Mules

**Look** at each word. **Say** it.
**Listen** for the sounds that **th, ch, sh,** and **ng** stand for.

| | **Write** each word. | **Check** it. |
|---|---|---|
| 1. the | the | the |
| 2. that | that | that |
| 3. with | with | with |
| 4. such | such | such |
| 5. fish | fish | fish |
| 6. long | long | long |

**Word Wall Words**
**Write** each word.

| | | |
|---|---|---|
| 7. four | four | four |
| 8. were | were | were |

**Notes for Home:** Your child spelled words with *th, ch, sh,* and *ng,* as well as two frequently used words: *four, were.* ***Home Activity:*** Help your child write a story about a fish, using these spelling words.

Level 1.4 Spelling: Initial and Final Digraphs 83

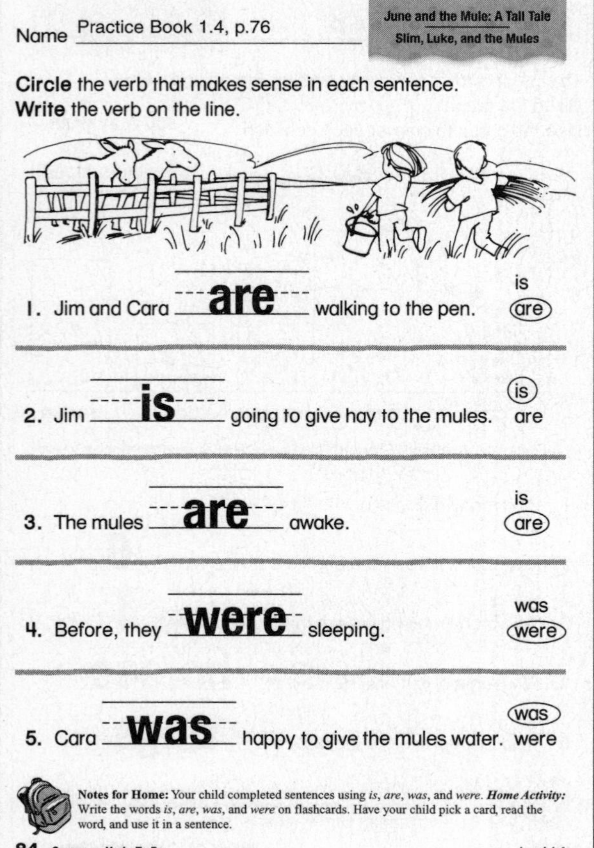

Name Practice Book 1.4, p.76

June and the Mule: A Tall Tale
Slim, Luke, and the Mules

**Circle** the verb that makes sense in each sentence.
**Write** the verb on the line.

1. Jim and Cara **are** walking to the pen. is (are)
2. Jim **is** going to give hay to the mules. (is) are
3. The mules **are** awake. is (are)
4. Before, they **were** sleeping. was (were)
5. Cara **was** happy to give the mules water. (was) were

**Notes for Home:** Your child completed sentences using *is, are, was,* and *were.* ***Home Activity:*** Write the words *is, are, was,* and *were* on flashcards. Have your child pick a card, read the word, and use it in a sentence.

84 Grammar: Verb: To Be Level 1.4

Name Practice Book 1.4, p.77

June and the Mule: A Tall Tale
Slim, Luke, and the Mules

## Part 1: Vocabulary

**Read** each sentence.
**Mark** the ⬭ for the word that fits.

1. There are _____ men.
 ⬬ four ⬭ soon ⬭ after

2. They went for a _____ ride.
 ⬭ something ⬬ long ⬭ very

3. They _____ going to get some food.
 ⬭ has ⬭ made ⬬ were

4. One man will _____ the truck.
 ⬬ watch ⬭ carry ⬭ funny

5. He will _____ the bags.
 ⬭ play ⬬ count ⬭ catch

GO ON

Level 1.4 Selection Test: Vocabulary 85

Name Practice Book 1.4, p.78

Slim, Luke, and the Mules

## Part 2: Comprehension

**Directions: You may wish to read the questions and answer choices to the children.**

**Read** each sentence.
**Mark** the ⊂⊃ for the answer.

6. What do Slim and Luke have to do?
   - ● go to town
   - ⊂⊃ rub down the mules
   - ⊂⊃ work on the ranch

7. How many mules do Slim and Luke have?
   - ⊂⊃ four
   - ● five
   - ⊂⊃ six

8. What happens when Slim counts the mules?
   - ● He does not count the one he is on.
   - ⊂⊃ A mule runs away.
   - ⊂⊃ He counts too many.

9. What will Slim and Luke do next?
   - ● go to buy food
   - ⊂⊃ count the mules again
   - ⊂⊃ let the mules go

10. Slim and Luke seem
   - ⊂⊃ sad.
   - ⊂⊃ mean.
   - ● silly.

STOP



Name Practice Book 1.4, p.79

June and the Mule: A Tall Tale
Slim, Luke, and the Mules

**Add -ed** and **-ing** to each word.
**Write** the new words on the lines.

fixing fixed

| | Add -ed | Add -ing |
|---|---|---|
| 1. play | played | playing |
| 2. rest | rested | resting |
| 3. talk | talked | talking |
| 4. help | helped | helping |
| 5. ask | asked | asking |

**Find** the word that makes sense in each sentence.
**Mark** the ⊂⊃ to show your answer.

6. Now, Kit is _____ her mom.
   - ⊂⊃ called
   - ⊂⊃ call
   - ● calling

7. Before, Kit _____ in the park.
   - ⊂⊃ play
   - ● played
   - ⊂⊃ playing

**Notes for Home:** Your child reviewed words with *-ed* and *-ing* endings. ***Home Activity:*** Make a list of action verbs like those above. Have your child add *-ed* and *-ing* to each word and use it in a sentence.



Name Practice Book 1.4, p.80

June and the Mule: A Tall Tale
Slim, Luke, and the Mules

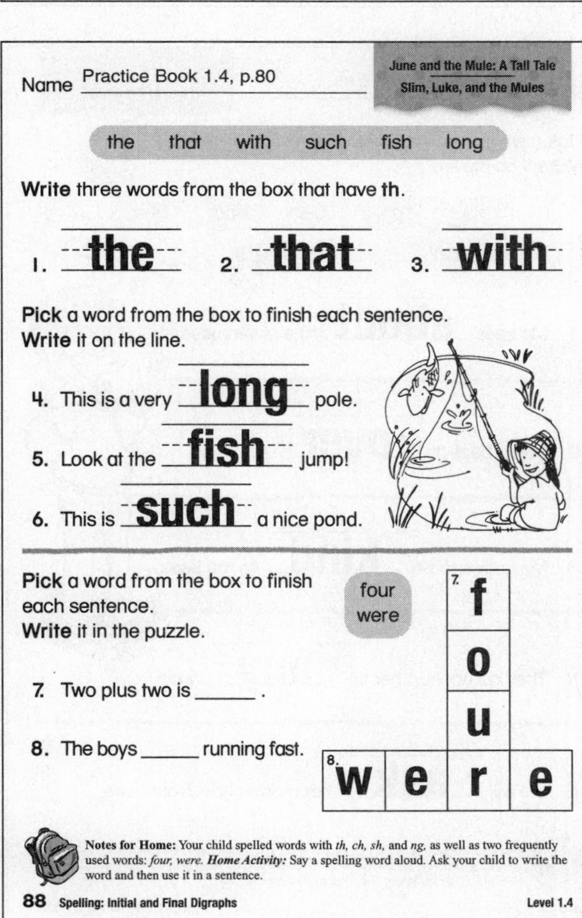

the that with such fish long

**Write** three words from the box that have **th**.

1. the 2. that 3. with

**Pick** a word from the box to finish each sentence.
**Write** it on the line.

4. This is a very long pole.
5. Look at the fish jump!
6. This is such a nice pond.

**Pick** a word from the box to finish each sentence.
**Write** it in the puzzle.

four were

7. Two plus two is _____.
8. The boys _____ running fast.

7. f o u r (down); 8. w e r e (across)

**Notes for Home:** Your child spelled words with *th, ch, sh,* and *ng,* as well as two frequently used words: *four, were.* ***Home Activity:*** Say a spelling word aloud. Ask your child to write the word and then use it in a sentence.



Name Grammar Practice Book, p.38

June and the Mule: A Tall Tale
Slim, Luke, and the Mules

RETEACHING

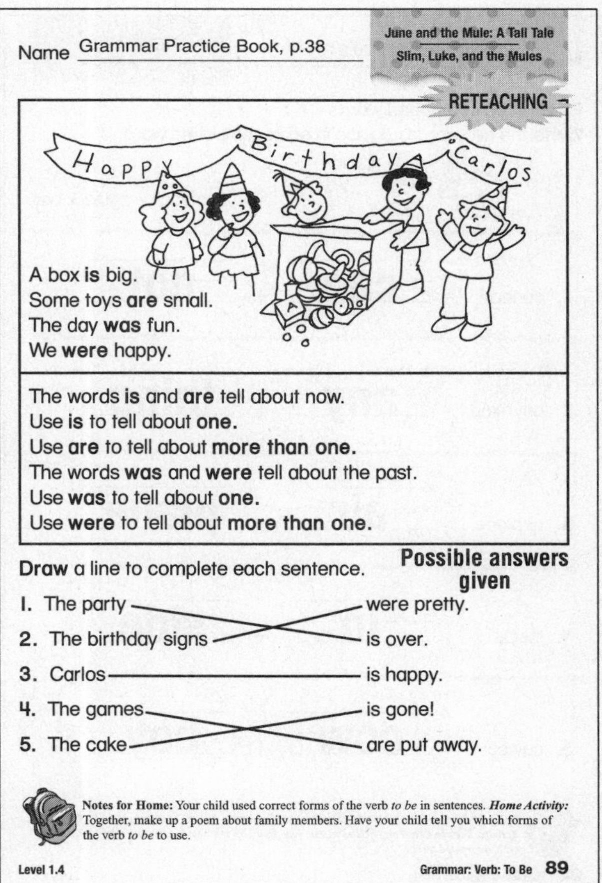


A box **is** big.
Some toys **are** small.
The day **was** fun.
We **were** happy.

The words **is** and **are** tell about now.
Use **is** to tell about **one.**
Use **are** to tell about **more than one.**
The words **was** and **were** tell about the past.
Use **was** to tell about **one.**
Use **were** to tell about **more than one.**

**Draw** a line to complete each sentence.

**Possible answers given**

1. The party — is over.
2. The birthday signs — were pretty.
3. Carlos — is happy.
4. The games — are put away.
5. The cake — is gone!

**Notes for Home:** Your child used correct forms of the verb *to be* in sentences. ***Home Activity:*** Together, make up a poem about family members. Have your child tell you which forms of the verb *to be* to use.

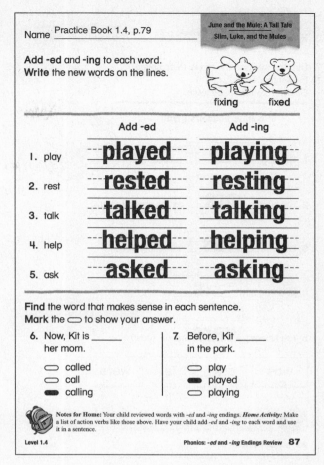

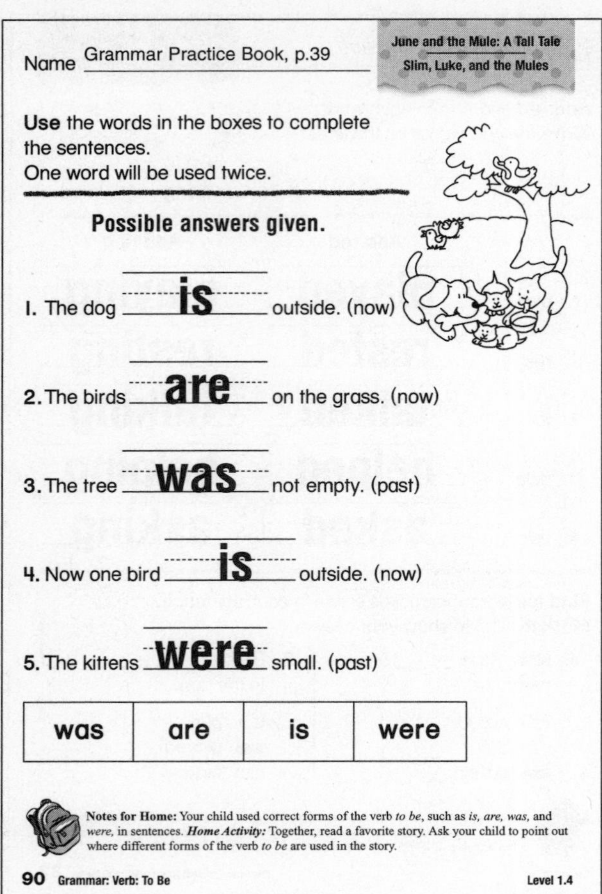
Name Grammar Practice Book, p.39

June and the Mule: A Tall Tale
Slim, Luke, and the Mules

**Use** the words in the boxes to complete the sentences.
One word will be used twice.

**Possible answers given.**

1. The dog **is** outside. (now)
2. The birds **are** on the grass. (now)
3. The tree **was** not empty. (past)
4. Now one bird **is** outside. (now)
5. The kittens **were** small. (past)

| was | are | is | were |
|---|---|---|---|

**Notes for Home:** Your child used correct forms of the verb *to be*, such as *is, are, was,* and *were,* in sentences. ***Home Activity:*** Together, read a favorite story. Ask your child to point out where different forms of the verb *to be* are used in the story.

90 Grammar: Verb: To Be Level 1.4

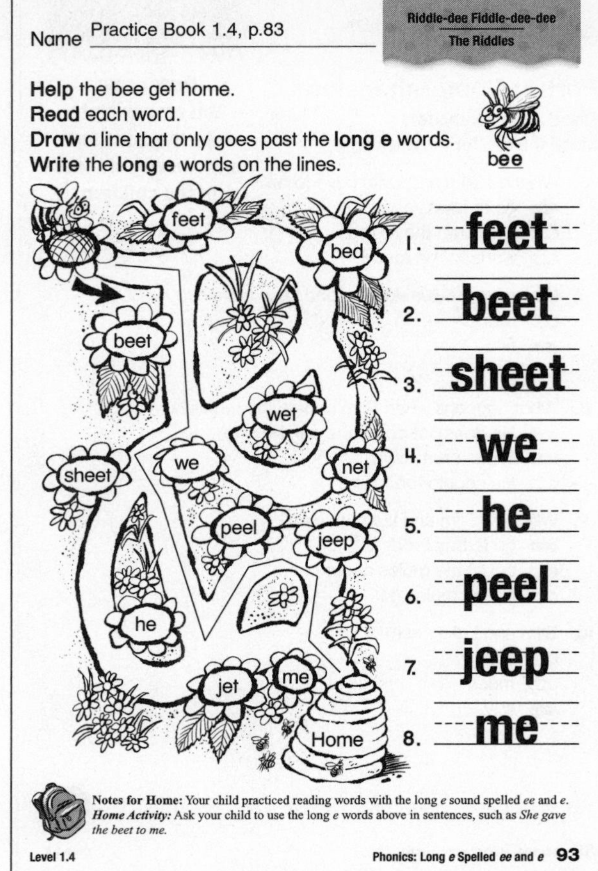
Name Practice Book 1.4, p.83

Riddle-dee Fiddle-dee-dee
The Riddles

**Help** the bee get home.
**Read** each word.
**Draw** a line that only goes past the **long e** words.
**Write** the **long e** words on the lines.



1. **feet**
2. **beet**
3. **sheet**
4. **we**
5. **he**
6. **peel**
7. **jeep**
8. **me**

**Notes for Home:** Your child practiced reading words with the long *e* sound spelled *ee* and *e*. ***Home Activity:*** Ask your child to use the long *e* words above in sentences, such as *She gave the beet to me.*

Level 1.4 Phonics: Long *e* Spelled *ee* and *e* 93

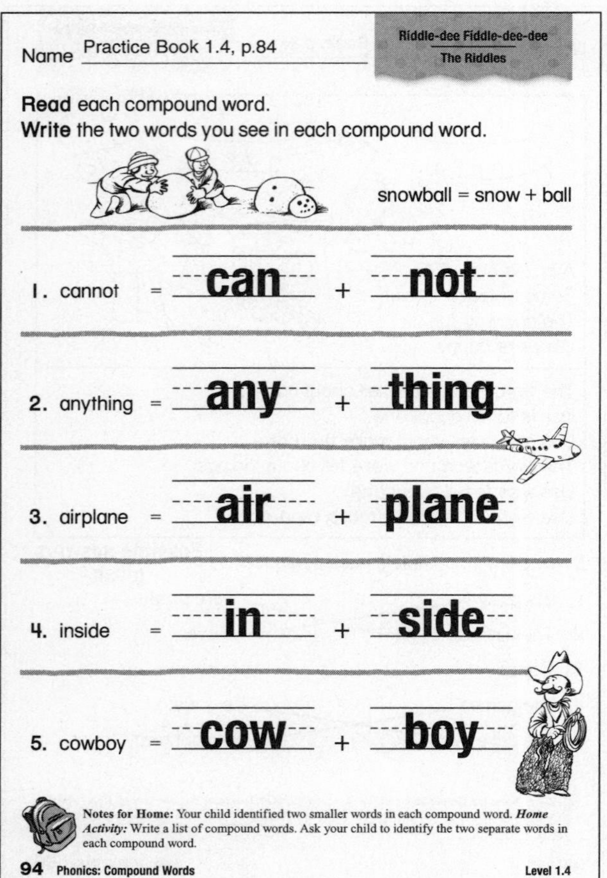
Name Practice Book 1.4, p.84

Riddle-dee Fiddle-dee-dee
The Riddles

**Read** each compound word.
**Write** the two words you see in each compound word.

snowball = snow + ball

1. cannot = **can** + **not**
2. anything = **any** + **thing**
3. airplane = **air** + **plane**
4. inside = **in** + **side**
5. cowboy = **cow** + **boy**

**Notes for Home:** Your child identified two smaller words in each compound word. ***Home Activity:*** Write a list of compound words. Ask your child to identify the two separate words in each compound word.

94 Phonics: Compound Words Level 1.4

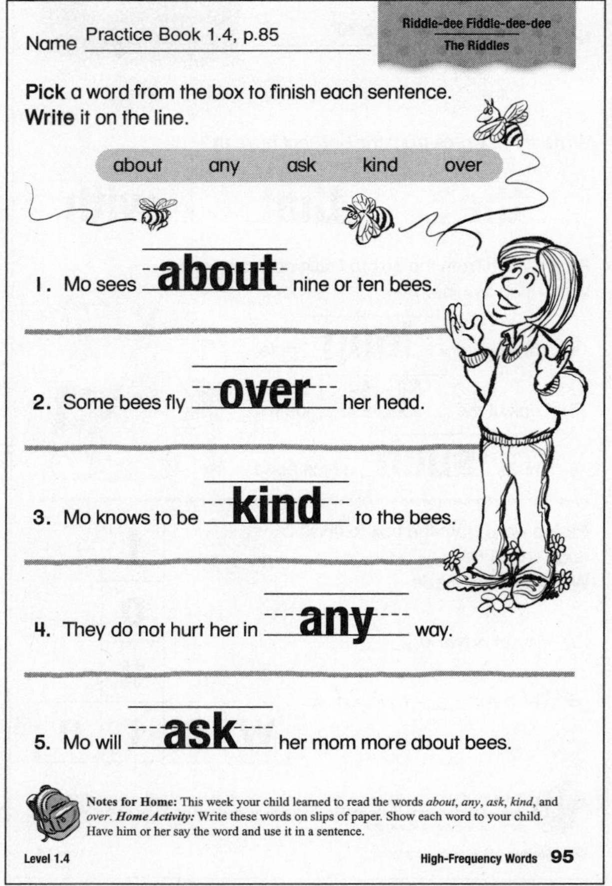
Name Practice Book 1.4, p.85

Riddle-dee Fiddle-dee-dee
The Riddles

**Pick** a word from the box to finish each sentence.
**Write** it on the line.

| about | any | ask | kind | over |
|---|---|---|---|---|

1. Mo sees **about** nine or ten bees.
2. Some bees fly **over** her head.
3. Mo knows to be **kind** to the bees.
4. They do not hurt her in **any** way.
5. Mo will **ask** her mom more about bees.

**Notes for Home:** This week your child learned to read the words *about, any, ask, kind,* and *over.* ***Home Activity:*** Write these words on slips of paper. Show each word to your child. Have him or her say the word and use it in a sentence.

Level 1.4 High-Frequency Words 95

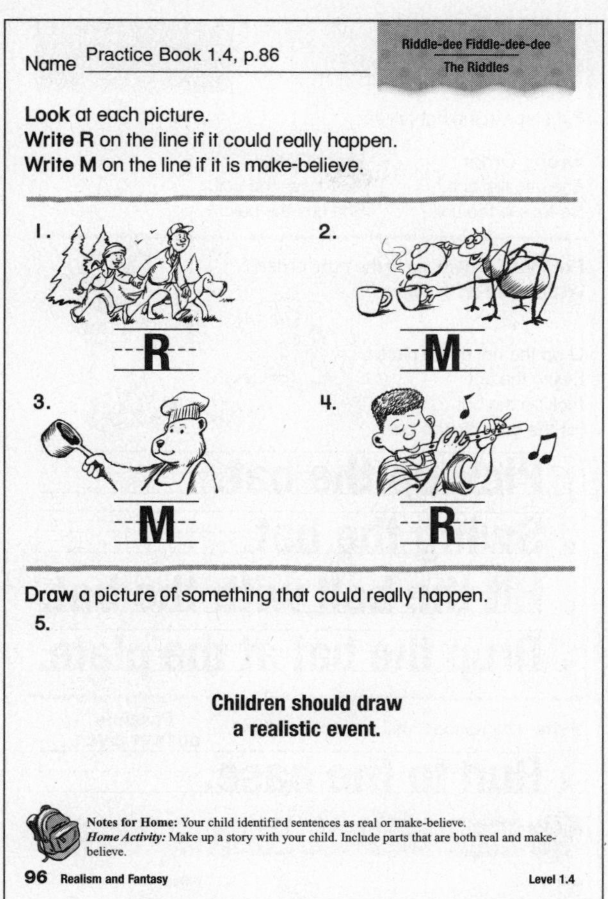
Riddle-dee Fiddle-dee-dee
The Riddles

Name Practice Book 1.4, p.86

**Look** at each picture.
**Write R** on the line if it could really happen.
**Write M** on the line if it is make-believe.

1. R
2. M
3. M
4. R

**Draw** a picture of something that could really happen.

5. **Children should draw a realistic event.**

**Notes for Home:** Your child identified sentences as real or make-believe. *Home Activity:* Make up a story with your child. Include parts that are both real and make-believe.

96 Realism and Fantasy Level 1.4

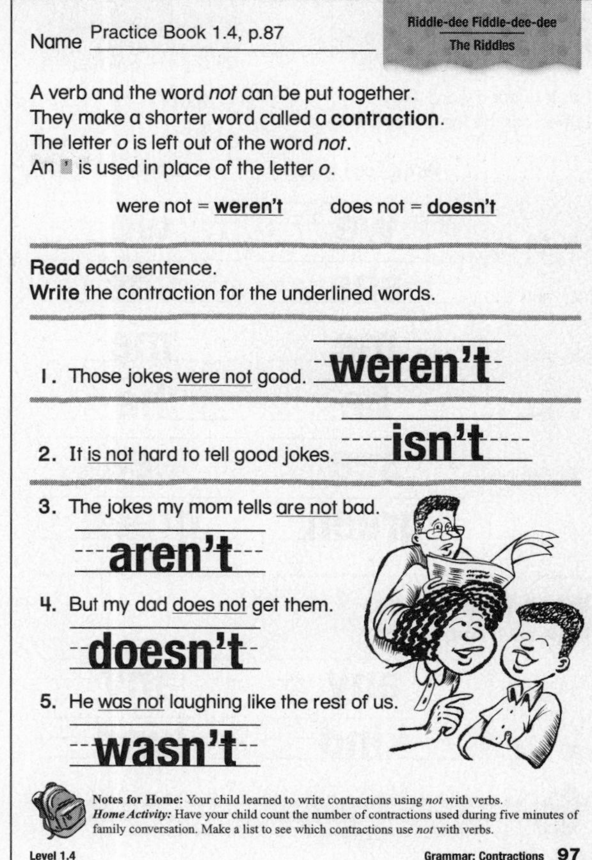
Riddle-dee Fiddle-dee-dee
The Riddles

Name Practice Book 1.4, p.87

A verb and the word *not* can be put together.
They make a shorter word called a **contraction**.
The letter *o* is left out of the word *not*.
An ' is used in place of the letter *o*.

were not = **weren't** does not = **doesn't**

**Read** each sentence.
**Write** the contraction for the underlined words.

1. Those jokes were not good. **weren't**
2. It is not hard to tell good jokes. **isn't**
3. The jokes my mom tells are not bad. **aren't**
4. But my dad does not get them. **doesn't**
5. He was not laughing like the rest of us. **wasn't**

**Notes for Home:** Your child learned to write contractions using *not* with verbs. *Home Activity:* Have your child count the number of contractions used during five minutes of family conversation. Make a list to see which contractions use *not* with verbs.

Level 1.4 Grammar: Contractions 97

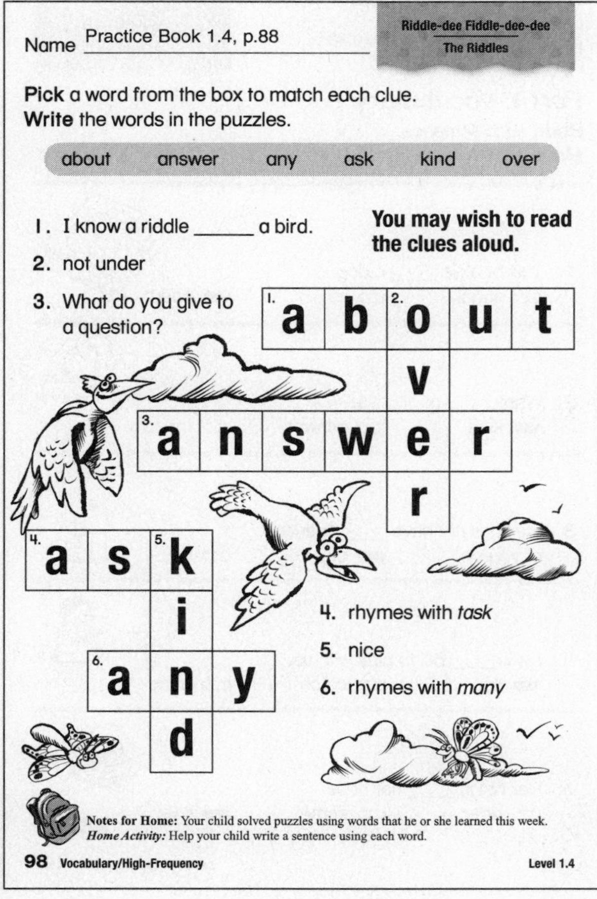
Riddle-dee Fiddle-dee-dee
The Riddles

Name Practice Book 1.4, p.88

**Pick** a word from the box to match each clue.
**Write** the words in the puzzles.

about answer any ask kind over

**You may wish to read the clues aloud.**

1. I know a riddle ______ a bird.
2. not under
3. What do you give to a question?
4. rhymes with *task*
5. nice
6. rhymes with *many*

1. about
2. over
3. answer
4. ask
5. kind
6. any

**Notes for Home:** Your child solved puzzles using words that he or she learned this week. *Home Activity:* Help your child write a sentence using each word.

98 Vocabulary/High-Frequency Level 1.4

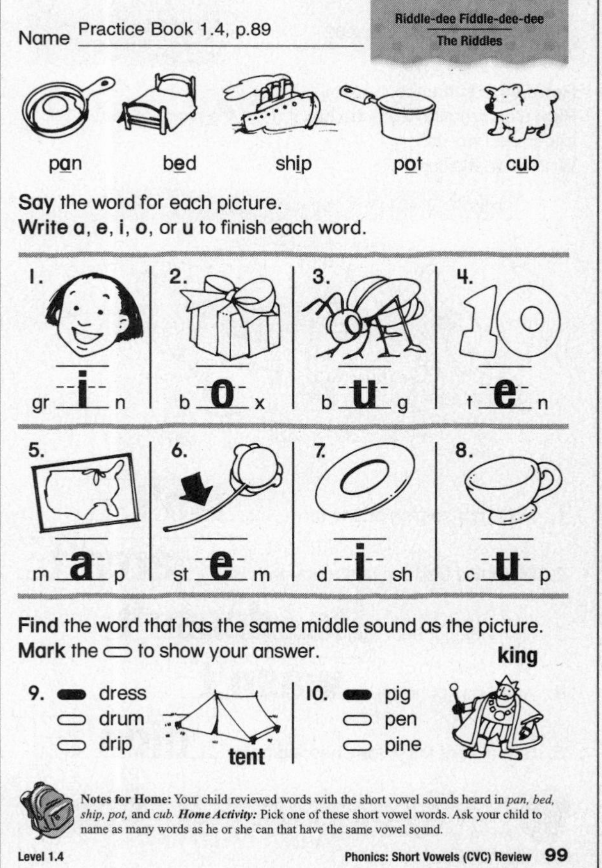
Riddle-dee Fiddle-dee-dee
The Riddles

Name Practice Book 1.4, p.89

pan bed ship pot cub

**Say** the word for each picture.
**Write a, e, i, o,** or **u** to finish each word.

1. gr**i**n
2. b**o**x
3. b**u**g
4. t**e**n
5. m**a**p
6. st**e**m
7. d**i**sh
8. c**u**p

**Find** the word that has the same middle sound as the picture.
**Mark** the ⬭ to show your answer.

9. tent: ● dress ○ drum ○ drip
10. king: ● pig ○ pen ○ pine

**Notes for Home:** Your child reviewed words with the short vowel sounds heard in *pan, bed, ship, pot,* and *cub.* *Home Activity:* Pick one of these short vowel words. Ask your child to name as many words as he or she can that have the same vowel sound.

Level 1.4 Phonics: Short Vowels (CVC) Review 99

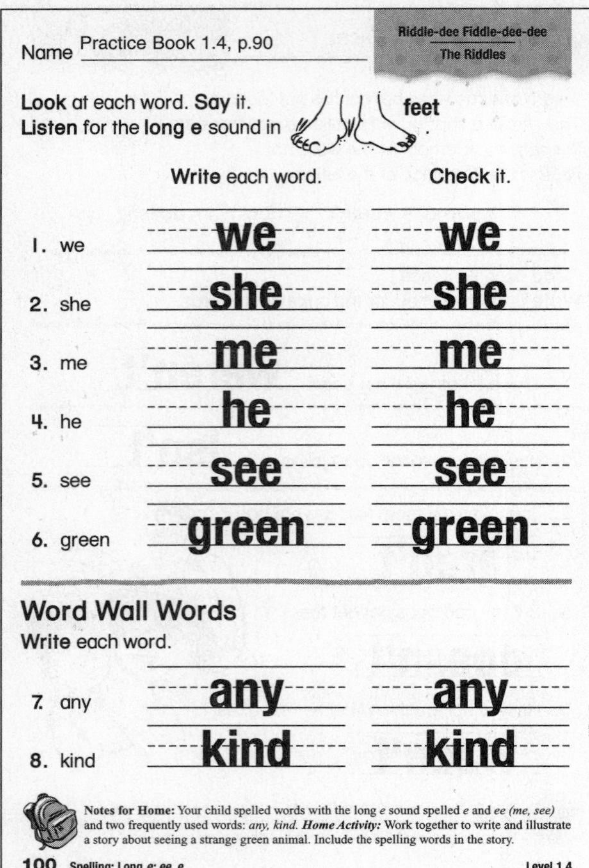

Name Practice Book 1.4, p.90

Riddle-dee Fiddle-dee-dee
The Riddles

**Look** at each word. **Say** it.
**Listen** for the **long e** sound in feet.

| | **Write** each word. | **Check** it. |
|---|---|---|
| 1. we | we | we |
| 2. she | she | she |
| 3. me | me | me |
| 4. he | he | he |
| 5. see | see | see |
| 6. green | green | green |

**Word Wall Words**
**Write** each word.

| | | |
|---|---|---|
| 7. any | any | any |
| 8. kind | kind | kind |

**Notes for Home:** Your child spelled words with the long *e* sound spelled *e* and *ee (me, see)* and two frequently used words: *any, kind. Home Activity:* Work together to write and illustrate a story about seeing a strange green animal. Include the spelling words in the story.

100 Spelling: Long *e: ee, e* Level 1.4

Name Practice Book 1.4, p.91

Riddle-dee Fiddle-dee-dee
The Riddles

Put steps in the right order.

| **Wrong Order** | **Right Order** |
|---|---|
| She hits the ball. | He tosses the ball. |
| He tosses the ball. | She hits the ball. |

**Put** these sentences in the right order.
**Write** them on the lines.

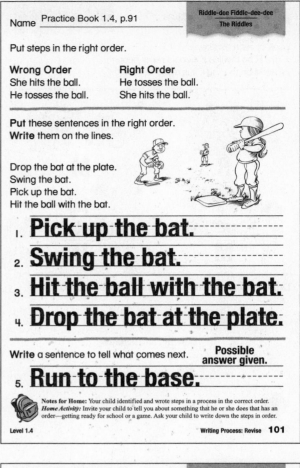

Drop the bat at the plate.
Swing the bat.
Pick up the bat.
Hit the ball with the bat.

1. Pick up the bat.
2. Swing the bat.
3. Hit the ball with the bat.
4. Drop the bat at the plate.

**Write** a sentence to tell what comes next. **Possible answer given.**

5. Run to the base.

**Notes for Home:** Your child identified and wrote steps in a process in the correct order. ***Home Activity:*** Invite your child to tell you about something that he or she does that has an order—getting ready for school or a game. Ask your child to write down the steps in order.

Level 1.4 Writing Process: Revise 101

Name Practice Book 1.4, p.92

Riddle-dee Fiddle-dee-dee
The Riddles

**Read** each sentence.
**Pick** a contraction from the box to take the place of the underlined words.
**Write** it on the line.

aren't didn't doesn't isn't wasn't

1. Hal <u>is not</u> helping on the farm. isn't
2. Mom and Dad <u>are not</u> happy with Hal. aren't
3. Hal <u>does not</u> hear them call. doesn't
4. Ann <u>was not</u> home. wasn't
5. She <u>did not</u> know they needed help. didn't

**Notes for Home:** Your child used *not* with verbs to make contractions. ***Home Activity:*** Write the words *is, are, was, were, do,* and *did* on flashcards. Have your child pick a card, add the word *not*, and tell you the contraction.

102 Grammar: Contractions Level 1.4

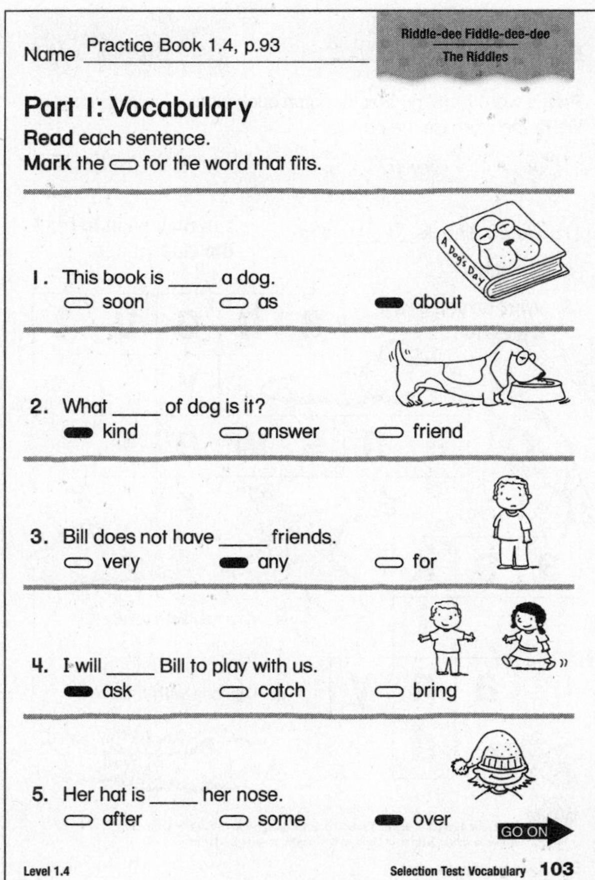

Name Practice Book 1.4, p.93

Riddle-dee Fiddle-dee-dee
The Riddles

**Part 1: Vocabulary**
**Read** each sentence.
**Mark** the ⊂⊃ for the word that fits.

1. This book is _____ a dog.
   - ○ soon ○ as ● about
2. What _____ of dog is it?
   - ● kind ○ answer ○ friend
3. Bill does not have _____ friends.
   - ○ very ● any ○ for
4. I will _____ Bill to play with us.
   - ● ask ○ catch ○ bring
5. Her hat is _____ her nose.
   - ○ after ○ some ● over

GO ON

Level 1.4 Selection Test: Vocabulary 103

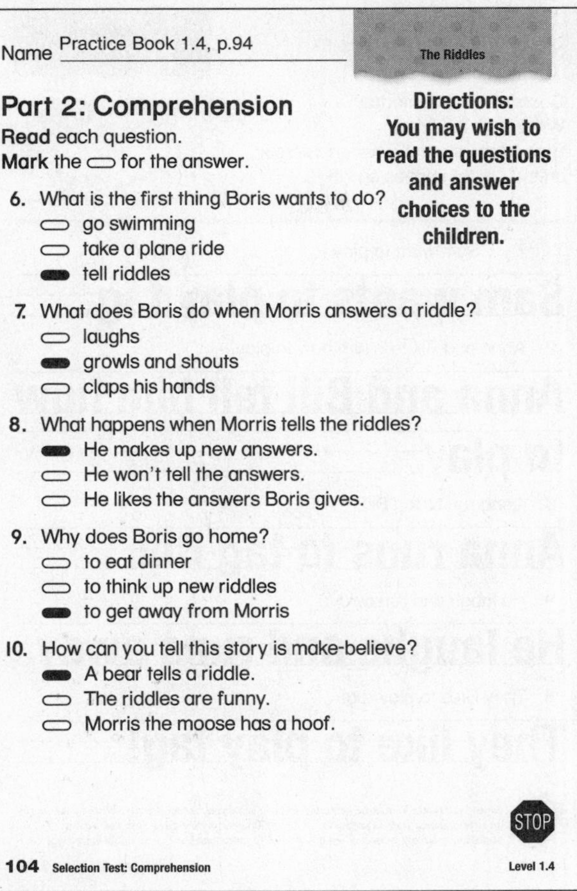

Name Practice Book 1.4, p.94

The Riddles

## Part 2: Comprehension

Read each question.
Mark the ⊂⊃ for the answer.

**Directions: You may wish to read the questions and answer choices to the children.**

6. What is the first thing Boris wants to do?
   - ⊂⊃ go swimming
   - ⊂⊃ take a plane ride
   - ⬬ tell riddles
7. What does Boris do when Morris answers a riddle?
   - ⊂⊃ laughs
   - ⬬ growls and shouts
   - ⊂⊃ claps his hands
8. What happens when Morris tells the riddles?
   - ⬬ He makes up new answers.
   - ⊂⊃ He won't tell the answers.
   - ⊂⊃ He likes the answers Boris gives.
9. Why does Boris go home?
   - ⊂⊃ to eat dinner
   - ⊂⊃ to think up new riddles
   - ⬬ to get away from Morris
10. How can you tell this story is make-believe?
   - ⬬ A bear tells a riddle.
   - ⊂⊃ The riddles are funny.
   - ⊂⊃ Morris the moose has a hoof.

STOP

104 Selection Test: Comprehension Level 1.4

Name Practice Book 1.4, p.95

Riddle-dee Fiddle-dee-dee
The Riddles

Circle the word for each picture.

tulip pillow

1. (butter) but
2. raft (rabbit)
3. (carrot) carpet
4. (ladder) letter
5. (papers) party
6. rubber (ruler)
7. (carpet) card
8. (diver) dinner

Find the word to match each picture.
Mark the ⊂⊃ to show your answer.

9. ⊂⊃ trigger ⬬ tiger ⊂⊃ time

10. ⬬ kitten ⊂⊃ kite ⊂⊃ carrot

Notes for Home: Your child reviewed words with two syllables that have one or two consonants in the middle. *Home Activity:* Have your child choose words from the page and use each word in a sentence. Check that your child is clearly saying the middle consonant sounds.

Level 1.4 Phonics: Medial Consonants Review 105

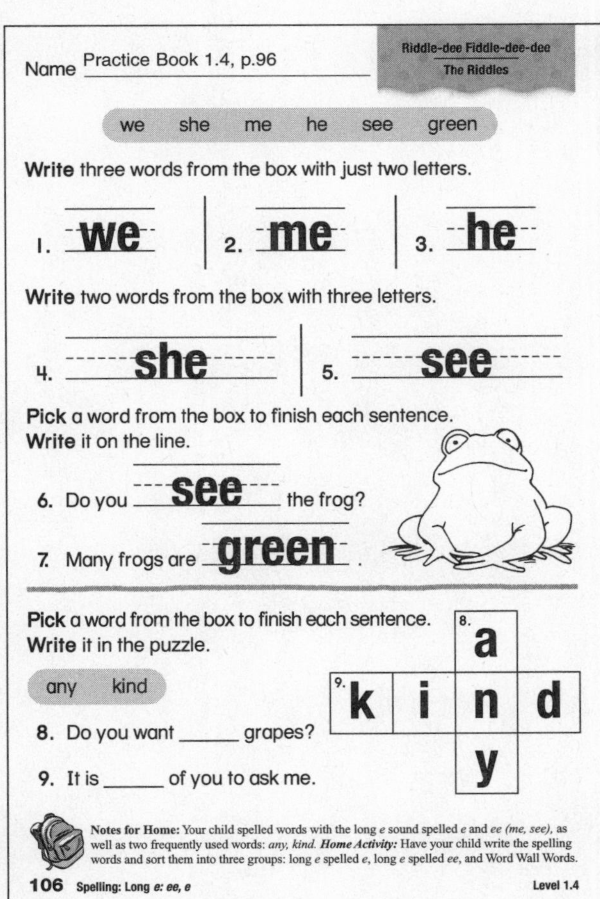

Name Practice Book 1.4, p.96

Riddle-dee Fiddle-dee-dee
The Riddles

we she me he see green

Write three words from the box with just two letters.

1. we 2. me 3. he

Write two words from the box with three letters.

4. she 5. see

Pick a word from the box to finish each sentence.
Write it on the line.

6. Do you see the frog?

7. Many frogs are green.

Pick a word from the box to finish each sentence.
Write it in the puzzle.

any kind

8. Do you want ______ grapes?

9. It is ______ of you to ask me.

8. (down) a n y
9. (across) k i n d

Notes for Home: Your child spelled words with the long *e* sound spelled *e* and *ee* (*me, see*), as well as two frequently used words: *any, kind. Home Activity:* Have your child write the spelling words and sort them into three groups: long *e* spelled *e*, long *e* spelled *ee*, and Word Wall Words.

106 Spelling: Long *e*: *ee, e* Level 1.4

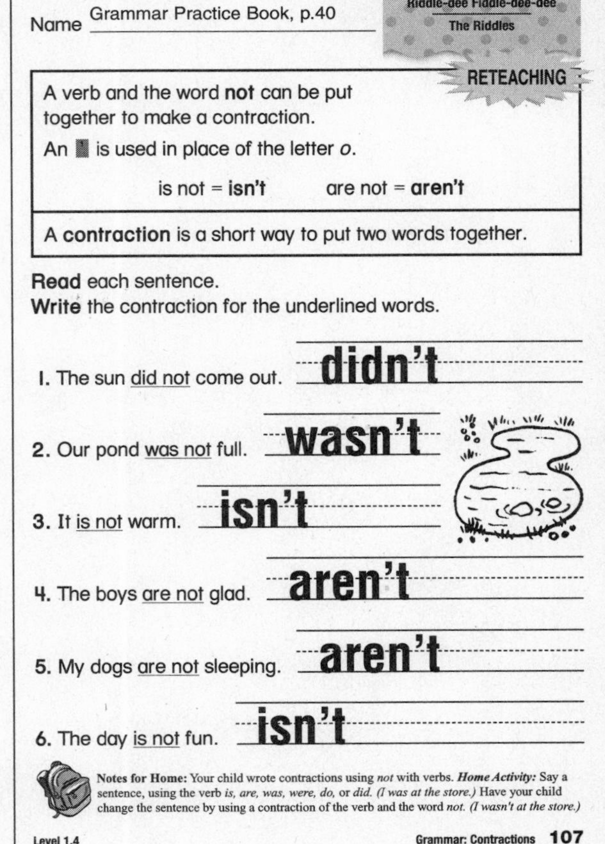

Name Grammar Practice Book, p.40

Riddle-dee Fiddle-dee-dee
The Riddles

RETEACHING

A verb and the word **not** can be put together to make a contraction.

An ' is used in place of the letter *o*.

is not = **isn't** are not = **aren't**

A **contraction** is a short way to put two words together.

Read each sentence.
Write the contraction for the underlined words.

1. The sun did not come out. didn't
2. Our pond was not full. wasn't
3. It is not warm. isn't
4. The boys are not glad. aren't
5. My dogs are not sleeping. aren't
6. The day is not fun. isn't

Notes for Home: Your child wrote contractions using *not* with verbs. *Home Activity:* Say a sentence, using the verb *is, are, was, were, do,* or *did.* (*I was at the store.*) Have your child change the sentence by using a contraction of the verb and the word *not.* (*I wasn't at the store.*)

Level 1.4 Grammar: Contractions 107

Name Grammar Practice Book, p.41

Riddle-dee Fiddle-dee-dee
The Riddles

**Word Bank**

is not = isn't  are not = aren't

was not = wasn't  were not = weren't

**Read** each sentence.
**Write** the two words for each contraction.

1. The farm wasn't noisy.
**was not**
2. Birds aren't flying.
**are not**
3. The sky isn't dark.
**is not**
4. The cows aren't mooing.
**are not**
5. Our chicken isn't clucking.
**is not**
6. Fields weren't plowed.
**were not**
7. Aunt Marge wasn't coming.
**was not**

**Write** a sentence. Use a contraction. **Answers will vary.**

**Notes for Home:** Your child separated contractions of verbs and the word *not.* (*isn't, aren't, wasn't, weren't*) ***Home Activity:*** Sing a familiar song with your child. Change the words by using contractions of verbs and the word *not.*



Name Practice Book 1.4, p.97

Riddle-dee Fiddle-dee-dee
The Riddles

**Correct** each sentence.
**Write** it on the line.
Hint: Verbs that tell what one person, animal, or thing does end in **-s**.

1. Sam want to play tag.
**Sam wants to play tag.**
2. Anna and Bill tells him how to play.
**Anna and Bill tell him how to play.**
3. Anna run to tag Bill.
**Anna runs to tag Bill.**
4. He laugh and run away.
**He laughs and runs away.**
5. They likes to play tag!
**They like to play tag!**

**Notes for Home:** Your child corrected verbs in sentences. ***Home Activity:*** Write action words on slips of paper, such as *jump, run,* and *play.* Take turns choosing a verb and saying sentences about one person doing the action and more than one person doing the action.

Name Practice Book 1.5, p.3

A Real Gift
Arthur's Reading Race

**Circle** a word to finish each sentence.
**Write** it on the line.

peach

1. I will **read** about a cat. (read) red

2. My cat likes **cream**. crate (cream)

3. My cat likes to **eat**. (eat) ant

4. I want to **teach** my cat a trick. tack (teach)

5. The trick is **fun**! flea (fun)

**Notes for Home:** Your child practiced reading words with the long *e* sound spelled *ea* as in *peach*. ***Home Activity:*** Work with your child to make a list of other words with the long *e* sound spelled *ea*. Ask your child to rhyme the new words with the words in these sentences.

Level 1.5 — Phonics: Long *e* Spelled *ea* 3

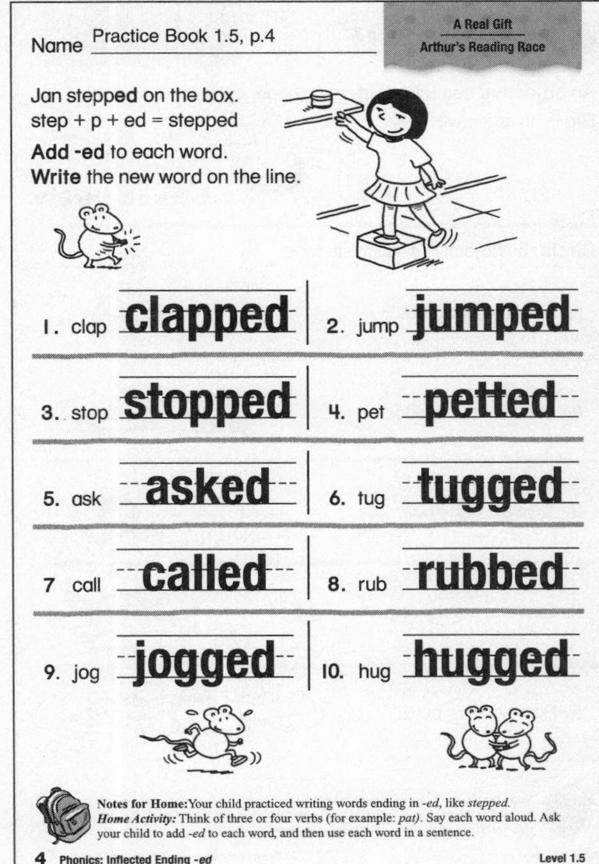

Name Practice Book 1.5, p.4

A Real Gift
Arthur's Reading Race

Jan stepp**ed** on the box.
step + p + ed = stepped

**Add -ed** to each word.
**Write** the new word on the line.

| | |
|---|---|
| 1. clap **clapped** | 2. jump **jumped** |
| 3. stop **stopped** | 4. pet **petted** |
| 5. ask **asked** | 6. tug **tugged** |
| 7 call **called** | 8. rub **rubbed** |
| 9. jog **jogged** | 10. hug **hugged** |

**Notes for Home:** Your child practiced writing words ending in *-ed*, like *stepped*. ***Home Activity:*** Think of three or four verbs (for example: *pat*). Say each word aloud. Ask your child to add *-ed* to each word, and then use each word in a sentence.

4 Phonics: Inflected Ending *-ed* — Level 1.5

Name Practice Book 1.5, p.5

A Real Gift
Arthur's Reading Race

**Pick** a word from the box to finish each sentence.
**Write** it on the line.

buy only or right think

1. Tom wants to **buy** a hat.

2. He can get **only** one hat.

3. Will he get this hat **or** that one?

4. He has to **think** a bit.

5. This hat fits just **right**.

**Notes for Home:** This week your child is learning to read the words *buy, only, or, right,* and *think*. ***Home Activity:*** Write each word on a slip of paper. Put all the slips in a bowl or hat. Ask your child to pick a word, say it aloud, and use it in a sentence.

Level 1.5 — High-Frequency Words 5

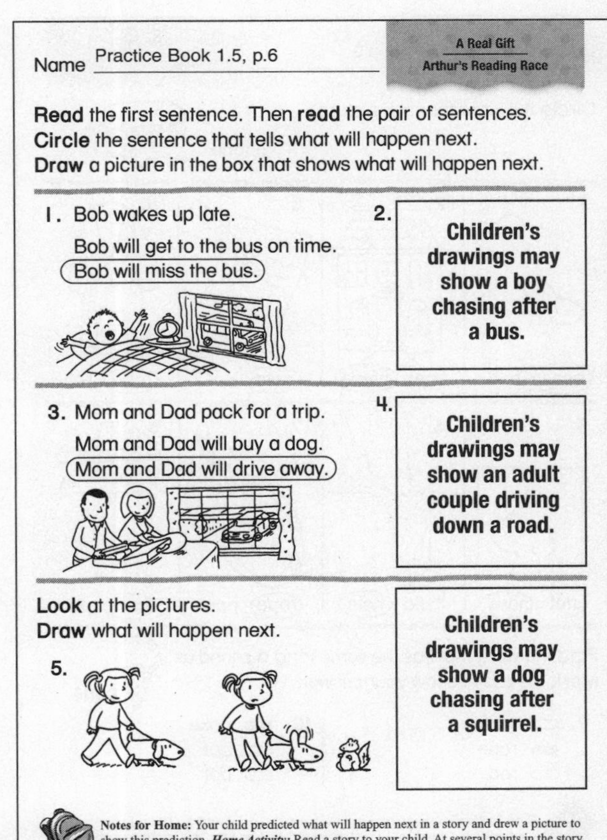

Name Practice Book 1.5, p.6

A Real Gift
Arthur's Reading Race

**Read** the first sentence. Then **read** the pair of sentences.
**Circle** the sentence that tells what will happen next.
**Draw** a picture in the box that shows what will happen next.

1. Bob wakes up late.
Bob will get to the bus on time.
(Bob will miss the bus.)

2. **Children's drawings may show a boy chasing after a bus.**

3. Mom and Dad pack for a trip.
Mom and Dad will buy a dog.
(Mom and Dad will drive away.)

4. **Children's drawings may show an adult couple driving down a road.**

**Look** at the pictures.
**Draw** what will happen next.

5. **Children's drawings may show a dog chasing after a squirrel.**

**Notes for Home:** Your child predicted what will happen next in a story and drew a picture to show this prediction. ***Home Activity:*** Read a story to your child. At several points in the story, stop and ask your child to predict what will happen next.

6 Predicting — Level 1.5

Name Practice Book 1.5, p.7

A Real Gift
Arthur's Reading Race

An **adjective** can tell about size, shape, color, or how many.
**Big** is an adjective.

Pat has a big hat.

**Circle** the adjective in each sentence.

1. Jim has a (long) bat.
2. Look at the (black) cat.
3. That's a (huge) ball.
4. Socks is a (cute) dog.
5. Pam has (five) hats.

**Notes for Home:** Your child identified adjectives that tell more about nouns—people, places, animals, or things. *Home Activity:* Look around the room. Point to an object and encourage your child to say an adjective that tells more about that object.

Level 1.5 Grammar: Adjectives (Describing Words) 7

Name Practice Book 1.5, p.8

A Real Gift
Arthur's Reading Race

**Pick** a word from the box to match each clue.
**Write** the words in the puzzles.

buy eight only or right think

1. Do you like cats ____ dogs? (or)
2. not wrong (right)
3. five, six, seven, ____ (eight)
4. I have ____ one cat. (only)
5. I ____ dogs are cute. (think)
6. not sell (buy)

**Notes for Home:** Your child solved puzzles using words learned this week. *Home Activity:* Work with your child to write a story using as many of these words as possible.

8 Vocabulary/High-Frequency Words Level 1.5

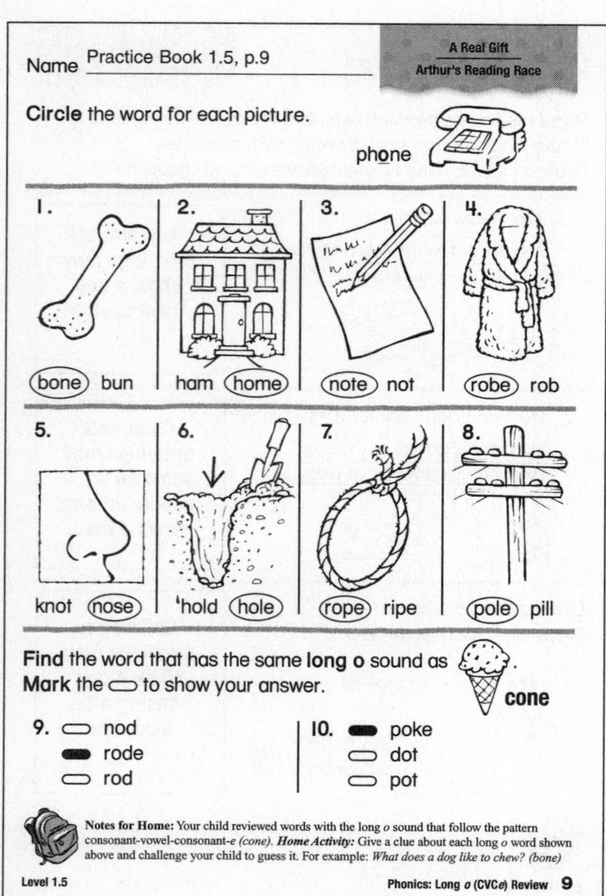
Name Practice Book 1.5, p.9

A Real Gift
Arthur's Reading Race

**Circle** the word for each picture.

phone

1. (bone) bun
2. ham (home)
3. (note) not
4. (robe) rob
5. knot (nose)
6. hold (hole)
7. (rope) ripe
8. (pole) pill

**Find** the word that has the same **long o** sound as cone.
**Mark** the ⬭ to show your answer.

9. ⬭ nod
● rode
⬭ rod

10. ● poke
⬭ dot
⬭ pot

**Notes for Home:** Your child reviewed words with the long *o* sound that follow the pattern consonant-vowel-consonant-*e* (*cone*). *Home Activity:* Give a clue about each long *o* word shown above and challenge your child to guess it. For example: *What does a dog like to chew? (bone)*

Level 1.5 Phonics: Long *o* (CVC*e*) Review 9

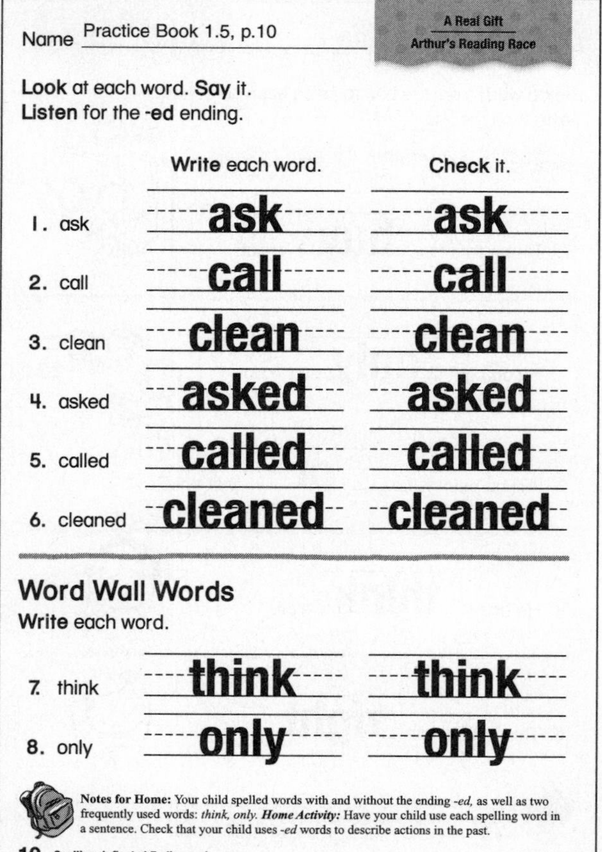
Name Practice Book 1.5, p.10

A Real Gift
Arthur's Reading Race

**Look** at each word. **Say** it.
**Listen** for the **-ed** ending.

| | Write each word. | Check it. |
|---|---|---|
| 1. ask | ask | ask |
| 2. call | call | call |
| 3. clean | clean | clean |
| 4. asked | asked | asked |
| 5. called | called | called |
| 6. cleaned | cleaned | cleaned |

**Word Wall Words**
**Write** each word.

| | | |
|---|---|---|
| 7. think | think | think |
| 8. only | only | only |

**Notes for Home:** Your child spelled words with and without the ending *-ed*, as well as two frequently used words: *think, only. Home Activity:* Have your child use each spelling word in a sentence. Check that your child uses *-ed* words to describe actions in the past.

10 Spelling: Inflected Ending *-ed* Level 1.5

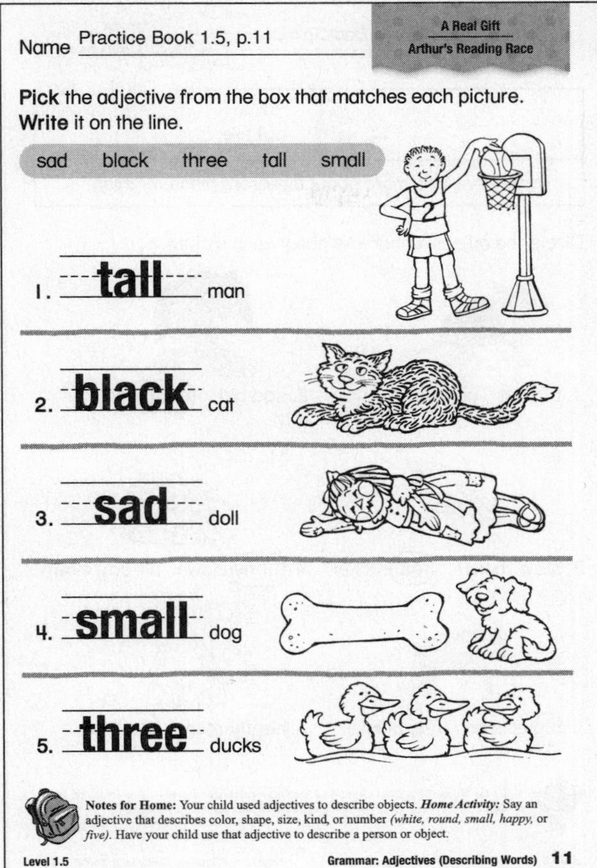

Name Practice Book 1.5, p.11

A Real Gift
Arthur's Reading Race

**Pick** the adjective from the box that matches each picture.
**Write** it on the line.

sad black three tall small

1. tall man
2. black cat
3. sad doll
4. small dog
5. three ducks

**Notes for Home:** Your child used adjectives to describe objects. ***Home Activity:*** Say an adjective that describes color, shape, size, kind, or number *(white, round, small, happy,* or *five).* Have your child use that adjective to describe a person or object.

Level 1.5 Grammar: Adjectives (Describing Words) 11

Name Practice Book 1.5, p.13

A Real Gift
Arthur's Reading Race

## Part 1: Vocabulary

**Read** each sentence.
**Mark** the ⬭ for the word that fits.



1. Dan wants to ______ a pet.
   - ⬭ only
   - ⬬ buy
   - ⬭ sleep

2. There are ______ four pets here.
   - ⬭ or
   - ⬭ out
   - ⬬ only



3. He has to ______ .
   - ⬬ think
   - ⬭ right
   - ⬭ thank

4. Does he want a dog ______ a cat?
   - ⬭ of
   - ⬬ or
   - ⬭ think

5. This cat is the ______ pet for Dan!
   - ⬬ right
   - ⬭ buy
   - ⬭ more

GO ON

Level 1.5 Selection Test: Vocabulary 13

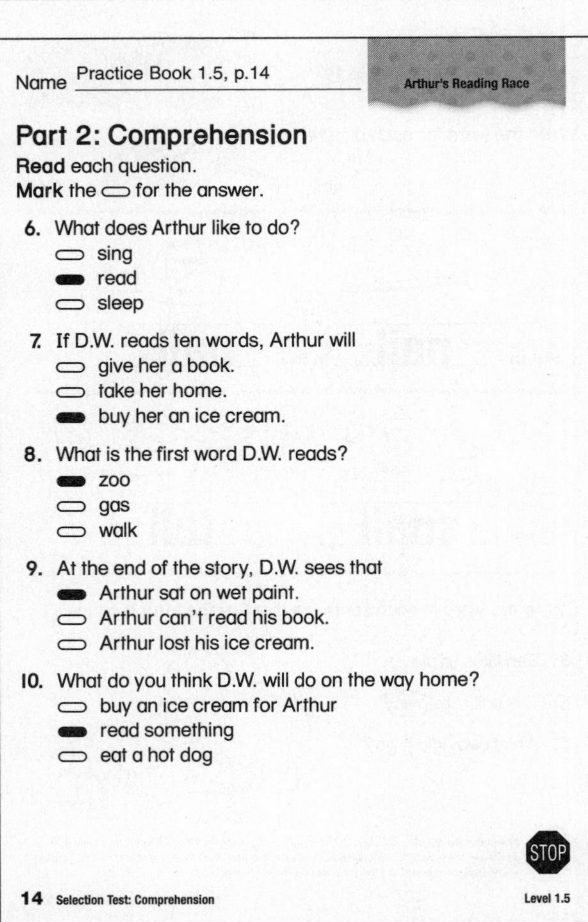

Name Practice Book 1.5, p.14

Arthur's Reading Race

## Part 2: Comprehension

**Read** each question.
**Mark** the ⬭ for the answer.

6. What does Arthur like to do?
   - ⬭ sing
   - ⬬ read
   - ⬭ sleep

7. If D.W. reads ten words, Arthur will
   - ⬭ give her a book.
   - ⬭ take her home.
   - ⬬ buy her an ice cream.

8. What is the first word D.W. reads?
   - ⬬ zoo
   - ⬭ gas
   - ⬭ walk

9. At the end of the story, D.W. sees that
   - ⬬ Arthur sat on wet paint.
   - ⬭ Arthur can't read his book.
   - ⬭ Arthur lost his ice cream.

10. What do you think D.W. will do on the way home?
    - ⬭ buy an ice cream for Arthur
    - ⬬ read something
    - ⬭ eat a hot dog

STOP

14 Selection Test: Comprehension Level 1.5

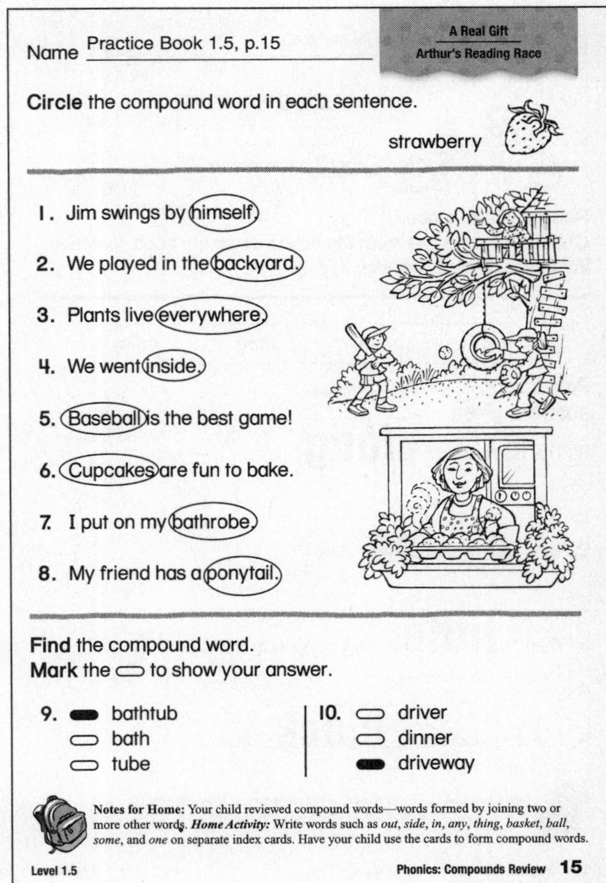

Name Practice Book 1.5, p.15

A Real Gift
Arthur's Reading Race

**Circle** the compound word in each sentence.

strawberry

1. Jim swings by (himself).
2. We played in the (backyard).
3. Plants live (everywhere).
4. We went (inside).
5. (Baseball) is the best game!
6. (Cupcakes) are fun to bake.
7. I put on my (bathrobe).
8. My friend has a (ponytail).

**Find** the compound word.
**Mark** the ⬭ to show your answer.

9. 
   - ⬬ bathtub
   - ⬭ bath
   - ⬭ tube

10. 
    - ⬭ driver
    - ⬭ dinner
    - ⬬ driveway

**Notes for Home:** Your child reviewed compound words—words formed by joining two or more other words. ***Home Activity:*** Write words such as *out, side, in, any, thing, basket, ball, some,* and *one* on separate index cards. Have your child use the cards to form compound words.

Level 1.5 Phonics: Compounds Review 15

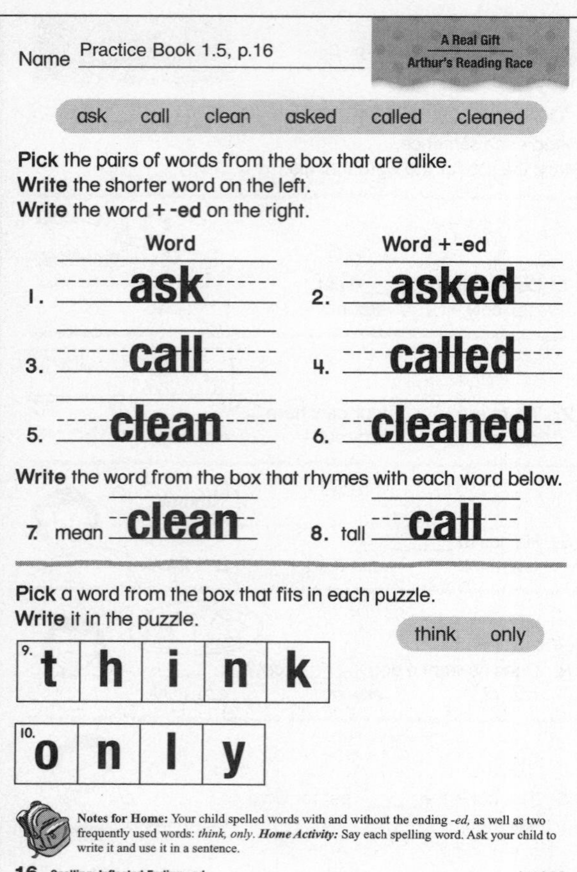

Name Practice Book 1.5, p.16

A Real Gift
Arthur's Reading Race

ask call clean asked called cleaned

**Pick** the pairs of words from the box that are alike.
**Write** the shorter word on the left.
**Write** the word + **-ed** on the right.

| | Word | | Word + -ed |
|---|---|---|---|
| 1. | ask | 2. | asked |
| 3. | call | 4. | called |
| 5. | clean | 6. | cleaned |

**Write** the word from the box that rhymes with each word below.

7. mean clean 8. tall call

**Pick** a word from the box that fits in each puzzle.
**Write** it in the puzzle.

think only

9. t h i n k

10. o n l y

**Notes for Home:** Your child spelled words with and without the ending *-ed,* as well as two frequently used words: *think, only.* ***Home Activity:*** Say each spelling word. Ask your child to write it and use it in a sentence.

16 Spelling: Inflected Ending *-ed* Level 1.5

Name Grammar Practice Book, p.42

A Real Gift
Arthur's Reading Race

RETEACHING

**hot** fire

An **adjective** tells more about a person, place, or thing.

**Circle** the adjective that tells about each picture.

1. **big** cat (small) cat 2. **sad** girl (happy) girl

3. **slow** rocket (fast) rocket 4. (funny) clown **sleepy** clown

5. (big) animal **tiny** animal 6. **happy** man (wet) man

**Notes for Home:** Your child identified adjectives—words that describe. ***Home Activity:*** Point to objects in the room. Have your child use adjectives to describe the objects.

Level 1.5 Grammar: Adjectives (Describing Words) 17

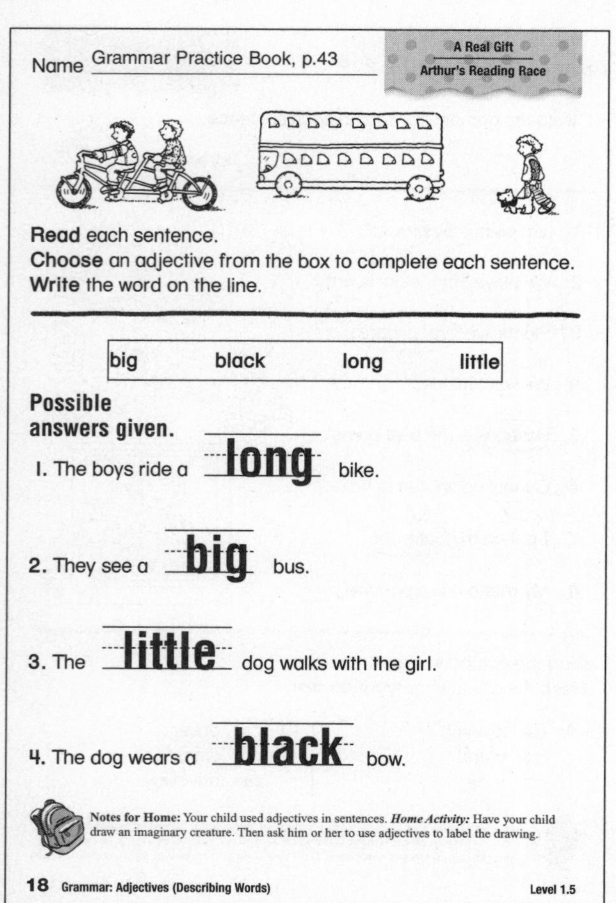

Name Grammar Practice Book, p.43

A Real Gift
Arthur's Reading Race

**Read** each sentence.
**Choose** an adjective from the box to complete each sentence.
**Write** the word on the line.

big black long little

**Possible answers given.**

1. The boys ride a long bike.

2. They see a big bus.

3. The little dog walks with the girl.

4. The dog wears a black bow.

**Notes for Home:** Your child used adjectives in sentences. ***Home Activity:*** Have your child draw an imaginary creature. Then ask him or her to use adjectives to label the drawing.

18 Grammar: Adjectives (Describing Words) Level 1.5

Name Practice Book 1.5, p.19

A Big Day for Jay
Lost!

**Write** the word for each picture.

n<u>ai</u>l h<u>ay</u>

1. Put the nail in the pail.

2. Does a snail have a tail?

**Circle** the word in each sentence that has the **long a** sound.

3. Ben likes to (play).

4. The ball rolls (away).

5. Which (way) did it go?

**Notes for Home:** Your child practiced writing and reading words with the long *a* sound spelled *ai* (as in *nail*) and *ay* (as in *hay*). ***Home Activity:*** Work with your child to write a short story using as many of the long *a* words on the page as possible.

Level 1.5 Phonics: Long *a* Spelled *ai, ay* 21

Name Practice Book 1.5, p.20

A Big Day for Jay
Lost!

**Pick** a word from the box that means the same as each pair of words.
**Write** it on the line.

She is tall.
She's tall.

| you'll | it's | that's | aren't |
|---|---|---|---|
| I'll | I'm | hadn't | don't |

1. it + is **it's**
2. that + is **that's**
3. are + not **aren't**
4. you + will **you'll**
5. I + will **I'll**
6. I + am **I'm**
7. do + not **don't**
8. had + not **hadn't**

**Notes for Home:** Your child learned to identify and write contractions, such as *I'll* and *She's*. ***Home Activity:*** Read each contraction on this page aloud. Challenge your child to use each one in a sentence. Work together to write each in a sentence.

22 Phonics: Contractions Level 1.5

Name Practice Book 1.5, p.21

A Big Day for Jay
Lost!

**Pick** a word from the box to finish each sentence.
**Write** it on the line.

| don't | from | hear | live | when |
|---|---|---|---|---|

1. I **hear** the mail truck beep.
2. I got a note **from** my friend.
3. My friend used to **live** here.
4. Now I **don't** see him anymore.
5. I am glad **when** he writes to me!

**Notes for Home:** This week your child is learning to read the words *don't, from, hear, live,* and *when*. ***Home Activity:*** Encourage your child to tell you a story using these words. Make a picture book of the completed story. Help your child write a caption for each picture.

Level 1.5 High-Frequency Words 23

Name Practice Book 1.5, p.22

A Big Day for Jay
Lost!

**Look** at both pictures.
**Write** sentences to tell how the pictures are the same and different.

Same **Possible answers given.**

1. **Rex and Pip are dogs.**
2. **Rex and Pip have hats.**

Different

3. **Rex is a big dog.**
4. **Rex has big feet.**
5. **Pip has long fur.**

Pip
Rex

**Notes for Home:** Your child used pictures to tell how two things are alike and different. ***Home Activity:*** Point out two objects to your child. Encourage your child to tell you how they are the same and how they are different.

24 Compare and Contrast Level 1.5

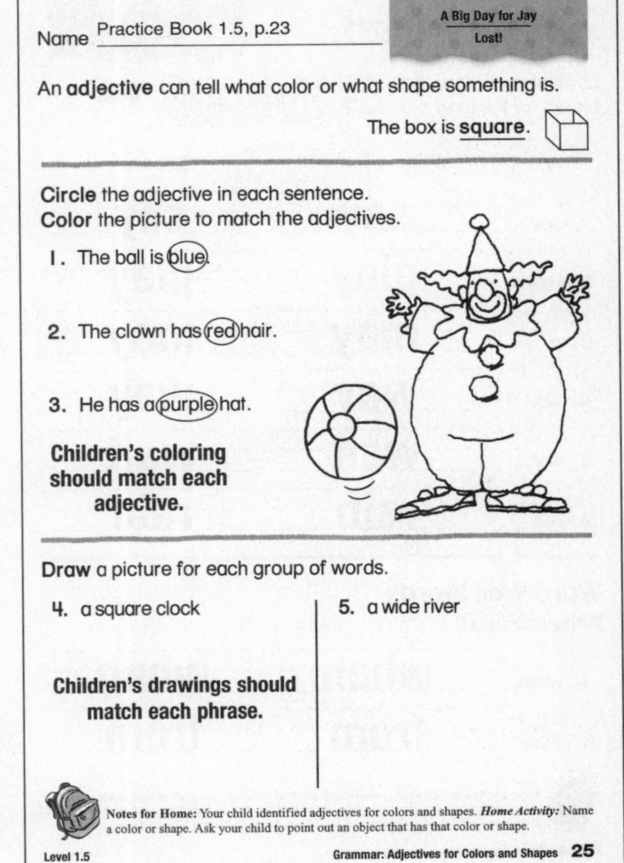

Name Practice Book 1.5, p.23

A Big Day for Jay
Lost!

An **adjective** can tell what color or what shape something is.

The box is **square**.

**Circle** the adjective in each sentence.
**Color** the picture to match the adjectives.

1. The ball is (blue).
2. The clown has (red) hair.
3. He has a (purple) hat.

**Children's coloring should match each adjective.**

**Draw** a picture for each group of words.

4. a square clock
5. a wide river

**Children's drawings should match each phrase.**

**Notes for Home:** Your child identified adjectives for colors and shapes. ***Home Activity:*** Name a color or shape. Ask your child to point out an object that has that color or shape.

Level 1.5 Grammar: Adjectives for Colors and Shapes 25

Name Practice Book 1.5, p.24

A Big Day for Jay
Lost!

**Pick** a word from the box to finish each sentence.
**Write** it on the line.

don't from hear hurt live when

1. I **hear** a pup.

2. Are you **hurt**, pup?

3. You **don't** look hurt.

4. Where do you **live**?

5. You are not **from** this block.

6. You will be glad **when** I find your home.

**Notes for Home:** Your child used new vocabulary words to complete a story. ***Home Activity:*** Read the vocabulary words aloud. Ask your child to write each word and explain its meaning.

26 Vocabulary/High-Frequency Words Level 1.5

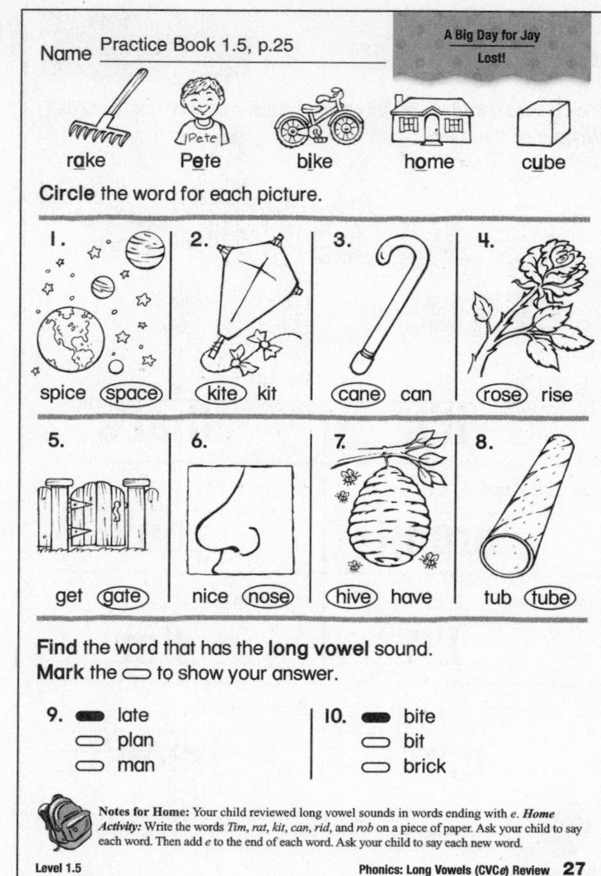

Name Practice Book 1.5, p.25

A Big Day for Jay
Lost!

rake Pete bike home cube

**Circle** the word for each picture.

1. spice (space)
2. (kite) kit
3. (cane) can
4. (rose) rise
5. get (gate)
6. nice (nose)
7. (hive) have
8. tub (tube)

**Find** the word that has the **long vowel** sound.
**Mark** the ⬭ to show your answer.

9. ● late ○ plan ○ man
10. ● bite ○ bit ○ brick

**Notes for Home:** Your child reviewed long vowel sounds in words ending with *e*. ***Home Activity:*** Write the words *Tim, rat, kit, can, rid,* and *rob* on a piece of paper. Ask your child to say each word. Then add *e* to the end of each word. Ask your child to say each new word.

Level 1.5 Phonics: Long Vowels (CVC*e*) Review 27

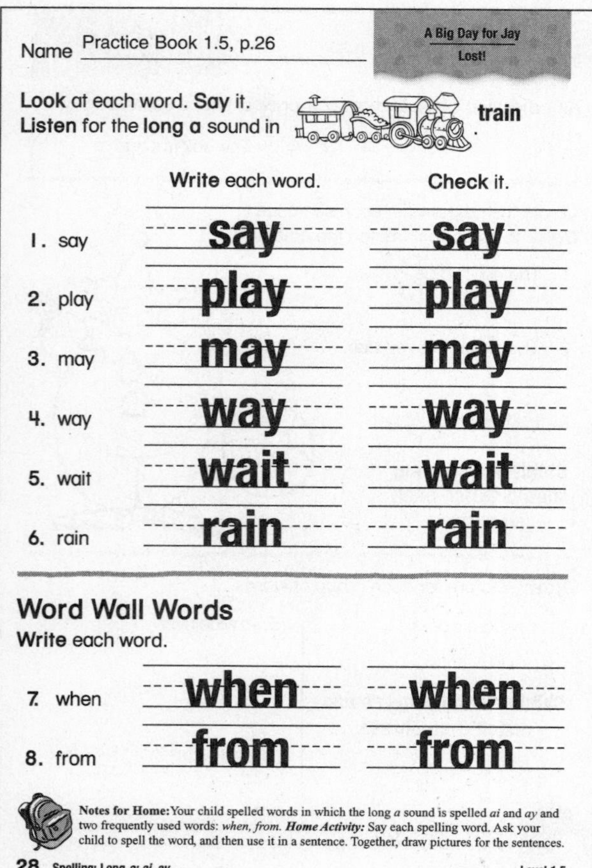

Name Practice Book 1.5, p.26

A Big Day for Jay
Lost!

**Look** at each word. **Say** it.
**Listen** for the **long a** sound in **train**.

| | Write each word. | Check it. |
|---|---|---|
| 1. say | say | say |
| 2. play | play | play |
| 3. may | may | may |
| 4. way | way | way |
| 5. wait | wait | wait |
| 6. rain | rain | rain |

**Word Wall Words**
**Write** each word.

| | | |
|---|---|---|
| 7. when | when | when |
| 8. from | from | from |

**Notes for Home:** Your child spelled words in which the long *a* sound is spelled *ai* and *ay* and two frequently used words: *when, from.* ***Home Activity:*** Say each spelling word. Ask your child to spell the word, and then use it in a sentence. Together, draw pictures for the sentences.

28 Spelling: Long *a: ai, ay* Level 1.5

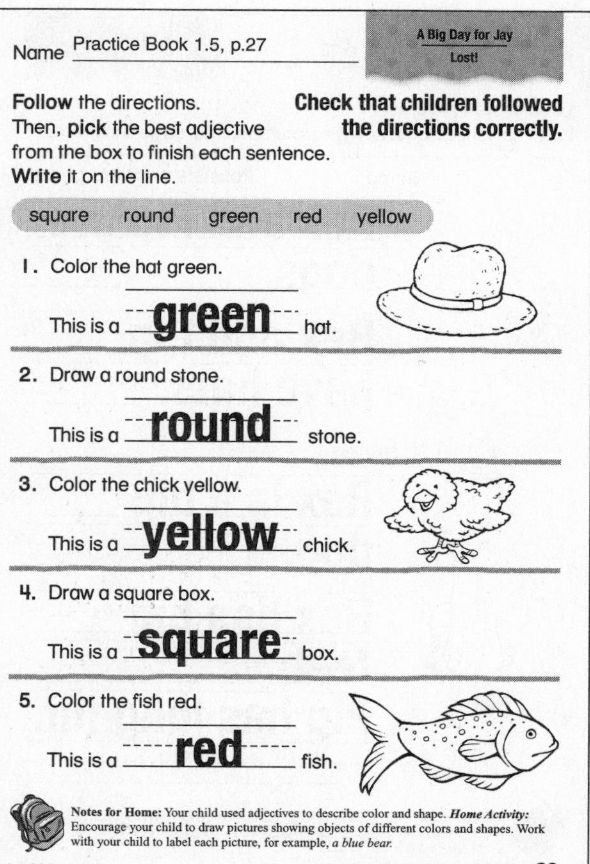

Name Practice Book 1.5, p.27

A Big Day for Jay
Lost!

**Follow** the directions.
Then, **pick** the best adjective from the box to finish each sentence.
**Write** it on the line.

**Check that children followed the directions correctly.**

square round green red yellow

1. Color the hat green.
This is a **green** hat.

2. Draw a round stone.
This is a **round** stone.

3. Color the chick yellow.
This is a **yellow** chick.

4. Draw a square box.
This is a **square** box.

5. Color the fish red.
This is a **red** fish.

**Notes for Home:** Your child used adjectives to describe color and shape. ***Home Activity:*** Encourage your child to draw pictures showing objects of different colors and shapes. Work with your child to label each picture, for example, *a blue bear.*

Level 1.5 Grammar: Adjectives for Colors and Shapes 29

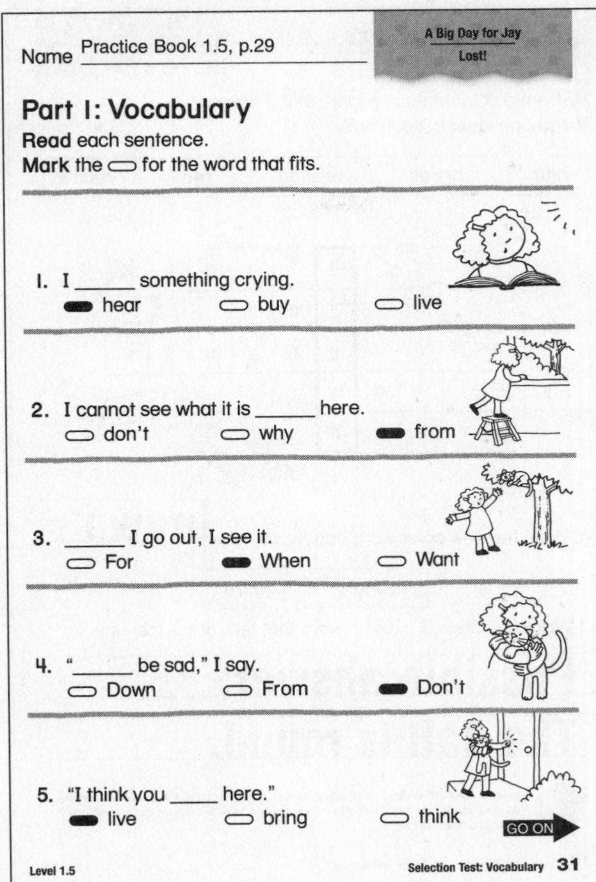

Name Practice Book 1.5, p.29

A Big Day for Jay
Lost!

## Part 1: Vocabulary

**Read** each sentence.
**Mark** the ⬭ for the word that fits.

1. I _____ something crying.
   - [x] hear
   - [ ] buy
   - [ ] live
2. I cannot see what it is _____ here.
   - [ ] don't
   - [ ] why
   - [x] from
3. _____ I go out, I see it.
   - [ ] For
   - [x] When
   - [ ] Want
4. "_____ be sad," I say.
   - [ ] Down
   - [ ] From
   - [x] Don't
5. "I think you _____ here."
   - [x] live
   - [ ] bring
   - [ ] think

GO ON

Level 1.5 Selection Test: Vocabulary 31

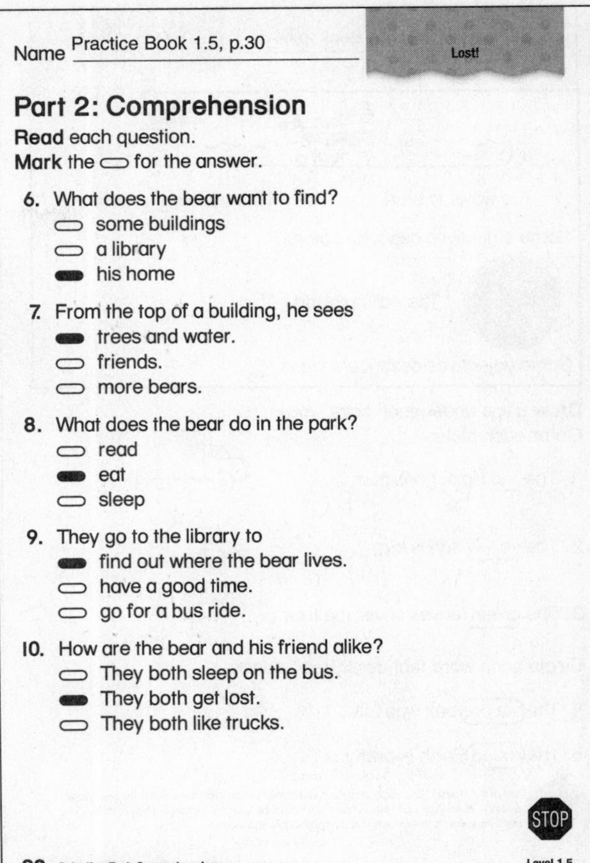

Name Practice Book 1.5, p.30

Lost!

## Part 2: Comprehension

**Read** each question.
**Mark** the ⬭ for the answer.

6. What does the bear want to find?
   - [ ] some buildings
   - [ ] a library
   - [x] his home
7. From the top of a building, he sees
   - [x] trees and water.
   - [ ] friends.
   - [ ] more bears.
8. What does the bear do in the park?
   - [ ] read
   - [x] eat
   - [ ] sleep
9. They go to the library to
   - [x] find out where the bear lives.
   - [ ] have a good time.
   - [ ] go for a bus ride.
10. How are the bear and his friend alike?
    - [ ] They both sleep on the bus.
    - [x] They both get lost.
    - [ ] They both like trucks.

STOP

32 Selection Test: Comprehension Level 1.5

Name Practice Book 1.5, p.31

A Big Day for Jay
Lost!



**ch**est **sh**op **th**in **wh**istle

**Circle** the word for each picture.

| 1. | 2. | 3. | 4. |
|---|---|---|---|
| (sheep) deep | gale (whale) | heat (wheat) | (thorn) torn |

| 5. | 6. | 7. | 8. |
|---|---|---|---|
| (ship) whip | there (chair) | thick (chick) | sell (shell) |

**Find** the word that has the same beginning sound as [chair]. **Mark** the ⬭ to show your answer.

chair

9.
- [x] cheap
- [ ] keep
- [ ] care

10.
- [ ] cold
- [ ] calm
- [x] child

**Notes for Home:** Your child reviewed digraphs—two letters that represent one sound—as in *chest, shop, thin,* and *whistle.* ***Home Activity:*** Together, write words beginning with *ch, sh, th,* and *wh* that have the same beginning sounds as the words shown above.

Level 1.5 Phonics: Initial Digraphs *ch, sh, th, wh* Review 33

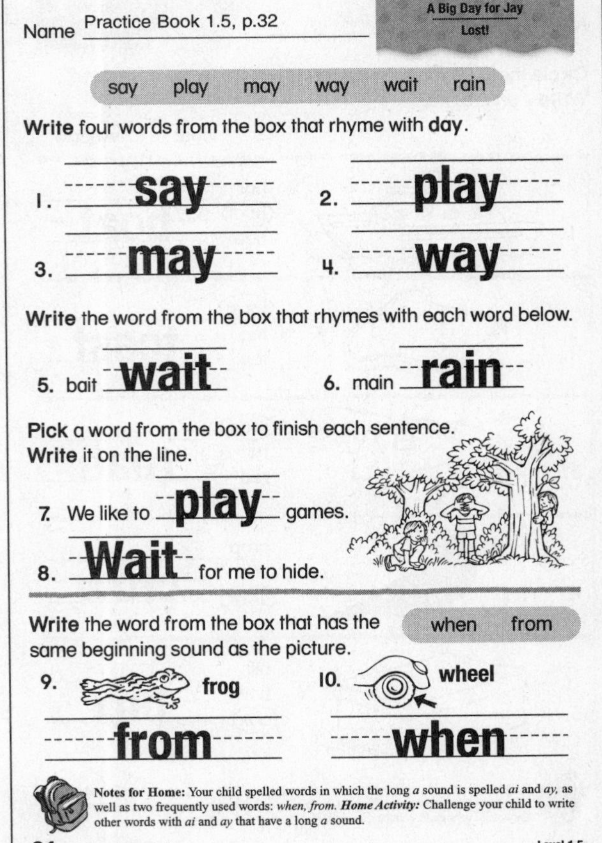

Name Practice Book 1.5, p.32

A Big Day for Jay
Lost!

say play may way wait rain

**Write** four words from the box that rhyme with **day**.

1. say
2. play
3. may
4. way

**Write** the word from the box that rhymes with each word below.

5. bait wait
6. main rain

**Pick** a word from the box to finish each sentence.
**Write** it on the line.

7. We like to play games.
8. Wait for me to hide.

**Write** the word from the box that has the same beginning sound as the picture.

when from

9. frog — from
10. wheel — when

**Notes for Home:** Your child spelled words in which the long *a* sound is spelled *ai* and *ay,* as well as two frequently used words: *when, from.* ***Home Activity:*** Challenge your child to write other words with *ai* and *ay* that have a long *a* sound.

34 Spelling: Long *a*: *ai, ay* Level 1.5

Name Grammar Practice Book, p.44

A Big Day for Jay
Lost!

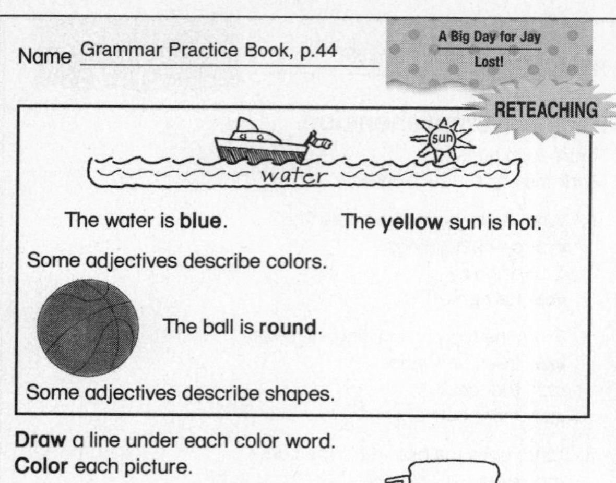
RETEACHING



The water is **blue**. The **yellow** sun is hot.

Some adjectives describe colors.

The ball is **round**.

Some adjectives describe shapes.

**Draw** a line under each color word.
**Color** each picture.

1. The red truck goes fast.

2. The yellow sun is big.

3. The green leaves cover the tree.

**Circle** each word that describes a shape.

4. The (square) box was full.

5. The (round) Earth is pretty.

**Notes for Home:** Your child identified adjectives that describe colors and shapes. ***Home Activity:*** Have your child cut out pictures from magazines or catalogs. Then have him or her label the pictures with words that describe colors and shapes.

Level 1.5 Grammar: Adjectives for Colors and Shapes 35

---

Name Grammar Practice Book , p.45

A Big Day for Jay
Lost!

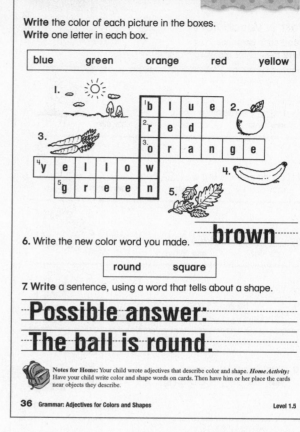

**Write** the color of each picture in the boxes.
**Write** one letter in each box.

blue green orange red yellow

| | | | | | | | | | | |
|---|---|---|---|---|---|---|---|---|---|---|
| | | | | | [1]b | l | u | e | | |
| | | | | | [2]r | e | d | | | |
| | | | | | [3]o | r | a | n | g | e |
| [4]y | e | l | l | o | w | | | | | |
| | [5]g | r | e | e | n | | | | | |

6. Write the new color word you made. **brown**

round square

7. **Write** a sentence, using a word that tells about a shape.

**Possible answer:**
**The ball is round.**

**Notes for Home:** Your child wrote adjectives that describe color and shape. ***Home Activity:*** Have your child write color and shape words on cards. Then have him or her place the cards near objects they describe.

36 Grammar: Adjectives for Colors and Shapes Level 1.5

---

Name Practice Book 1.5, p.35

Baby Otter Grows Up
Foal

**Circle** the word for each picture.
**Write** it on the line.

coat window

1. bat (boat) beet **boat**
2. (toast) tea top **toast**
3. (road) run red **road**
4. crop cap (crow) **crow**
5. bill bowl (box) **box**

**Notes for Home:** Your child practiced reading words with the long *o* sound spelled *oa* (as in *coat*) and *ow* (as in *window*). ***Home Activity:*** Read each long *o* word on this page aloud. Encourage your child to think of a word that rhymes with each word.

Level 1.5 Phonics: Long *o* Spelled *oa, ow* 39

---

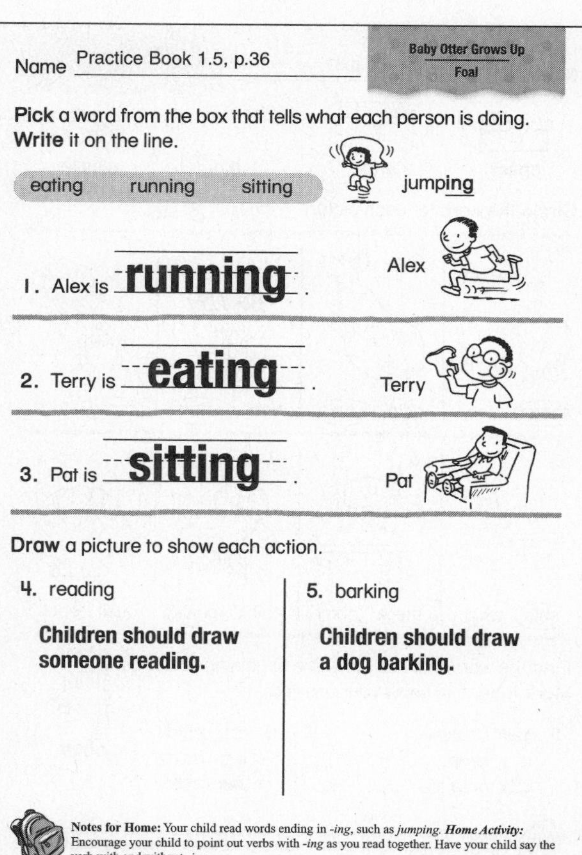

Name Practice Book 1.5, p.36

Baby Otter Grows Up
Foal

**Pick** a word from the box that tells what each person is doing.
**Write** it on the line.

eating running sitting

jumping

1. Alex is **running**. Alex
2. Terry is **eating**. Terry
3. Pat is **sitting**. Pat

**Draw** a picture to show each action.

4. reading
**Children should draw someone reading.**

5. barking
**Children should draw a dog barking.**

**Notes for Home:** Your child read words ending in *-ing*, such as *jumping*. ***Home Activity:*** Encourage your child to point out verbs with *-ing* as you read together. Have your child say the verb with and without *-ing*.

40 Phonics: Inflected Ending *-ing* Level 1.5

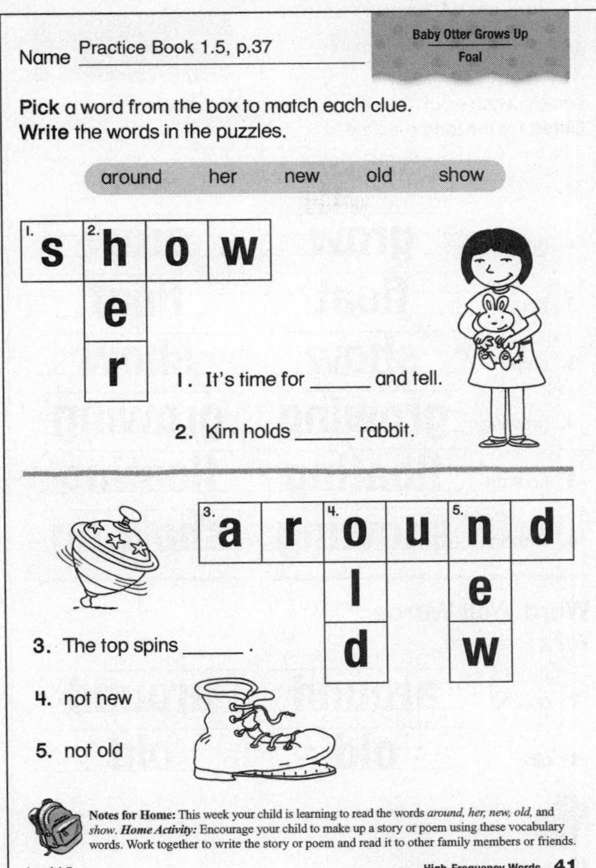

Baby Otter Grows Up
Foal

Name Practice Book 1.5, p.37

**Pick** a word from the box to match each clue.
**Write** the words in the puzzles.

around her new old show

1. s 2. h o w
e
r

1. It's time for _____ and tell.
2. Kim holds _____ rabbit.

3. a r 4. o u 5. n d
l e
d w

3. The top spins _____ .
4. not new
5. not old

**Notes for Home:** This week your child is learning to read the words *around, her, new, old,* and *show.* ***Home Activity:*** Encourage your child to make up a story or poem using these vocabulary words. Work together to write the story or poem and read it to other family members or friends.

Level 1.5 High-Frequency Words 41

Baby Otter Grows Up
Foal

Name Practice Book 1.5, p.38

**Look** at the pictures.
**Write 1, 2, 3** to put the sentences in order.

1. Then Dan picked a puppy. 2
2. Dan played with his new puppy at home. 3
3. Dan and his mother went to the pet store. 1

4. Jen and Sam went home. 3
5. First Jen and Sam went to the park. 1
6. Jen and Sam played on the slide. 2

**Notes for Home:** Your child put a sequence of events in order to form a story. ***Home Activity:*** Ask your child to draw a series of pictures showing three events in the order in which they happened.

42 Sequence Level 1.5

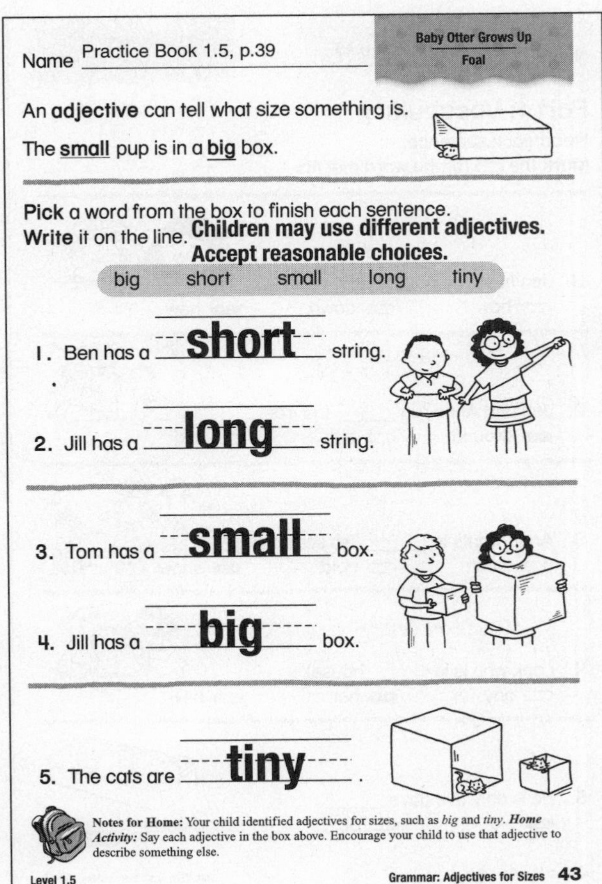

Baby Otter Grows Up
Foal

Name Practice Book 1.5, p.39

An **adjective** can tell what size something is.
The <u>small</u> pup is in a <u>big</u> box.

**Pick** a word from the box to finish each sentence.
**Write** it on the line. **Children may use different adjectives. Accept reasonable choices.**

big short small long tiny

1. Ben has a **short** string.
2. Jill has a **long** string.
3. Tom has a **small** box.
4. Jill has a **big** box.
5. The cats are **tiny** .

**Notes for Home:** Your child identified adjectives for sizes, such as *big* and *tiny.* ***Home Activity:*** Say each adjective in the box above. Encourage your child to use that adjective to describe something else.

Level 1.5 Grammar: Adjectives for Sizes 43

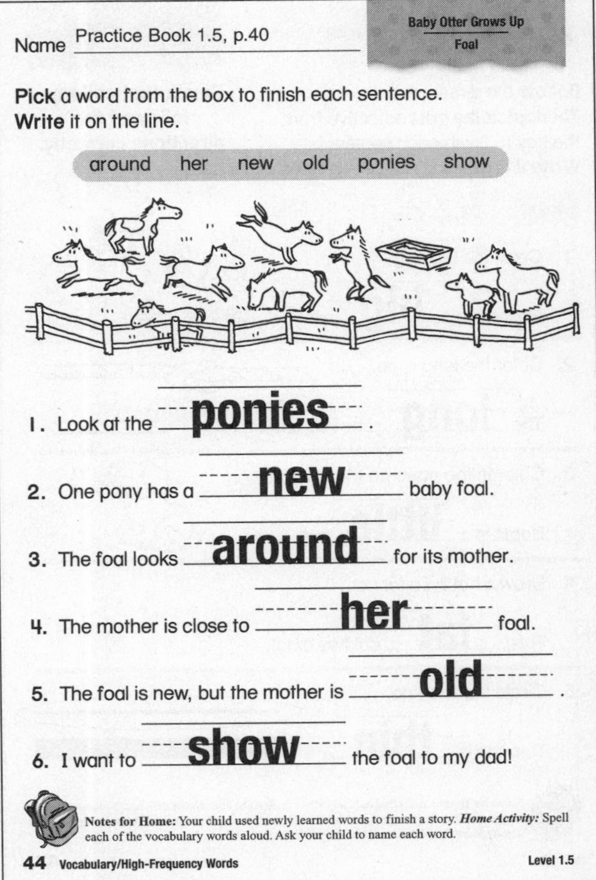

Baby Otter Grows Up
Foal

Name Practice Book 1.5, p.40

**Pick** a word from the box to finish each sentence.
**Write** it on the line.

around her new old ponies show

1. Look at the **ponies** .
2. One pony has a **new** baby foal.
3. The foal looks **around** for its mother.
4. The mother is close to **her** foal.
5. The foal is new, but the mother is **old** .
6. I want to **show** the foal to my dad!

**Notes for Home:** Your child used newly learned words to finish a story. ***Home Activity:*** Spell each of the vocabulary words aloud. Ask your child to name each word.

44 Vocabulary/High-Frequency Words Level 1.5

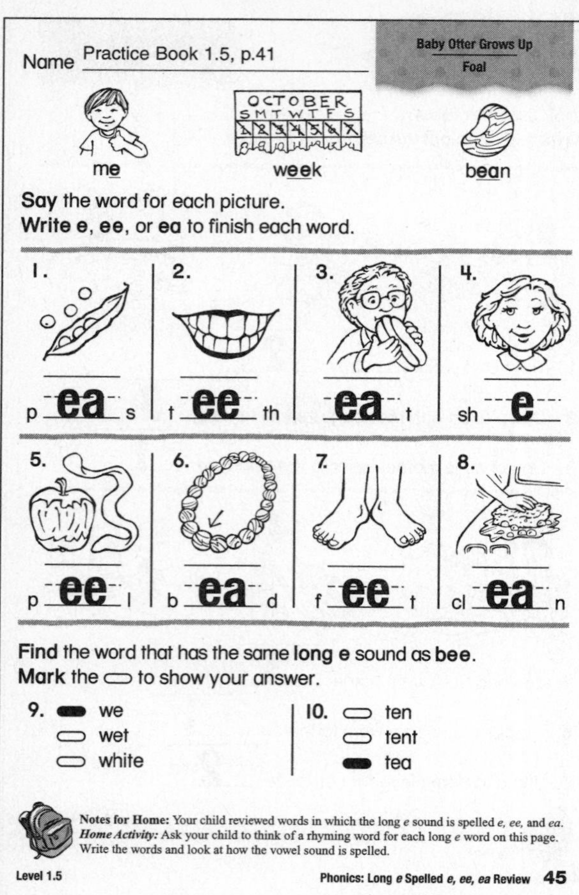

Baby Otter Grows Up
Foal

Name Practice Book 1.5, p.41

me week bean

**Say** the word for each picture.
**Write e, ee,** or **ea** to finish each word.

1. p **ea** s
2. t **ee** th
3. **ea** t
4. sh **e**
5. p **ee** l
6. b **ea** d
7. f **ee** t
8. cl **ea** n

**Find** the word that has the same **long e** sound as **bee**.
**Mark** the ⬭ to show your answer.

9. ● we ○ wet ○ white
10. ○ ten ○ tent ● tea

**Notes for Home:** Your child reviewed words in which the long *e* sound is spelled *e, ee,* and *ea*. ***Home Activity:*** Ask your child to think of a rhyming word for each long *e* word on this page. Write the words and look at how the vowel sound is spelled.

Level 1.5 Phonics: Long *e* Spelled *e, ee, ea* Review 45

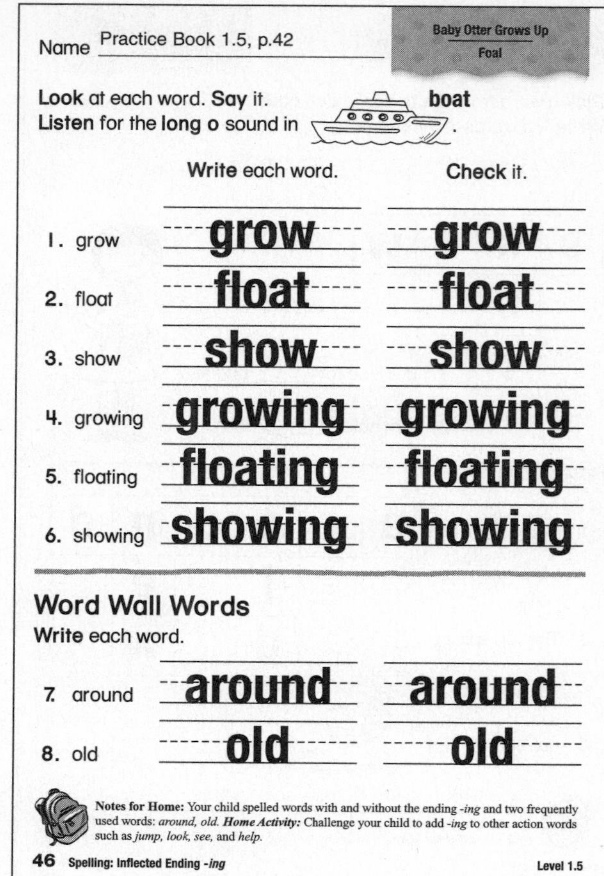

Baby Otter Grows Up
Foal

Name Practice Book 1.5, p.42

**Look** at each word. **Say** it.
**Listen** for the **long o** sound in **boat**.

| | Write each word. | Check it. |
|---|---|---|
| 1. grow | grow | grow |
| 2. float | float | float |
| 3. show | show | show |
| 4. growing | growing | growing |
| 5. floating | floating | floating |
| 6. showing | showing | showing |

**Word Wall Words**
**Write** each word.

| | | |
|---|---|---|
| 7. around | around | around |
| 8. old | old | old |

**Notes for Home:** Your child spelled words with and without the ending *-ing* and two frequently used words: *around, old.* ***Home Activity:*** Challenge your child to add *-ing* to other action words such as *jump, look, see,* and *help.*

46 Spelling: Inflected Ending *-ing* Level 1.5

Baby Otter Grows Up
Foal

Name Practice Book 1.5, p.43

**Follow** the directions.
Then, **pick** the best adjective from the box to finish each sentence.
**Write** it on the line. Use each word only once.

**Check that children followed the directions correctly.**

thin long big fat little

1. Color the big dog.
Rover is a **big** dog.

2. Color the long rope.
The **long** rope has a knot.

3. Color in the paws on the little pup.
Boots is a **little** pup.

4. Draw a hat on a fat cat.
This **fat** cat has a hat.

5. Circle the thin line.
This line is **thin**.

**Notes for Home:** Your child used adjectives to describe size. ***Home Activity:*** Go for a walk with your child. Encourage him or her to describe the objects and people you see using size adjectives, such as *big, small, tall,* and *short, huge, tiny.*

Level 1.5 Grammar: Adjectives for Sizes 47

Baby Otter Grows Up
Foal

Name Practice Book 1.5, p.45

**Part 1: Vocabulary**
**Read** each sentence.
**Mark** the ⬭ for the word that fits.

1. Jen has a _____ friend.
○ how ○ down ● new

2. Jen and Anna run _____ the tree.
● around ○ old ○ with

3. Anna wants to _____ Jen something.
○ catch ○ hold ● show

4. Look who is in _____ house!
○ any ● her ○ new

5. He is only five days _____ .
● old ○ or ○ around

GO ON

Level 1.5 Selection Test: Vocabulary 49

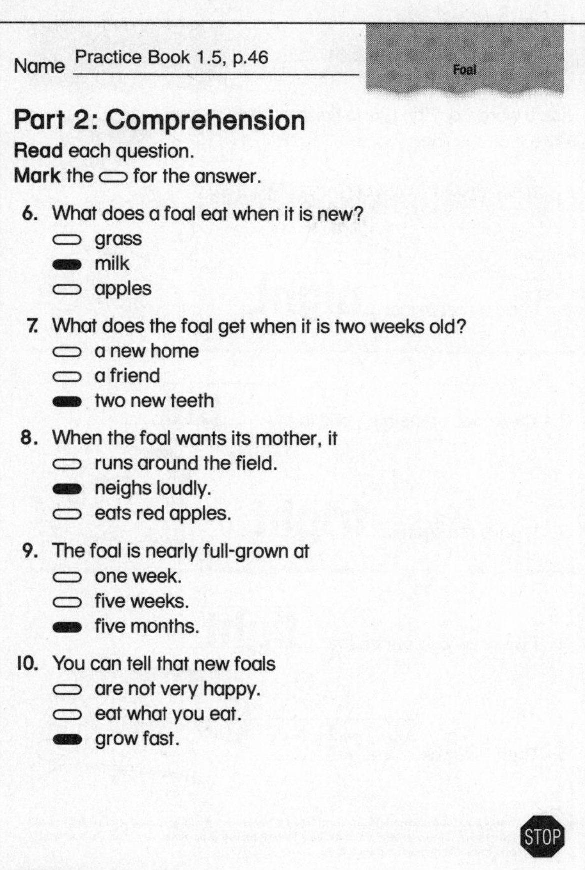

Name Practice Book 1.5, p.46
Foal
Part 2: Comprehension
Read each question.
Mark the ⊂⊃ for the answer.
6. What does a foal eat when it is new?
grass
milk
apples
7. What does the foal get when it is two weeks old?
a new home
a friend
two new teeth
8. When the foal wants its mother, it
runs around the field.
neighs loudly.
eats red apples.
9. The foal is nearly full-grown at
one week.
five weeks.
five months.
10. You can tell that new foals
are not very happy.
eat what you eat.
grow fast.
STOP
50 Selection Test: Comprehension
Level 1.5


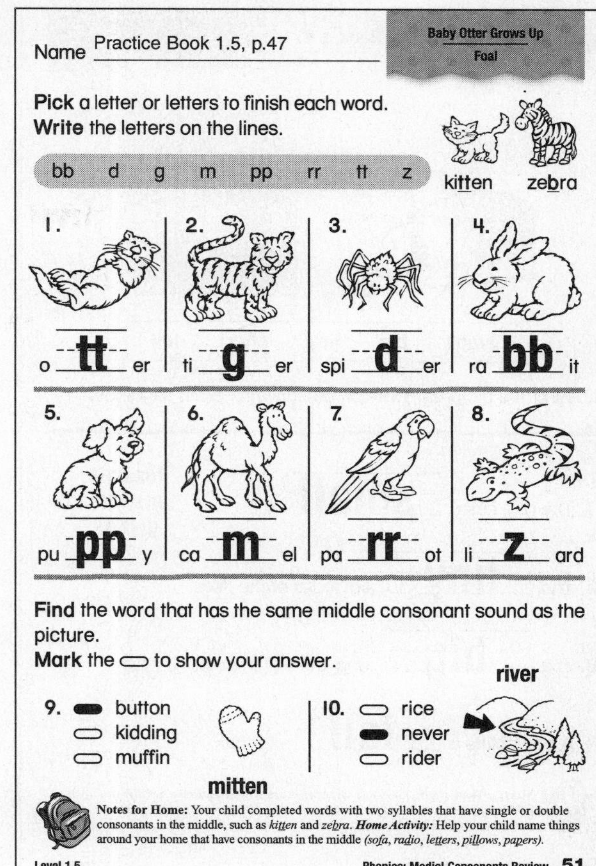

Name Practice Book 1.5, p.47
Baby Otter Grows Up
Foal
Pick a letter or letters to finish each word.
Write the letters on the lines.
bb d g m pp rr tt z
kitten zebra
1. o tt er
2. ti g er
3. spi d er
4. ra bb it
5. pu pp y
6. ca m el
7. pa rr ot
8. li z ard
Find the word that has the same middle consonant sound as the picture.
Mark the ⊂⊃ to show your answer.
9. button
kidding
muffin
mitten
10. rice
never
rider
river
Notes for Home: Your child completed words with two syllables that have single or double consonants in the middle, such as kitten and zebra. Home Activity: Help your child name things around your home that have consonants in the middle (sofa, radio, letters, pillows, papers).
Level 1.5
Phonics: Medial Consonants Review 51


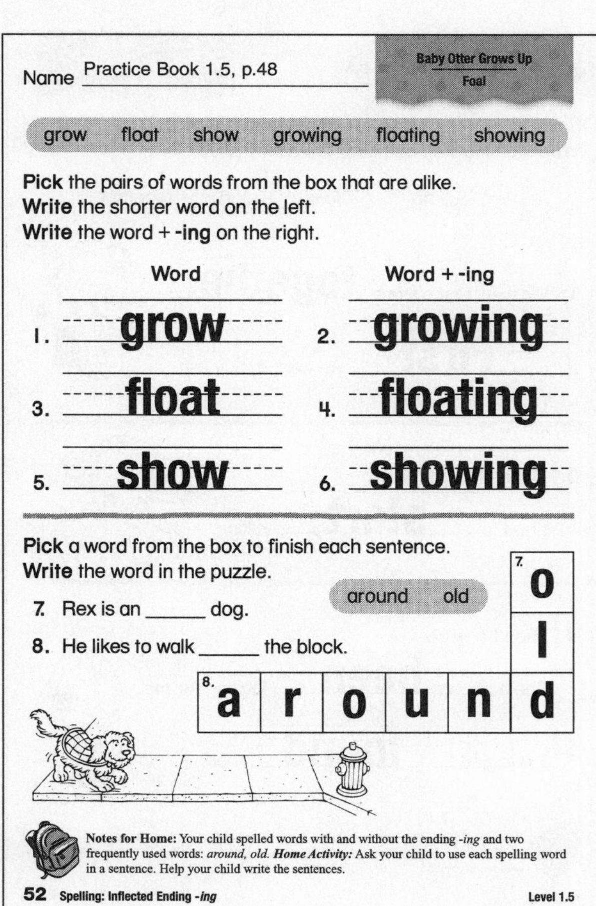

Name Practice Book 1.5, p.48
Baby Otter Grows Up
Foal
grow float show growing floating showing
Pick the pairs of words from the box that are alike.
Write the shorter word on the left.
Write the word + -ing on the right.
Word
Word + -ing
1. grow
2. growing
3. float
4. floating
5. show
6. showing
Pick a word from the box to finish each sentence.
Write the word in the puzzle.
around old
7. Rex is an ______ dog.
8. He likes to walk ______ the block.
7. o l d
8. a r o u n d
Notes for Home: Your child spelled words with and without the ending -ing and two frequently used words: around, old. Home Activity: Ask your child to use each spelling word in a sentence. Help your child write the sentences.
52 Spelling: Inflected Ending -ing
Level 1.5


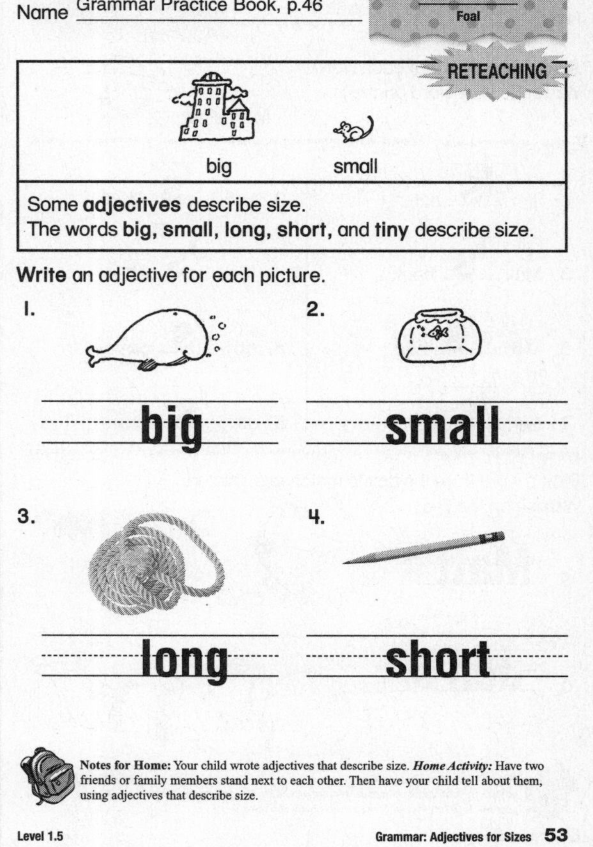

Name Grammar Practice Book, p.46
Baby Otter Grows Up
Foal
RETEACHING
big
small
Some adjectives describe size.
The words big, small, long, short, and tiny describe size.
Write an adjective for each picture.
1. big
2. small
3. long
4. short
Notes for Home: Your child wrote adjectives that describe size. Home Activity: Have two friends or family members stand next to each other. Then have your child tell about them, using adjectives that describe size.
Level 1.5
Grammar: Adjectives for Sizes 53

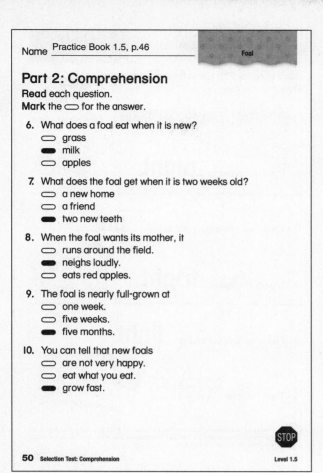

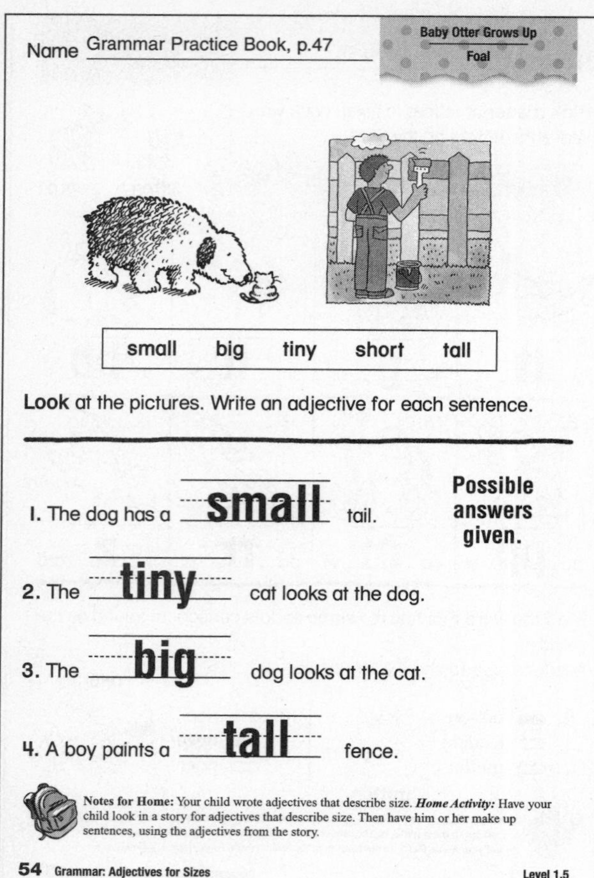

Name Grammar Practice Book, p.47

Baby Otter Grows Up
Foal

small big tiny short tall

**Look** at the pictures. Write an adjective for each sentence.

**Possible answers given.**

1. The dog has a **small** tail.
2. The **tiny** cat looks at the dog.
3. The **big** dog looks at the cat.
4. A boy paints a **tall** fence.

**Notes for Home:** Your child wrote adjectives that describe size. ***Home Activity:*** Have your child look in a story for adjectives that describe size. Then have him or her make up sentences, using the adjectives from the story.

54 Grammar: Adjectives for Sizes Level 1.5

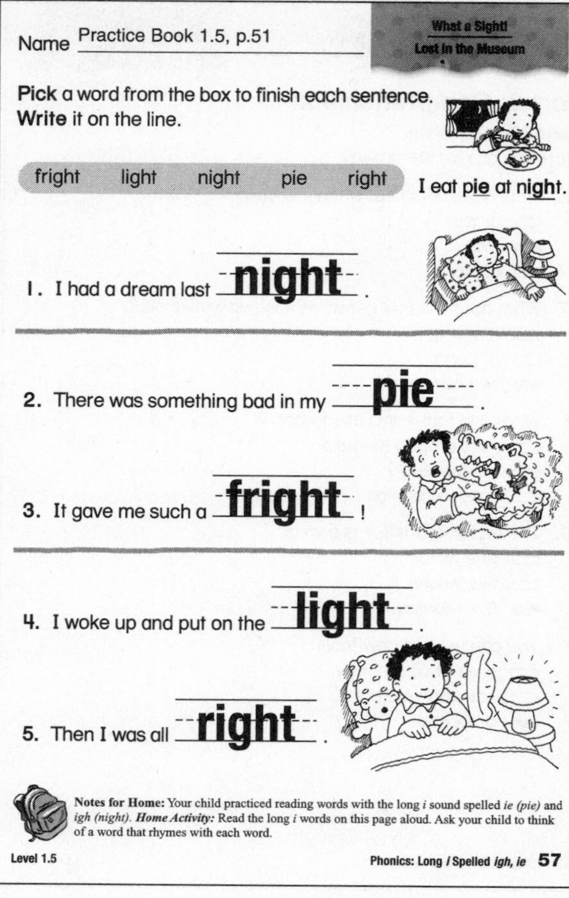

Name Practice Book 1.5, p.51

What a Sight!
Lost in the Museum

**Pick** a word from the box to finish each sentence.
**Write** it on the line.

fright light night pie right

I eat pi<u>e</u> at ni<u>gh</u>t.

1. I had a dream last **night**.
2. There was something bad in my **pie**.
3. It gave me such a **fright**!
4. I woke up and put on the **light**.
5. Then I was all **right**.

**Notes for Home:** Your child practiced reading words with the long *i* sound spelled *ie (pie)* and *igh (night)*. ***Home Activity:*** Read the long *i* words on this page aloud. Ask your child to think of a word that rhymes with each word.

Level 1.5 Phonics: Long *i* Spelled *igh, ie* 57

Name Practice Book 1.5, p.52

What a Sight!
Lost in the Museum

**Add 's** to the end of each word.
**Write** the new word on the line.

Meg's hat

1. Jim **'s** bat
2. baby **'s** laugh
3. Max **'s** book
4. Kate **'s** kite
5. Mom **'s** cup
6. boy **'s** games
7. Ben **'s** cat
8. Jill **'s** horn

**Pick** a word from the box to match each picture.
**Write** it on the line.

Jen's Matt's

9. **Matt's** hat
10. **Jen's** ball

**Notes for Home:** Your child wrote words with *'s* to show ownership. ***Home Activity:*** Point out objects in your home or outside that are owned by one person. Ask your child to use a possessive to tell you who owns each object *(Mike's bike)*.

58 Phonics: Possessives Level 1.5

Name Practice Book 1.5, p.53

What a Sight!
Lost in the Museum

**Pick** a word from the box to finish each sentence.
**Write** it on the line. Use each word only once.

been first found start together

1. We went to the store **together**.
2. **First** we went to buy fish.
3. My mother got lost.
I had to **start** yelling.
4. Then I saw her.
She had **been** looking for me.
5. I was glad I **found** her!

**Notes for Home:** This week your child is learning the words *been, first, found, start,* and *together.* ***Home Activity:*** Use each of these words in a simple sentence. Help your child read each sentence aloud.

Level 1.5 High-Frequency Words 59

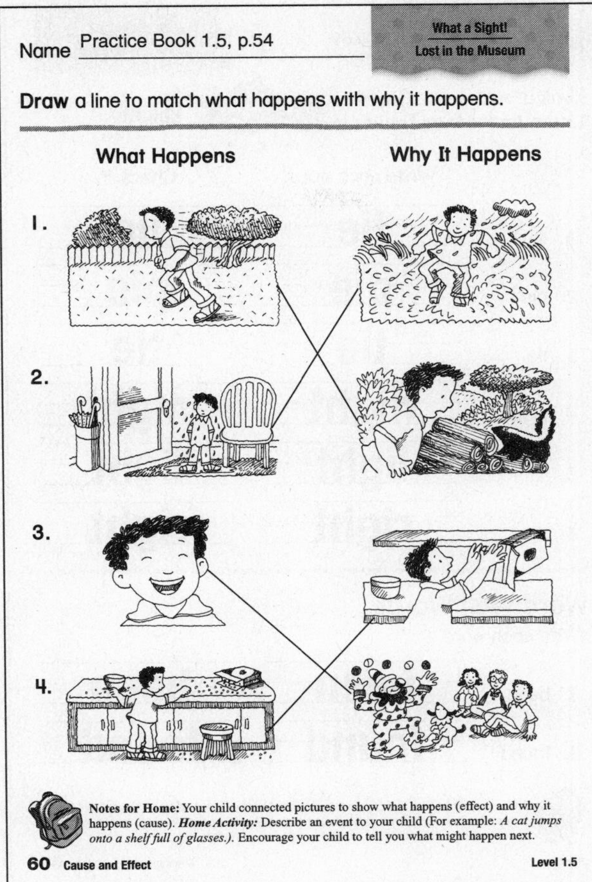

Name Practice Book 1.5, p.54

What a Sight!
Lost in the Museum

**Draw** a line to match what happens with why it happens.

| What Happens | Why It Happens |
| --- | --- |
| 1. | |
| 2. | |
| 3. | |
| 4. | |

**Notes for Home:** Your child connected pictures to show what happens (effect) and why it happens (cause). *Home Activity:* Describe an event to your child (For example: *A cat jumps onto a shelf full of glasses.*). Encourage your child to tell you what might happen next.

60 Cause and Effect Level 1.5

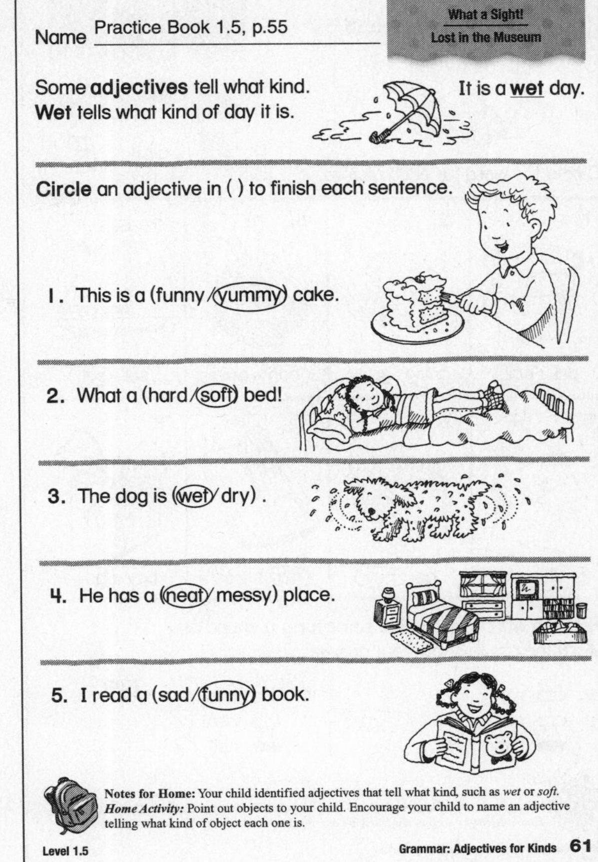

Name Practice Book 1.5, p.55

What a Sight!
Lost in the Museum

Some **adjectives** tell what kind.
**Wet** tells what kind of day it is.

It is a **wet** day.

**Circle** an adjective in ( ) to finish each sentence.

1. This is a (funny / yummy) cake.
2. What a (hard / soft) bed!
3. The dog is (wet / dry).
4. He has a (neat / messy) place.
5. I read a (sad / funny) book.

**Notes for Home:** Your child identified adjectives that tell what kind, such as *wet* or *soft*. *Home Activity:* Point out objects to your child. Encourage your child to name an adjective telling what kind of object each one is.

Level 1.5 Grammar: Adjectives for Kinds 61

Name Practice Book 1.5, p.56

What a Sight!
Lost in the Museum

**Pick** a word from the box that is the opposite of each word below.
**Write** it on the line.

been first found start together

1. stop **start**
2. last **first**
3. lost **found**
4. apart **together**

**Write** a sentence with the word *been*. **Possible answer given.**

5. **I have been good.**

*Notes for Home:* Your child identified opposites and wrote a sentence using words learned this week. *Home Activity:* Encourage your child to make up a song or poem using as many of these words as possible.

62 Vocabulary/High-Frequency Words Level 1.5

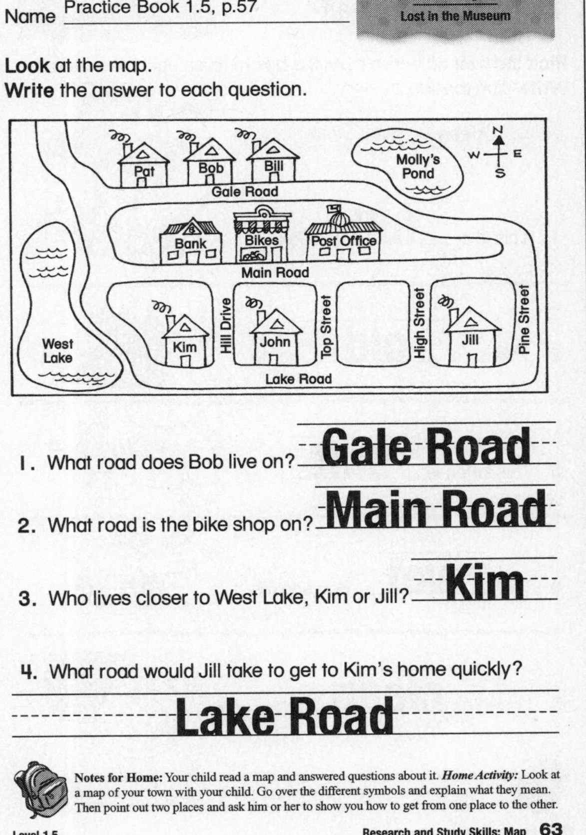

Name Practice Book 1.5, p.57

What a Sight!
Lost in the Museum

**Look** at the map.
**Write** the answer to each question.



1. What road does Bob live on? **Gale Road**
2. What road is the bike shop on? **Main Road**
3. Who lives closer to West Lake, Kim or Jill? **Kim**
4. What road would Jill take to get to Kim's home quickly? **Lake Road**

**Notes for Home:** Your child read a map and answered questions about it. *Home Activity:* Look at a map of your town with your child. Go over the different symbols and explain what they mean. Then point out two places and ask him or her to show you how to get from one place to the other.

Level 1.5 Research and Study Skills: Map 63

Name Practice Book 1.5, p.58

What a Sight!
Lost in the Museum

tail play

**Circle** the word for each picture.

1. pal (pail)
2. (gray) grow
3. (pan) pain
4. sell (sail)
5. (mail) mill
6. he (hay)
7. (tray) tree
8. bay (bow)

**Find** the word that has the same **long a** sound as rain. **Mark** the ⬭ to show your answer.

9. ⬭ rap
⬭ clap
⬬ clay

10. ⬭ nap
⬭ neat
⬬ nail

**Notes for Home:** Your child reviewed words in which the long *a* sound is spelled *ai* and *ay*. ***Home Activity:*** Ask your child to think of a rhyming word for each long *a* word on this page.

64 Phonics: Long *a* Spelled *ai, ay* Review Level 1.5

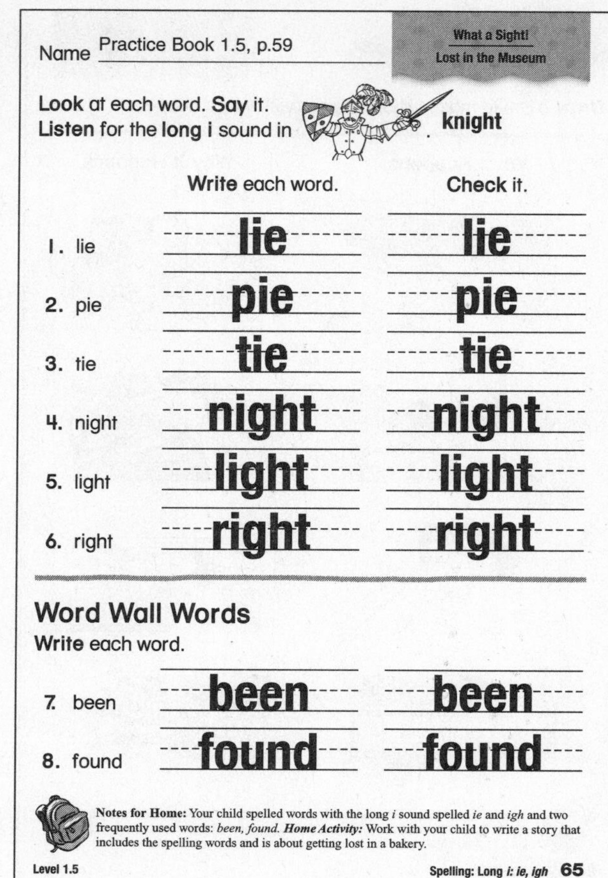

Name Practice Book 1.5, p.59

What a Sight!
Lost in the Museum

**Look** at each word. **Say** it.
**Listen** for the **long i** sound in knight.

| | Write each word. | Check it. |
|---|---|---|
| 1. lie | lie | lie |
| 2. pie | pie | pie |
| 3. tie | tie | tie |
| 4. night | night | night |
| 5. light | light | light |
| 6. right | right | right |

**Word Wall Words**
**Write** each word.

| | | |
|---|---|---|
| 7. been | been | been |
| 8. found | found | found |

**Notes for Home:** Your child spelled words with the long *i* sound spelled *ie* and *igh* and two frequently used words: *been, found. **Home Activity:*** Work with your child to write a story that includes the spelling words and is about getting lost in a bakery.

Level 1.5 Spelling: Long *i*: *ie, igh* 65

Name Practice Book 1.5, p.60

What a Sight!
Lost in the Museum

**Pick** the best adjective from the box to finish each sentence.
**Write** it on the line.

soft clean wet old full

1. This is a full box.
2. This is an old home.
3. This kitten is soft.
4. The wet dog shakes.
5. I need a clean dish to use.

**Notes for Home:** Your child used adjectives that tell what kind of object something is, such as *full box* or *wet dog*. ***Home Activity:*** Play *I Spy* with your child. Encourage your child to describe an object using adjectives for kind, and see if you can guess what object he or she is talking about.

66 Grammar: Adjectives for Kinds Level 1.5

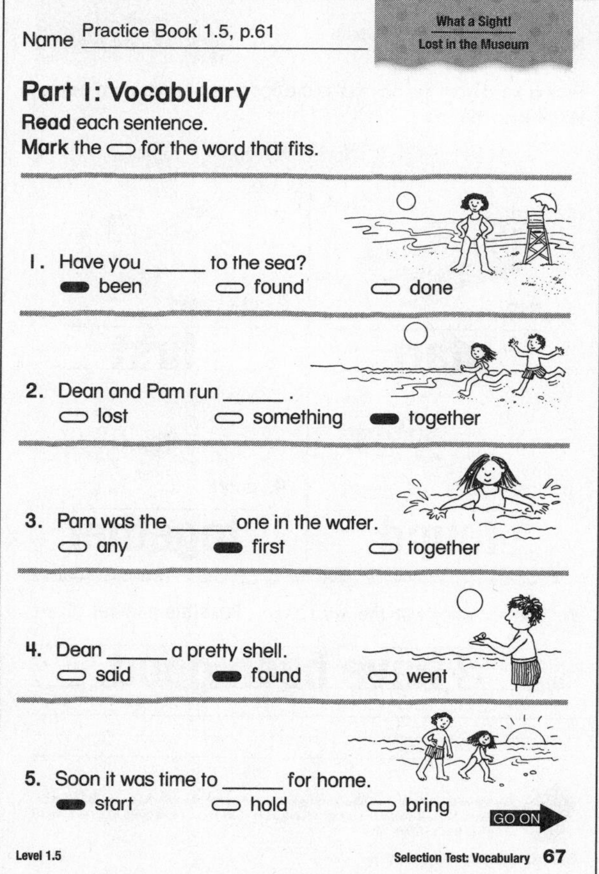

Name Practice Book 1.5, p.61

What a Sight!
Lost in the Museum

**Part 1: Vocabulary**
**Read** each sentence.
**Mark** the ⬭ for the word that fits.

1. Have you _____ to the sea?
⬬ been ⬭ found ⬭ done

2. Dean and Pam run _____ .
⬭ lost ⬭ something ⬬ together

3. Pam was the _____ one in the water.
⬭ any ⬬ first ⬭ together

4. Dean _____ a pretty shell.
⬭ said ⬬ found ⬭ went

5. Soon it was time to _____ for home.
⬬ start ⬭ hold ⬭ bring

GO ON

Level 1.5 Selection Test: Vocabulary 67

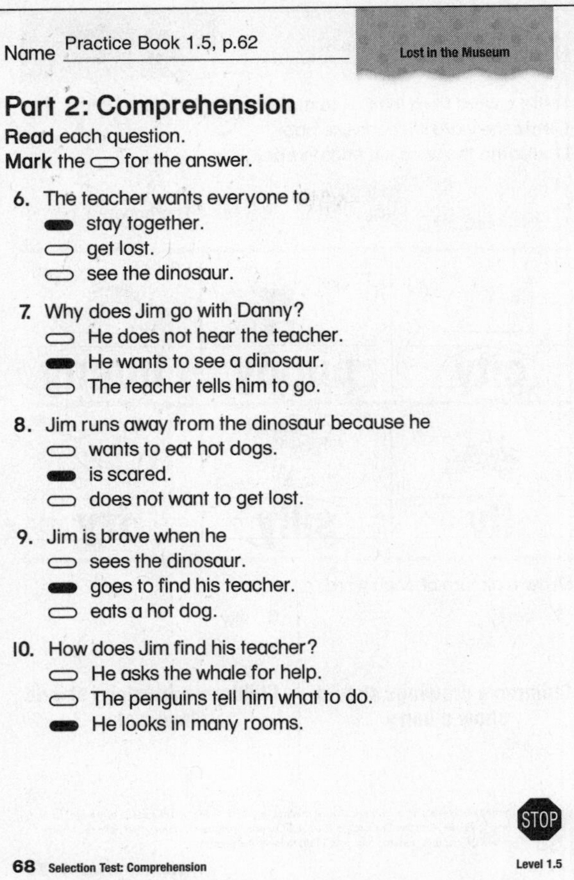
Name Practice Book 1.5, p.62

Lost in the Museum

## Part 2: Comprehension

**Read** each question.
**Mark** the ⬭ for the answer.

6. The teacher wants everyone to
   - ⬬ stay together.
   - ⬭ get lost.
   - ⬭ see the dinosaur.
7. Why does Jim go with Danny?
   - ⬭ He does not hear the teacher.
   - ⬬ He wants to see a dinosaur.
   - ⬭ The teacher tells him to go.
8. Jim runs away from the dinosaur because he
   - ⬭ wants to eat hot dogs.
   - ⬬ is scared.
   - ⬭ does not want to get lost.
9. Jim is brave when he
   - ⬭ sees the dinosaur.
   - ⬬ goes to find his teacher.
   - ⬭ eats a hot dog.
10. How does Jim find his teacher?
    - ⬭ He asks the whale for help.
    - ⬭ The penguins tell him what to do.
    - ⬬ He looks in many rooms.

STOP

68 Selection Test: Comprehension Level 1.5

Name Practice Book 1.5, p.63

What a Sight!
Lost in the Museum

**Write** the contraction for each pair of words.

1. I + am = **I'm**
2. you + will = **you'll**
3. is + not = **isn't**
4. they + are = **they're**
5. could + not = **couldn't**
6. she + had = **she'd**
7. do + not = **don't**
8. would + not = **wouldn't**

**Find** the contraction.
**Mark** the ⬭ to show your answer.

9. ⬬ it's ⬭ hits ⬭ its

10. ⬭ were ⬬ we're ⬭ worry

**Notes for Home:** Your child reviewed contractions—words made up of two words and an apostrophe. ***Home Activity:*** Write the words *it, is, did, not, I, am, we,* and *are* on separate index cards. Ask your child to see how many different contractions he or she can form.

Level 1.5 Phonics: Contractions Review 69

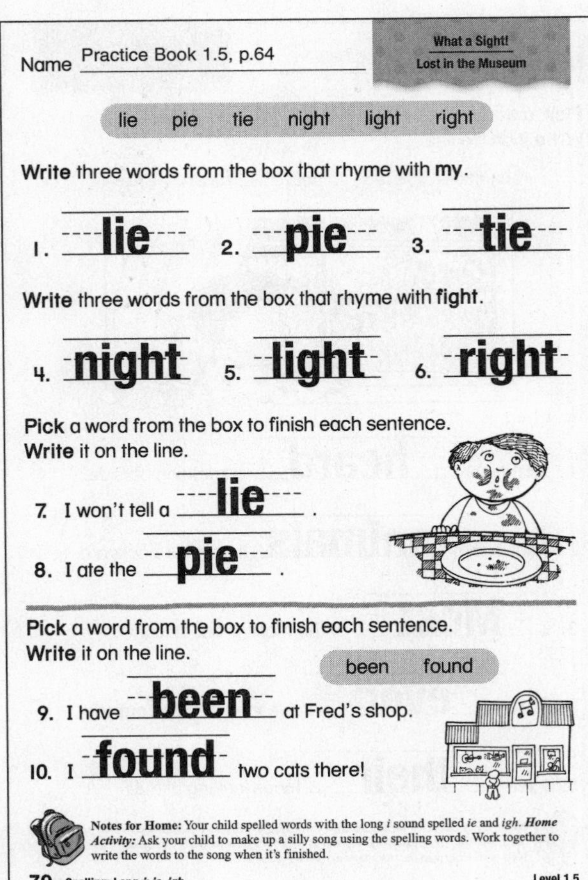
Name Practice Book 1.5, p.64

What a Sight!
Lost in the Museum

lie pie tie night light right

**Write** three words from the box that rhyme with **my**.

1. **lie** 2. **pie** 3. **tie**

**Write** three words from the box that rhyme with **fight**.

4. **night** 5. **light** 6. **right**

**Pick** a word from the box to finish each sentence.
**Write** it on the line.

7. I won't tell a **lie**.
8. I ate the **pie**.

**Pick** a word from the box to finish each sentence.
**Write** it on the line.

been found

9. I have **been** at Fred's shop.
10. I **found** two cats there!

**Notes for Home:** Your child spelled words with the long *i* sound spelled *ie* and *igh*. ***Home Activity:*** Ask your child to make up a silly song using the spelling words. Work together to write the words to the song when it's finished.

70 Spelling: Long *i*: *ie, igh* Level 1.5

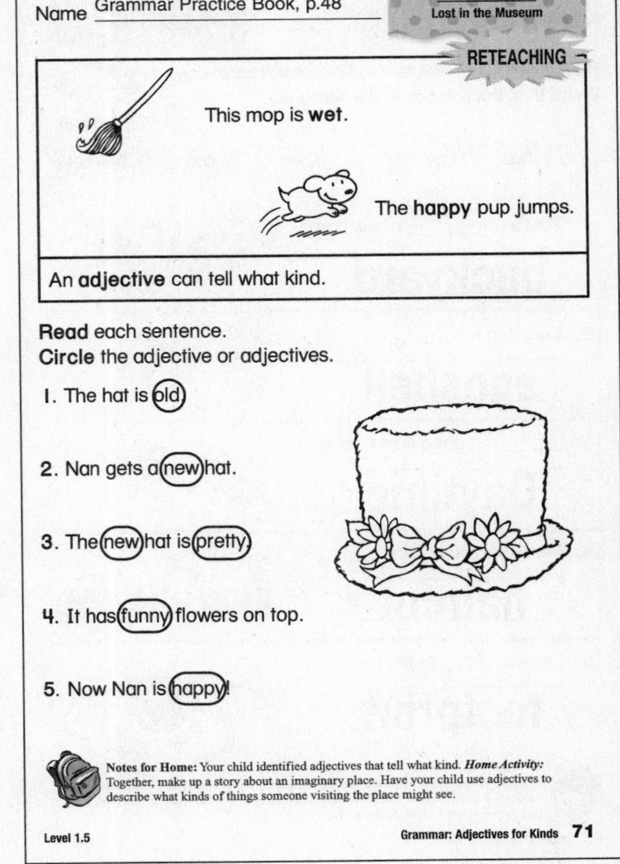
Name Grammar Practice Book, p.48

What a Sight!
Lost in the Museum

RETEACHING

This mop is **wet**.

The **happy** pup jumps.

An **adjective** can tell what kind.

**Read** each sentence.
**Circle** the adjective or adjectives.

1. The hat is (old).
2. Nan gets a (new) hat.
3. The (new) hat is (pretty).
4. It has (funny) flowers on top.
5. Now Nan is (happy)!

**Notes for Home:** Your child identified adjectives that tell what kind. ***Home Activity:*** Together, make up a story about an imaginary place. Have your child use adjectives to describe what kinds of things someone visiting the place might see.

Level 1.5 Grammar: Adjectives for Kinds 71

What a Sight!
Lost in the Museum

Name Grammar Practice Book, p.49

**Read** each sentence.
**Choose** the correct adjective in ( ).
**Write** it on the line.

1. I like to pet the (soft/hard) rabbit.
   **soft**
2. The children are (sad/happy).
   **happy**
3. The (fast/slow) snail is moving.
   **slow**
4. This duck was very (bad/good)!
   **bad**
5. Don't touch the (hot/cold) fire!
   **hot**
6. That is a (long/sad) bat.
   **long**

**Notes for Home:** Your child identified appropriate adjectives—words that describe—in sentences. ***Home Activity:*** Put three objects on a table. (For example: apple, orange, banana) Have your child use adjectives in sentences to describe what kinds of objects they are.

72 Grammar: Adjective for Kinds Level 1.5

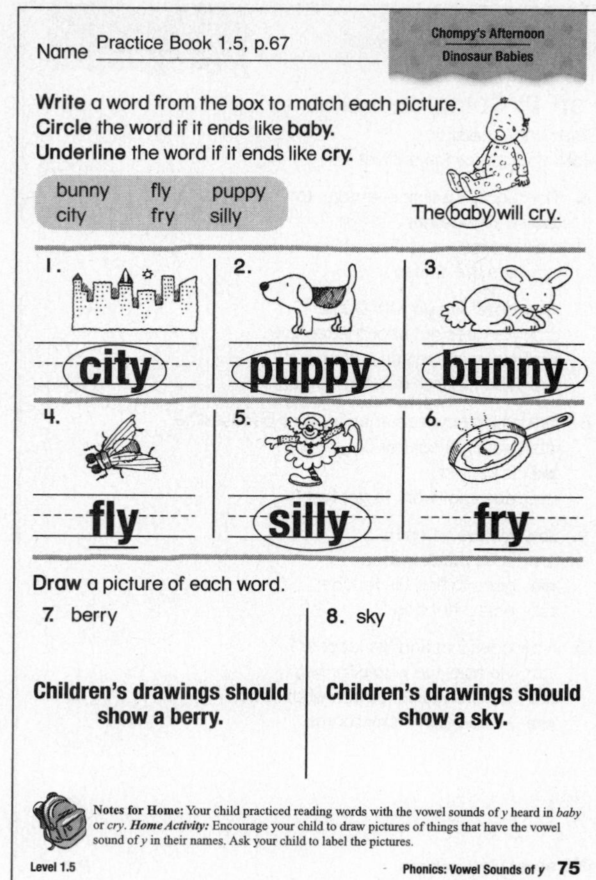

Chompy's Afternoon
Dinosaur Babies

Name Practice Book 1.5, p.67

**Write** a word from the box to match each picture.
**Circle** the word if it ends like **baby.**
**Underline** the word if it ends like **cry.**

| bunny | fly | puppy |
|---|---|---|
| city | fry | silly |

The baby will cry.

1. **city**
2. **puppy**
3. **bunny**
4. **fly**
5. **silly**
6. **fry**

**Draw** a picture of each word.

7. berry

**Children's drawings should show a berry.**

8. sky

**Children's drawings should show a sky.**

**Notes for Home:** Your child practiced reading words with the vowel sounds of *y* heard in *baby* or *cry*. ***Home Activity:*** Encourage your child to draw pictures of things that have the vowel sound of *y* in their names. Ask your child to label the pictures.

Level 1.5 Phonics: Vowel Sounds of *y* 75

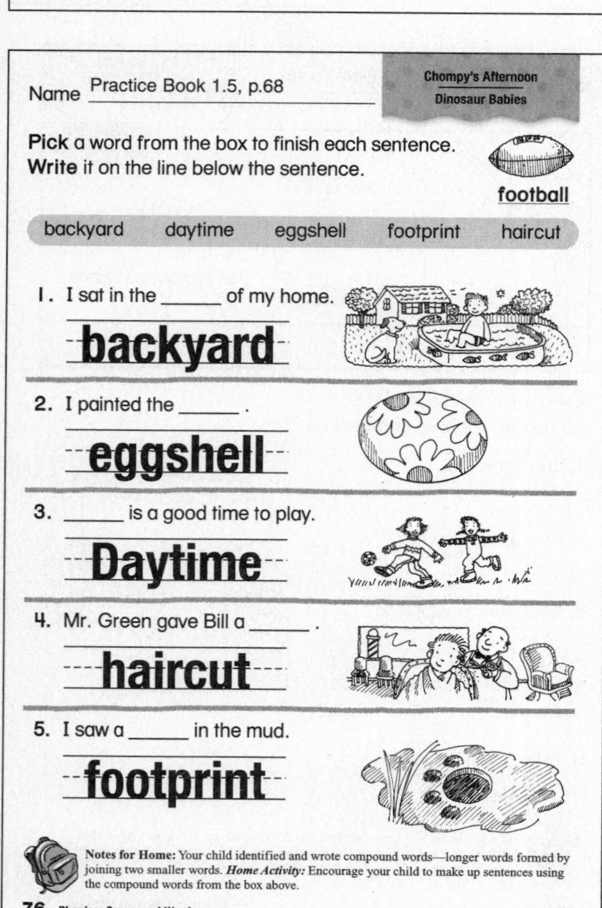

Chompy's Afternoon
Dinosaur Babies

Name Practice Book 1.5, p.68

**Pick** a word from the box to finish each sentence.
**Write** it on the line below the sentence.

football

| backyard | daytime | eggshell | footprint | haircut |
|---|---|---|---|---|

1. I sat in the ____ of my home.
   **backyard**
2. I painted the ____.
   **eggshell**
3. ____ is a good time to play.
   **Daytime**
4. Mr. Green gave Bill a ____.
   **haircut**
5. I saw a ____ in the mud.
   **footprint**

**Notes for Home:** Your child identified and wrote compound words—longer words formed by joining two smaller words. ***Home Activity:*** Encourage your child to make up sentences using the compound words from the box above.

76 Phonics: Compound Words Level 1.5

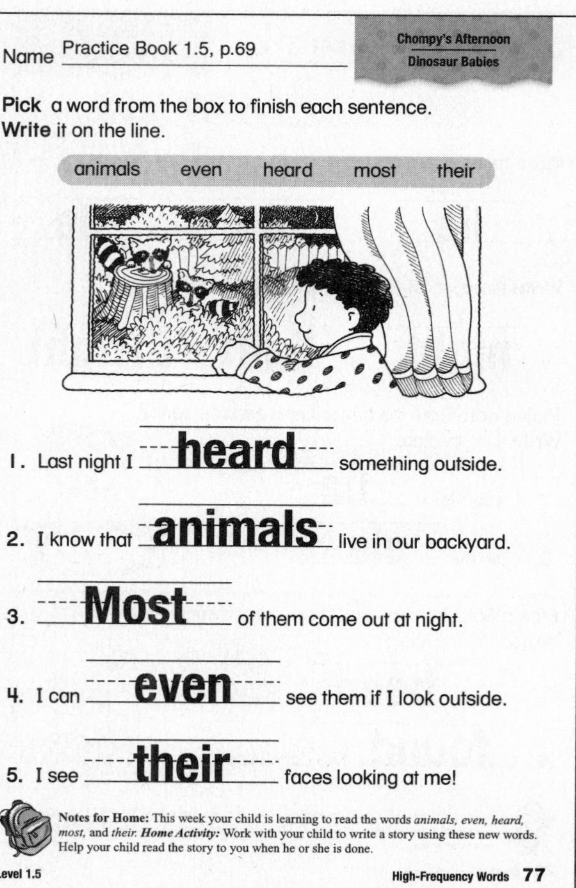

Chompy's Afternoon
Dinosaur Babies

Name Practice Book 1.5, p.69

**Pick** a word from the box to finish each sentence.
**Write** it on the line.

| animals | even | heard | most | their |
|---|---|---|---|---|

1. Last night I **heard** something outside.
2. I know that **animals** live in our backyard.
3. **Most** of them come out at night.
4. I can **even** see them if I look outside.
5. I see **their** faces looking at me!

**Notes for Home:** This week your child is learning to read the words *animals, even, heard, most,* and *their.* ***Home Activity:*** Work with your child to write a story using these new words. Help your child read the story to you when he or she is done.

Level 1.5 High-Frequency Words 77

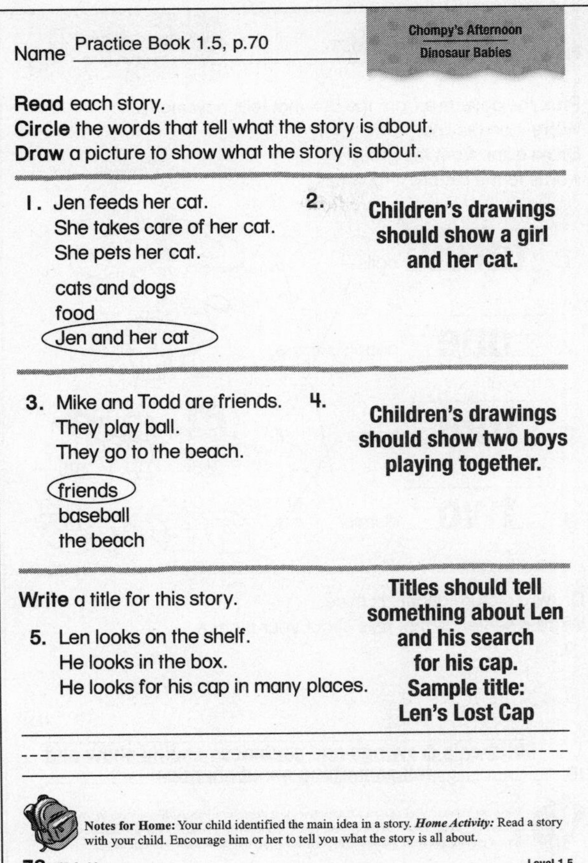

Name Practice Book 1.5, p.70

Chompy's Afternoon
Dinosaur Babies

**Read** each story.
**Circle** the words that tell what the story is about.
**Draw** a picture to show what the story is about.

1. Jen feeds her cat.
She takes care of her cat.
She pets her cat.

cats and dogs
food
(Jen and her cat)

2. **Children's drawings should show a girl and her cat.**

3. Mike and Todd are friends.
They play ball.
They go to the beach.

(friends)
baseball
the beach

4. **Children's drawings should show two boys playing together.**

**Write** a title for this story.

5. Len looks on the shelf.
He looks in the box.
He looks for his cap in many places.

**Titles should tell something about Len and his search for his cap. Sample title: Len's Lost Cap**

**Notes for Home:** Your child identified the main idea in a story. ***Home Activity:*** Read a story with your child. Encourage him or her to tell you what the story is all about.

78 Main Idea Level 1.5

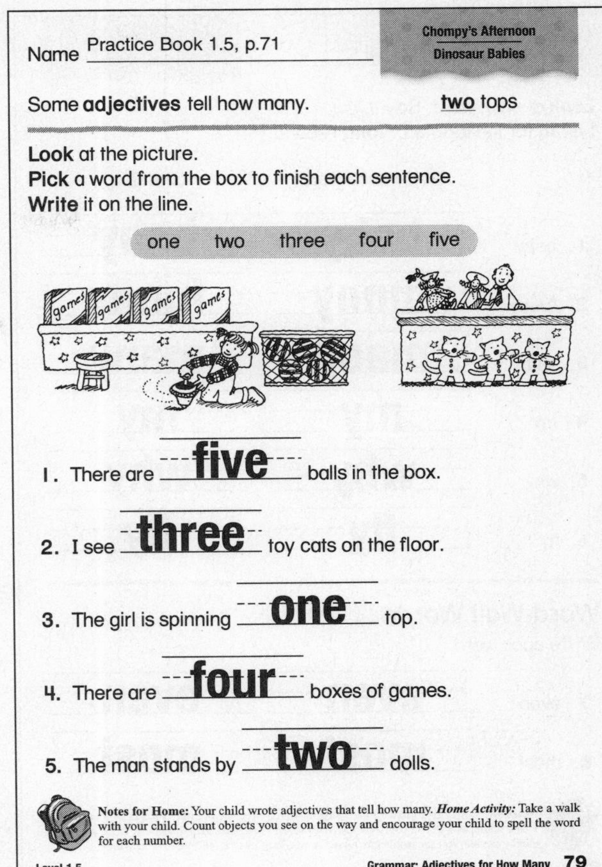

Name Practice Book 1.5, p.71

Chompy's Afternoon
Dinosaur Babies

Some **adjectives** tell how many. **two** tops

**Look** at the picture.
**Pick** a word from the box to finish each sentence.
**Write** it on the line.

one two three four five



1. There are **five** balls in the box.
2. I see **three** toy cats on the floor.
3. The girl is spinning **one** top.
4. There are **four** boxes of games.
5. The man stands by **two** dolls.

**Notes for Home:** Your child wrote adjectives that tell how many. ***Home Activity:*** Take a walk with your child. Count objects you see on the way and encourage your child to spell the word for each number.

Level 1.5 Grammar: Adjectives for How Many 79

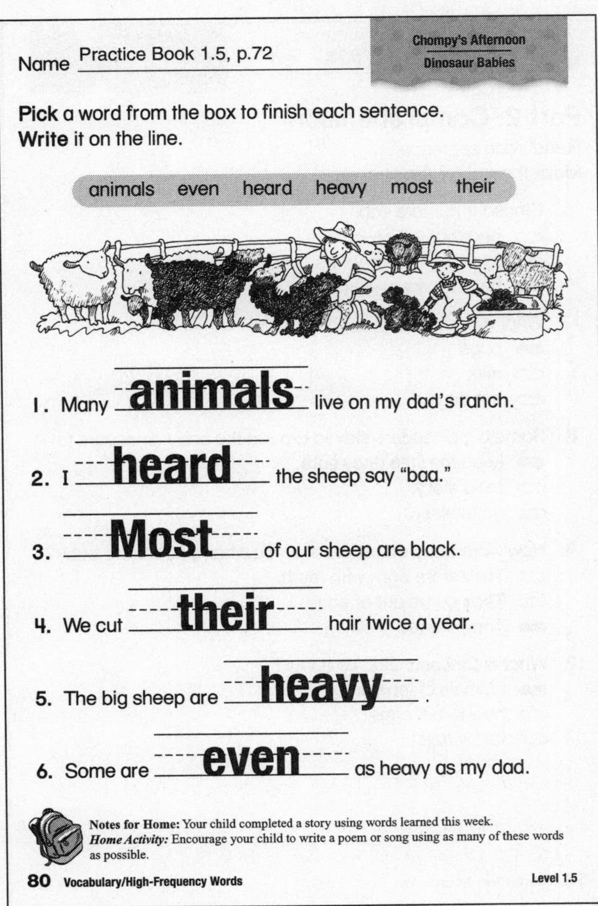

Name Practice Book 1.5, p.72

Chompy's Afternoon
Dinosaur Babies

**Pick** a word from the box to finish each sentence.
**Write** it on the line.

animals even heard heavy most their

1. Many **animals** live on my dad's ranch.
2. I **heard** the sheep say "baa."
3. **Most** of our sheep are black.
4. We cut **their** hair twice a year.
5. The big sheep are **heavy**.
6. Some are **even** as heavy as my dad.

**Notes for Home:** Your child completed a story using words learned this week. ***Home Activity:*** Encourage your child to write a poem or song using as many of these words as possible.

80 Vocabulary/High-Frequency Words Level 1.5

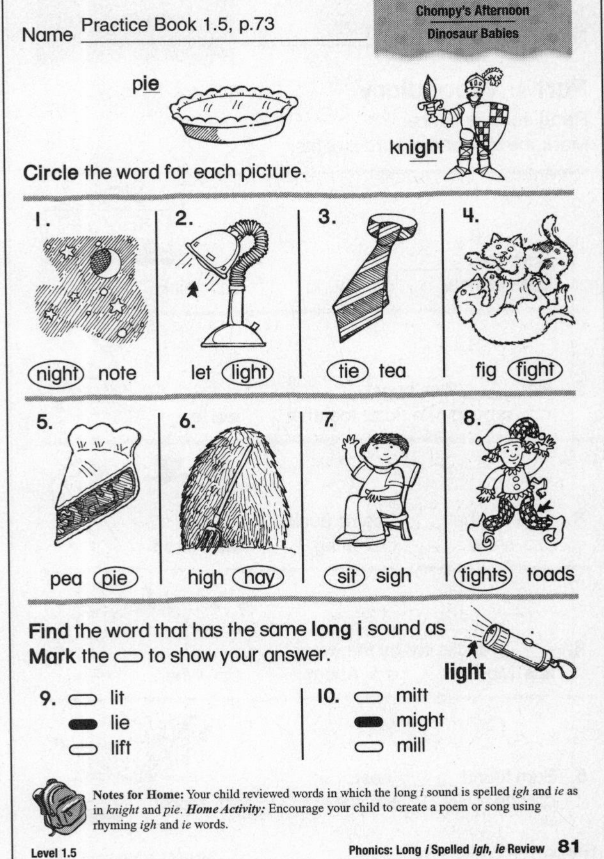

Name Practice Book 1.5, p.73

Chompy's Afternoon
Dinosaur Babies

pie
knight

**Circle** the word for each picture.

1. (night) note
2. let (light)
3. (tie) tea
4. fig (fight)
5. pea (pie)
6. high (hay)
7. (sit) sigh
8. (tights) toads

**Find** the word that has the same **long i** sound as **light**.
**Mark** the ⊂⊃ to show your answer.

9. ⊂⊃ lit
▬ lie
⊂⊃ lift

10. ⊂⊃ mitt
▬ might
⊂⊃ mill

**Notes for Home:** Your child reviewed words in which the long *i* sound is spelled *igh* and *ie* as in *knight* and *pie*. ***Home Activity:*** Encourage your child to create a poem or song using rhyming *igh* and *ie* words.

Level 1.5 Phonics: Long *i* Spelled *igh, ie* Review 81

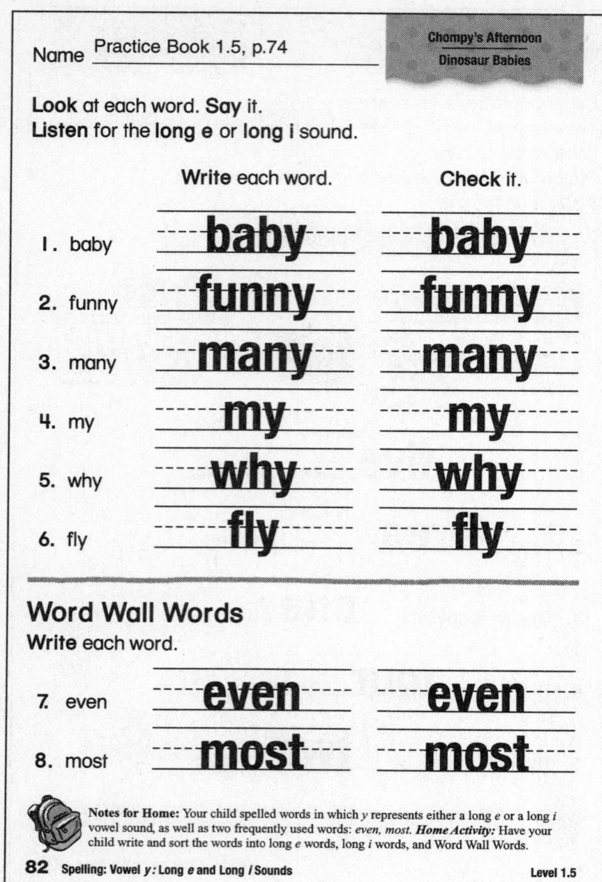

Name Practice Book 1.5, p.74

Chompy's Afternoon
Dinosaur Babies

**Look** at each word. **Say** it.
**Listen** for the **long e** or **long i** sound.

| | **Write** each word. | **Check** it. |
|---|---|---|
| 1. baby | baby | baby |
| 2. funny | funny | funny |
| 3. many | many | many |
| 4. my | my | my |
| 5. why | why | why |
| 6. fly | fly | fly |

## Word Wall Words

**Write** each word.

| | | |
|---|---|---|
| 7. even | even | even |
| 8. most | most | most |

**Notes for Home:** Your child spelled words in which *y* represents either a long *e* or a long *i* vowel sound, as well as two frequently used words: *even, most. Home Activity:* Have your child write and sort the words into long *e* words, long *i* words, and Word Wall Words.

82 Spelling: Vowel *y*: Long *e* and Long *i* Sounds Level 1.5

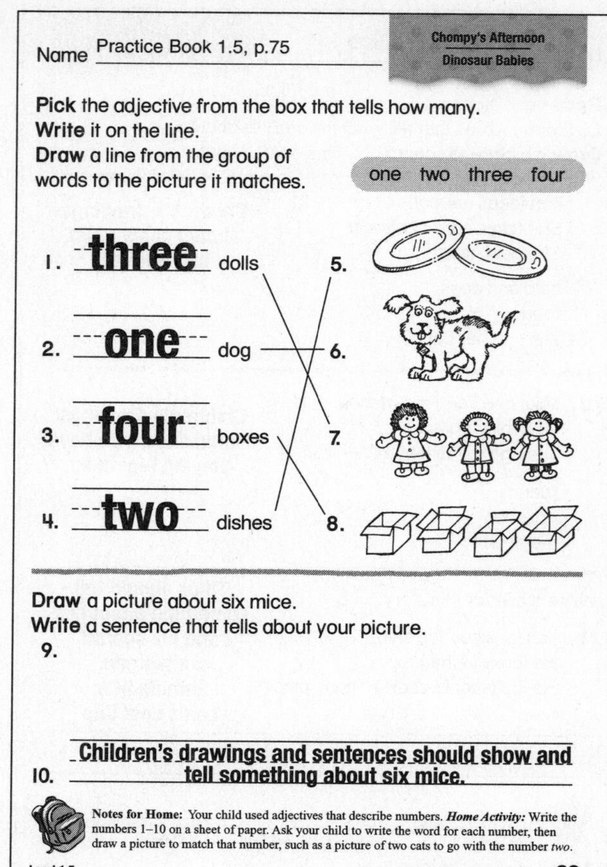

Name Practice Book 1.5, p.75

Chompy's Afternoon
Dinosaur Babies

**Pick** the adjective from the box that tells how many.
**Write** it on the line.
**Draw** a line from the group of words to the picture it matches.

one two three four

1. three dolls — 7.
2. one dog — 6.
3. four boxes — 8.
4. two dishes — 5.

**Draw** a picture about six mice.
**Write** a sentence that tells about your picture.

9.

10. Children's drawings and sentences should show and tell something about six mice.

**Notes for Home:** Your child used adjectives that describe numbers. *Home Activity:* Write the numbers 1–10 on a sheet of paper. Ask your child to write the word for each number, then draw a picture to match that number, such as a picture of two cats to go with the number *two.*

Level 1.5 Grammar: Adjectives for How Many 83

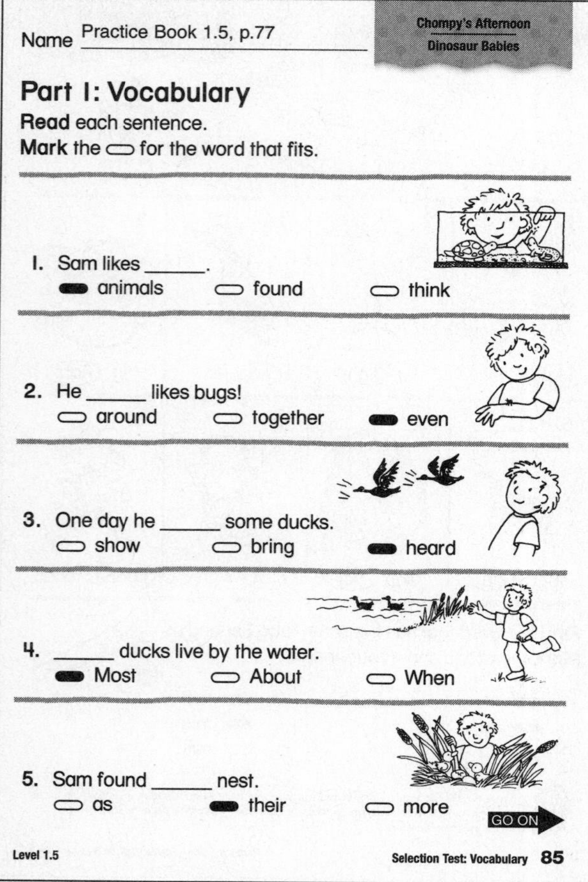

Name Practice Book 1.5, p.77

Chompy's Afternoon
Dinosaur Babies

## Part 1: Vocabulary

**Read** each sentence.
**Mark** the ⊂⊃ for the word that fits.

1. Sam likes ______.
   - ● animals
   - ○ found
   - ○ think

2. He ______ likes bugs!
   - ○ around
   - ○ together
   - ● even

3. One day he ______ some ducks.
   - ○ show
   - ○ bring
   - ● heard

4. ______ ducks live by the water.
   - ● Most
   - ○ About
   - ○ When

5. Sam found ______ nest.
   - ○ as
   - ● their
   - ○ more

GO ON

Level 1.5 Selection Test: Vocabulary 85

Name Practice Book 1.5, p.78

Dinosaur Babies

## Part 2: Comprehension

**Read** each sentence.
**Mark** the ⊂⊃ for the answer.

6. Dinosaur hunters can
   - ○ hear baby dinosaurs.
   - ○ see dinosaur mothers.
   - ● find dinosaur eggs.

7. What did some baby dinosaurs eat?
   - ● bugs
   - ○ milk
   - ○ hot dogs

8. Some big dinosaurs stayed around the baby dinosaurs to
   - ● keep the little ones safe.
   - ○ tell a story.
   - ○ go to sleep.

9. How were baby dinosaurs like you when you were a baby?
   - ○ They were born with teeth.
   - ○ They came out of eggs.
   - ● They started growing.

10. What is *Dinosaur Babies* about?
    - ● animals of long ago
    - ○ how to eat eggs
    - ○ funny tails

STOP

86 Selection Test: Comprehension Level 1.5

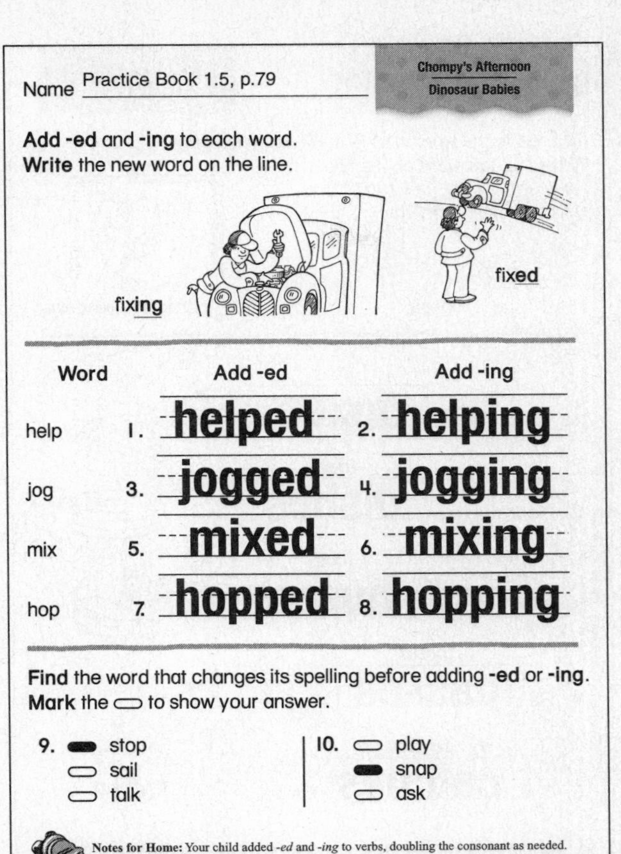

Chompy's Afternoon
Dinosaur Babies

Name Practice Book 1.5, p.79

**Add -ed** and **-ing** to each word.
**Write** the new word on the line.



| Word | | Add -ed | | Add -ing |
|---|---|---|---|---|
| help | 1. | helped | 2. | helping |
| jog | 3. | jogged | 4. | jogging |
| mix | 5. | mixed | 6. | mixing |
| hop | 7. | hopped | 8. | hopping |

**Find** the word that changes its spelling before adding **-ed** or **-ing**.
**Mark** the ⬭ to show your answer.

9. ● stop ○ sail ○ talk

10. ○ play ● snap ○ ask

**Notes for Home:** Your child added *-ed* and *-ing* to verbs, doubling the consonant as needed. ***Home Activity:*** Have your child read aloud the words with *-ed* and *-ing* endings. Talk about whether the spelling changed before the endings were added.

Level 1.5 Phonics: *-ed* and *-ing* Endings Review 87

Chompy's Afternoon
Dinosaur Babies

Name Practice Book 1.5, p.80

baby funny many my why fly

**Write** three words from the box that have the **long e** sound.

1. baby 2. funny 3. many

**Write** three words from the box that have the **long i** sound.

4. my 5. why 6. fly

**Pick** a word from the box to match each clue.
**Write** it in the puzzle.

7. go in plane
8. a lot

Puzzle: 7. f l y (down); 8. m a n y (across)

**Pick** a word from the box to finish each sentence.
**Write** it on the line.

even most

9. I did most of my tasks.
10. I even made my bed!

**Notes for Home:** Your child spelled words in which *y* represents either a long *e* or a long *i* vowel sound, as well as two frequently used words: *even, most.* ***Home Activity:*** Challenge your child to write other long *e* and long *i* words with *y*.

88 Spelling: Vowel *y*: Long *e* and Long *i* Sounds Level 1.5

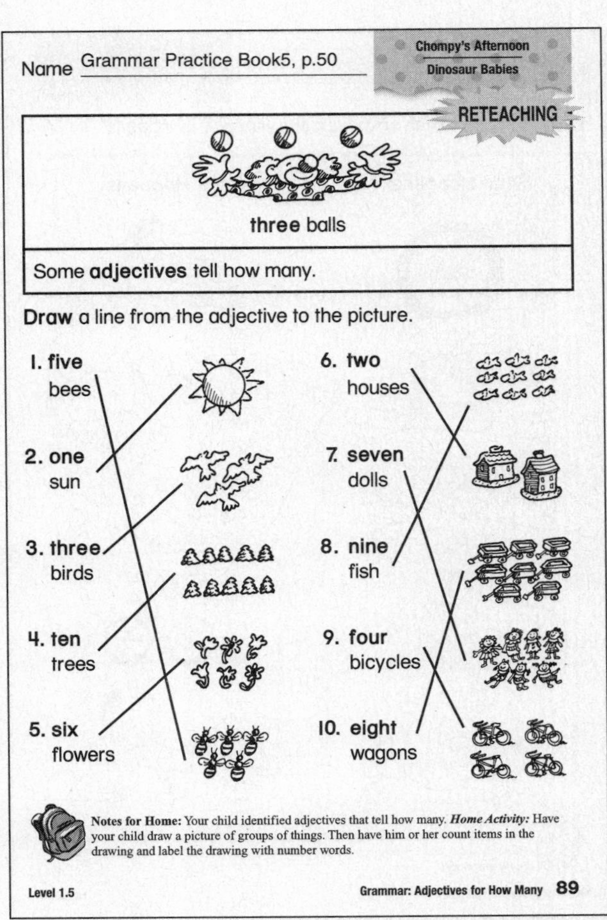

Chompy's Afternoon
Dinosaur Babies

Name Grammar Practice Book5, p.50

RETEACHING

three balls

Some **adjectives** tell how many.

**Draw** a line from the adjective to the picture.

1. five bees
2. one sun
3. three birds
4. ten trees
5. six flowers
6. two houses
7. seven dolls
8. nine fish
9. four bicycles
10. eight wagons

**Notes for Home:** Your child identified adjectives that tell how many. ***Home Activity:*** Have your child draw a picture of groups of things. Then have him or her count items in the drawing and label the drawing with number words.

Level 1.5 Grammar: Adjectives for How Many 89

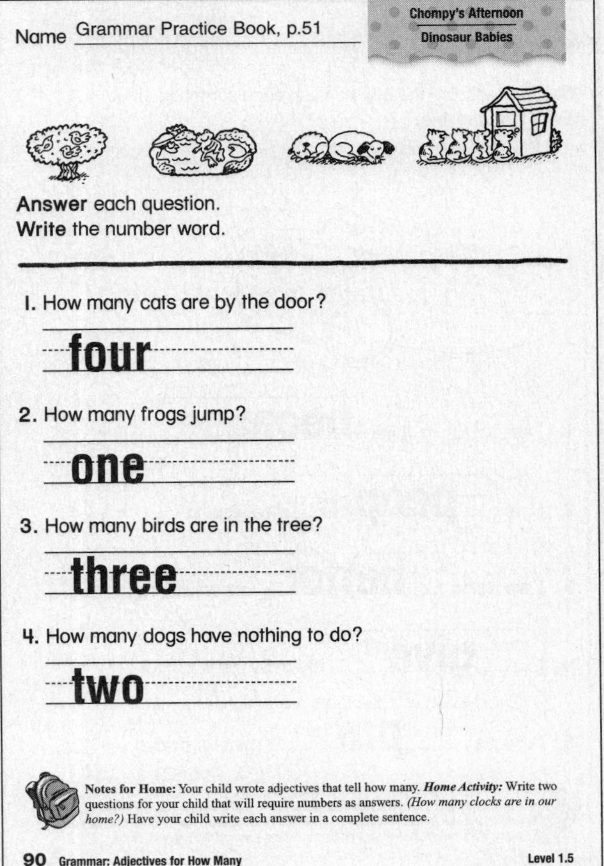

Chompy's Afternoon
Dinosaur Babies

Name Grammar Practice Book, p.51

**Answer** each question.
**Write** the number word.

1. How many cats are by the door?
four

2. How many frogs jump?
one

3. How many birds are in the tree?
three

4. How many dogs have nothing to do?
two

**Notes for Home:** Your child wrote adjectives that tell how many. ***Home Activity:*** Write two questions for your child that will require numbers as answers. *(How many clocks are in our home?)* Have your child write each answer in a complete sentence.

90 Grammar: Adjectives for How Many Level 1.5

Name Practice Book 1.5, p.83

The True Story of Abbie Burgess
The Bravest Cat!

**Read** the name of each child below.
**Pick** words from the box with vowel sounds that are spelled the same.
**Write** the words on the lines.



blue chew clue few glue grew knew true

Sue

1. blue
2. clue
3. glue
4. true

**Word order may vary.**

Stewart

5. chew
6. few
7. grew
8. knew

**Word order may vary.**

**Notes for Home:** Your child practiced writing words with the vowel patterns *ew* and *ue*. ***Home Activity:*** Help your child think of other ways to spell the sound made by *ew* and *ue*.



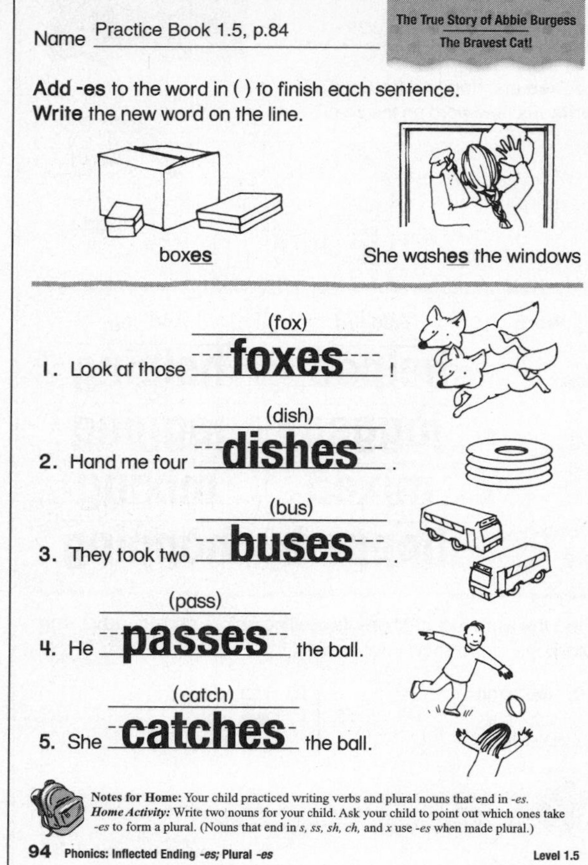
Name Practice Book 1.5, p.84

The True Story of Abbie Burgess
The Bravest Cat!

**Add -es** to the word in ( ) to finish each sentence.
**Write** the new word on the line.



1. Look at those (fox) foxes !
2. Hand me four (dish) dishes .
3. They took two (bus) buses .
4. He (pass) passes the ball.
5. She (catch) catches the ball.

**Notes for Home:** Your child practiced writing verbs and plural nouns that end in *-es*. ***Home Activity:*** Write two nouns for your child. Ask your child to point out which ones take *-es* to form a plural. (Nouns that end in *s, ss, sh, ch,* and *x* use *-es* when made plural.)



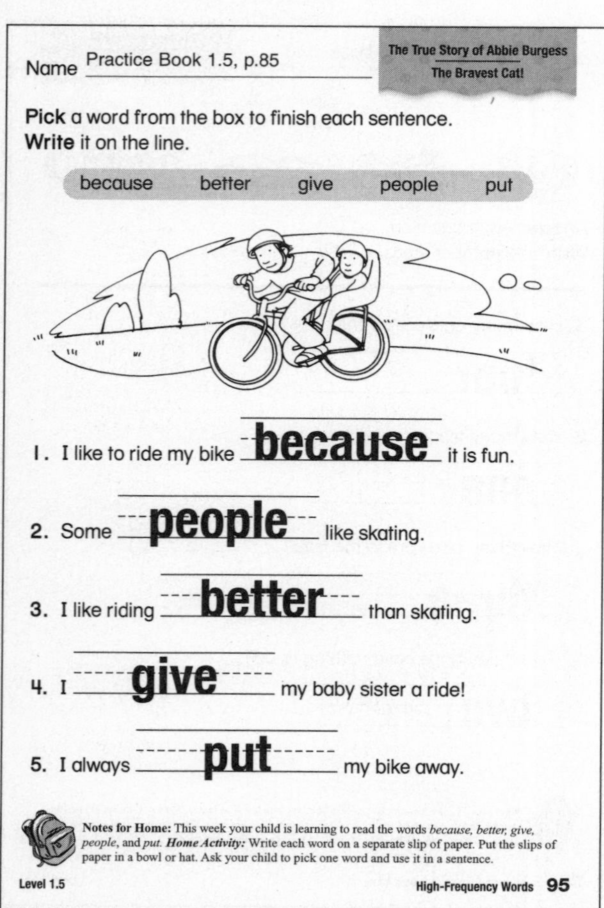
Name Practice Book 1.5, p.85

The True Story of Abbie Burgess
The Bravest Cat!

**Pick** a word from the box to finish each sentence.
**Write** it on the line.

because better give people put

1. I like to ride my bike because it is fun.
2. Some people like skating.
3. I like riding better than skating.
4. I give my baby sister a ride!
5. I always put my bike away.

**Notes for Home:** This week your child is learning to read the words *because, better, give, people,* and *put*. ***Home Activity:*** Write each word on a separate slip of paper. Put the slips of paper in a bowl or hat. Ask your child to pick one word and use it in a sentence.



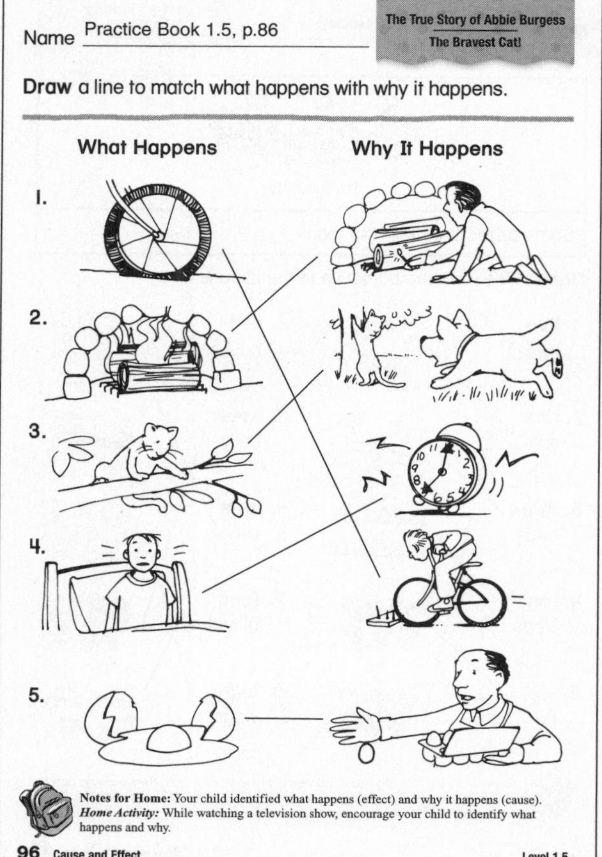
Name Practice Book 1.5, p.86

The True Story of Abbie Burgess
The Bravest Cat!

**Draw** a line to match what happens with why it happens.

**What Happens** **Why It Happens**

1.
2.
3.
4.
5.

**Notes for Home:** Your child identified what happens (effect) and why it happens (cause). ***Home Activity:*** While watching a television show, encourage your child to identify what happens and why.

Name Practice Book 1.5, p.87

The True Story of Abbie Burgess
The Bravest Cat!

An **adjective** tells more about a person, place, or thing.
**Cute** tells more about Mary's cat.

Mary has a **cute** cat.

**Pick** a word from the box that helps each sentence tell more.
**Write** it on the line.

black hot tall three wet

1. Dad sips a **hot** drink.
2. Tom is a **tall** man.
3. I have a **black** cat.
4. I have **three** sisters.
5. Take off your **wet** coat.

**Notes for Home:** Your child used adjectives to improve sentences. ***Home Activity:*** Make up simple sentences for your child. Encourage your child to add adjectives to make each sentence more interesting.

Level 1.5 Grammar: Writing with Adjectives 97

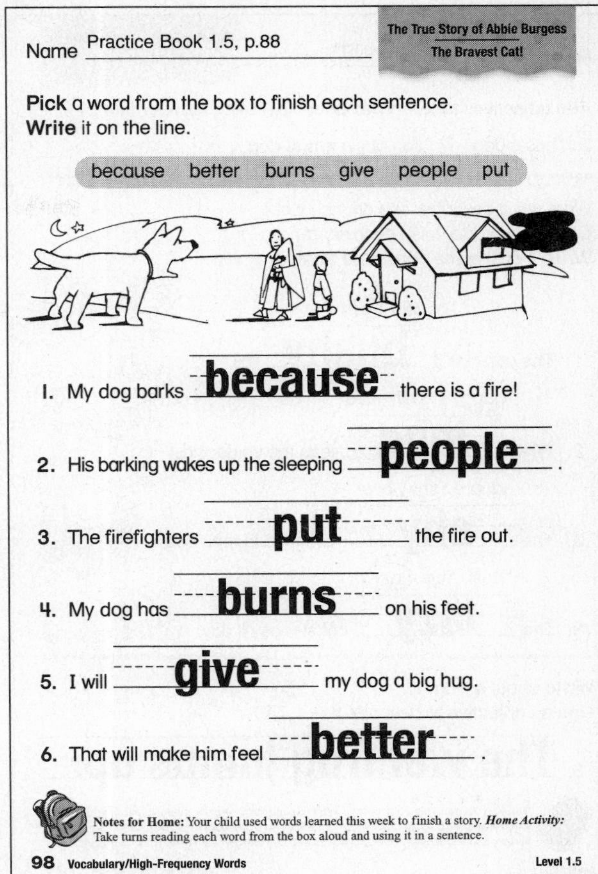

Name Practice Book 1.5, p.88

The True Story of Abbie Burgess
The Bravest Cat!

**Pick** a word from the box to finish each sentence.
**Write** it on the line.

because better burns give people put

1. My dog barks **because** there is a fire!
2. His barking wakes up the sleeping **people**.
3. The firefighters **put** the fire out.
4. My dog has **burns** on his feet.
5. I will **give** my dog a big hug.
6. That will make him feel **better**.

**Notes for Home:** Your child used words learned this week to finish a story. ***Home Activity:*** Take turns reading each word from the box aloud and using it in a sentence.

98 Vocabulary/High-Frequency Words Level 1.5

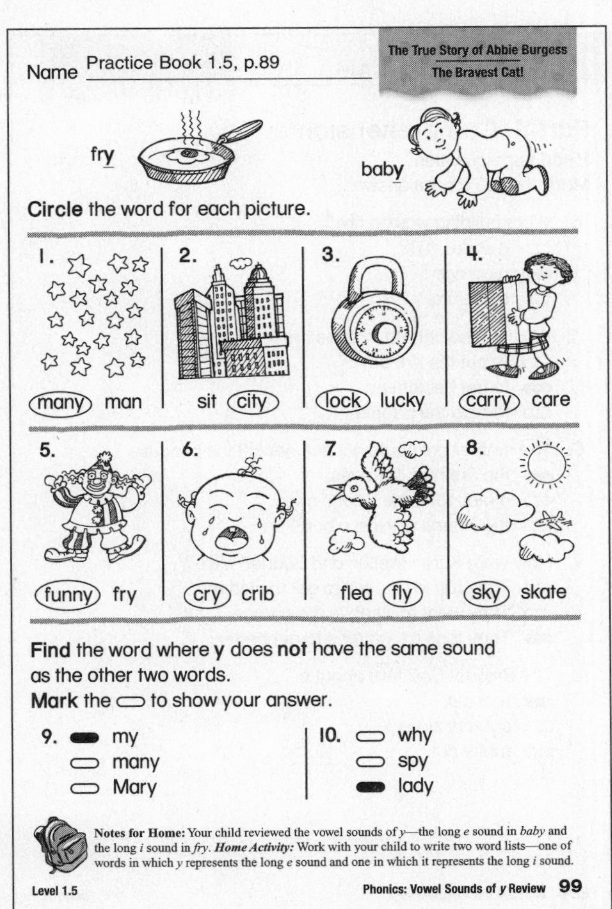

Name Practice Book 1.5, p.89

The True Story of Abbie Burgess
The Bravest Cat!

fry baby

**Circle** the word for each picture.

1. (many) man
2. sit (city)
3. (lock) lucky
4. (carry) care
5. (funny) fry
6. (cry) crib
7. flea (fly)
8. (sky) skate

**Find** the word where **y** does **not** have the same sound as the other two words.
**Mark** the ⬭ to show your answer.

9. ● my ○ many ○ Mary
10. ○ why ○ spy ● lady

**Notes for Home:** Your child reviewed the vowel sounds of *y*—the long *e* sound in *baby* and the long *i* sound in *fry*. ***Home Activity:*** Work with your child to write two word lists—one of words in which *y* represents the long *e* sound and one in which it represents the long *i* sound.

Level 1.5 Phonics: Vowel Sounds of *y* Review 99

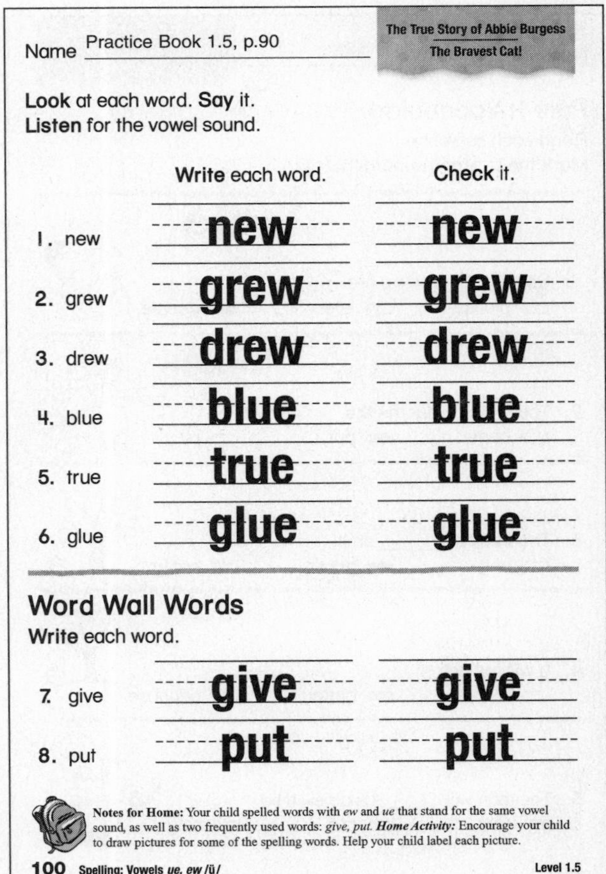

Name Practice Book 1.5, p.90

The True Story of Abbie Burgess
The Bravest Cat!

**Look** at each word. **Say** it.
**Listen** for the vowel sound.

| | Write each word. | Check it. |
|---|---|---|
| 1. new | **new** | **new** |
| 2. grew | **grew** | **grew** |
| 3. drew | **drew** | **drew** |
| 4. blue | **blue** | **blue** |
| 5. true | **true** | **true** |
| 6. glue | **glue** | **glue** |

**Word Wall Words**

Write each word.

| | | |
|---|---|---|
| 7. give | **give** | **give** |
| 8. put | **put** | **put** |

**Notes for Home:** Your child spelled words with *ew* and *ue* that stand for the same vowel sound, as well as two frequently used words: *give, put.* ***Home Activity:*** Encourage your child to draw pictures for some of the spelling words. Help your child label each picture.

100 Spelling: Vowels *ue, ew* /ü/ Level 1.5

Name Practice Book 1.5, p.91

The True Story of Abbie Burgess
The Bravest Cat!

Add adjectives to tell more about a person, place, or thing.

Jan has a dog. Jan has a **small** dog.

What word describes the animal best?
**Circle** a word to finish each sentence.
**Write** it on the line. **Possible answer given.**

old (bushy) new
1. The pup has a **bushy** tail.

(long) sweet nice
2. What **long** legs the spider has!

square (shy) best
3. The **shy** mice hide in their cage.

fast fine (lazy)
4. The **lazy** cat sleeps all day.

**Write** about a frog.
**Use** an adjective to describe it.

5. **The wet frog jumps up.**

**Notes for Home:** Your child used adjectives (words that describe a person, place, or thing) to improve sentences. ***Home Activity:*** Write some simple sentences for your child. *(I saw a cow.)* Invite your child to improve the sentences with one or more adjectives. *(I saw a big, fat cow.)*

Level 1.5 Writing Process: Revise 101

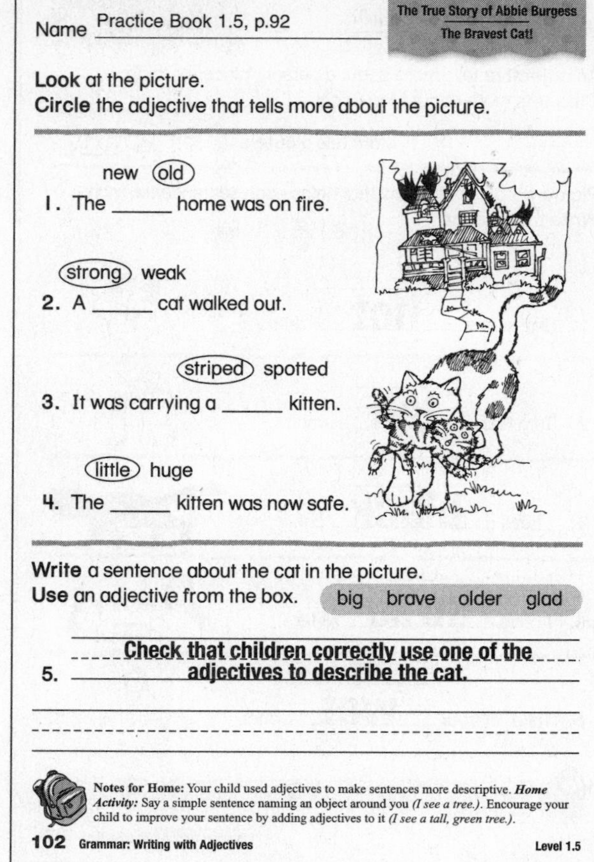
Name Practice Book 1.5, p.92

The True Story of Abbie Burgess
The Bravest Cat!

**Look** at the picture.
**Circle** the adjective that tells more about the picture.

new (old)
1. The ______ home was on fire.

(strong) weak
2. A ______ cat walked out.

(striped) spotted
3. It was carrying a ______ kitten.

(little) huge
4. The ______ kitten was now safe.

**Write** a sentence about the cat in the picture.
**Use** an adjective from the box.

big brave older glad

5. **Check that children correctly use one of the adjectives to describe the cat.**

**Notes for Home:** Your child used adjectives to make sentences more descriptive. ***Home Activity:*** Say a simple sentence naming an object around you *(I see a tree.)*. Encourage your child to improve your sentence by adding adjectives to it *(I see a tall, green tree.)*.

102 Grammar: Writing with Adjectives Level 1.5

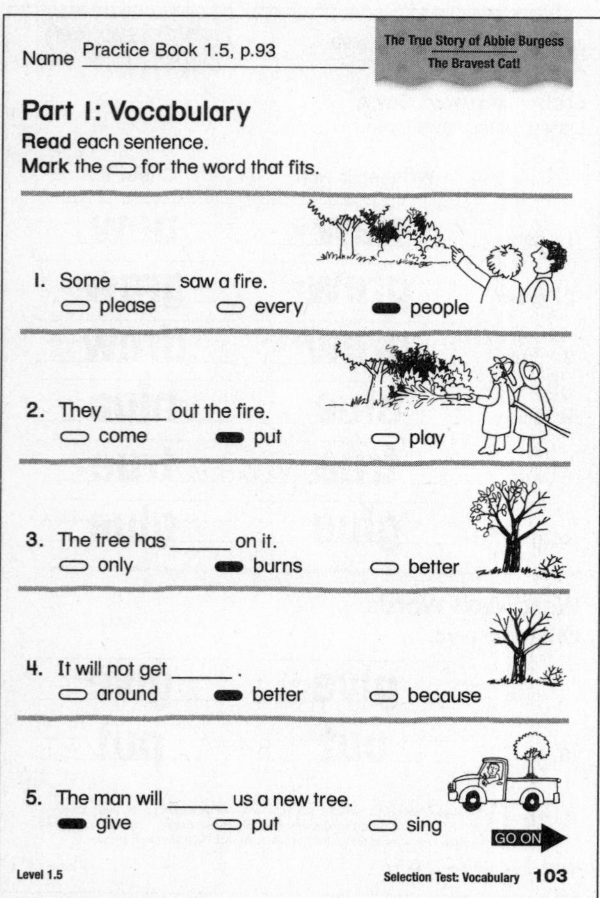
Name Practice Book 1.5, p.93

The True Story of Abbie Burgess
The Bravest Cat!

## Part 1: Vocabulary

**Read** each sentence.
**Mark** the ⬭ for the word that fits.

1. Some ______ saw a fire.
⬭ please ⬭ every ⬬ people

2. They ______ out the fire.
⬭ come ⬬ put ⬭ play

3. The tree has ______ on it.
⬭ only ⬬ burns ⬭ better

4. It will not get ______.
⬭ around ⬬ better ⬭ because

5. The man will ______ us a new tree.
⬬ give ⬭ put ⬭ sing

GO ON

Level 1.5 Selection Test: Vocabulary 103

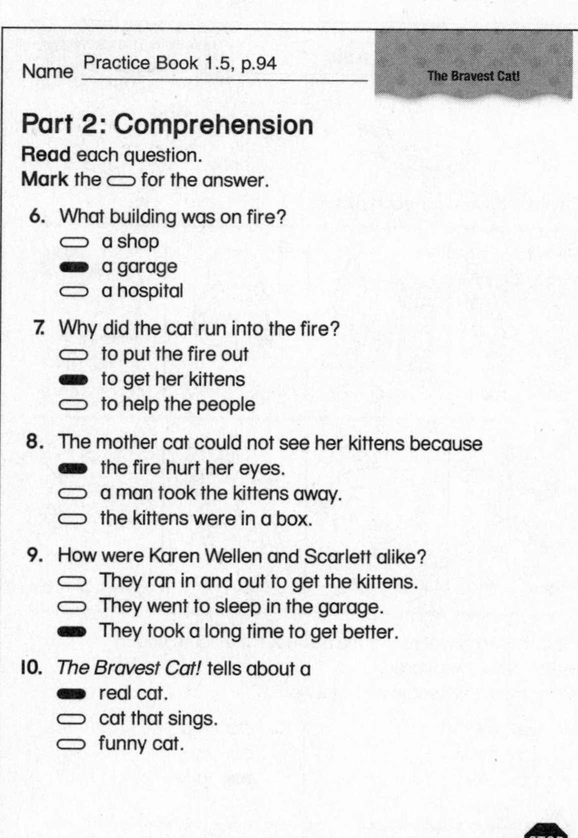
Name Practice Book 1.5, p.94

The Bravest Cat!

## Part 2: Comprehension

**Read** each question.
**Mark** the ⬭ for the answer.

6. What building was on fire?
⬭ a shop
⬬ a garage
⬭ a hospital

7. Why did the cat run into the fire?
⬭ to put the fire out
⬬ to get her kittens
⬭ to help the people

8. The mother cat could not see her kittens because
⬬ the fire hurt her eyes.
⬭ a man took the kittens away.
⬭ the kittens were in a box.

9. How were Karen Wellen and Scarlett alike?
⬭ They ran in and out to get the kittens.
⬭ They went to sleep in the garage.
⬬ They took a long time to get better.

10. *The Bravest Cat!* tells about a
⬬ real cat.
⬭ cat that sings.
⬭ funny cat.

STOP

104 Selection Test: Comprehension Level 1.5

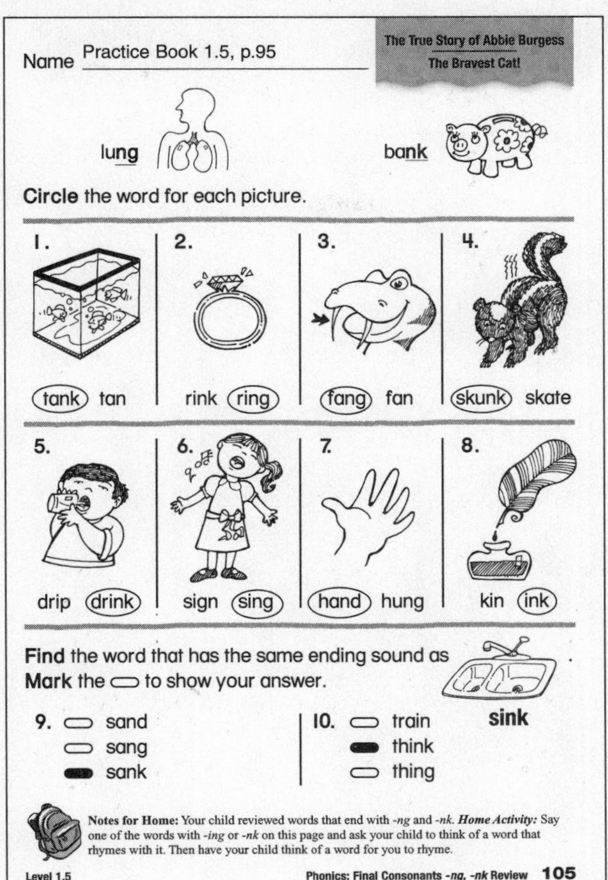

Name Practice Book 1.5, p.95

The True Story of Abbie Burgess
The Bravest Cat!

lung bank

**Circle** the word for each picture.

1. (tank) tan
2. rink (ring)
3. (fang) fan
4. (skunk) skate
5. drip (drink)
6. sign (sing)
7. (hand) hung
8. kin (ink)

**Find** the word that has the same ending sound as sink
**Mark** the ⬭ to show your answer.

9. ⬭ sand
⬭ sang
⬬ sank

10. ⬭ train
⬬ think
⬭ thing

**Notes for Home:** Your child reviewed words that end with *-ng* and *-nk*. ***Home Activity:*** Say one of the words with *-ing* or *-nk* on this page and ask your child to think of a word that rhymes with it. Then have your child think of a word for you to rhyme.

Level 1.5 Phonics: Final Consonants *-ng, -nk* Review 105

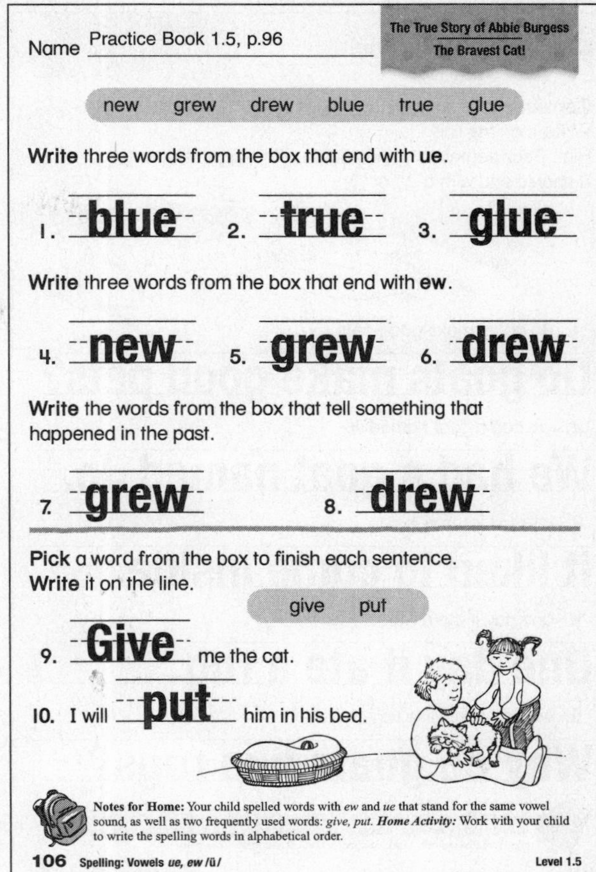

Name Practice Book 1.5, p.96

The True Story of Abbie Burgess
The Bravest Cat!

new grew drew blue true glue

**Write** three words from the box that end with **ue**.

1. blue 2. true 3. glue

**Write** three words from the box that end with **ew**.

4. new 5. grew 6. drew

**Write** the words from the box that tell something that happened in the past.

7. grew 8. drew

**Pick** a word from the box to finish each sentence.
**Write** it on the line.

give put

9. Give me the cat.

10. I will put him in his bed.

**Notes for Home:** Your child spelled words with *ew* and *ue* that stand for the same vowel sound, as well as two frequently used words: *give, put.* ***Home Activity:*** Work with your child to write the spelling words in alphabetical order.

106 Spelling: Vowels *ue, ew* /ü/ Level 1.5

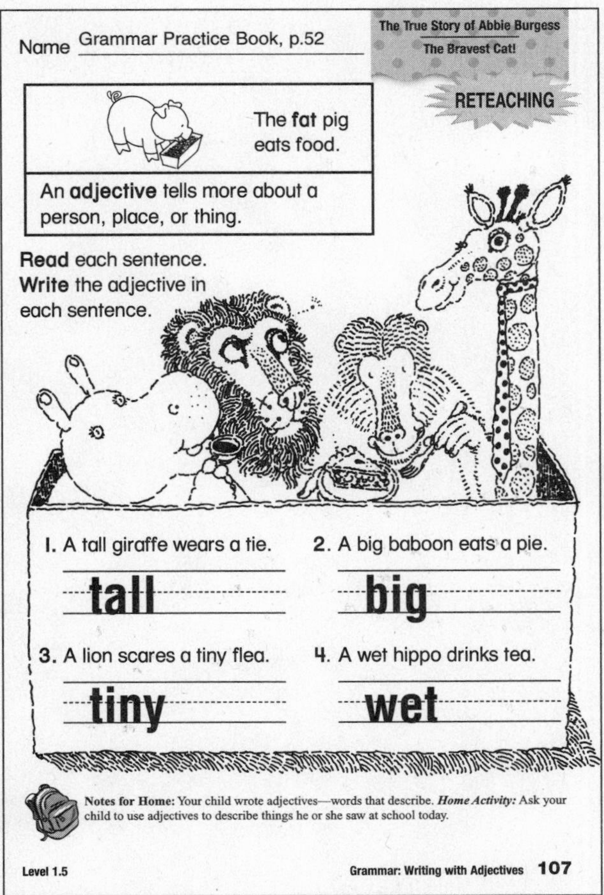

Name Grammar Practice Book, p.52

The True Story of Abbie Burgess
The Bravest Cat!

RETEACHING

The **fat** pig eats food.

An **adjective** tells more about a person, place, or thing.

**Read** each sentence.
**Write** the adjective in each sentence.

1. A tall giraffe wears a tie.
tall

2. A big baboon eats a pie.
big

3. A lion scares a tiny flea.
tiny

4. A wet hippo drinks tea.
wet

**Notes for Home:** Your child wrote adjectives—words that describe. ***Home Activity:*** Ask your child to use adjectives to describe things he or she saw at school today.

Level 1.5 Grammar: Writing with Adjectives 107

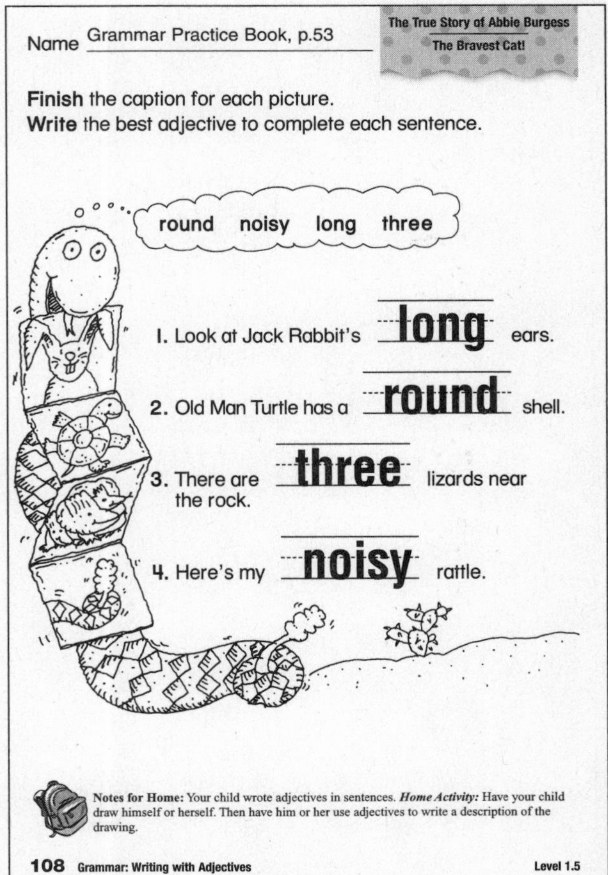

Name Grammar Practice Book, p.53

The True Story of Abbie Burgess
The Bravest Cat!

**Finish** the caption for each picture.
**Write** the best adjective to complete each sentence.

round noisy long three

1. Look at Jack Rabbit's long ears.
2. Old Man Turtle has a round shell.
3. There are three lizards near the rock.
4. Here's my noisy rattle.

**Notes for Home:** Your child wrote adjectives in sentences. ***Home Activity:*** Have your child draw himself or herself. Then have him or her use adjectives to write a description of the drawing.

108 Grammar: Writing with Adjectives Level 1.5

Name Practice Book 1.5, p.97

The True Story of Abbie Burgess
The Bravest Cat!

**Correct** each sentence.
**Write** it on the line.
Hint: Each sentence should begin with a capital letter.
It should end with a . or ?.

1. do goats make good pets

**Do goats make good pets?**

2. we had a goat named Jo

**We had a goat named Jo.**

3. it liked to come inside

**It liked to come inside.**

4. one day it ate a rug

**One day it ate a rug.**

5. why do goats like rugs

**Why do goats like rugs?**

**Notes for Home:** Your child corrected sentences using capital letters and end marks. ***Home Activity:*** Help your child find out about a favorite animal. Invite your child to write a short report on that animal. Make sure that sentences are written correctly.

Level 1.5 Writing Process: Edit 109

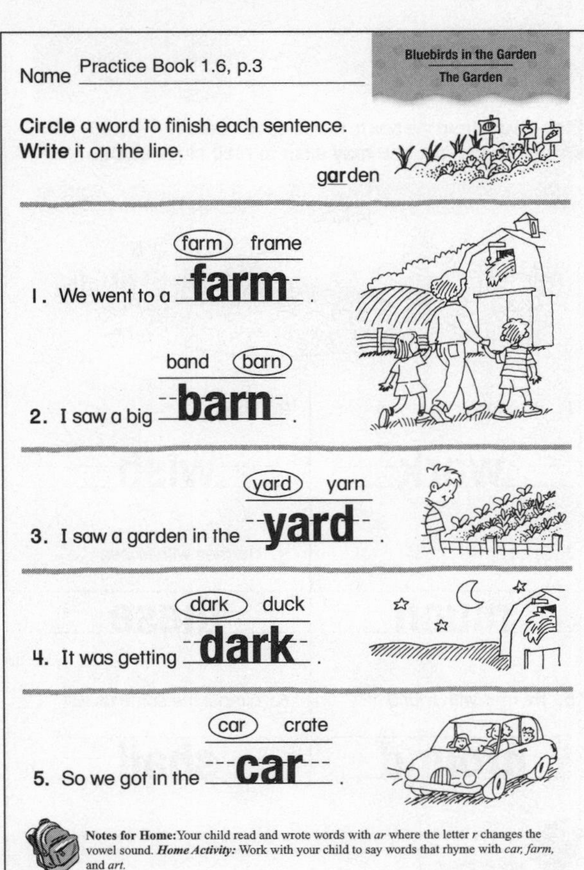

Name Practice Book 1.6, p.3

Bluebirds in the Garden
The Garden

**Circle** a word to finish each sentence.
**Write** it on the line.

garden

1. We went to a **farm**. (farm) frame
2. I saw a big **barn**. band (barn)
3. I saw a garden in the **yard**. (yard) yarn
4. It was getting **dark**. (dark) duck
5. So we got in the **car**. (car) crate

**Notes for Home:** Your child read and wrote words with *ar* where the letter *r* changes the vowel sound. ***Home Activity:*** Work with your child to say words that rhyme with *car, farm,* and *art.*

Level 1.6 Phonics: *r*-Controlled *ar* 3

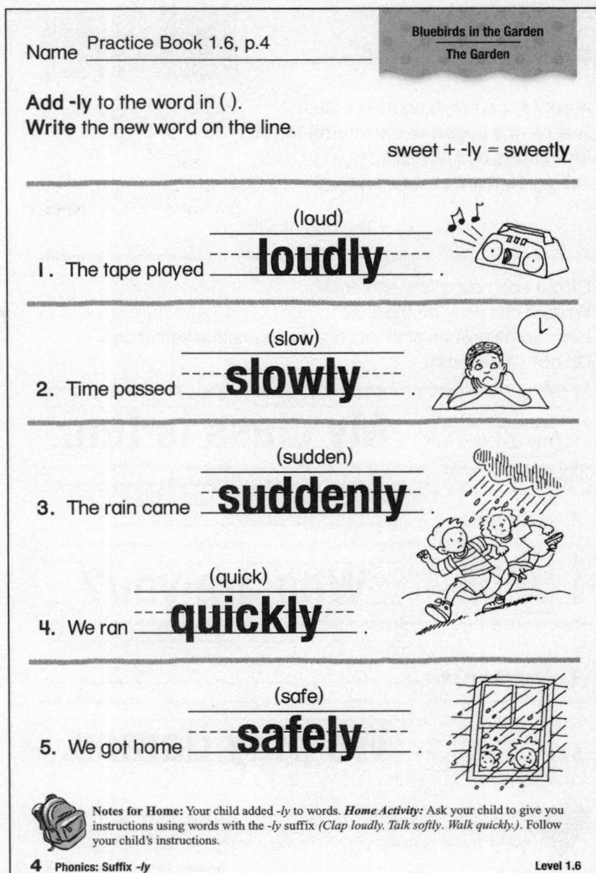

Name Practice Book 1.6, p.4

Bluebirds in the Garden
The Garden

**Add -ly** to the word in ( ).
**Write** the new word on the line.

sweet + -ly = sweetly

1. The tape played **loudly**. (loud)
2. Time passed **slowly**. (slow)
3. The rain came **suddenly**. (sudden)
4. We ran **quickly**. (quick)
5. We got home **safely**. (safe)

**Notes for Home:** Your child added *-ly* to words. ***Home Activity:*** Ask your child to give you instructions using words with the *-ly* suffix *(Clap loudly. Talk softly. Walk quickly.)*. Follow your child's instructions.

4 Phonics: Suffix *-ly* Level 1.6

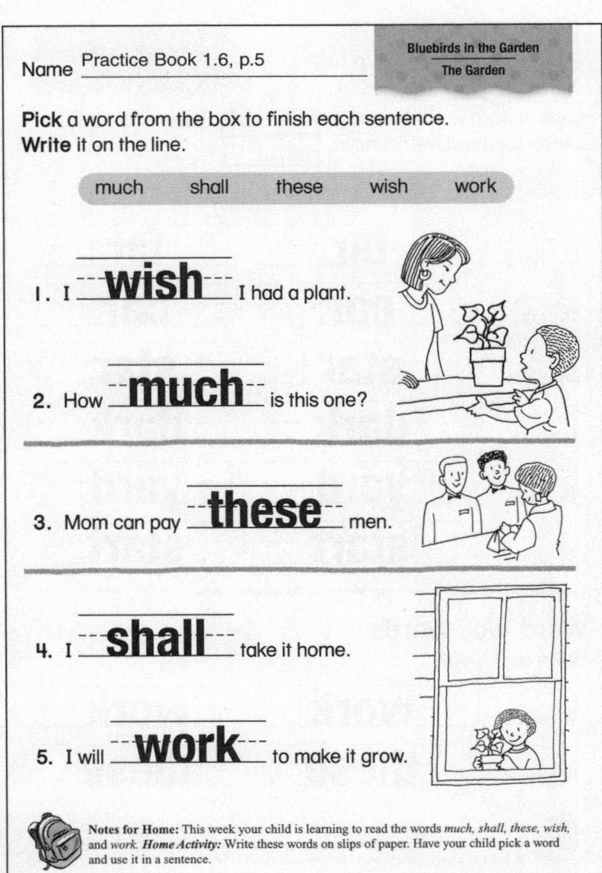

Name Practice Book 1.6, p.5

Bluebirds in the Garden
The Garden

**Pick** a word from the box to finish each sentence.
**Write** it on the line.

much shall these wish work

1. I **wish** I had a plant.
2. How **much** is this one?
3. Mom can pay **these** men.
4. I **shall** take it home.
5. I will **work** to make it grow.

**Notes for Home:** This week your child is learning to read the words *much, shall, these, wish,* and *work.* ***Home Activity:*** Write these words on slips of paper. Have your child pick a word and use it in a sentence.

Level 1.6 High-Frequency Words 5

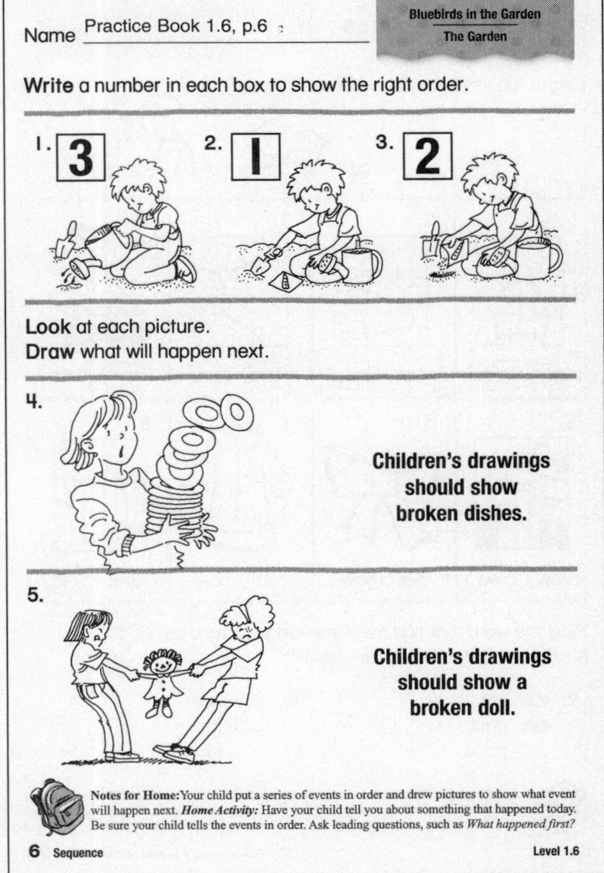

Name Practice Book 1.6, p.6

Bluebirds in the Garden
The Garden

**Write** a number in each box to show the right order.

1. **3** 2. **1** 3. **2**

**Look** at each picture.
**Draw** what will happen next.

4. **Children's drawings should show broken dishes.**

5. **Children's drawings should show a broken doll.**

**Notes for Home:** Your child put a series of events in order and drew pictures to show what event will happen next. ***Home Activity:*** Have your child tell you about something that happened today. Be sure your child tells the events in order. Ask leading questions, such as *What happened first?*

6 Sequence Level 1.6

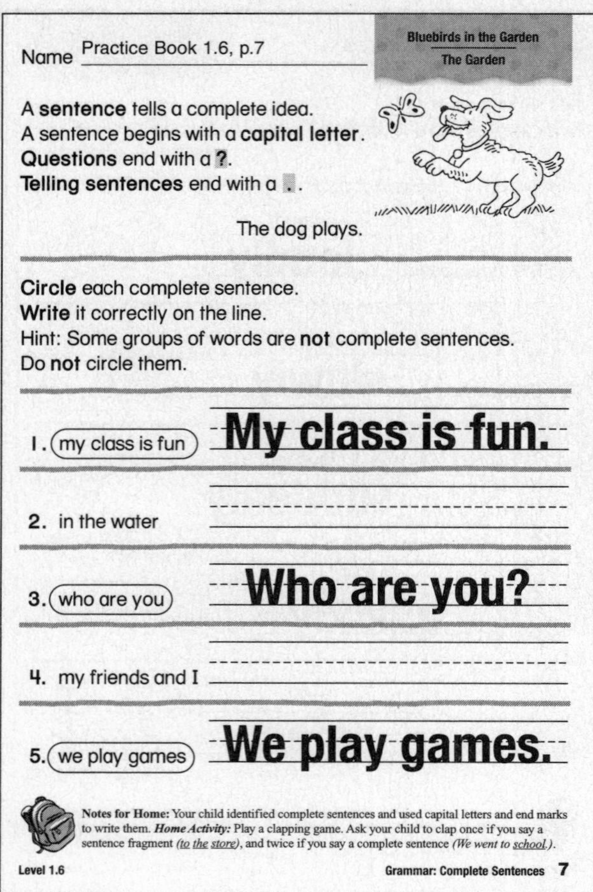

Name Practice Book 1.6, p.7

Bluebirds in the Garden
The Garden

A **sentence** tells a complete idea.
A sentence begins with a **capital letter**.
**Questions** end with a **?**.
**Telling sentences** end with a **.**.

The dog plays.

**Circle** each complete sentence.
**Write** it correctly on the line.
Hint: Some groups of words are **not** complete sentences.
Do **not** circle them.

1. (my class is fun) **My class is fun.**
2. in the water
3. (who are you) **Who are you?**
4. my friends and I
5. (we play games) **We play games.**

**Notes for Home:** Your child identified complete sentences and used capital letters and end marks to write them. ***Home Activity:*** Play a clapping game. Ask your child to clap once if you say a sentence fragment *(to the store)*, and twice if you say a complete sentence *(We went to school.)*.

Level 1.6 Grammar: Complete Sentences 7

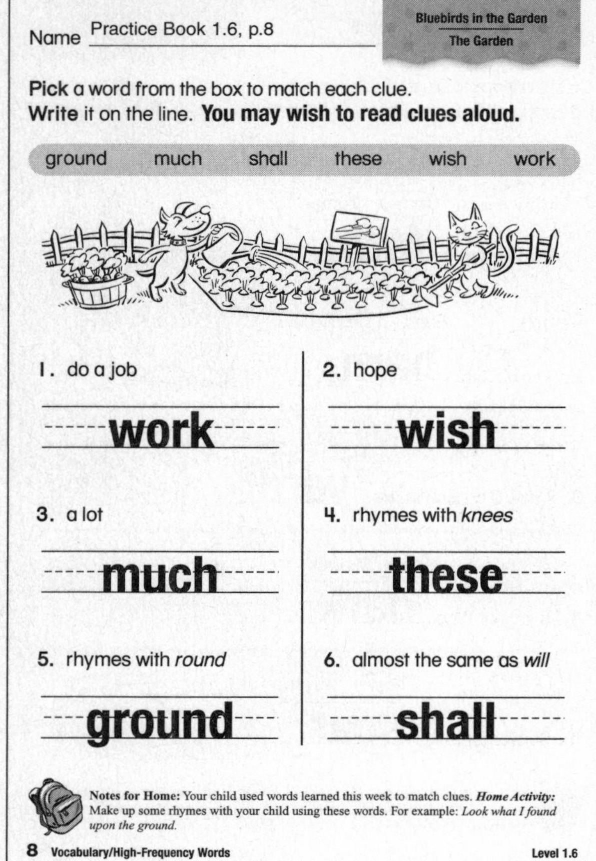

Name Practice Book 1.6, p.8

Bluebirds in the Garden
The Garden

**Pick** a word from the box to match each clue.
**Write** it on the line. **You may wish to read clues aloud.**

ground much shall these wish work

1. do a job **work**
2. hope **wish**
3. a lot **much**
4. rhymes with *knees* **these**
5. rhymes with *round* **ground**
6. almost the same as *will* **shall**

**Notes for Home:** Your child used words learned this week to match clues. ***Home Activity:*** Make up some rhymes with your child using these words. For example: *Look what I found upon the ground.*

8 Vocabulary/High-Frequency Words Level 1.6

Name Practice Book 1.6, p.9

Bluebirds in the Garden
The Garden

**Circle** the word for each picture.

toad blow

1. wins (window)
2. snap (snow)
3. (road) read
4. (boat) beat
5. crow (crew)
6. bee (bow)
7. (coat) cost
8. goat (gate)

**Find** the word that has the same **long o** sound as goat.
**Mark** the ⬭ to show your answer.

goat

9. ⬭ got
   ⬬ goal
   ⬭ good

10. ⬬ low
    ⬭ lost
    ⬭ look

**Notes for Home:** Your child reviewed words in which the long *o* sound is spelled *oa* and *ow*, as in *toad* and *blow*. ***Home Activity:*** Together, list as many words with the long *o* sound in their names as possible. Then ask your child to sort the words by their spellings.

Level 1.6 Phonics: Long *o* Spelled *oa, ow* Review 9

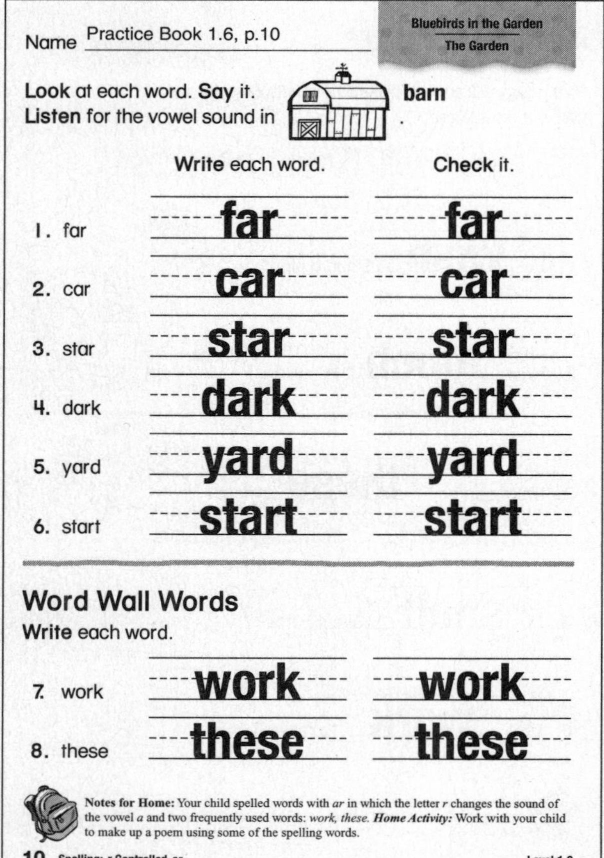

Name Practice Book 1.6, p.10

Bluebirds in the Garden
The Garden

**Look** at each word. **Say** it.
**Listen** for the vowel sound in **barn**.

| | Write each word. | Check it. |
|---|---|---|
| 1. far | **far** | **far** |
| 2. car | **car** | **car** |
| 3. star | **star** | **star** |
| 4. dark | **dark** | **dark** |
| 5. yard | **yard** | **yard** |
| 6. start | **start** | **start** |

## Word Wall Words

Write each word.

| | | |
|---|---|---|
| 7. work | **work** | **work** |
| 8. these | **these** | **these** |

**Notes for Home:** Your child spelled words with *ar* in which the letter *r* changes the sound of the vowel *a* and two frequently used words: *work, these.* ***Home Activity:*** Work with your child to make up a poem using some of the spelling words.

10 Spelling: *r*-Controlled *ar* Level 1.6

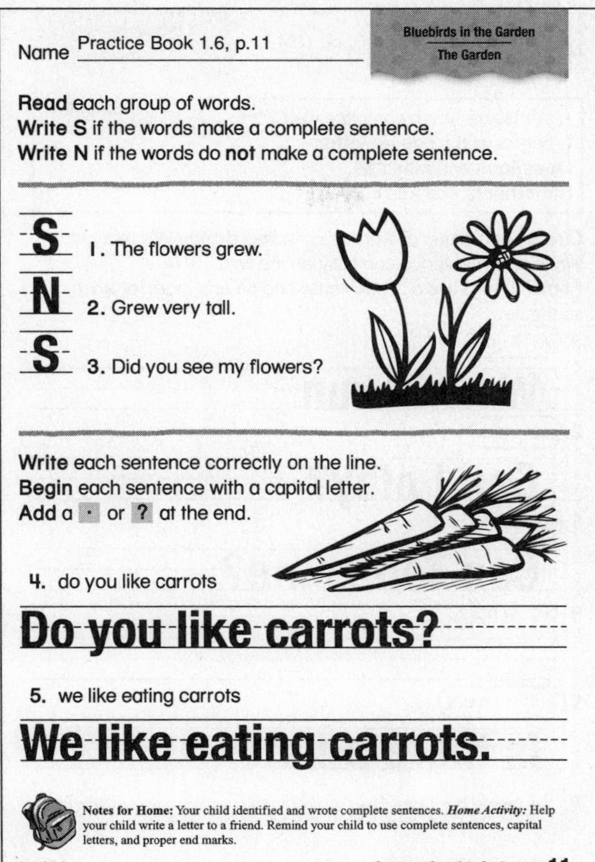

Bluebirds in the Garden
The Garden

Name Practice Book 1.6, p.11

**Read** each group of words.
**Write S** if the words make a complete sentence.
**Write N** if the words do **not** make a complete sentence.

S 1. The flowers grew.
N 2. Grew very tall.
S 3. Did you see my flowers?

**Write** each sentence correctly on the line.
**Begin** each sentence with a capital letter.
**Add** a . or ? at the end.

4. do you like carrots
**Do you like carrots?**

5. we like eating carrots
**We like eating carrots.**

**Notes for Home:** Your child identified and wrote complete sentences. ***Home Activity:*** Help your child write a letter to a friend. Remind your child to use complete sentences, capital letters, and proper end marks.

Level 1.6 Grammar: Complete Sentences 11

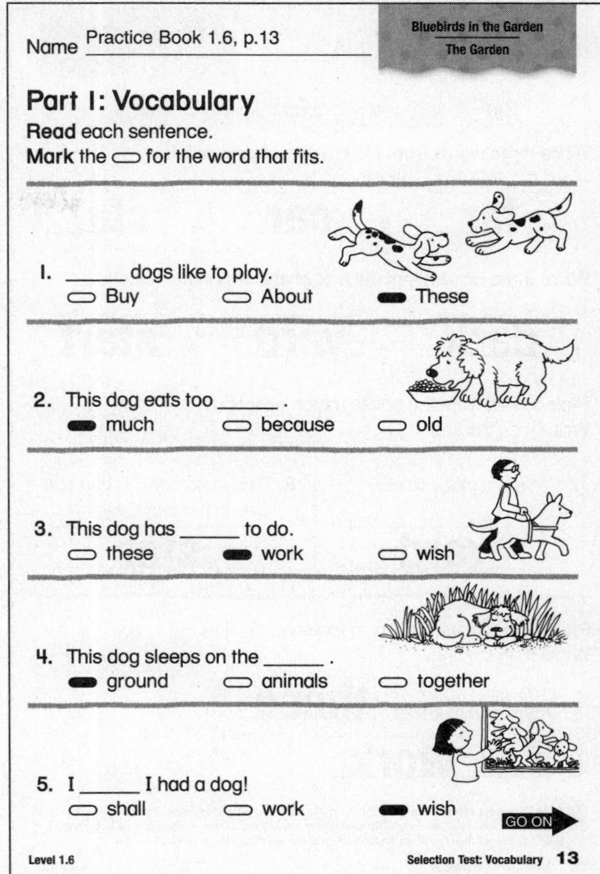

Bluebirds in the Garden
The Garden

Name Practice Book 1.6, p.13

## Part 1: Vocabulary

**Read** each sentence.
**Mark** the ⬭ for the word that fits.

1. _____ dogs like to play.
⬭ Buy ⬭ About ⬬ These

2. This dog eats too _____ .
⬬ much ⬭ because ⬭ old

3. This dog has _____ to do.
⬭ these ⬬ work ⬭ wish

4. This dog sleeps on the _____ .
⬬ ground ⬭ animals ⬭ together

5. I _____ I had a dog!
⬭ shall ⬭ work ⬬ wish

GO ON

Level 1.6 Selection Test: Vocabulary 13

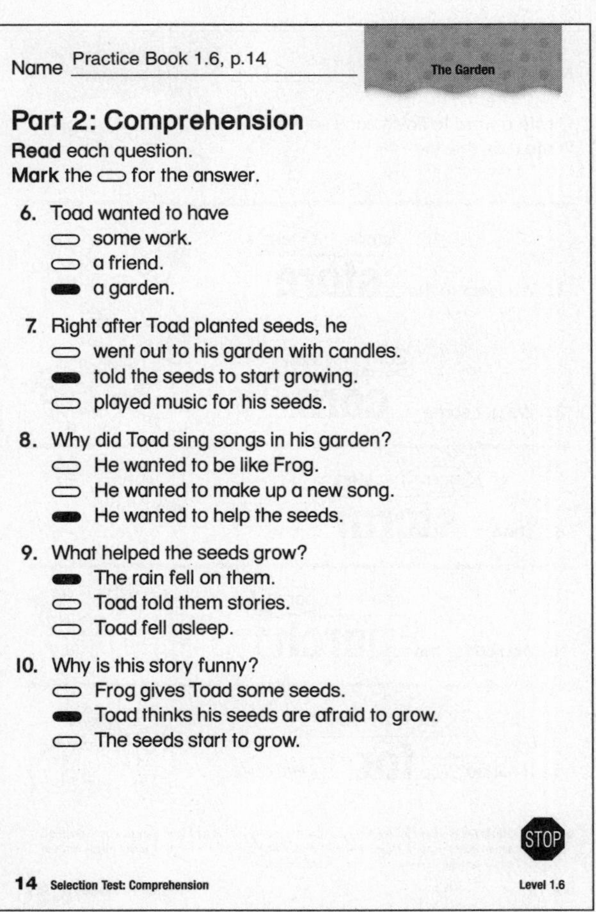

The Garden

Name Practice Book 1.6, p.14

## Part 2: Comprehension

**Read** each question.
**Mark** the ⬭ for the answer.

6. Toad wanted to have
⬭ some work.
⬭ a friend.
⬬ a garden.

7. Right after Toad planted seeds, he
⬭ went out to his garden with candles.
⬬ told the seeds to start growing.
⬭ played music for his seeds.

8. Why did Toad sing songs in his garden?
⬭ He wanted to be like Frog.
⬭ He wanted to make up a new song.
⬬ He wanted to help the seeds.

9. What helped the seeds grow?
⬬ The rain fell on them.
⬭ Toad told them stories.
⬭ Toad fell asleep.

10. Why is this story funny?
⬭ Frog gives Toad some seeds.
⬬ Toad thinks his seeds are afraid to grow.
⬭ The seeds start to grow.

STOP

14 Selection Test: Comprehension Level 1.6

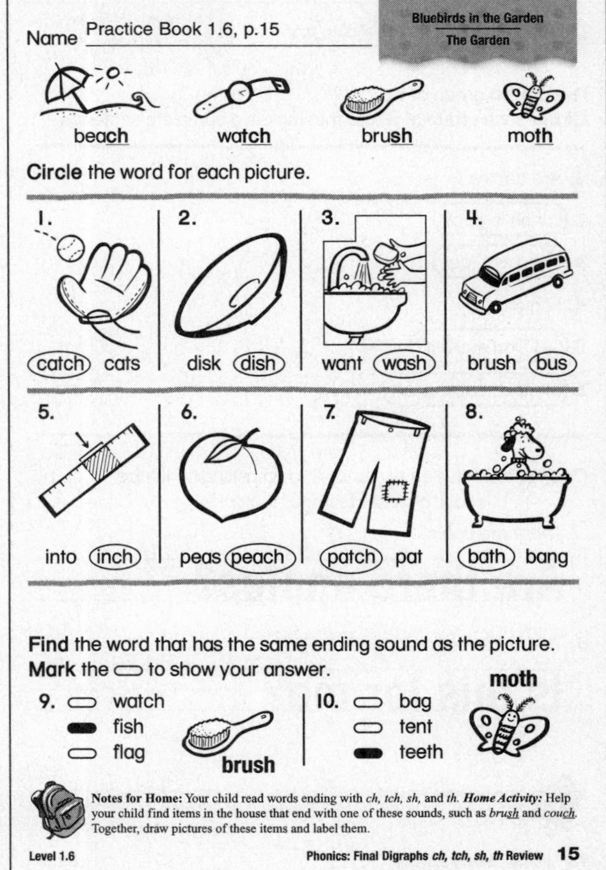

Bluebirds in the Garden
The Garden

Name Practice Book 1.6, p.15

beach watch brush moth

**Circle** the word for each picture.

1. (catch) cats
2. disk (dish)
3. want (wash)
4. brush (bus)
5. into (inch)
6. peas (peach)
7. (patch) pat
8. (bath) bang

**Find** the word that has the same ending sound as the picture.
**Mark** the ⬭ to show your answer.

9. ⬭ watch ⬬ fish ⬭ flag — brush
10. ⬭ bag ⬭ tent ⬬ teeth — moth

**Notes for Home:** Your child read words ending with *ch, tch, sh,* and *th.* ***Home Activity:*** Help your child find items in the house that end with one of these sounds, such as *brush* and *couch.* Together, draw pictures of these items and label them.

Level 1.6 Phonics: Final Digraphs *ch, tch, sh, th* Review 15

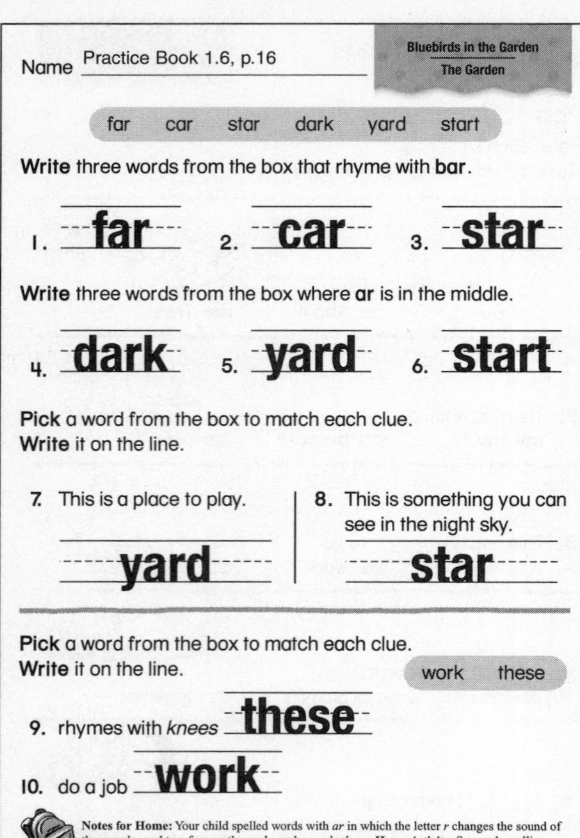
Name Practice Book 1.6, p.16

Bluebirds in the Garden
The Garden

far car star dark yard start

**Write** three words from the box that rhyme with **bar**.

1. far 2. car 3. star

**Write** three words from the box where **ar** is in the middle.

4. dark 5. yard 6. start

**Pick** a word from the box to match each clue.
**Write** it on the line.

7. This is a place to play. yard

8. This is something you can see in the night sky. star

**Pick** a word from the box to match each clue.
**Write** it on the line.

work these

9. rhymes with *knees* these

10. do a job work

**Notes for Home:** Your child spelled words with *ar* in which the letter *r* changes the sound of the vowel *a* and two frequently used words: *work, these.* ***Home Activity:*** Say each spelling word, and then use it in a sentence. Repeat the word and have your child write it.

16 Spelling: *r*-Controlled *ar* Level 1.6

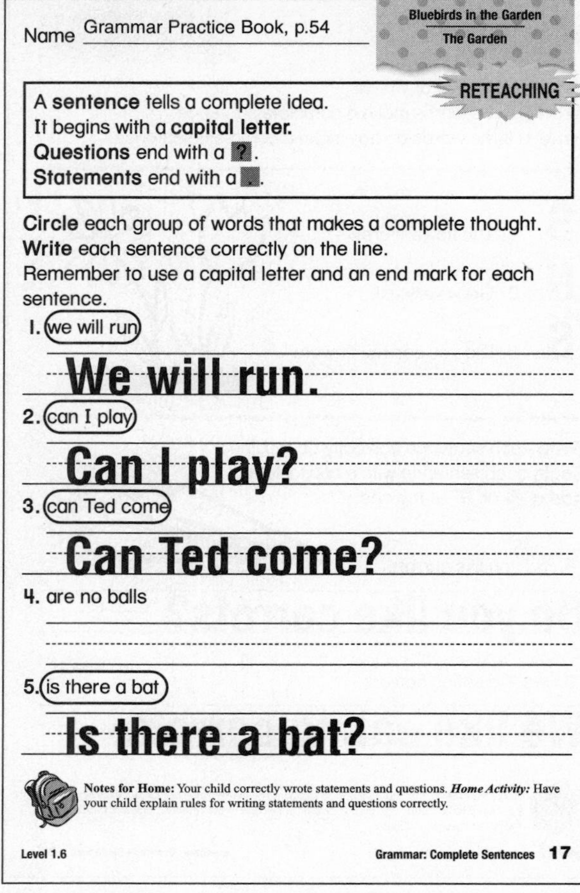
Name Grammar Practice Book, p.54

Bluebirds in the Garden
The Garden

RETEACHING

A **sentence** tells a complete idea.
It begins with a **capital letter.**
**Questions** end with a **?**.
**Statements** end with a **.**.

**Circle** each group of words that makes a complete thought.
**Write** each sentence correctly on the line.
Remember to use a capital letter and an end mark for each sentence.

1. (we will run)
We will run.

2. (can I play)
Can I play?

3. (can Ted come)
Can Ted come?

4. are no balls

5. (is there a bat)
Is there a bat?

**Notes for Home:** Your child correctly wrote statements and questions. ***Home Activity:*** Have your child explain rules for writing statements and questions correctly.

Level 1.6 Grammar: Complete Sentences 17

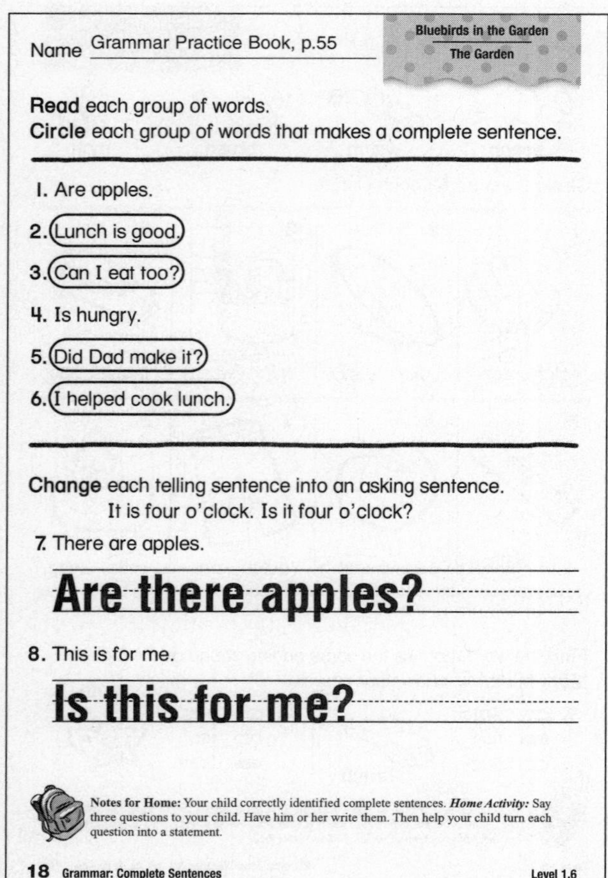
Name Grammar Practice Book, p.55

Bluebirds in the Garden
The Garden

**Read** each group of words.
**Circle** each group of words that makes a complete sentence.

1. Are apples.
2. (Lunch is good.)
3. (Can I eat too?)
4. Is hungry.
5. (Did Dad make it?)
6. (I helped cook lunch.)

**Change** each telling sentence into an asking sentence.
It is four o'clock. Is it four o'clock?

7. There are apples.
Are there apples?

8. This is for me.
Is this for me?

**Notes for Home:** Your child correctly identified complete sentences. ***Home Activity:*** Say three questions to your child. Have him or her write them. Then help your child turn each question into a statement.

18 Grammar: Complete Sentences Level 1.6

Name Practice Book 1.6, p.19

Jordan Makes a New Friend
Ice-Cold Birthday

**Circle** a word to finish each sentence.
**Write** it on the line.

horn

stare (store)
1. We went to the store.

(corn) can
2. We got some corn.

(storm) start
3. Then a storm came.

port (porch)
4. We ran for the porch.

(for) far
5. It rained for two days.

**Notes for Home:** This week your child is learning to read words with *or* that have the same sound heard in *horn.* ***Home Activity:*** Work with your child to see how many words you can come up with to rhyme with *corn, score,* and *short.*

Level 1.6 Phonics: r-Controlled *or* 21

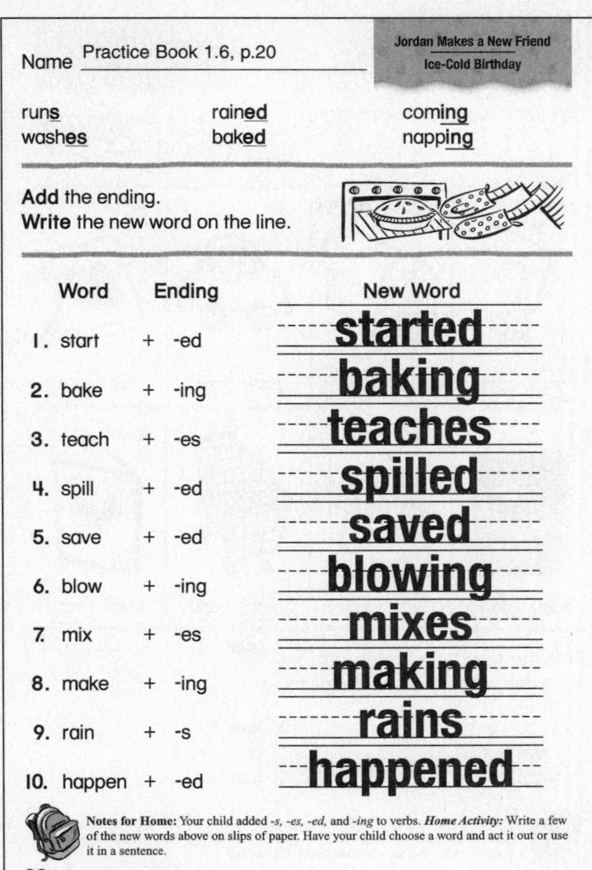

Name Practice Book 1.6, p.20

Jordan Makes a New Friend
Ice-Cold Birthday

runs rained coming
washes baked napping

**Add** the ending.
**Write** the new word on the line.

| | Word | | Ending | New Word |
|---|---|---|---|---|
| 1. | start | + | -ed | **started** |
| 2. | bake | + | -ing | **baking** |
| 3. | teach | + | -es | **teaches** |
| 4. | spill | + | -ed | **spilled** |
| 5. | save | + | -ed | **saved** |
| 6. | blow | + | -ing | **blowing** |
| 7. | mix | + | -es | **mixes** |
| 8. | make | + | -ing | **making** |
| 9. | rain | + | -s | **rains** |
| 10. | happen | + | -ed | **happened** |

**Notes for Home:** Your child added *-s, -es, -ed,* and *-ing* to verbs. ***Home Activity:*** Write a few of the new words above on slips of paper. Have your child choose a word and act it out or use it in a sentence.

22 Phonics: Inflected Endings *-s, -es, -ed, -ing* Level 1.6

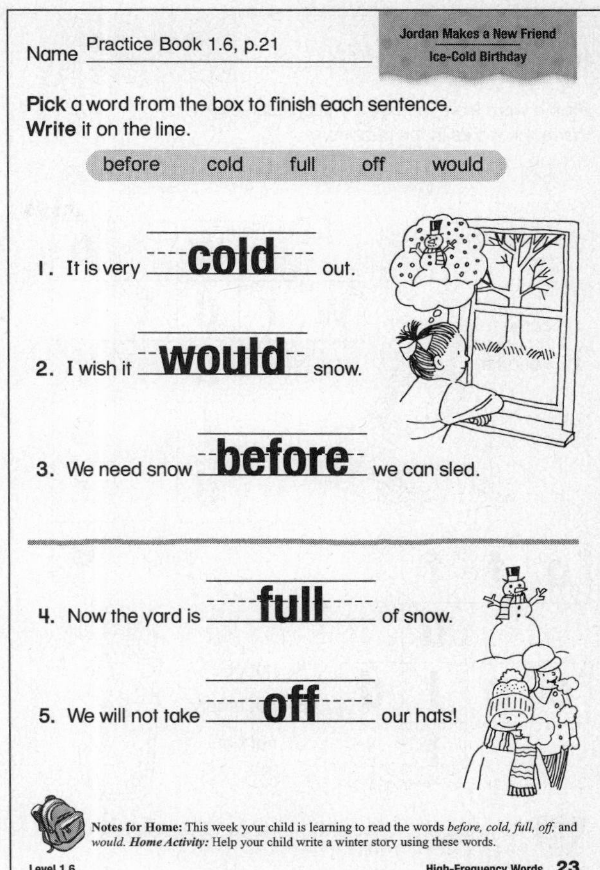

Name Practice Book 1.6, p.21

Jordan Makes a New Friend
Ice-Cold Birthday

**Pick** a word from the box to finish each sentence.
**Write** it on the line.

before cold full off would

1. It is very **cold** out.
2. I wish it **would** snow.
3. We need snow **before** we can sled.
4. Now the yard is **full** of snow.
5. We will not take **off** our hats!

**Notes for Home:** This week your child is learning to read the words *before, cold, full, off,* and *would.* ***Home Activity:*** Help your child write a winter story using these words.

Level 1.6 High-Frequency Words 23

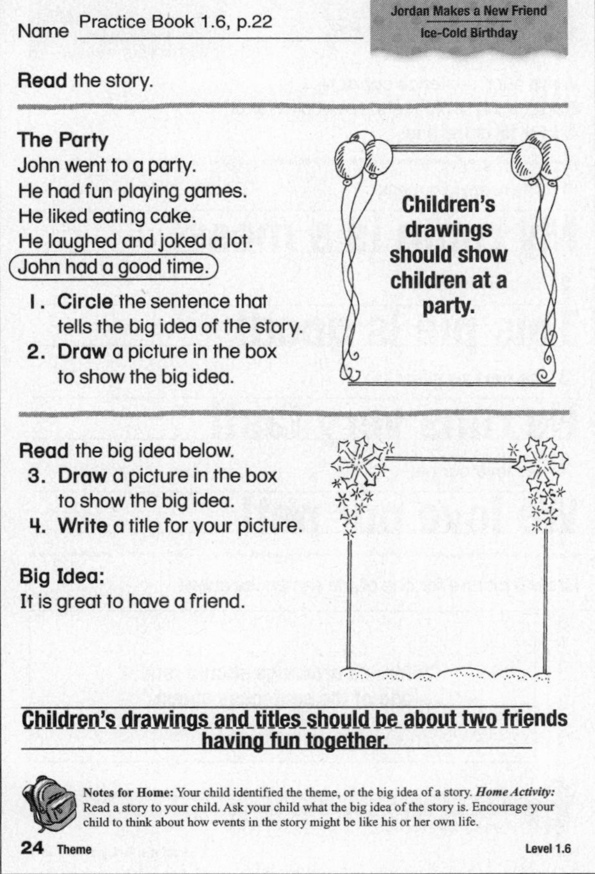

Name Practice Book 1.6, p.22

Jordan Makes a New Friend
Ice-Cold Birthday

**Read** the story.

**The Party**
John went to a party.
He had fun playing games.
He liked eating cake.
He laughed and joked a lot.
(John had a good time.)

1. **Circle** the sentence that tells the big idea of the story.
2. **Draw** a picture in the box to show the big idea.

**Children's drawings should show children at a party.**

**Read** the big idea below.
3. **Draw** a picture in the box to show the big idea.
4. **Write** a title for your picture.

**Big Idea:**
It is great to have a friend.

**Children's drawings and titles should be about two friends having fun together.**

**Notes for Home:** Your child identified the theme, or the big idea of a story. ***Home Activity:*** Read a story to your child. Ask your child what the big idea of the story is. Encourage your child to think about how events in the story might be like his or her own life.

24 Theme Level 1.6

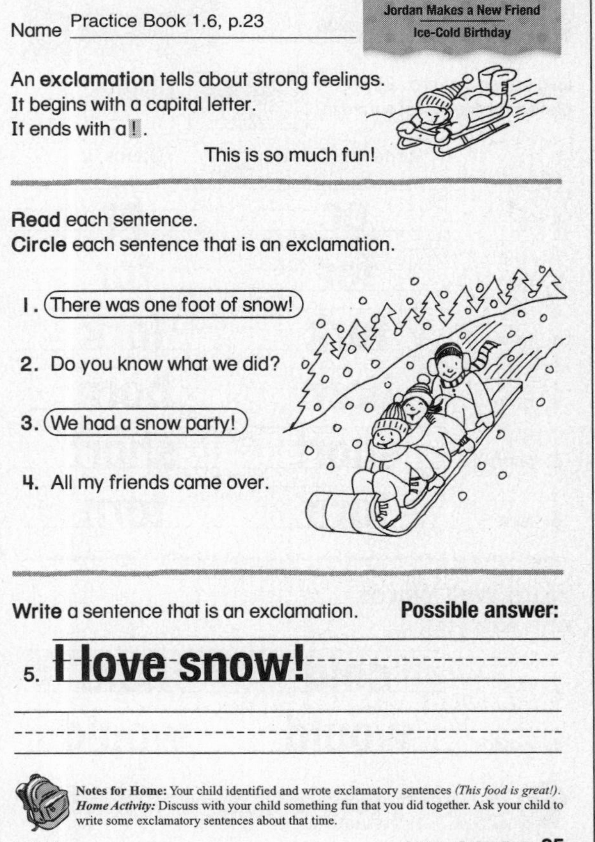

Name Practice Book 1.6, p.23

Jordan Makes a New Friend
Ice-Cold Birthday

An **exclamation** tells about strong feelings.
It begins with a capital letter.
It ends with a **!**.

This is so much fun!

**Read** each sentence.
**Circle** each sentence that is an exclamation.

1. (There was one foot of snow!)
2. Do you know what we did?
3. (We had a snow party!)
4. All my friends came over.

**Write** a sentence that is an exclamation. **Possible answer:**

5. **I love snow!**

**Notes for Home:** Your child identified and wrote exclamatory sentences *(This food is great!).* ***Home Activity:*** Discuss with your child something fun that you did together. Ask your child to write some exclamatory sentences about that time.

Level 1.6 Grammar: Exclamations 25

Name Practice Book 1.6, p.24

Jordan Makes a New Friend
Ice-Cold Birthday

**Pick** a word from the box to match each clue.
**Write** the words in the puzzles.

before cold full off would wrote

1. ______ you like to come to my party?
2. not after
3.

4. not on
5. not empty
6. not hot



**Notes for Home:** Your child used words learned this week to solve a puzzle. *Home Activity:* Help your child write a poem using some of these words above.

26 Vocabulary/High-Frequency Words Level 1.6

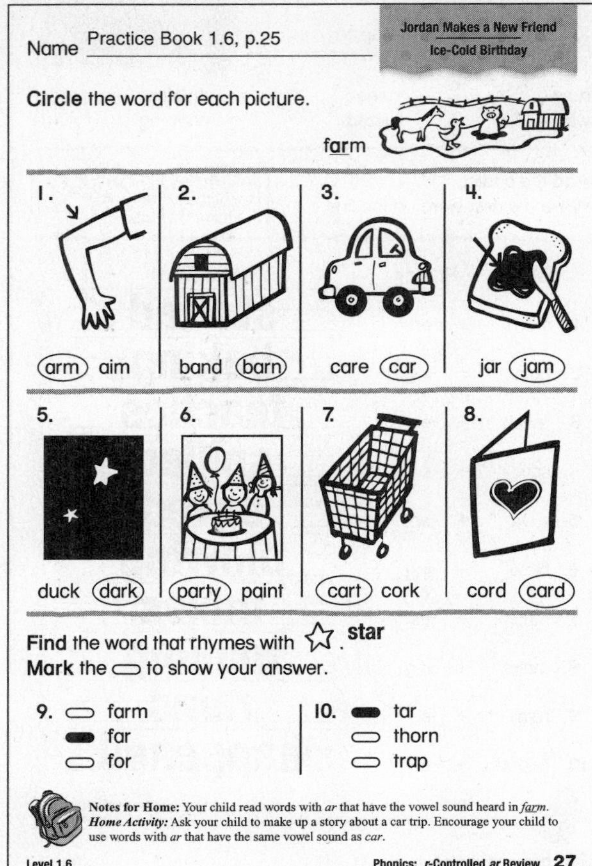
Name Practice Book 1.6, p.25

Jordan Makes a New Friend
Ice-Cold Birthday

**Circle** the word for each picture.

farm

1. (arm) aim
2. band (barn)
3. care (car)
4. jar (jam)
5. duck (dark)
6. (party) paint
7. (cart) cork
8. cord (card)

**Find** the word that rhymes with star.
**Mark** the ⬭ to show your answer.

9. ⬭ farm ⬬ far ⬭ for
10. ⬬ tar ⬭ thorn ⬭ trap

**Notes for Home:** Your child read words with *ar* that have the vowel sound heard in *farm*. *Home Activity:* Ask your child to make up a story about a car trip. Encourage your child to use words with *ar* that have the same vowel sound as *car*.

Level 1.6 Phonics: *r*-Controlled *ar* Review 27

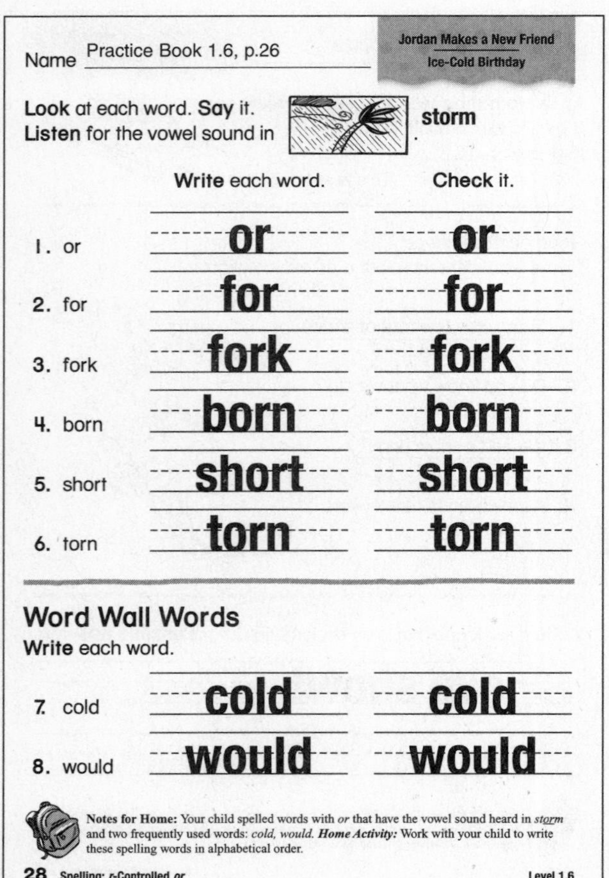
Name Practice Book 1.6, p.26

Jordan Makes a New Friend
Ice-Cold Birthday

**Look** at each word. **Say** it.
**Listen** for the vowel sound in storm.

| | Write each word. | Check it. |
|---|---|---|
| 1. or | or | or |
| 2. for | for | for |
| 3. fork | fork | fork |
| 4. born | born | born |
| 5. short | short | short |
| 6. torn | torn | torn |

**Word Wall Words**
**Write** each word.

| | | |
|---|---|---|
| 7. cold | cold | cold |
| 8. would | would | would |

**Notes for Home:** Your child spelled words with *or* that have the vowel sound heard in *storm* and two frequently used words: *cold, would. Home Activity:* Work with your child to write these spelling words in alphabetical order.

28 Spelling: *r*-Controlled *or* Level 1.6

Name Practice Book 1.6, p.27

Jordan Makes a New Friend
Ice-Cold Birthday

**Write** each sentence correctly.
**Begin** each sentence with a capital letter.
**Add** a ! at the end.

1. my room is a mess
**My room is a mess!**
2. this pie is good
**This pie is good!**
3. he runs very fast
**He runs very fast!**
4. we love our pet
**We love our pet!**

**Draw** a picture for one of the sentences above.

5. **Children's drawings should reflect one of the sentences above.**

**Notes for Home:** Your child wrote exclamations—sentences that express strong feelings. *Home Activity:* Take turns saying sentences that express strong feelings. Encourage your child to speak with emotion.

Level 1.6 Grammar: Exclamations 29

Name Practice Book 1.6, p.29

Jordan Makes a Friend
Ice-Cold Birthday

## Part 1: Vocabulary

**Read** each sentence.
**Mark** the ○ for the word that fits.

1. I will have some water ______ I run.
   ● before ○ new ○ around
2. Jack ______ like some water too.
   ○ bring ● would ○ think
3. The glass is ______ .
   ○ when ● full ○ off
4. I shut ______ the water.
   ○ before ○ four ● off
5. This water is very ______ !
   ● cold ○ would ○ old

GO ON

Level 1.6 Selection Test: Vocabulary 31

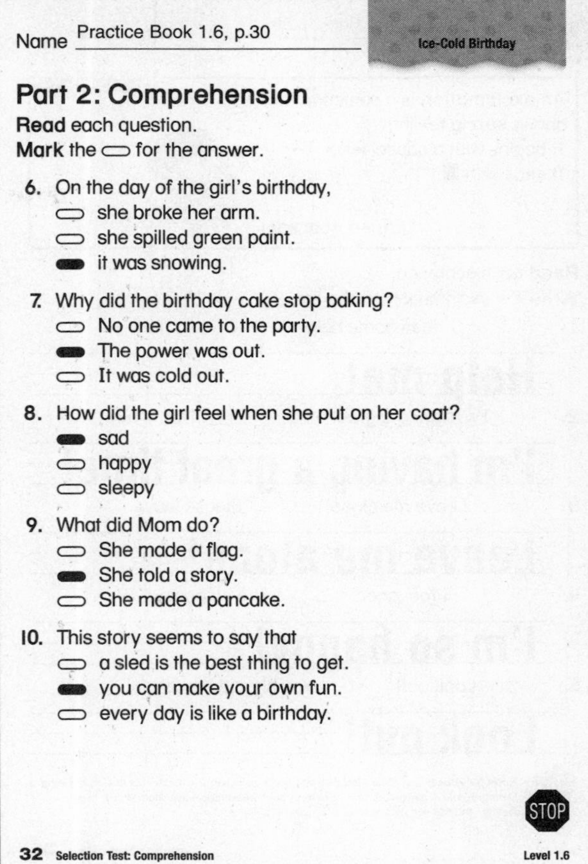

Name Practice Book 1.6, p.30

Ice-Cold Birthday

## Part 2: Comprehension

**Read** each question.
**Mark** the ○ for the answer.

6. On the day of the girl's birthday,
   ○ she broke her arm.
   ○ she spilled green paint.
   ● it was snowing.
7. Why did the birthday cake stop baking?
   ○ No one came to the party.
   ● The power was out.
   ○ It was cold out.
8. How did the girl feel when she put on her coat?
   ● sad
   ○ happy
   ○ sleepy
9. What did Mom do?
   ○ She made a flag.
   ● She told a story.
   ○ She made a pancake.
10. This story seems to say that
   ○ a sled is the best thing to get.
   ● you can make your own fun.
   ○ every day is like a birthday.

STOP

32 Selection Test: Comprehension Level 1.6

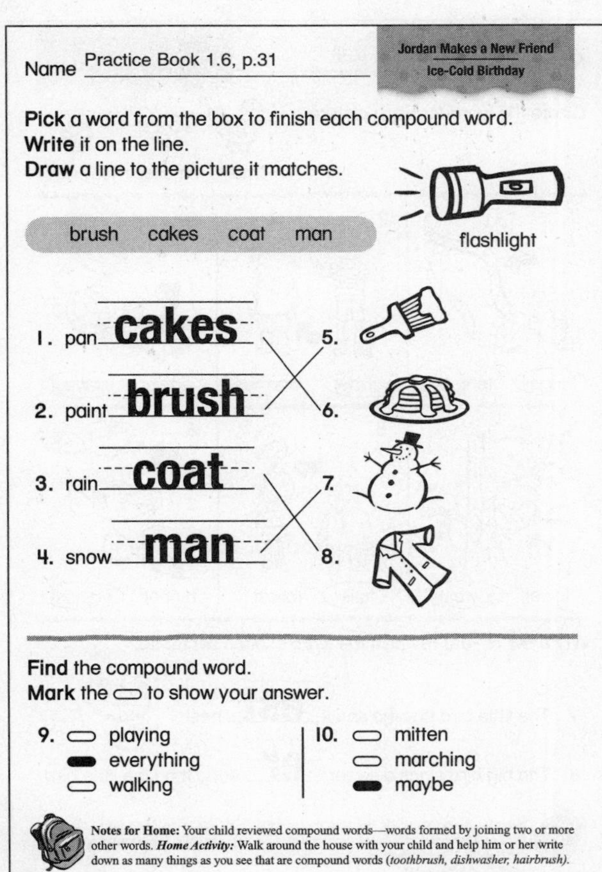

Name Practice Book 1.6, p.31

Jordan Makes a New Friend
Ice-Cold Birthday

**Pick** a word from the box to finish each compound word.
**Write** it on the line.
**Draw** a line to the picture it matches.

brush cakes coat man

flashlight

1. pan**cakes** 5.
2. paint**brush** 6.
3. rain**coat** 7.
4. snow**man** 8.

**Find** the compound word.
**Mark** the ○ to show your answer.

9. ○ playing
   ● everything
   ○ walking

10. ○ mitten
   ○ marching
   ● maybe

**Notes for Home:** Your child reviewed compound words—words formed by joining two or more other words. ***Home Activity:*** Walk around the house with your child and help him or her write down as many things as you see that are compound words (*toothbrush, dishwasher, hairbrush*).

Level 1.6 Phonics: Compounds Review 33

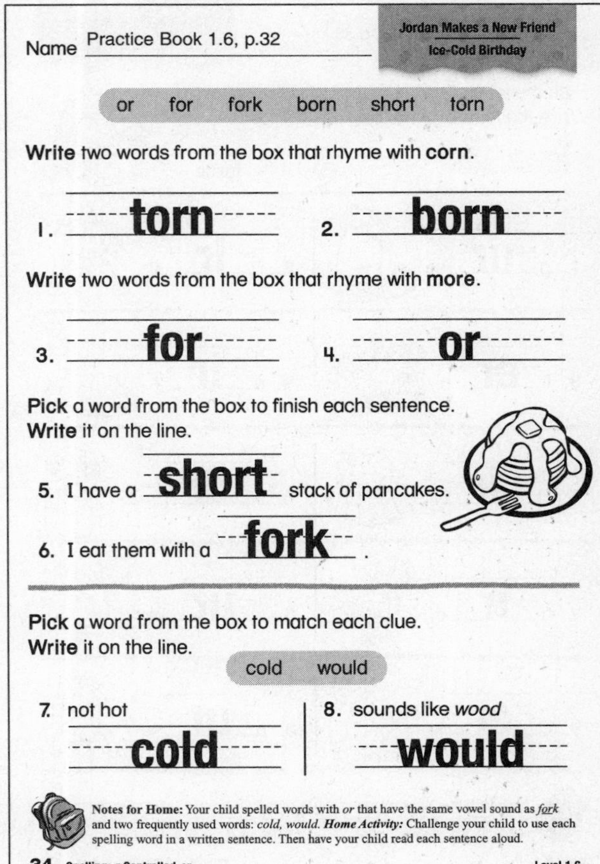

Name Practice Book 1.6, p.32

Jordan Makes a New Friend
Ice-Cold Birthday

or for fork born short torn

**Write** two words from the box that rhyme with **corn**.

1. **torn** 2. **born**

**Write** two words from the box that rhyme with **more**.

3. **for** 4. **or**

**Pick** a word from the box to finish each sentence.
**Write** it on the line.

5. I have a **short** stack of pancakes.
6. I eat them with a **fork** .

**Pick** a word from the box to match each clue.
**Write** it on the line.

cold would

7. not hot **cold**
8. sounds like *wood* **would**

**Notes for Home:** Your child spelled words with *or* that have the same vowel sound as *fork* and two frequently used words: *cold, would.* ***Home Activity:*** Challenge your child to use each spelling word in a written sentence. Then have your child read each sentence aloud.

34 Spelling: *r*-Controlled *or* Level 1.6

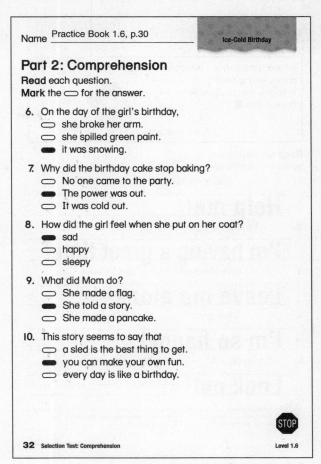

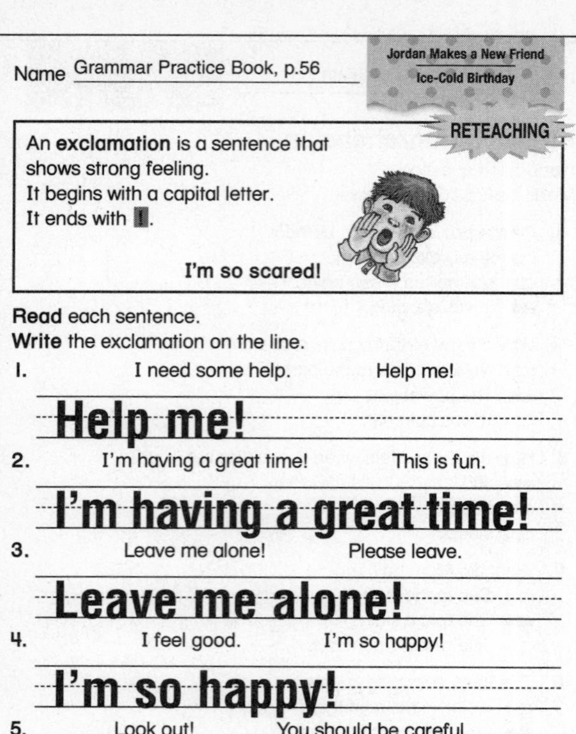
Name Grammar Practice Book, p.56

Jordan Makes a New Friend
Ice-Cold Birthday

RETEACHING

An **exclamation** is a sentence that shows strong feeling.
It begins with a capital letter.
It ends with **!**.

I'm so scared!

**Read** each sentence.
**Write** the exclamation on the line.

1. I need some help. Help me!
**Help me!**
2. I'm having a great time! This is fun.
**I'm having a great time!**
3. Leave me alone! Please leave.
**Leave me alone!**
4. I feel good. I'm so happy!
**I'm so happy!**
5. Look out! You should be careful.
**Look out!**

**Notes for Home:** Your child identified and wrote exclamations—sentences that show strong feeling. ***Home Activity:*** Ask your child to write short sentences that show strong, happy feelings and that end with exclamation marks (!).

Level 1.6 Grammar: Exclamations 35

Name Grammar Practice Book, p.57

Jordan Makes a New Friend
Ice-Cold Birthday

**Look** at each picture.
**Write** an exclamation about it. **Possible answers given.**

1. **It is pretty!**
2. **That was bad!**
3. **Watch out!**
4. **She's so happy!**
5. **That dinosaur is huge!**

**Notes for Home:** Your child wrote exclamations—sentences that express strong feeling. ***Home Activity:*** Write an exclamation and have your child act it out. Then change roles.

36 Grammar: Exclamations Level 1.6

Name Practice Book 1.6, p.35

Show Time: Your First Play
Do You Live in a Nest?

**Pick** the letters from the box to finish each word.
**Write** the letters on the line.

er ir ur

turtle

1. p**ur**se
2. f**ir**st
3. f**er**n
4. d**ir**t
5. sk**ir**t
6. h**er**
7. b**ir**d
8. t**ur**key
9. cl**er**k
10. n**ur**se

**Notes for Home:** Your child wrote words in which the letters *er, ir,* and *ur* represent the same vowel sound heard in *her, shirt,* and *turtle.* ***Home Activity:*** Make a list of the words with *er, ir,* and *ur* that have this vowel sound. Ask your child to sort the words by their spelling.

Level 1.6 Phonics: *r*-Controlled *er, ir, ur* 39

Name Practice Book 1.6, p.36

Show Time: Your First Play
Do You Live in a Nest?

**Circle** the word for each picture.

small smaller smallest

1. (longer) longest
2. (warmer) warmest
3. slower (slowest)
4. lower (lowest)
5. (taller) tallest
6. higher (highest)

**Write -er** or **-est** to finish the word in each sentence.

7. The little bird has the small**est** nest.
8. The big bird sings a sweet**er** song than the little bird.

**Notes for Home:** Your child identified the comparative endings *-er* and *-est* as in *smaller* and *smallest.* ***Home Activity:*** Compare different animals with your child. Use *-er* when comparing two animals. Use *-est* when comparing more than two.

40 Phonics: Comparative Endings *-er, -est* Level 1.6

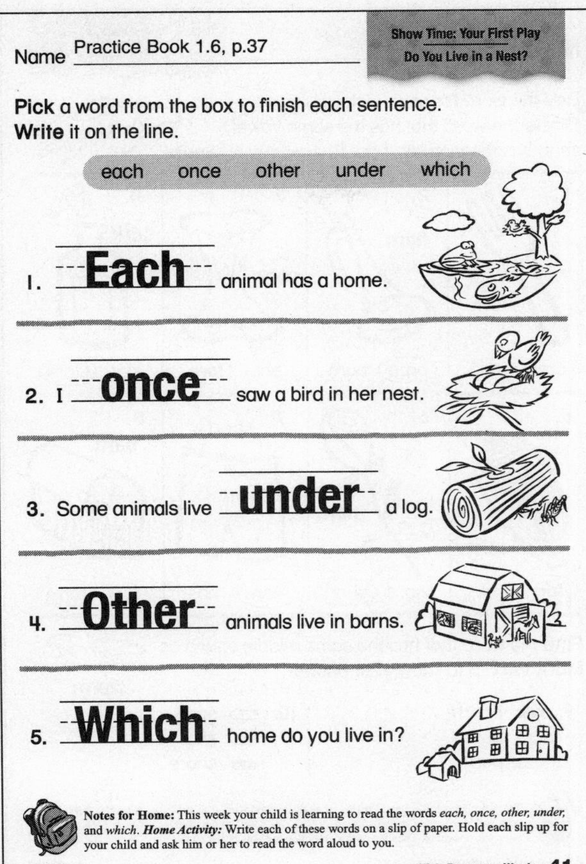
Show Time: Your First Play
Do You Live in a Nest?

Name Practice Book 1.6, p.37

**Pick** a word from the box to finish each sentence.
**Write** it on the line.

each once other under which

1. **Each** animal has a home.
2. I **once** saw a bird in her nest.
3. Some animals live **under** a log.
4. **Other** animals live in barns.
5. **Which** home do you live in?

**Notes for Home:** This week your child is learning to read the words *each, once, other, under,* and *which*. ***Home Activity:*** Write each of these words on a slip of paper. Hold each slip up for your child and ask him or her to read the word aloud to you.

Level 1.6 High-Frequency Words 41

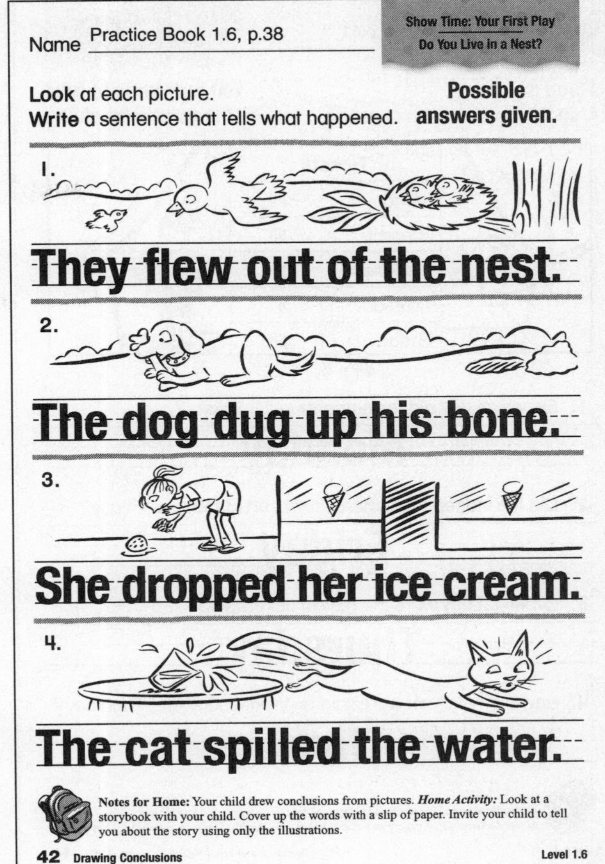
Show Time: Your First Play
Do You Live in a Nest?

Name Practice Book 1.6, p.38

**Look** at each picture.
**Write** a sentence that tells what happened. **Possible answers given.**

1. **They flew out of the nest.**
2. **The dog dug up his bone.**
3. **She dropped her ice cream.**
4. **The cat spilled the water.**

**Notes for Home:** Your child drew conclusions from pictures. ***Home Activity:*** Look at a storybook with your child. Cover up the words with a slip of paper. Invite your child to tell you about the story using only the illustrations.

42 Drawing Conclusions Level 1.6

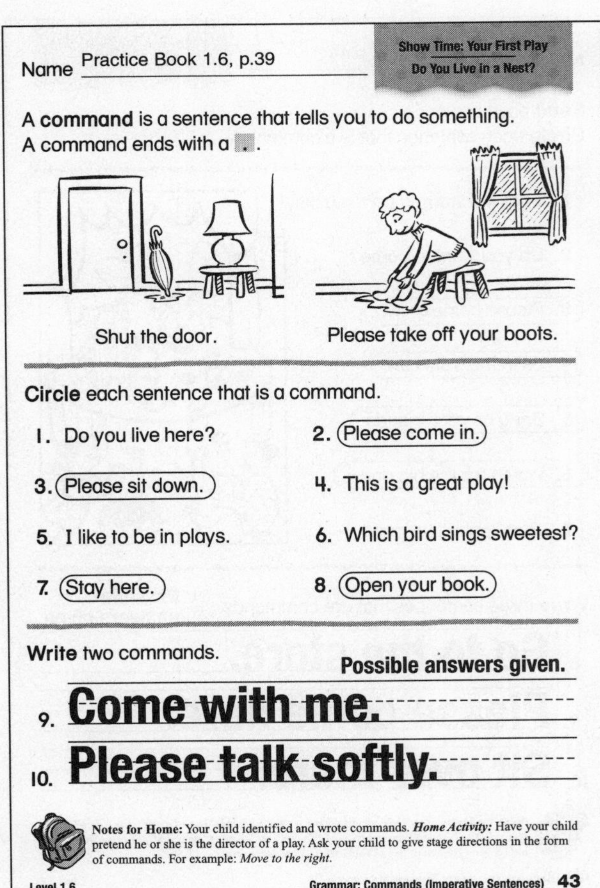
Show Time: Your First Play
Do You Live in a Nest?

Name Practice Book 1.6, p.39

A **command** is a sentence that tells you to do something.
A command ends with a **.**.

Shut the door. Please take off your boots.

**Circle** each sentence that is a command.

1. Do you live here?
2. (Please come in.)
3. (Please sit down.)
4. This is a great play!
5. I like to be in plays.
6. Which bird sings sweetest?
7. (Stay here.)
8. (Open your book.)

**Write** two commands. **Possible answers given.**

9. **Come with me.**
10. **Please talk softly.**

**Notes for Home:** Your child identified and wrote commands. ***Home Activity:*** Have your child pretend he or she is the director of a play. Ask your child to give stage directions in the form of commands. For example: *Move to the right.*

Level 1.6 Grammar: Commands (Imperative Sentences) 43

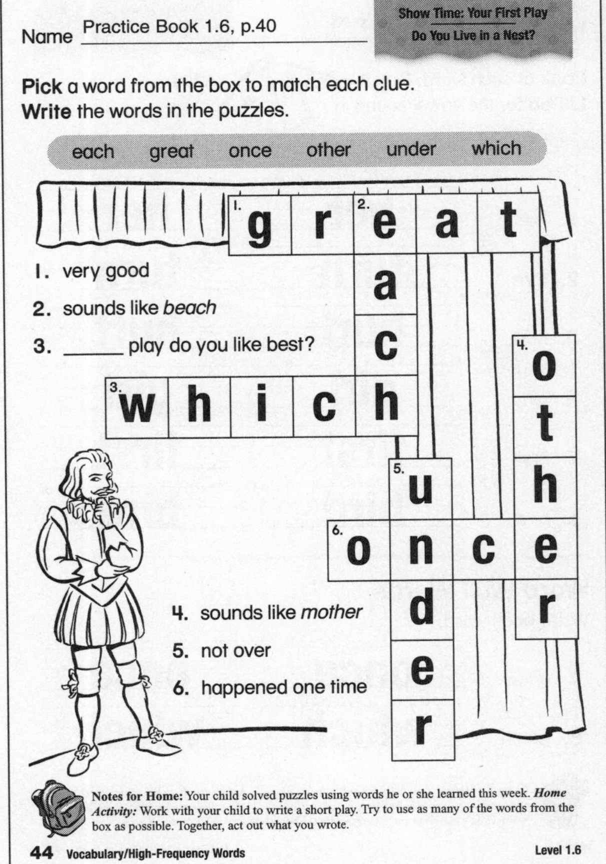
Show Time: Your First Play
Do You Live in a Nest?

Name Practice Book 1.6, p.40

**Pick** a word from the box to match each clue.
**Write** the words in the puzzles.

each great once other under which

1. very good — **great**
2. sounds like *beach* — **each**
3. ______ play do you like best? — **which**
4. sounds like *mother* — **other**
5. not over — **under**
6. happened one time — **once**

**Notes for Home:** Your child solved puzzles using words he or she learned this week. ***Home Activity:*** Work with your child to write a short play. Try to use as many of the words from the box as possible. Together, act out what you wrote.

44 Vocabulary/High-Frequency Words Level 1.6

Name Practice Book 1.6, p.41

Show Time: Your First Play
Do You Live in a Nest?

**Read** the chart.
**Use** it to answer each question.

**You may wish to read the questions aloud.**

| Tickets | |
|---|---|
| Monday | 𝍸 |
| Tuesday | IIII |
| Wednesday | III |
| Thursday | II |
| Friday | 𝍸 I |

𝍸 = 5

1. On which day did the students sell 5 tickets?

**Monday**

2. Did the students sell more tickets on Monday or Friday?

**Friday**

3. On which day were the fewest tickets sold?

**Thursday**

4. How many tickets were sold on Wednesday and Thursday?

**five**

**Notes for Home:** Your child used a chart to find information and answer questions. ***Home Activity:*** Together, create a chart showing chores that family members do at home.



Name Practice Book 1.6, p.42

Show Time: Your First Play
Do You Live in a Nest?

**Say** the word for each picture.
**Circle** the word that has the same vowel sound as the picture.

storm

1. fork — cart (cork)
2. horn — (born) burn
3. core — shirt (tore)
4. cork — car (store)
5. corn — (fort) first
6. thorn — share (short)
7. shorts — (more) most
8. barn — fork (farm)

**Find** the word that has the same middle sound as storm.
**Mark** the ⬭ to show your answer.

9. ● porch ○ perch ○ part

10. ○ such ○ shut ● shore

**Notes for Home:** Your child reviewed words spelled with *or* as in *storm*. ***Home Activity:*** Help your child make up a story using words with this vowel sound, such as *unicorn, horn, stork, popcorn,* or *boring.* Then have your child illustrate his or her story.



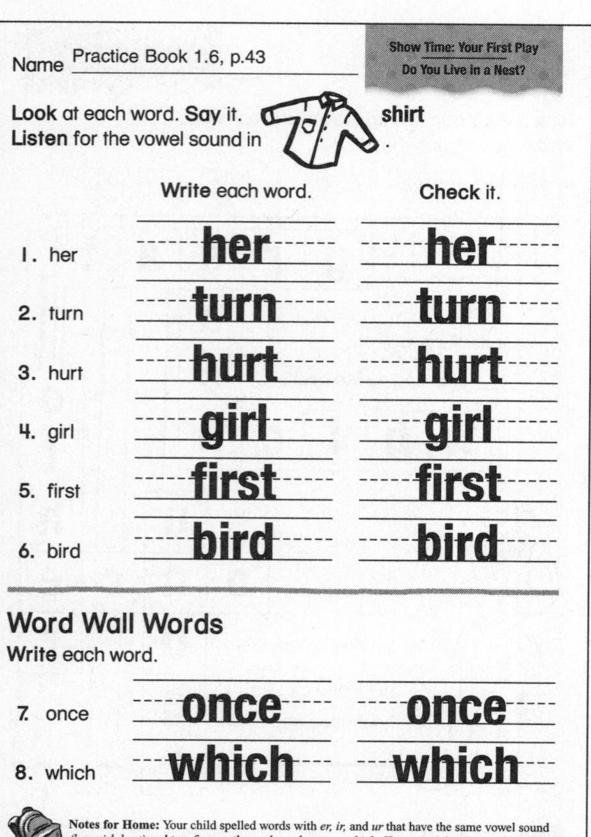

Name Practice Book 1.6, p.43

Show Time: Your First Play
Do You Live in a Nest?

**Look** at each word. **Say** it.
**Listen** for the vowel sound in shirt.

| | **Write** each word. | **Check** it. |
|---|---|---|
| 1. her | her | her |
| 2. turn | turn | turn |
| 3. hurt | hurt | hurt |
| 4. girl | girl | girl |
| 5. first | first | first |
| 6. bird | bird | bird |

**Word Wall Words**

**Write** each word.

| | | |
|---|---|---|
| 7. once | once | once |
| 8. which | which | which |

**Notes for Home:** Your child spelled words with *er, ir,* and *ur* that have the same vowel sound (*her, girl, hurt*) and two frequently used words: *once, which.* ***Home Activity:*** Say each spelling word. Have your child use it in a sentence. Then have your child write it down.

Level 1.6 Spelling: r-Controlled er, ir, ur 47

Name Practice Book 1.6, p.44

Show Time: Your First Play
Do You Live in a Nest?

**Read** each sentence.
**Circle** each sentence that is a command.

1. I got the starring part in a play!
2. Do you want to come?
3. (Please come at two.)
4. (Sit in the front row.)
5. (Bring all your friends.)
6. (Watch for the big dog.)
7. That dog will be me!

**Write** three sentences that are commands. **Possible answers given.**

8. **Go to the store.**
9. **Please come here.**
10. **Sit over there.**

**Notes for Home:** Your child identified and wrote commands (For example: *Bring me that bag.*). ***Home Activity:*** Play a version of "Simon Says" where your child follows the directions *only* if you give him or her a command. Then change roles.

48 Grammar: Commands (Imperative Sentences) Level 1.6

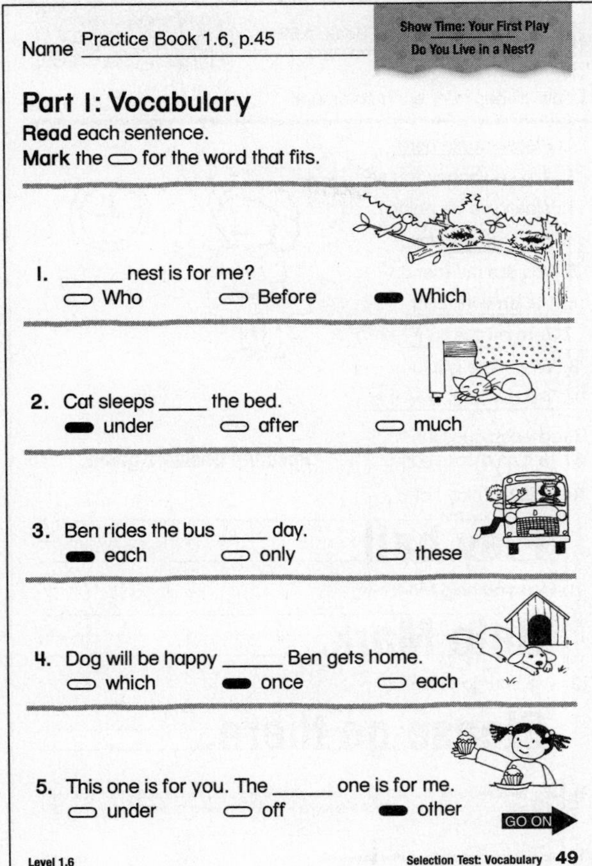

Name Practice Book 1.6, p.45

Show Time: Your First Play
Do You Live in a Nest?

## Part 1: Vocabulary

**Read** each sentence.
**Mark** the ○ for the word that fits.

1. ______ nest is for me?
○ Who ○ Before ● Which

2. Cat sleeps _____ the bed.
● under ○ after ○ much

3. Ben rides the bus _____ day.
● each ○ only ○ these

4. Dog will be happy ______ Ben gets home.
○ which ● once ○ each

5. This one is for you. The ______ one is for me.
○ under ○ off ● other

GO ON

Level 1.6 Selection Test: Vocabulary 49

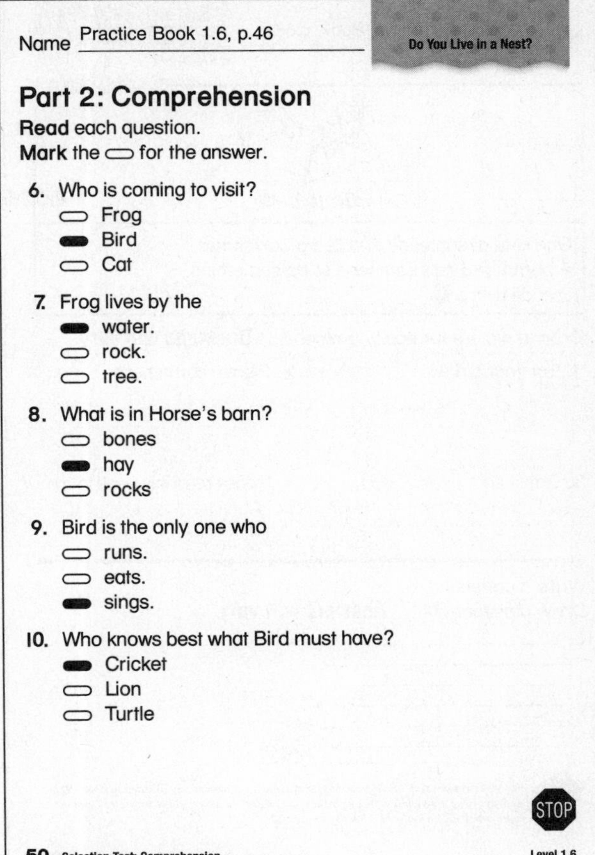

Name Practice Book 1.6, p.46

Do You Live in a Nest?

## Part 2: Comprehension

**Read** each question.
**Mark** the ○ for the answer.

6. Who is coming to visit?
○ Frog
● Bird
○ Cat

7. Frog lives by the
● water.
○ rock.
○ tree.

8. What is in Horse's barn?
○ bones
● hay
○ rocks

9. Bird is the only one who
○ runs.
○ eats.
● sings.

10. Who knows best what Bird must have?
● Cricket
○ Lion
○ Turtle

STOP

50 Selection Test: Comprehension Level 1.6

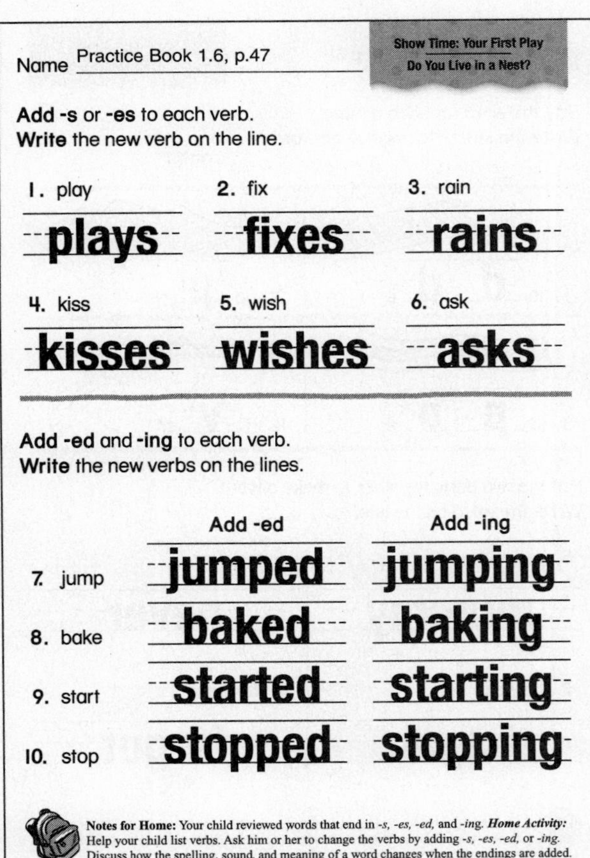

Name Practice Book 1.6, p.47

Show Time: Your First Play
Do You Live in a Nest?

**Add -s** or **-es** to each verb.
**Write** the new verb on the line.

1. play — plays
2. fix — fixes
3. rain — rains
4. kiss — kisses
5. wish — wishes
6. ask — asks

**Add -ed** and **-ing** to each verb.
**Write** the new verbs on the lines.

| | Add -ed | Add -ing |
|---|---|---|
| 7. jump | jumped | jumping |
| 8. bake | baked | baking |
| 9. start | started | starting |
| 10. stop | stopped | stopping |

**Notes for Home:** Your child reviewed words that end in *-s, -es, -ed,* and *-ing*. ***Home Activity:*** Help your child list verbs. Ask him or her to change the verbs by adding *-s, -es, -ed,* or *-ing*. Discuss how the spelling, sound, and meaning of a word changes when the endings are added.

Level 1.6 Phonics: Inflected Endings *-s, -es, -ed, -ing* Review 51

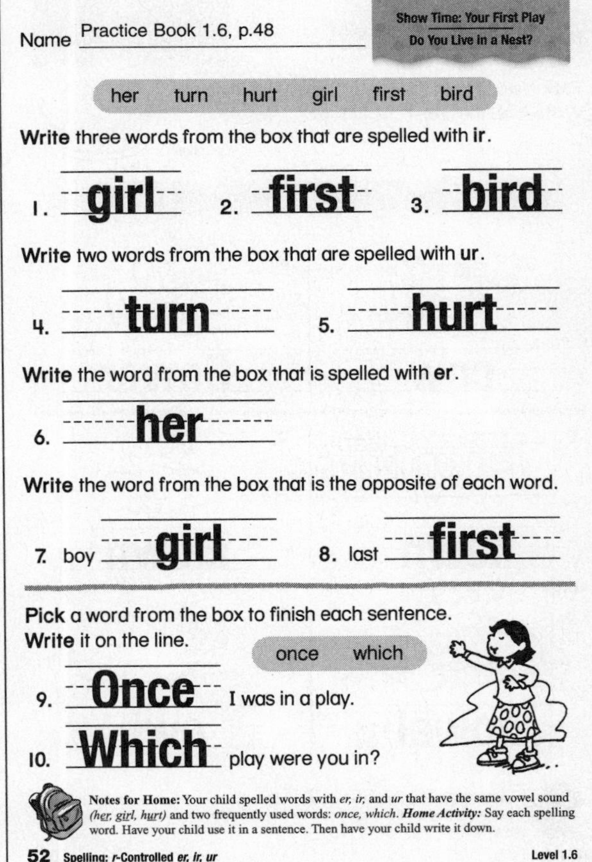

Name Practice Book 1.6, p.48

Show Time: Your First Play
Do You Live in a Nest?

her turn hurt girl first bird

**Write** three words from the box that are spelled with **ir**.

1. girl 2. first 3. bird

**Write** two words from the box that are spelled with **ur**.

4. turn 5. hurt

**Write** the word from the box that is spelled with **er**.

6. her

**Write** the word from the box that is the opposite of each word.

7. boy girl 8. last first

**Pick** a word from the box to finish each sentence.
**Write** it on the line.

once which

9. Once I was in a play.

10. Which play were you in?

**Notes for Home:** Your child spelled words with *er, ir,* and *ur* that have the same vowel sound (*her, girl, hurt*) and two frequently used words: *once, which.* ***Home Activity:*** Say each spelling word. Have your child use it in a sentence. Then have your child write it down.

52 Spelling: *r*-Controlled *er, ir, ur* Level 1.6

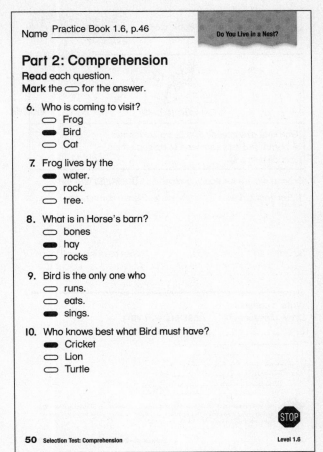

Name Grammar Practice Book, p.58

Show Time: Your First Play
Do You Live in a Nest?

RETEACHING

Go to bed.

One kind of sentence is called a **command**.
A **command** tells someone to do something.
It ends with a ▪.

**Draw** a picture for each command. **Drawings will vary.**

1. Eat your dinner.
2. Please come here.
3. Get in line.
4. Please read this book to me.

**Write** a command.
**Draw** a picture of it. **Answers will vary.**

5. ______

**Notes for Home:** Your child showed understanding of commands by illustrating them. ***Home Activity:*** Have your child write commands that lead to a treasure. *(Take ten steps. Open the cupboard. Look on the shelf. Find the cookie.)*



Name Grammar Practice Book, p.59

Show Time: Your First Play
Do You Live in a Nest?

**Draw** a line under each command.

1. Please come here.
2. Are you happy today?
3. When are we going?
4. Help me with this.
5. You are my friend.
6. Put on your coat.
7. Turn off the light.
8. What time is it?
9. Tell me what time it is.

**Read** each question.
**Write** it as a command. **Possible answers given.**

10. Will you play ball?
**Play ball.**

11. Can you help Mark?
**Help Mark.**

12. Will you go there?
**Please go there.**

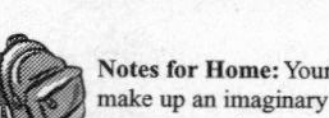

**Notes for Home:** Your child identified and wrote commands. ***Home Activity:*** Have your child make up an imaginary pet. Then help him or her write commands for the pet. *(Come here. Eat your carrots.)*



Name Practice Book 1.6, p.51

What's New/Class
Fox on Stage

**Pick** a word from the box to match each picture.
**Write** it on the line.

crown

clown cow flower owl towel town

1.  **cow**
2.  **flower**
3.  **town**
4.  **clown**
5.  **towel**
6.  **owl**

**Notes for Home:** Your child read and wrote words with *ow* that have the vowel sound heard in *crown*. ***Home Activity:*** Encourage your child to think of other words with *ow* that rhyme with *cow* and *brown*.



Name Practice Book 1.6, p.52

What's New/Class
Fox on Stage

**Say** the word for each picture.
**Write** the letters to finish each word.

rabbit

1. la **d d** er

2. pa **p** er

3. zi **p p** er

4. ri **v** er

**Put** the two parts together to make a word.
**Write** the word on the line.

5. mum · my **mummy**
6. nev · er **never**
7. be · gan **began**
8. for · got **forgot**

**Notes for Home:** Your child practiced reading and writing two-syllable words. ***Home Activity:*** Look in your refrigerator. Name different items in the refrigerator. Decide whether each name has one syllable or more than one syllable.

Name Practice Book 1.6, p.53

What's New/Class
Fox on Stage

**Pick** a word from the box to finish each sentence.
**Write** it on the line.

along goes great idea pull

1. We have a **great** big dog.
2. He **goes** outside to play.
3. We run **along** the fence.
4. We have a good **idea**.
5. He can **pull** the wagon.

**Notes for Home:** This week your child is learning to read the words *along, goes, great, idea,* and *pull. Home Activity:* Help your child write sentences that contain each of these words. Ask your child to draw pictures showing what happens in each sentence.

Level 1.6 High-Frequency Words 59

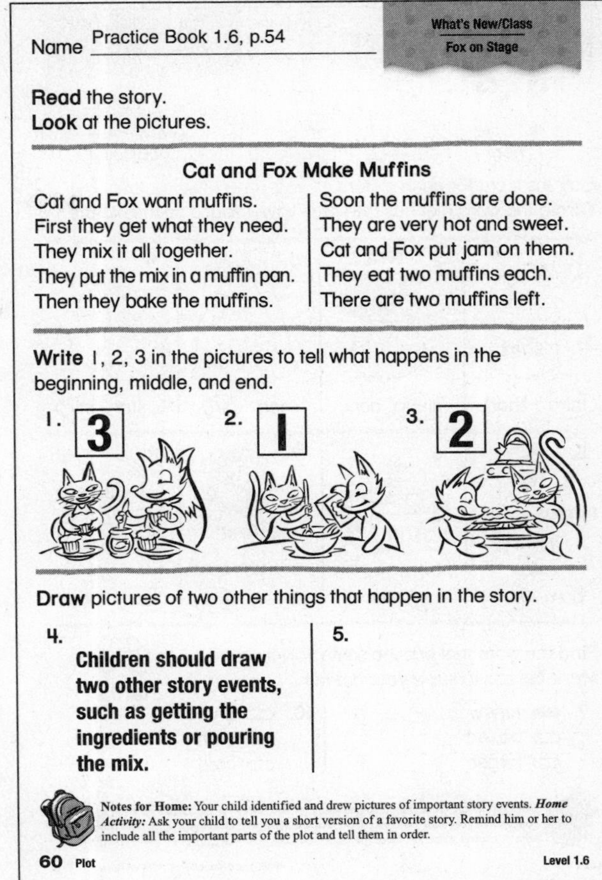

Name Practice Book 1.6, p.54

What's New/Class
Fox on Stage

**Read** the story.
**Look** at the pictures.

**Cat and Fox Make Muffins**

Cat and Fox want muffins.
First they get what they need.
They mix it all together.
They put the mix in a muffin pan.
Then they bake the muffins.
Soon the muffins are done.
They are very hot and sweet.
Cat and Fox put jam on them.
They eat two muffins each.
There are two muffins left.

**Write** 1, 2, 3 in the pictures to tell what happens in the beginning, middle, and end.

1. **3** 2. **1** 3. **2**

**Draw** pictures of two other things that happen in the story.

4. 5.

**Children should draw two other story events, such as getting the ingredients or pouring the mix.**

**Notes for Home:** Your child identified and drew pictures of important story events. *Home Activity:* Ask your child to tell you a short version of a favorite story. Remind him or her to include all the important parts of the plot and tell them in order.

60 Plot Level 1.6

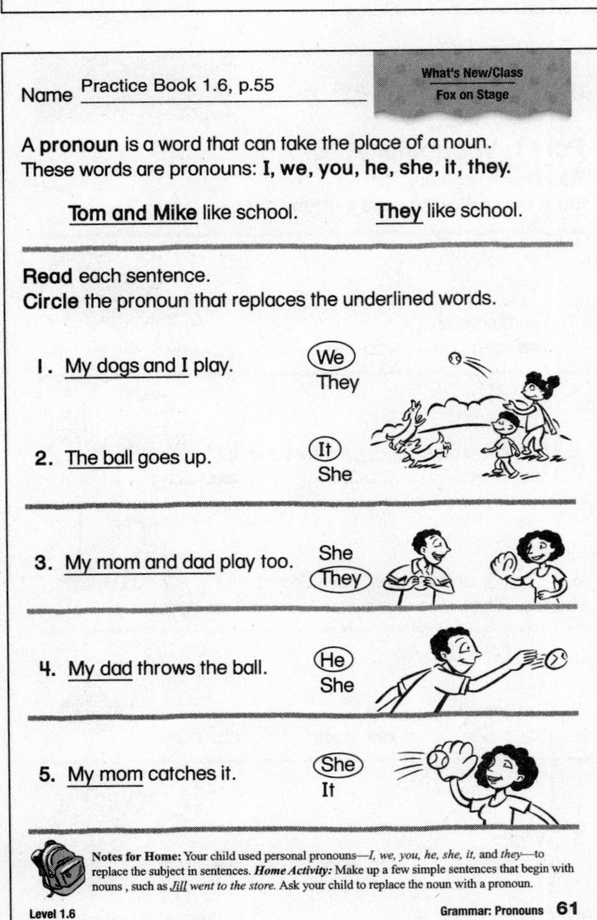

Name Practice Book 1.6, p.55

What's New/Class
Fox on Stage

A **pronoun** is a word that can take the place of a noun.
These words are pronouns: **I, we, you, he, she, it, they.**

<u>Tom and Mike</u> like school. <u>They</u> like school.

**Read** each sentence.
**Circle** the pronoun that replaces the underlined words.

1. <u>My dogs and I</u> play. (We) They
2. <u>The ball</u> goes up. (It) She
3. <u>My mom and dad</u> play too. She (They)
4. <u>My dad</u> throws the ball. (He) She
5. <u>My mom</u> catches it. (She) It

**Notes for Home:** Your child used personal pronouns—*I, we, you, he, she, it,* and *they*—to replace the subject in sentences. *Home Activity:* Make up a few simple sentences that begin with nouns, such as *<u>Jill</u> went to the store.* Ask your child to replace the noun with a pronoun.

Level 1.6 Grammar: Pronouns 61

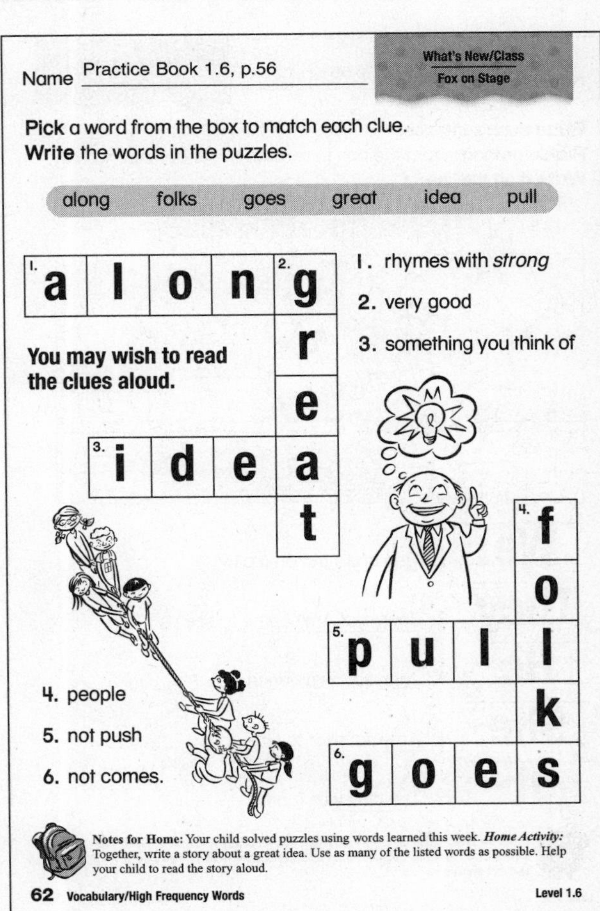

Name Practice Book 1.6, p.56

What's New/Class
Fox on Stage

**Pick** a word from the box to match each clue.
**Write** the words in the puzzles.

along folks goes great idea pull

1. rhymes with *strong*
2. very good
3. something you think of

**You may wish to read the clues aloud.**

4. people
5. not push
6. not comes.

1. along 2. great 3. idea 4. folks 5. pull 6. goes

**Notes for Home:** Your child solved puzzles using words learned this week. *Home Activity:* Together, write a story about a great idea. Use as many of the listed words as possible. Help your child to read the story aloud.

62 Vocabulary/High Frequency Words Level 1.6

Name Practice Book 1.6, p.57

What's New/Class?
Fox on Stage

her bird curtain

**Say** the word for each picture.
**Circle** the word that has the same vowel sound as the picture.

1. shirt — (third) short
2. fern — (clerk) cork
3. skirt — dart (dirt)
4. bird — star (stir)
5. nurse — barn (surf)
6. herd — (her) harm
7. first — forest (girl)
8. purse — (turn) track

**Find** the word that has the same vowel sound as turtle.
**Mark** the ⬭ to show your answer.

9. ⬬ turkey
⬭ basket
⬭ target

10. ⬭ brand
⬬ burn
⬭ card

**Notes for Home:** Your child reviewed words spelled with *er, ir,* and *ur* that have the same vowel sound (*her, bird, curtain*). ***Home Activity:*** Help your child make up rhymes using words with this vowel sound and these spellings *(You can't wear that shirt. It is covered in dirt!).*

Level 1.6 Phonics: *r*-Controlled *er, ir, ur* Review 63

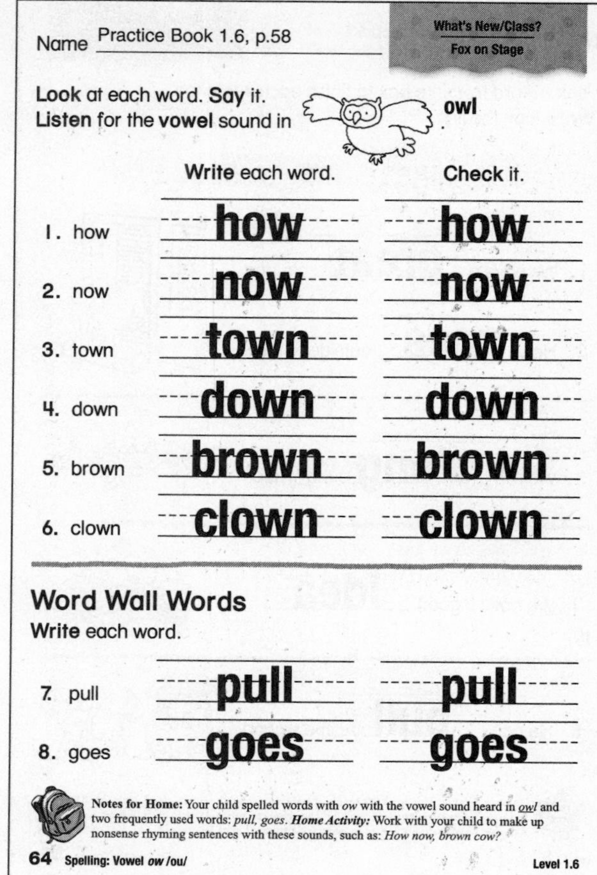

Name Practice Book 1.6, p.58

What's New/Class?
Fox on Stage

**Look** at each word. **Say** it.
**Listen** for the **vowel** sound in owl.

| | Write each word. | Check it. |
|---|---|---|
| 1. how | how | how |
| 2. now | now | now |
| 3. town | town | town |
| 4. down | down | down |
| 5. brown | brown | brown |
| 6. clown | clown | clown |

**Word Wall Words**
**Write** each word.

| | | |
|---|---|---|
| 7. pull | pull | pull |
| 8. goes | goes | goes |

**Notes for Home:** Your child spelled words with *ow* with the vowel sound heard in *owl* and two frequently used words: *pull, goes.* ***Home Activity:*** Work with your child to make up nonsense rhyming sentences with these sounds, such as: *How now, brown cow?*

64 Spelling: Vowel *ow* /ou/ Level 1.6

Name Practice Book 1.6, p.59

What's New/Class?
Fox on Stage

**Read** each sentence.
**Pick** a pronoun from the box to replace the underlined words.
**Write** it on the line.

he it she they we

We 1. Bob and I put on a play.
They 2. John and Amy came to see us.
He 3. John sat on a bench.
She 4. Amy sat next to him.
It 5. The play was funny.

**Notes for Home:** Your child replaced nouns with pronouns in sentences. ***Home Activity:*** Read a story with your child. Point out the pronouns and ask your child what person, place, or thing each pronoun represents.

Level 1.6 Grammar: Pronouns 65

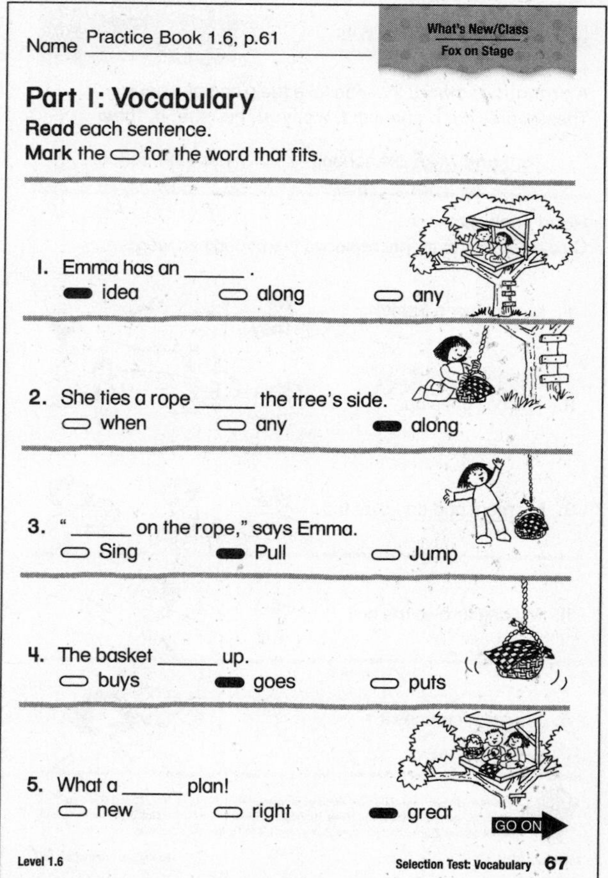

Name Practice Book 1.6, p.61

What's New/Class
Fox on Stage

**Part 1: Vocabulary**
**Read** each sentence.
**Mark** the ⬭ for the word that fits.

1. Emma has an ______ .
⬬ idea ⬭ along ⬭ any

2. She ties a rope ______ the tree's side.
⬭ when ⬭ any ⬬ along

3. " ______ on the rope," says Emma.
⬭ Sing ⬬ Pull ⬭ Jump

4. The basket ______ up.
⬭ buys ⬬ goes ⬭ puts

5. What a ______ plan!
⬭ new ⬭ right ⬬ great

GO ON

Level 1.6 Selection Test: Vocabulary 67

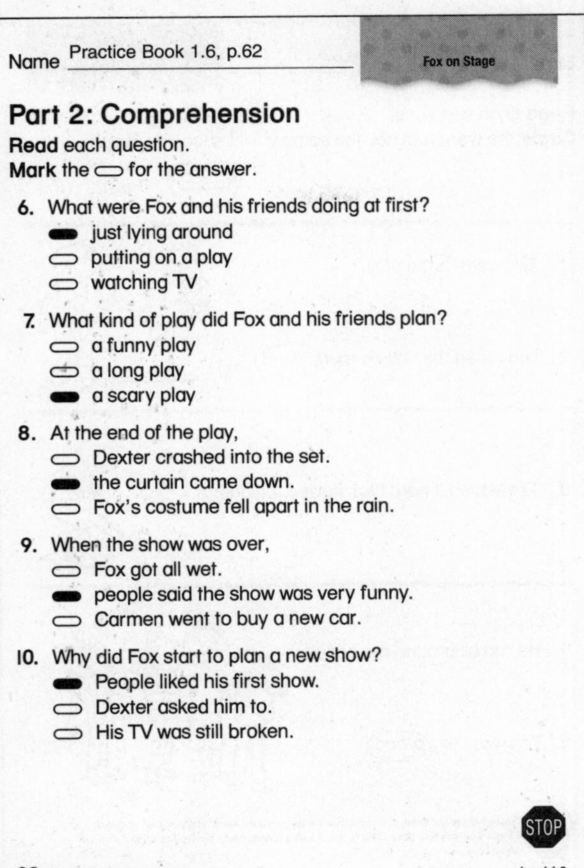
Name Practice Book 1.6, p.62

Fox on Stage

## Part 2: Comprehension

**Read** each question.
**Mark** the ⬭ for the answer.

6. What were Fox and his friends doing at first?
   - ⬬ just lying around
   - ⬭ putting on a play
   - ⬭ watching TV
7. What kind of play did Fox and his friends plan?
   - ⬭ a funny play
   - ⬭ a long play
   - ⬬ a scary play
8. At the end of the play,
   - ⬭ Dexter crashed into the set.
   - ⬬ the curtain came down.
   - ⬭ Fox's costume fell apart in the rain.
9. When the show was over,
   - ⬭ Fox got all wet.
   - ⬬ people said the show was very funny.
   - ⬭ Carmen went to buy a new car.
10. Why did Fox start to plan a new show?
   - ⬬ People liked his first show.
   - ⬭ Dexter asked him to.
   - ⬭ His TV was still broken.

STOP

68 Selection Test: Comprehension Level 1.6

Name Practice Book 1.6, p.63

What's New/Class? Fox on Stage

**Look** at each picture.
**Add 's** to a word to tell who owns something.
**Write** the new word on the line.



1. **Mom's** mug
2. **baby's** bib
3. **Sue's** room
4. **Fox's** chair
5. **Bob's** ball
6. **Rex's** dish

**Find** the words that tell who owns something.
**Mark** the ⬭ to show your answer.

7. ⬭ Mom gems
   ⬬ Mom's gems
   ⬭ Moms gems
8. ⬭ Dad tie
   ⬭ Dads tie
   ⬬ Dad's tie

**Notes for Home:** Your child used *'s* to tell who owns something. ***Home Activity:*** Draw pictures with your child of objects that someone in your family owns. Help your child label each picture, such as *the cat's dish* or *the baby's crib.*

Level 1.6 Phonics: -'s Possessives Review 69

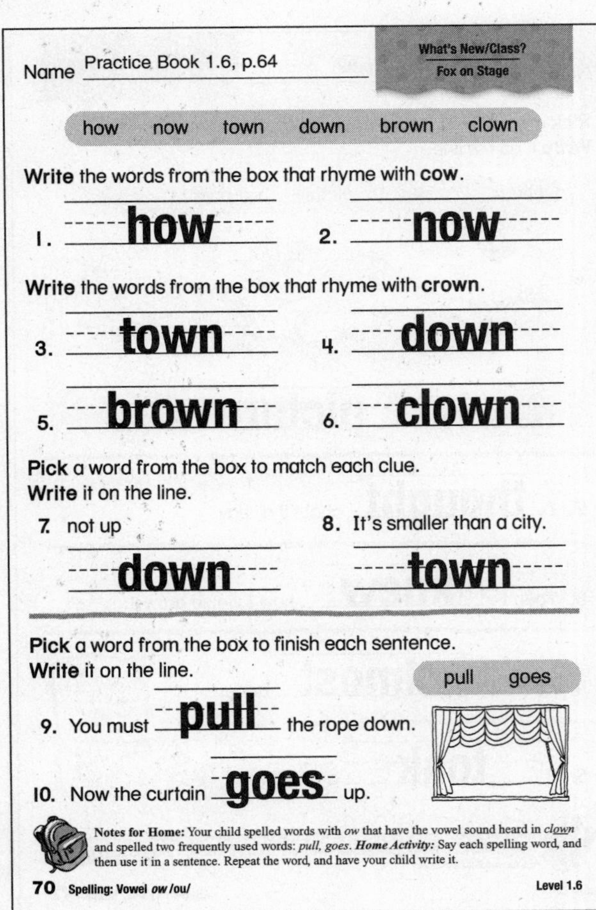
Name Practice Book 1.6, p.64

What's New/Class? Fox on Stage

how now town down brown clown

**Write** the words from the box that rhyme with **cow**.

1. **how**
2. **now**

**Write** the words from the box that rhyme with **crown**.

3. **town**
4. **down**
5. **brown**
6. **clown**

**Pick** a word from the box to match each clue.
**Write** it on the line.

7. not up **down**
8. It's smaller than a city. **town**

**Pick** a word from the box to finish each sentence.
**Write** it on the line.

pull goes

9. You must **pull** the rope down.
10. Now the curtain **goes** up.

**Notes for Home:** Your child spelled words with *ow* that have the vowel sound heard in *clown* and spelled two frequently used words: *pull, goes.* ***Home Activity:*** Say each spelling word, and then use it in a sentence. Repeat the word, and have your child write it.

70 Spelling: Vowel *ow* /ou/ Level 1.6

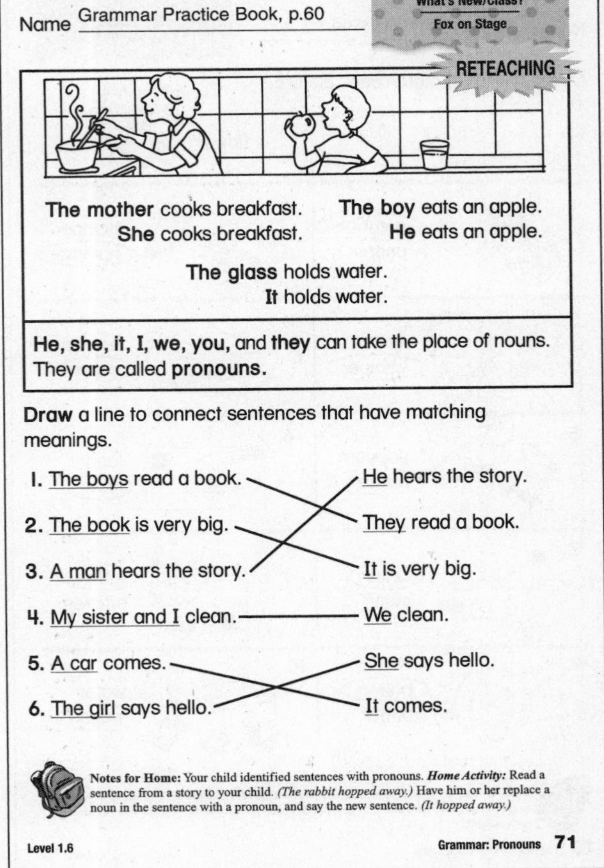
Name Grammar Practice Book, p.60

What's New/Class? Fox on Stage

RETEACHING

**The mother** cooks breakfast.
**She** cooks breakfast.

**The boy** eats an apple.
**He** eats an apple.

**The glass** holds water.
**It** holds water.

**He, she, it, I, we, you,** and **they** can take the place of nouns. They are called **pronouns.**

**Draw** a line to connect sentences that have matching meanings.

1. The boys read a book. — They read a book.
2. The book is very big. — It is very big.
3. A man hears the story. — He hears the story.
4. My sister and I clean. — We clean.
5. A car comes. — It comes.
6. The girl says hello. — She says hello.

**Notes for Home:** Your child identified sentences with pronouns. ***Home Activity:*** Read a sentence from a story to your child. *(The rabbit hopped away.)* Have him or her replace a noun in the sentence with a pronoun, and say the new sentence. *(It hopped away.)*

Level 1.6 Grammar: Pronouns 71

Name Grammar Practice Book, p.61

What's New/Class?
Fox on Stage

**Circle** the correct word in each box.
**Write** it in each sentence.

I (me)

1. Sally sees Mrs. Bear and **me**.

(We) it

2. **We** say hello to Sally.

(It) They

3. **It** is big and dark.

**Notes for Home:** Your child wrote pronouns in sentences. ***Home Activity:*** Have your child write a short poem about two animals or people. Challenge him or her to use pronouns in the poem.

72 Grammar: Pronouns Level 1.6

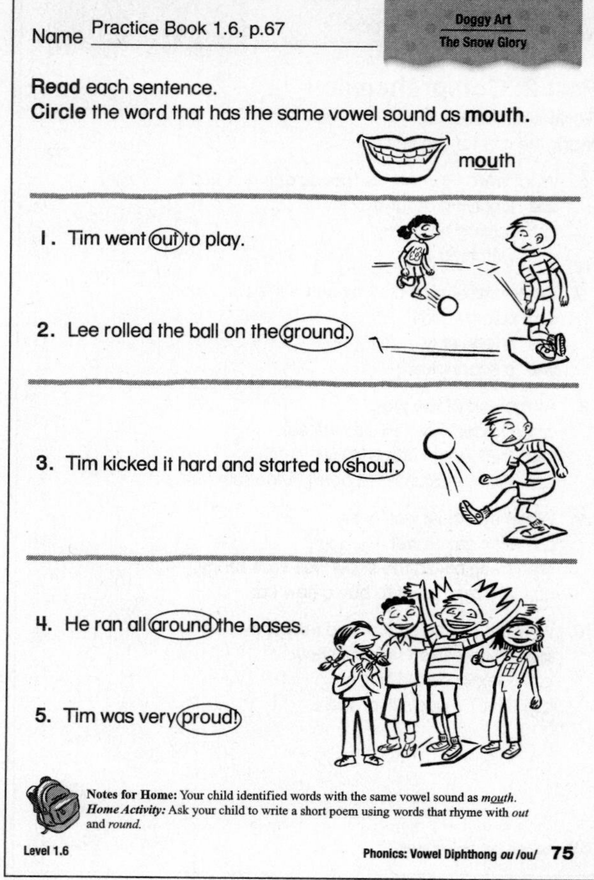

Name Practice Book 1.6, p.67

Doggy Art
The Snow Glory

**Read** each sentence.
**Circle** the word that has the same vowel sound as **mouth.**

mouth

1. Tim went (out) to play.

2. Lee rolled the ball on the (ground).

3. Tim kicked it hard and started to (shout).

4. He ran all (around) the bases.

5. Tim was very (proud)!

**Notes for Home:** Your child identified words with the same vowel sound as *mouth*. ***Home Activity:*** Ask your child to write a short poem using words that rhyme with *out* and *round.*

Level 1.6 Phonics: Vowel Diphthong *ou* /ou/ 75

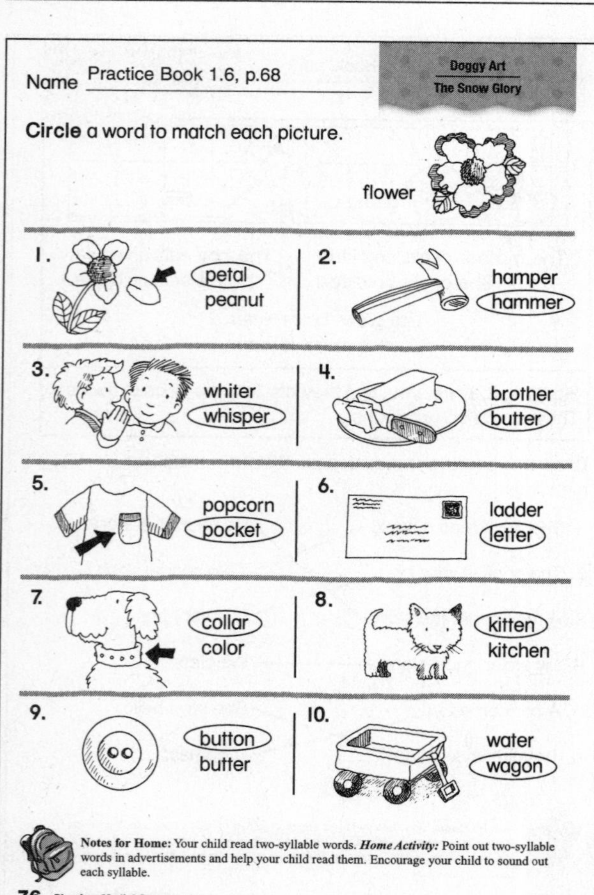

Name Practice Book 1.6, p.68

Doggy Art
The Snow Glory

**Circle** a word to match each picture.

flower

1. (petal) peanut
2. hamper (hammer)
3. whiter (whisper)
4. brother (butter)
5. popcorn (pocket)
6. ladder (letter)
7. (collar) color
8. (kitten) kitchen
9. (button) butter
10. water (wagon)

**Notes for Home:** Your child read two-syllable words. ***Home Activity:*** Point out two-syllable words in advertisements and help your child read them. Encourage your child to sound out each syllable.

76 Phonics: Medial Consonants Level 1.6

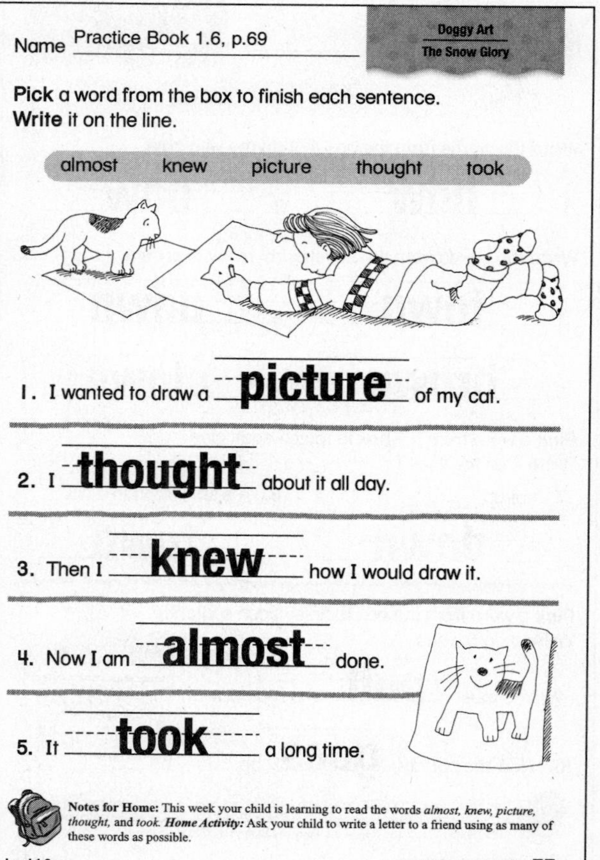

Name Practice Book 1.6, p.69

Doggy Art
The Snow Glory

**Pick** a word from the box to finish each sentence.
**Write** it on the line.

almost knew picture thought took

1. I wanted to draw a **picture** of my cat.

2. I **thought** about it all day.

3. Then I **knew** how I would draw it.

4. Now I am **almost** done.

5. It **took** a long time.

**Notes for Home:** This week your child is learning to read the words *almost, knew, picture, thought,* and *took.* ***Home Activity:*** Ask your child to write a letter to a friend using as many of these words as possible.

Level 1.6 High-Frequency Words 77

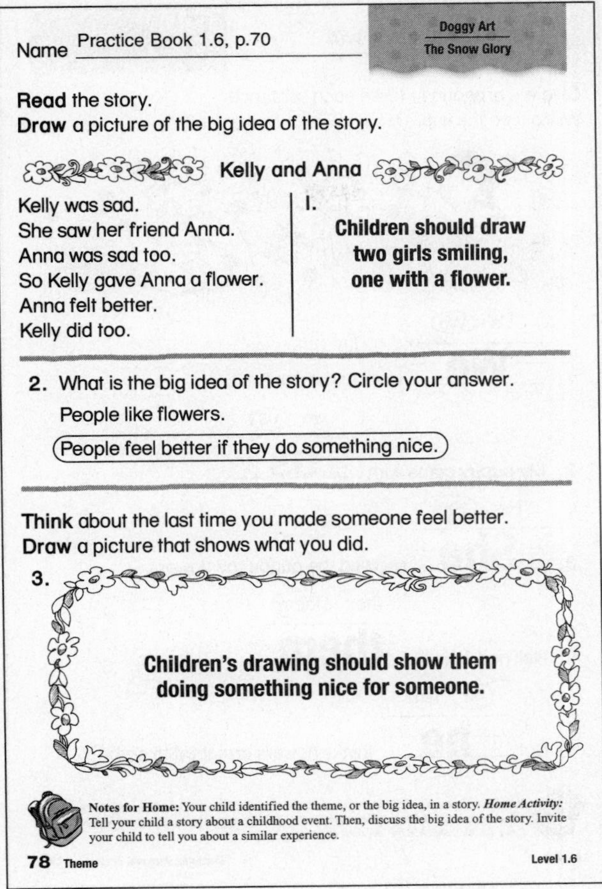

Name Practice Book 1.6, p.70

Doggy Art
The Snow Glory

**Read** the story.
**Draw** a picture of the big idea of the story.

Kelly and Anna

Kelly was sad.
She saw her friend Anna.
Anna was sad too.
So Kelly gave Anna a flower.
Anna felt better.
Kelly did too.

1. **Children should draw two girls smiling, one with a flower.**

2. What is the big idea of the story? Circle your answer.
People like flowers.
(People feel better if they do something nice.)

**Think** about the last time you made someone feel better.
**Draw** a picture that shows what you did.

3. **Children's drawing should show them doing something nice for someone.**

**Notes for Home:** Your child identified the theme, or the big idea, in a story. *Home Activity:* Tell your child a story about a childhood event. Then, discuss the big idea of the story. Invite your child to tell you about a similar experience.

78 Theme Level 1.6

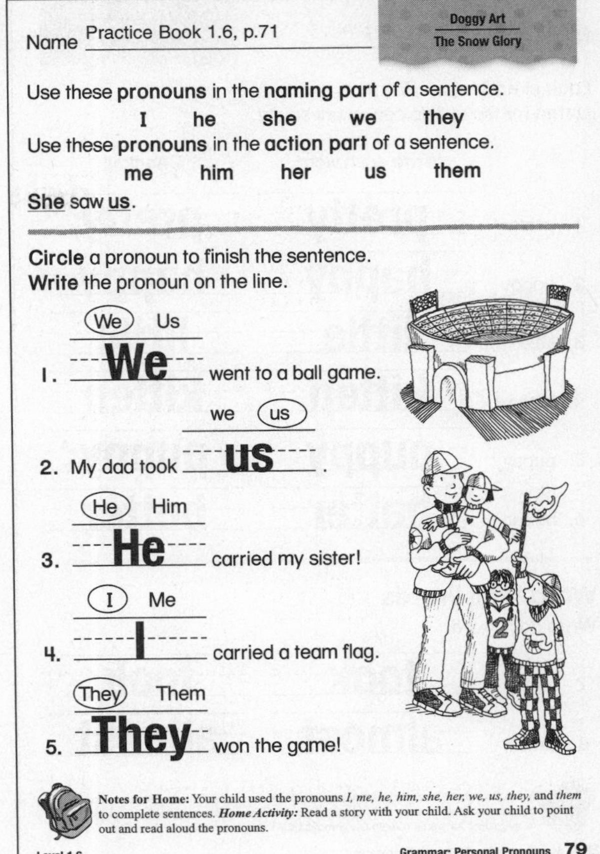

Name Practice Book 1.6, p.71

Doggy Art
The Snow Glory

Use these **pronouns** in the **naming part** of a sentence.
**I he she we they**
Use these **pronouns** in the **action part** of a sentence.
**me him her us them**
She saw us.

**Circle** a pronoun to finish the sentence.
**Write** the pronoun on the line.

(We) Us
1. **We** went to a ball game.

we (us)
2. My dad took **us**.

(He) Him
3. **He** carried my sister!

(I) Me
4. **I** carried a team flag.

(They) Them
5. **They** won the game!

**Notes for Home:** Your child used the pronouns *I, me, he, him, she, her, we, us, they,* and *them* to complete sentences. *Home Activity:* Read a story with your child. Ask your child to point out and read aloud the pronouns.

Level 1.6 Grammar: Personal Pronouns 79

Name Practice Book 1.6, p.72

Doggy Art
The Snow Glory

**Pick** a word from the box that means the opposite.
**Write** it on the line.

almost knew picture stood thought took

1. sat **stood**
2. gave **took**

**Pick** a word from the box to match each clue.
**Write** it on the line.

3. You can find *most* hidden here. **almost**
4. It sounds like *new*. **knew**
5. It is what you think. **thought**
6. You may see this in a book. **picture**

**Notes for Home:** Your child found words that mean the opposite and answered clues. *Home Activity:* Take turns saying a word and giving a word that means the opposite.

80 Vocabulary/High-Frequency Words Level 1.6

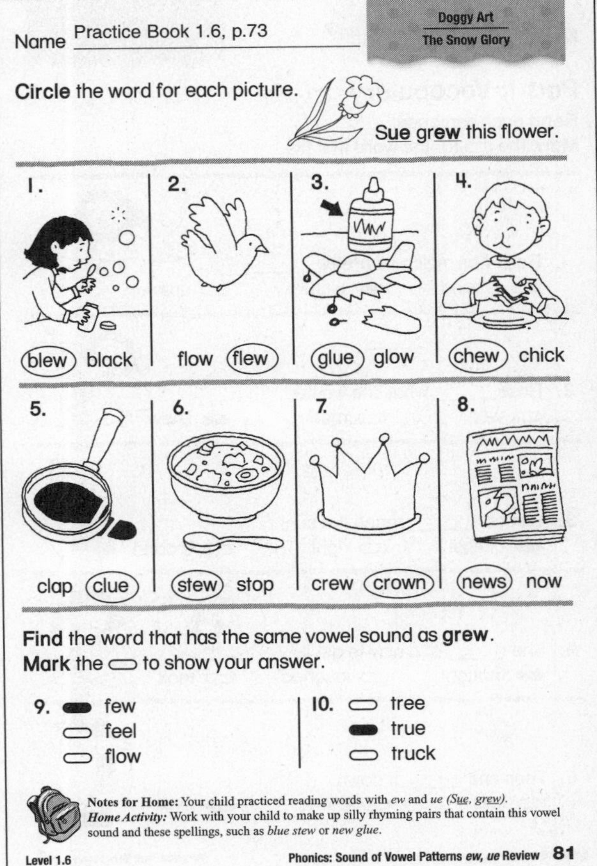

Name Practice Book 1.6, p.73

Doggy Art
The Snow Glory

**Circle** the word for each picture.

Sue grew this flower.

1. (blew) black
2. flow (flew)
3. (glue) glow
4. (chew) chick
5. clap (clue)
6. (stew) stop
7. crew (crown)
8. (news) now

**Find** the word that has the same vowel sound as **grew**.
**Mark** the ⊂⊃ to show your answer.

9. ● few
○ feel
○ flow

10. ○ tree
● true
○ truck

**Notes for Home:** Your child practiced reading words with *ew* and *ue* (*Sue, grew*). *Home Activity:* Work with your child to make up silly rhyming pairs that contain this vowel sound and these spellings, such as *blue stew* or *new glue.*

Level 1.6 Phonics: Sound of Vowel Patterns *ew, ue* Review 81

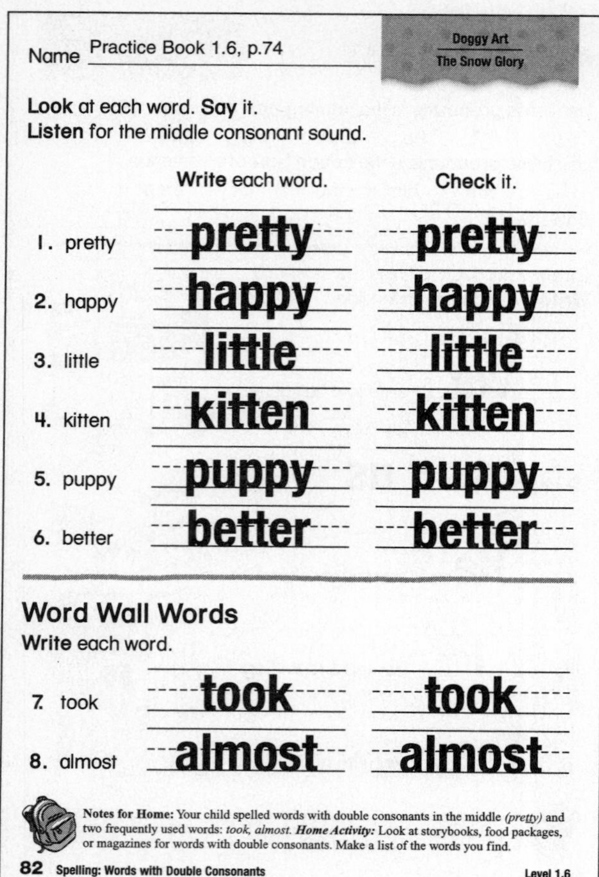

Name Practice Book 1.6, p.74

Doggy Art
The Snow Glory

**Look** at each word. **Say** it.
**Listen** for the middle consonant sound.

| | **Write** each word. | **Check** it. |
|---|---|---|
| 1. pretty | pretty | pretty |
| 2. happy | happy | happy |
| 3. little | little | little |
| 4. kitten | kitten | kitten |
| 5. puppy | puppy | puppy |
| 6. better | better | better |

## Word Wall Words

**Write** each word.

| | | |
|---|---|---|
| 7. took | took | took |
| 8. almost | almost | almost |

**Notes for Home:** Your child spelled words with double consonants in the middle *(pretty)* and two frequently used words: *took, almost.* ***Home Activity:*** Look at storybooks, food packages, or magazines for words with double consonants. Make a list of the words you find.

82 Spelling: Words with Double Consonants Level 1.6

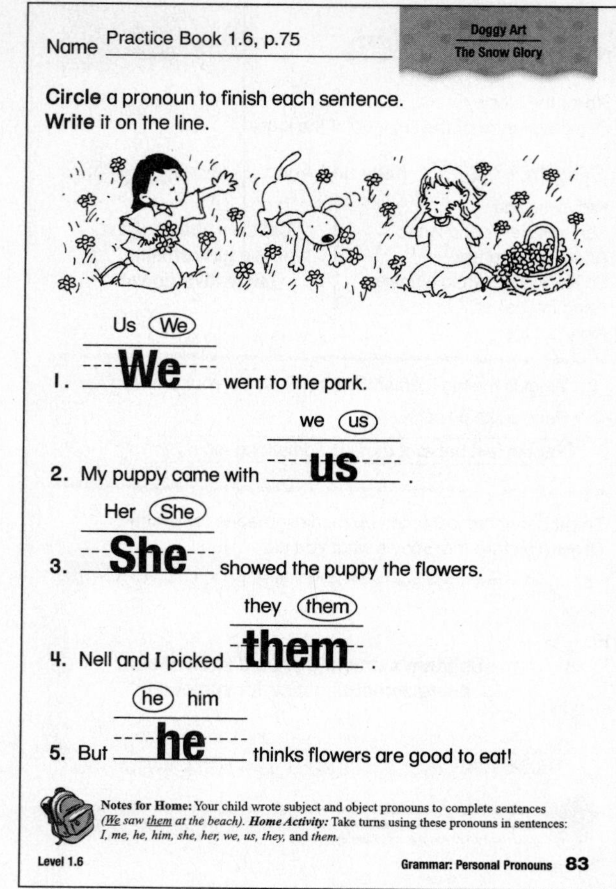

Name Practice Book 1.6, p.75

Doggy Art
The Snow Glory

**Circle** a pronoun to finish each sentence.
**Write** it on the line.

Us (We)
1. We went to the park.

we (us)
2. My puppy came with us.

Her (She)
3. She showed the puppy the flowers.

they (them)
4. Nell and I picked them.

(he) him
5. But he thinks flowers are good to eat!

**Notes for Home:** Your child wrote subject and object pronouns to complete sentences *(We saw them at the beach).* ***Home Activity:*** Take turns using these pronouns in sentences: *I, me, he, him, she, her, we, us, they,* and *them.*

Level 1.6 Grammar: Personal Pronouns 83

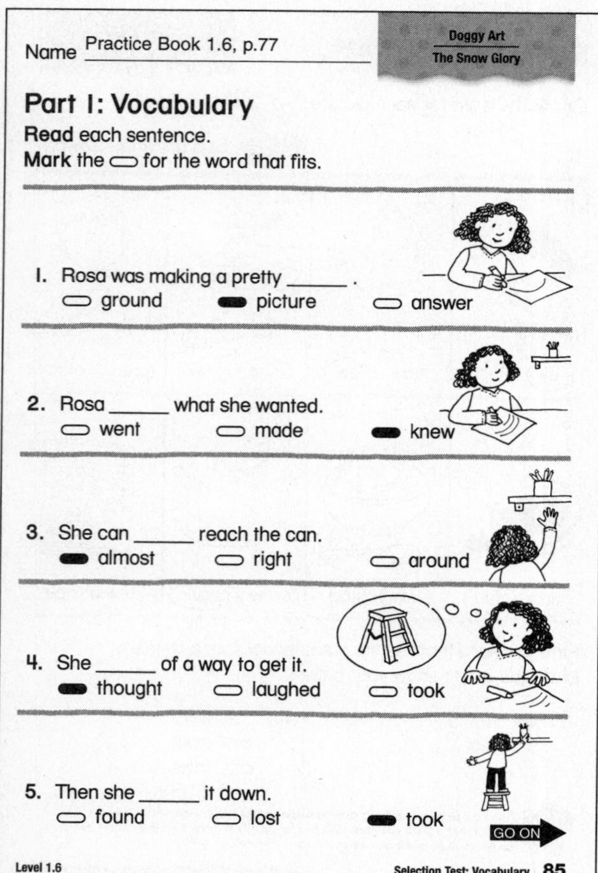

Name Practice Book 1.6, p.77

Doggy Art
The Snow Glory

## Part 1: Vocabulary

**Read** each sentence.
**Mark** the ⬭ for the word that fits.

1. Rosa was making a pretty _____ .
   - ⬭ ground
   - ● picture
   - ⬭ answer

2. Rosa _____ what she wanted.
   - ⬭ went
   - ⬭ made
   - ● knew

3. She can _____ reach the can.
   - ● almost
   - ⬭ right
   - ⬭ around

4. She _____ of a way to get it.
   - ● thought
   - ⬭ laughed
   - ⬭ took

5. Then she _____ it down.
   - ⬭ found
   - ⬭ lost
   - ● took

GO ON

Level 1.6 Selection Test: Vocabulary 85

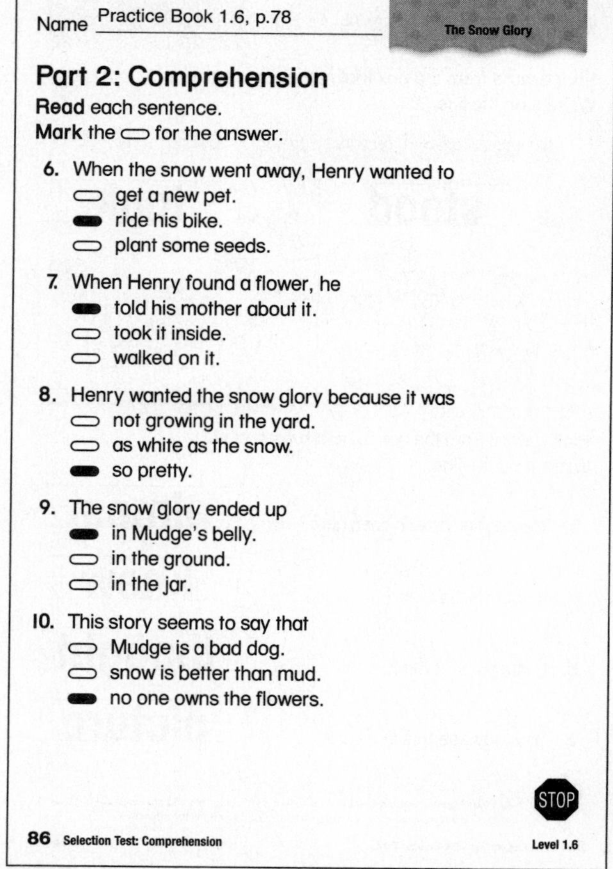

Name Practice Book 1.6, p.78

The Snow Glory

## Part 2: Comprehension

**Read** each sentence.
**Mark** the ⬭ for the answer.

6. When the snow went away, Henry wanted to
   - ⬭ get a new pet.
   - ● ride his bike.
   - ⬭ plant some seeds.

7. When Henry found a flower, he
   - ● told his mother about it.
   - ⬭ took it inside.
   - ⬭ walked on it.

8. Henry wanted the snow glory because it was
   - ⬭ not growing in the yard.
   - ⬭ as white as the snow.
   - ● so pretty.

9. The snow glory ended up
   - ● in Mudge's belly.
   - ⬭ in the ground.
   - ⬭ in the jar.

10. This story seems to say that
    - ⬭ Mudge is a bad dog.
    - ⬭ snow is better than mud.
    - ● no one owns the flowers.

STOP

86 Selection Test: Comprehension Level 1.6

Name Practice Book 1.6, p.79

Doggy Art
The Snow Glory

**Circle** the word for each picture.

tall taller tallest

1. (fatter) fattest
2. thinner (thinnest)
3. younger (youngest)
4. older (oldest)
5. (smaller) smallest
6. (colder) coldest

**Find** the word that could be used to compare **two** things.
**Mark** the ⊂⊃ to show your answer.

7. ⊂⊃ warm
   ● warmer
   ⊂⊃ warmest

8. ⊂⊃ loud
   ● louder
   ⊂⊃ loudest

**Notes for Home:** Your child reviewed words with the comparative endings *-er* and *-est*. *Home Activity:* With your child, look at family photos or photos in a magazine. Ask your child to compare people or objects in the photos using words with *-er* and *-est* endings.

Level 1.6 Phonics: Comparative Endings *-er, -est* Review 87

Name Practice Book 1.6, p.80

Doggy Art
The Snow Glory

pretty happy little kitten puppy better

**Write** four words from the box that have the letters **tt**.

1. pretty
2. little
3. kitten
4. better

**Write** two words from the box that have the letters **pp**.

5. happy
6. puppy

**Pick** a word from the box to match each clue.
**Write** it on the line.

7. a baby cat kitten
8. not big little

**Pick** a word from the box to finish each sentence.
**Write** it on the line.

took almost

9. The dog almost ate the flower.
10. The boy took it away from the dog.

**Notes for Home:** Your child practiced spelling words with double consonants in the middle (*pretty*) and two frequently-used words: *took, almost. Home Activity:* Together, make up a story about a kitten and a puppy using these spelling words. Help your child write the story.

88 Spelling: Words with Double Consonants Level 1.6

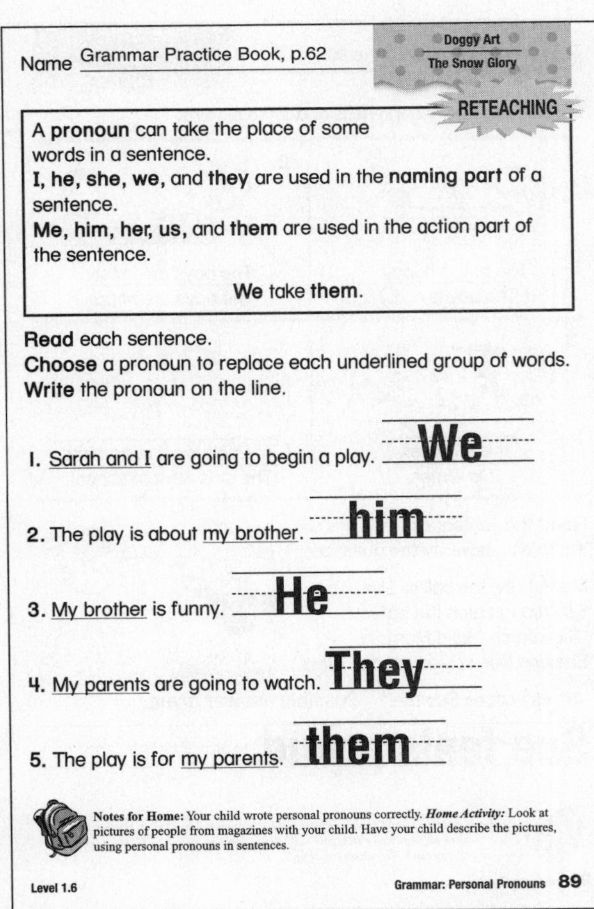

Name Grammar Practice Book, p.62

Doggy Art
The Snow Glory

RETEACHING

A **pronoun** can take the place of some words in a sentence.
**I, he, she, we,** and **they** are used in the **naming part** of a sentence.
**Me, him, her, us,** and **them** are used in the action part of the sentence.

**We** take **them.**

**Read** each sentence.
**Choose** a pronoun to replace each underlined group of words.
**Write** the pronoun on the line.

1. Sarah and I are going to begin a play. We
2. The play is about my brother. him
3. My brother is funny. He
4. My parents are going to watch. They
5. The play is for my parents. them

**Notes for Home:** Your child wrote personal pronouns correctly. *Home Activity:* Look at pictures of people from magazines with your child. Have your child describe the pictures, using personal pronouns in sentences.

Level 1.6 Grammar: Personal Pronouns 89

Name Grammar Practice Book, p.63

Doggy Art
The Snow Glory

**Read** each sentence.
**Circle** the correct word in ( ).
**Write** it on the line.

1. ((I)/me) got a snake today. I
2. A man told (I/(me)) about the snake. me
3. ((We)/It) looked at the snake. We
4. The snake looked at (her/(us)). us
5. I gave water to ((it)/me). it

**Notes for Home:** Your child wrote personal pronouns that fit in sentences. *Home Activity:* Together, find personal pronouns in a favorite story. Then have your child make up new sentences, using the personal pronouns from the story.

90 Grammar: Personal Pronouns Level 1.6

Name Practice Book 1.6, p.83

I'll Join You
Leon and Bob

**Circle** the word for each picture.

The boy makes a noise.

1. tie (toy)
2. (soil) sail
3. (joy) jay
4. bays (boys)
5. paint (point)
6. (coil) cold
7. (oil) owl
8. (boil) ball

**Draw** a picture for each word.

9. coin — **Children should draw a coin.**

10. toys — **Children should draw more than one toy.**

**Notes for Home:** Your child practiced reading words with *oi* and *oy (coin, boy)*. ***Home Activity:*** Write the words above with *oi* and *oy* on slips of paper. Have your child pick a word and use it in a sentence.

Level 1.6 Phonics: Vowel Diphthongs *oi, oy* 93

Name Practice Book 1.6, p.84

I'll Join You
Leon and Bob

**Circle** a word in ( ) to finish each sentence.

walking

1. Bob ate his (broken/(breakfast)).
2. He ((grabbed)/graded) his hat.
3. He went (outer/(outside)).
4. He ((walked)/watched) to the bus stop.
5. He ((waited)/wanted) for the bus.



**Notes for Home:** Your child read words with more than one syllable. ***Home Activity:*** When you read longer words with your child, encourage him or her to sound out the smaller, more familiar word parts.

94 Phonics: Decoding Multisyllabic Words Level 1.6

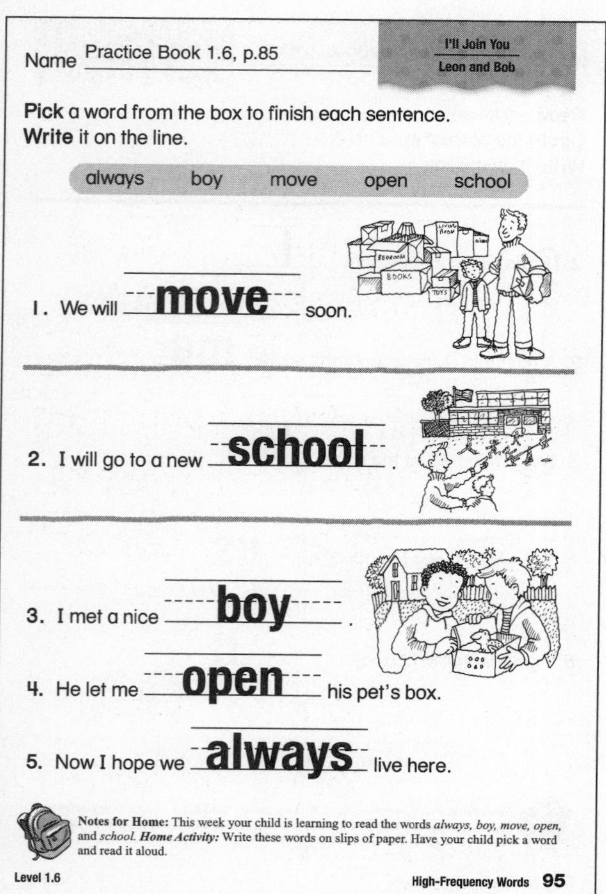

Name Practice Book 1.6, p.85

I'll Join You
Leon and Bob

**Pick** a word from the box to finish each sentence.
**Write** it on the line.

always boy move open school

1. We will **move** soon.
2. I will go to a new **school**.
3. I met a nice **boy**.
4. He let me **open** his pet's box.
5. Now I hope we **always** live here.



**Notes for Home:** This week your child is learning to read the words *always, boy, move, open,* and *school.* ***Home Activity:*** Write these words on slips of paper. Have your child pick a word and read it aloud.

Level 1.6 High-Frequency Words 95

Name Practice Book 1.6, p.86

I'll Join You
Leon and Bob

**Circle** the sentence that tells about the picture.

1. The boy is happy. / (The boy is sad.)
2. The boys are lonely. / (The boys are happy.)
3. (It is summer.) / It is winter.
4. (The girls went swimming.) / The girls went to school.

**Read** the sentences.
**Write** an answer to the question.

Mom threw the ball to Sue.
Sue ran to catch the ball.
"Nice catch," said Mom.
She and Sue smiled at each other.

5. How does Sue feel? **Possible answer given.**

**Sue feels proud.**

**Notes for Home:** Your child drew conclusions using picture and word clues. ***Home Activity:*** Look at pictures of your family with your child. Ask questions, such as: *"What are we doing here? How do you think this person is feeling?"*

96 Drawing Conclusions Level 1.6

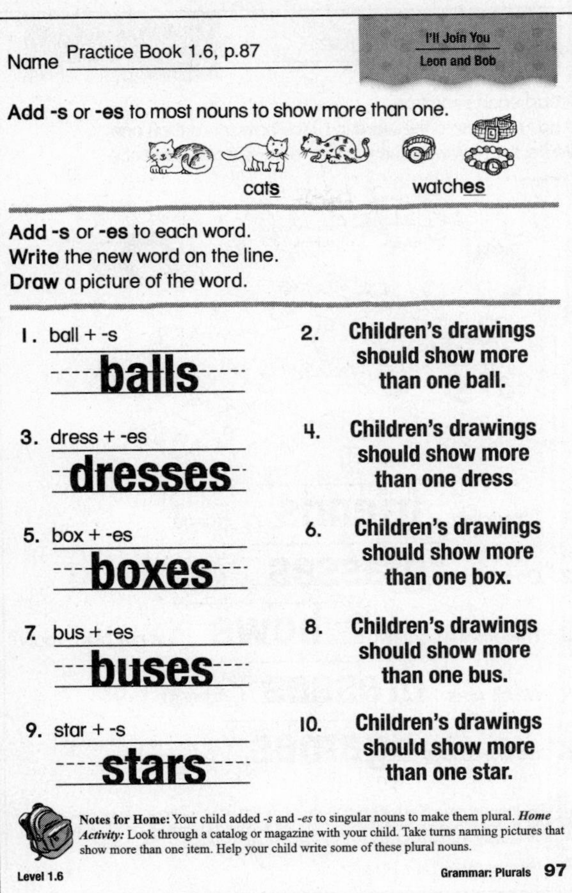

Name Practice Book 1.6, p.87

I'll Join You
Leon and Bob

**Add -s** or **-es** to most nouns to show more than one.

cats watches

**Add -s** or **-es** to each word.
**Write** the new word on the line.
**Draw** a picture of the word.

1. ball + -s **balls**
2. **Children's drawings should show more than one ball.**
3. dress + -es **dresses**
4. **Children's drawings should show more than one dress**
5. box + -es **boxes**
6. **Children's drawings should show more than one box.**
7. bus + -es **buses**
8. **Children's drawings should show more than one bus.**
9. star + -s **stars**
10. **Children's drawings should show more than one star.**

**Notes for Home:** Your child added *-s* and *-es* to singular nouns to make them plural. ***Home Activity:*** Look through a catalog or magazine with your child. Take turns naming pictures that show more than one item. Help your child write some of these plural nouns.

Level 1.6 Grammar: Plurals 97

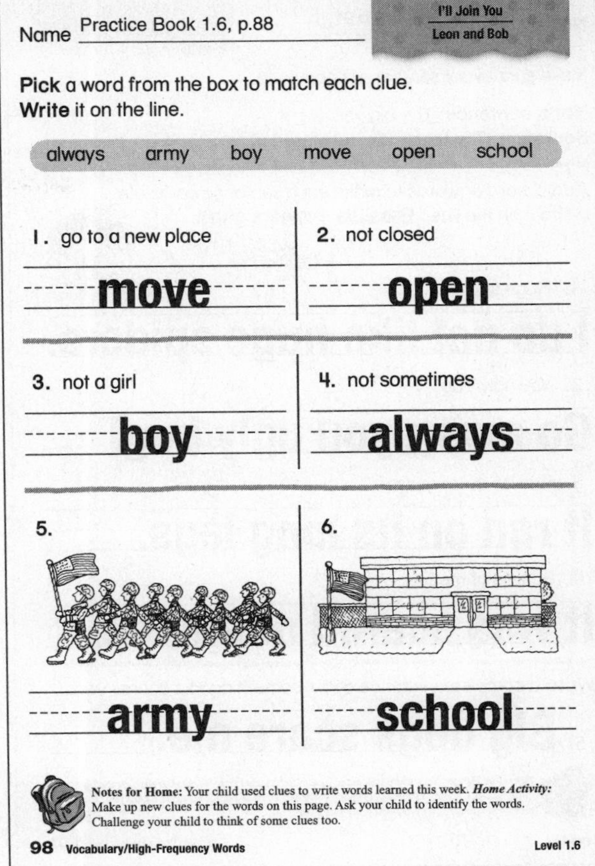

Name Practice Book 1.6, p.88

I'll Join You
Leon and Bob

**Pick** a word from the box to match each clue.
**Write** it on the line.

always army boy move open school

1. go to a new place **move**
2. not closed **open**
3. not a girl **boy**
4. not sometimes **always**
5. **army**
6. **school**

**Notes for Home:** Your child used clues to write words learned this week. ***Home Activity:*** Make up new clues for the words on this page. Ask your child to identify the words. Challenge your child to think of some clues too.

98 Vocabulary/High-Frequency Words Level 1.6

Name Practice Book 1.6, p.89

I'll Join You
Leon and Bob

**Circle** the word for each picture.

crown house

1. floor (flower)
2. (couch) crush
3. month (mouth)
4. tile (towel)
5. (mouse) mess
6. chew (cow)
7. (clown) clean
8. (owl) oil

**Find** the word that has the same vowel sound as cloud.
**Mark** the ⬭ to show your answer.

9. ⬭ need ⬭ hide ⬬ hound
10. ⬭ been ⬬ brown ⬭ brain

**Notes for Home:** Your child reviewed words with the vowel sound heard in *crown* and *house*. ***Home Activity:*** Make up the first line of a rhyme. It should end with a word with this vowel sound. Ask your child to make up the second line that ends with a rhyming word.

Level 1.6 Phonics: Vowel Diphthongs *ow, ou* /ou/ Review 99

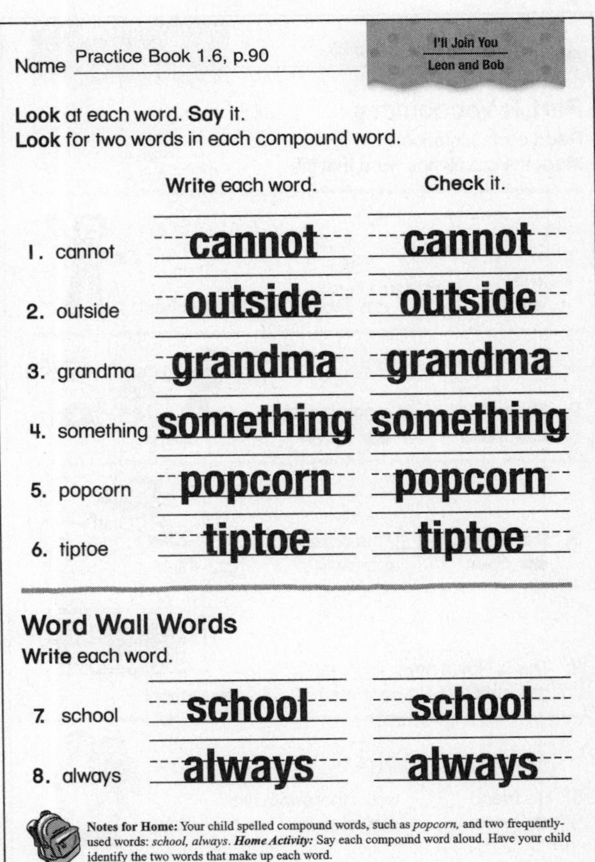

Name Practice Book 1.6, p.90

I'll Join You
Leon and Bob

**Look** at each word. **Say** it.
**Look** for two words in each compound word.

| | Write each word. | Check it. |
|---|---|---|
| 1. cannot | **cannot** | **cannot** |
| 2. outside | **outside** | **outside** |
| 3. grandma | **grandma** | **grandma** |
| 4. something | **something** | **something** |
| 5. popcorn | **popcorn** | **popcorn** |
| 6. tiptoe | **tiptoe** | **tiptoe** |

**Word Wall Words**
**Write** each word.

| | | |
|---|---|---|
| 7. school | **school** | **school** |
| 8. always | **always** | **always** |

**Notes for Home:** Your child spelled compound words, such as *popcorn,* and two frequently-used words: *school, always.* ***Home Activity:*** Say each compound word aloud. Have your child identify the two words that make up each word.

100 Spelling: Compound Words Level 1.6

Name Practice Book 1.6, p.91

I'll Join You
Leon and Bob

Make sure every sentence is complete.

**Not a sentence:** The big yellow cat.
**Sentence:** The big yellow cat hissed at me.

**Add** a word or words to make each sentence complete.
**Write** it on the line. **Possible answers given.**

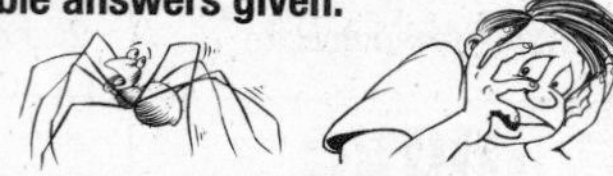

1. Huge spiders.
**I do not like huge spiders.**
2. You ugly bug.
**Go away, you ugly bug!**
3. Ran on its long legs.
**It ran on its long legs.**
4. Scared of me too.
**It was scared of me too.**

**Write** a complete sentence about something that scares you.

5. **Big dogs scare me.**

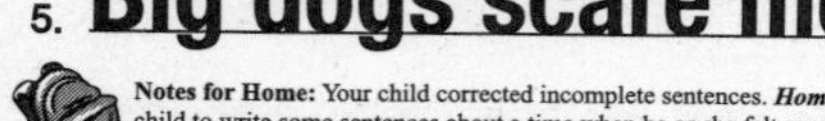

**Notes for Home:** Your child corrected incomplete sentences. ***Home Activity:*** Encourage your child to write some sentences about a time when he or she felt scared or frightened. Check that your child has formed complete sentences.



Name Practice Book 1.6, p.92

I'll Join You
Leon and Bob

**Read** each sentence.
**Add -s** or **-es** to the word in ( ) to show more than one.
**Write** the new word on the line to finish each sentence.

1. I have two **friends**. (friend)
2. One wears **glasses**. (glass)
3. The other wears two **bows** in her hair. (bow)
4. We all wear **dresses**. (dress)
5. We like to play **games**. (game)

**Notes for Home:** Your child wrote plurals ending with *-s* and *-es*. ***Home Activity:*** Look at newspaper or magazine ads with your child and point out the plurals. Talk about which words have just *-s* added to the singular noun *(tire, tires)* and which have *-es (box, boxes)*.



Name Practice Book 1.6, p.93

I'll Join You
Leon and Bob

## Part 1: Vocabulary

**Read** each sentence.
**Mark** the ⬭ for the word that fits.

1. This ______ is Ray.
● boy ⬭ mother ⬭ school

2. Ray will ______ to a new house.
⬭ make ● move ⬭ open

3. It is time to ______ the boxes.
● open ⬭ walk ⬭ think

4. This is Ray's new ______.
⬭ cold ⬭ idea ● school

5. His friend ______ walks there with him.
⬭ very ● always ⬭ about

GO ON



Name Practice Book 1.6, p.94

Leon and Bob

## Part 2: Comprehension

**Read** each question.
**Mark** the ⬭ for the answer.

6. Where was Leon's dad?
⬭ in town
● in the army
⬭ at home

7. What do you know about the first Bob in this story?
● He is not real.
⬭ He runs a lot.
⬭ He can sing.

8. You can tell that Leon is
● sad because his dad is away.
⬭ happy because he likes his new home.
⬭ mad because his mom can't take him to school.

9. Why did Leon keep thinking about the new boy?
⬭ He had never seen a boy like that.
⬭ He did not like the new boy.
● He wanted the boy to be a friend.

10. How does the story end?
⬭ Leon goes home.
● Leon has a new friend.
⬭ Leon knows two boys named Bob.

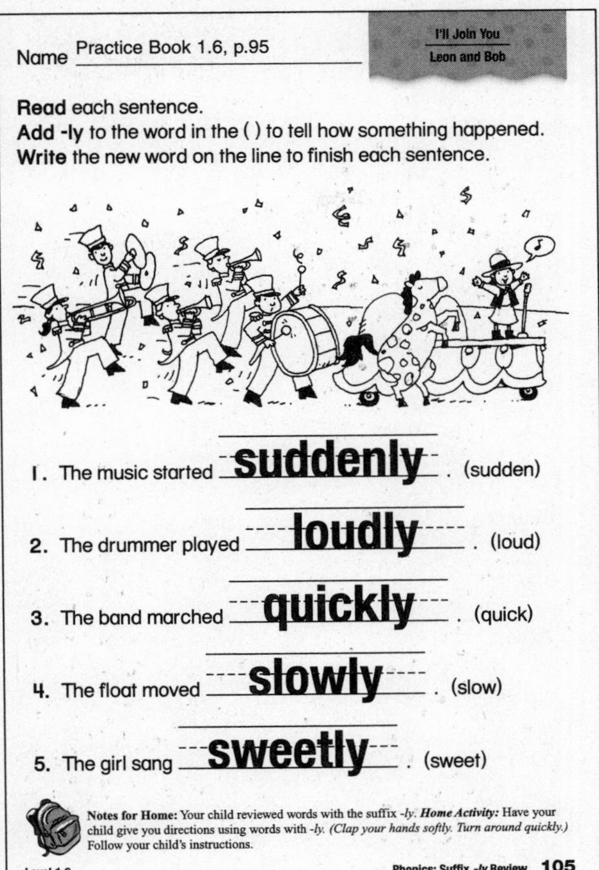
I'll Join You
Leon and Bob

Name Practice Book 1.6, p.95

**Read** each sentence.
**Add -ly** to the word in the ( ) to tell how something happened.
**Write** the new word on the line to finish each sentence.

1. The music started **suddenly**. (sudden)
2. The drummer played **loudly**. (loud)
3. The band marched **quickly**. (quick)
4. The float moved **slowly**. (slow)
5. The girl sang **sweetly**. (sweet)

**Notes for Home:** Your child reviewed words with the suffix *-ly*. ***Home Activity:*** Have your child give you directions using words with *-ly*. *(Clap your hands softly. Turn around quickly.)* Follow your child's instructions.

Level 1.6 Phonics: Suffix *-ly* Review 105

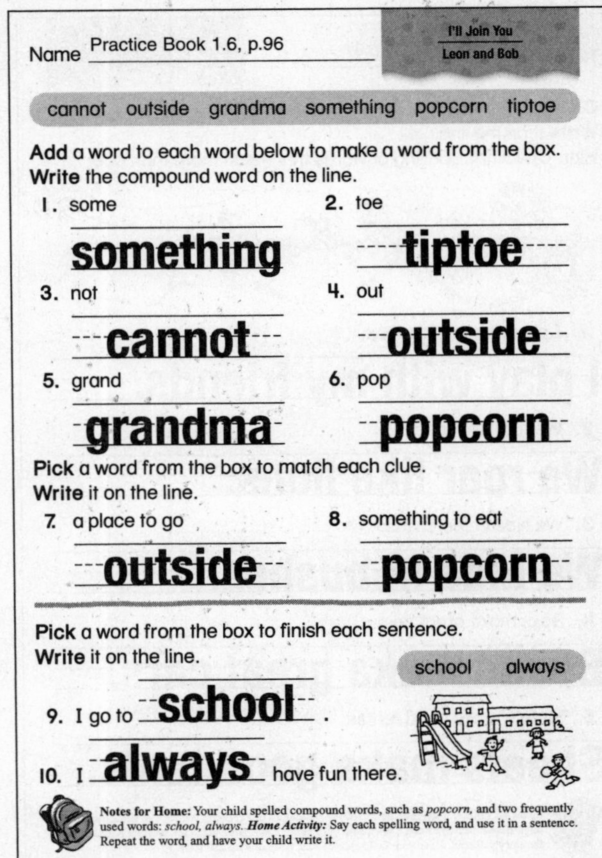
I'll Join You
Leon and Bob

Name Practice Book 1.6, p.96

cannot outside grandma something popcorn tiptoe

**Add** a word to each word below to make a word from the box.
**Write** the compound word on the line.

1. some **something**
2. toe **tiptoe**
3. not **cannot**
4. out **outside**
5. grand **grandma**
6. pop **popcorn**

**Pick** a word from the box to match each clue.
**Write** it on the line.

7. a place to go **outside**
8. something to eat **popcorn**

**Pick** a word from the box to finish each sentence.
**Write** it on the line.

school always

9. I go to **school**.
10. I **always** have fun there.

**Notes for Home:** Your child spelled compound words, such as *popcorn*, and two frequently used words: *school, always*. ***Home Activity:*** Say each spelling word, and use it in a sentence. Repeat the word, and have your child write it.

106 Spelling: Compound Words Level 1.6

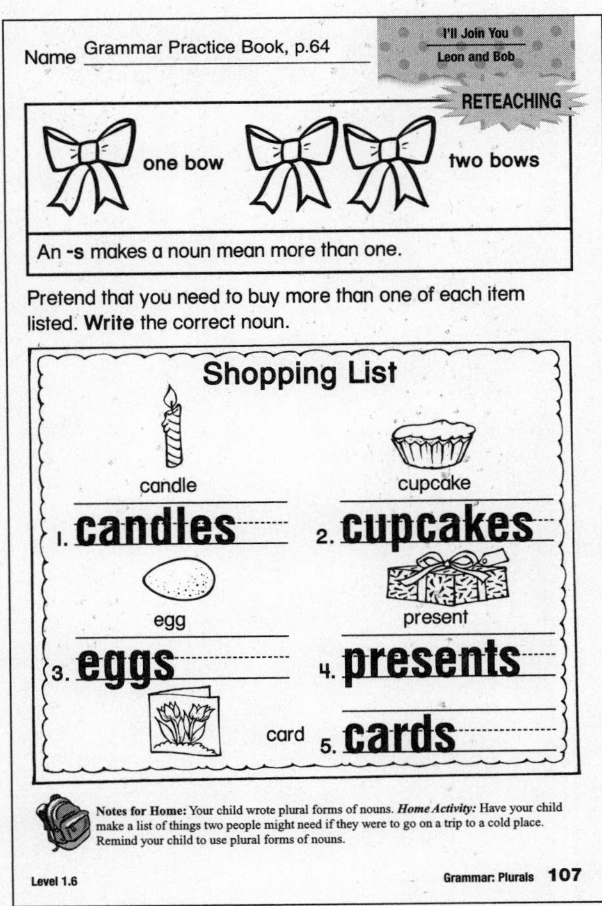
I'll Join You
Leon and Bob

Name Grammar Practice Book, p.64

RETEACHING

one bow two bows

An **-s** makes a noun mean more than one.

Pretend that you need to buy more than one of each item listed. **Write** the correct noun.

Shopping List

candle cupcake
1. **candles** 2. **cupcakes**
egg present
3. **eggs** 4. **presents**
card 5. **cards**

**Notes for Home:** Your child wrote plural forms of nouns. ***Home Activity:*** Have your child make a list of things two people might need if they were to go on a trip to a cold place. Remind your child to use plural forms of nouns.

Level 1.6 Grammar: Plurals 107

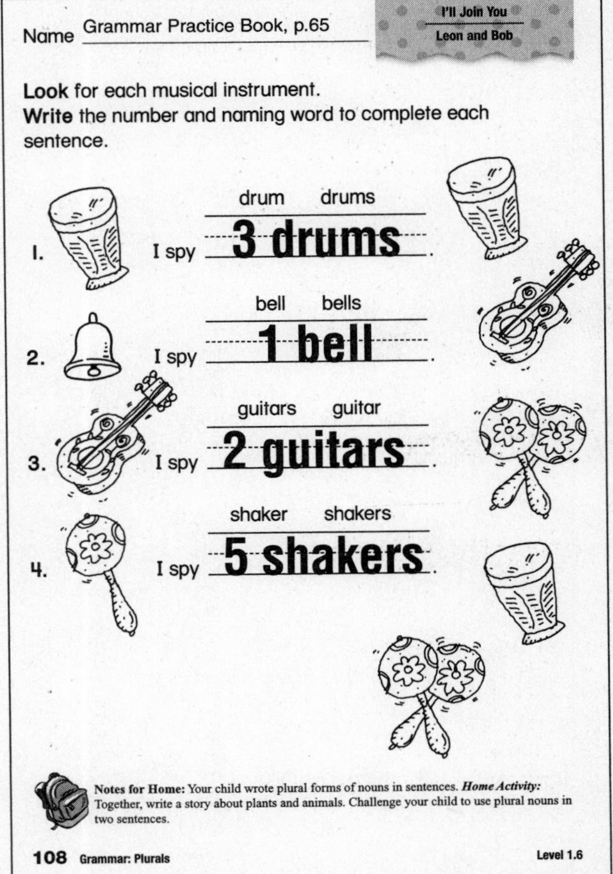
I'll Join You
Leon and Bob

Name Grammar Practice Book, p.65

**Look** for each musical instrument.
**Write** the number and naming word to complete each sentence.

1. drum drums — I spy **3 drums**.
2. bell bells — I spy **1 bell**.
3. guitars guitar — I spy **2 guitars**.
4. shaker shakers — I spy **5 shakers**.

**Notes for Home:** Your child wrote plural forms of nouns in sentences. ***Home Activity:*** Together, write a story about plants and animals. Challenge your child to use plural nouns in two sentences.

108 Grammar: Plurals Level 1.6

Name Practice Book 1.6, p.97

I'll Join You
Leon and Bob

**Correct** each sentence.
**Write** it on the line.
Hint: Check the spelling of words that mean more than one.

1. I play with my friendes.

**I play with my friends.**

2. We roar like liones.

**We roar like lions.**

3. We hide in the bushs.

**We hide in bushes.**

4. Boxs make great cars.

**Boxes make great cars.**

5. Sheets make good tentes.

**Sheets make good tents.**

**Notes for Home:** Your child corrected the spelling of plural nouns (words that show more than one). ***Home Activity:*** Read a story with your child. Later, point out some singular nouns from the story you read. Have your child change each noun to its plural form by adding *-s* or *-es*.

Level 1.6 Writing Process: Edit 109

# Teacher's Notes

# Teacher's Notes

# Teacher's Notes

# Teacher's Notes